A

THE MACMILLAN COMPANY
NEW YORK · BOSTON · CHICAGO
DALLAS · ATLANTA · SAN FRANCISCO

MACMILLAN AND CO., LIMITED
LONDON · BOMBAY · CALCUTTA
MADRAS · MELBOURNE

THE MACMILLAN COMPANY
OF CANADA, LIMITED
TORONTO

# *Story and Verse for Children*

# STORY and VERSE for CHILDREN

*Selected and Edited by*

MIRIAM BLANTON HUBER, Ph.D.

*Decorations by Boris Artzybasheff*

THE MACMILLAN COMPANY
New York

PRINTED IN THE UNITED STATES OF AMERICA

*Published May, 1940*
*Tenth Printing March, 1947*

# ACKNOWLEDGMENTS

GRATEFUL acknowledgment is made to the following publishers and authors for permission to reprint copyrighted material:

D. APPLETON-CENTURY COMPANY—"The Tar Baby," and "The Well Story," from *The Uncle Remus Book,* by Miriam Blanton Huber, retold from *Uncle Remus: His Songs and Sayings,* by Joel Chandler Harris; illustration by A. B. Frost, from *Uncle Remus: His Songs and Sayings,* by Joel Chandler Harris; "The Duck," and "The Rabbit," from *Fifty New Poems for Children,* by Edith King.

DOROTHY W. BARUCH—"Merry-Go-Round," from *I Like Machinery,* by Dorothy W. Baruch.

THE BOBBS-MERRILL COMPANY—"Little Orphant Annie," and "The Raggedy Man," from *Rhymes of Childhood,* by James Whitcomb Riley, copyright 1890, 1918; used by special permission of the Bobbs-Merrill Company, publishers.

BERTON BRALEY—"The Thinker," by Berton Braley, copyright by Berton Braley; all rights reserved.

BRANDT AND BRANDT—"A Nautical Extravagance," from *Random Rhymes and Odd Numbers,* by Wallace Irwin; "The Horseshoe," from *Poems Selected for Young People,* by Edna St. Vincent Millay; "Travel," from *Second April,* by Edna St. Vincent Millay.

W. COLLINS SONS AND COMPANY, LTD.—"Wild Animals," from *Gammon and Spinach,* by Elizabeth Fleming.

DODD, MEAD AND COMPANY, INC.—"A Vagabond Song," from *Vagabondia,* by Bliss Carman; "Lullaby," from *Lyrics of the Hearthside,* by Paul Laurence Dunbar.

DOUBLEDAY, DORAN AND COMPANY, INC.—"Mr. Murdle's Large Heart," from *A Street of Little Shops,* by Margery Bianco, copyright, 1932; "The Birches," from *Echoes and Realities,* by Walter Pritchard Eaton, copyright, 1918; "Taxis," from *Taxis and Toadstools,* by Rachel Field, copyright, 1926; "Fairies," from *Fairies and Chimneys,* by Rose Fyleman, copyright, 1920; "The First Christmas Tree," from *A Little Christmas Book,* by Rose Fyleman, copyright, 1927; "If Only . . . ," from *Gay Go Up,* by Rose Fyleman, copyright, 1929, 1930; "Mice," from *Fifty-One New Nursery Rhymes,* by Rose Fyleman, copyright, 1932; "The

Poplars," from *Dreamers, and Other Poems,* by Theodosia Garrison, copyright, 1917; "The House with Nobody in It," from *Poems, Essays and Letters,* by Joyce Kilmer, copyright, 1914, 1917, 1918; "The Elephant's Child," and illustration by Rudyard Kipling, from *Just So Stories,* by Rudyard Kipling; "The Secret of the Machines," from *A History of England,* by Rudyard Kipling; "A Hot-Weather Song," by Don Marquis; "The Ghost of the Great White Stag," from *Skunny Wundy, and Other Indian Tales,* by Arthur C. Parker, copyright, 1926; "Paul Bunyan," from *Paul Bunyan and His Great Blue Ox,* by Wallace Wadsworth, copyright, 1926; "O Captain! My Captain!" "I Hear America Singing," and "Miracles," from *Leaves of Grass,* by Walt Whitman, copyright, 1924; "The Blackbird," from *Kensington Gardens,* by Humbert Wolfe; reprinted by permission of Doubleday, Doran and Company, Inc.

GEORGES DUPLAIX—"Plouf, the Little Wild Duck," from *Plouf, the Little Wild Duck,* by Lida.

E. P. DUTTON AND COMPANY, INC.—"The Night Will Never Stay," from *Gypsy and Ginger,* by Eleanor Farjeon, copyrighted by E. P. Dutton and Company, Inc., New York.

FRONTIER AND MIDLAND—"The Oregon Trail: 1851," by Jim Marshall.

ELIZABETH FLEMING—"Wild Animals," from *Gammon and Spinach,* by Elizabeth Fleming.

HAMLIN GARLAND—"A Night Ride in a Prairie Schooner," from *Boy Life on the Prairie,* by Hamlin Garland; "Books of My Childhood," "Horses Chawin' Hay," "The Passing of the Buffalo," "Plowing: A Memory," and "The Plowman of Today," by Hamlin Garland.

GINN AND COMPANY—"Mark Twain," from *Young Americans: How History Looked to Them While It Was in the Making,* by Cornelia Meigs, reprinted by permission of Ginn and Company, publishers.

HARCOURT, BRACE AND COMPANY, INC.—"Between Two Loves," from *Selected Poems of T. A. Daly;* "The Merry Miner," from *Troupers of the Gold Coast,* by Constance Rourke; "Abe Lincoln Grows Up," from *Abe Lincoln Grows Up,* by Carl Sandburg; "Milk-White Moon, Put the Cows To Sleep," from *Good Morning, America,* by Carl Sandburg; "Children of the Wind," from *The People, Yes,* by Carl Sandburg; "Primer Lesson," from *Slabs of the Sunburnt West,* by Carl Sandburg.

HARPER AND BROTHERS—"Merry-Go-Round," from *I Like Machinery,* by Dorothy W. Baruch; "Tom Sawyer and His Pirate Crew," from *The Adventures of Tom Sawyer,* by Samuel L. Clemens; "Plouf, the Little Wild Duck," from *Plouf, the Little Wild Duck,* by Lida; "The Horseshoe," from *Poems Selected for Young People,* by Edna St. Vincent Millay, copyright, 1929; "Travel," from *Second April,* by Edna St. Vincent Millay, copyright, 1921.

HARPER'S MAGAZINE—"The Ticket Agent," by Edmund Leamy.

GEORGE G. HARRAP AND COMPANY, LTD.—"The Straw Ox," from *Cossack Fairy Tales,* by R. Nisbet Bain.

LUCIEN HARRIS—"The Tar Baby," and "The Well Story," from *The Uncle*

*Remus Book,* by Miriam Blanton Huber, retold from *Uncle Remus: His Songs and Sayings,* by Joel Chandler Harris.

RUPERT SARGENT HOLLAND—"Jack-in-the-Pulpit," by Rupert Sargent Holland.

HENRY HOLT AND COMPANY—"A Child's Day Begins," from *A Child's Day,* by Walter de la Mare; "The Huntsmen," and "Silver," from *Collected Poems,* by Walter de la Mare; "Seeds," from *Poems for Children,* by Walter de la Mare; "Some One," from *Peacock Pie,* by Walter de la Mare; "The Pasture," "The Runaway," and "Stopping by Woods on a Snowy Evening," from *New Hampshire,* by Robert Frost; "Loveliest of Trees," from *A Shropshire Lad,* by A. E. Housman; "Fog," from *Chicago Poems,* by Carl Sandburg; "Psalm of Those Who Go Forth before Daylight," from *Cornhuskers,* by Carl Sandburg.

HOUGHTON MIFFLIN COMPANY—"A Nautical Ballad," and "The Plaint of the Camel," from *Davy and the Goblin,* by Charles Edward Carryl; "The Leak in the Dike," by Phoebe Cary; "The Bird's Nest," from *All about Me,* by John Drinkwater; "Washing," from *More about Me,* by John Drinkwater; "The Concord Hymn," by Ralph Waldo Emerson; "The Queen of the Pirate Isle," from *The Queen of the Pirate Isle,* by Bret Harte; "The Pine-Tree Shillings," from *Grandfather's Chair,* by Nathaniel Hawthorne; "The Winged Horse," from *A Wonder Book for Boys and Girls,* by Nathaniel Hawthorne; "The Deacon's Masterpiece; or, The Wonderful 'One-Hoss Shay,'" and "The Height of the Ridiculous," by Oliver Wendell Holmes; "The Discoverer of the North Cape," "Hiawatha's Canoe," "Hiawatha's Childhood," "Hymn to the Night," "The Leap of Roushan Beg," "Paul Revere's Ride," "Three Kings Came Riding," and "The Village Blacksmith," by Henry Wadsworth Longfellow; "The Sea Shell," from *A Dome of Many-Colored Glass,* by Amy Lowell; "Aladdin," "The Courtin'," and "The Singing Leaves," by James Russell Lowell; "Baron Munchausen Goes to the Moon," from *The Children's Munchausen,* by John Martin, retold from *Adventures of Baron Munchausen,* by Rudolph Erich Raspe; "The Blind Men and the Elephant," by John Godfrey Saxe; "Darius Green and His Flying Machine," and "Evening at the Farm," by John Townsend Trowbridge; "Being a Boy," from *Being a Boy,* by Charles Dudley Warner; "Barbara Frietchie," "In School Days," "Skipper Ireson's Ride," and "The Snow," by John Greenleaf Whittier; reprinted by permission of Houghton Mifflin Company, authorized publishers.

WALLACE IRWIN—"A Nautical Extravagance," from *Random Rhymes and Odd Numbers,* by Wallace Irwin.

MRS. DAVID STARR JORDAN—"The Story of a Stone," from *Science Sketches,* by David Starr Jordan.

JOHN McCRAE KILGOUR—"In Flanders Fields," from *In Flanders Fields, and Other Poems,* by John McCrae.

MRS. RUDYARD KIPLING—"The Elephant's Child," and illustration by Rudyard Kipling, from *Just So Stories,* by Rudyard Kipling; "The Secret of the Machines," from *A History of England,* by Rudyard Kipling.

ALFRED A. KNOPF, INC.—"Mother to Son," from *The Dream Keeper, and Other Poems,* by Langston Hughes; "Pita's Painted Pig," from *The Painted Pig,* by Elizabeth Morrow; "Velvet Shoes," from *Nets to Catch the Wind,* by Elinor Wylie; reprinted by permission of and special arrangement with Alfred A. Knopf, Inc., authorized publishers.

JOHN A. LOMAX—"Whoopee Ti Yi Yo, Get Along, Little Dogies," and "The Zebra Dun," from *Cowboy Songs and Other Frontier Ballads,* by John A. and Alan Lomax.

LITTLE, BROWN AND COMPANY—"Little Women Plan Christmas," from *Little Women,* by Louisa May Alcott; "A Bird," and "The Sun," from *The Poems of Emily Dickinson;* "Invincible Louisa as a Nurse," from *Invincible Louisa: The Story of the Author of Little Women,* by Cornelia Meigs; "The Pearl Diver," from *The Pearl Lagoon,* by Charles Nordhoff; "Navaho Prayer," from *Shackled Youth,* by Edward S. Yeomans.

J. B. LIPPINCOTT COMPANY—"Song for a Little House," from *Chimney Smoke,* by Christopher Morley.

LONGMANS, GREEN AND COMPANY—"Aladdin and the Wonderful Lamp," from *The Arabian Nights' Entertainments,* by Andrew Lang; "Drakesbill," from *The Red Fairy Book,* by Andrew Lang.

DAVID McCORD—"The Frost Pane," and "This Is My Rock," by David McCord; used by permission of the author.

THE MACMILLAN COMPANY—"Billy and Blaze," from *Billy and Blaze,* by C. W. Anderson; "The Hairy Dog," and "Skating," from *Pillicock Hill,* by Herbert Asquith; "The Lion-Hearted Kitten," from *The Lion-Hearted Kitten, and Other Stories,* by Peggy Bacon; "The Making of the Hammer," from *Stories from Northern Myths,* by Emilie Kip Baker; "Pandora," from *Stories of Old Greece and Rome,* by Emilie Kip Baker; "My Dog," from *Foothills of Parnassus,* by John Kendrick Bangs; "What We Found in a Fox Den," from *The Sprite: The Story of a Red Fox,* by Ernest Harold Baynes; "A Gentleman in Brown," from *More about Animals,* by Margery Bianco; "Children of Haiti," from *Popo and Fifina: Children of Haiti,* by Arna Bontemps and Langston Hughes; "Caddie and the Indian Chief," and illustration by Kate Seredy, from *Caddie Woodlawn,* by Carol Ryrie Brink; "By Covered Wagon," from *Drusilla,* by Emma L. Brock; "Paddlewings Grows Up," from *Paddlewings: The Penguin of Galápagos,* by Wilfrid S. Bronson; "Stories of Other Days in Old Bergen," from *Wandering Monday,* by Ragnhild Chevalier; "Birthdays," and "Presents," from *Rhymes about Ourselves,* by Marchette Gaylord Chute; "Calypso," and "Song of the Parrot," from *Alice-All-by-Herself,* by Elizabeth Coatsworth; "Oak Leaves," "Swift Things Are Beautiful," and "The Wilderness Is Tamed," from *Away Goes Sally,* by Elizabeth Coatsworth; "Pinocchio," from *The Adventures of Pinocchio,* by C. Collodi (translated by Carol della Chiesa); "The First Harp," from *The Big Tree of Bunlahy,* by Padraic Colum; "The Story of Odysseus," from *The Children's Homer,* by Padraic Colum; "Jimmie, the White Sparrow," from *The White Sparrow,* by Padraic Colum; "The Old Woman of the Roads," from *Wild Earth, and Other Poems,* by Padraic Colum; "The Small Yellow Train," from *America Travels,* by Alice Dalgliesh; "The Blue Teapot," from *The Blue Teapot,* by Alice Dalgliesh; "The White Cat," and illustration by Elizabeth MacKinstry, from *The White Cat, and Other Old French Fairy Tales,* by Madame la Comtesse D'Aulnoy (edited by Rachel Field); "The Capture of the Giant

Armadillo," from *The Forest of Adventure,* by Raymond L. Ditmars; "A Circus Garland," from *Branches Green,* by Rachel Field; "Hitty Goes to Sea," from *Hitty: Her First Hundred Years,* by Rachel Field; "Roads," and "Skyscrapers," from *The Pointed People,* by Rachel Field; "Ask Mr. Bear," from *Ask Mr. Bear,* by Marjorie Flack; "Lucky Little Lena," from *Lucky Little Lena,* by Marjorie Flack; "Rusty Pete, Cow Pony," from *Rusty Pete of the Lazy A B,* by Doris Fogler and Nina Nicol; "Jacques and the Little Chief," from *The Painted Arrow,* by Frances Gaither; "The Prince and the Giant's Daughter," from *The Book of Celtic Stories,* by Elizabeth W. Grierson; "Bridget Goes Prospecting," from *Midget and Bridget,* by Berta and Elmer Hader; "Behind the Battlements," from *Medieval Days and Ways,* by Gertrude Hartman; "Grandmother's Buttons," from *Buttons,* by George and Doris Hauman; "Little Tonino," from *Little Tonino,* by Helen Hill and Violet Maxwell; "Rocky Billy Goes Visiting," from *Rocky Billy: The Story of a Rocky Mountain Goat,* by Holling Clancy Holling; "Sigurd the Volsung," from *Sons of the Volsungs,* by Dorothy Hosford; "The Far-Distant Oxus," from *The Far-Distant Oxus,* by Katharine Hull and Pamela Whitlock; "A Nautical Extravagance," from *Random Rhymes and Odd Numbers,* by Wallace Irwin, copyright, 1906; "The Heroes of Asgard," from *The Heroes of Asgard,* by A. and E. Keary; "Talking Wires," from *Talking Wires,* by Clara Lambert; "Hide and Go Seek," from *Hide and Go Seek,* by Dorothy P. Lathrop; illustration from *The Little White Goat,* by Dorothy P. Lathrop; "Schumann-Heink's First Contract," from *Schumann-Heink, Last of the Titans,* by Mary Lawton, and *When I Was a Girl,* by Helen Ferris; "Tony, the Steam Shovel Man," from *Diggers and Builders,* by Henry B. Lent; "Plowing," from *Grindstone Farm,* by Henry B. Lent; "An Explanation of the Grasshopper," "In Praise of Johnny Appleseed," "An Indian Summer Day on the Prairie," "The Little Turtle," "The Moon's the North Wind's Cooky," "The Mysterious Cat," and "Yet Gentle Will the Griffin Be," from *Johnny Appleseed, and Other Poems,* by Vachel Lindsay; "Whoopee Ti Yi Yo, Get Along, Little Dogies," and "The Zebra Dun," from *Cowboy Songs and Other Frontier Ballads,* by John A. and Alan Lomax; "Buck, the Lead-Dog," from *The Call of the Wild,* by Jack London; "Chris Farrington: Able Seaman," from *Dutch Courage,* by Jack London; "Goethals, the Prophet Engineer," from *The Present Hour,* by Percy MacKaye; illustration by Lynd Ward, from *Waif Maid,* by May McNeer; "The Bears of Blue River," from *The Bears of Blue River,* by Charles Major; "The Midnight Voyage," from *The Midnight Folk,* by John Masefield; "Sea Fever," from *Salt Water Poems and Ballads,* by John Masefield; "Dick Finds the 'Wheel of Fortune,' " from *Wind in the Chimney,* by Cornelia Meigs; "Cat," from *Menagerie,* by Mary Britton Miller; "Swiss Family Robinson," from *Swiss Family Robinson,* by Johann David Wyss (edited by C. E. Mitton); "Riding the Girders," and "Sand Hogs," from *Heroes and Hazards,* by Margaret Norris; "Alone," from *Green Pipes,* by Joseph Paget-Fredericks; "Skunks," from *First Lessons in Nature Study,* by Edith M. Patch; "The Horny Ones," from *Desert Neighbors,* by Edith M. Patch and Carroll Lane Fenton; "The Prairie Schooner," from *Barbed Wire and Wayfarers,* by Edwin Ford Piper; "Keeping Still in the Woods," from *Children of the Wilds,* by Charles G. D. Roberts; "Beasts of the Tar Pits," from *Beasts of the Tar Pits,* by W. W. Robinson; "Boats Sail on the Rivers," "The Caterpillar," "The City Mouse and the Garden Mouse," "Do You Know?" "Is the Moon Tired?" "The Swallow," "Who Has Seen the Wind?" and "Woolly Lambkins," from *Sing-Song,* by Christina G. Rossetti; "Way Ping, Master of Boats," from *The Rabbit Lantern, and Other Stories of Chinese Children,* by Dorothy Rowe; "Blue Barns," from *Blue Barns,* by Helen Sewell; "The Pony Express," from *Riding West on the Pony Express,* by Charles L. Skelton; "Blue Arrow and the Outlaws," from *Andy Breaks Trail,* by Constance Lindsay Skinner; illustration by Arthur Rackham, from *English Fairy Tales,* by Flora Annie Steel; "The King of the Crocodiles," from *Tales of the Punjab,* by Flora Annie Steel; "Night Was Creeping," and "The White Window," from *Collected Poems,* by James Stephens; "April," from *Rivers to the Sea,* by Sara Teasdale; "The Falling Star," and "It Is Not Far," from *Stars Tonight,* by Sara Teasdale; "The Angel in the Apple Tree," "Behind the Waterfall," "Dogs and Weather," "Green Moth," "The Lucky Snail," and "Three Lovely Holes," from *Skipping Along Alone,* by Winifred Welles; "Jangwa Begins to Hunt," from *Jangwa: The Story of a Jungle Prince,* by Walter J. Wilwerding; reprinted by permission of The Macmillan Company, publishers.

MRS. DOUGLAS MALLOCH—"When the Drive Goes Down: A Lumberjack's Story," by Douglas Malloch; reprinted by special permission.

VIRGIL MARKHAM—"A Prayer," by Edwin Markham; reprinted by special permission.

BERNICE M. MARQUIS—"A Hot-Weather Song," by Don Marquis.

JIM MARSHALL—"The Oregon Trail: 1851," by Jim Marshall.

H. G. MERRIAM—"The Oregon Trail: 1851," by Jim Marshall.

JUANITA MILLER—"Columbus," by Joaquin Miller.

DAVID MORTON—"Old Ships," from *Ships in Harbour,* by David Morton.

G. P. PUTNAM'S SONS—"Skipping Ropes," from *Everything and Anything,* by Dorothy Aldis; "Troubles," from *Here, There, and Everywhere,* by Dorothy Aldis; "With Helmet and Hose," from *Exploring with Beebe,* by William Beebe; "Jack and the Beanstalk," from *English Fairy Tales,* by Joseph Jacobs; "New York to Paris," from *We,* by Charles A. Lindbergh; "In Flanders Fields," from *In Flanders Fields, and Other Poems,* by John McCrae; "Old Ships," from *Ships in Harbour,* by David Morton.

RAND McNALLY AND COMPANY—"To China," from *Peter Patter Book,* by Leroy F. Jackson; "Letters to Channy," from *Letters to Channy,* by Heluiz Chandler Washburne, copyright, 1932; reprinted by permission of Rand McNally and Company, publishers.

ROW, PETERSON AND COMPANY—"Aiken-Drum, the Brownie," from *After the Sun Sets, The Wonder Story Books, Book III,* by Miriam Blanton Huber, Frank Seely Salisbury, and Mabel O'Donnell; reprinted by permission of Row, Peterson and Company, publishers.

THE SATURDAY REVIEW OF LITERATURE—"Books of My Childhood," by Hamlin Garland; "This Is My Rock," by David McCord.

SCOTT, FORESMAN AND COMPANY—"Gareth and Lynette," from *Six Great Stories,* by Gertrude Moderow, Mary Yost Sandrus, Josephine Mitchell, and Ernest C. Noyes, copyright, 1937; reprinted by permission of Scott, Foresman and Company, publishers.

CHARLES SCRIBNER'S SONS—"The Sleepy Song," from *Poems,* by Josephine Daskam Bacon; "Hans Brinker and His Sister," from *Hans Brinker; or, The Silver Skates,* by Mary Mapes Dodge; "The Duel," and "Wynken, Blynken, and Nod," from *Poems of Childhood,* by Eugene Field; "Dear Land of All My Love," from *Centennial Ode,* by Sidney Lanier; "Two Little Confederates," from *Two Little Confederates,* by Thomas Nelson Page; "The Truce on Treasure Island," from *Treasure Island,* by Robert Louis Stevenson; "The Angler's Reveille," and "Trees," from *Complete Poems,* by Henry van Dyke.

IRVING SHEPARD—"Chris Farrington: Able Seaman," from *Dutch Courage,* by Jack London.

LIONEL STEVENSON—"In a Desert Town," by Lionel Stevenson; used by permission of the author.

MABEL ROSE STEVENSON—"Springtime in Donegal," by Mabel Rose Stevenson; used by permission of the author.

FREDERICK A. STOKES COMPANY—"Little Black Sambo," from *The Story of Little Black Sambo,* by Helen Bannerman; "The Winning of Atalanta," from *Children of the Dawn,* by Elsie Finnimore Buckley; "Mouse," and "Hills," from *Poems by a Little Girl,* by Hilda Conkling, copyright, 1920; "Over the Garden Wall," from *Over the Garden Wall,* by Eleanor Farjeon, copyright, 1933; "Doctor Dolittle and the Pushmi-Pullyu," from *The Story of Doctor Dolittle,* by Hugh Lofting, copyright, 1920; "The House Cat," and "Indian Children," from *For Days and Days: A Year-Round Treasury of Verse for Children,* by Annette Wynne, copyright, 1919; reprinted by permission of Frederick A. Stokes Company.

THE VIKING PRESS, INC.—Illustration from *The Seven Simeons,* by Boris Artzybasheff, copyright, 1937; "Lone Dog," from *Songs To Save a Soul,* by Irene Rutherford McLeod; "The Butterbean Tent," "Christmas Morning," "The Hens," and "The Woodpecker," from *Under the Tree,* by Elizabeth Madox Roberts, copyright, 1922, 1930; "Jancsi and Kate," from *The Good Master,* by Kate Seredy, copyright, 1935; "Glimpse in Autumn," from *Dreams out of Darkness,* by Jean Starr Untermeyer, copyright, 1921.

FREDERICK WARNE AND COMPANY, INC.—Illustration from *The Panjandrum Picture Book,* by Randolph Caldecott; illustration from *Mother Goose; or, The Old Nursery Rhymes,* by Kate Greenaway; "Nonsense Verses," "The Owl and the Pussy Cat," and "The Table and the Chair," by Edward Lear; "Mother Goose Rhymes," and illustration by L. Leslie Brooke, from *The Nursery Rhyme Book,* by Andrew Lang; "The Tale of Peter Rabbit," from *The Tale of Peter Rabbit,* by Beatrix Potter; reprinted by permission of Frederick Warne and Company, Inc., authorized publishers.

A. P. WATT AND SON—"The Elephant's Child," and illustration by Rudyard Kipling, from *Just So Stories,* by Rudyard Kipling; "The Secret of the Machines," from *A History of England,* by Rudyard Kipling.

WORLD BOOK COMPANY—"Busy Carpenters," from *Busy Carpenters,* by James S. Tippett, copyright, 1929; reprinted by permission of World Book Company, Yonkers, New York.

YALE UNIVERSITY PRESS—"Watching Clouds," from *Songs for Parents,* by John Farrar.

CHARLES SCRIBNER'S SONS: [illegible] *Stories* [illegible] [illegible] [illegible] and the [illegible] [illegible] by Mary Mapes Dodge; [illegible] [illegible] *Poems of Childhood* by Eugene Field; [illegible] *Treasure Island* by Robert Louis Stevenson; [illegible] Complete [illegible] by Henry van Dyke.

[illegible] SHEPARD: [illegible] by John Lockwood.

[illegible] STEVENSON: [illegible] by [illegible] Stevenson, used by permission of the author.

MABEL ROSS STEVENSON: [illegible] by Mabel Ross Stevenson, used by permission of the author.

FREDERICK A. STOKES COMPANY: [illegible] *Little Black Sambo* by Helen Bannerman; [illegible] by Elsie Singmaster [illegible] by Hilda Conkling, copyright [illegible] *Garden Wall* [illegible] by Hilda Conkling [illegible] and the [illegible] Conkling [illegible] *Young Children* [illegible] [illegible] reprinted by permission of Frederick A. Stokes Company.

THE VIKING PRESS, INC.: [illegible] [illegible] [illegible] [illegible] Rachel [illegible] [illegible] copyright [illegible] [illegible] *Bridge*, [illegible] [illegible] [illegible].

[illegible] HOUGHTON MIFFLIN COMPANY: [illegible] Randolph Caldecott [illegible] [illegible] *Old Mother Hubbard* [illegible] [illegible] and the Pussy-Cat [illegible] illustration by [illegible] *Rhymes* by Andrew Lang [illegible] reprinted by permission of Frederick Warne and Company, Inc., authorized publishers.

A. P. WATT & SON: [illegible] illustration by Rudyard Kipling, from *Just So Stories* by Rudyard Kipling [illegible] *History of* [illegible] by Rudyard Kipling.

WORLD BOOK COMPANY: [illegible] copyright [illegible] reprinted by permission of World Book Company, Yonkers, New York.

YALE UNIVERSITY PRESS: [illegible] by John Farrar.

# CONTENTS

## BOOKS AND CHILDREN


PAGE

ENJOYMENT OF LITERATURE 3

CHILDREN'S BOOKS 6
Books of My Childhood, *Hamlin Garland* 6

SELECTING BOOKS FOR CHILDREN 9

CHILDREN'S INTERESTS IN READING 12

ILLUSTRATED BOOKS FOR CHILDREN 19

*SUGGESTIONS FOR STUDENTS* 41

*STUDENT ACTIVITIES* 42

*REFERENCES FOR STUDENTS*
Enjoyment of Literature 44
Guides to Children's Books 44
Children's Interests in Reading 45
The Illustration of Children's Books 45


## MOTHER GOOSE RHYMES


*MOTHER GOOSE: ORIGIN AND SIGNIFICANCE* 49

MOTHER GOOSE RHYMES

1. Ride a cock-horse to Banbury Cross 53
2. This little pig went to market 53
3. Diddle, diddle, dumpling 53
4. Bow, wow, wow 53
5. Bye, baby bunting 53
6. Hush-a-bye, baby 53
7. Pat-a-cake 53
8. To market, to buy a fat pig 53
9. Polly, put the kettle on 54
10. Come, butter, come 54

| | PAGE |
|---|---|
| 11. The rose is red | 54 |
| 12. Hey, diddle, diddle | 54 |
| 13. Jack and Jill | 54 |
| 14. Hickory, dickory, dock | 54 |
| 15. Cushy cow bonny | 54 |
| 16. Pussy cat, where have you been | 54 |
| 17. Mistress Mary | 54 |
| 18. A farmer went riding | 54 |
| 19. Little Betty Blue | 55 |
| 20. Jack be nimble | 55 |
| 21. Three blind mice | 55 |
| 22. Higgledy, piggledy, my black hen | 55 |
| 23. There was an old woman lived under a hill | 55 |
| 24. Wee Willie Winkie | 55 |
| 25. Little Jack Horner | 55 |
| 26. Little Miss Muffet | 55 |
| 27. Little Boy Blue | 55 |
| 28. Cock-a-doodle-doo | 55 |
| 29. Little Robin Redbreast | 56 |
| 30. The north wind doth blow | 56 |
| 31. Once I saw a little bird | 56 |
| 32. God bless the master of this house | 56 |
| 33. There were three jovial huntsmen | 56 |
| 34. I had a little nut-tree | 56 |
| 35. I saw a ship a-sailing | 56 |
| 36. Girls and boys, come out to play | 57 |
| 37. Ding, dong, dell | 57 |
| 38. Sing a song of sixpence | 57 |
| 39. There was an old woman who lived in a shoe | 57 |
| 40. One, two, buckle my shoe | 57 |
| 41. I had a little pony | 57 |
| 42. Old King Cole | 58 |
| 43. Little Bo-peep | 58 |
| 44. Willy boy, where are you going | 58 |
| 45. Blow, wind, blow | 58 |
| 46. Baa, baa, black sheep | 58 |
| 47. Cobbler, cobbler, mend my shoe | 58 |
| 48. A cat came fiddling | 58 |
| 49. Little King Boggen | 58 |
| 50. Intery, mintery, cutery-corn | 58 |
| 51. Pease-porridge hot | 58 |
| 52. Humpty-Dumpty | 59 |
| 53. I have a little sister | 59 |
| 54. Twenty white horses | 59 |
| 55. Little Nancy Etticoat | 59 |

PAGE

56. As round as an apple 59
57. In marble walls as white as milk 59
58. As I was going to St. Ives 59
59. Thirty days hath September 59
60. Monday's child 59
61. If all the seas were one sea 59
62. There was an old woman tossed up in a basket 60
63. There was a crooked man 60
64. There was a man in our town 60
65. Simple Simon 60
66. Peter Piper 60
67. Robert Rowley 60
68. Three children sliding on the ice 60
69. This is the house that Jack built 60
70. Old Mother Hubbard 61
71. There was an old man who lived in a wood 62

*MOTHER GOOSE RHYMES: SUGGESTED GRADES* 63

*BOOKS OF MOTHER GOOSE RHYMES* 64

*STUDENT ACTIVITIES* 65

*REFERENCES FOR STUDENTS* 66

## *VERSE*

*VERSE FOR CHILDREN* 69

BOYS AND GIRLS

The Huntsmen, *Walter de la Mare* 73
Time to Rise, *Robert Louis Stevenson* 73
A Child's Day Begins, *Walter de la Mare* 73
Bed in Summer, *Robert Louis Stevenson* 74
My Bed Is a Boat, *Robert Louis Stevenson* 74
Lullaby, *Paul Laurence Dunbar* 74
The Sleepy Song, *Josephine Duskam Bacon* 75
Wynken, Blynken, and Nod, *Eugene Field* 75
Sweet and Low, *Alfred Tennyson* 76
My Shadow, *Robert Louis Stevenson* 76
Washing, *John Drinkwater* 76
Birthdays, *Marchette Gaylord Chute* 77
Presents, *Marchette Gaylord Chute* 77
Troubles, *Dorothy Aldis* 77
Skipping Ropes, *Dorothy Aldis* 77
To China, *Leroy F. Jackson* 77
At the Seaside, *Robert Louis Stevenson* 78

PAGE

Merry-Go-Round, *Dorothy W. Baruch* 78
The Swing, *Robert Louis Stevenson* 78
Three Lovely Holes, *Winifred Welles* 78
The Land of Counterpane, *Robert Louis Stevenson* 78
Alone, *Joseph Paget-Fredericks* 79
Over the Garden Wall, *Eleanor Farjeon* 79
A Good Play, *Robert Louis Stevenson* 79
If Only . . . , *Rose Fyleman* 80
The Raggedy Man, *James Whitcomb Riley* 80
Skating, *Herbert Asquith* 80
The Butterbean Tent, *Elizabeth Madox Roberts* 81
Thanksgiving Day, *Lydia Maria Child* 81
Christmas Morning, *Elizabeth Madox Roberts* 82
Mr. Nobody, *Author Unknown* 82
A Circus Garland, *Rachel Field* 82
A Boy's Song, *James Hogg* 83
Little Orphant Annie, *James Whitcomb Riley* 83

*BOYS AND GIRLS: SUGGESTED GRADES* 84

FAIRIES AND MAKE-BELIEVE

Fairies, *Rose Fyleman* 86
Some One, *Walter de la Mare* 86
The Child and the Fairies, *Author Unknown* 87
Queen Mab, *Thomas Hood* 87
The Elf Singing, *William Allingham* 87
Up the Airy Mountain, *William Allingham* 88
A Visit from St. Nicholas, *Clement C. Moore* 88
Yet Gentle Will the Griffin Be, *Vachel Lindsay* 89
Skyscrapers, *Rachel Field* 89
The Angel in the Apple Tree, *Winifred Welles* 90
Behind the Waterfall, *Winifred Welles* 90
Green Moth, *Winifred Welles* 90
Springtime in Donegal, *Mabel Rose Stevenson* 90
Aladdin, *James Russell Lowell* 91
The Bugle Song, *Alfred Tennyson* 91

*FAIRIES AND MAKE-BELIEVE: SUGGESTED GRADES* 91

IN FEATHERS AND FUR AND SUCH

The Woodpecker, *Elizabeth Madox Roberts* 93
The Rabbit, *Edith King* 93
The Bird's Nest, *John Drinkwater* 93
Woolly Lambkins, *Christina G. Rossetti* 94
The Squirrel, *Author Unknown* 94

PAGE

The Little Turtle, *Vachel Lindsay* 94
The Caterpillar, *Christina G. Rossetti* 94
Mouse, *Hilda Conkling* 94
Mice, *Rose Fyleman* 94
Frogs at School, *George Cooper* 95
An Explanation of the Grasshopper, *Vachel Lindsay* 95
Choosing a Kitten, *Author Unknown* 95
The House Cat, *Annette Wynne* 95
The Hairy Dog, *Herbert Asquith* 95
The Cow, *Robert Louis Stevenson* 96
Pretty Cow, *Ann Taylor* 96
The Pasture, *Robert Frost* 96
The Duck, *Edith King* 96
A Friend in the Garden, *Juliana Horatia Ewing* 96
A Bird, *Emily Dickinson* 97
Bob White, *George Cooper* 97
The Secret, *Author Unknown* 97
The Lucky Snail, *Winifred Welles* 97
Wild Animals, *Elizabeth Fleming* 98
The Blackbird, *Humbert Wolfe* 98
The Swallow, *Christina G. Rossetti* 98
The City Mouse and the Garden Mouse, *Christina G. Rossetti* 98
Cat, *Mary Britton Miller* 98
Dogs and Weather, *Winifred Welles* 99
Do You Know? *Christina G. Rossetti* 99
The Runaway, *Robert Frost* 99
The Hens, *Elizabeth Madox Roberts* 100
My Dog, *John Kendrick Bangs* 100
The Mysterious Cat, *Vachel Lindsay* 100
Lone Dog, *Irene Rutherford McLeod* 101
Horses Chawin' Hay, *Hamlin Garland* 101
Brown Bee, *William Brighty Rands* 101
Little Busy Bee, *Isaac Watts* 101
Children of the Wind, *Carl Sandburg* 102
The Angler's Reveille, *Henry van Dyke* 102

*IN FEATHERS AND FUR AND SUCH: SUGGESTED GRADES* 103

THE WORLD AND ALL

The White Window, *James Stephens* 105
The Moon's the North Wind's Cooky, *Vachel Lindsay* 105
Is the Moon Tired? *Christina G. Rossetti* 105
Who Has Seen the Wind? *Christina G. Rossetti* 105
The Wind, *Robert Louis Stevenson* 106
Rain, *Robert Louis Stevenson* 106

PAGE

Clouds, *Author Unknown* 106
Watching Clouds, *John Farrar* 106
Boats Sail on the Rivers, *Christina G. Rossetti* 106
Night Was Creeping, *James Stephens* 106
Jack-in-the-Pulpit, *Rupert Sargent Holland* 107
The Birches, *Walter Pritchard Eaton* 107
April, *Sara Teasdale* 107
Seeds, *Walter de la Mare* 107
The Sun's Travels, *Robert Louis Stevenson* 108
Little Star, *Jane Taylor* 108
Silver, *Walter de la Mare* 108
The Night Will Never Stay, *Eleanor Farjeon* 108
The Wonderful World, *William Brighty Rands* 108
The Frost Pane, *David McCord* 109
The Wonderful Weaver, *George Cooper* 109
Wintertime, *Robert Louis Stevenson* 109
Stopping by Woods on a Snowy Evening, *Robert Frost* 110
The Garden Year, *Sara Coleridge* 110
Glimpse in Autumn, *Jean Starr Untermeyer* 110
Oak Leaves, *Elizabeth Coatsworth* 111
The Year's at the Spring, *Robert Browning* 111
In a Desert Town, *Lionel Stevenson* 111
Hills, *Hilda Conkling* 111
The Wind in a Frolic, *William Howitt* 111
The Wind and the Moon, *George MacDonald* 112
Milk-White Moon, Put the Cows To Sleep, *Carl Sandburg* 113
The Falling Star, *Sara Teasdale* 113
Swift Things Are Beautiful, *Elizabeth Coatsworth* 114
Fog, *Carl Sandburg* 114
Autumn Fancies, *Author Unknown* 114
Loveliest of Trees, *A. E. Housman* 114
The Poplars, *Theodosia Garrison* 114
The Planting of the Apple-Tree, *William Cullen Bryant* 115
A Salute to Trees, *Henry van Dyke* 115
July, *Susan Hartley Swett* 115
An Indian Summer Day on the Prairie, *Vachel Lindsay* 116
This Is My Rock, *David McCord* 116
The Sun, *Emily Dickinson* 116
It Is Not Far, *Sara Teasdale* 116
Hymn to the Night, *Henry Wadsworth Longfellow* 117
The Snow, *John Greenleaf Whittier* 117
Velvet Shoes, *Elinor Wylie* 118
Daffodils, *William Wordsworth* 118
A Vagabond Song, *Bliss Carman* 118
Miracles, *Walt Whitman* 119

PAGE

*THE WORLD AND ALL: SUGGESTED GRADES* 119

FOR FUN

The Plaint of the Camel, *Charles Edward Carryl* 121
The Owl and the Pussy-Cat, *Edward Lear* 121
The Duel, *Eugene Field* 122
A Lobster Quadrille, *Lewis Carroll* 122
The Table and the Chair, *Edward Lear* 123
The Height of the Ridiculous, *Oliver Wendell Holmes* 123
A Strange Wild Song, *Lewis Carroll* 124
Nonsense Verses, *Edward Lear* 124
The Strange Man, *Author Unknown* 125
A Tragic Story, *William Makepeace Thackeray* 126
The Twins, *Henry S. Leigh* 126
The Walrus and the Carpenter, *Lewis Carroll* 126
A Nautical Ballad, *Charles Edward Carryl* 128
The Yarn of the Nancy Bell, *William S. Gilbert* 128
A Nautical Extravagance, *Wallace Irwin* 130
The Merry Miner, *Author Unknown* 130
A Hot-Weather Song, *Don Marquis* 131
Darius Green and His Flying Machine, *John Townsend Trowbridge* 131
Between Two Loves, *T. A. Daly* 134
The Deacon's Masterpiece; or, The Wonderful "One-Hoss Shay," *Oliver Wendell Holmes* 135

*FOR FUN: SUGGESTED GRADES* 136

ROADS TO ANYWHERE

Roads, *Rachel Field* 138
Where Go the Boats? *Robert Louis Stevenson* 138
The Horseshoe, *Edna St. Vincent Millay* 138
Taxis, *Rachel Field* 139
The Peddler's Caravan, *William Brighty Rands* 139
Travel, *Edna St. Vincent Millay* 139
The Sea Shell, *Amy Lowell* 140
Song of the Parrot, *Elizabeth Coatsworth* 140
Travel, *Robert Louis Stevenson* 140
Old Ships, *David Morton* 141
Sea Fever, *John Masefield* 141
The Ticket Agent, *Edmund Leamy* 141

*ROADS TO ANYWHERE: SUGGESTED GRADES* 142

THE DAY'S WORK

Busy Carpenters, *James S. Tippett* 143

PAGE

Carpenter, *E. V. Lucas* 143
Psalm of Those Who Go Forth before Daylight, *Carl Sandburg* 143
Evening at the Farm, *John Townsend Trowbridge* 144
Plowing: A Memory, *Hamlin Garland* 144
The Plowman of Today, *Hamlin Garland* 145
The Village Blacksmith, *Henry Wadsworth Longfellow* 145
I Hear America Singing, *Walt Whitman* 145
When the Drive Goes Down, *Douglas Malloch* 146
The Zebra Dun, *Author Unknown* 146
Whoopee Ti Yi Yo, Git Along, Little Dogies, *Author Unknown* 147
The Clinker, *Author Unknown* 148
Goethals, the Prophet Engineer, *Percy MacKaye* 148
The Secret of the Machines, *Rudyard Kipling* 149
The Thinker, *Berton Braley* 150

*THE DAY'S WORK: SUGGESTED GRADES* 150

OUR COUNTRY

Dear Land of All My Love, *Sidney Lanier* 152
Indian Children, *Annette Wynne* 152
The Wilderness Is Tamed, *Elizabeth Coatsworth* 152
Columbus, *Joaquin Miller* 153
Concord Hymn, *Ralph Waldo Emerson* 153
Paul Revere's Ride, *Henry Wadsworth Longfellow* 153
In Praise of Johnny Appleseed, *Vachel Lindsay* 155
The Passing of the Buffalo, *Hamlin Garland* 156
The Prairie Schooner, *Edwin Ford Piper* 157
The Oregon Trail: 1851, *Jim Marshall* 157
Barbara Frietchie, *John Greenleaf Whittier* 158
O Captain! My Captain! *Walt Whitman* 159
In Flanders Fields, *John McCrae* 160
My Own, My Native Land, *Sir Walter Scott* 160

*OUR COUNTRY: SUGGESTED GRADES* 160

GUIDEPOSTS

Mother to Son, *Langston Hughes* 162
Primer Lesson, *Carl Sandburg* 162
A Child's Grace, *Robert Burns* 162
He Prayeth Best, *Samuel Taylor Coleridge* 162
All Things Bright and Beautiful, *Cecil Frances Alexander* 163
Cradle Hymn, *Martin Luther* 163
As Joseph Was A-Walking, *Old Carol* 163
The Lamb, *William Blake* 163
The Old Woman of the Roads, *Padraic Colum* 164

PAGE

Song for a Little House, *Christopher Morley* 164
The House with Nobody in It, *Joyce Kilmer* 164
A Thing of Beauty, *John Keats* 165
A Prayer, *Edwin Markham* 165
Navaho Prayer, *Edward S. Yeomans* 165
Abou Ben Adhem, *Leigh Hunt* 166
The Lord Is My Shepherd, *The Bible: Psalm 23* 166
Thanksgiving, *The Bible: Psalm 100* 166
A Merry Heart, *The Bible: Proverbs 15* 167
Charity, *The Bible: I Corinthians 13* 167

*GUIDEPOSTS: SUGGESTED GRADES* 168

STORIES IN VERSE

The Three Little Kittens, *Eliza Lee Follen* 169
A Visit from Mr. Fox, *Old Folk Rhyme* 169
Hiawatha's Childhood, *Henry Wadsworth Longfellow* 170
The Leak in the Dike, *Phoebe Cary* 171
The Raggle, Taggle Gypsies, *Old Folk Song* 173
King Bruce and the Spider, *Eliza Cook* 173
How They Brought the Good News from Ghent to Aix, *Robert Browning* 174
The Blind Men and the Elephant, *John Godfrey Saxe* 176
The Battle of Blenheim, *Robert Southey* 176
Three Kings Came Riding, *Henry Wadsworth Longfellow* 177
Hiawatha's Canoe, *Henry Wadsworth Longfellow* 178
Robin Hood and the Ranger, *Old Ballad* 179
Robin Hood and Little John, *Old Ballad* 181
Robin Hood and Allen-a-Dale, *Old Ballad* 182
Meg Merrilies, *John Keats* 184
The Discoverer of the North Cape, *Henry Wadsworth Longfellow* 184
In School Days, *John Greenleaf Whittier* 186
The Courtin', *James Russell Lowell* 186
Lochinvar, *Sir Walter Scott* 188
Lady Clare, *Alfred Tennyson* 189
The Singing Leaves, *James Russell Lowell* 190
Annabel Lee, *Edgar Allan Poe* 191
The Leap of Roushan Beg, *Henry Wadsworth Longfellow* 192
The Pied Piper of Hamelin, *Robert Browning* 193
Skipper Ireson's Ride, *John Greenleaf Whittier* 196
John Anderson, My Jo, *Robert Burns* 198

*STORIES IN VERSE: SUGGESTED GRADES* 198

*COLLECTIONS OF VERSE*

For Younger Children 200
For Older Children 200

PAGE

*BOOKS OF VERSE*
For Younger Children 201
For Older Children 202

*STUDENT ACTIVITIES* 202

*REFERENCES FOR STUDENTS* 203

# *OLD TALES AND LEGENDS*

*FOLK TALES: VALUE AND ORIGIN* 207

OLD TALES

The Three Billy Goats Gruff 213
The Gingerbread Boy 214
The Three Bears 215
The Old Woman and Her Pig 216
The Straw Ox 218
Little Red Riding Hood 219
Aiken-Drum, the Brownie 221
Mr. Vinegar 224
Lazy Jack 225
The Three Little Pigs 226
The Traveling Musicians 229
Why the Bear Is Stumpy-Tailed 230
The Wolf and the Seven Young Goslings 231
The Lad Who Went to the North Wind 232
Jack and the Beanstalk 234
The Elves and the Shoemaker 237
Drakesbill 238
Boots and His Brothers 241
Snow-White and the Seven Dwarfs 243
Hansel and Gretel 247
Snow-White and Rose-Red 251
Cinderella; or, The Little Glass Slipper 254
Brier Rose 258
The Princess on the Glass Hill 259
East of the Sun and West of the Moon 264
The King of the Crocodiles 270
Tom Thumb 272
Puss in Boots 275
Aladdin and the Wonderful Lamp 278
The Prince and the Giant's Daughter 285
Riquet with the Tuft 296
The Tiger, the Brahman, and the Jackal 298

PAGE

The Fables of Aesop
The Lion and the Mouse 299
The Wind and the Sun 300
The Frog and the Ox 300
The Hare and the Tortoise 300
The Crow and the Pitcher 300
The Ant and the Grasshopper 301
The Mice in Council 301
The Dog and the Shadow 301
The Fox and the Grapes 301
The Town Mouse and the Country Mouse 302
Hercules and the Wagoner 302
The Milkmaid and Her Pail 302

*OLD TALES: SUGGESTED GRADES* 303

*BOOKS OF OLD TALES* 304

*MYTHS AND LEGENDS: SIGNIFICANCE AND USE* 307

LEGENDS AND HERO TALES

The Ghost of the Great White Stag, *Arthur C. Parker* 309
Fin McCoul and the Giant, *Joseph Jacobs* 313
The First Harp, *Padraic Colum* 317
The Heroes of Asgard, *A. and E. Keary* 318
The Making of the Hammer, *Emilie Kip Baker* 320
Sigurd the Volsung, *Dorothy Hosford* 324
Pandora, *Emilie Kip Baker* 334
The Winged Horse, *Nathaniel Hawthorne* 337
The Story of Odysseus, *Padraic Colum* 345
The Winning of Atalanta, *Elsie Finnimore Buckley* 350
Gareth and Lynette, *retold from Alfred Tennyson* 362
The Fair Jehane, *Katharine Gibson* 369

*LEGENDS AND HERO TALES: SUGGESTED GRADES* 376

*BOOKS OF LEGENDS AND HERO TALES* 377

*STUDENT ACTIVITIES* 379

*REFERENCES FOR STUDENTS*

Folk Tales 380
Legends and Hero Tales 380
Story Telling 381
Puppets and Plays 381

## *STORIES OF THEN AND NOW*

PAGE

*MODERN LITERATURE FOR CHILDREN* 385

MAKE-BELIEVE STORIES

Ask Mr. Bear, *Marjorie Flack* 393
The First Christmas Tree, *Rose Fyleman* 394
The Tinder Box, *Hans Christian Andersen* 395
The Midnight Voyage, *John Masefield* 399
The Princess and the Pea, *Hans Christian Andersen* 406
The White Cat, *Madame la Comtesse D'Aulnoy* 407
Fairyfoot, *Frances Browne* 415
Pinocchio, *C. Collodi* 420
Little Daylight, *George MacDonald* 423
The Ugly Duckling, *Hans Christian Andersen* 430
The Emperor's New Clothes, *Hans Christian Andersen* 434
Rip Van Winkle, *Washington Irving* 436
The Nightingale, *Hans Christian Andersen* 445

*MAKE-BELIEVE STORIES: SUGGESTED GRADES* 450

*BOOKS OF MAKE-BELIEVE STORIES* 451

STORIES FOR FUN

The Tale of Peter Rabbit, *Beatrix Potter* 455
Little Black Sambo, *Helen Bannerman* 456
The Lion-Hearted Kitten, *Peggy Bacon* 458
The Magic Fish-Bone, *Charles Dickens* 459
The Tar Baby, *Joel Chandler Harris* 465
The Well Story, *Joel Chandler Harris* 466
The Elephant's Child, *Rudyard Kipling* 467
Doctor Dolittle and the Pushmi-Pullyu, *Hugh Lofting* 471
Alice Goes Down the Rabbit-Hole, *Lewis Carroll* 473
Paul Bunyan, *Wallace Wadsworth* 478
The Bold Dragoon, *Washington Irving* 482
Baron Munchausen Goes to the Moon, *Rudolph Erich Raspe* 485

*STORIES FOR FUN: SUGGESTED GRADES* 487

*BOOKS FOR FUN* 488

THE WORLD AND ITS CREATURES

Blue Barns, *Helen Sewell* 490
Plouf, the Little Wild Duck, *Lida* 491
The Gentleman in Brown, *Margery Bianco* 493
Hide and Go Seek, *Dorothy P. Lathrop* 496

PAGE

Skunks, *Edith M. Patch* 501
Rocky Billy Goes Visiting, *Holling Clancy Holling* 502
Keeping Still in the Woods, *Charles G. D. Roberts* 505
The Horny Ones, *Edith M. Patch* and *Carroll Lane Fenton* 511
Jimmie, the White Sparrow, *Padraic Colum* 513
Beasts of the Tar Pits, *W. W. Robinson* 519
Paddlewings Grows Up, *Wilfrid S. Bronson* 521
What We Found in a Fox Den, *Ernest Harold Baynes* 525
With Helmet and Hose, *William Beebe* 527
Jangwa Begins to Hunt, *Walter J. Wilwerding* 530
The Story of a Stone, *David Starr Jordan* 535
The Capture of the Giant Armadillo, *Raymond L. Ditmars* 538

*THE WORLD AND ITS CREATURES: SUGGESTED GRADES* 546

*BOOKS ABOUT THE WORLD AND ITS CREATURES* 547

STORIES ABOUT BOYS AND GIRLS

Lucky Little Lena, *Marjorie Flack* 550
Billy and Blaze, *C. W. Anderson* 551
Grandmother's Buttons, *George* and *Doris Hauman* 552
Pita's Painted Pig, *Elizabeth Morrow* 553
Letters to Channy, *Helvin Chandler Washburne* 554
Mr. Murdle's Large Heart, *Margery Bianco* 557
The Blue Teapot, *Alice Dalgliesh* 560
Jancsi and Kate, *Kate Seredy* 565
Calypso, *Elizabeth Coatsworth* 568
Stories of Other Days in Old Bergen, *Ragnhild Chevalier* 570
Swiss Family Robinson, *Johann David Wyss* 574
The Queen of the Pirate Isle, *Bret Harte* 583
Little Goody Two-Shoes, *ascribed to Oliver Goldsmith* 591
The Bears of Blue River, *Charles Major* 596
Hans Brinker and His Sister, *Mary Mapes Dodge* 599
David and Goliath, *The Bible: I Samuel 17* 602
The Far-Distant Oxus, *Katherine Hull* and *Pamela Whitlock* 605
Little Women Plan Christmas, *Louisa M. Alcott* 609
Christmas with the Cratchits, *Charles Dickens* 611
"Mark Twain," *Cornelia Meigs* 613
Tom Sawyer and His Pirate Crew, *Samuel L. Clemens* 619
The Truce on Treasure Island, *Robert Louis Stevenson* 626

*STORIES ABOUT BOYS AND GIRLS: SUGGESTED GRADES* 629

*BOOKS ABOUT BOYS AND GIRLS* 630

PAGE

THE MAKING OF AMERICA

By Covered Wagon, *Emma L. Brock* 635
Caddie and the Indian Chief, *Carol Ryrie Brink* 639
Two Little Confederates, *Thomas Nelson Page* 644
Hitty Goes to Sea, *Rachel Field* 648
A Night Ride in a Prairie Schooner, *Hamlin Garland* 655
The Pine-Tree Shillings, *Nathaniel Hawthorne* 657
Jacques and the Little Chief, *Frances Gaither* 659
Dick Finds the "Wheel of Fortune," *Cornelia Meigs* 666
Abe Lincoln Grows Up, *Carl Sandburg* 672
Invincible Louisa as a Nurse, *Cornelia Meigs* 675
Blue Arrow and the Outlaws, *Constance Lindsay Skinner* 679
Being a Boy, *Charles Dudley Warner* 685
The Hoosier Schoolmaster, *Edward Eggleston* 691
The Pony Express, *Charles L. Skelton* 695

*THE MAKING OF AMERICA: SUGGESTED GRADES* 702

*BOOKS ABOUT THE MAKING OF AMERICA* 702

WORKERS AND THEIR WORK

Tony, the Steam Shovel Man, *Henry B. Lent* 705
Way Ping, Master of Boats, *Dorothy Rowe* 706
The Small Yellow Train, *Alice Dalgliesh* 709
Rusty Pete, Cow Pony, *Doris Fogler* and *Nina Nicol* 711
Children of Haiti, *Arna Bontemps* and *Langston Hughes* 715
Little Tonino, *Helen Hill* and *Violet Maxwell* 719
Plowing, *Henry B. Lent* 725
Bridget Goes Prospecting, *Berta* and *Elmer Hader* 729
The French Jongleurs, *Katharine Gibson* 733
Behind the Battlements, *Gertrude Hartman* 734
Buck, the Lead-Dog, *Jack London* 736
Talking Wires, *Clara Lambert* 739
The Pearl Diver, *Charles Nordhoff* 740
Chris Farrington: Able Seaman, *Jack London* 743
New York to Paris, *Charles A. Lindbergh* 747
Sand Hogs, *Margaret Norris* 751
Riding the Girders, *Margaret Norris* 751
Robinson Crusoe, *Daniel Defoe* 753
Schumann-Heink's First Contract, *Mary Lawton* 758
John Halifax Faces the Rioters, *Dinah Maria Mulock Craik* 764

*WORKERS AND THEIR WORK: SUGGESTED GRADES* 773

*BOOKS ABOUT WORKERS AND THEIR WORK* 774

PAGE

*BOOKS OF BIOGRAPHY* 777

*NEWBERY MEDAL BOOKS* 779

*CALDECOTT MEDAL BOOKS* 780

*BOOKS THAT ARE EASY TO READ* 781

*STUDENT ACTIVITIES* 785

*REFERENCES FOR STUDENTS* 786

## *APPENDIX*

AUTHORS OF CHILDREN'S BOOKS 791

*REFERENCES FOR STUDENTS* 840

LIST OF SELECTIONS: SUGGESTED GRADES 841

PRONOUNCING GLOSSARY 853

*REFERENCES FOR STUDENTS* 855

INDEX 857

*Books and Children*

# *BOOKS AND CHILDREN*

## *Enjoyment of Literature*

STORY AND VERSE FOR CHILDREN *is designed for prospective teachers, teachers in service, librarians, mothers, and all those whose privilege it is to make books available to children and to share with children their own love of good books.*

There is really no specialized body of literature to be known as *children's literature*. All the world of literature is open to children and to those who work with children; from it they may take those books (or parts of books) that satisfy the needs and interests of children at varying levels of development and growth. Many books that children have taken for their own were not written for children at all, and the great body of traditional literature now so commonly thought of as belonging to children is the best of national literatures of distant times and places—the expression of the hopes and aspirations of whole nations of people now preserved for us and thought of as children's stories. It is in recent times, historically, that poems, stories, and informational materials have been written consciously for children, but it is only when the writers of these materials identify themselves with the world of literature in general and create books that express in simple form the universality of truth and clearness of purpose characteristic of great literature that their books may hope to endure and find a place in children's regard.

This does not mean that adult selections or adult standards shall govern the choice of books for children. Far from it. Emotional and social maturity (or immaturity) of children has its own demands, and these demands must be recognized if children are to cultivate a love for literature that will bring them satisfactions as children and persist as satisfactions throughout their entire lives. The teacher, the librarian, the mother, or the father who aspires to be the agent through whom children come to know and love literature must, first and foremost, have an understanding of children—their needs, desires, thoughts, interests, and daily lives. Then the teacher (or parent) may stand ready to offer a book, a story, a poem at the particular time that it will find an audience. He or she will know well the effect of timeliness and will allow for the fact that groups and individuals vary in their interests. Requirement and compulsion and competition will not be a part of her program. She will know the degree of understanding of which a group or a child is capable; she will know that ability to understand is the result of intelligence, of experience, and of environment. She will know that among children of school age, pleasure from reading books is dependent upon skill in reading; if a selection suitable and interesting in content is too difficult for a child to read himself, she will read it to him; she is too wise to let the mechanical difficulties of reading destroy a child's interest and enthusiasm. She immediately sets about, however, to find other books suitable in content but simple enough in form for the child to read himself, and as he grows in reading ability she continues to provide books adapted to his developing skill.

Some one has said that love of literature cannot be "taught," but it may be "caught." A trite saying, perhaps, but a true one. Love and enthusiasm for good books shared with children, communicates itself to them. That is a sincere and genuine love does. Children are quick to recognize superficiality and insincerity in praise of books, and in such a situation, up go barriers of defense. If children suspect that an adult has an ulterior motive in the recommendation of a book, the book is immediately condemned. Requirement may force the reading of a particular book, but love of reading cannot be built by requirement; it is much more likely that all reading will stop when the requirement is fulfilled. On the other hand, true love of books and enjoyment of them can be shared, and children are quick to respond and participate in a cooperative venture that gives them so much pleasure.

There are then two things needed in the equipment of one who wishes to teach literature to children—an understanding of children and a genuine appreciation of literature. An appreciation of literature is deepened and broadened by acquaintance with it. By acquaintance we do not mean analysis and dissection of literature but a wide reading and enjoyment of it. In the words of Mrs. Browning:

"We get no good
By being ungenerous, even to a book,
And calculating profits,—so much help
By so much reading. It is rather when
We gloriously forget ourselves and plunge
Soul-forward, headlong, into a book's profound,
Impassioned for its beauty and salt of truth—
'Tis then we get the right good from a book."
(Elizabeth Barrett Browning: *Aurora Leigh*)

This is not to say that knowledge and benefit cannot be got from reading, as every student knows. It is rather to say that deeper and more enduring values are there, values that can be made the permanent possession of those who desire them. Further, it is not to say that one's reading should be confined to the so-called masterpieces of literature. An acquaintance with books reveals many pleasant books—not great books but pleasant books--that bring satisfaction for the moment and may be forgotten. One who reads widely realizes that relaxation alone is the legitimate function of some books and that within limits an escape from reality is a desirable balance in living.

A college student who is a member of a class in *Children's Literature* may easily combine two purposes in her study. Her strongest objective, of course, is to acquire a wide acquaintance with children's books and to develop a sensitiveness that will enable her to choose such books wisely and to offer them to children in ways that will be acceptable to children themselves. In addition, a student may enlarge her own experience with literature through exploring children's books. Worthwhile books for children have the same enduring qualities that mark worthwhile books for adults. If a student will give herself up to the beauty, truth, and fun to be found in children's books, reading them may be a delightful experience in itself as well as a valuable preparation for her future work as a teacher. Reading books for children requires no special set of attitudes and no method of approach peculiar to the books themselves. Simply read and enjoy them, as children do. Sometimes the business of reading books is thought of as a process of great seriousness and not to be undertaken lightly. Such a point of view tends to hedge about with restrictions an experience that should be pleasant, natural, and satisfying.

# *Children's Books*

IT HAS been said that all great artists maintain a directness and simplicity in thinking that is childlike in quality. Many fortunate adults maintain this childlikeness throughout their entire lives. There is no quality of thinking more important in the equipment of one who would teach literature to children. Can we as adults recapture some of the thoughts and feelings of childhood? It will give us insight in selecting books for children if we can.

Perhaps the best beginning for developing the insight needed to select books for children is to try to recall the reading of one's own childhood. What stories, poems, and books did you like so well as a child that you still remember them? Would the story of the reading you did as a child be at all like the following account written by Hamlin Garland?

## BOOKS OF MY CHILDHOOD [1]

*Hamlin Garland*

My childhood's reading was entirely catch-as-catch-can. My father's family were New Englanders and essentially bookish, but when they migrated from Maine to Wisconsin in 1850 they took very few books with them, and the McClintock's, my mother's people, though highly musical were not given to reading in any unusual degree. I cannot recall any books in their home other than the Bible. I do not recall that grandfather Hugh took any periodical other than the county paper. His sons and daughters who played the dulcimer, organ, and violin were not given to the buying of books and our neighbors were all equally "shy" on print. I cannot say that I grew up in a library.

One of the earliest of my books was a Christmas present, a very tiny little volume called *Aladdin and His Wonderful Lamp,* which had in it all the magic of the East. It told of a poor boy and his magic lamp which needed only to be rubbed to furnish forth a palace and a glorious table laden with meat and fruits. Included in this book was "Beauty and the Beast" and no novel of today has anything better than the enthralling power of that romance. It swept me away into regions where gold and silver and silken raiment were at the command of a Sorcerer and where men and beasts could change forms under spell. For fifty years I have been trying to write, but I am not able to put into words the witchery of these tales. They stirred me vaguely, powerfully, and inexplicably.

[1] From *The Saturday Review of Literature,* VII:347. Reference to *Authors of Children's Books,* in the Appendix of this volume, will give information concerning the authors of all the selections which are included in this book.

In 1870 we moved from my native valley in Wisconsin out upon the wild prairies of Iowa, and almost before we were settled I began borrowing books from our neighbors. My search yielded *Ivanhoe, Tempest and Sunshine, The Scottish Chief,* and a tattered volume of adventures on the seas.

The village of Osage had not yet established its public library or if it had I did not know it. We owned Franklin's *Autobiography, The Life of P. T. Barnum, The Female Spy,* and Milton's *Paradise Lost.* Among these books *Ivanhoe* was naturally my favorite. I read it with such complete absorption that time and place were lost. My interest in Richard the Lion-hearted had been whetted by two selections in McGuffey's Reader, the one called "The Storming of the Castle" and the other, "The Duel in the Desert" or some such title. From that time to this, I have read every new and careful study of Richard, who is still one of the most attractive of all the English kings, notwithstanding the fact that he was a Norman and lived in England only a few months of his reign. In truth, I got my first taste for Longfellow, Whittier, Scott, Dickens, Hawthorne, and Shakespeare from McGuffey's Readers. They cannot be left out of the record. Gray's "Elegy," Scott's "Marmion," Campbell's "Lochiel's Warning," and many other poems read for the first time in these schoolbooks, remain in memory to this day.

With nothing else handy, I read and reread Franklin's *Autobiography, The Life of P. T. Barnum,* and *The Spy of the Rebellion.* Barnum made me aware of New York City and Bridgeport (to my thinking they were of equal importance), and Franklin's writing was like the almanac, wise, dryly humorous in such chapters as that in which he told of paying too much for his whistle, but he did not succeed in interesting me as Scott did.

As this is to be a truthful account of my early reading, I shall be obliged to confess that I borrowed from a neighbor a huge pile of back-numbers of a weekly paper called *The New York Saturday Night,* a story paper which was the complement of *The New York Ledger.* I read these pages with such delight as I have never since known. Only my father's voice could rouse me from their magic and secure my services in such household chores as bringing in wood or water. I came to my meals in a daze. At last my father took stern measures and ordered the return of these papers.

My reading of *The Ledger* and *The Saturday Night* led to the discovery of Beadle's Dime Novels. This may be another shocking confession, but I shall include it and let the editor blue-pencil it if he thinks it harmful. These novels were small volumes bound in yellow paper and with most alluring titles. *The Phantom Horsemen of the Plains, The Quaker Detective, Buckskin Bill, Dare Devil Dan, King of the Rockies,* and the like. They cost ten cents each, but if you kept your copy clean you could exchange it at Dailey's drugstore for another by paying five cents. In this way you could read twenty of these tales for a dollar, and by exchanging among your neighbors you could almost double this number. Whether this kind of reading did me any harm or not is a question, but I am certain that it gave me more pleasure than anything else of that time except the circus, for the circus came only once a year while Beadle's Dime Novels were always on sale at the drugstore.

It is only justice to add that I soon gained a perception of something different and better. One day in the autumn of 1871 my father brought home from Osage a little magazine called *Hearth and Home* in which was a story about people whose amusements, like our own, included singing schools, revival meetings, and spelling bees. It was called "The Hoosier School Master" and was written by a man named Edward Eggleston, and so keen was our interest in this serial story, I struggled with my sister each month to see who should win the first chance to read the continuation of the tale.

This speaks well for the novel and reflects some credit on me as well as on my sister. We did not know where the Hoosiers lived, but we understood them. They were somewhat like the folk who lived over on the Little Cedar, sort of backwoods people, but we felt in "Ralph Hartsook" something very like our own teacher. We knew a man like "Bud Means," in fact one of the big boys in my class was of that muscular, thick-headed sort. I admired "Ivanhoe," but I was able also to rejoice over Bud's victory and Hannah's release from bondage.

In this singular mixture of Franklin, Scott, Eggleston, and Old Sleuth I approached my sixteenth year, when my father gave up his farm and moved into the village of Osage to be the grain merchant for the Grange. In the autumn of that year I became a student in the Cedar Valley Seminary, which was the pride of the county, and in its library I came upon two small volumes which changed my world for me. They were *Mosses from an Old Manse,* by Nathaniel Hawthorne. Here was magic of a higher sort, words with a nobler music. For days I neglected my studies. I carried one of these volumes in my pocket and read it at every opportunity. I read it while walking along the street. I read it while eating my supper, pondering on such tales as "The Artist of the Beautiful," feeling something vast and timeless in them.

With these volumes my boyish reading ended. Thereafter I read as a student, vaguely aware of the problems which beset the American novelist, the poet, and the playwright.

# *Selecting Books for Children*

THE teacher or parent who wishes a child to have freedom in the choice of books is not in the position of doing nothing about the matter. The way in which we can best serve the reading needs of children is to make books available to them in as large number and variety and of as high quality as possible. If we discover that a child is reading a book that seems to us unworthy, we need not put a premium upon the book by condemning it. We know that to condemn books, even with adults, is to advertise them. Instead, we may offer a book of genuine merit that contains the same qualities that attracted the child to the unworthy book. Surprise, suspense, vivid characters, and fast-moving action are the qualities that the child seeks and we can make sure that he finds them in books of genuine value.

As a friendly counselor, we also attempt to provide for each child a variety of experiences in reading. A child whose reading is confined to one kind of book may become interested in books of entirely different content if the latter are attractive and suited to his understanding. This does not mean that a child shall be expected to give up the literature that he likes best. He may, however, by friendly suggestion be led to explore books that are new to him and as a result widen and deepen his experiences.

The reading interests of children may find satisfaction in a variety of subjects presented in a variety of forms. Poetry, fanciful and realistic fiction, humor and nonsense, science, history, biography—all have their place in literature for children. The material in *Story and Verse for Children* has been selected to present a well-rounded and balanced program of children's reading. Reference to the table of Contents will show that selections representative of a wide range of material have been included. In addition to the selections themselves, the book lists that follow each group of selections will serve as guides to other materials of similar content.

Every year hundreds of books are published for children. Their quality varies. Some endure and find a permanent place in literature, many are forgotten. Discrimination in selecting the books to be offered to children is needed. We want to keep in children's libraries books that have met the test of time and to add new publications of quality and value. There are no rigid or fixed measures by which a book may be selected or rejected. But we grow in judgment as we increase our acquaintance with children's books and with children.

It is true that conditions of present-day living have added new demands in children's reading. Children want to understand the scientific and industrial age in which we live, and as a result informational books for children are being written and published in larger number than at any period in the history of children's literature. We want such books in children's libraries, but their selection should be made with the same care that is given to the selection of imaginative literature. Too often the only standards applied to such books are the accuracy and the extent of the facts they contain. This is a short-sighted standard for selection. Facts have a way of not remaining facts; experiments and discoveries displace them with newer facts. Facts alone may contribute little to an understanding of the reality of human relations, but an understanding of human relations can give significance to facts. It is a combination of these factors that makes an informational book valuable. The authors of such books for children sometimes think that their books are easier to understand if the information is condensed. Just the opposite is really the case. Children need more details to understand clearly than do adults, for the child's limited experience gives him a limited background with which to understand. It seems not too much to ask also that such books, even in their simplest forms, shall have literary excellence and be free of artificial devices for conveying information.

Provision for well-rounded experiences in literature will give an important place to poetry. Poetry is ages old and in its varied forms has always been the way mankind has given expression to something more than ideas. Like music, its rhythms and cadences are universal in their emotional appeal. Children find great pleasure in hearing poetry; that is, if their experience has been free of unfortunate happenings, such as most adults can easily call to mind, in connection with it. A suitable poem read casually but well, often without comment, will find an audience. The teacher who continues to read well-selected verse and read it well, will soon have eager listeners. It is a natural step for children to attempt to write verses of their own and even to put them to music.

In the varied experiences which literature can give to children, there is a place for the old folk and fairy tales. Children now as ever need the faculty of idealizing human relations and a belief in the possibility of improving human situations. In the old tales daring, bravery, originality, and clear thinking often transform a commonplace character into a hero. There are no confused issues remaining when the tales are done; justice and right win. The old folk tales have a quality indispensable in children's stories—that of robustness. They are free of sickly sentimentality and artificiality, which are the elements most to be avoided in all literature for children.

Children love to find funny and ridiculous things in stories. The humor they like is not always the humor adults think they will like. For young children it is largely a love of the grotesque and of situations in which things "tumble down." Even children who are older relish humor that is clear cut and lacking in subtlety. They resent satire that wounds at the same time that it pretends to amuse. People of all ages need fun and nonsense as a balance to the over-serious tendency of living. We can find many excellent poems and stories for children that violate no canons of good taste but offer abundant opportunity for the wholesome release in laughter so necessary to well-being.

The reading needs of adolescent children require special consideration. Such children want books that picture life as a "flashing river of bright adventure." Romance, chivalry, and accounts of everyday living—all have their appeal. Studies of children's interests in books have shown differences in the preferences of adolescent boys and adolescent girls, particularly at the ages of about twelve and thirteen years when girls develop a strong interest in domestic life. Present-day girls, however, lead such active lives that more and more they are demanding forceful books with plenty of action such as boys like, rather than the sentimental stories labeled girls' books.

In efforts to select books to satisfy the varied and changing interests of children, one needs to draw upon acquaintance with literature and with life and upon knowledge and understanding of children. We try to make our judgments of the books we offer as discriminating as possible, but the final evaluation of them must always rest with children themselves.

# Children's Interests in Reading

ONE of the most profitable experiences a prospective teacher can have is to spend an afternoon in the children's room of a busy public library. She will note with pleasure the physical arrangements for the comfort of children—the low tables and chairs and the book shelves that children can reach. She will notice the attractive bulletin boards, the posters announcing new books, and special exhibits of interest to children. Perhaps the library she is visiting has a fireplace or other favored spot where the librarian holds story hours for children at convenient times.

We will assume that our observer is familiar with the classification system in use and the position of the shelves containing the different types of books. By looking at the appearance of books she can learn much that is enlightening in regard to children's interests in reading. The books they love are worn and soiled and require frequent rebinding. There are several duplicate copies of the books most in demand. A book that has been in the library for some time and has its original covers fresh and unsoiled has failed to attract children. It is interesting to speculate why.

When the children arrive for their daily selection of books, the unobtrusive observer can learn a great deal. She will probably be astonished at the businesslike way in which children choose their books. There is much less indecision in their actions than in those of a group of adults. As a rule children know what they want and where to find it. When they consult a librarian, their explanations are clear and to the point. They may be uncertain as to exact titles of books, but they are certain in their likes and dislikes among books.

When the children's room closes for the day, perhaps our observer may borrow duplicate copies of some of the books that have been in demand. Perhaps she may take some of them home with her and attempt to discover what it is that makes them satisfying to children.

Observations such as we have described are helpful in understanding children's interests in reading. In working with children, however, we learn to study the interests of each group and each child and make the best provision we can to satisfy them. Needs and interests vary, but the wider one's observation, the more sensitive one becomes to the variations in groups and in individuals.

There is no doubt that children are discriminating in their choices and that they recognize good books. A number of careful experimental studies of children's reading interests have been made and they show that children, at all levels of intelligence, are appreciative of the quality of the materials they read. They really do discriminate and express consistent preferences.

Jordan[1] reports a carefully conducted investigation of children's reading based upon library withdrawals and upon questionnaires to children. After an interval of five years he gave the same questionnaire to other children and found a striking similarity in the returns of the investigations. The boys and girls he studied ranged in age from 9 to 18 years. He found marked differences in the interests of boys and of girls, with the greatest difference in interests at the ages of 12 and 13 years. The major interest of the boys at all ages was adventure. The literature most popular with them pictured strenuous adventure, mastery, love of sensory life, loyalty, and self-control. The major interests of the girls were home life and stories that pictured kindliness, attention to others, and response to approval and to scornful behavior. *The Call of the Wild, Treasure Island,* Boy Scout books, and books by Joseph Altsheler stood high in boys' choices; the most popular book among girls was *Little Women.*

From the Stanford research on gifted children in California, Terman and Lima[2] report on the reading of 1,000 children of very high intelligence compared with 1,000 unselected children, the ages ranging from 6 to 16 years. The types of material standing highest in the regard of both the gifted boys and the boys of the unselected group were adventure and informational fiction, but the reading of the gifted boys showed a much larger proportion of books of science, history, and biography than that of the boys of the unselected group. The books best liked by both groups of girls were stories of home and school life and of adventure, but the girls of the unselected group revealed a greater liking for emotional fiction than the gifted girls. The children of all four groups showed an interest in fairy tales and animal stories. The books reported by the children in this investigation were uniformly books of value and literary merit, due, the investigators believe, to the fact that the children had access to good books.

An extensive investigation of children's reading was made by Washburne and Vogel[3] assisted by committees of the American Library Association. In thirty-four cities, 36,750 children furnished reports giving their opinions of all the books they read during a school year. Over 9,000 different books were reported. Librarians rated the literary merit of the 800 books most frequently reported and considered 100 of them low in quality. The books high in children's choices, however, were in the main considered acceptable by the librarians. Among the books given high rank by children were the following: Grade IV—*Grimms' Fairy Tales, Peter Pan, Fairies and Chimneys,* and *The Story of Mrs. Tubbs;* Grade V—*Black Beauty, Pinocchio, The Story of Dr. Dolittle,* and *Alice's Adventures in Wonderland;* Grade VI—*Heidi, Hans Brinker, Toby Tyler,* and *The Peterkin Papers;* Grade VII—*Tom Sawyer, Little Women, Huckleberry Finn,* and *Treasure Island;* Grade VIII

[1] Arthur M. Jordan, *Children's Interests in Reading.* University of North Carolina Press.

[2] Lewis M. Terman and Margaret Lima, *Children's Reading.* D. Appleton-Century Company.

[3] Carleton Washburne and Mabel Vogel, *Winnetka Graded Book List,* American Library Association; *The Right Book for the Right Child,* The John Day Company.

—*The Call of the Wild, Kidnapped, Penrod,* and *The Dark Frigate;* Grade IX—*Jim Davis, Sherlock Holmes, Lorna Doone,* and *A Tale of Two Cities.*

Seegers[1] reports an analysis of the undirected, uncontrolled reading of books done outside school hours by 924 pupils in a large city. These children read a wide variety of books, many of good quality and others of doubtful value. He believes that most of the selections were due to availability. He found that many of the children were susceptible to suggestion and read and enjoyed a great number of desirable books recommended by their teachers. *Tom Sawyer* was read by a larger number of boys than any other book, and *Little Women* by a larger number of girls. Seegers reports also that among the most frequently read books were many that the children had recently seen produced as motion pictures. This was true not only of the classics, but of less desirable books. Librarians from various parts of the United States have reported the same result from books pictured upon the screen, and this seems to indicate that motion pictures may be a means of stimulating reading instead of supplanting it. It has been observed, too, that children express pleasure when they find a screen version faithful to the original book.

Huber, Bruner, and Curry[2] conducted an experiment involving 50,000 children and 1,500 teachers geographically distributed over the United States, to determine the poetry most suitable for children in the elementary and junior high schools. From the opinion of teachers and writers and from courses of study, 100 poems for each school grade were chosen and published in experimental booklets which were put into the hands of children taking part in the experiment. The procedure was so worked out that each booklet was used over a range of five grades. During a period of a year each child came in contact with at least 60 poems. The reactions of each child were recorded and studied, and the findings have had a marked influence upon the selection and grade placement of poetry for children.

In the Huber-Bruner-Curry experiment it was found that children at all age levels have decided preferences and that these preferences differ at different age levels. Exception to this was found in the case of 59 poems which were high in children's choices over a range of three or more grades; these poems appear to contain elements of compelling interest for children of various ages. This situation seems to suggest that certain literature for children belongs in any grade—that certain poems, and probably stories also, hold the interest of readers of all ages, perhaps from "seven to seventy." Other materials, in themselves good but lacking the qualities of universal appeal, need to be considered more carefully and offered to children of the particular ages to which they are suited.

In this experiment, "The Raggedy Man,"[3] by James Whitcomb Riley, was used in the first five grades and called out a reaction of preference far ex-

[1] J. C. Seegers, "A Study of Children's Reading," *Elementary English Review,* XIII : 251.

[2] Miriam Blanton Huber, Herbert B. Bruner, and Charles M. Curry, *Children's Interests in Poetry.* Rand McNally and Company.

[3] "The Raggedy Man," by James Whitcomb Riley, may be found on page 80 of this volume.

ceeding any other poem. In the first, second, and fourth grades it ranked first in children's choices; in the third, second; and in the fifth grade, fifth. It, however, held in the second grade a weighted score that indicated its greatest interest there. Why do children like "The Raggedy Man" so much? Is it the dialect or the social situation? Or is it one of the following: animals, play, outdoor activities, fairies, magic, humor, surprise, choosing a life career, kindness, or a vivid lovable character? Or do all of these combine in the poem to give satisfaction to children?

In reading the poems arranged for each grade according to children's choices as shown by this experiment, it seems possible to detect a growing maturity in taste; there appears to be some unity of interest in a grade, but each grade shows a variety of interests. In Grade I the greatest interests appear to be animals and play; in Grade II many lullabies and poems about children are liked; in Grade III many fairy poems are found to be of interest as are poems of the outdoors; in Grade IV humor and nonsense make a high appeal, as do poems of patriotism; in Grade V many ballads and poems of heroes are liked; in Grade VI interest divides between home and danger, but poems of romance also receive recognition; in Grade VII humor continues to rank high, but the humorous situations become more complex, there are fewer hero poems although many bloody encounters, and there is an increased love of romance; in Grade VIII romance, tragedy, and retribution hold the stage; in Grade IX the poems high in regard are more reflective and thoughtful, as if the readers are seeking the causes of things. A surprisingly large number of the poems strongly preferred by boys and girls in this experiment are written in dialect. Children unhesitatingly delight in the human quality and homely artistry of dialect in literature. Their choices throughout show the satisfaction children find in verse that pictures action and the vivid quality of living.

Workers in children's literature are indebted to Dunn[1] for a study of the factors in stories that hold the greatest interest for children in the primary grades. Her study reports stories that children like and, by a process of analysis, the qualities in them that are believed to appeal most highly to young children. Thirty-one samples of primary reading material were arranged in forty pairs and read to 195 different classes in Grades I, II, and III. After each pair was read, the children expressed their preference. Among the stories that stood high in children's choices were "One Eye, Two Eyes, and Three Eyes," "The Wolf and the Seven Kids," "Epaminondas," "Boots and His Brothers," and "A Story of Washington's Boyhood." The thirty-one stories were analyzed by adult judges for the presence of one or more of twenty characteristics previously selected as significant in interest to children. The data statistically treated led to the following conclusions: The interests of boys and girls of these ages are very similar. The characteristics of greatest interest are *surprise* and *plot* for both boys and girls; *animalness* (presence of animals in the story) for boys; *childness* (presence of child

[1] Fannie Wyche Dunn, *Interest Factors in Primary Reading.* Teachers College Bureau of Publications.

characters in the story), *familiar experience,* and to a lesser extent *repetition* and *conversation* for girls.

It is interesting to find that in this experiment *liveliness* had an unfavorable effect upon children's choices. Children are quick to detect artificial sprightliness and reject it in favor of genuine plot in which things really happen. The fact that *surprise* outranks *plot* leads to some interesting speculations also. Factual material in nature study and science may be made very attractive to children if unexpected phenomena are presented simply enough for them to understand.

Many questions have arisen in regard to the reading interests of dull children and superior children. Do dull and superior children wish to read about the same things? Do children of average intelligence have the same reading interests as children of more intelligence or less intelligence? To find an answer to these questions, Huber[1] presented selections from children's literature to groups of children of different levels of intelligence under experimental conditions and made comparisons of their reactions and preferences.

Thirty poems and stories were selected as representative of the following types of material: *familiar experience, unusual experience, humor, fancy, information,* and *heroism and service.* Groups of expert judges rated each selection for literary quality, for suitability, and for difficulty. The selections were arranged in pairs so that each type of material might be presented in comparison with all the other types.

The subjects of the experiment were 408 children in fifteen classes in five typical good public schools. Six of the fifteen classes were considered in their schools as dull, five as average, and four as superior. The dull groups were organized in "special" or ungraded classes, and the average and superior groups were taken from Grades I, II, III, IV, and V. An intelligence rating was secured for each child from an individual Stanford-Binet Intelligence Test. The experiment was conducted with each class separately in its individual classroom, but for greater accuracy the pupils were re-sorted into three groups before the results were tabulated. These groups were arranged so that they were approximately equal in average chronological age, about nine years, and in number of years in school; and the children of the average and bright groups were approximately equal in grade status. The one marked difference in the groups was intelligence.

The stories and poems in pairs were read to the children under pleasant and enjoyable conditions. Each child indicated a preference in each pair. The resulting data were treated by statistical methods which made provision for the relation between children's preferences and the judges' ratings of quality and difficulty. The results showed clearly that the reading interests of children at different levels of intelligence, as measured by the materials used in this experiment, are strikingly similar. The material liked best by the dull, the average, and the bright children was unmistakably that of the

[1] Miriam Blanton Huber, *The Influence of Intelligence upon Children's Reading Interests.* Teachers College Bureau of Publications.

fourth type, *fancy*. The stories and poems of that type used were: "The Gingerbread Boy," "A Visit from St. Nicholas," "The Tinder Box," "A Story of the Springtime," and "The Selfish Giant."

The order of preference of the other five types of material was the same for the average and the superior children as were the choices of the dull, except that the dull children placed *humor* lower than did the average and bright children. The dull children liked the selections of *familiar experience* better than did the average and bright children, but they liked them least, as did all the children, though the adult judges rated those selections less difficult than the others. The order of preference of the average and bright children in the types of material was as follows: (1) *fancy*, (2) *humor*, (3) *unusual experience*, (4) *heroism and service*, (5) *information*, and (6) *familiar experience*. The choices of the dull children were in the same order, except that *humor* fell to fourth place, with *unusual experience* second and *heroism and service* third. The humorous selections used were: "Frogs at School," "The Baby Elephant and the Red Cap," "The Tar Baby," "The Elephant's Child," and "The Walrus and the Carpenter."

The results of this experiment indicate that the reading interests of dull children are strikingly similar to the reading interests of average and superior children. Dull children, however, are more influenced by difficulty and complexity than are more intelligent children. It follows, then, that dull children, attempting to read for themselves, find difficulty of language and complexity of ideas serious handicaps. To provide satisfying books that dull children can read is an opportunity for service that no teacher or librarian should overlook. Many dull children have special abilities, and many have integrity and strength of character that enable them to become useful members of society. Provision for enjoyment in reading is as necessary for them as for children more fortunately endowed in intelligence. Often the problem is met by offering the dull child a book written for younger children because it is easy reading. The dull boy, however, wants to read about the same things that other boys of his age like to read about, and a "babyish" book not only fails to interest him but disgusts him. An over-age girl also cannot be satisfied by literary fare suitable for younger children; she would like to read about the things that interest girls of her own age *if she could read the books*. Struggles with difficult words, involved sentence structure, and abstract ideas soon lead to discouragement and reading is abandoned. On pages 781-784 of this volume may be found a list of books which have proved satisfying to over-age children and children retarded in reading. These books are simple in language and style but their content is high in general interest. The reading needs of dull children have not received sufficient attention and the supply of suitable books is limited.

Experimental studies of children's interests in reading have resulted in a wholesome respect for children's tastes. Today a child's book is judged not only by literary standards but in the light of whether children will like it or not. Regard for children's preferences has not lowered literary standards, for children prove themselves excellent judges of literary quality. When they choose books of little merit, it is largely because that is the kind of books available to them. When they are given access to good books, they develop an appreciation of them. This is a different situation from one in which adults make the choices for children, and this changed emphasis is the very heart of providing successful experiences in literature.

In the studies of children's interests, the conditions of the experiments were purposely arranged to discover the reactions of children to the literature itself, with as little influence of other factors as possible. In ordinary situations, many factors peculiar to the situation are present, and the alert teacher or parent takes advantage of them. Groups of children, and individual children, have special interests that may be capitalized. A stamp collection may lead to absorbed reading of history and travel. The natural environment or industrial environment in which children live may be the starting point for wide reading. The activities and experiences of the school offer rich opportunities for exploration in books. With these special incentives and purposes, children will find satisfaction in books that under other conditions they might consider uninteresting. Even difficulties in language and style may sometimes be surmounted by the drive of real purposes. The teacher who is sensitive to all such possibilities modifies what she knows of children's interests in general to suit the needs and desires of the children about her.

# *Illustrated Books for Children*

THE student of children's literature will be interested not only in the content of the children's books she examines but will be delighted with the beautiful illustrations they contain. In her observation of children's reactions to books, she will be alert to discover the influence that illustrations have upon children's choices of books. This is particularly true of recent books, for there has been no development in the field of children's books so significant as that of illustration. An understanding of the pleasure that children find in books requires consideration of this aspect of the question and it is, in itself, a subject of absorbing interest. If one has not previously given much attention to the pictures in children's books, a study of them will be valuable.

The physical make-up of a book is often taken for granted or, if thought of, is considered a mechanical process with little relation to the subject of literature. As a matter of fact, beautiful and satisfying books for children result from a combination of three arts—the art of the writer, the typographer, and the illustrator. The text is the author's expression of life as he sees it, given in a form that children can understand and share. But the author's creation must reach his readers through the medium of print and paper, and to capture and hold within the covers of a book the author's spirit and purpose is much more than a mechanical process; the selection of type, engraving, binding—the whole process of book designing—calls for imagination and insight. Last but not least is the illustrator, whose pictures may enrich and expand the author's meaning and add immeasurably to the delight of the children who read the book.

The illustrations in a book may be beautiful and significant, but the illustrations, like the text, are set in a frame of typographical design that can enhance or mar their value. The pleasing appearance of a page, the texture of paper and binding, the satisfying "feel" of the book in the hand are not accidental, nor are they the result of mechanical skill alone. Designing the format of a book is a creative process, and a design of beauty is the work of an artist.

The first principle in all good design is "fitness to purpose"; a book is intended to be read, therefore legibility is of paramount importance. Legibility in children's books is dependent upon clear type of ample size in comparatively short lines. White space, or leading, between lines is essential, as are fairly wide margins. Paper, binding, and stitching of leaves need to be sturdy. These considerations are practical, but they may be attained without sacrifice of beauty and charm and without undue expense in manufacture.

The history of printing and book designing is a long and honorable one. The creation and development of type faces is an interesting chapter in that history. One who designs a book today has the choice of a number of different styles of type, a heritage of several centuries of fine craftsmanship. A fairly recent development in books for young children is hand lettering of text to take the place of type. The purpose is to secure unity of text and illustration and to give a feeling of informality. In only a few instances has the plan been successful; on the whole the hand-lettered text is inferior in design to well-selected type and is much more difficult for children to read.

In the majority of cases, the manuscript of a book comes to the publisher without illustrations, and the designer, or editor, secures the illustrator who seems best suited to express the author's mood and purpose. The successfully illustrated book is one in which the text and pictures have the same atmosphere and feeling, the same dramatic quality.

The choice of binding is the final step in making a book. Not only should the binding be strong enough for much handling, but it should tie together the typography and illustrations and in color and design give the reader a clue to the content of the book.

Harmony of workmanship that produces a beautiful book is the result of much care and thoughtful planning. Such care and consideration given to large numbers of children's books is a development of the present century. Today dozens of publishers are giving to the production of children's books the attention formerly given only to limited and expensive editions of adult books, and today beautiful children's books in most cases sell for less than the average popular novel. Recognition of fine production in the juvenile field has been given by the American Institute of Graphic Arts, which annually selects the fifty books published during the year deemed to be outstanding in typography and illustration. Two well-known children's books that have received this award are *Hitty: Her First Hundred Years* by Rachel Field, illustrated by Dorothy Lathrop, and *Seven Simeons,* written and illustrated by Boris Artzybasheff.

That children are sensitive to the physical make-up of books cannot be doubted. The limited amount of experimental evidence available shows that even young children have definite preferences in the formats of books. Bamberger[1] conducted a series of experiments with children of the first, second, and third grades, in which the children had an opportunity to select their favorite among five different editions of well-loved stories. An analysis of results shows that numerous illustrations make a book desirable to children and that large pictures are preferred to small ones. Younger children prefer colors with a great deal of brightness and older children gradually grow into a preference for softer tints and tones. Pictures that tell a story and contain humor and action are favored. In these experiments size appeared to be a factor in book selection. Small, diminutive books were not

[1] Florence E. Bamberger, *The Effect of the Physical Make-up of a Book upon Children's Selection.* Johns Hopkins University Press.

liked as well as large ones, and the editions with the largest type were chosen. The cover appeared to exert a strong influence; children prefer an illustrated cover and a binding of bright color.

Mellinger[1] secured evidence concerning the kind of pictures children like. She conducted a series of experiments with children of the first, third, and fifth grades, in which they made choices between realistic representation and conventionalized representation of the same subjects presented in black and white and in color. The children in all three grades definitely preferred the realistic pictures to the conventionalized or stylized drawings, and they preferred color to black and white.

Experimental data concerning specific items of format, such as size of type, length of line, etc., are limited due to the difficulty of keeping other factors constant so that justifiable conclusions may be drawn. The story content, the child's previous experience, the timeliness of contact with a book —so many elements influence preferences. Observation also bears out the fact that beautiful illustration and format alone will not hold children's attention; if the text is dull, superficial, or insincere, children will neglect the book no matter how elaborate its dress. On the other hand, if the content is high in interest, beautiful illustration and design deepen and enrich the child's enjoyment and such a book will be literally worn out with much reading and handling.

Some of the well-loved characters of children's stories have been given such distinctive personalities by the artists who pictured them that it is impossible to visualize the characters in any other form than that given by the artists. *Alice* would not be *Alice* in any other dress than that of John Tenniel; in fact, an edition of *Alice's Adventures in Wonderland* with new illustrations published a few years ago met with loud protest from both children and adults. There are many such examples, and a student to be well acquainted with children's books needs to be familiar with the work of outstanding artists who have illustrated books for children, artists of historical importance and of contemporary interest.

The hard usage to which children's books are subjected accounts for the comparatively few examples of juvenile books of earlier times that are still in existence. Children wore them out. Those that have come down to us are prized by collectors and hold honored places in museums, libraries, and private collections. From them we can reconstruct the history of children's books, aided by accounts and references in adult books of the same periods. We have to depend upon the latter for our knowledge of some of the well-loved children's books of even a century ago, as no copies are known to exist.

The large number of beautiful children's books available today makes it difficult to imagine how the early books must have looked. The earliest of

[1] Bonnie E. Mellinger, *Children's Interests in Pictures.* Teachers College Bureau of Publications.

which we have any knowledge was the *Hornbook,*[1] which was almost the only child's book in existence in the sixteenth and seventeenth centuries. It was really not a book at all, but a single sheet of paper covered with horn and mounted on thin oak, with a handle for the reader to hold. The one illustrated on this page is the famous Bateman *Hornbook,* now in the Bateman Museum in England, believed to have been made about 1649. The back is covered with leather and stamped with an equestrian statue of Charles I. The initials T. H. are thought to refer to the engraver.

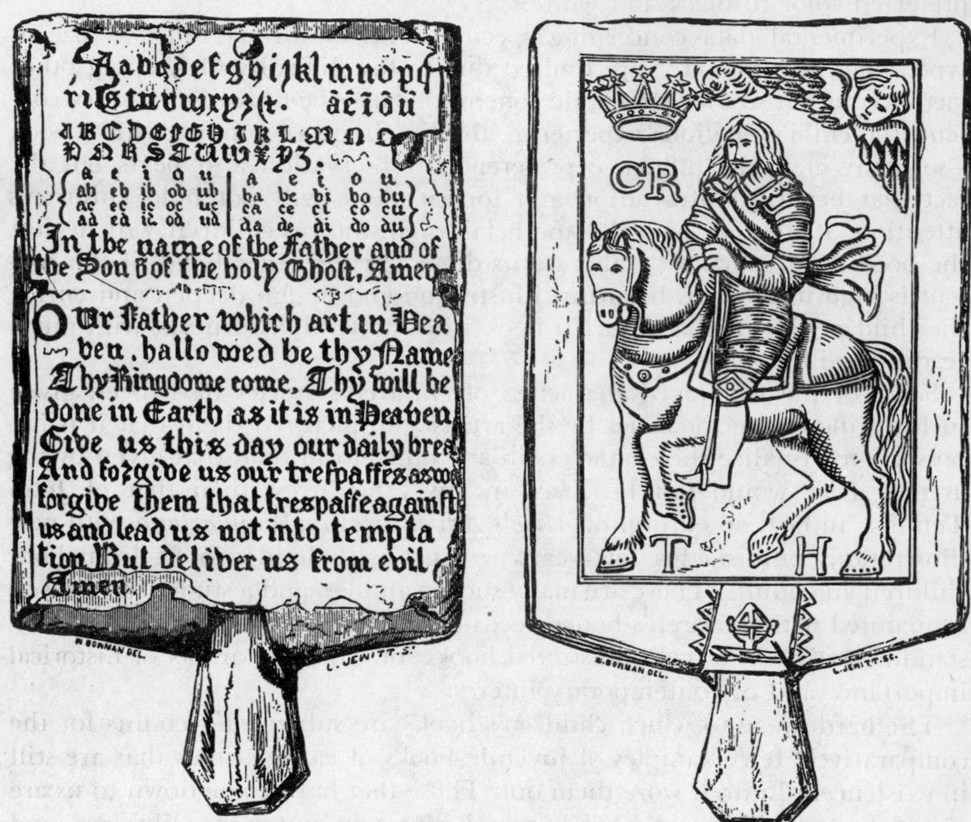


The Bateman *Hornbook,* believed to have been made in England in 1649.

The first child's book printed in America was *The New England Primer,* issued in the latter part of the seventeenth century. It contained about 100 small pages, filled with lessons, Bible quotations, and the catechism. The content that most nearly approached a child's book as we know it today was the alphabet with accompanying rhymes. The examples shown here are

[1] Further details concerning hornbooks and *The New England Primer* may be found on pages 385, 386.

reproduced from the oldest copy of *The New England Primer* extant, printed by Kneeland and Green in Boston in 1727, now in the Lenox Collection of the New York Public Library.

The first picture book made for children of which we have any knowledge was the *Orbis Pictus* of Comenius. Johann Amos Comenius, a Moravian, or Czech, bishop of the seventeenth century, exercised a wide influence on education. "Pictures," he said, "are the most intelligible books that children can look upon." He carried out his belief by publishing the *Orbis Pictus* in 1658 in Nuremberg. It was translated into English by Charles Hoole in London in 1664 and went through innumerable editions up to 1777. The title given to the English translation was *Visible World: or, a Picture and*

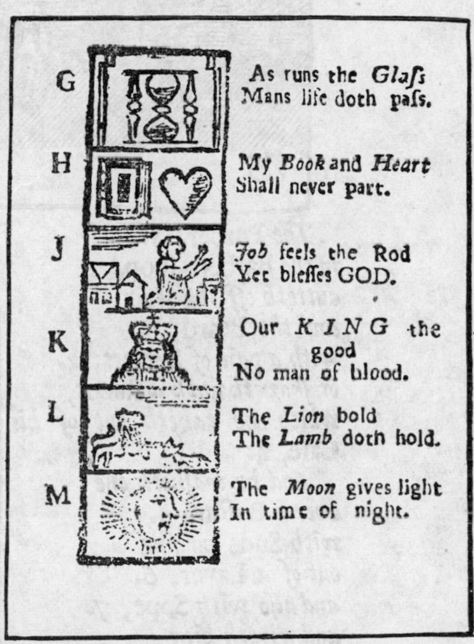


Two pages of *The New England Primer,* from a copy published in Boston in 1727.

*Nomenclature of all the chief Things that are in the World.* Every kind of subject that children could be expected to learn was given, from religious topics to "crawling vermin," but games and subjects of real interest to children were included. The text appeared in parallel columns, in Latin and in English (or German in the original). Each page was accompanied by a woodcut, and the woodcuts, though crude, actually illustrated the text as may be seen from the example shown on the following page. In this respect the *Orbis Pictus* was superior to other books of the period, for it was common practice to use the same "cuts" in different books and even to repeat them in the same book without reference to the text.

## The Barbers Shop. LXXV. *Tonſtrina.*

| | |
|---|---|
| *The* Barber, 1. | *Tonſor,* 1. |
| *in the* Barbers-ſhop, 2. | in *Tonſtrina,* 2. |
| *cutteth off the* Hair | tondet *Crines* |
| *and the* Beard | & *Barbam* |
| *with a pair of* Sizzars, 3. | *Forcipe,* 3. |
| *or ſhaveth with a* Razor, | vel radit *Novaculâ,* |
| *which he taketh out of his* Caſe, 4. | quam è *Theca,* 4. depromit. |
| *And he waſheth one* | Et lavat |
| *over a* Baſon, 5. | ſuper *Pelvim,* 5. |
| *with* Suds *running* | *Lixivio* defluente |
| *out of a* Laver, 6. | è *Gutturnio,* 6. |
| *and alſo with* Sope, 7. | ut & *Sapone,* 7. |
| *and wipeth him* | & tergit |
| *with a* Towel, 8. | *Linteo,* 8. |
| *combeth him with a* Comb, 9. | pectit *Pectine,* 9. |
| *and curleth him* | criſpat |
| *with a* Criſping Iron, 10. | *Calamiſtro,* 10. |
| *Sometimes he cutteth a Vein* | Interdum Venam ſecat |
| *with a* Pen-knife, 11. | *Scalpello,* 11. |
| *where the Blood ſpirteth out,* 12. | ubi Sanguis propullulat, 12. |

*The*

A page from the *Orbis Pictus,* by Comenius. The illustration and Latin text are from the original edition of 1658, the English text from an edition of 1727.

Before printing with movable type was invented, the art of wood engraving was employed to reproduce both text and pictures. It was natural, therefore, that early printed books continued to be illustrated by woodcuts. In most of the examples that have come down to us, the illustrations are more interesting than the text; the pictures are primitive and quaint but attractive. Very few books of the time, however, were intended for children, but just as many adult books today are appropriated by children, so they must have been in an earlier day. Children were taught to read and they read whatever was available; in the eighteenth century much of their reading was undoubtedly from chapbooks,[1] which were numerous and cheap. The illustration given here is from a chapbook published in England about

From a chapbook, *Dick Whittington and His Cat,* published in England about 1770.

1770. The story is the traditional tale of Dick Whittington, the sale of whose cat made him rich and eventually Lord Mayor of London.

In the latter part of the eighteenth century Thomas Bewick, an Englishman, so improved the technique of cutting wood blocks for wood engraving that he was able to produce a finer line than any of his predecessors. Bewick's graceful wood engravings were much in demand, and from the beginning he was interested in illustrating books for children. One of the earliest books illustrated by Bewick that has been preserved is an alphabet picture book, entitled *A New Lottery Book of Birds and Beasts, for Children to Learn Their Letters As Soon as They Can Speak* (1771). Another rare one is *A New Years Gift for Little Masters & Misses* (1777), from which the two pictures of Red Riding Hood reproduced on the next page are taken. The fine line of the leaves and tree trunk in Bewick's wood engraving is the forerunner of the many exquisite reproductions that are possible today through the processes

[1] For further discussion of chapbooks, see page 387.

of lithography and photo-engraving. Without these processes, especially the latter, the wealth of beautifully illustrated books for children today would be impossible.

Illustrations by Thomas Bewick, from "Little Red Riding Hood," in *A New Years Gift for Little Masters & Misses,* 1777.

The first picture book for children in the modern sense was the translation by Edgar Taylor of *Grimms' Popular Stories,* illustrated by George Cruikshank. The first volume of these stories, published in 1823, contained

Illustration by George Cruikshank, from the title page of *Grimms' Popular Stories,* 1823.

twelve etchings by Cruikshank, and to the second, published three years later, Cruikshank contributed ten more. Up to this time pictures had been included in children's books almost entirely for the purpose of driving home a moral, but Cruikshank's pictures inaugurated a new era—that of giving pleasure. Ruskin said that Cruikshank's etchings for the stories of Grimm were "unrivalled in masterfulness of touch since Rembrandt; in some qualities of delineation unrivalled even by him." Certainly Cruikshank's draw-

Illustration by George Cruikshank, from "The Elves and the Shoemaker," in *Grimms' Popular Stories,* 1823.

ings were for children as truly as those of any present-day illustrator. He was a genius as a caricaturist, and his pictures are full of the grotesque and lively humor in which children delight. He himself regarded as one of his best the picture reproduced on this page which shows the elves dancing into their new clothes while the shoemaker and his wife peep around the curtain.

The cartoon type of illustration was also employed by Sir John Tenniel in illustrating *Alice's Adventures in Wonderland* (1866) and *Through the Looking-Glass* (1872). Lewis Carroll regarded them as perfect illustration of his text.

Cruikshank and Tenniel worked in black and white. Colored illustrations in books for children were common, but they were poorly drawn and crudely colored. Improvement in color printing about the middle of the nineteenth century made possible the reproduction of the work of three artists whose illustrations in color set high standards—Walter Crane, Kate Greenaway, and Randolph Caldecott. In 1865, the first of Crane's "toy-books" appeared

Illustration by John Tenniel, from *Alice's Adventures in Wonderland.*

with pictures of "The House That Jack Built," "Cock Robin," and "Dame Trot and Her Comical Cat." During the next ten years Crane illustrated a number of such "toy-books," containing many of the old nursery tales. In 1877 Crane's ambitious *The Baby's Opera* was published and immediately became popular. It was followed by *The Baby's Bouquet* and *Baby's Own Aesop.* In these books, the artist's sister, Lucy, supplied the rhymes and tales. Lucy Crane also made a translation of a number of the Grimm stories which, published as *Household Stories from the Bros. Grimm,* contained drawings by her brother. Crane's drawings, while beautiful and charming, are decorative rather than dramatic, and the amount of detail is confusing

Illustration by Walter Crane, from "The Goose Girl," in *Household Stories from the Bros. Grimm.*

to younger children. His careful work, however, did much to lend dignity and prestige to the illustration of books for children and artists still study his work.

Kate Greenaway's illustrations were the first to demonstrate that pictures *of* children could be made delightful *to* children. Her pictured children are not shown in unusual or exciting situations but doing quite ordinary things such as rolling a hoop, walking in the garden, or eating supper. The

Illustration by Kate Greenaway, from the title page of *Mother Goose.*

striking thing about them is their charming dress. Kate Greenaway considered the clothes worn by children of her own day as ugly so she designed quaint, picturesque costumes for her characters. Her costumes became immensely popular and their influence upon the clothing worn by children in real life may be seen even today. Kate Greenaway illustrated very few books written by other people but supplied her own text, mostly light verse. *Under the Window, Marigold Garden,* and *Kate Greenaway's Al-*

*manacks* were among the best-loved books of the nineteenth century, not only in England but in America as well.

The drawings of Randolph Caldecott possess a timelessness and freshness lacking in the work of Walter Crane and Kate Greenaway. His picture books are favorites today, as they were fifty years ago, and it is fitting that the annual award for the best picture book published each year in the United States should be called the Caldecott Medal.

Illustration by Randolph Caldecott, from "Ride a Cock-Horse to Banbury Cross," in *The Panjandrum Picture Book.*

The first illustrations that established Caldecott's fame were made for *Old Christmas,* a selection of chapters from Irving's *Sketch-Book,* but it is his work in the *Randolph Caldecott's Picture Books* that is best known. There are sixteen of the picture books, all in print today, and they contain Mother Goose rhymes and old-fashioned poems illustrated in inimitable style, with action and vitality, clear color, and genuine humor. The feel of rural England and an abundant love of life are in all of Randolph Caldecott's pictures.

The latter part of the nineteenth century brought the work of another English artist who upheld the standards set by Caldecott. Leslie Brooke's drawings lack the action and sweep found in Caldecott's work, but they are alive, full of humor, and appealing to both children and adults. His first work published in America was *The Nursery Rhyme Book,* edited by Andrew Lang. It was followed by other collections of rhymes and tales and climaxed by *Johnny Crow's Garden* and *Johnny Crow's Party* for which he not only made the pictures but also wrote the delightful rhymes. These books are in great demand by children in libraries today.

Equally popular has been the work of Reginald Birch, an Englishman who has long lived in America. He it was who created the "long-curled, velvet-suited, and lace-collared" hero of Mrs. Burnett's *Little Lord Fauntleroy*. Mr. Birch has since done much finer work, notably his illustrations for a 1937 edition of *The Night before Christmas,* by Clement C. Moore.

One of the first American illustrators of children's books to become famous was Howard Pyle. Before his death in 1911, he wrote and illustrated a number of books, among them *The Merry Adventures of Robin Hood,*

Illustration by L. Leslie Brooke, from *The Nursery Rhyme Book.*

*Men of Iron, The Wonder Clock,* and a series of King Arthur stories. His pictures of pirates and man-to-man combats have been immensely popular with boys. For many years he dominated the illustration of children's books in the United States and his fine workmanship influenced many other artists. A number of present-day illustrators carry forward the Pyle tradition; among them is James Daugherty. Mr. Daugherty's pictures have the same robustness and vigor, and he surpasses Pyle in infectious good humor and buoyancy. His illustrations of frontier life are particularly notable. He has illustrated some fifty books; among them Irving's *The Bold Dragoon and Other Ghostly Tales,* Sandburg's *Abe Lincoln Grows Up,* and *Their Weight in Wildcats*—the last, a collection of stories of frontiersmen for which he also wrote the text.

American artists have also been particularly successful in illustrating books that contain animal characters. Among the first to gain this distinction was A. B. Frost, whose delineations of Brer Rabbit and the other animal characters of *Uncle Remus* have long been a significant part of those stories.

Another of the older artists responsible for high standards in book illustration is Francis D. Bedford, whose training and interest in architecture contributed to beautiful balanced composition in the pictures he made for children. Many of the English editions he illustrated have been issued in America, among them Dickens' *A Christmas Carol* and MacDonald's *At the Back of the North Wind.*

Illustration by A. B. Frost, from *Uncle Remus: His Songs and Sayings.*

For the excellent engraving, printing, and binding that is the rule in children's books today, we are greatly indebted to Arthur Rackham, an example of whose work is shown on the following page. His illustrations for Barrie's *Peter Pan in Kensington Gardens,* published in 1906, did much to stimulate a demand for children's books in elaborate format. Mr. Rackham illustrated many books for children. His imagery and inventiveness were best shown in his pictures of fairies, but the wealth of detail and the soft colors he employed are better suited to older than younger children.

The year 1920 marked an expansion in the production of children's books in the United States. Before that date a few books each year were outstanding in illustration, but each new season since then has brought a number of beautifully illustrated and carefully designed books for children. This comparatively recent development includes also the rise of the picture book as we know it today—the book in which the picture space equals or exceeds the amount of space given to the text. In some cases the books for very young children contain no text at all and the entire story is told by pictures alone. This rapid rise in popularity of the picture book has brought its attendant evil—the production of a certain number of poorly conceived and poorly executed books. It is fortunate for the status of children's literature, however, that the number of such books is outweighed by the number of really desirable ones.

Among the artists of the present day who give pleasure to young children is Wanda Gág. Her strong wood-block technique and rounded forms make the animal characterizations in *Millions of Cats* and *The Funny Thing* very satisfying to children. Her pictures to accompany her own selection of *Tales from Grimm* add another name to the list of fine artists who have pictured the characters of these old tales.

Illustration by Arthur Rackham, from "Jack and the Beanstalk," in *English Fairy Tales.*

The simplicity and realness of Marjorie Flack's animals make them ideal for children of kindergarten and early primary ages. The lovable Scottie, "Angus," and the dachshund, "Lena," romp across gay pages and seem very much alive. The text, which Miss Flack writes, is also extremely simple and childlike. The work of a Swedish artist, Elsa Beskow, shows also the same quality of strength and assurance.

Several attempts to illustrate children's books with photographs have been made. Travel, nature, and other informational materials lend themselves to this treatment and are very much liked by children. A few books for very young children have been successfully illustrated by photographs, but they are realistic accounts of simple, everyday happenings. Efforts to illustrate narratives with photographs have been disappointing. They lack spontaneity and are devoid of the imaginative touches that an artist can give.

An interesting development in present-day books for children is the growing number of books written and illustrated by the same person. One of the earlier and most notable examples of this was the *Just So Stories,* for which Rudyard Kipling made the drawings to accompany his own inimitable text.

Illustration by Rudyard Kipling, from "The Elephant's Child," in *Just So Stories.*

In some more recent examples, many critics feel that illustration has been brought to a high state of perfection without a corresponding high quality of text, but in many such books, particularly those for young children, a fine harmony of text and illustration has resulted.

It is interesting to note that three pairs of artist-authors producing children's books today are teams of husband and wife working together: Ingri and Edgar Parin d'Aulaire, Berta and Elmer Hader, and Maud and Miska

Petersham. Edgar d'Aulaire is Swiss and Ingri, Norwegian. Their books about *Ola,* a little Norwegian boy, have large full-page pictures in beautiful colors, in which they have achieved effects of movement and distance. Since coming to America they have also illustrated several books by other writers.

Illustration by Kate Seredy, from *Caddie Woodlawn.*

Berta and Elmer Hader are Americans whose illustrations and stories show a genuine understanding of the things children enjoy. *Midget and Bridget* is an outstanding example of their work. Miska Petersham is from Hungary, and his wife Maud is an American. Their handling of color has a foreign flavor and brilliance. *Miki, Auntie,* and *The Christ Child* are well liked.

One of the recent illustrators to become well known is Kate Seredy, a Hungarian who makes her home in the United States. *The White Stag,* which she wrote and illustrated, was awarded the John Newbery Medal [1]

[1] For further discussion of books receiving the Newbery Medal, see page 779.

in 1938 as "the most distinguished book for children" of the year. Miss Seredy's pictures for *The White Stag* are breath-taking in power and sweep. Her previous book, *The Good Master,* is also beautifully illustrated. *Caddie Woodlawn* by Brink, an earlier Newbery prize winner, was illustrated by Kate Seredy.

Illustration by Boris Artzybasheff, from *Seven Simeons.*

Boris Artzybasheff, one of the most skilled of contemporary illustrators, is a Russian who came to America after the Russian revolution. He has illustrated books by Padraic Colum, Dhan Gopal Mukerji, Ella Young, and others. Much of his work is pronounced black and white, but *Seven Simeons,* which he wrote, is illustrated in delicate designs of red, green, and black. *Seven Simeons* is much liked by children younger than those to whom his earlier illustrations appeal.

Two artists who have obtained a sculptured effect in book illustration are Helen Sewell and Elizabeth MacKinstry. The pictures of both give the impression of having a third dimension. Miss MacKinstry's illustrations for the old French fairy tale, *The White Cat,* show also a pleasing use of color. Helen Sewell's illustrations are for younger children; her picture book of *Cinderella* is outstanding, and the firm, rhythmic lines of the pictures in *A Head for Happy, Blue Barns,* and other stories of her own writing are much liked by children.

Illustration by Elizabeth MacKinstry, from *The White Cat, and Other Old French Fairy Tales.*

Alphabet books for young children have interested nearly as many well-known artists as have the old folk tales. The *A B C* Book, by Charles B. Falls, is an attractive example. Lois Lenski's quaint pictures of make-believe characters and Emma Brock's *The Runaway Sardine* are also liked by little children, as are William Nicholson's pictures of the gallant toy soldier, *Clever Bill,* and his more serious pictures for Bianco's *The Velveteen Rabbit.* Robert Lawson's striking drawings for *The Story of Ferdinand,* by Munro Leaf, are an essential part of that story; other books of his illustration have strong and interesting animal characterizations.

Kurt Wiese's stories and pictures of *Wallie, the Walrus* and *Ella, the Elephant* delight young children. Mr. Wiese is very versatile and is successful in drawing both for young children and for older ones. Years spent in China enable him to illustrate with especial charm books with Chinese backgrounds. Another artist whose intimate acquaintance with China is revealed in his pictures is Thomas Handforth, whose beautiful *Mei Li* was awarded the Caldecott Medal in 1939. In the extraordinary lithographs on each page of that book, Chinese children are portrayed with gaiety, strength, and dignity.

An outstanding example of perfect harmony between author and illustrator is found in *The Cat Who Went to Heaven,* by Elizabeth Coatsworth, in which Lynd Ward's fine brush drawings in black and gray have captured the spirit of the Japanese story. In this book Mr. Ward has succeeded in

Illustration by Lynd Ward, from *Waif Maid.*

being what he believes every illustrator should be, "a functional being rather than a mere complementary decorator."

Lovers of beautifully illustrated books for children felt it particularly fitting that the first award of the Caldecott Medal should have been made to Dorothy Lathrop for her *Animals of the Bible.* No illustrations in contemporary children's books surpass Miss Lathrop's in sincerity, grace, and beauty. Her pictures of animals have great softness and naturalness. She has peopled a fairy world with figures the child (and the adult who has never entirely grown up) recognizes at once as the true land of "faery." Dorothy Lathrop has illustrated some thirty books for children: books of verse, ad-

Illustration by Dorothy P. Lathrop, from *The Little White Goat.*

venture, and fairy tales written by famous writers, as well as the fairy and animal books for which she has written the text as well as made the illustrations. Some are illustrated with pen and ink drawings, some in color, and some with a lithographic pencil. The last medium is that employed in *Animals of the Bible, Who Goes There?* and *Hide and Go Seek,* in which the animals appear in full-page pictures and in double-page processions.

It has not been possible to mention in this discussion all the artists who have contributed to making the production of children's books the art it is today. A student who explores the materials of children's literature will discover the work of the artists discussed and of others whose pictures delight children, and will experience pleasure in a widening acquaintance with illustrators as well as authors.

# Suggestions for Students

The classification of materials in *Story and Verse for Children* has been made for convenience in studying the field of children's literature—a very broad field, drawn from many sources. These sources range geographically over the entire world and historically from the ancient past to the present.

The material in this book has been selected as representative of types and subjects in literature which are high in interest to children of various ages. Through the suggested references and book lists, the student may extend her acquaintance with any type or topic more widely if she desires. While the book is organized to present a survey of the field of children's literature, provision is made for intensive study of various problems by students if such procedure is desired. Suggestions for extension of many lines of study are found in the introductions, footnotes, cross references, collateral reading, biographical notes, and suggested student activities.

For convenience, prose and poetry have been placed in separate sections. For the same reason, fanciful stories and realistic stories, literature from traditional sources and literature from modern sources, have been grouped separately. In working with children, however, our constant purpose is to interest them in a varied and well-balanced program of reading. As a teacher becomes acquainted with the materials of children's literature, she will see many possibilities for combining verse and prose, fiction and facts, on related subjects to satisfy children's needs.

The stories and poems in this anthology have been grouped about childlike themes. It has been thought that this arrangement will increase the pleasure of the adult student and provide for her a greater variety of reading experience. A student or teacher who has a specific purpose to serve may wish to make quite new and different groupings of the material. She should be encouraged to do so. After reading and enjoying the stories and poems, many interesting combinations may suggest themselves. For example, material about wild animals may be found in the following groups: in verse, *Boys and Girls, In Feathers and Fur and Such, For Fun, Our Country,* and *Stories in Verse;* in prose, *Old Tales, Legends and Hero Tales, Stories for Fun, The World and Its Creatures,* and *Stories about Boys and Girls*—the subject being treated differently of course in each group. Should one want stories about a particular animal, perhaps the elephant, several may be found. For further example, a large number of selections having to do with the American Indian have been included, though only a few are found in a single section. They range from myth and legend to realistic fiction and factual material; if desired, they may be read and used together.

A prospective teacher sometimes finds it difficult to determine the age of children to whom a poem or story or book is suited. If firsthand contacts with children are limited, the problem is still more difficult. The content of the poem or story or book is the first consideration, but other elements, such as difficulty of language and ideas and the point of view of the author, require attention. To aid students in developing insight for such judgments, suggestions for the grades in which selections in this anthology may be used are given at the end of each group of material. It is desirable, however, that the student have first a pleasant and enjoyable experience with the material and, after a real acquaintance with the stories and poems themselves, turn her attention to the grades in which they can be used to advantage. It is not intended that this grading be accepted literally. Factors operating in particular situations may indicate that material be used in higher grades or in lower grades than those suggested. Children's reading should not be subject to hard and fast rules, and the plans of teachers and parents should be flexible and easily adapted to children's needs.

A study of children's literature is not primarily concerned with teaching children to read; its purpose is to help children enjoy books and learn to love them. Learning to read, however, is an allied problem and its demands must be recognized in adapting literary experiences to the reading ability of children. It should be noted that in this volume the selections for young children are intended to be read *to* children, at least until the time that the teacher is certain the child can read them for himself easily and without loss of pleasure in the stories themselves. Many of the fine old tales are better told than read. Many children have had rich literary experiences before coming to school, in stories and verse told and read to them and in picture books which they have interpreted for themselves. For the majority of children with such background, learning to read should come easily and thus add a new avenue of enjoyment. To less fortunate children, the teacher who brings story and verse is opening a world of enchantment.

The student should look upon literature as serving many purposes in the schoolroom, as in life. A student, or group of students, may find it interesting to organize the literature that could be used by a group of real or imaginary children engaged in some activity or studying some theme or topic. Children themselves enjoy the search for such material when they are really interested, and it is good experience for them to assist in finding material suited to their purposes and to their abilities. The story and verse, however, should have genuine relation to the theme and purpose; there should be no place for artificial and superficial tie-ups. Because the purpose is practical is no reason for the material to be lacking in quality; fine literature should find its place in supplementing and enriching children's experiences in real life and in the classroom.

There are other purposes for literature. There are many pieces of literature that are their "own excuse for being" because of their strength and beauty. Still other books without claim to greatness, some books of humor or adventure perhaps, may have their place because of the pleasure they give.

Literature is as broad as life. In choice of materials and plan of organization, *Story and Verse for Children* reveals the variety and scope of the contacts which literature may have with child life.

## *Student Activities*

1. After reading Hamlin Garland's "Books of My Childhood," pages 6 to 8, write a brief sketch that will reveal the nature and extent of your own early reading. What books do you remember most vividly? How did your taste in books

change as you grew into the "teens"? It might be interesting to get a composite picture of the early reading of your entire class.

2. Hold interviews with one or more children to determine what books they are reading and what books they like best. Perhaps you may get them to tell you how they decide whether or not they want to read an unfamiliar book. Do they judge by the pictures, the amount of conversation, whether the book is hard to read, or do they have other methods? Write up your interviews and compare them with those of other members of your class. Do certain books seem to be popular with a number of children?

3. What significant conclusions, if any, seem to be indicated by a comparison of the reports of early reading of members of the class and that of present-day children?

4. In the light of the studies reviewed on pages 12 to 18, "Children's Interest in Reading," did the children interviewed by you "run true to form," or did you chance to find some young "individualists"?

5. Spend an hour in a children's library when books are being chosen and withdrawn, and note the way children go about their business. The discussion on page 12 will help you plan your visit.

6. A committee of one or two members of the class may wish to interview a children's librarian and report to the class on the provisions for acquainting children with the library. How are children encouraged to "break the ice" and make their first withdrawals? How are individuals helped when they come to the library? Do groups of children come to the library for instruction and exploration? Is there a story hour at the library?

7. You may find yourself at a loss to know how to use the materials in the children's library. Perhaps the class may go to the library and become familiar with the classification and arrangement of the books. Individual students will find it an interesting experience to "browse" through the shelves and examine the books, old and new, used and unused.

8. Ask the librarian what changes have taken place in the last ten years in the demand for different types of books. How do you account for such changes?

9. Arrange an exhibit of children's books illustrated by outstanding artists. What are the features of each artist's work that seem to be high in appeal to children? If possible, secure several editions of well-known children's classics illustrated by different artists. In the illustrations of these different artists do you observe a difference in interpretation of the author's meaning and purpose? Which do you consider best suited to the age of children who read the book? Do you find that different artists select for illustration the same episodes in these stories, or is there wide variation? Have you discovered the work of any particular artist illustrating books for boys and girls that appeals especially to you? How much variety and adaptability to different types of stories do you find in the work of your favorite artist?

## References for Students

### Enjoyment of Literature

Bennett, Arnold, *Literary Taste: How To Form It*. Doubleday, Doran.

Crothers, Samuel McChord, *The Gentle Reader*. Houghton Mifflin.

Drew, Elizabeth, *The Enjoyment of Literature*. Norton.

Eastman, Max, *Enjoyment of Poetry*. Scribner.

Erskine, John, *The Delight of Great Books*. Bobbs-Merrill.

Finger, Charles J., *After the Great Companions*. Dutton.

Kerfoot, J. B., *How To Read*. Houghton Mifflin.

Pritchard, F. H., *Training in Literary Appreciation*. Crowell.

Sprau, George, *The Meaning of Literature*. Scribner.

Woodberry, George E., *The Appreciation of Literature*. Harcourt, Brace.

### Guides to Children's Books

Becker, May Lamberton, *Adventures in Reading*. Stokes.

———, *First Adventures in Reading*. Stokes.

Beust, Nora, *Graded List of Books for Children*. American Library Assn.

Bianco, Margery, "Our Youngest Critics," *The Bookman*, LXII: 249.

Center, Stella S., and Max J. Herzberg (editors), *Leisure Reading* (book list for Grades VII, VIII, and IX). National Council of Teachers of English.

Dalgliesh, Alice, *First Experiences with Literature*. Scribner.

Fay, Lucy E., and Anne T. Eaton, *Instruction in the Use of Books and Libraries*. Faxon.

Field, Walter Taylor, *A Guide to Literature for Children*. Ginn.

Frank, Josette, *What Books for Children?* Doubleday, Doran.

Gardner, Emelyn E., and Eloise Ramsey, *A Handbook of Children's Literature*. Scott, Foresman.

Mahony, Bertha E. (editor), *The Horn Book Magazine: Books and Reading for Young People*, published bi-monthly (Boston).

Mahony, Bertha E., and Elinor Whitney, *Realms of Gold in Children's Books*. Doubleday, Doran.

———, *Five Years of Children's Books*. Doubleday, Doran.

Moore, Anne Carroll, *My Roads*. Doubleday, Doran.

———, *The Three Owls*, Book I, Macmillan; Books II and III, Coward-McCann.

Moore, Annie E., *Literature Old and New for Children*. Houghton Mifflin.

Olcott, Frances Jenkins, *The Children's Reading*. Houghton Mifflin.

Ramsey, Eloise (editor), *Reading for Fun* (book list for elementary schools). National Council of Teachers of English.

Richards, Laura E., *What Shall the Children Read?* Appleton-Century.

Washburne, Carlcton, *The Right Book for the Right Child*. John Day.

Weekes, Blanche E., *Literature and the Child*. Silver, Burdett.

## *Children's Interests in Reading*

Bamberger, Florence E., and Angela M. Broening, *A Guide to Children's Literature,* Chapter 2. Johns Hopkins.

Bradshaw, Ruth E., "Children's Choices in Poetry in the First Grade," *The Elementary English Review,* XIV: 168.

Dunn, Fannie Wyche, *Interest Factors in Primary Reading*. Teachers College.

Faegre, Marion, "Understanding Our Children," *Children's Library Yearbook,* No. 3. American Library Assn.

Gardner, Emelyn E., and Eloise Ramsey, *A Handbook of Children's Literature,* Chapter 1. Scott, Foresman.

Gates, Arthur I., *Interest and Ability in Reading*. Macmillan.

Hatfield, W. Wilbur (editor), *An Experience Curriculum in English*. Appleton-Century, for National Council of Teachers of English.

Huber, Miriam Blanton, *The Influence of Intelligence upon Children's Reading Interests*. Teachers College.

Huber, Miriam Blanton, Herbert B. Bruner, and Charles M. Curry, *Children's Interests in Poetry*. Rand McNally.

Jordan, A. M., *Children's Interests in Reading*. University of North Carolina.

Kangley, Lucy, *Poetry Preferences in the Junior High School*. Teachers College.

Starbuck, Edwin D., and Frank H. Shuttleworth, *A Guide to Literature for Character Training*. Macmillan.

Terman, Lewis M., and Margaret Lima, *Children's Reading*. Appleton-Century.

Uhl, Willis L., *The Materials of Reading*. Silver, Burdett.

Washburne, Carleton, and Mabel Vogel, *Winnetka Graded Book List,* American Library Assn.: *The Right Book for the Right Child,* John Day.

## *The Illustration of Children's Books*

Bamberger, Florence E., *The Effect of the Physical Make-up of a Book upon Children's Selection*. Johns Hopkins.

Darton, F. J. Harvey, *Children's Books in England*. Macmillan.

Darton, F. J. Harvey, *Modern Book Illustration in Great Britain and America.* The Studio (London).

Hamilton, Elizabeth B., *Reginald Birch—His Book.* Harcourt, Brace.

James, Philip, *Children's Books of Yesterday.* The Studio (London).

Kunitz, Stanley J., and Howard Haycraft, *The Junior Book of Authors.* Wilson.

Mahony, Bertha E., and Elinor Whitney, *Contemporary Illustrators of Children's Books.* Women's Educational and Industrial Union (Boston).

Martin, Helen, "Children's Interests in Pictures," *Western Reserve Bulletin,* XXXIV: 10.

Mellinger, Bonnie E., *Children's Interests in Pictures.* Teachers College.

Miller, Bertha Mahony, "Artists Triumph," *The Horn Book,* XIV: 201.

Miller, William A., "The Picture Choices of Primary Children," *Elementary School Journal,* XXXVII: 273.

Newton, Lesley, "Modern Trends in Book Illustration for Children," *Elementary English Review,* IX: 89.

Ramsey, Eloise, "Introducing the Illustrator," *Childhood Education,* XIV: 344.

# *Mother Goose Rhymes*

# MOTHER GOOSE RHYMES

## Mother Goose: Origin and Significance

WHAT *Mother Goose Rhymes* do you remember from your childhood? You probably learned them from your mother, or grandmother, or other children, long before you could read them in books. For centuries these rhymes have been handed down from one generation to another. Many of them are believed to be of "dateless antiquity." People in far-away times and far-away places sang the same rhymes that American children today repeat so naturally and carelessly, but often the people of long ago had serious uses for these rhymes. The same counting-out rhymes that children today use to determine who shall be "It" in a game may have been the means of deciding what man in the tribe should face a threatening danger to protect his people. Many of the rhymes, such as "Come, butter, come" and "Cushy cow bonny" were charms that the users believed brought success in household chores. "Little Jack Horner" is thought to be rhymed ridicule of an official who long ago profited unduly from the public treasury. Many others undoubtedly were made up to illustrate events of current political importance—the events themselves, and the people concerned in them, have been forgotten long ago, but the jingles continue to please generations of children who care nothing for their origin and little for their meaning.

Many scholars have given years of study and research to tracing the history not only of the rhymes but of *Mother Goose* herself. Such information has no value for children, but it is interesting to the student of children's literature. Who was *Mother Goose?* When did she live? Much effort by antiquarians and folklorists has failed to find the answers to these questions. Mother Goose probably did not live anywhere and never existed as a person. It seems likely that she is a myth, a personification of the well-loved storytellers who have existed since the world began. For it is as a storyteller, not a maker of rhymes, that we first discover Mother Goose in written record. In 1650 a French poem refers to fanciful stories known in France at that time as tales of Mother Goose, and in 1697 Charles Perrault published in France a little book of eight prose tales known as *Contes de Ma Mère l'Oye (Tales of My*

*Mother Goose).* In Perrault's collection[1] were some of the most widely known fairy tales in all literature; among them, "Cinderella" and "Little Red Riding Hood."

Perrault's tales were translated into English in a comparatively short time and were later issued in London by John Newbery.[2] John Newbery has been called the "father of children's literature" for he was the first publisher to conceive the idea of publishing books intended for children. From his shop in St. Paul's Churchyard in London between 1744 and 1767 issued a flood of tiny books bound in "flowery and gilt" Dutch paper, which delighted the hearts of children. Perrault's *Tales of Mother Goose* ran into many editions, and when Newbery published a collection of favorite nursery rhymes, the book was called *Mother Goose's Melody.* Newbery was a good business man and perhaps the success of the *Tales of Mother Goose* led him to use the name of Mother Goose for the book of rhymes. It is possible, however, that people telling and singing the rhymes had themselves appropriated the name of Mother Goose and associated the name with the rhymes before Newbery printed them in a book. Oliver Goldsmith[3] was in Newbery's employ, and it is believed that he collected and arranged the rhymes and wrote the preface, but no copies of this first collection of Mother Goose rhymes are in existence. From that time on, however, the name of Mother Goose has been connected with rhymes instead of tales. This is particularly true in America, where the name of Mother Goose is seen in books more frequently than in England. The rhymes themselves are the same, however, in England and in the United States, and in many languages all over the world.

A few years after Newbery's *Mother Goose's Melody* appeared in England it was reprinted in Boston and achieved a favored place in the literature of the newly established United States. Mother Goose became so much loved in America that several attempts have been made to establish her identity as a real woman of colonial Boston who originated the rhymes and sang them to her grandchildren.[4] No proof of this claim has ever been produced, and it is probable that this American Mother Goose is the same legendary old lady who appeared in France a century earlier. Her mythical existence in no way lessens her charm, rather it insures for her an immortality in the love of succeeding generation of children who repeat her rhymes.

The old lady has had her detractors, however, as well as her admirers. Some literal-minded adults have attacked the rhymes as "unfit for infant minds." They have pointed out that some of the rhymes have elements of cruelty; moreover, they fear that the gross exaggerations will give children distorted notions of the world in which they live. Fortunately no such doubts disturb children themselves, in fact they do not see at all the things that give

[1] For further discussion of Perrault, see pages 208-209, 827.

[2] Charles Welsh, *A Bookseller of the Last Century,* Griffith, Farran, Okeden, and Welsh, London, 1885.

[3] For further discussion of Newbery and Goldsmith, see pages 387-388, 809.

[4] See notes on William A. Wheeler, page 838.

concern to these over-serious elders. To children the rhymes are fun and meaning is unimportant. In repeating "Little Miss Muffet" no child gives a thought to what a "tuffet" may be. If he were asked, he would probably answer in the words of Dr. Samuel Crothers,[1] "A tuffet is the kind of thing that Miss Muffet sat on," and the matter would be ended as far as the child was concerned. There are, however, so many Mother Goose rhymes that teachers and parents may choose among them and omit those that seem objectionable. There will be enough left to give present-day children the same happiness and satisfaction that this literature has supplied throughout the centuries.

Why do children like the rhymes so much? Perhaps it is the rhythm they love; certainly they never tire of the regular and strongly marked accents. Perhaps it is the gay jingle, with rhyming words, alliteration, and unexpected combinations of sound. Children find in the rhymes the kind of humor that to them is really funny. To a child, "A farmer went riding" pictures a completely humorous situation. "Humpty-Dumpty" supplies the "tumble-down" elements of humor that are more satisfying to a child than any clever lines of double-edged meaning. The presence of child characters in the rhymes appeals to children—the *little* characters: "Little Jack Horner," "Little Boy Blue," "Little Miss Muffet" and others. Some of the rhymes carry a story, or the germ of one, such as "Old King Cole," "Pussy-cat," and "Old Mother Hubbard." Others serve a purpose in action games and pantomime, such as "Ride a cock-horse to Banbury Cross" and "Cobbler, cobbler, mend my shoe." A few of the rhymes have the quality of genuine verse; a true lyric quality is found in "I saw a ship a-sailing," "I had a little nut-tree," and "Cushy cow bonny."

The rhymes given in the following collection are drawn from Halliwell, with the exception of six from Andrew Lang and two from William A. Wheeler, which are indicated by footnotes. In 1842 James Orchard Halliwell (also known as Halliwell-Phillips) published for a learned society in England a collection entitled *Nursery Rhymes of England,* upon which he had spent much scholarly research. A few years later he issued *Nursery Rhymes and Nursery Tales of England,* which is the recognized source of the most authentic versions of English traditional rhymes and tales. The book is out of print, but there are copies in a few public and private libraries in the United States. Anyone who has access to a copy will be deeply interested in Halliwell's notes and discussions and in the several versions of some of the rhymes which he was able to collect.

A student of children's literature will find it interesting to compare the form of the Mother Goose rhymes learned in childhood with the form in which they appear in the pages to follow. "Hey! diddle, diddle" appears to be current in a number of slightly different versions. A form known by children in northern Indiana, which is probably older than Halliwell's preferred version, is as follows:

[1] Samuel McChord Crothers, *Miss Muffet's Christmas Party,* page 4.

Hi! diddy, diddle,
The cat played the fiddle,
The cow jumped over the moon;
The little dog laughed
To see such a craft,
And the dish ran away with the spoon.

The rhymes given here are arranged in order approximately as children hear them. "Ride a cock-horse to Banbury Cross" may accompany a bouncing ride that Baby takes on Mother's or Father's knee or foot; the lullabies are sung to children before they learn to talk; and so on, to the final "There was an old man who lived in a wood," which tells a homely story in a form somewhat like that of the old ballads.

# Mother Goose Rhymes

1

Ride a cock-horse to Banbury Cross,
To see an old lady upon a white horse;
Rings on her fingers, and bells on her toes,
And so she makes music wherever she goes.

2

*(A song for five toes)*

This little pig went to market;
This little pig stayed at home;
This little pig had roast beef;
And this little pig had none;
This little pig said, "Wee, wee, wee!
I can't find my way home."

3

Diddle, diddle, dumpling, my son John,
Went to bed with his stockings on;
One shoe off, the other shoe on,
Diddle, diddle, dumpling, my son John.

4

Bow, wow, wow,
Whose dog art thou?
Little Tom Tinker's dog,
Bow, wow, wow.

5

Bye, baby bunting,
Daddy's gone a-hunting,
To get a little rabbit skin
To wrap the baby bunting in.

6

Hush-a-bye, baby, on the tree top,
When the wind blows, the cradle will rock;
When the bough bends, the cradle will fall.
Down will come baby, bough, cradle, and all.

7

Pat-a-cake, pat-a-cake, baker's man!
So I will, master, as fast as I can;
Pat it, and prick it, and mark it with T,
Put it in the oven for Tommy and me.

8

To market, to market, to buy a fat pig,
Home again, home again, dancing a jig;
To market, to market, to buy a fat hog;
Home again, home again, jiggety-jog;
To market, to market, to buy a plum bun,
Home again, home again, market is done.

9

Polly, put the kettle on,
  Polly, put the kettle on,
Polly, put the kettle on,
  And let's drink tea.

10

Come, butter, come,
Come, butter, come!
Peter stands at the gate,
Waiting for a buttered cake;
Come, butter, come.

11

*(A valentine)*

The rose is red,
  The violet's blue;
Pinks are sweet,
  And so are you!

12

Hey! diddle, diddle,
  The cat and the fiddle,
The cow jumped over the moon;
  The little dog laughed
  To see such sport,
And the dish ran away with the spoon.

13

Jack and Jill went up the hill,
  To fetch a pail of water;
Jack fell down, and broke his crown,
  And Jill came tumbling after.

14

Hickory, dickory, dock,
The mouse ran up the clock;
  The clock struck one,
  The mouse ran down;
Hickory, dickory, dock.[1]

15

Cushy cow bonny, let down thy milk,
And I will give thee a gown of silk;
A gown of silk and a silver tee,
If thou wilt let down thy milk to me.

16

Pussy-cat, pussy-cat, where have you been?
"I've been to London to look at the queen."
Pussy-cat, pussy-cat, what did you there?
"I frightened a little mouse under the chair."

17

Mistress Mary, quite contrary,
  How does your garden grow?
With cockle-shells, and silver bells,
  And pretty maids all in a row.[2]

18

A farmer went riding
  Upon his gray mare;
Bumpety, bumpety, bump!
With his daughter behind him,
  So rosy and fair;
Lumpety, lumpety, lump!

A raven cried "Croak!"
  And they all tumbled down;
Bumpety, bumpety, bump!
The mare broke her knees,
  And the farmer his crown;
Lumpety, lumpety, lump!

The mischievous raven
  Flew laughing away;
Bumpety, bumpety, bump!
And vowed he would serve them
  The same the next day;
Lumpety, lumpety, lump! [3]

[1] From William A. Wheeler, *Mother Goose's Melodies.*
[2] From Andrew Lang, *The Nursery Rhyme Book.*
[3] *Ibid.*

19

Little Betty Blue
Lost her holiday shoe;
What can little Betty do?
Give her another
To match the other,
And then she may walk in two.

20

Jack be nimble,
And Jack be quick;
And Jack jump over
The candlestick.

21

Three blind mice! See, how they run!
They all ran after the farmer's wife,
Who cut off their tails with the carving knife!
Did you ever see such a thing in your life?
Three blind mice!

22

Higgledy, piggledy, my black hen,
She lays eggs for gentlemen;
Sometimes nine, sometimes ten;
Higgledy, piggledy, my black hen.

23

There was an old woman
Lived under a hill;
And if she's not gone,
She lives there still.

24

Wee Willie Winkie runs through the town,
Upstairs and downstairs in his nightgown,
Rapping at the window, crying through the lock,
"Are the children in their beds, for now it's eight o'clock?" [1]

25

Little Jack Horner
Sat in a corner,
Eating his Christmas pie.
He put in his thumb,
And he pulled out a plum,
And said, "What a good boy am I!"

26

Little Miss Muffet
Sat on a tuffet,
Eating of curds and whey;
There came a spider,
And sat down beside her,
And frightened Miss Muffet away.[2]

27

Little Boy Blue, come blow your horn,
The sheep's in the meadow, the cow's in the corn.
Where is the boy that looks after the sheep?
"He's under the haycock, fast asleep."
Will you wake him? "No, not I;
For if I do, he'll be sure to cry."

28

Cock-a-doodle-doo!
My dame has lost her shoe;
My master's lost his fiddling stick,
And don't know what to do.

Cock-a-doodle-doo!
What is my dame to do?
Till master finds his fiddling stick,
She'll dance without her shoe.

Cock-a-doodle-doo!
My dame has found her shoe,
And master's found his fiddling stick,
Sing doodle-doodle-doo!

Cock-a-doodle-doo!
My dame will dance with you,
While master fiddles his fiddling stick
For dame and doodle-doo.

[1] From Andrew Lang, *The Nursery Rhyme Book.*
[2] *Ibid.*

29

Little Robin Redbreast
  Sat upon a rail;
Niddle, naddle, went his head,
  Wiggle, waggle, went his tail.

30

The north wind doth blow,
And we shall have snow,
And what will the robin do then?
  Poor thing!

He will sit in a barn,
And to keep himself warm,
Will hide his head under his wing.
  Poor thing!

31

Once I saw a little bird
  Come hop, hop, hop;
So I cried, "Little bird,
  Will you stop, stop, stop?"
And was going to the window
  To say, "How do you do?"
But he shook his little tail,
  And far away he flew.

32

God bless the master of this house,
  The mistress, also,
And all the little children,
  That round the table go;
And all your kin and kinsmen
  That dwell both far and near;
I wish you a Merry Christmas,
  And a Happy New Year.

33

There were three jovial huntsmen,
  As I have heard them say,
And they would go a-hunting
  All on a summer's day.

All the day they hunted,
  And nothing could they find
But a ship a-sailing,
  A-sailing with the wind.

One said it was a ship,
  The other he said nay;
The third said it was a house
  With the chimney blown away.

And all the night they hunted,
  And nothing could they find
But the moon a-gliding,
  A-gliding with the wind.

One said it was the moon,
  The other he said nay;
The third said it was a cheese,
  And half o't cut away.

34

I had a little nut-tree, nothing would it bear
But a silver nutmeg and a golden pear;
The king of Spain's daughter came to visit me,
And all because of my little nut-tree.
I skipped over water, I danced over sea,
And all the birds in the air couldn't catch me.

35

I saw a ship a-sailing,
  A-sailing on the sea;
And oh, it was all laden
  With pretty things for thee!

There were comfits in the cabin,
  And apples in the hold;
The sails were made of silk,
  And the masts were made of gold.

The four and twenty sailors,
  That stood between the decks,
Were four and twenty white mice,
  With chains about their necks.

The captain was a duck,
  With a packet on his back;
And when the ship began to move,
  The captain said, "Quack! Quack!"

36

Girls and boys, come out to play,
The moon is shining as bright as day.

Leave your supper, and leave your sleep,
And come with your playfellows into the
street.

Come with a whoop, come with a call,
Come with a good will or not at all.

Up the ladder and down the wall,
A halfpenny roll will serve us all.

You find milk, and I'll find flour,
And we'll have pudding in half an hour.

37

Ding, dong, bell,
Pussy's in the well!
Who put her in?
Little Tommy Green.
Who pulled her out?
Big Johnny Stout.
What a naughty boy was that,
To drown poor pussy-cat,
Who never did him any harm,
But killed the mice in his father's barn! [1]

38

Sing a song of sixpence,
A pocket full of rye;
Four and twenty blackbirds
Baked in a pie;

When the pie was opened,
The birds began to sing;
Was not that a dainty dish
To set before the king?

The king was in his counting-house
Counting out his money;
The queen was in the parlor
Eating bread and honey;

The maid was in the garden
Hanging out the clothes,
When along came a blackbird
And pecked off her nose.

39

There was an old woman who lived in a
shoe,
She had so many children, she didn't know
what to do;
She gave them some broth without any
bread,
She whipped them all soundly, and put
them to bed.

40

One, two,
Buckle my shoe;
Three, four,
Shut the door;
Five, six,
Pick up sticks;
Seven, eight,
Lay them straight;
Nine, ten,
A good fat hen;
Eleven, twelve,
Who will delve?
Thirteen, fourteen,
Maids a-courting;
Fifteen, sixteen,
Maids a-kissing;
Seventeen, eighteen,
Maids a-waiting;
Nineteen, twenty,
My stomach's empty.

41

I had a little pony,
His name was Dapple-gray,
I lent him to a lady,
To ride a mile away;
She whipped him, she slashed him,
She rode him through the mire;
I would not lend my pony now
For all the lady's hire.

[1] From William A. Wheeler, *Mother Goose's Melodies.*

42

Old King Cole
Was a merry old soul,
And a merry old soul was he;
He called for his pipe,
And he called for his bowl,
And he called for his fiddlers three.
Every fiddler, he had a fiddle,
And a very fine fiddle had he;
Twee-tweedle-dee, tweedle-dee, went the fiddlers.
Oh, there's none so rare,
As can compare
With old King Cole and his fiddlers three!

43

Little Bo-peep has lost her sheep,
And can't tell where to find them;
Leave them alone, and they'll come home,
And bring their tails behind them.

Little Bo-peep fell fast asleep,
And dreamt she heard them bleating;
But when she awoke, she found it a joke,
For they were still a-fleeting.

Then up she took her little crook,
Determined for to find them;
She found them indeed, but it made her heart bleed,
For they'd left all their tails behind them.

44

Willy boy, Willy boy, where are you going?
I'll go with you, if I may.
"I'm going to the meadow to see them a-mowing,
I'm going to help them make hay."

45

Blow, wind, blow! And go, mill, go!
That the miller may grind his corn;
That the baker may take it,
And into rolls make it,
And send us some hot in the morn.

46

Baa, baa, black sheep,
Have you any wool?
"Yes, marry, have I,
Three bags full;
One for my master,
And one for my dame,
And one for the little boy
Who lives in the lane."

47

Cobbler, cobbler, mend my shoe,
Give it a stitch and that will do.
Here's a nail, and there's a prod,
And now my shoe is well shod.

48

A cat came fiddling out of a barn,
With a pair of bagpipes under her arm;
She could sing nothing but fiddle cum fee,
The mouse has married the bumblebee.

49

Little King Boggen he built a fine hall,
Pie-crust and pastry-crust, that was the wall;
The windows were made of black puddings and white,
And slated with pancakes—you ne'er saw the like.

50

*(A counting-out rhyme)*

Intery, mintery, cutery-corn,
Apple seed and apple thorn;
Wire, brier, limber-lock,
Five geese in a flock;
Sit and sing by a spring,
O-U-T, and in again.

51

*(A game with the hands)*

Pease-porridge hot,
Pease-porridge cold,
Pease-porridge in the pot,
Nine days old;
Some like it hot,
Some like it cold,
Some like it in the pot,
Nine days old.[1]

[1] From Andrew Lang, *The Nursery Rhyme Book.*

52

Humpty-Dumpty sat on a wall,
Humpty-Dumpty had a great fall;
Threescore men and threescore more
Cannot place Humpty-Dumpty as he was
before.

*(An egg.)*

53

I have a little sister, they call her Peep,
Peep;
She wades the waters deep, deep, deep;
She climbs the mountains high, high, high;
Poor little creature, she has but one eye.

*(A star.)*

54

Twenty white horses
Upon a red hill;
Now they tramp,
Now they champ,
Now they stand still.

*(A child's teeth.)*

55

Little Nancy Etticoat,
In a white petticoat,
And a red nose;
The longer she stands,
The shorter she grows.

*(A candle.)*

56

As round as an apple,
As deep as a cup,
All the king's horses
Can't pull it up.

*(A well.)*

57

In marble walls as white as milk,
Lined with a skin as soft as silk,
Within a fountain crystal clear,
A golden apple doth appear;
No doors there are to this stronghold,
Yet thieves break in and steal the gold.

*(An egg.)*

58

As I was going to St. Ives,
I met a man with seven wives;
Every wife had seven sacks,
Every sack had seven cats,
Every cat had seven kits;
Kits, cats, sacks, and wives,
How many were there going to St. Ives?

*(One.)*

59

Thirty days hath September,
April, June, and November;
February has twenty-eight alone,
All the rest have thirty-one,
Excepting leap year, that's the time
When February's days are twenty-nine.

60

Monday's child is fair of face,
Tuesday's child is full of grace;
Wednesday's child is full of woe,
Thursday's child has far to go;
Friday's child is loving and giving,
Saturday's child works hard for its living;
But the child that is born on the Sabbath
day
Is bonny and blithe, and good and gay.[1]

61

If all the seas were one sea,
What a *great* sea that would be!
If all the trees were one tree,
What a *great* tree that would be!
If all the axes were one axe,
What a *great* axe that would be!
If all the men were one man,
What a *great* man he would be!
And if the *great* man took the *great* axe,
And cut down the *great* tree,
And let it fall into the *great* sea,
What a *great* splash-splash *that* would be!

[1] From Andrew Lang, *The Nursery Rhyme Book.*

62

There was an old woman tossed up in a basket
Nineteen times as high as the moon;
Where she was going I couldn't but ask it,
For in her hand she carried a broom.

"Old woman, old woman, old woman," quoth I,
"O whither, O whither, O whither, so high?"
"To brush the cobwebs off the sky!"
"Shall I go with thee?" "Aye, by and by."

63

There was a crooked man, and he went a crooked mile,
And found a crooked sixpence against a crooked stile;
He bought a crooked cat, which caught a crooked mouse,
And they all lived together in a little crooked house.

64

There was a man in our town,
And he was wondrous wise;
He jumped into a brier bush,
And scratched out both his eyes;
And when he saw his eyes were out,
With all his might and main
He jumped into another bush,
And scratched 'em in again.

65

Simple Simon met a pieman
Going to the fair;
Says Simple Simon to the pieman,
"Let me taste your ware."

Says the pieman to Simple Simon,
"Show me first your penny."
Says Simple Simon to the pieman,
"Indeed, I have not any."

Simple Simon went a fishing
For to catch a whale:
All the water he had got
Was in his mother's pail!

66

Peter Piper picked a peck of pickled peppers;
A peck of pickled peppers Peter Piper picked;
If Peter Piper picked a peck of pickled peppers,
Where's the peck of pickled peppers Peter Piper picked?

67

Robert Rowley rolled a round roll 'round;
A round roll Robert Rowley rolled 'round;
If Robert Rowley rolled a round roll 'round,
Where rolled the round roll Robert Rowley rolled 'round?

68

Three chiidren sliding on the ice
Upon a summer's day,
As it fell out, they all fell in,
The rest they ran away.

Now had these children been at home,
Or sliding on dry ground,
Ten thousand pounds to one penny
They had not all been drowned.

You parents all that children have,
And you that have got none,
If you would have them safe abroad,
Pray keep them safe at home.

69

This is the house that Jack built.

This is the malt
That lay in the house that Jack built.

This is the rat,
That ate the malt
That lay in the house that Jack built.

This is the cat,
That killed the rat,
That ate the malt
That lay in the house that Jack built.

This is the dog,
That worried the cat,
That killed the rat,
That ate the malt
That lay in the house that Jack built.

This is the cow with the crumpled horn,
That tossed the dog,
That worried the cat,
That killed the rat,
That ate the malt
That lay in the house that Jack built.

This is the maiden all forlorn,
That milked the cow with the crumpled
horn,
That tossed the dog,
That worried the cat,
That killed the rat,
That ate the malt
That lay in the house that Jack built.

This is the man all tattered and torn,
That kissed the maiden all forlorn,
That milked the cow with the crumpled
horn,
That tossed the dog,
That worried the cat,
That killed the rat,
That ate the malt
That lay in the house that Jack built.

This is the priest all shaven and shorn,
That married the man all tattered and torn,
That kissed the maiden all forlorn,
That milked the cow with the crumpled
horn,
That tossed the dog,
That worried the cat,
That killed the rat,
That ate the malt
That lay in the house that Jack built.

This is the cock that crowed in the morn,
That waked the priest all shaven and shorn,
That married the man all tattered and torn,
That kissed the maiden all forlorn,
That milked the cow with the crumpled
horn,
That tossed the dog,
That worried the cat,
That killed the rat,
That ate the malt
That lay in the house that Jack built.

This is the farmer sowing his corn,
That kept the cock that crowed in the
morn,
That waked the priest all shaven and shorn,
That married the man all tattered and torn,
That kissed the maiden all forlorn,
That milked the cow with the crumpled
horn,
That tossed the dog,
That worried the cat,
That killed the rat,
That ate the malt
That lay in the house that Jack built.

70

Old Mother Hubbard
Went to the cupboard
To get her poor dog a bone;
But when she came there
The cupboard was bare,
And so the poor dog had none.

She went to the baker's
To buy him some bread;
But when she came back
The poor dog was dead.

She went to the joiner's
To buy him a coffin;
But when she came back
The poor dog was laughing.

She took a clean dish,
To get him some tripe;
But when she came back
He was smoking his pipe.

She went to the hatter's
To buy him a hat;
But when she came back
He was feeding the cat.

She went to the barber's
To buy him a wig;
But when she came back
He was dancing a jig.

She went to the fruiterer's
  To buy him some fruit;
But when she came back
  He was playing the flute.

She went to the tailor's
  To buy him a coat;
But when she came back
  He was riding a goat.

She went to the cobbler's
  To buy him some shoes;
But when she came back
  He was reading the news.

She went to the seamstress
  To buy him some linen;
But when she came back
  The dog was spinning.

She went to the hosier's
  To buy him some hose;
But when she came back
  He was dressed in his clothes.

The dame made a curtsey,
  The dog made a bow;
The dame said, "Your servant,"
  The dog said, "Bow-wow."

71

There was an old man, who lived in a wood,
  As you may plainly see;
He said he could do as much work in a day,
  As his wife could do in three.
"With all my heart," the old woman said,
  "If that you will allow,
Tomorrow you'll stay at home in my stead,
  And I'll go drive the plow.

"But you must milk the Tidy cow,
  For fear that she go dry;
And you must feed the little pigs
  That are within the sty;
And you must mind the speckled hen,
  For fear she lay away;
And you must reel the spool of yarn,
  That I spun yesterday."

The old woman took a staff in her hand,
  And went to drive the plow.
The old man took a pail in his hand,
  And went to milk the cow;
But Tidy hinched, and Tidy flinched,
  And Tidy broke his nose,
And Tidy gave him such a blow,
  That the blood ran down to his toes.

"High! Tidy! ho! Tidy! high!
  Tidy! do stand still;
If ever I milk you, Tidy, again,
  'Twill be sore against my will!"

He went to feed the little pigs
  That were within the sty;
He hit his head against the beam,
  And he made the blood to fly.
He went to mind the speckled hen,
  For fear she'd lay astray,
And he forgot the spool of yarn
  His wife spun yesterday.

So he swore by the sun, the moon, and the stars,
  And the green leaves on the tree,
"If my wife doesn't do a day's work in her life,
  She shall ne'er be ruled by me."

## *Mother Goose Rhymes: Suggested Grades*

Most children know some of the Mother Goose rhymes before entering school; they learn others from hearing the teacher say or sing them. Comprehension of meaning and ability to read are not involved in the child's enjoyment of the rhymes, and grading has less significance here than in other types of material. The grades given are those in which children appear to take the greatest pleasure in hearing and repeating the particular rhymes, though they may have learned them much earlier, as indeed we hope they have.

*Grade One*

1. Ride a cock-horse to Banbury Cross
2. This little pig went to market
3. Diddle, diddle, dumpling
4. Bow, wow, wow
5. Bye, baby bunting
6. Hush-a-bye, baby
7. Pat-a-cake
8. To market, to buy a fat pig
9. Polly, put the kettle on
10. Come, butter, come
11. The rose is red
12. Hey! diddle, diddle
13. Jack and Jill
14. Hickory, dickory, dock
15. Cushy cow bonny
16. Pussy-cat, where have you been
17. Mistress Mary
18. A farmer went riding
19. Little Betty Blue
20. Jack be nimble
22. Higgledy, piggledy, my black hen
23. There was an old woman lived under a hill
24. Wee Willie Winkie
25. Little Jack Horner
26. Little Miss Muffet
27. Little Boy Blue
29. Little Robin Redbreast
30. The north wind doth blow
31. Once I saw a little bird
33. There were three jovial huntsmen
36. Girls and boys, come out to play
37. Ding, dong, bell
38. Sing a song of sixpence
39. There was an old woman who lived in a shoe

40. One, two, buckle my shoe
42. Old King Cole
43. Little Bo-peep
44. Willy boy, where are you going
45. Blow, wind, blow
46. Baa, baa, black sheep
47. Cobbler, cobbler, mend my shoe
52. Humpty-Dumpty
53. I have a little sister
54. Twenty white horses

*Grade Two*

21. Three blind mice
32. God bless the master of this house
41. I had a little pony
48. A cat came fiddling
49. Little King Boggen
50. Intery, mintery, cutery-corn
51. Pease-porridge hot
55. Little Nancy Etticoat
56. As round as an apple
61. If all the seas were one sea
69. This is the house that Jack built
70. Old Mother Hubbard

*Grade Three*

28. Cock-a-doodle-doo
34. I had a little nut-tree
35. I saw a ship a-sailing
57. In marble walls as white as milk
58. As I was going to St. Ives
60. Monday's child
62. There was an old woman tossed up in a basket
63. There was a crooked man
65. Simple Simon
71. There was an old man who lived in a wood

*Grade Four*

59. Thirty days hath September
64. There was a man in our town
66. Peter Piper
67. Robert Rowley
68. Three children sliding on the ice

## *Books of Mother Goose Rhymes*

Anderson, Anne (illustrator), *The Old Mother Goose Nursery Rhyme Book.* Nelson.

Brooke, L. Leslie (illustrator), *Ring o' Roses.* Warne.

Caldecott, Randolph (illustrator), *Randolph Caldecott's Picture Book No. 2.* Warne.

———, *Randolph Caldecott's The Hey Diddle Diddle Picture Book.* Warne.

Daglish, Alice, and Ernest Rhys, *The Land of Nursery Rhyme,* illus. by Charles Folkard. Dutton.

Dalgliesh, Alice, *The Gay Mother Goose,* illus. by Francoise Seignobosc. Scribner.

Falls, Charles B. (illustrator), *Mother Goose.* Doubleday, Doran.

Fraser, C. Lovat (illustrator), *Nursery Rhymes.* Knopf.

Greenaway, Kate (illustrator), *Mother Goose.* Warne.

Grover, Eulalie L., *The Volland Mother Goose,* illus. by Frederick Richardson. Donohue.

Hader, Berta, and Elmer Hader (illustrators), *Picture Book of Mother Goose.* Coward-McCann.

Lang, Andrew, *The Nursery Rhyme Book,* illus. by L. Leslie Brooke. Warne.

Lenski, Lois (illustrator), *Lois Lenski's Mother Goose.* Harper.

Rackham, Arthur (illustrator), *Mother Goose.* Appleton-Century.

Smith, E. Boyd (illustrator), *Mother Goose.* Putnam.

Smith, Jessie Willcox (illustrator), *Mother Goose.* Dodd, Mead.

Walter, L. Edna, *Mother Goose's Nursery Rhymes,* illus. by Charles Folkard. Macmillan.

Wright, Blanche Fisher (illustrator), *The Real Mother Goose.* Rand McNally.

## *Student Activities*

1. Do you find that the versions of *Mother Goose Rhymes* given here vary in form from those you knew as a child? Do you have any emotional reaction to these changes?

2. Can you contribute to the class discussion any modern rhymes similar in pattern to Mother Goose? Perhaps they come from your own childhood, present-day political life, or some other area of experience. Could some of our college yells, e.g. "Oski-wow-wow! Wiski-wee-wee!" etc., be properly classified as folk rhymes?

3. Can you contribute examples of corruptions by neighborhood children of Mother Goose rhymes to fit their present purposes? Such as the following:

Roses are red,
Violets are blue;
Elephants are fat,
And so are you!

——— is mad,
And I am glad,
And I know what will please her;
(followed by a line appropriate to the situation)

4. Do you think of other evidence pointing in the direction that the same human motives behind the old Mother Goose rhymes are operating today?

## *References for Students*

Barnes, Walter, *The Children's Poets,* Chapter 2. World Book.

Darton, F. J. Harvey, *Children's Books in England,* pages 98 to 105, 122 to 140. Macmillan.

Field, Walter T., *A Guide to Literature for Children,* Chapter 10. Ginn.

Hale, Edward Everett (introduction), *The Only True Mother Goose* (reproduction of edition printed in Boston in 1833). Lothrop.

Homer, Sydney, *Songs from Mother Goose.* Macmillan.

Moffat, A. E., *Little Songs of Long Ago,* illus. by H. Willebeek Le Mair. McKay.

———, *Our Old Nursery Rhymes,* illus. by H. Willebeek Le Mair. McKay.

Moore, Annie E., *Literature Old and New for Children,* Chapter 2. Houghton Mifflin.

Moses, Montrose J., *Children's Books and Reading,* Chapter 2. Mitchell Kennerly.

Welsh, Charles (editor), *A Book of Nursery Rhymes.* Heath.

Wheeler, William A. (editor), *Mother Goose's Melodies.* Houghton Mifflin.

# *Verse*

# VERSE FOR CHILDREN

CHILDREN like poetry. There are many reasons why they should. Children and poets have much in common. Not only are both sensitive to rhythm, but they have much the same way of looking at things. To them the world is always new and experience is vivid and intense. Things seen and heard and touched are full of meaning and significance. The poet is able to catch these qualities and put them into words. His feeling is easily communicated to children, for they, in their childish ways, have the same eager desire to taste experience to the full. Natural, also, to the child is the high value the poet places on his own experience; he paints something that *he sees,* not a picture that some one else saw but *his own* personal experience or the experience of *his own* imagination. To him words are living things as they are to children, who often make up words for themselves for the fun of it. Indeed, when conditions are favorable many children make their own verse, thus sharing the poet's joy in giving creative expression to their experience.

Most children have a happy introduction to poetry, and the teacher's concern should be to continue and to enhance the joy that children get from verse. Before his school life began, lullabies sang the child to sleep, jingles satisfied his love of rhythm, and nursery rhymes associated poetry with the commonplace things of the world about him. It is unfortunate if the school cannot continue poetry as a simple, natural experience of childhood. But the enchantment will be destroyed if chores and requirements and obligations become a part of the program. All that is really needed is to let children hear poetry, read casually and pleasantly but well. At first they may not talk much about a poem, but they will listen. Before long they will ask to hear certain poems again, then again and again. Then they begin saying certain lines with the reader and perhaps even repeating whole poems for themselves. This happens, though, only in an atmosphere free from compulsion. It cannot be forced or hurried.

Because of the delicacy of the thing called appreciation, it can be so easily spoiled. The teacher or parent who wants to preserve for children the beauty and enjoyment that lie in poetry is alert to the effect of *timeliness* in offering a poem. Circumstances, interests, conditions of various sorts, affect the reception children will accord a poem. If a teacher is familiar with a great deal of verse suitable for children, it is easy to bring out the poem that fits best at a particular time, often with as happy results as if she were a magician producing a white rabbit from a hat.

One of the outstanding developments in the field of verse for children is the comparatively recent change that has taken place in the choice of poetry considered suitable for children. Not so long ago, any poems high in sentiment and purpose were thought desirable for children; the fact that many of these poems were difficult and abstract in thought and language was given little attention. The same lack of insight caused any poem that pictured children or childhood to be regarded as a child's poem. Often such poems were reflective and philosophical, the poet looked back upon his childhood from an adult point of view that had little reality to children themselves. In the same way many poems were offered to children, which though beautiful in themselves, dealt with mature experiences far beyond the child's ability to comprehend. An example is Eugene Field's "Little Boy Blue," which until fairly recently was commonly included in children's books. True, the poem speaks of a child and his toys, but its theme is a parent's grief and sorrow. Better understanding of children has brought marked changes in other respects in the verse thought desirable for them. We have learned the value of starting with children *where they are*. This may sometimes mean that the verse we offer may not be great poetry, but it will be simple and clear to children. As they grow in experience with poetry and love of it, they grow in taste and understanding that welcomes finer and finer things.

A necessary quality in verse for children is vividness and singleness of purpose. A poem should present one clear image, or a succession of images, but each one clear and complete. Vague and confused shapes and fragments of experience are not for children. Completeness in a poem does not mean, however, that the child's mind and imagination may not be led from the poem into a further exploration of its ideas and feeling. Just as a great painter puts in a picture a space from which the imagination of the observer leaves the picture, so the poet leads the reader into a world of the reader's own making.

The appeal of verse lies not only in the thought, feeling, and images which the poet invokes, but in the music and rhythm of his language. To children the appeal of rhythm is especially strong, and young children delight in the music of poetry before the words come to have meaning. As they grow older and the content of poems adds to their enjoyment, a strongly rhythmic setting continues to give satisfaction. They find great delight in verse that describes physical action. Such verse, in a rhythm that is in itself descriptive of the action, invites them to dance and skip and devise bodily movements which dramatize the rhythm.

The impulse to join words and movement is one of the oldest art experiences of the race. Primitive man undoubtedly made songs about his hunting and his wars. There are many work songs of great antiquity that have come down to us. Rowing a boat, chopping a tree, or similar activities shared by two or more people lent themselves to song-making. It was a short step to a community song to celebrate a victory or to express the sorrow of defeat. Then when a hero performed a great deed it was natural to commemorate his exploit in a song—and ballads were born.

The old ballads, which we now think of as belonging especially to children's literature, were not made or sung for children; they were the literature of all the people. They were handed down orally from generation to generation for centuries before books were made. After printing was invented, many found their way into early books and have been appropriated by children, especially those that deal with the beloved figure of Robin Hood. The strong rhythm and the recurring rhymes of ballads delight children today just as they did hundreds of years ago when as songs they were companions of the old folk tales. The old ballads always tell a story, they were made to be sung to tunes, and they have no known authors.

It was not until early in the eighteenth century that poetry definitely intended for children appeared. Dr. Isaac Watts' *Divine and Moral Songs for Children* (1715) was written not to give pleasure but to teach moral and religious truths. Many of these poems are stern, but others show kindliness and genuine love of children. "How Doth the Little Busy Bee" has kept its place in children's verse to the present day.

Unfortunately Dr. Watts had many imitators who lacked his gentleness, and for a century the verse written for children was terrifying in its content. The writers, both in England and America, were preoccupied with such themes as early death and punishment for misbehavior. Many of these old cautionary poems seem funny today because the threats and forebodings were pushed to such extremes. Let us hope that the children who had to read and memorize them saw something in them to giggle over when their elders were out of hearing.

William Blake is an exception to the period in which he lived. His *Songs of Innocence,* first printed in 1789, is an expression of true poetic genius that even now is not fully appreciated.

Ann and Jane Taylor were the first poets who wrote only for children. Their *Original Poems for Infant Minds* (1804) shows more of the influence of Watts than of Blake, but they wrote *for* children and *about* children. "Pretty Cow" and "Twinkle, Twinkle, Little Star" have a secure place in children's verse.

The work of Edward Lear cannot be explained in terms of any influences at the time he lived, though of course nonsense needs no explanation. Most of the juvenile books of the period were concerned with moral and practical lessons; hence Lear's *Book of Nonsense* (1846) literally burst upon children and grownups and sent them into gales of laughter, laughter that continues today. Lear's "Limericks" and "The Owl and the Pussy Cat" are unsurpassed in humorous verse.

With the appearance of Christina Rossetti's *Sing-Song* (1871) and Robert Louis Stevenson's *A Child's Garden of Verses* (1885) began an era of beautiful verse for children that has continued until the present day. Many distinguished poets have contributed to this childlike and delightful literature.

Outstanding among the children's poets of today are Walter de la Mare,[1] Elizabeth Madox Roberts, Rachel Field, Winifred Welles, Rose Fyleman, Eleanor Farjeon, and A. A. Milne. Other poets, such as Robert Frost and John Masefield, who are poets for adults, have written some beautiful poems that appeal strongly to children.

Two contemporary American poets, who began writing for grownups but have been claimed by children, are Vachel Lindsay and Carl Sandburg. These poets have an honesty of expression and a treatment of original themes that are very significant in modern poetry. Vachel Lindsay's "ripping, roaring rhythms" are after a child's own heart. Carl Sandburg does not always follow the established and expected forms of verse and he writes about everyday things that have been considered by many writers too prosaic to be the subject of poetry, but his verse has at times great beauty and at all times strength and vigor. It seems natural to children that poetry should deal with ordinary things in a tempo expressive of modern living. Another reason for the popularity of modern verse is its freedom from obscure language and difficult literary allusions. There are no references and archaic words to be looked up. These poets speak not only in the language of the time in which our children live but in the very speech which children themselves use. It is evident that our vigorous, living American language can take its place in genuine literature.

A sympathetic understanding of children will provide abundant experience in hearing and enjoying humorous verse. Laughter is as necessary as food for the development of wholesome, happy children. Let us not be afraid of verse that abounds in fun and pleasure. Let our children laugh.

[1] Further information about the work of these poets and of all the authors whose writings appear in this book may be found in *Authors of Children's Books,* in the Appendix.

# Boys and Girls

## THE HUNTSMEN [1]

*Walter de la Mare*

Three jolly gentlemen,
  In coats of red,
Rode their horses
  Up to bed.

Three jolly gentlemen
  Snored till morn,
Their horses champing
  The golden corn.

Three jolly gentlemen,
  At break of day,
Came clitter-clatter down the stairs
  And galloped away.

## TIME TO RISE [2]

*Robert Louis Stevenson*

A birdie with a yellow bill
Hopped upon the window sill,
Cocked his shining eye and said:
"Ain't you 'shamed, you sleepyhead!"

## A CHILD'S DAY BEGINS [3]

*Walter de la Mare*

Softly, drowsily,
Out of sleep;
Into the world again
Ann's eyes peep;
Over the pictures
Across the walls
One little quivering
Sunbeam falls.
A thrush in the garden
Seems to say,
Wake, little Ann,
'Tis day, 'tis day;
Faint sweet breezes
The casement stir,
Breathing of pinks
And lavender.
At last from her pillow,
With cheeks bright red,
Up comes her round little
Tousled head;
And out she tumbles
From her warm bed.

[1] From Walter de la Mare, *Collected Poems.*
[2] From Robert Louis Stevenson, *A Child's Garden of Verses.*
[3] From Walter de la Mare, *A Child's Day.*

## BED IN SUMMER [1]

*Robert Louis Stevenson*

In winter I get up at night
And dress by yellow candlelight.
In summer, quite the other way,
I have to go to bed by day.

I have to go to bed and see
The birds still hopping on the tree,
Or hear the grown-up people's feet
Still going past me in the street.

And does it not seem hard to you,
When all the sky is clear and blue,
And I should like so much to play,
To have to go to bed by day?

## MY BED IS A BOAT [2]

*Robert Louis Stevenson*

My bed is like a little boat;
  Nurse helps me in when I embark;
She girds me in my sailor's coat
  And starts me in the dark.

At night, I go on board and say
  Good night to all my friends on shore;
I shut my eyes and sail away
  And see and hear no more.

And sometimes things to bed I take,
  As prudent sailors have to do;
Perhaps a slice of wedding cake,
  Perhaps a toy or two.

All night across the dark we steer;
  But when the day returns at last,
Safe in my room, beside the pier,
  I find my vessel fast.

## LULLABY [3]

*Paul Laurence Dunbar*

Bedtime's come fu' little boys,
  Po' little lamb.
Too tiahed out to make a noise,
  Po' little lamb.
You gwine t' have to-morrer sho'?
Yes, you tole me dat befo',
Don't you fool me, chile, no mo',
  Po' little lamb.

You been bad the livelong day,
  Po' little lamb.
Th'owin' stones an' runnin' 'way,
  Po' little lamb.
My, but you's a-runnin' wil',
Look jes' lak some po' folks' chile;
Mam' gwine whup you atter while,
  Po' little lamb.

Come hyeah! you mos' tiahed to def,
  Po' little lamb.
Played yo'se'f clean out o' bref,
  Po' little lamb.
See dem han's now—sich a sight!
Would you evah b'lieve dey's white?
Stan' still twell I wash 'em right,
  Po' little lamb.

Jes' cain't hol' yo' haid up straight,
  Po' little lamb.
Hadn't oughter played so late,
  Po' little lamb.
Mammy do' know whut she'd do,
Ef de chillun's all lak you;
You's a caution now fu' true,
  Po' little lamb.

Lay yo' haid down in my lap,
  Po' little lamb.
Y' ought to have a right good slap,
  Po' little lamb.
You been runnin' roun' a heap.
Shet dem eyes an' don't you peep,
Dah now, dah now, go to sleep,
  Po' little lamb.

[1] From Robert Louis Stevenson, *A Child's Garden of Verses.*
[2] *Ibid.*
[3] From Paul Laurence Dunbar, *Lyrics of the Hearthside.*

## THE SLEEPY SONG [1]

*Josephine Daskam Bacon*

As soon as the fire burns red and low,
And the house upstairs is still,
She sings me a queer little sleepy song,
Of sheep that go over the hill.

The good little sheep run quick and soft,
Their colors are gray and white;
They follow their leader nose to tail,
For they must be home by night.

And one slips over and one comes next,
And one runs after behind,
The gray one's nose at the white one's tail,
The top of the hill they find.

And when they get to the top of the hill
They quietly slip away,
But one runs over and one comes next—
Their colors are white and gray.

And over they go, and over they go,
And over the top of the hill,
The good little sheep run quick and soft,
And the house upstairs is still.

And one slips over and one comes next,
The good little, gray little sheep!
I watch how the fire burns red and low,
And she says that I fall asleep.

## WYNKEN, BLYNKEN, AND NOD [2]

*Eugene Field*

Wynken, Blynken, and Nod one night
  Sailed off in a wooden shoe—
Sailed on a river of crystal light,
  Into a sea of dew.
"Where are you going, and what do you wish?"
  The old moon asked the three.
"We have come to fish for the herring fish
  That live in this beautiful sea;
  Nets of silver and gold have we,"
      Said Wynken,
      Blynken,
      And Nod.

The old moon laughed and sang a song,
  As they rocked in the wooden shoe,
And the wind that sped them all night long
  Ruffled the waves of dew.
The little stars were the herring fish
  That lived in that beautiful sea—
"Now cast your nets wherever you wish,
  Never afeared are we!"
So cried the stars to the fishermen three:
      Wynken,
      Blynken,
      And Nod.

All night long their nets they threw
  To the stars in the twinkling foam—
Then down from the sky came the wooden shoe,
  Bringing the fishermen home;
'Twas all so pretty a sail, it seemed
  As if it could not be;
And some folk thought 'twas a dream they'd dreamed
  Of sailing that beautiful sea;
  But I shall name you the fishermen three:
      Wynken,
      Blynken,
      And Nod.

Wynken and Blynken are two little eyes,
  And Nod is a little head,
And the wooden shoe that sailed the skies
  Is a wee one's trundle-bed;
So shut your eyes while Mother sings
  Of wonderful sights that be,
And you shall see the beautiful things
  As you rock in the misty sea
  Where the old shoe rocked the fishermen three:
      Wynken,
      Blynken,
      And Nod.

[1] From Josephine Daskam Bacon, *Poems.*
[2] From Eugene Field, *Poems of Childhood.*

## SWEET AND LOW[1]

*Alfred Tennyson*

Sweet and low, sweet and low,
Wind of the western sea,
Low, low, breathe and blow,
Wind of the western sea!
Over the rolling waters go,
Come from the dying moon, and blow,
Blow him again to me;
While my little one, while my pretty one, sleeps.

Sleep and rest, sleep and rest,
Father will come to thee soon;
Rest, rest on mother's breast,
Father will come to thee soon;
Father will come to his babe in the nest,
Silver sails all out of the west
Under the silver moon;
Sleep, my little one, sleep, my pretty one, sleep.

## MY SHADOW[2]

*Robert Louis Stevenson*

I have a little shadow that goes in and out with me,
And what can be the use of him is more than I can see.
He is very, very like me from the heels up to the head;
And I see him jump before me when I jump into my bed.

The funniest thing about him is the way he likes to grow—
Not at all like proper children, which is always very slow;
For he sometimes shoots up taller like an india-rubber ball,
And he sometimes gets so little that there's none of him at all.

He hasn't got a notion of how children ought to play,
And can only make a fool of me in every sort of way.
He stays so close beside me, he's a coward you can see;
I'd think shame to stick to nursie as that shadow sticks to me!

One morning, very early, before the sun was up,
I rose and found the shining dew on every buttercup;
But my lazy little shadow, like an arrant sleepy-head,
Had stayed at home behind me and was fast asleep in bed.

## WASHING[3]

*John Drinkwater*

What is all this washing about,
Every day, week in, week out?
From getting up till going to bed,
I'm tired of hearing the same thing said.
Whether I'm dirty or whether I'm not,
Whether the water is cold or hot,
Whether I like or whether I don't
Whether I will or whether I won't—
"Have you washed your hands, and washed your face?"
I seem to *live* in the washing-place.

Whenever I go for a walk or ride,
As soon as I put my nose inside
The door again, there's some one there
With a sponge and soap, and a lot they care
If I have something better to do,
"Now wash your face and your fingers too."

Before a meal is ever begun,
And after ever a meal is done,
It's time to turn on the waterspout.

Please, what *is* all this washing about?

1 From Alfred Tennyson, *The Princess.*
2 From Robert Louis Stevenson, *A Child's Garden of Verses.*
3 From John Drinkwater, *More about Me.*

## BIRTHDAYS [1]

*Marchette Gaylord Chute*

We had waffles-with-syrup for breakfast,
As many as we could hold;
And I had some presents extra,
Because I am six years old.

I've thanked everyone for my presents,
And kissed 'em, and now that that's done
The family's all ready to do things,
Whatever I think would be fun.

When Timothy had his birthday
We went to the circus, and Tim
Laughed so hard at the seals and the monkeys
That a real clown winked at him.

And Dorothy chose a picnic
On the shore of a little lake,
With tadpoles, and buns, and diving,
And a four-layer birthday cake.

And now that it's my turn for choosing,
I'm going to ask if we might
Take all our family of rabbits
To bed with us just for tonight.

## PRESENTS [2]

*Marchette Gaylord Chute*

I wanted a rifle for Christmas,
I wanted a bat and a ball,
I wanted some skates and a bicycle,
But I didn't want mittens at all.

I wanted a whistle
And I wanted a kite,
I wanted a pocketknife
That shut up tight.
I wanted some books
And I wanted a kit,
But I didn't want mittens one little bit.

I told them I didn't want mittens,
I told them as plain as plain.
I told them I didn't *want* mittens,
And they've given me mittens again!

## TROUBLES [3]

*Dorothy Aldis*

Stockings are a trouble; so many times my toes
Try to climb in where a heel generally goes.

And mittens are not easy, for lots of days my thumbs
Go wandering and crawling into other fingers' homes.

But rubbers are the hardest because, it seems to me,
I always put one rubber where the other one should be.

## SKIPPING ROPES [4]

*Dorothy Aldis*

Someday
Jane shall
Have, she
Hopes,
Rainbows
For her
Skipping
Ropes.

## TO CHINA [5]

*Leroy F. Jackson*

Buster's got a popper gun,
A reg'lar one that shoots,
And Teddy's got an engine
With a whistler that toots.

[1] From Marchette Gaylord Chute, *Rhymes about Ourselves.*
[2] *Ibid.*
[3] From Dorothy Aldis, *Here, There and Everywhere.*
[4] From Dorothy Aldis, *Everything and Anything.*
[5] From Leroy F. Jackson, *The Peter Patter Book.*

But I've got something finer yet—
A pair of rubber boots—
Oh, it's boots, boots, boots,
A pair of rubber boots!
I could walk from here to China
In a pair of rubber boots.

## AT THE SEASIDE [1]

*Robert Louis Stevenson*

When I was down beside the sea,
A wooden spade they gave to me
  To dig the sandy shore.

My holes were empty like a cup.
In every hole the sea came up,
  Till it could come no more.

## MERRY-GO-ROUND [2]

*Dorothy W. Baruch*

I climbed up on the merry-go-round,
And it went round and round.

I climbed up on a big brown horse,
And it went up and down.

  Around and round
  And up and down,
  Around and round
  And up and down.
  I sat high up
  On a big brown horse
  And rode around
  On the merry-go-round
    And rode around

On the merry-go-round
I rode around
On the merry-go-round
  Around
    And round
      And
        Round.

## THE SWING [3]

*Robert Louis Stevenson*

How do you like to go up in a swing,
  Up in the air so blue?
Oh, I do think it the pleasantest thing
  Ever a child can do!

Up in the air and over the wall,
  Till I can see so wide,
Rivers and trees and cattle and all
  Over the countryside—

Till I look down on the garden green,
  Down on the roof so brown—
Up in the air I go flying again,
  Up in the air and down!

## THREE LOVELY HOLES [4]

*Winifred Welles*

Our barn roof has three lovely holes.
At dusk they are pink as coals,
But they are blue as eyes by day.
I love to lie upon the hay,
Staring up at them and see
How they are staring down at me.

## THE LAND OF COUNTERPANE [5]

*Robert Louis Stevenson*

When I was sick and lay a-bed,
I had two pillows at my head,
And all my toys beside me lay
To keep me happy all the day.

[1] From Robert Louis Stevenson, *A Child's Garden of Verses.*
[2] From Dorothy W. Baruch, *I Like Machinery.*
[3] From Robert Louis Stevenson, *A Child's Garden of Verses.*
[4] From Winifred Welles, *Skipping Along Alone.*
[5] From Robert Louis Stevenson, *A Child's Garden of Verses.*

And sometimes for an hour or so
I watched my leaden soldiers go,
With different uniforms and drills,
Among the bedclothes, through the hills;

And sometimes sent my ships in fleets
All up and down among the sheets;
Or brought my trees and houses out,
And planted cities all about.

I was the giant great and still
That sits upon the pillow-hill
And sees before him, dale and plain,
The pleasant land of counterpane.

## ALONE [1]

*Joseph Paget-Fredericks*

I never had walked quite so far
Alone,
And as I closed the garden gate
And slipped into the leafy lane
And saw the winding road ahead,
I felt so very quite alone,
Walking along alone.

I hadn't gone so very far
Alone,
When all the staring huge oak trees
Came shuffling, crowding round me;
And then I wished I was at home.
I felt so very quite alone,
Walking along alone.

A few more steps to the road's bend
Alone,
And then I stole a glance ahead.
It's awfully shady, dark beyond,
So I just turned and ran and ran.
I felt so very quite alone;
But better, . . . running home.

## OVER THE GARDEN WALL [2]

*Eleanor Farjeon*

Over the garden wall
Where unseen children play,
Somebody threw a ball
One fine summer day;
I caught it as it came
Straight from the hand unknown
Playing a happy game
It would not play alone.

A pretty ball with bands
Of gold and stars of blue;
I turned it in my hands
And wondered, then I threw
Over the garden wall
Again the treasure round—
And somebody caught the ball
With a laughing sound.

## A GOOD PLAY [3]

*Robert Louis Stevenson*

We built a ship upon the stairs
All made of the back-bedroom chairs,
And filled it full of sofa pillows
To go a-sailing on the billows.

We took a saw and several nails,
And water in the nursery pails;
And Tom said, "Let us also take
An apple and a slice of cake";
Which was enough for Tom and me
To go a-sailing on, till tea.

We sailed along for days and days,
And had the very best of plays;
But Tom fell out and hurt his knee,
So there was no one left but me.

[1] From Joseph Paget-Fredericks, *Green Pipes.*
[2] From Eleanor Farjeon, *Over the Garden Wall.*
[3] From Robert Louis Stevenson, *A Child's Garden of Verses.*

## IF ONLY . . .[1]

*Rose Fyleman*

If only I'd some money,
  I'd buy a jolly boat
And get a pair of sea boots
  And a furry sort of coat,
A case or two of salted beef
  And a seaman's wooden chest,
And I'd sail away to the North Pole,
Or I'd sail away to the South Pole,
  Whichever I thought was best.

I'd get up very early—
  They wouldn't see me go—
Jimmy would be with me
  But no one else would know.
Dogs are very useful,
  And I couldn't part with Jim,
And whether I went to the North Pole,
Or whether I went to the South Pole,
  It would be all the same to him.

Perhaps we'd see a mountain
  That no one else had seen;
Perhaps we'd find a country
  Where no one else had been.
Suppose we climbed an iceberg
  And saw the midnight sun! . . .
Oh, whether we went to the North Pole,
Or whether we went to the South Pole,
  Wouldn't it all be fun?

## THE RAGGEDY MAN[2]

*James Whitcomb Riley*

O The Raggedy Man! He works fer Pa;
An' he's the goodest man ever you saw!
He comes to our house every day,
An' waters the horses, an' feeds 'em hay;
An' he opens the shed—an' we all ist laugh
When he drives out our little old wobblely
    calf;
An' nen—ef our hired girl says he can—
He milks the cow fer 'Lizabuth Ann.
  Aint he a' awful good Raggedy Man?
    Raggedy! Raggedy! Raggedy Man!

W'y, The Raggedy Man—he's ist so good
He splits the kindlin' an' chops the wood;
An' nen he spades in our garden, too,
An' does most things 'at *boys* can't do!
He clumbed clean up in our big tree
An' shooked a' apple down fer me—
An' nother'n', too, fer 'Lizabuth Ann—
An' nother'n', too, fer The Raggedy Man.
  Aint he a' awful kind Raggedy Man?
    Raggedy! Raggedy! Raggedy Man!

An' The Raggedy Man, he knows most
    rhymes
An' tells 'em, ef I be good, sometimes;
Knows 'bout Giunts, an' Griffuns, an' Elves,
An' the Squidgicum-Squees 'at swallers
    therselves!
An', wite by the pump in our pasture-lot,
He showed me the hole 'at the Wunks is got,
'At lives 'way deep in the ground, an' can
Turn into me, er 'Lizabuth Ann!
  Aint he a funny old Raggedy Man?
    Raggedy! Raggedy! Raggedy Man!

The Raggedy Man—one time when he
Wuz makin' a little bow-'n'-orry fer me,
Says "When *you're* big like your Pa is,
Air you go' to keep a fine store like his—
An' be a rich merchunt—an' wear fine
    clothes?
Er what *air* you go' to be, goodness knows!"
An' nen he laughed at 'Lizabuth Ann,
An' I says " 'M go' to be a Raggedy Man!
  I'm ist go' to be a nice Raggedy Man!
    Raggedy! Raggedy! Raggedy Man!"

## SKATING[3]

*Herbert Asquith*

When I try to skate,
My feet are so wary
They grit and grate;
And then I watch Mary
Easily gliding,
Like an ice-fairy;
Skimming and curving,

[1] From Rose Fyleman, *Gay Go Up*.
[2] From James Whitcomb Riley, *Rhymes of Childhood*.
[3] From Herbert Asquith, *Pillicock Hill*.

Out and in,
With a turn of her head,
And a lift of her chin,
And a gleam of her eye,
And a twirl and a spin;
Sailing under
The breathless hush
Of the willows, and back
To the frozen rush;
Out to the island
And round the edge,
Skirting the rim
Of the crackling sedge,
Swerving close
To the poplar root,
And round the lake
On a single foot,
With a three, and an eight,
And a loop and a ring;
Where Mary glides,
The lake will sing!
Out in the mist
I hear her now
Under the frost
Of the willow-bough
Easily sailing,
Light and fleet,
With the song of the lake
Beneath her feet.

## THE BUTTERBEAN TENT [1]

*Elizabeth Madox Roberts*

All through the garden I went and went,
And I walked in under the butterbean tent.

The poles leaned up like a good tepee
And made a nice little house for me.

I had a hard brown clod for a seat,
And all outside was a cool green street.

A little green worm and a butterfly
And a cricket-like thing that could hop
 went by.

Hidden away there were flocks and flocks
Of bugs that could go like little clocks.

Such a good day it was when I spent
A long, long while in the butterbean tent.

[1] From Elizabeth Madox Roberts, *Under the Tree.*

## THANKSGIVING DAY

*Lydia Maria Child*

Over the river and through the wood,
 To grandfather's house we go;
  The horse knows the way
  To carry the sleigh
 Through the white and drifted snow.

Over the river and through the wood—
 Oh, how the wind does blow!
  It stings the toes
  And bites the nose,
 As over the ground we go.

Over the river and through the wood,
 To have a first-rate play.
  Hear the bells ring,
  "Ting-a-ling-ding!"
 Hurrah for Thanksgiving Day!

Over the river and through the wood,
 Trot fast, my dapple-gray!
  Spring over the ground,
  Like a hunting-hound!
 For this is Thanksgiving Day.

Over the river and through the wood,
 And straight through the barnyard gate.
  We seem to go
  Extremely slow,
 It is so hard to wait!

Over the river and through the wood—
 Now grandmother's cap I spy!
  Hurrah for the fun!
  Is the pudding done?
 Hurrah for the pumpkin pie!

## CHRISTMAS MORNING[1]

*Elizabeth Madox Roberts*

If Bethlehem were here today,
Or this were very long ago,
There wouldn't be a winter time
Nor any cold or snow.

I'd run out through the garden gate,
And down along the pasture walk;
And off beside the cattle barns
I'd hear a kind of gentle talk.

I'd move the heavy iron chain
And pull away the wooden pin;
I'd push the door a little bit
And tiptoe very softly in.

The pigeons and the yellow hens
And all the cows would stand away;
Their eyes would open wide to see
A lady in the manger hay,

If this were very long ago
And Bethlehem were here today.

And Mother held my hand and smiled—
I mean the lady would—and she
Would take the woolly blankets off
Her little boy so I could see.

His shut-up eyes would be asleep,
And he would look like our John,
And he would be all crumpled too,
And have a pinkish color on.

I'd watch his breath go in and out,
His little clothes would all be white.
I'd slip my finger in his hand
To feel how he could hold it tight.

And she would smile and say, "Take care,"
The mother, Mary, would, "Take care";
And I would kiss his little hand
And touch his hair.

While Mary put the blankets back
The gentle talk would soon begin.
And when I'd tiptoe softly out
I'd meet the Wise Men going in.

## MR. NOBODY

*Author Unknown*

I know a funny little man,
  As quiet as a mouse,
Who does the mischief that is done
  In everybody's house!
There's no one ever sees his face,
  And yet we all agree
That every plate we break was cracked
  By Mr. Nobody.

'Tis he who always tears our books,
  Who leaves the door ajar,
He pulls the buttons from our shirts,
  And scatters pins afar;
That squeaking door will always squeak,
  For, prithee, don't you see,
We leave the oiling to be done
  By Mr. Nobody.

The finger marks upon the door
  By none of us are made;
We never leave the blinds unclosed,
  To let the curtains fade.
The ink we never spill; the boots
  That lying round you see
Are not our boots—they all belong
  To Mr. Nobody.

## A CIRCUS GARLAND[2]

*Rachel Field*

### PARADE

This is the day the circus comes
With blare of brass, with beating drums,
And clashing cymbals, and with roar
Of wild beasts never heard before
Within town limits. Spick and span
Will shine each gilded cage and van;
Cockades at every horse's head
Will nod, and riders dressed in red
Or blue trot by. There will be floats
In shapes like dragons, thrones and boats,
And clowns on stilts; freaks big and small,
Till leisurely and last of all
Camels and elephants will pass
Beneath our elms, along our grass.

[1] From Elizabeth Madox Roberts, *Under the Tree.*
[2] From Rachel Field, *Branches Green.*

### THE PERFORMING SEAL

Who is so proud
As not to feel
A secret awe
Before a seal
That keeps such sleek
And wet repose
While twirling candles
On his nose?

### ACROBAT

Surely that is not a man
Balanced on a thread in air,
But a brightly colored fan
Folding and unfolding there?

### THE ELEPHANT

With wrinkled hide and great frayed ears,
Gunga, the elephant, appears.
Colored like city smoke he goes
As gingerly on blunted toes
As if he held the earth in trust
And feared to hurt the very dust.

### THE GIRL ON THE MILK-WHITE HORSE

See, they are clearing the sawdust course
For the girl in pink on the milk-white horse.
Her spangles twinkle; his pale flanks shine,
Every hair of his tail is fine
And bright as a comet's; his mane blows free,
And she points a toe and bends a knee,
The while his hoofbeats fall like rain
Over and over and over again.
And nothing that moves on land or sea
Will seem so beautiful to me
As the girl in pink on the milk-white horse
Cantering over the sawdust course.

### NEXT DAY

Nothing now to mark the spot
But a littered vacant lot;
Sawdust in a heap, and there
Where the ring was, grass worn bare
In a circle, scuffed and brown,
And a paper hoop the clown
Made his little dog jump through,
And a pygmy pony-shoe.

## A BOY'S SONG

*James Hogg*

Where the pools are bright and deep,
Where the gray trout lies asleep,
Up the river, and o'er the lea,
That's the way for Billy and me.

Where the blackbird sings the latest,
Where the hawthorn blooms the sweetest,
Where the nestlings chirp and flee,
That's the way for Billy and me.

Where the mowers mow the cleanest,
Where the hay lies thick and greenest;
There to track the homeward bee,
That's the way for Billy and me.

Where the hazel bank is steepest,
Where the shadow falls the deepest,
Where the clustering nuts fall free,
That's the way for Billy and me.

Why the boys should drive away
Little sweet maidens from the play,
Or love to banter and fight so well,
That's the thing I never could tell.

But this I know, I love to play
Through the meadow, among the hay;
Up the water and o'er the lea,
That's the way for Billy and me.

## LITTLE ORPHANT ANNIE[1]

*James Whitcomb Riley*

Little Orphant Annie's come to our house
to stay,
An' wash the cups and saucers up, an' brush
the crumbs away,
An' shoo the chickens off the porch, an'
dust the hearth, an' sweep,
An' make the fire, an' bake the bread, an'
earn her board-an'-keep;
An' all us other childern, when the supper
things is done,
We set around the kitchen fire an' has the
mostest fun

[1] From James Whitcomb Riley, *Rhymes of Childhood.*

A-list'nin' to the witch tales 'at Annie tells about,
An' the Gobble-uns 'at gits you
Ef you
Don't
Watch
Out!

Onc't they was a little boy wouldn't say his pray'rs—
An' when he went to bed at night, away upstairs,
His mammy heerd him holler, an' his daddy heerd him bawl,
An' when they turn't the kivvers down, he wasn't there at all!
An' they seeked him in the rafter room, an' cubby-hole, an' press,
An' seeked him up the chimbly flue, an' ever'wheres, I guess;
But all they ever found was thist his pants an' round about!
An' the Gobble-uns 'll git you
Ef you
Don't
Watch
Out!

An' one time a little girl 'ud allus laugh an' grin,
An' make fun of ever' one, an' all her blood-an'-kin;
An' onc't when they was "company," an' ole folks was there,
She mocked 'em an' shocked 'em an' said she didn't care!
An' thist as she kicked her heels, an' turn't to run an' hide,
They was two great big Black Things a-standin' by her side,
An' they snatched her through the ceilin' 'fore she knowed what she's about!
An' the Gobble-uns 'll git you
Ef you
Don't
Watch
Out!

An' little Orphant Annie says, when the blaze is blue,
An' the lampwick sputters, an' the wind goes woo-oo!
An' you hear the crickets quit, an' the moon is gray,
An' the lightnin'-bugs in dew is all squenched away—
You better mind yer parents, an' yer teachers fond an' dear,
An' churish them 'at loves you, an' dry the orphant's tear,
An' he'p the pore an' needy ones 'at clusters all about,
Er the Gobble-uns 'll git you
Ef you
Don't
Watch
Out!

## *Boys and Girls: Suggested Grades*

*Grade One*

The Huntsmen
Time to Rise
Bed in Summer
The Sleepy Song
Washing
Birthdays

Presents
Troubles
To China
At the Seaside
Merry-Go-Round
The Swing

*Grade Two*

A Child's Day Begins
My Bed Is a Boat
Lullaby
Wynken, Blynken, and Nod
Sweet and Low
My Shadow
Skipping Ropes
Three Lovely Holes
The Land of Counterpane
Alone
Over the Garden Wall
A Good Play
The Raggedy Man
Christmas Morning

*Grade Three*

If Only . . .
Skating
The Butterbean Tent
Thanksgiving Day

*Grade Four*

Mr. Nobody
A Circus Garland

*Grade Five*

A Boy's Song
Little Orphant Annie

# *Fairies and Make-Believe*

## FAIRIES [1]

*Rose Fyleman*

There are fairies at the bottom of our garden!
It's not so very, very far away;
You pass the gardener's shed and you just keep straight ahead—
I do so hope they've really come to stay.
There's a little wood, with moss in it and beetles,
And a little stream that quietly runs through;
You wouldn't think they'd dare to come merry-making there—
Well, they do.

There are fairies at the bottom of our garden!
They often have a dance on summer nights;
The butterflies and bees make a lovely little breeze,
And the rabbits stand about and hold the lights.
Did you know that they could sit upon the moonbeams
And pick a little star to make a fan,
And dance away up there in the middle of the air?
Well, they can.

There are fairies at the bottom of our garden!
You cannot think how beautiful they are;
They all stand up and sing when the Fairy Queen and King
Come gently floating down upon their car.
The King is very proud and *very* handsome;
The Queen—now can you guess who that could be
(She's a little girl all day, but at night she steals away)?
Well—it's *Me!*

## SOME ONE [2]

*Walter de la Mare*

Some one came knocking
At my wee, small door;
Some one came knocking,
I'm sure—sure—sure;

[1] From Rose Fyleman, *Fairies and Chimneys.*
[2] From Walter de la Mare, *Peacock Pie.*

I listened, I opened,
  I looked to left and right,
But nought there was a-stirring
  In the still dark night;
Only the busy beetle
  Tap-tapping in the wall,
Only from the forest
  The screech-owl's call,
Only the cricket whistling
  While the dewrops fall,
So I know not who came knocking,
  At all, at all, at all.

## THE CHILD AND THE FAIRIES

*Author Unknown*

The woods are full of fairies!
  The trees are all alive;
The river overflows with them,
  See how they dip and dive!
What funny little fellows!
  What dainty little dears!
They dance and leap, and prance and peep,
  And utter fairy cheers!

I'd like to tame a fairy,
  To keep it on a shelf,
To see it wash its little face,
  And dress its little self.
I'd teach it pretty manners,
  It always should say, "Please!"
And then, you know, I'd make it sew,
  And courtesy with its knees!

## QUEEN MAB

*Thomas Hood*

A little fairy comes at night,
  Her eyes are blue, her hair is brown,
With silver spots upon her wings,
  And from the moon she flutters down.

She has a little silver wand,
  And when a good child goes to bed
She waves her hand from right to left,
  And makes a circle round its head.

And then it dreams of pleasant things,
  And fountains filled with fairy fish,
And trees that bear delicious fruit,
  And bow their branches at a wish;

Of arbors filled with dainty scents
  From lovely flowers that never fade;
Bright flies that glitter in the sun,
  And glowworms shining in the shade.

And talking birds with gifted tongues,
  For singing songs and telling tales,
And funny dwarfs to show the way
  Through fairy hills and fairy dales.

## THE ELF SINGING [1]

*William Allingham*

An Elf sat on a twig,
He was not very big,
He sang a little song,
He did not think it wrong;
But he was on a Wizard's ground,
Who hated all sweet sound.

Elf, Elf,
Take care of yourself,
He's coming behind you,
To seize you and bind you
And stifle your song.
The Wizard! the Wizard!
He changes his shape
In crawling along,
An ugly old ape,
A poisonous lizard,
A spotted spider,
A wormy glider,
The Wizard! the Wizard!
He's up on the bough,
He'll bite through your gizzard,
He's close to you now!

The Elf went on with his song,
It grew more clear and strong,
  It lifted him into air,
    He floated singing away,
  With rainbows in his hair;

[1] From William Allingham, *Robin Redbreast and Other Verses.*

While the Wizard-worm from his creep
  Made a sudden leap,
  Fell down into a hole,
And, ere his magic word he could say,
  Was eaten up by a Mole.

## UP THE AIRY MOUNTAIN[1]

*William Allingham*

Up the airy mountain,
  Down the rushy glen,
We daren't go a-hunting
  For fear of little men;
Wee folk, good folk,
  Trooping all together;
Green jacket, red cap,
  And white owl's feather!

Down along the rocky shore
  Some make their home;
They live on crispy pancakes
  Of yellow tide-foam;
Some in the reeds
  Of the black mountain lake,
With frogs for their watchdogs,
  All night awake.

High on the hilltop
  The old King sits;
He is now so old and gray
  He's nigh lost his wits.
With a bridge of white mist
  Columbkill he crosses,
On his stately journeys
  From Slieveleague to Rosses;
Or going up with music
  On cold starry nights,
To sup with the Queen
  Of the gay Northern Lights.

By the craggy hillside,
  Through the mosses bare,
They have planted thorn-trees
  For pleasure here and there.
Is any man so daring
  As dig them up in spite,
He shall find their sharpest thorns
  In his bed at night.

Up the airy mountain,
  Down the rushy glen,
We daren't go a-hunting
  For fear of little men;
Wee folk, good folk,
  Trooping all together;
Green jacket, red cap,
  And white owl's feather!

## A VISIT FROM ST. NICHOLAS

*Clement C. Moore*

'Twas the night before Christmas, when all through the house
Not a creature was stirring, not even a mouse.
The stockings were hung by the chimney with care,
In hopes that St. Nicholas soon would be there.
The children were nestled all snug in their beds,
While visions of sugar-plums danced in their heads;
And mamma in her kerchief, and I in my cap,
Had just settled our brains for a long winter's nap—
When out on the lawn there arose such a clatter,
I sprang from my bed to see what was the matter.
Away to the window I flew like a flash,
Tore open the shutters and threw up the sash.
The moon on the breast of the new-fallen snow
Gave the lustre of midday to objects below;
When, what to my wondering eyes should appear,
But a miniature sleigh and eight tiny reindeer,
With a little old driver, so lively and quick,
I knew in a moment it must be St. Nick!
More rapid than eagles his coursers they came,
And he whistled, and shouted, and called them by name:

[1] From William Allingham, *Robin Redbreast and Other Verses.*

"Now, *Dasher!* now, *Dancer!* now, *Prancer* and *Vixen!*
On, *Comet!* on, *Cupid!* on, *Donder* and *Blitzen!*
To the top of the porch, to the top of the wall,
Now, dash away, dash away, dash away all!"
As dry leaves that before the wild hurricane fly,
When they meet with an obstacle, mount to the sky,
So up to the housetop the coursers they flew,
With a sleigh full of toys—and St. Nicholas too.
And then, in a twinkling, I heard on the roof
The prancing and pawing of each little hoof.
As I drew in my head and was turning around,
Down the chimney St. Nicholas came with a bound.
He was dressed all in fur from his head to his foot,
And his clothes were all tarnished with ashes and soot;
A bundle of toys he had flung on his back,
And he looked like a peddler just opening his pack.
His eyes, how they twinkled! his dimples, how merry!
His cheeks were like roses, his nose like a cherry;
His droll little mouth was drawn up like a bow,
And the beard on his chin was as white as the snow.
The stump of a pipe he held tight in his teeth,
And the smoke, it encircled his head like a wreath.
He had a broad face, and a little round belly
That shook, when he laughed, like a bowlful of jelly.
He was chubby and plump—a right jolly old elf,
And I laughed when I saw him, in spite of myself;
A wink of his eye, and a twist of his head,
Soon gave me to know I had nothing to dread.
He spoke not a word, but went straight to his work,
And filled all the stockings; then turned with a jerk,
And laying his finger aside of his nose,
And giving a nod, up the chimney he rose.
He sprang to his sleigh, to his team gave a whistle,
And away they all flew like the down of a thistle.
But I heard him exclaim, ere he drove out of sight,
*"Happy Christmas to all, and to all a good-night!"*

## YET GENTLE WILL THE GRIFFIN BE [1]

*Vachel Lindsay*

The moon? It is a griffin's egg,
Hatching tomorrow night.
And how the little boys will watch
With shouting and delight
To see him break the shell and stretch
And creep across the sky.
The boys will laugh. The little girls,
I fear, may hide and cry.
Yet gentle will the griffin be,
Most decorous and fat,
And walk up to the Milky Way
And lap it like a cat.

## SKYSCRAPERS [2]

*Rachel Field*

Do skyscrapers ever grow tired
Of holding themselves up high?
Do they ever shiver on frosty nights
With their tops against the sky?

[1] From Vachel Lindsay, *Johnny Appleseed and Other Poems.*
[2] From Rachel Field, *The Pointed People.*

Do they feel lonely sometimes
Because they have grown so tall?
Do they ever wish they could lie right down
And never get up at all?

## THE ANGEL IN THE APPLE TREE [1]

*Winifred Welles*

Early in the morning, before the day began,
Out along the hillside, glittering and cold,
And down into the orchard that was all dim gold,
Barefoot, and by myself, breathlessly I ran.

There I saw an Angel resting in an apple tree,
A lovely, silver Person up among the leaves—
From deep in the folds of one of her blue sleeves,
She took a yellow apple, and she dropped it down to me.

I clasped my hands around it, I lifted up my eyes
To smile at her and thank her, but already she was gone.
I stood among the grasses very still and all alone—
While the green leaves rustled and the sun began to rise.

## BEHIND THE WATERFALL [2]

*Winifred Welles*

A little old woman
In a thin white shawl,
Stepped straight through the column
Of the silver waterfall,
As if the fall of water
Were not anything at all.
I saw her crook her finger,
I heard her sweetly call.
Over stones all green and glossy
I fled and did not fall;
I ran along the river
And through the waterfall,
And that heavy curve of water
Never hindered me at all.
The little old woman
In the thin white shawl
Took my hand and laughed and led me
Down a cool, still hall,
Between two rows of pillars
That were glistening and tall.
At her finger's tap swung open
A wide door in the wall,
And I saw the crystal city
That's behind the waterfall.

## GREEN MOTH [3]

*Winifred Welles*

The night the green moth came for me,
A creamy moon poured down the hill,
The meadow seemed a silver sea,
Small pearls were hung in every tree,
And all so still, so still.

He floated in on my white bed,
A strange and soundless fellow.
I saw the horns wave on his head,
He stepped across my pillow
In tiny ermine boots, and spread
His cape of green and yellow.

He came so close that I could see
His golden eyes, and sweet and chill,
His faint breath wavered over me.
"Come Child, my Beautiful," said he,
And all so still, so still.

## SPRINGTIME IN DONEGAL [4]

*Mabel Rose Stevenson*

It's springtime in Donegal,
The primroses are blowing;
I shut my eyes and see it all
With certitude of knowing.

[1] From Winifred Welles, *Skipping Along Alone.*
[2] *Ibid.*
[3] *Ibid.*
[4] Used by permission of the author.

I see the glen below the road,
Where screening brackens cluster,
And where in magical abode
The Little People muster.

I have not seen them with my eyes,
But dreaming by the river
I've heard the rustle of their spies
And seen the grasses quiver;
Findaragh has his palace there,
And Maeve is wont to hover
And weave her glamor in the air
About each trysting lover.

The dainty bluebells nod and swing,
Tho' few are born to hearing
The faint and fragrant chimes they ring
Or catch the elfin cheering.
For spring has come to Donegal
And primroses are peeping
In answer to the trumpet call
That wakes the world from sleeping.

### ALADDIN

*James Russell Lowell*

When I was a beggarly boy,
And lived in a cellar damp,
I had not a friend nor a toy,
But I had Aladdin's lamp;
When I could not sleep for the cold,
I had fire enough in my brain,
And builded, with roofs of gold,
My beautiful castles in Spain!

### THE BUGLE SONG[1]

*Alfred Tennyson*

The splendor falls on castle walls
And snowy summits old in story;
The long light shakes across the lakes,
And the wild cataract leaps in glory.
Blow, bugle, blow, set the wild echoes flying,
Blow, bugle; answer, echoes, dying, dying,
dying.

O hark, O hear! how thin and clear,
And thinner, clearer, farther going!
O sweet and far from cliff and scar
The horns of Elfland faintly blowing!
Blow, let us hear the purple glens replying;
Blow, bugle; answer, echoes, dying, dying,
dying.

O love, they die in yon rich sky,
They faint on hill or field or river;
Our echoes roll from soul to soul,
And grow forever and forever.
Blow, bugle, blow, set the wild echoes flying,
And answer, echoes, answer, dying, dying,
dying.

## *Fairies and Make-Believe: Suggested Grades*

*Grade One*
- A Visit from St. Nicholas
- Skyscrapers

*Grade Two*
- The Child and the Fairies

*Grade Three*
- Fairies
- Some One
- The Elf Singing
- The Angel in the Apple Tree
- Behind the Waterfall
- Green Moth

[1] From Alfred Tennyson, *The Princess.*

*Grade Four*
Queen Mab
Up the Airy Mountain
Yet Gentle Will the Griffin Be
Springtime in Donegal

*Grade Five*
Aladdin

*Grade Seven*
The Bugle Song

# *In Feathers and Fur and Such*

## THE WOODPECKER [1]

*Elizabeth Madox Roberts*

The woodpecker pecked out a little round hole
And made him a house in the telephone pole.

One day when I watched he poked out his head,
And he had on a hood and a collar of red.

When the streams of rain pour out of the sky,
And the sparkles of lightning go flashing by,

And the big, big wheels of thunder roll,
He can snuggle back in the telephone pole.

## THE RABBIT [2]

*Edith King*

Brown bunny sits inside his burrow
Till everything is still,
Then out he slips along the furrow,
Or up the grassy hill.

He nibbles all about the bushes
Or sits to wash his face,
But at a sound he stamps, and rushes
At a surprising pace.

You see some little streaks and flashes,
A last sharp twink of white,
As down his hidy-hole he dashes
And disappears from sight.

## THE BIRD'S NEST [3]

*John Drinkwater*

I know a place, in the ivy on a tree,
Where a bird's nest is, and the eggs are three,
And the bird is brown, and the eggs are blue,
And the twigs are old, but the moss is new,
And I go quite near, though I think
I should have heard
The sound of me watching, if
I had been a bird.

[1] From Elizabeth Madox Roberts, *Under the Tree.*
[2] From Edith King, *Fifty New Poems for Children.*
[3] From John Drinkwater, *All about Me.*

## WOOLLY LAMBKINS [1]

*Christina G. Rossetti*

On the grassy banks
Lambkins at their pranks;
Woolly sisters, woolly brothers,
  Jumping off their feet,
While their woolly mothers
  Watch by them and bleat.

## THE SQUIRREL

*Author Unknown*

Whisky, frisky,
Hippity hop,
Up he goes
To the tree top!

Whirly, twirly,
Round and round,
Down he scampers
To the ground.

Furly, curly
What a tail!
Tall as a feather
Broad as a sail!

Where's his supper?
In the shell.
Snappity, crackity,
Out it fell!

## THE LITTLE TURTLE [2]

*Vachel Lindsay*

There was a little turtle.
He lived in a box.
He swam in a puddle.
He climbed on the rocks.

He snapped at a mosquito.
He snapped at a flea.
He snapped at a minnow.
And he snapped at me.

He caught the mosquito.
He caught the flea.
He caught the minnow.
But he didn't catch me.

## THE CATERPILLAR [3]

*Christina G. Rossetti*

Brown and furry
Caterpillar in a hurry;
Take your walk
To the shady leaf, or stalk.

May no toad spy you,
May the little birds pass by you;
Spin and die,
To live again a butterfly.

## MOUSE [4]

*Hilda Conkling*

Little mouse in gray velvet,
Have you had a cheese-breakfast?
There are no crumbs on your coat,
Did you use a napkin?
I wonder what you had to eat,
And who dresses you in gray velvet.

## MICE [5]

*Rose Fyleman*

I think mice
Are rather nice.

  Their tails are long,
  Their faces small,
  They haven't any
  Chins at all.

[1] From Christina G. Rossetti, *Sing-Song.*
[2] From Vachel Lindsay, *Johnny Appleseed and Other Poems.*
[3] From Christina G. Rossetti, *Sing-Song.*
[4] From Hilda Conkling, *Poems by a Little Girl.*
[5] From Rose Fyleman, *Fifty-One New Nursery Rhymes.*

Their ears are pink,
Their teeth are white,
They run about
The house at night.
They nibble things
They shouldn't touch
And no one seems
To like them much.

But I think mice
Are nice.

## FROGS AT SCHOOL

*George Cooper*

Twenty froggies went to school
Down beside a rushy pool;
Twenty little coats of green,
Twenty vests all white and clean.

"We must be in time," said they,
"First we study, then we play;
That is how we keep the rule,
When we froggies go to school."

Master Bullfrog, grave and stern,
Called the classes in their turn;
Taught them how to nobly strive,
Likewise how to leap and dive.

From his seat upon a log,
Showed them how to say, "Ker-chog!"
Also how to dodge a blow
From the sticks which bad boys throw.

Twenty froggies grew up fast;
Bullfrogs they became at last.
Not one dunce was in the lot,
Not one lesson they forgot.

Polished in a high degree,
As each froggy ought to be,
Now they sit on other logs,
Teaching other little frogs.

## AN EXPLANATION OF THE GRASSHOPPER [1]

*Vachel Lindsay*

The Grasshopper, the Grasshopper,
I will explain to you:
He is the Brownies' racehorse,
The fairies' Kangaroo.

## CHOOSING A KITTEN

*Author Unknown*

A black-nosed kitten will slumber all the day;
A white-nosed kitten is ever glad to play;
A yellow-nosed kitten will answer to your call;
And a gray-nosed kitten I like best of all.

## THE HOUSE CAT [2]

*Annette Wynne*

The house cat sits
And smiles and sings.
He knows a lot
Of secret things.

## THE HAIRY DOG [3]

*Herbert Asquith*

My dog's so furry I've not seen
His face for years and years;
His eyes are buried out of sight,
I only guess his ears.

When people ask me for his breed,
I do not know or care;
He has the beauty of them all
Hidden beneath his hair.

[1] From Vachel Lindsay, *Johnny Appleseed and Other Poems.*
[2] From Annette Wynne, *For Days and Days.*
[3] From Herbert Asquith, *Pillicock Hill.*

## THE COW [1]

*Robert Louis Stevenson*

The friendly cow all red and white,
  I love with all my heart;
She gives me cream with all her might,
  To eat with apple-tart.

She wanders lowing here and there,
  And yet she cannot stray,
All in the pleasant open air,
  The pleasant light of day;

And blown by all the winds that pass
  And wet with all the showers,
She walks among the meadow grass
  And eats the meadow flowers.

## PRETTY COW [2]

*Ann Taylor*

Thank you, pretty cow, that made
Pleasant milk to soak my bread,
Every day and every night,
Warm, and fresh, and sweet, and white.

Do not chew the hemlock rank,
Growing on the weedy bank;
But the yellow cowslip eat,
That will make it very sweet.

Where the purple violet grows,
Where the bubbling water flows,
Where the grass is fresh and fine,
Pretty cow, go there and dine.

## THE PASTURE [3]

*Robert Frost*

I'm going out to clean the pasture spring;
I'll only stop to rake the leaves away
(And wait to watch the water clear, I may);
I sha'n't be gone long.—You come too.
I'm going out to fetch the little calf
That's standing by the mother. It's so young,
It totters when she licks it with her tongue.
I sha'n't be gone long.—You come too.

## THE DUCK [4]

*Edith King*

If I were in a fairy tale,
And it were my good luck
To have a wish, I'd choose to be
A lovely snow-white duck.

When she puts off into the pond
And leaves me on the brink,
She wags her stumpy tail at me,
And gives a saucy wink,

Which says as plain as words could say
I'm safe as safe can be,
Stay there, or you will drown yourself,
The pond was made for me.

She goes a-sailing to and fro,
Just like a fishing-boat,
And steers and paddles all herself,
And never wets her coat.

Then in the water, upside down,
I've often seen her stand,
More neatly than the little boys
Who do it on the land.

And, best of all, her children are
The ducklings, bright as gold,
Who swim about the pond with her
And do as they are told.

## A FRIEND IN THE GARDEN

*Juliana Horatia Ewing*

He is not John the gardener,
  And yet the whole day long
Employs himself most usefully
  The flower-beds among.

1 From Robert Louis Stevenson, *A Child's Garden of Verses.*
2 From Ann and Jane Taylor, *Original Poems for Infant Minds.*
3 From Robert Frost, *New Hampshire.*
4 From Edith King, *Fifty New Poems for Children.*

He is not Tom the pussy-cat;
And yet the other day,
With stealthy stride and glistening eye,
He crept upon his prey.

He is not Dash, the dear old dog,
And yet, perhaps, if you
Took pains with him and petted him,
You'd come to love him too.

He's not a blackbird though he chirps,
And though he once was black;
And now he wears a loose, gray coat,
All wrinkled on the back.

He's got a very dirty face,
And very shining eyes;
He sometimes comes and sits indoors;
He looks—and p'r'aps is—wise.

But in a sunny flower-bed
He has his fixed abode;
He eats the things that eat my plants—
He is a friendly Toad.

## A BIRD [1]

*Emily Dickinson*

A bird came down the walk:
He did not know I saw;
He bit an angle-worm in halves
And ate the fellow, raw.

And then he drank a dew
From a convenient grass,
And then hopped sidewise to the wall
To let a beetle pass.

## BOB WHITE

*George Cooper*

There's a plump little chap in a speckled coat,
And he sits on the zigzag rails remote,
Where he whistles at breezy, bracy morn,
When the buckwheat is ripe and stacked is the corn:
"Bob White! Bob White! Bob White!"

Is he hailing some comrade as blithe as he?
Now I wonder where Robert White can be!
O'er the billows of gold and amber grain
There is no one in sight—but hark again:
"Bob White! Bob White! Bob White!"

Ah! I see why he calls; in the stubble there
Hide his plump little wife and babies fair!
So contented is he, and so proud of the same,
That he wants all the world to know his name:
"Bob White! Bob White! Bob White!"

## THE SECRET

*Author Unknown*

We have a secret, just we three,
The robin, and I, and the sweet cherry-tree;
The bird told the tree, and the tree told me,
And nobody knows it but just us three.

But of course the robin knows it best,
Because he built the—I shan't tell the rest;
And laid the four little—something in it—
I'm afraid I shall tell it every minute.

But if the tree and the robin don't peep,
I'll try my best the secret to keep;
Though I know when the little birds fly about
Then the whole secret will be out.

## THE LUCKY SNAIL [2]

*Winifred Welles*

The snail's a lucky fellow, he can go
The whole world over if he chooses,
Through blazing suns, or where the white flakes blow,
Yet his own home he never loses.
He can behold what's strange and beautiful,
While still remaining very comfortable.

[1] From Emily Dickinson, *Poems for Youth.*
[2] From Winifred Welles, *Skipping Along Alone.*

He goes afar yet never is away,
Whose house rests always on his shoulder—
He dreams beneath a fern's soft spray,
Or dares to climb the hardest boulder.
He can be cozy and yet love to roam,
A traveler who always is at home.

## WILD ANIMALS [1]

*Elizabeth Fleming*

I like a mouse
When he's not in my house,
And a rat
When he goes nibble, nibble, like that.
I like a mole; he's a kind little soul,
And a stoat
With a smudge like snow on his throat.
I like a shrew
With his nose in the dew,
And a hare,
For he leaps and runs everywhere;
I like a fox
With his little white socks,
And rabbits and squirrels and other brown things,
I'm in love with them all,
So funny and furry and furtive and frightened and small.

## THE BLACKBIRD [2]

*Humbert Wolfe*

In the far corner
close by the swings,
every morning
a blackbird sings.

His bill's so yellow,
his coat's so black,
that he makes a fellow
whistle back.

Ann, my daughter,
thinks that he
sings for us two
especially.

## THE SWALLOW [3]

*Christina G. Rossetti*

Fly away, fly away over the sea,
Sun-loving swallow, for summer is done;
Come again, come again, come back to me,
Bringing the summer and bringing the sun.

## THE CITY MOUSE AND THE GARDEN MOUSE [4]

*Christina G. Rossetti*

The city mouse lives in a house;
The garden mouse lives in a bower,
He's friendly with the frogs and toads,
And sees the pretty plants in flower.

The city mouse eats bread and cheese;
The garden mouse eats what he can;
We will not grudge him seeds and stalks,
Poor little timid furry man.

## CAT [5]

*Mary Britton Miller*

The black cat yawns,
Opens her jaws,
Stretches her legs,
And shows her claws.

Then she gets up
And stands on four
Long stiff legs
And yawns some more.

[1] From Elizabeth Fleming, *Gammon and Spinach.*
[2] From Humbert Wolfe, *Kensington Gardens.*
[3] From Christina G. Rossetti, *Sing-Song.*
[4] *Ibid.*
[5] From Mary Britton Miller, *Menagerie.*

She shows her sharp teeth,
She stretches her lip,
Her slice of a tongue
Turns up at the tip.

Lifting herself
On her delicate toes,
She arches her back
As high as it goes.

She lets herself down
With particular care,
And pads away
With her tail in the air.

## DOGS AND WEATHER[1]

*Winifred Welles*

I'd like a different dog
For every kind of weather—
A narrow greyhound for a fog,
A wolfhound strange and white,
With a tail like a silver feather
To run with in the night,
When snow is still and winter stars are bright.

In the fall I'd like to see
In answer to my whistle,
A golden spaniel look at me.
But best of all for rain
A terrier, hairy as a thistle,
To trot with fine disdain
Beside me down the soaked, sweet-smelling lane.

## DO YOU KNOW?[2]

*Christina G. Rossetti*

When the cows come home the milk is coming;
Honey's made while the bees are humming;
Duck and drake on the rushy lake,
And the deer live safe in the breezy brake;
And timid, funny, pert little bunny
Winks his nose, and sits all sunny.

## THE RUNAWAY[3]

*Robert Frost*

Once, when the snow of the year was beginning to fall,
We stopped by a mountain pasture to say "Whose colt?"
A little Morgan had one forefoot on the wall,
The other curled at his breast. He dipped his head
And snorted to us. And then he had to bolt.
We heard the miniature thunder where he fled
And we saw him or thought we saw him dim and gray,
Like a shadow against the curtain of falling flakes.
"I think the little fellow's afraid of the snow.
He isn't winter-broken. It isn't play
With the little fellow at all. He's running away.
I doubt if even his mother could tell him, 'Sakes,
It's only weather.' He'd think she didn't know.
Where is his mother? He can't be out alone."
And now he comes again with a clatter of stone
And mounts the wall again with whited eyes
And all his tail that isn't hair up straight.
He shudders his coat as if to throw off flies.
"Whoever it is that leaves him out so late,
When other creatures have gone to stall and bin,
Ought to be told to come and take him in."

1 From Winifred Welles, *Skipping Along Alone.*
2 From Christina G. Rossetti, *Sing-Song.*
3 From Robert Frost, *New Hampshire.*

## THE HENS[1]

*Elizabeth Madox Roberts*

The night was coming very fast
It reached the gate as I ran past.

The pigeons had gone to the tower of the church,
And all the hens were on their perch

Up in the barn, and I thought I heard
A piece of a little purring word.

I stopped inside, waiting and staying,
To try to hear what the hens were saying.

They were asking something, that was plain,
Asking it over and over again.

One of them moved and turned around,
Her feathers made a ruffled sound,

A ruffled sound, like a bushful of birds,
And she said her little asking words.

She pushed her head close into her wing,
But nothing answered anything.

## MY DOG[2]

*John Kendrick Bangs*

I have no dog, but it must be
Somewhere there's one belongs to me—
A little chap with wagging tail,
And dark brown eyes that never quail,
But look you through, and through, and through
With love unspeakable, but true.

Somewhere it must be, I opine,
There is a little dog of mine
With cold black nose that sniffs around
In search of what things may be found
In pocket, or some nook hard by
Where I have hid them from his eye.

Somewhere my doggie pulls and tugs
The fringes of rebellious rugs,
Or with the mischief of the pup
Chews all my shoes and slippers up,
And when he's done it to the core
With eyes all eager pleads for more.

Somewhere a little dog doth wait,
It may be by some garden gate,
With eyes alert and tail attent—
You know the kind of tail that's meant—
With stores of yelps of glad delight
To bid me welcome home at night.

Somewhere a little dog is seen,
His nose two shaggy paws between,
Flat on his stomach, one eye shut
Held fast in dreamy slumber, but
The other open, ready for
His master coming through the door.

## THE MYSTERIOUS CAT[3]

*Vachel Lindsay*

I saw a proud, mysterious cat,
I saw a proud, mysterious cat,
Too proud to catch a mouse or rat—
Mew, mew, mew.

But catnip she would eat, and purr,
But catnip she would eat, and purr,
And goldfish she did much prefer—
Mew, mew, mew.

I saw a cat—'twas but a dream,
I saw a cat—'twas but a dream,
Who scorned the slave that brought her cream—
Mew, mew, mew.

Unless the slave were dressed in style,
Unless the slave were dressed in style,
And knelt before her all the while—
Mew, mew, mew.

[1] From Elizabeth Madox Roberts, *Under the Tree.*
[2] From John Kendrick Bangs, *Foothills of Parnassus.*
[3] From Vachel Lindsay, *Johnny Appleseed and Other Poems.*

Did you ever hear of a thing like that?
Did you ever hear of a thing like that?
Did you ever hear of a thing like that?
Oh, what a proud mysterious cat.
Oh, what a proud mysterious cat.
Oh, what a proud mysterious cat.
Mew . . . mew . . . mew.

## LONE DOG [1]

*Irene Rutherford McLeod*

I'm a lean dog, a keen dog, a wild dog, and
  lone;
I'm a rough dog, a tough dog, hunting on
  my own;
I'm a bad dog, a mad dog, teasing silly
  sheep;
I love to sit and bay the moon, to keep fat
  souls from sleep.

I'll never be a lap dog, licking dirty feet,
A sleek dog, a meek dog, cringing for my
  meat,
Not for me the fireside, the well-filled plate,
But shut door, and sharp stone, and cuff
  and kick and hate.

Not for me the other dogs, running by my
  side,
Some have run a short while, but none of
  them would bide.
O mine is still the lone trail, the hard trail,
  the best,
Wide wind, the wild stars, and hunger of
  the quest!

## HORSES CHAWIN' HAY [2]

*Hamlin Garland*

I tell yeh whut! The chankin'
  Which the tired horses makes
When you've slipped the harness off'm
  And shoved the hay in flakes
From the hay-mow overhead,
  Is jest about the equal of any pi-any;
They's nothin' soun's s' cumftabul
  As horses chawin' hay.

I love to hear 'em chankin',
  Jest a-grindin' slow and low,
With their snoots a-rootin' clover
  Deep as their ol' heads'll go.
It's kind o' sort o' restin'
  To a feller's bones, I say.
It soun's s' mighty cumftabul—
  The horses chawin' hay.

*Gra-onk, gra-onk, gra-onk!*
  In a stiddy kind o' tone,
Not a tail a-waggin' to 'em,
  N'r another sound 'r groan—
Fer the flies is gone a-snoozin'.
Then I loaf around an' watch 'em
  In a sleepy kind o' way,
F'r they soun' so mighty cumftabul
  As they root and chaw their hay.

## BROWN BEE [3]

*William Brighty Rands*

The bee is a rover;
  The brown bee is gay;
To feed on the clover,
  He passes this way.
Brown bee, humming over,
  What is it you say?
"The world is so happy—
  So happy today!"

## LITTLE BUSY BEE [4]

*Isaac Watts*

How doth the little busy bee
  Improve each shining hour,
And gather honey all the day
  From every opening flower!

[1] From Irene Rutherford McLeod, *Songs to Save a Soul.*
[2] Used by permission of the author.
[3] From William Brighty Rands, *Lilliput Lyrics.*
[4] From Isaac Watts, *Divine and Moral Songs for Children.*

How skilfully she builds her cell,
  How neat she spreads the wax!
And labors hard to store it well
  With the sweet food she makes.

## CHILDREN OF THE WIND[1]

*Carl Sandburg*

On the shores of Lake Michigan
high on a wooden pole, in a box,
two purple martins had a home,
and taken away down to Martinique
and let loose, they flew home,
thousands of miles to be home again.

The birds let out began flying
north, north-by-west, north,
till they were back home.
How their instruments told them
of ceiling, temperature, air pressure,
how their control-boards gave them
reports of fuel, ignition, speeds,
is out of the record, out.

Across spaces of sun and cloud,
in rain and fog, through air pockets,
wind with them, wind against them,
stopping for subsistence rations,
whirling in gust and spiral,
these people of the air,
these children of the wind,
had a sense of where to go and how,
how to go north, north-by-west, north,
till they came to one wooden pole,
till they were home again.

## THE ANGLER'S REVEILLE[2]

*Henry van Dyke*

What time the rose of dawn is laid across
  the lips of night,
And all the drowsy little stars have fallen
  asleep in light;
'Tis then a wandering wind awakes, and
  runs from tree to tree,
And borrows words from all the birds to
  sound the reveille.

This is the carol the Robin throws
  Over the edge of the valley;
Listen how boldly it flows,
  Sally on sally:

Tirra-lirra,
Down the river,
Laughing water
All a-quiver.
Day is near,
Clear, clear.
Fish are breaking,
Time for waking.
Tup, tup, tup!
Do you hear?
All clear—
Wake up!

The phantom flood of dreams has ebbed
  and vanished with the dark,
And like a dove the heart forsakes the
  prison of the ark;
Now forth she fares through friendly woods
  and diamond-fields of dew,
While every voice cries out "Rejoice!" as if
  the world were new.

This is the ballad the Bluebird sings,
  Unto his mate replying,
Shaking the tune from his wings
  While he is flying:

Surely, surely, surely,
Life is dear
Even here.
Blue above,
You to love,
Purely, purely, purely.

[1] From Carl Sandburg, *The People, Yes.*
[2] From Henry van Dyke, *Complete Poems.*

There's wild azalea on the hill, and roses down the dell,
And just one spray of lilac still abloom beside the well;
The columbine adorns the rocks, the laurel buds grow pink,
Along the stream white arums gleam, and violets bend to drink.

This is the song of the Yellowthroat,
Fluttering gaily beside you;
Hear how each voluble note
Offers to guide you:

Which way, sir?
I say, sir,
Let me teach you,
I beseech you!
Are you wishing
Jolly fishing?
This way, sir!
I'll teach you.

Then come, my friend, forget your foes, and leave your fears behind,
And wander forth to try your luck, with cheerful, quiet mind;
For be your fortune great or small, you'll take what God may give,
And all the day your heart shall say, " 'Tis luck enough to live."

This is the song the Brown Thrush flings,
Out of his thicket of roses;
Hark how it warbles and rings,
Mark how it closes:

Luck, luck,
What luck?
Good enough for me!
I'm alive, you see.
Sun shining,
No repining;
Never borrow
Idle sorrow;
Drop it!
Cover it up!
Hold your cup!
Joy will fill it,
Don't spill it,
Steady, be ready,
Good luck!

## *In Feathers and Fur and Such: Suggested Grades*

*Grade One*

The Woodpecker
The Bird's Nest
Woolly Lambkins
The Squirrel
The Rabbit
The Little Turtle
The Caterpillar
Mouse
Mice
Choosing a Kitten
The House Cat
The Hairy Dog
Frogs at School

*Grade Two*

An Explanation of the Grasshopper
The Cow
Pretty Cow
The Pasture
The Duck
A Friend in the Garden
A Bird
Bob White
The Secret

*Grade Three*

The Lucky Snail
Wild Animals
The Blackbird
The Swallow
The City Mouse and the Garden Mouse
Cat
Dogs and Weather
Do You Know?
The Hens
Brown Bee

*Grade Four*

The Runaway
My Dog
The Mysterious Cat

*Grade Five*

Lone Dog
Horses Chawin' Hay
Little Busy Bee
Children of the Wind

*Grade Six*

The Angler's Reveille

# *The World and All*

## THE WHITE WINDOW [1]

*James Stephens*

The Moon comes every night to peep
Through the window where I lie;
But I pretend to be asleep;
And watch the Moon go slowly by,
  And she never makes a sound!

She stands and stares! And then she goes
To the house that's next to me,
Stealing by on tippy-toes;
To peep at folk asleep maybe
  And she never makes a sound!

## THE MOON'S THE NORTH WIND'S COOKY [2]

*Vachel Lindsay*

The Moon's the North Wind's cooky.
He bites it, day by day,
Until there's but a rim of scraps
That crumble all away.
The South Wind is a baker.
He kneads clouds in his den,
And bakes a crisp new moon *that . . greedy*
*North . . Wind . . eats . . again!*

## IS THE MOON TIRED? [3]

*Christina G. Rossetti*

Is the moon tired? She looks so pale
Within her misty veil;
She scales the sky from east to west,
And takes no rest.

Before the coming of the night
The moon shows papery white;
Before the dawning of the day
She fades away.

## WHO HAS SEEN THE WIND? [4]

*Christina G. Rossetti*

Who has seen the wind?
  Neither I nor you;
But when the leaves hang trembling,
  The wind is passing through.

Who has seen the wind?
  Neither you nor I;
But when the trees bow down their heads,
  The wind is passing by.

[1] From James Stephens, *Collected Poems.*
[2] From Vachel Lindsay, *Johnny Appleseed and Other Poems.*
[3] From Christina G. Rossetti, *Sing-Song*
[4] *Ibid.*

## THE WIND [1]

*Robert Louis Stevenson*

I saw you toss the kites on high
And blow the birds about the sky;
And all around I heard you pass,
Like ladies' skirts across the grass—
  O wind, a-blowing all day long,
  O wind, that sings so loud a song!

I saw the different things you did,
But always you yourself you hid.
I felt you push, I heard you call,
I could not see yourself at all—
  O wind, a-blowing all day long,
  O wind, that sings so loud a song!

O you that are so strong and cold,
O blower, are you young or old?
Are you a beast of field and tree,
Or just a stronger child than me?
  O wind, a-blowing all day long,
  O wind, that sings so loud a song!

## RAIN [2]

*Robert Louis Stevenson*

The rain is raining all around,
  It falls on field and tree,
It rains on the umbrellas here,
  And on the ships at sea.

## CLOUDS

*Author Unknown*

White sheep, white sheep,
  On a blue hill,
When the wind stops,
  You all stand still.

When the wind blows,
  You walk away slow.
White sheep, white sheep,
  Where do you go?

## WATCHING CLOUDS [3]

*John Farrar*

I've watched the clouds by day and night,
Great fleecy ones all filled with light,
Gray beasts that steal across the sky,
And little fellows slipping by.

Sometimes they seem like sheep at play,
Sometimes when they are dull and gray
The pale sun seems a ship to me,
Sailing through a rolling sea;

And I've seen faces in them, too,
Funny white men on the blue;
But on across the heavens they blow—
I often wonder where they go.

## BOATS SAIL ON THE RIVERS [4]

*Christina G. Rossetti*

Boats sail on the rivers,
  And ships sail on the seas;
But clouds that sail across the sky
  Are prettier far than these.

There are bridges on the rivers,
  As pretty as you please;
But the bow that bridges heaven,
  And overtops the trees,
And builds a road from earth to sky,
  Is prettier far than these.

## NIGHT WAS CREEPING [5]

*James Stephens*

The Night was creeping on the ground!
She crept and did not make a sound,

Until she reached the tree; and then
She covered it, and stole again

Along the grass beside the wall!
I heard the rustling of her shawl

[1] From Robert Louis Stevenson, *A Child's Garden of Verses.*
[2] *Ibid.*
[3] From John Farrar, *Songs for Parents.*
[4] From Christina G. Rossetti, *Sing-Song.*
[5] From James Stephens. *Collected Poems.*

As she threw blackness everywhere,
Along the sky, the ground, the air,

And in the room where I was hid!
But, no matter what she did

To everything that was without,
She could not put my candle out!

So I stared at the Night! And she
Stared solemnly back at me!

## JACK-IN-THE-PULPIT [1]

*Rupert Sargent Holland*

Four of us went to the woods one day,
Keeping the trail in the Indian way,
Creeping, crawling,
Sometimes sprawling,
Pushing through bushes, and there we found
A little green pulpit stuck in the ground;
And in the pulpit a brown man stood
Preaching to all the folk in the wood.

We lay as quiet as Indians do,
Because each one of the four of us knew
At any sound,
The creatures 'round,
The squirrels and chipmunks, birds and bees,
Would fly away through the ring of trees;
And Jack-in-the-Pulpit would stop his speech
If he knew we four were in easy reach.

We listened as hard as ever we could,
But not a one of us understood,
Or even heard
A single word.
Though I saw a chipmunk nod his head
As if he knew what the preacher said;
And a big gray squirrel clapped his paws
When he thought it was time for some applause.
Many and many a Jack we've found,
But none of us ever heard a sound;
So I suppose
That Jackie knows
When children try to hear him preach,
And talks in some peculiar speech.
I wonder if we could find a way
To hear what Jacks-in-the-Pulpit say!

## THE BIRCHES [2]

*Walter Pritchard Eaton*

The little birches, white and slim,
Gleaming in the forest dim,
Must think the day is almost gone,
For each one has her nightie on.

## APRIL [3]

*Sara Teasdale*

The roofs are shining from the rain,
The sparrows twitter as they fly,
And with a windy April grace
The little clouds go by.

Yet the back-yards are bare and brown
With only one unchanging tree—
I could not be so sure of Spring
Save that it sings in me.

## SEEDS [4]

*Walter de la Mare*

The seeds I sowed—
For weeks unseen—
Have pushed up pygmy
Shoots of green;
So frail you'd think
The tiniest stone
Would never let
A glimpse be shown.

[1] Used by permission of the author.
[2] From Walter Pritchard Eaton, *Echoes and Realities.*
[3] From Sara Teasdale, *Rivers to the Sea.*
[4] From Walter de la Mare, *Poems for Children.*

But no, a pebble
Near them lies,
At least a cherry-stone
In size,
Which that mere sprout
Has heaved away,
To bask in sun,
And see the day.

## THE SUN'S TRAVELS [1]

*Robert Louis Stevenson*

The sun is not a-bed, when I
At night upon my pillow lie;
Still round the earth his way he takes,
And morning after morning makes.

While here at home, in shining day,
We round the sunny garden play,
Each little Indian sleepyhead
Is being kissed and put to bed.

And when at eve I rise from tea,
Day dawns beyond the Atlantic Sea;
And all the children in the West
Are getting up and being dressed.

## LITTLE STAR [2]

*Jane Taylor*

Twinkle, twinkle, little star,
How I wonder what you are!
Up above the world so high,
Like a diamond in the sky.

When the blazing sun is gone,
When he nothing shines upon,
Then you show your little light,
Twinkle, twinkle, all the night.

## SILVER [3]

*Walter de la Mare*

Slowly, silently, now the moon
Walks the night in her silver shoon;
This way, and that, she peers, and sees
Silver fruit upon silver trees;
One by one the casements catch
Her beams beneath the silvery thatch;
Couched in his kennel, like a log,
With paws of silver, sleeps the dog;
From their shadowy cote the white breasts peep
Of doves in a silver-feathered sleep;
A harvest mouse goes scampering by,
With silver claws, and silver eye;
And moveless fish in the water gleam,
By silver reeds in a silver stream.

## THE NIGHT WILL NEVER STAY [4]

*Eleanor Farjeon*

The night will never stay,
The night will still go by,
Though with a million stars
You pin it to the sky,
Though you bind it with the blowing wind
And buckle it with the moon,
The night will slip away
Like sorrow or a tune.

## THE WONDERFUL WORLD [5]

*William Brighty Rands*

Great, wide, beautiful, wonderful World,
With the wonderful water round you curled,
And the wonderful grass upon your breast—
World, you are beautifully dressed!

[1] From Robert Louis Stevenson, *A Child's Garden of Verses.*
[2] From Ann and Jane Taylor, *Original Poems for Infant Minds.*
[3] From Walter de la Mare, *Collected Poems.*
[4] From Eleanor Farjeon, *Gypsy and Ginger.*
[5] From William Brighty Rands, *Lilliput Lyrics.*

The wonderful air is over me,
And the wonderful wind is shaking the tree—
It walks on the water, and whirls the mills,
And talks to itself on the top of the hills.

You friendly Earth, how far do you go,
With the wheat-fields that nod and the rivers that flow,
With cities and gardens and cliffs and isles,
And the people upon you for thousands of miles?

### THE FROST PANE [1]

*David McCord*

What's the use of breathing
On the window
Pane
In summer?
You can't make a frost
On the window pane
In summer.

You can't make a
Nalphabet,
You can't make a
Nelephant;
You can't make a smudge
With your nose
(In summer).

Lots of good, breathing
On the window
Pane
In winter.
You can make a frost
On the window pane
In winter.
A white frost, a light frost,
A thick frost, a quick frost,
A write-me-out-a-picture frost
Across
The pane
In
Winter.

### THE WONDERFUL WEAVER

*George Cooper*

There's a wonderful weaver
High up in the air,
And he weaves a white mantle
For cold earth to wear,
With the wind for his shuttle,
The cloud for his loom,
How he weaves! how he weaves!
In the light, in the gloom.

Oh! with finest of laces
He decks bush and tree,
On the bare flinty meadows
A cover lays he.
Then a quaint cap he places
On pillar and post,
And he changes the pump
To a grim, silent ghost.

But this wonderful weaver
Grows weary at last,
And the shuttle lies idle
That once flew so fast;
Then the sun peeps abroad
On the work that is done;
And he smiles: "I'll unravel
It all just for fun!"

### WINTERTIME [2]

*Robert Louis Stevenson*

Late lies the wintry sun a-bed,
A frosty, fiery, sleepyhead;
Blinks but an hour or two; and then,
A blood-red orange, sets again.

Before the stars have left the skies,
At morning in the dark I rise,
And shivering in my nakedness,
By the cold candle bathe and dress.

Close by the jolly fire I sit
To warm my frozen bones a bit;
Or with a reindeer sled explore
The colder countries round the door.

[1] From *The Saturday Review of Literature,* II:25.
[2] From Robert Louis Stevenson, *A Child's Garden of Verses.*

When to go out my nurse doth wrap
Me in my comforter and cap,
The cold wind burns my face and blows
Its frosty pepper up my nose.

Black are my steps on silver sod;
Thick blows my frosty breath abroad;
And tree and house, and hill and lake,
Are frosted like a wedding-cake.

## STOPPING BY WOODS ON A SNOWY EVENING[1]

*Robert Frost*

Whose woods these are I think I know.
His house is in the village though;
He will not see me stopping here
To watch his woods fill up with snow.

My little horse must think it queer
To stop without a farmhouse near
Between the woods and frozen lake
The darkest evening of the year.

He gives his harness bells a shake
To ask if there is some mistake.
The only other sound's the sweep
Of easy wind and downy flake.

The woods are lovely, dark, and deep.
But I have promises to keep,
And miles to go before I sleep,
And miles to go before I sleep.

## THE GARDEN YEAR[2]

*Sara Coleridge*

January brings the snow,
Makes our feet and fingers glow.

February brings the rain,
Thaws the frozen lake again.

March brings breezes, loud and shrill,
To stir the dancing daffodil.

April brings the primrose sweet,
Scatters daisies at our feet.

May brings flocks of pretty lambs
Skipping by their fleecy dams.

June brings tulips, lilies, roses,
Fills the children's hands with posies.

Hot July brings cooling showers,
Apricots, and gillyflowers.

August brings the sheaves of corn,
Then the harvest home is borne.

Warm September brings the fruit;
Sportsmen then begin to shoot.

Fresh October brings the pheasant;
Then to gather nuts is pleasant.

Dull November brings the blast;
Then the leaves are whirling fast.

Chill December brings the sleet,
Blazing fire, and Christmas treat.

## GLIMPSE IN AUTUMN[3]

*Jean Starr Untermeyer*

Ladies at a ball
  Are not so fine as these
  Richly brocaded trees
That decorate the fall.

They stand against a wall
  Of crisp October sky,
  Their plumed heads held high,
Like ladies at a ball.

[1] From Robert Frost, *New Hampshire.*
[2] From Sara Coleridge, *Pretty Lessons in Verse for Good Children.*
[3] From Jean Starr Untermeyer, *Dreams Out of Darkness.*

## OAK LEAVES [1]

*Elizabeth Coatsworth*

When all the other leaves are gone
The brown oak leaves still linger on,
Their branches obstinately lifted
To frozen wind and snow deep-drifted.

But when the winter is well passed
The brown oak leaves drop down at last,
To let the little buds appear
No larger than a mouse's ear.

## THE YEAR'S AT THE SPRING [2]

*Robert Browning*

The year's at the spring
And day's at the morn;
Morning's at seven;
The hillside's dew-pearled;
The lark's on the wing;
The snail's on the thorn;
God's in his heaven—
All's right with the world!

## IN A DESERT TOWN [3]

*Lionel Stevenson*

We have a mountain at the end of our street,
Changing from day to day;
Sometimes it is prim and distant and neat,
Vestured in sober gray.

Sunset bewitches it to drift and glow
Like a castle with opal walls;
Winter transfigures its cliffs with snow
Into spell-bound waterfalls.

We have a mountain at the end of our street
Where other towns have a church,
Promising refuge from the clamor and heat
Like the goal of a weary search.

Moonlight is magical on the mountain, too;
The shadows grow deep and dim
Till the gazer strays into the dreamy blue
And sleep comes beckoning him.

Certain that beauty is lingering to greet
Our homecoming from any place,
Having a mountain at the end of our street
We do not lack for grace.

## HILLS [4]

*Hilda Conkling*

The Hills are going somewhere;
They have been on the way a long time.
They are like camels in a line,
But they move more slowly.
Sometimes at sunset they carry silks,
But most of the time silver birch trees,
Heavy rocks, heavy trees, gold leaves
On heavy branches till they are aching . . .
Birches like silver bars they can hardly lift
With grass so thick about their feet to hinder . . .
They have not gone far
In the time I've watched them . . .

## THE WIND IN A FROLIC

*William Howitt*

The wind one morning sprang up from sleep,
Saying, "Now for a frolic! now for a leap!
Now for a madcap galloping chase!
I'll make a commotion in every place!"

So it swept with a bustle right through a great town,
Cracking the signs and scattering down
Shutters; and whisking, with merciless squalls,
Old women's bonnets and gingerbread stalls,

[1] From Elizabeth Coatsworth, *Away Goes Sally.*
[2] From Robert Browning, *Pippa Passes.*
[3] Used by permission of the author.
[4] From Hilda Conkling, *Poems by a Little Girl.*

There never was heard a much lustier shout,
As the apples and oranges trundled about;
And the urchins that stand with their thievish eyes
For ever on watch ran off each with a prize.

Then away to the field it went, blustering and humming,
And the cattle all wondered whatever was coming;
It plucked by the tails the grave matronly cows,
And tossed the colts' manes all over their brows;
Till, offended at such an unusual salute,
They all turned their backs, and stood sulky and mute.

'Twas so bold that it feared not to play its joke
With the doctor's wig or the gentleman's cloak.
Through the forest it roared, and cried gaily, "Now,
You sturdy old oaks, I'll make you bow!"
And it made them bow without more ado,
Or it cracked their great branches through and through.

Then it rushed like a monster on cottage and farm,
Striking their dwellers with sudden alarm;
And they ran out like bees in a midsummer swarm;
There were dames with their kerchiefs tied over their caps,
To see if their poultry were free from mishaps;
The turkeys they gobbled, the geese screamed aloud,
And the hens crept to roost in a terrified crowd;
There was rearing of ladders, and logs laying on,
Where the thatch from the roof threatened soon to be gone.

But the wind had swept on, and had met in a lane
With a schoolboy, who panted and struggled in vain;
For it tossed him and twirled him, then passed, and he stood
With his hat in a pool and his shoes in the mud.

Then away went the wind in its holiday glee,
And now it was far on the billowy sea,
And the lordly ships felt its staggering blow,
And the little boats darted to and fro.

But lo! it was night, and it sank to rest
On the sea-birds' rock in the gleaming West,
Laughing to think, in its fearful fun,
How little of mischief it really had done.

## THE WIND AND THE MOON

*George MacDonald*

Said the Wind to the Moon, "I will blow you out;
You stare
In the air
Like a ghost in a chair,
Always looking what I am about;
I hate to be watched; I will blow you out."

The Wind blew hard, and out went the Moon.
So, deep
On a heap
Of clouds to sleep,
Down lay the Wind, and slumbered soon—
Muttering low, "I've done for that Moon."

He turned in his bed; she was there again!
On high,
In the sky,
With her one ghost eye,
The Moon shone white and alive and plain.
Said the Wind—"I will blow you out again."

The Wind blew hard, and the Moon grew dim.
"With my sledge
And my wedge
I have knocked off her edge!
If only I blow right fierce and grim,
The creature will soon be dimmer than dim."

He blew and he blew, and she thinned to a thread.
"One puff
More's enough
To blow her to snuff!
One good puff more where the last was bred,
And glimmer, glimmer, glum will go that thread!"

He blew a great blast and the thread was gone.
In the air
Nowhere
Was a moonbeam bare;
Far-off and harmless the shy stars shone;
Sure and certain the Moon was gone!

The Wind he took to his revels once more;
On down,
In town,
Like a merry-mad clown,
He leaped and halloed with whistle and roar—
"What's that?" The glimmering thread once more!

He flew in a rage—he danced and blew;
But in vain
Was the pain
Of his bursting brain;
For still the broader the Moon-scrap grew
The broader he swelled his big cheeks and blew.

Slowly she grew—till she filled the night,
And shone
On her throne
In the sky alone,
A matchless, wonderful, silvery light,
Radiant and lovely, the Queen of the night.

Said the Wind, "What a marvel of power am I!
With my breath,
Good faith,
I blew her to death—
First blew her away right out of the sky—
Then blew her in; what a strength am I!"

But the Moon she knew nothing about the affair;
For high
In the sky,
With her one white eye,
Motionless, miles above the air,
She had never heard the great Wind blare.

## MILK-WHITE MOON, PUT THE COWS TO SLEEP [1]

*Carl Sandburg*

Milk-white moon, put the cows to sleep.
Since five o'clock in the morning,
Since they stood up out of the grass,
Where they slept on their knees and hocks,
They have eaten grass and given their milk,
And kept their heads and teeth at the earth's face.
Now they are looking at you, milk-white moon.
Carelessly as they look at the level landscapes,
Carelessly as they look at a pail of new white milk,
They are looking at you, wondering not at all, at all.
If the moon is the skim face top of a pail of milk,
Wondering not at all, carelessly looking.
Put the cows to sleep, milk-white moon,
Put the cows to sleep.

## THE FALLING STAR [2]

*Sara Teasdale*

I saw a star slide down the sky,
Blinding the north as it went by,

[1] From Carl Sandburg, *Good Morning, America.*
[2] From Sara Teasdale, *Stars Tonight.*

Too burning and too quick to hold,
Too lovely to be bought or sold,
Good only to make wishes on
And then forever to be gone.

## SWIFT THINGS ARE BEAUTIFUL[1]

*Elizabeth Coatsworth*

Swift things are beautiful:
Swallows and deer,
And lightning that falls
Bright-veined and clear,
Rivers and meteors,
Wind in the wheat,
The strong-withered horse,
The runner's sure feet.

## FOG[2]

*Carl Sandburg*

The fog comes
on little cat feet.

It sits looking
over harbor and city
on silent haunches
and then moves on.

## AUTUMN FANCIES

*Author Unknown*

The maple is a dainty maid,
The pet of all the wood,
Who lights the dusky forest glade
With scarlet cloak and hood.

The elm a lovely lady is,
In shimmering robes of gold,
That catch the sunlight when she moves,
And glisten, fold on fold.

The sumach is a Gypsy queen,
Who flaunts in crimson drest,
And wild along the roadside runs,
Red blossoms in her breast.

And towering high above the wood,
All in his purple cloak,
A monarch in his splendor is
The proud and princely oak.

## LOVELIEST OF TREES[3]

*A. E. Housman*

Loveliest of trees, the cherry now
Is hung with bloom along the bough,
And stands about the woodland ride
Wearing white for Eastertide.

Now, of my threescore years and ten,
Twenty will not come again,
And take from seventy springs a score,
It only leaves me fifty more.

And since to look at things in bloom
Fifty springs are little room,
About the woodland I will go
To see the cherry hung with snow.

## THE POPLARS[4]

*Theodosia Garrison*

My poplars are like ladies trim,
Each conscious of her own estate;
In costume somewhat over prim,
In manner cordially sedate,
Like two old neighbors met to chat
Beside my garden gate.

My stately old aristocrats—
I fancy still their talk must be
Of rose-conserves and Persian cats,
And lavender and Indian tea;
I wonder sometimes as I pass
If they approve of me.

[1] From Elizabeth Coatsworth, *Away Goes Sally.*
[2] From Carl Sandburg, *Chicago Poems.*
[3] From A. E. Housman, *A Shropshire Lad.*
[4] From Theodosia Garrison, *Dreamers, and Other Poems.*

I give them greeting night and morn,
I like to think they answer, too,
With that benign assurance born
When youth gives age the reverence due,
And bend their wise heads as I go
As courteous ladies do.

Long may you stand before my door,
Oh, kindly neighbors garbed in green,
And bend with rustling welcome o'er
The many friends who pass between;
And where the little children play
Look down with gracious mien.

## THE PLANTING OF THE APPLE-TREE

*William Cullen Bryant*

Come, let us plant the apple-tree!
Cleave the tough greensward with the spade;
Wide let its hollow bed be made;
There gently lay the roots, and there
Sift the dark mold with kindly care,
And press it o'er them tenderly,
As round the sleeping infant's feet
We softly fold the cradle sheet;
So plant we the apple-tree.

What plant we in this apple-tree?
Buds which the breath of summer days
Shall lengthen into leafy sprays;
Boughs where the thrush with crimson breast
Shall haunt, and sing, and hide her nest;
We plant upon the sunny lea
A shadow for the noontide hour,
A shelter from the summer shower,
When we plant the apple-tree.

## A SALUTE TO TREES[1]

*Henry van Dyke*

Many a tree is found in the wood,
And every tree for its use is good.
Some for the strength of the gnarled root,
Some for the sweetness of flower or fruit,
Some for shelter against the storm,
And some to keep the hearthstone warm,
Some for the roof and some for the beam,
And some for a boat to breast the storm.
In the wealth of the wood since the world began,
The trees have offered their gifts to man.

I have camped in the whispering forest of pines
I have slept in the shadow of olives and vines;
In the knees of an oak, at the foot of a palm,
I have found good rest and slumber's balm.
And now, when the morning gilds the boughs
Of the vaulted elm at the door of my house,
I open the window and make a salute:
"God bless thy branches and feed thy root!
Thou hast lived before, live after me,
Thou ancient, friendly, faithful tree!"

## JULY

*Susan Hartley Swett*

When the scarlet cardinal tells
Her dream to the dragonfly,
And the lazy breeze makes a nest in the trees,
And murmurs a lullaby,
It is July.

When the tangled cobweb pulls
The cornflower's cap awry,
And the lilies tall lean over the wall
To bow to the butterfly,
It is July.

When the heat like a mist-veil floats,
And poppies flame in the rye,
And the silver note in the streamlet's throat
Has softened almost to a sigh,
It is July.

[1] From Henry van Dyke, *Complete Poems*.

When the hours are so still that time
  Forgets them, and lets them lie
'Neath petals pink till the night stars wink
  At the sunset in the sky,
    It is July.

## AN INDIAN SUMMER DAY ON THE PRAIRIE [1]

*Vachel Lindsay*

### IN THE BEGINNING

The sun is a huntress young,
The sun is a red, red joy,
The sun is an Indian girl,
Of the tribe of the Illinois.

### MID-MORNING

The sun is a smoldering fire,
That creeps through the high gray plain,
And leaves not a bush of cloud
To blossom with flowers of rain.

### NOON

The sun is a wounded deer,
That treads pale grass in the skies,
Shaking his golden horns,
Flashing his baleful eyes.

### SUNSET

The sun is an eagle old,
There in the windless west,
Atop of the spirit-cliffs
He builds him a crimson nest.

## THIS IS MY ROCK [2]

*David McCord*

This is my rock
And here I run
To steal the secret of the sun;

This is my rock
And here come I
Before the night has swept the sky;

This is my rock,
This is the place
I meet the evening face to face.

## THE SUN [3]

*Emily Dickinson*

I'll tell you how the sun rose—
A ribbon at a time.
The steeples swam in amethyst,
The news like squirrels ran.

The hills untied their bonnets.
The bobolinks begun.
Then I said softly to myself,
"That must have been the sun!"

But how he set, I know not.
There seemed a purple stile
Which little yellow boys and girls
Were climbing all the while

Till when they reached the other side,
A dominie in gray
Put gently up the evening bars,
And led the flock away.

## IT IS NOT FAR [4]

*Sara Teasdale*

Stars over snow,
  And in the west a planet
Swinging below a star—
  Look for a lovely thing and you will
    find it,
It is not far—
  It never will be far.

[1] From Vachel Lindsay, *Johnny Appleseed and Other Poems.*
[2] From *The Saturday Review of Literature,* VI:17.
[3] From Emily Dickinson, *Poems for Youth.*
[4] From Sara Teasdale, *Stars Tonight.*

## HYMN TO THE NIGHT[1]

*Henry Wadsworth Longfellow*

I heard the trailing garments of the Night
  Sweep through her marble halls!
I saw her sable skirts all fringed with light
  From the celestial walls!

I felt her presence, by its spell of might,
  Stoop o'er me from above;
The calm, majestic presence of the Night,
  As of the one I love.

## THE SNOW[2]

*John Greenleaf Whittier*

The sun that brief December day
Rose cheerless over hills of gray,
And, darkly circled, gave at noon
A sadder light than waning moon.
Slow tracing down the thickening sky
Its mute and ominous prophecy,
A portent seeming less than threat,
It sank from sight before it set.
A chill no coat, however stout,
Of homespun stuff could quite shut out,
A hard, dull bitterness of cold,
  That checked, mid-vein, the circling race
  Of life-blood in the sharpened face,
The coming of the snow-storm told.
The wind blew east; we heard the roar
Of Ocean on his wintry shore,
And felt the strong pulse throbbing there
Beat with low rhythm our inland air.

Meanwhile we did our nightly chores—
Brought in the wood from out of doors,
Littered the stalls, and from the mows
Raked down the herd's-grass for the cows;
Heard the horse whinnying for his corn;
And, sharply clashing horn on horn,
Impatient down the stanchion rows
The cattle shake their walnut bows;
While, peering from his early perch
Upon the scaffold's pole of birch,
The cock his crested helmet bent
And down his querulous challenge sent.

Unwarmed by any sunset light
The gray day darkened into night,
A night made hoary with the swarm
And whirl-dance of the blinding storm,
As, zigzag wavering to and fro,
Crossed and recrossed the wingèd snow;
And ere the early bed-time came
The white drift piled the window-frame,
And through the glass the clothes-line posts
Looked in like tall and sheeted ghosts.

So all night long the storm roared on;
The morning broke without a sun;
In tiny spherule traced with lines
Of Nature's geometric signs,
In starry flake, and pellicle,
All day the hoary meteor fell;
And, when the second morning shone,
We looked upon a world unknown,
On nothing we could call our own.
Around the glistening wonder bent
The blue walls of the firmament,
No cloud above, no earth below—
A universe of sky and snow!
The old familiar sights of ours
Took marvellous shapes; strange domes and towers
Rose up where sty or corn-crib stood,
Or garden wall, or belt of wood;
A smooth white mound the brush-pile showed,
A fenceless drift what once was road;
The bridle-post an old man sat
With loose-flung coat and high cocked hat;
The well-curb had a Chinese roof;
And even the long sweep, high aloof,
In its slant splendor, seemed to tell
Of Pisa's leaning miracle.

A prompt, decisive man, no breath
Our father wasted: "Boys, a path!"
Well pleased (for when did farmer boy
Count such a summons less than joy?),
Our buskins on our feet we drew;
  With mittened hands, and caps drawn low,
  To guard our necks and ears from snow,
We cut the solid whiteness through;

[1] From Henry Wadsworth Longfellow, *Voices of the Night.*
[2] From John Greenleaf Whittier, *Snow-Bound.*

And, where the drift was deepest, made
A tunnel walled and overlaid
With dazzling crystal; we had read
Of rare Aladdin's wondrous cave,
And to our own his name we gave,
With many a wish the luck were ours
To test his lamp's supernal powers.
We reached the barn with merry din,
And roused the prisoned brutes within.
The old horse thrust his long head out,
And grave with wonder gazed about;
The cock his lusty greeting said,
And forth his speckled harem led;
The oxen lashed their tails, and hooked,
And mild reproach of hunger looked;
The hornèd patriarch of the sheep,
Like Egypt's Amun roused from sleep,
Shook his sage head with gesture mute,
And emphasized with stamp of foot.

## VELVET SHOES [1]

*Elinor Wylie*

Let us walk in the white snow
  In a soundless space;
With footsteps quiet and slow,
  At a tranquil pace,
  Under veils of white lace.

I shall go shod in silk,
  And you in wool,
White as a white cow's milk,
  More beautiful
  Than the breast of a gull.

We shall walk through the still town
  In a windless peace;
We shall step upon the white down,
  Upon silver fleece,
  Upon softer than these.

We shall walk in velvet shoes;
  Wherever we go
Silence will fall like dews
  On white silence below.
  We shall walk in the snow.

[1] From Elinor Wylie, *Nets To Catch the Wind.*
[2] From Bliss Carman, *Vagabondia.*

## DAFFODILS

*William Wordsworth*

I wandered lonely as a cloud
  That floats on high o'er vales and hills,
When all at once I saw a crowd,
  A host, of golden daffodils;
Beside the lake, beneath the trees,
  Fluttering and dancing in the breeze.

Continuous as the stars that shine
  And twinkle on the milky way,
They stretched in never-ending line
  Along the margin of a bay;
Ten thousand saw I at a glance,
  Tossing their heads in sprightly dance.

The waves beside them danced, but they
  Outdid the sparkling waves in glee—
A poet could not but be gay,
  In such a jocund company!
I gazed—and gazed—but little thought
  What wealth the show to me had brought;

For oft, when on my couch I lie
  In vacant or in pensive mood,
They flash upon that inward eye
  Which is the bliss of solitude;
And then my heart with pleasure fills,
  And dances with the daffodils.

## A VAGABOND SONG [2]

*Bliss Carman*

There is something in the autumn that is native to my blood—
  Touch of manner, hint of mood;
  And my heart is like a rime,
With the yellow and the purple and the crimson keeping time.

The scarlet of the maples can shake me like a cry
  Of bugles going by.
  And my lonely spirit thrills
To see the frosty asters like a smoke upon the hills.

There is something in October sets the
  gypsy blood astir;
 We must rise and follow her,
 When from every hill of flame
She calls and calls each vagabond by name.

### MIRACLES[1]

*Walt Whitman*

Why, who makes much of a miracle?
As to me I know of nothing else but
  miracles,
Whether I walk the streets of Manhattan,
Or dart my sight over the roofs of houses
  toward the sky,
Or wade with naked feet along the beach
  just in the edge of the water,
Or stand under trees in the woods,
Or talk by day with any one I love,
Or sit at table at dinner with the rest,
Or look at strangers opposite me riding in
  the car,
Or watch honey-bees busy around the hive
  of a summer forenoon,
Or animals feeding in the fields,
Or birds, or the wonderfulness of insects
  in the air,
Or the wonderfulness of the sundown, or
  of stars shining so quiet and bright,
Or the exquisite, delicate, thin curve of
  the new moon in spring;
These with the rest, one and all, are to me
  miracles,
The whole referring, yet each distinct and
  in its place.

To me every hour of the light and dark is
  a miracle,
Every cubic inch of space is a miracle,
Every square yard of the surface of the
  earth is spread with the same,
Every foot of the interior swarms with the
  same.

To me the sea is a continual miracle,
The fishes that swim—the rocks—the motion of the waves, the ships with men
  in them,
What stranger miracles are there?

## *The World and All: Suggested Grades*

*Grade One*

The White Window
The Moon's the North Wind's Cooky
Who Has Seen the Wind?
The Wind
Rain
Clouds
Watching Clouds
Jack-in-the-Pulpit

*Grade Two*

Is the Moon Tired?
Boats Sail on the Rivers
Night Was Creeping
The Birches
Little Star
The Frost Pane

[1] From Walt Whitman, *Leaves of Grass.*

*Grade Three*

Seeds
The Sun's Travels
Silver
The Night Will Never Stay
The Wonderful World
The Wonderful Weaver
Wintertime
Oak Leaves

*Grade Four*

April
Stopping by Woods on a Snowy Evening
The Garden Year
Glimpse in Autumn
The Year's at the Spring
In a Desert Town
Hills
The Wind and the Moon

*Grade Five*

The Wind in a Frolic
Milk-White Moon, Put the Cows To Sleep
Swift Things Are Beautiful
Fog
Autumn Fancies
A Salute to Trees

*Grade Six*

The Falling Star
The Poplars
The Planting of the Apple-Tree
July
An Indian Summer Day on the Prairie
This Is My Rock

*Grade Seven*

Loveliest of Trees
The Sun
Hymn to the Night
Daffodils
A Vagabond Song

*Grade Eight*

It Is Not Far
The Snow
Velvet Shoes
Miracles

# *For Fun*

## THE PLAINT OF THE CAMEL [1]

*Charles Edward Carryl*

Canary birds feed on sugar and seed,
  Parrots have crackers to crunch;
And as for the poodles, they tell me the noodles
  Have chicken and cream for their lunch.
    But there's never a question
    About *my* digestion
    *Anything* does for me!

Cats, you're aware, can repose in a chair,
  Chickens can roost upon rails;
Puppies are able to sleep in a stable,
  And oysters can slumber in pails.
    But no one supposes
    A poor Camel dozes—
    *Any place* does for me!

Lambs are enclosed where it's never exposed,
  Coops are constructed for hens;
Kittens are treated to houses well heated,
  And pigs are protected by pens.
    But a Camel comes handy
    Wherever it's sandy—
    *Anywhere* does for me!

People would laugh if you rode a giraffe,
  Or mounted the back of an ox;
It's nobody's habit to ride on a rabbit,
  Or try to bestraddle a fox.
    But as for a Camel, he's
    Ridden by families—
    *Any load* does for me!

A snake is as round as a hole in the ground,
  And weasels are wavy and sleek;
And no alligator could ever be straighter
  Than lizards that live in a creek.
    But a Camel's all lumpy
    And bumpy and humpy—
    *Any shape* does for me!

## THE OWL AND THE PUSSY-CAT [2]

*Edward Lear*

The Owl and the Pussy-Cat went to sea
  In a beautiful pea-green boat;
They took some honey, and plenty of money
  Wrapped up in a five-pound note.
The Owl looked up to the stars above,
  And sang to a small guitar,
"O lovely Pussy, O Pussy, my love,
  What a beautiful Pussy you are,
        You are,
        You are!
  What a beautiful Pussy you are!"

[1] From Charles Edward Carryl, *Davy and the Goblin.*
[2] From Edward Lear, *Nonsense Songs and Stories.*

Pussy said to the Owl, "You elegant fowl,
  How charmingly sweet you sing!
Oh! let us be married; too long we have tarried—
  But what shall we do for a ring?"
They sailed away, for a year and a day,
  To the land where the bong-tree grows;
And there in a wood a Piggy-Wig stood,
  With a ring in the end of his nose.
      His nose,
      His nose,
  With a ring in the end of his nose.

"Dear Pig, are you willing to sell for one shilling
  Your ring?" Said the Piggy, "I will."
So they took it away, and were married next day
  By the Turkey who lives on the hill.
They dined upon mince and slices of quince,
  Which they ate with a runcible spoon;
And hand in hand on the edge of the sand
  They danced by the light of the moon,
      The moon,
      The moon,
  They danced by the light of the moon.

## THE DUEL[1]

*Eugene Field*

The gingham dog and the calico cat
Side by side on the table sat;
'Twas half past twelve, and (what do you think!)
Nor one nor t'other had slept a wink!
  The old Dutch clock and the Chinese plate
  Appeared to know as sure as fate
There was going to be a terrible spat.
  *(I wasn't there; I simply state*
  *What was told to me by the Chinese plate!)*

The gingham dog went "Bow-wow-wow!"
And the calico cat replied "Mee-ow!"
The air was littered, an hour or so,
With bits of gingham and calico,
  While the old Dutch clock in the chimney place
  Up with its hands before its face,
For it always dreaded a family row!
  *(Now mind: I'm only telling you*
  *What the old Dutch clock declares is true!)*

The Chinese plate looked very blue,
And wailed, "Oh, dear! what shall we do!"
But the gingham dog and the calico cat
Wallowed this way and tumbled that,
  Employing every tooth and claw
  In the awfullest way you ever saw—
And, oh! how the gingham and calico flew!
  *(Don't fancy I exaggerate—*
  *I got my news from the Chinese plate!)*

Next morning, where the two had sat
They found no trace of dog or cat:
And some folks think unto this day
That burglars stole that pair away!
  But the truth about the cat and pup
  Is this: they ate each other up!
Now what do you really think of that!
  *(The old Dutch clock it told me so,*
  *And that is how I came to know.)*

## A LOBSTER QUADRILLE[2]

*Lewis Carroll*

"Will you walk a little faster?"
  Said a whiting to a snail,
"There's a porpoise close behind us,
  And he's treading on my tail.
See how eagerly the lobsters
  And the turtles all advance!
They are waiting on the shingle—
  Will you come and join the dance?
Will you, won't you, will you, won't you,
  Will you join the dance?
Will you, won't you, will you, won't you,
  Won't you join the dance?

[1] From Eugene Field, *Poems of Childhood.*
[2] From Lewis Carroll, *Alice's Adventures in Wonderland.*

"You can really have no notion
How delightful it will be
When they take us up and throw us,
With the lobsters, out to sea!"
But the snail replied, "Too far, too far!"
And gave a look askance—
Said he thanked the whiting kindly,
But he would not join the dance.
Would not, could not, would not, could not,
Would not join the dance.
Would not, could not, would not, could not,
Could not join the dance.

"What matters it how far we go?"
His scaly friend replied.
"There is another shore, you know,
Upon the other side.
The further off from England
The nearer is to France —
Then turn not pale, beloved snail,
But come and join the dance.
Will you, won't you, will you, won't you,
Will you join the dance?
Will you, won't you, will you, won't you,
Won't you join the dance?"

## THE TABLE AND THE CHAIR [1]

*Edward Lear*

Said the Table to the Chair,
"You can hardly be aware
How I suffer from the heat
And from chilblains on my feet.
If we took a little walk,
We might have a little talk;
Pray let us take the air,"
Said the Table to the Chair.

Said the Chair unto the Table,
"Now, you *know* we are not able:
How foolishly you talk,
When you know we *cannot* walk!"
Said the Table with a sigh,
"It can do no harm to try.
I've as many legs as you;
Why can't we walk on two?"

[1] From Edward Lear, *Nonsense Songs and Stories.*

So they both went slowly down,
And walked about the town
With a cheerful bumpy sound
As they toddled round and round;
And everybody cried,
As they hastened to their side,
"See! the Table and the Chair
Have come out to take the air!"

But in going down an alley
To a castle in a valley,
They completely lost their way,
And wandered all the day;
Till, to see them safely back,
They paid a Ducky-quack,
And a Beetle, and a Mouse,
Who took them to their house.

Then they whispered to each other,
"O delightful little brother,
What a lovely walk we've taken!
Let us dine on beans and bacon."
So the Ducky and the leetle
Browny-Mousy and the Beetle
Dined, and danced upon their heads
Till they toddled to their beds.

## THE HEIGHT OF THE RIDICULOUS

*Oliver Wendell Holmes*

I wrote some lines once on a time,
In wondrous merry mood,
And thought, as usual, men would say
They were exceeding good.

They were so queer, so very queer,
I laughed as I would die;
Albeit, in the general way,
A sober man am I.

I called my servant, and he came;
How kind it was of him
To mind a slender man like me,
He of the mighty limb.

"These to the printer," I exclaimed,
And, in my humorous way,
I added (as a trifling jest),
"There'll be the devil to pay."

He took the paper, and I watched,
  And saw him peep within;
At the first line he read, his face
  Was all upon the grin.

He read the next; the grin grew broad,
  And shot from ear to ear;
He read the third; a chuckling noise
  I now began to hear.

The fourth; he broke into a roar;
  The fifth; his waistband split;
The sixth; he burst five buttons off,
  And tumbled in a fit.

Ten days and nights, with sleepless eye,
  I watched that wretched man,
And since, I never dare to write
  As funny as I can.

## A STRANGE WILD SONG[1]

*Lewis Carroll*

He thought he saw a Buffalo
  Upon the chimney-piece;
He looked again, and found it was
  His Sister's Husband's Niece.
"Unless you leave this house," he said,
  "I'll send for the Police."

He thought he saw a Rattlesnake
  That questioned him in Greek;
He looked again, and found it was
  The Middle of Next Week.
"The one thing I regret," he said,
  "Is that it cannot speak!"

He thought he saw a Banker's Clerk
  Descending from the 'bus;
He looked again, and found it was
  A Hippopotamus.
"If this should stay to dine," he said,
  "There won't be much for us!"

He thought he saw a Kangaroo
  That worked a coffee-mill;
He looked again, and found it was
  A Vegetable-Pill.
"Were I to swallow this," he said,
  "I should be very ill."

He thought he saw a Coach and Four
  That stood beside his bed;
He looked again, and found it was
  A Bear without a Head.
"Poor thing," he said, "poor silly thing!
  "It's waiting to be fed!"

He thought he saw an Albatross
  That fluttered round the Lamp;
He looked again, and found it was
  A Penny Postage-Stamp.
"You'd best be getting home," he said:
  "The nights are very damp!"

He thought he saw a Garden Door
  That opened with a key;
He looked again, and found it was
  A Double-Rule-of-Three.
"And all its mystery," he said,
  "Is clear as day to me!"

## NONSENSE VERSES[2]

*Edward Lear*

### I

There was an Old Man with a beard
Who said, "It is just as I feared!
  Two Owls and a Hen,
  Four Larks and a Wren,
Have all built their nests in my beard!"

### II

There was a Young Lady whose bonnet
Came untied when the birds sat upon it;
  But she said, "I don't care!
  All the birds in the air
Are welcome to sit on my bonnet!"

[1] From Lewis Carroll, *Sylvie and Bruno.*
[2] From Edward Lear. *A Book of Nonsense.*

III

There was an Old Man who said, "How
Shall I flee from that horrible cow?
  I will sit on this stile
  And continue to smile,
Which may soften the heart of that cow."

IV

There was a Young Lady of Bute,
Who played on a silver-gilt flute;
  She played several jigs
  To her uncle's white pigs,
That amusing Young Lady of Bute.

V

There was an Old Man who said, "Hush!
I perceive a young bird in this bush!"
  When they said, "Is it small?"
  He replied, "Not at all!
It is four times as big as the bush!"

VI

There was an Old Man in a boat,
Who said, "I'm afloat! I'm afloat!"
  When they said, "No, you ain't!"
  He was ready to faint,
That unhappy Old Man in a boat.

VII

There was a Young Lady of Norway,
Who casually sat in a doorway;
  When the door squeezed her flat,
  She exclaimed, "What of that?"
This courageous Young Lady of Norway.

VIII

There was an Old Man of the Isles,
Whose face was pervaded with smiles;
  He sang "High dum diddle,"
  And played on the fiddle,
That amiable man of the Isles.

## THE STRANGE MAN

*Author Unknown*

His face was the oddest that ever was seen,
His mouth stood across 'twixt his nose and his chin;
Whenever he spoke it was then with his voice,
And in talking he always made some sort of noise.
*Derry down.*

He'd an arm on each side to work when he pleased,
But he never worked hard when he lived at his ease;
Two legs he had got to make him complete,
And what is more odd, at each end were his feet.

His legs, as folks say, he could move at his will,
And when he was walking he never stood still.
If you were to see him, you'd laugh till you burst,
For one leg or the other would always be first.

If this whimsical fellow had a river to cross,
If he could not get over, he stayed where he was;
He seldom or ever got off the dry ground,
So great was his luck that he never was drowned.

But the reason he died and the cause of his death
Was owing, poor soul, to the want of more breath;
And now he is left in the grave for to molder,
Had he lived a day longer, he'd have been a day older.
*Derry down.*

## A TRAGIC STORY

*William Makepeace Thackeray*

There lived a sage in days of yore,
And he a handsome pigtail wore;
But wondered much and sorrowed more
Because it hung behind him.

He mused upon this curious case,
And swore he'd change the pigtail's place,
And have it hanging at his face,
Not dangling there behind him.

Said he, "The mystery I've found,
I'll turn me round";
He turned him round;
But still it hung behind him.

Then round and round, and out and in,
All day the puzzled sage did spin;
In vain—it mattered not a pin—
The pigtail hung behind him.

And right, and left, and round about,
And up, and down, and in, and out,
He turned; but still the pigtail stout
Hung steadily behind him.

And though his efforts never slack,
And though he twist, and twirl, and tack,
Alas! still faithful to his back,
The pigtail hangs behind him.

## THE TWINS

*Henry S. Leigh*

In form and feature, face and limb,
I grew so like my brother,
That folks got taking me for him,
And each for one another.
It puzzled all our kith and kin,
It reached an awful pitch;
For one of us was born a twin,
Yet not a soul knew which.

One day (to make the matter worse),
Before our names were fixed,
As we were being wash'd by nurse
We got completely mixed;
And thus, you see, by Fate's decree
(Or rather nurse's whim),
My brother John got christened me,
And I got christened him.

This fatal likeness even dogg'd
My footsteps when at school,
And I was always getting flogg'd,
For John turned out a fool.
I put this question hopelessly
To every one I knew—
What would you do, if you were me,
To prove that you were you?

Our close resemblance turned the tide
Of my domestic life;
For somehow my intended bride
Became my brother's wife.
In short, year after year the same
Absurd mistakes went on;
And when I died—the neighbors came
And buried brother John!

## THE WALRUS AND THE CARPENTER [1]

*Lewis Carroll*

The sun was shining on the sea,
Shining with all his might;
He did his very best to make
The billows smooth and bright—
And this was odd, because it was
The middle of the night.

The moon was shining sulkily,
Because she thought the sun
Had got no business to be there
After the day was done—
"It's very rude of him," she said,
"To come and spoil the fun!"

[1] From Lewis Carroll, *Through the Looking-Glass.*

The sea was wet as wet could be,
  The sands were dry as dry,
You could not see a cloud, because
  No cloud was in the sky;
No birds were flying overhead—
  There were no birds to fly.

The Walrus and the Carpenter
  Were walking close at hand;
They wept like anything to see
  Such quantities of sand;
"If this were only cleared away,"
  They said, "it *would* be grand!"

"If seven maids with seven mops
  Swept it for half a year,
Do you suppose," the Walrus said,
  "That they could get it clear?"
"I doubt it," said the Carpenter,
  And shed a bitter tear.

"O Oysters, come and walk with us!"
  The Walrus did beseech.
"A pleasant walk, a pleasant talk,
  Along the briny beach;
We cannot do with more than four,
  To give a hand to each."

The eldest Oyster looked at him,
  But never a word he said;
The eldest Oyster winked his eye,
  And shook his heavy head—
Meaning to say he did not choose
  To leave the oyster bed.

But four young Oysters hurried up,
  All eager for the treat;
Their coats were brushed, their faces washed,
  Their shoes were clean and neat—
And this was odd, because, you know,
  They hadn't any feet.

Four other Oysters followed them,
  And yet another four;
And thick and fast they came at last,
  And more, and more, and more—
All hopping through the frothy waves,
  And scrambling to the shore.

The Walrus and the Carpenter
  Walked on a mile or so,
And then they rested on a rock
  Conveniently low;
And all the little Oysters stood
  And waited in a row.

"The time has come," the Walrus said,
  "To talk of many things:
Of shoes—and ships—and sealing wax—
  Of cabbages—and kings—
And why the sea is boiling hot—
  And whether pigs have wings."

"But wait a bit," the Oysters cried,
  "Before we have our chat;
For some of us are out of breath,
  And all of us are fat!"
"No hurry!" said the Carpenter.
  They thanked him much for that.

"A loaf of bread," the Walrus said,
  "Is what we chiefly need;
Pepper and vinegar besides
  Are very good indeed—
Now if you're ready, Oysters dear,
  We can begin to feed."

"But not on us!" the Oysters cried,
  Turning a little blue.
"After such kindness, that would be
  A dismal thing to do!"
"The night is fine!" the Walrus said,
  "Do you admire the view?

"It was so kind of you to come!
  And you are very nice!"
The Carpenter said nothing but
  "Cut us another slice;
I wish you were not quite so deaf—
  I've had to ask you twice!"

"It seems a shame," the Walrus said,
  "To play them such a trick,
After we've brought them out so far,
  And made them trot so quick!"
The Carpenter said nothing but
  "The butter's spread too thick!"

"I weep for you," the Walrus said,
 "I deeply sympathize."
With sobs and tears he sorted out
 Those of the largest size,
Holding his pocket handkerchief
 Before his streaming eyes.

"O Oysters," said the Carpenter,
 "You've had a pleasant run!
Shall we be trotting home again?"
 But answer came there none—
And this was scarcely odd, because
 They'd eaten every one.

## A NAUTICAL BALLAD [1]

*Charles Edward Carryl*

A capital ship for an ocean trip,
 Was the Walloping Window-Blind;
No gale that blew dismayed her crew.
 Nor troubled the captain's mind.

The man at the wheel was taught to feel
 Contempt for the wildest blow;
And it often appeared—when the weather had cleared—
 He had been in his bunk below.

The boatswain's mate was very sedate,
 Yet fond of amusement too;
And he played hopscotch with the starboard watch,
 While the captain tickled the crew.

And the gunner we had was apparently mad,
 For he sat on the after-rail
And fired salutes with the captain's boots
 In the teeth of the booming gale.

The captain sat on the commodore's hat,
 And dined, in a royal way,
Off toasted pigs and pickles and figs
 And gummery bread each day.

The cook was Dutch and behaved as such,
 For the diet he gave the crew,
Was a number of tons of hot-cross buns,
 Served up with sugar and glue.

All nautical pride we laid aside,
 And we cast our vessel ashore,
On the Gulliby Isles, where the Poo-Poo smiles
 And the Rumpletum-Bunders roar.

We sat on the edge of a sandy ledge,
 And shot at the whistling bee;
And the cinnamon bats wore waterproof hats,
 As they danced by the sounding sea.

On Rug-gub bark, from dawn till dark,
 We fed, till we all had grown
Uncommonly shrunk; when a Chinese junk
 Came in from the Torriby Zone.

She was stubby and square, but we didn't much care,
 So we cheerily put to sea;
And we left the crew of the junk to chew
 The bark of the Rug-gub tree.

## THE YARN OF THE NANCY BELL [2]

*William S. Gilbert*

'T was on the shores that round our coast
 From Deal to Ramsgate span,
That I found alone on a piece of stone
 An elderly naval man.

His hair was weedy, his beard was long,
 And weedy and long was he,
And I heard this wight on the shore recite,
 In a singular minor key:

"Oh, I am a cook and a captain bold,
 And the mate of the Nancy brig,
And a bo'sun tight, and a midshipmite,
 And the crew of the captain's gig."

[1] From Charles Edward Carryl, *Davy and the Goblin.*
[2] From William S. Gilbert, *Bab Ballads.*

And he shook his fists and he tore his hair,
  Till I really felt afraid,
For I couldn't help thinking the man had
    been drinking,
  And so I simply said:

"Oh, elderly man, it's little I know
  Of the duties of men of the sea,
And I'll eat my hand if I understand
  However you can be

"At once a cook, and a captain bold,
  And the mate of the Nancy brig,
And a bo'sun tight, and a midshipmite,
  And the crew of the captain's gig."

Then he gave a hitch to his trousers, which
  Is a trick all seamen larn,
And having got rid of a thumping quid,
  He spun this painful yarn:

" 'T was in the good ship Nancy Bell
  That we sailed to the Indian Sea,
And there on a reef we come to grief,
  Which has often occurred to me.

"And pretty nigh all the crew was drowned
  (There was seventy-seven o' soul),
And only ten of the Nancy's men
  Said 'Here!' to the muster-roll.

"There was me and the cook and the cap-
    tain bold,
  And the mate of the Nancy brig,
And the bo'sun tight, and a midshipmite,
  And the crew of the captain's gig.

"For a month we'd neither wittles nor
    drink,
  Till a-hungry we did feel,
So we drawed a lot, and accordin' shot
  The captain for our meal.

"The next lot fell to the Nancy's mate,
  And a delicate dish he made;
Then our appetite with the midshipmite
  We seven survivors stayed.

"And then we murdered the bo'sun tight,
  And he much resembled pig;
Then we wittled free, did the cook and me,
  On the crew of the captain's gig.

"Then only the cook and me was left,
  And the delicate question, 'Which
Of us two goes to the kettle?' arose,
  And we argued it out as sich.

"For I loved that cook as a brother, I did,
  And the cook he worshipped me;
But we'd both be blowed if we'd either be
    stowed
  In the other chap's hold, you see.

" 'I'll be eat if you dines off me,' says Tom;
  'Yes, that,' says I, 'you'll be'—
'I'm boiled if I die, my friend,' quoth I;
  And 'Exactly so,' quoth he.

"Says he, 'Dear James, to murder me
  Were a foolish thing to do;
For don't you see that you can't cook me,
  While I can—and will—cook *you!*'

"So he boils the water, and takes the salt
  And the pepper in portions true
(Which he never forgot), and some chopped
    shalot,
  And some sage and parsley, too.

" 'Come here,' says he, with a proper pride,
  Which his smiling features tell,
' 'T will soothing be if I let you see
  How extremely nice you'll smell.'

"And he stirred it round and round and
    round
  And he sniffed at the foaming froth;
When I ups with his heels and smothers his
    squeals
  In the scum of the boiling broth.

"And I eat that cook in a week or less,
  And—as I eating be
The last of his chops, why, I almost drops,
  For a wessel in sight I see!

. . . . . . .

"And I never larf, and never smile,
  And I never lark nor play,
But sit and croak, and a single joke
  I have—which is to say:

" 'Oh, I am a cook and a captain bold,
  And the mate of the Nancy brig,
And a bo'sun tight, and a midshipmite,
  And the crew of the captain's gig!' "

## A NAUTICAL EXTRAVAGANCE[1]

*Wallace Irwin*

I stood one day by the breezy bay
A-watching the ships go by,
When a tired tar said, with a shake of his head:
"I wisht I could tell a lie!

"I've seen some sights as would jigger yer lights,
And they've jiggered me own, in sooth,
But I ain't wuth a darn at spinnin' a yarn
What wanders away from the truth.

"We were out in the gig, the Rigagajig,
Jest a mile and a half to sea,
When Capting Snook, with a troubled look,
He came and he says to me:

" 'O Bos'n Smith, make haste forthwith
And hemstitch the fo'ard sail;
Accordeon pleat the dory sheet,
For there's going to be a gale.'

"I straightway did as the capting bid—
No sooner the job was through
When the north wind, whoof, bounced over the roof,
And, murderin' lights, she blew!

"She blew the tars right off the spars,
And the spars right off the mast,
Sails and pails and anchors and nails
Flew by on the wings o' the blast.

"The galley shook as she blew our cook
Straight out o' the porthole glim,
While pots and pans, kettles and cans
Went clatterin' after him.

"She blew the fire from our gallant stove
And the coal from our gallant bin,
She whistled apace past the capting's face
And blew the beard off his chin!

" 'O wizzel me dead!' the capting said
(And the words blew out of his mouth);
'We're lost, I fear, if the wind don't veer
And blow a while from the south.'

"And wizzel me dead, no sooner he'd said
Them words that blew from his mouth,
Than the wind switched round with a hurricane sound
And blew straight in from the south.

"We opened our eyes with a wild surprise,
And never a word to say—
In changin' her tack the wind blew back
The things that she'd blew away!

"She blew the tars back onto the spars,
And the spars back onto the mast;
Back flew the pails, the sails and the nails,
Which into the ship stuck fast.

"And 'fore we could look she blew back the cook
Straight into the galley coop,
Back dropped the pans, kettles and cans,
Without even spillin' the soup.

"She blew the fire back into the stove
Where it burnt in its proper place—
And all of us cheered as she blew the beard
Back on the capting's face.

"There's more o' me tale," said the sailor hale,
"As would jigger yer lights, in sooth,
But I ain't wuth a darn at spinnin' a yarn
What wanders away from the truth."

## THE MERRY MINER[2]

*Author Unknown*

Go roll a prairie up like cloth,
Drink Mississippi dry,
Put Allegheny in your hat,
A steamboat in your eye—
And for your breakfast, buffalo
Some five and twenty fry.

[1] Used by permission of the author.
[2] From Constance Rourke, *Troupers of the Gold Coast.*

Go kill the whole Comanche tribe,
Some day before you dine;
Pick out to make your walking stick
A California pine;
And then turn round and frown so dark
The sun won't dare to shine.

Go whip a ton of grizzly bears
With nothing but a tan;
And prove yourself by all these feats
To be a Western man;
And you can write a poem grand
If anybody can.

## A HOT-WEATHER SONG [1]

*Don Marquis*

I feel so exceedingly lazy,
I neglect what I oughtn't to should!
My notion of work is so hazy
That I couldn't to toil if I would!

I feel so exceedingly silly
That I say all I shouldn't to ought!
And my mind is as frail as a lily;
It would break with the weight of a thought!

## DARIUS GREEN AND HIS FLYING MACHINE

*John Townsend Trowbridge*

If ever there lived a Yankee lad,
Wise or otherwise, good or bad,
Who, seeing the birds fly, didn't jump
With flapping arms from stake or stump,
Or, spreading the tail
Of his coat for a sail,
Take a soaring leap from post or rail,
And wonder why
He couldn't fly,
And flap and flutter and wish and try—
If ever you knew a country dunce
Who didn't try that as often as once,
All I can say is, that's a sign
He never would do for a hero of mine.

[1] Used by permission of Bernice M. Marquis.

An aspiring genius was D. Green;
The son of a farmer—age fourteen;
His body was long and lank and lean—
Just right for flying, as will be seen;
He had two eyes each bright as a bean,
And a freckled nose that grew between,
A little awry—for I must mention
That he had riveted his attention
Upon his wonderful invention,
Twisting his tongue as he twisted the strings,
And working his face as he worked the wings,
And with every turn of gimlet and screw
Turning and screwing his mouth round, too,
Till his nose seemed bent
To catch the scent,
Around some corner, of new-baked pies,
And his wrinkled cheeks and his squinting eyes
Grew puckered into a queer grimace,
That made him look very droll in the face,
And also very wise.

And wise he must have been, to do more
Than ever a genius did before,
Excepting Daedalus of yore
And his son Icarus, who wore
Upon their backs
Those wings of wax
He had read of in the old almanacs.
Darius was clearly of the opinion,
That the air was also man's dominion,
And that with paddle or fin or pinion,
We soon or late
Shall navigate
The azure as now we sail the sea.
The thing looks simple enough to me;
And, if you doubt it,
Hear how Darius reasoned about it:

"Birds can fly,
An' why can't I?
Must we give in,"
Says he with a grin,
" 'T the bluebird an' phoebe
Are smarter'n we be?

Jest fold our hands, an' see the swaller
An' blackbird an' catbird beat us holler?
Does the leetle chatterin', sassy wren,
No bigger'n my thumb, know more than men?
    Jest show me that!
    Er prove 't the bat
Hez got more brains than's in my hat,
An' I'll back down, an' not till then!"

He argued further: "Ner I can't see
What's th' use o' wings to a bumble-bee,
Fer to git a livin' with, more'n to me;
    Ain't my business
    Important's his'n is?
    That Icarus
    Was a silly cuss—
Him an' his daddy Daedalus;
They might 'a'knowed wings made o' wax
Wouldn't stan' sun-heat an' hard whacks.
    I'll make mine o' luther,
    Er suthin' er other."

And he said to himself, as he tinkered and planned:
"But I ain't goin' to show my hand
To mummies that never can understand
The fust idee that's big an' grand.
    They'd 'a' laft an' made fun
O' Creation itself afore it was done!"
So he kept his secret from all the rest,
Safely buttoned within his vest;
And in the loft above the shed
Himself he locks, with thimble and thread
And wax and hammer and buckles and screws,
And all such things as geniuses use;
Two bats for patterns, curious fellows!
A charcoal-pot and a pair of bellows;
An old hoop-skirt or two, as well as
Some wire, and several old umbrellas;
A carriage-cover, for tail and wings;
A piece of harness; and straps and strings;
    And a big strong box,
    In which he locks
These and a hundred other things.

His grinning brothers, Reuben and Burke
And Nathan and Jotham and Solomon, lurk
Around the corner to see him work—
Sitting cross-legged, like a Turk,
Drawing the waxed-end through with a jerk,
And boring the holes with a comical quirk
Of his wise old head, and a knowing smirk.
But vainly they mounted each other's backs,
And poked through knot-holes and pried through cracks;
With wood from the pile and straw from the stacks
He plugged the knot-holes and calked the cracks;
And a bucket of water, which one would think
He had brought up into the loft to drink
    When he chanced to be dry,
    Stood always nigh,
    For Darius was sly!
And, whenever at work he happened to spy,
At chink or crevice a blinking eye,
He let a dipper of water fly.
"Take that! an', ef ever ye git a peep,
Guess ye'll ketch a weasel asleep!"
    And he sings as he locks
    His big strong box:

"The weasel's head is small an' trim,
An' he is leetle an' long an' slim,
An' quick of motion an' nimble of limb,
    An' ef yeou'll be
    Advised by me,
Keep wide awake when ye're ketching him!"

    So day after day
He stitched and tinkered and hammered away,
    Till at last 'twas done—
The greatest invention under the sun.
"An' now," says Darius, "hooray fer some fun!"

    'Twas the Fourth of July,
    And the weather was dry,
And not a cloud was in all the sky,
Save a few light fleeces, which here and there,
    Half mist, half air,

Like foam on the ocean went floating by—
Just as lovely a morning as ever was seen
For a nice little trip in a flying-machine.
Thought cunning Darius: "Now I shan't go
Along 'ith the fellers to see the show.
I'll say I've got sich a terrible cough!
An' then, when the folks have all gone off,
I'll hev full swing
Fer to try the thing,
An' practyse a little on the wing."

"Ain't goin' to see the celebration?"
Says brother Nate. "No; botheration!
I've got sich a cold—a toothache—I—
My gracious! feel's though I should fly!"
Said Jotham, "Sho!
Guess ye better go."
But Darius said, "No!
Shouldn't wonder 'f yeou might see me, though,
'Long 'bout noon, ef I git red
O' this jumpin', thumpin' pain in my head."
For all the while to himself he said:

"I tell ye what!
I'll fly a few times around the lot,
To see how 't seems; then soon's I've got
The hang o' the thing, ez likely's not,
I'll astonish the nation,
An' all creation,
By flying over the celebration!
Over their heads I'll sail like an eagle;
I'll balance myself on my wings like a sea-gull;
I'll dance on the chimbleys; I'll stan' on the steeple;
I'll flop up to winders an' scare the people!
I'll light on the libbe'ty-pole, an' crow;
An' I'll say to the gawpin' fools below,
'What world's this 'ere
That I've come near?'
Fer I'll make 'em b'lieve I'm a chap f'm the moon;
An' I'll try a race 'ith their ol' balloon!"
He crept from his bed;
And, seeing the others were gone, he said,
"I'm a-gittin' over the cold 'n my head."
And away he sped,
To open the wonderful box in the shed.

His brothers had walked but a little way
When Jotham to Nathan chanced to say,
"What on airth is he up to, hey?"
"Don'o'—the' 's suthin' er other to pay,
Er he wouldn't 'a' stayed to hum to-day."
Says Burke, "His toothache's all 'n his eye!
*He* never'd miss a Fo'th-o'-July,
Ef he hadn't got some machine to try.
Le's hurry back, an' hide 'n the barn,
An' pay him fer tellin' us that yarn!"
"Agreed!" Through the orchard they creep back,
Along by the fences, behind the stack,
And one by one, through a hole in the wall,
In under the dusty barn they crawl,
Dressed in their Sunday garments all;
And a very astonishing sight was that,
When each in his cobwebbed coat and hat
Came up through the floor like an ancient rat.
And there they hid;
And Reuben slid
The fastenings back, and the door undid.
"Keep dark," said he,
"While I squint an' see what the' is to see."

As knights of old put on their mail—
From head to foot
In an iron suit,
Iron jacket and iron boot,
Iron breeches, and on the head
No hat, but an iron pot instead,
And under the chin the bail
(I believe they call the thing a helm)—
And, thus accoutred, they took the field,
Sallying forth to overwhelm
The dragons and pagans that plagued the realm;
So this modern knight
Prepared for flight,
Put on his wings and strapped them tight—
Jointed and jaunty, strong and light—
Buckled them fast to shoulder and hip,
Ten feet they measured from tip to tip!
And a helm he had, but that he wore,
Not on his head, like those of yore,
But more like the helm of a ship.

"Hush!" Reuben said,
"He's up in the shed!
He's opened the winder—I see his head!
He stretches it out,
An' pokes it about,
Lookin' to see 'f the coast is clear,
An' nobody near;
Guess he don'o' who's hid in here!
He's riggin' a spring-board over the sill!
Stop laffin', Solomon! Burke, keep still!
He's climbin' out now—Of all the things!
What's he got on? I vum, it's wings!
An' that t'other thing? I vum, it's a tail!
And there he sets like a hawk on a rail!
Steppin' careful, he travels the length
Of his spring-board, and teeters to try its strength;
Now he stretches his wings, like a monstrous bat;
Peeks over his shoulder, this way an' that,
Fer to see 'f the' 's anyone passin' by;
But the' 's o'ny a ca'f an' a goslin' nigh.
*They* turn up at him a wonderin' eye,
To see—The dragon! he's goin' to fly!
Away he goes! Jimminy! what a jump!
Flop—flop—an' plump
To the ground with a thump!
Flutt'rin' an' flound'rin', all'n a lump!"

As a demon is hurled by an angel's spear,
Heels over head, to his proper sphere—
Heels over head, and head over heels,
Dizzily down the abyss he wheels—
So fell Darius. Upon his crown,
In the midst of the barnyard, he came down,
In a wonderful whirl of tangled strings,
Broken braces and broken springs,
Broken tail and broken wings,
Shooting stars, and various things!
Away with a bellow flew the calf,
And what was that? Did the gosling laugh?
'Tis a merry roar
From the old barn-door,
And he hears the voice of Jotham crying,
"Say, D'rius! how de yeou like flyin'?"

Slowly, ruefully, where he lay,
Darius just turned and looked that way,
As he stanched his sorrowful nose with his cuff.
"Wal, I like flyin' well enough,"
He said, "but the' ain't sich a thunderin' sight
O' fun in 't when ye come to light."

I just have room for the MORAL here:
And this is the moral—Stick to your sphere.
Or, if you insist, as you have the right,
On spreading your wings for a loftier flight,
The moral is—Take care how you light.

## BETWEEN TWO LOVES[1]

*T. A. Daly*

I gotta lov' for Angela,
I lov' Carlòtta, too.
I no can marry both o' dem,
So w'at I gona do?

O! Angela ees pretta girl,
She gotta hair so black, so curl,
An' teeth so white as anytheeng.
An' O! she gotta voice to seeng,
Dat mak' your hearta feel eet must
Jump up an' dance or eet weell bust.
An' alla time she seeng, her eyes
Dey smila like Italia's skies,
An' makin' flirtin' looks at you—
But dat ees all w'at she can do.

Carlotta ees no gotta song,
But she ees twice so big an' strong
As Angela, an' she no look
So beautiful—but she can cook.
You oughta see her carry wood!
I tal you w'at, eet do you good.
When she ees be som'body wife
She worka hard, you bat my life!
She never gattin' tired, too—
But dat ees all w'at she can do.

O! my! I weesh dat Angela
Was strong for carry wood,
Or else Carlotta gotta song
An' looka pretta good.

[1] From *Selected Poems of T. A. Daly*.

I gotta lov' for Angela,
  I lov' Carlotta, too.
I no can marry both o' dem,
  So w'at I gona do?

## THE DEACON'S MASTERPIECE
### OR, THE WONDERFUL "ONE-HOSS SHAY"

*Oliver Wendell Holmes*

Have you heard of the wonderful one-hoss
    shay,
That was built in such a logical way
It ran a hundred years to a day,
And then, of a sudden, it—ah, but stay,
I'll tell you what happened without delay,
Scaring the parson into fits,
Frightening people out of their wits—
Have you ever heard of that, I say?

Seventeen hundred and fifty-five.
*Georgius Secundus* was then alive—
Snuffy old drone from the German hive.
That was the year when Lisbon-town
Saw the earth open and gulp her down,
And Braddock's army was done so brown,
Left without a scalp to its crown,
It was on the terrible Earthquake day
That the Deacon finished the one-hoss
    shay.

Now in building of chaises, I tell you what,
There is always *somewhere* a weakest spot—
In hub, tire, felloe, in spring or thill,
In panel, or crossbar, or floor, or sill,
In screw, bolt, thoroughbrace—lurking still,
Find it somewhere you must and will—
Above or below, or within or without—
And that's the reason, beyond a doubt,
A chaise *breaks down,* but doesn't *wear
    out.*

But the Deacon swore (as Deacons do,
With an "I dew vum," or an "I tell *yeou*")
He would build one shay to beat the taown
'N' the keounty 'n' all the kentry raoun';
It should be so built that it *couldn't* break
    daown.
"Fur," said the Deacon, "'t's mighty plain
Thut the weakes' place mus' stan' the
    strain;
'N' the way t' fix it, uz I maintain,
    Is only jest
T' make that place uz strong uz the rest."

So the Deacon inquired of the village folk
Where he could find the strongest oak,
That couldn't be split nor bent nor broke—
That was for spokes and floor and sills;
He sent for lancewood to make the thills;
The crossbars were ash, from the straightest
    trees;
The panels of white-wood, that cuts like
    cheese,
But lasts like iron for things like these;
The hubs of logs from the "Settler's
    ellum"—
Last of its timber—they couldn't sell 'em,
Never an ax had seen their chips,
And the wedges flew from between their
    lips,
Their blunt ends frizzled like celery tips;
Step and prop-iron, bolt and screw,
Spring, tire, axle, and linchpin too,
Steel of the finest, bright and blue;
Thoroughbrace bison-skin, thick and wide;
Boot, top, dasher, from tough old hide
Found in the pit when the tanner died.
That was the way he "put her through."
"There!" said the Deacon, "naow she'll
    dew!"

Do! I tell you, I rather guess
She was a wonder, and nothing less!
Colts grew horses, beards turned gray,
Deacon and deaconess dropped away,
Children and grandchildren—where were
    they?
But there stood the stout old one-hoss shay
As fresh as on Lisbon earthquake day!

EIGHTEEN HUNDRED—it came and found
The Deacon's masterpiece strong and sound.
Eighteen hundred increased by ten—
"Hahnsum kerridge" they called it then.
Eighteen hundred and twenty came—
Running as usual; much the same.
Thirty and forty at last arrive,
And then come fifty, and FIFTY-FIVE.

Little of all we value here
Wakes on the morn of its hundredth year
Without both feeling and looking queer.
In fact, there's nothing that keeps its youth,
So far as I know, but a tree and truth.
(This is a moral that runs at large;
Take it. – You're welcome. – No extra charge.)

First of November—the earthquake day,
There are traces of age in the one-hoss shay,
A general flavor of mild decay,
But nothing local, as one may say.
There couldn't be—for the Deacon's art
Had made it so like in every part
That there wasn't a chance for one to start.
For the wheels were just as strong as the thills,
And the floor was just as strong as the sills,
And the panels just as strong as the floor,
And the whippletree neither less nor more,
And the back crossbar as strong as the fore,
And spring and axle and hub *encore*.
And yet, *as a whole,* it is past a doubt
In another hour it will be *worn out!*

First of November, 'Fifty-five!
This morning the parson takes a drive.
Now, small boys, get out of the way!
Here comes the wonderful one-hoss shay,
Drawn by a rat-tailed, ewe-necked bay.
"Huddup!" said the parson.—Off went they.

The parson was working his Sunday's text—
Had got to *fifthly,* and stopped perplexed
At what the—Moses—was coming next.
All at once the horse stood still,
Close by the meet'n'-house on the hill.
First a shiver, and then a thrill,
Then something decidedly like a spill,
And the parson was sitting upon a rock,
At half-past nine by the meet'n'-house clock—
Just the hour of the earthquake shock!
What do you think the parson found,
When he got up and stared around?
The poor old chaise in a heap or mound,
As if it had been to the mill and ground!
You see, of course, if you're not a dunce,
How it went to pieces all at once—
All at once, and nothing first—
Just as bubbles do when they burst.

End of the wonderful one-hoss shay.
Logic is logic. That's all I say.

## *For Fun: Suggested Grades*

*Grade Two*
The Owl and the Pussy Cat

*Grade Three*
The Duel

*Grade Four*
The Plaint of the Camel
The Lobster Quadrille
The Table and the Chair
A Strange Wild Song
Nonsense Verses
The Strange Man
A Tragic Story

*Grade Five*

The Height of the Ridiculous
The Twins
The Walrus and the Carpenter

*Grade Six*

A Nautical Ballad
The Yarn of the Nancy Bell
A Hot-Weather Song

*Grade Seven*

The Merry Miner
Darius Green and His Flying Machine

*Grade Eight*

A Nautical Extravagance
Between Two Loves
The Deacon's Masterpiece

# *Roads to Anywhere*

## ROADS [1]

*Rachel Field*

A road might lead to anywhere—
  To harbor towns and quays,
Or to a witch's pointed house,
  Hidden by bristly trees.
It might lead past the tailor's door,
  Where he sews with needle and thread;
Or by Miss Pim's, the milliner's,
  With her hats for every head.

It might be a road to a great dark cave,
  With treasure and gold piled high;
Or a road with a mountain tied to its end,
  Blue-humped against the sky.
Oh, a road might lead to anywhere,
  To Mexico or Maine;
But then it might just fool you, and—
  Lead you back home again!

## WHERE GO THE BOATS? [2]

*Robert Louis Stevenson*

Dark brown is the river,
  Golden is the sand,
It flows along forever,
  With trees on either hand.

Green leaves a-floating,
  Castles of the foam,
Boats of mine a-boating—
  Where will all come home?

On goes the river
  And out past the mill,
Away down the valley,
  Away down the hill.

Away down the river,
  A hundred miles or more,
Other little children
  Shall bring my boats ashore.

## THE HORSESHOE [3]

*Edna St. Vincent Millay*

Wonder where this horseshoe went.
Up and down, up and down,
Up and past the monument,
Maybe into town.

Wait a minute. "Horseshoe,
How far have you been?"
*Says it's been to Salem*
*And halfway to Lynn.*

[1] From Rachel Field, *The Pointed People.*
[2] From Robert Louis Stevenson, *A Child's Garden of Verses.*
[3] From Edna St. Vincent Millay, *Poems Selected for Young People.*

Wonder who was in the team.
Wonder what they saw.
Wonder if they passed a bridge—
Bridge with a draw.

*Says it went from one bridge*
*Straight upon another.*
*Says it took a little girl*
*Driving with her mother.*

## TAXIS [1]

*Rachel Field*

Ho, for taxis green or blue,
  Hi, for taxis red,
They roll along the avenue
  Like spools of colored thread!

Jack-o'Lantern yellow,
Orange as the moon,
Greener than the greenest grass
Ever grew in June.
Gayly striped or checked in squares,
Wheels that twinkle bright,
Don't you think that taxis make
A very pleasant sight?
Taxis shiny in the rain,
Scudding through the snow,
Taxis flashing back the sun
Waiting in a row.

Ho, for taxis red and green,
  Hi, for taxis blue,
I wouldn't be a private car
  In sober black, would you?

## THE PEDDLER'S CARAVAN [2]

*William Brighty Rands*

I wish I lived in a caravan,
With a horse to drive, like a peddler man!
Where he comes from nobody knows,
Or where he goes to, but on he goes!

His caravan has windows two,
And a chimney of tin, that the smoke comes
    through;
He has a wife, with a baby brown,
And they go riding from town to town.

Chairs to mend, and delf to sell!
He clashes the basins like a bell;
Tea trays, baskets ranged in order,
Plates, with alphabets round the border!

The roads are brown, and the sea is green,
But his house is like a bathing machine;
The world is round, and he can ride,
Rumble and slash, to the other side!

With the peddler man I should like to
    roam,
And write a book when I came home;
All the people would read my book,
Just like the Travels of Captain Cook!

## TRAVEL [3]

*Edna St. Vincent Millay*

The railroad track is miles away,
  And the day is loud with voices speaking,
Yet there isn't a train goes by all day
  But I hear its whistle shrieking.

All night there isn't a train goes by,
  Though the night is still for sleep and
    dreaming,
But I see its cinders in the sky,
  And hear its engine steaming.

My heart is warm with the friends I make,
  And better friends I'll not be knowing,
Yet there isn't a train I wouldn't take,
  No matter where it's going.

[1] From Rachel Field, *Taxis and Toadstools.*
[2] From William Brighty Rands, *Lilliput Lyrics.*
[3] From Edna St. Vincent Millay, *Second April.*

## THE SEA SHELL [1]

*Amy Lowell*

Sea Shell, Sea Shell,
  Sing me a song, O please!
A song of ships, and sailor men,
  Of parrots and tropical trees;

Of islands lost in the Spanish Main
Which no man ever may find again,
Of fishes and corals under the waves,
And sea-horses stabled in great green caves.

Sea Shell, Sea Shell,
Sing of the things you know so well.

## SONG OF THE PARROT [2]

*Elizabeth Coatsworth*

Far off, far off
Those forests lie
Beneath a heavy
Molten sky

Where I was born.
Oh, never more
At dusk shall I hear
Lions roar,

Nor see the monkeys
Leap and sway
From branch to branch
At dawn of day!

Behold me now,
Across the sea,
Watching mild ladies
Pour out tea!

## TRAVEL [3]

*Robert Louis Stevenson*

I should like to rise and go
Where the golden apples grow;
Where below another sky
Parrot islands anchored lie,
And, watched by cockatoos and goats,
Lonely Crusoes building boats;
Where in sunshine reaching out
Eastern cities, miles about,
Are with mosque and minaret
Among sandy gardens set,
And the rich goods from near and far
Hang for sale in the bazaar;
Where the Great Wall round China goes,
And on one side the desert blows,
And with bell and voice and drum,
Cities on the other hum;
Where are forests, hot as fire,
Wide as England, tall as a spire,
Full of apes and cocoanuts
And the negro hunters' huts;
Where the knotty crocodile
Lies and blinks in the Nile,
And the red flamingo flies
Hunting fish before his eyes;
Where in jungles, near and far,
Man-devouring tigers are,
Lying close and giving ear,
Lest the hunt be drawing near,
Or a comer-by be seen
Swinging in a palanquin;
Where among the desert sands
Some deserted city stands,
All its children, sweep and prince,
Grown to manhood ages since,
Not a foot in street or house,
Not a stir of child or mouse,
And when kindly falls the night,
In all the town no spark of light.
There I'll come when I'm a man
With a camel caravan;
Light a fire in the gloom
Of some dusty dining-room;
See the pictures on the walls,
Heroes, fights and festivals;
And in a corner find the toys
Of the Old Egyptian boys.

[1] From Amy Lowell, *A Dome of Many-Colored Glass.*
[2] From Elizabeth Coatsworth, *Alice-All-by-Herself.*
[3] From Robert Louis Stevenson, *A Child's Garden of Verses.*

## OLD SHIPS [1]

*David Morton*

There is a memory stays upon old ships,
 A weightless cargo in the musty hold,
Of bright lagoons and prow-caressing lips,
 Of stormy midnights, and a tale untold.
They have remembered islands in the dawn,
 And windy capes that tried their slender spars,
And tortuous channels where their keels have gone,
 And calm blue nights of stillness and the stars.

Ah, never think that ships forget a shore,
 Or bitter seas, or winds that made them wise;
There is a dream upon them, evermore;
 And there be some who say that sunk ships rise
To seek familiar harbors in the night,
 Blowing in mists, their spectral sails like light.

## SEA FEVER [2]

*John Masefield*

I must go down to the seas again, to the lonely sea and the sky,
And all I ask is a tall ship and a star to steer her by;
And the wheel's kick and the wind's song and the white sail's shaking,
And a gray mist on the sea's face, and a gray dawn breaking.

I must go down to the seas again, for the call of the running tide
Is a wild call and a clear call that may not be denied;
And all I ask is a windy day with the white clouds flying,
And the flung spray and the blown spume and the sea-gulls crying.

I must go down to the seas again, to the vagrant gipsy life,
To the gull's way and the whale's way where the wind's like a whetted knife;
And all I ask is a merry yarn from a laughing fellow rover,
And quiet sleep and a sweet dream when the long trick's over.

## THE TICKET AGENT [3]

*Edmund Leamy*

Like any merchant in a store
Who sells things by the pound or score,

He deals with scarce perfunctory glance
Small pass-keys to the world's Romance.

He takes dull money, turns and hands
The roadways to far distant lands.

Bright shining rail and fenceless sea
Are partners to his wizardry.

He calls off names as if they were
Just names to cause no heart to stir.

For listening you'll hear him say
". . . and then to Aden and Bombay . . ."

Or ". . . 'Frisco and then to Nome,
Across the Rocky Mountains—Home . . ."

And never catch of voice to tell
He knows the lure or feels the spell.

Like any salesman in a store,
He sells but tickets—nothing more.

And casual as any clerk
He deals in dreams, and calls it—work!

[1] From David Morton, *Ships in Harbour.*
[2] From John Masefield, *Salt-Water Poems and Ballads.*
[3] From *Harper's Magazine,* CXLVI: 170.

## *Roads to Anywhere: Suggested Grades*

*Grade Two*
- Where Go the Boats?
- Taxis

*Grade Three*
- Roads
- The Horseshoe
- The Peddler's Caravan

*Grade Four*
- The Sea Shell

*Grade Five*
- Song of the Parrot
- Travel (Stevenson)

*Grade Six*
- Travel (Millay)

*Grade Seven*
- Old Ships

*Grade Eight*
- Sea Fever
- The Ticket Agent

# The Day's Work

## BUSY CARPENTERS [1]

*James S. Tippett*

The song of the saw
Is true
As we cut the boards
In two.

The song of the plane
Is sweet
As the shavings curl
At our feet.

And the song of the hammer
Is good
As we drive the nails
In the wood.

## CARPENTER [2]

*E. V. Lucas*

I thought I could saw, and I thought I could plane,
And I thought I was clever with nails,
And I mended a chair (though it's broken again),
And I once made a couple of bails.

But directly the carpenter came to our house
To put up some shelves in the hall,
And I sat by his side as still as a mouse,
I knew I knew nothing at all.

He measured each part with the greatest of care,
(A footrule's a thing I don't use)
He labored to make the joints perfectly square,
And he always bored holes for the screws.

Now it's all very well to go hammering round,
And to look on a tool-chest as fun,
But in future my carpenter-work shall be sound,
And done once for all, if it's done.

## PSALM OF THOSE WHO GO FORTH BEFORE DAYLIGHT [3]

*Carl Sandburg*

The policeman buys shoes slow and careful; the teamster buys gloves slow and careful; they take care of their feet and hands; they live on their feet and hands.

[1] From James S. Tippett, *Busy Carpenters.*
[2] From E. V. Lucas, *Four and Twenty Toilers.*
[3] From Carl Sandburg, *Cornhuskers.*

The milkman never argues; he works alone and no one speaks to him; the city is asleep when he is on the job; he puts a bottle on six hundred porches and calls it a day's work; he climbs two hundred wooden stairways; two horses are company for him; he never argues.

The rolling-mill men and the sheet-steel men are brothers of cinders; they empty cinders out of their shoes after the day's work; they ask their wives to fix burnt holes in the knees of their trousers; their necks and ears are covered with a smut; they scour their necks and ears; they are brothers of cinders.

## EVENING AT THE FARM

*John Townsend Trowbridge*

Over the hill the farm-boy goes.
His shadow lengthens along the land,
A giant staff in a giant hand;
In the poplar-tree, above the spring,
The katydid begins to sing;
  The early dews are falling;
Into the stone-heap darts the mink;
The swallows skim the river's brink;
And home to the woodland fly the crows,
When over the hill the farm-boy goes,
  Cheerily calling,
  "Co', boss! co', boss! co'! co'! co'!"
Farther, farther, over the hill,
Faintly calling, calling still,
  "Co', boss co', boss! co'! co'!"

Into the yard the farmer goes,
With grateful heart, at the close of day;
Harness and chain are hung away;
In the wagon-shed stand yoke and plow,
The straw's in the stack, the hay in the mow,
  The cooling dews are falling;
The friendly sheep his welcome bleat,
The pigs come grunting to his feet,
And the whinnying mare her master knows,
When into the yard the farmer goes,
  His cattle calling,
  "Co', boss! co', boss! co'! co'! co'!"
While still the cow-boy, far away,
Goes seeking those that have gone astray,
  "Co', boss! co', boss! co'! co'! co'!"

Now to her task the milkmaid goes.
The cattle come crowding through the gate,
Lowing, pushing, little and great;
About the trough, by the farmyard pump,
The frolicsome yearlings frisk and jump,
  While the pleasant dews are falling;
The new milch heifer is quick and shy,
But the old cow waits with tranquil eye,
And the white stream into the bright pail flows,
When to her task the milkmaid goes,
  Soothingly calling,
  "So, boss! so, boss! so! so! so!"
The cheerful milkmaid takes her stool,
And sits and milks in the twilight cool,
  Saying, "So! so, boss! so! so!"

To supper at last the farmer goes.
The apples are pared, the paper read,
The stories are told, then all to bed;
Without, the crickets' ceaseless song
Makes shrill the silence all night long;
  The heavy dews are falling.
The housewife's hand has turned the lock;
Drowsily ticks the kitchen clock;
The household sinks to deep repose,
But still in sleep the farm-boy goes
  Singing, calling,
  "Co', boss! co', boss! co'! co'! co'!"
And oft the milkmaid, in her dreams,
Drums in the pail with the flashing streams,
  Murmuring, "So, boss! so!"

## PLOWING: A MEMORY[1]

*Hamlin Garland*

A lonely task it is to plow!
All day the black and shining soil
Rolls like a ribbon from the mold-board's
Glistening curve. All day the horses toil
And battle with the flies, and strain
Their creaking harnesses. All day
The crickets jeer from wind-blown shocks of grain.

[1] Used by permission of the author.

October brings the frosty dawn,
The still warm noon and cold, clear night,
When stiffened crickets make no sound
And wild ducks in their southward flight
Go by in haste—and still the boy
And toiling team gnaw round after round
On weather-beaten stubble band by band,
Until at last, to his great joy,
The winter's frost seals up the unplowed land.

## THE PLOWMAN OF TODAY[1]

*Hamlin Garland*

Upon his tractor's steady seat
He sits and drives his triple-share,
Hearing his steel bright pistons beat
Their tireless tattoo on the air.
Unwearied, recking neither wind nor snow,
Nor burning sun, scorning all insects' sting,
The ponderous monster wallows to and fro
Like some vast, captive dinosaurian King!

## THE VILLAGE BLACKSMITH

*Henry Wadsworth Longfellow*

Under a spreading chestnut-tree
The village smithy stands;
The smith, a mighty man is he,
With large and sinewy hands;
And the muscles of his brawny arms
Are strong as iron bands.

His hair is crisp, and black, and long,
His face is like the tan;
His brow is wet with honest sweat,
He earns whate'er he can,
And looks the whole world in the face,
For he owes not any man.

Week in, week out, from morn till night,
You can hear his bellows blow;
You can hear him swing his heavy sledge,
With measured beat and slow,
Like a sexton ringing the village bell,
When the evening sun is low.

[1] Used by permission of the author.
[2] From Walt Whitman, *Leaves of Grass.*

And children coming home from school
Look in at the open door;
They love to see the flaming forge,
And hear the bellows roar,
And catch the burning sparks that fly
Like chaff from a threshing-floor.

He goes on Sunday to the church,
And sits among his boys;
He hears the parson pray and preach,
He hears his daughter's voice,
Singing in the village choir,
And it makes his heart rejoice.

It sounds to him like her mother's voice,
Singing in Paradise!
He needs must think of her once more,
How in the grave she lies;
And with his hard, rough hand he wipes
A tear out of his eyes.

Toiling, rejoicing, sorrowing,
Onward through life he goes;
Each morning sees some task begun,
Each evening sees it close;
Something attempted, something done,
Has earned a night's repose.

Thanks, thanks to thee, my worthy friend,
For the lesson thou hast taught!
Thus at the flaming forge of life
Our fortunes must be wrought;
Thus on its sounding anvil shaped
Each burning deed and thought.

## I HEAR AMERICA SINGING[2]

*Walt Whitman*

I hear America singing, the varied carols I hear,
Those of mechanics, each one singing his, as it should be, blithe and strong,
The carpenter singing his, as he measures his plank or beam,
The mason singing his, as he makes ready for work, or leaves off work,
The boatman singing what belongs to him in his boat, the deckhand singing on the steamboat deck,

The shoemaker singing as he sits on his bench, the hatter singing as he stands,
The wood-cutter's song, the ploughboy's on his way in the morning, or at the noon intermission, or at sundown,
The delicious singing of the mother, or of the young wife at work, or of the girl sewing or washing,
Each singing what belongs to him or her and to none else,
The day what belongs to the day—at night the party of young fellows, robust, friendly,
Singing, with open mouths their strong melodious songs.

## WHEN THE DRIVE GOES DOWN [1]

### A Lumberjack's Story

*Douglas Malloch*

There's folks that like the good dry land, an' folks that like the sea,
But rock an' river, shoal an' sand, are good enough for me.
There's folks that like the ocean crest, an' folks that like the town—
But when I really feel the best is when the drive goes down.

So pole away, you river rats,
From landin' down to lake—
There's miles of pine to keep in line,
A hundred jams to break!

There's folks that like to promenade along the boulevard,
But here's a spot I wouldn't trade for all their pavement hard;
Ten thousand logs by currents birled an' waters white that hiss—
Oh, where's the sidewalk in the world that's half as fine as this?

So leap away, you river rats,
From landin' down to sluice;
There's logs to run, there's peavy fun
To break the timber loose!

An' ev'ry rollin' of a stick that starts her down the stream
An' ev'ry bit of water quick where runnin' ripples gleam
Means gittin' nearer to the end, to wife an' babe an' rest—
An' ev'ry time you turn a bend the next bend looks the best.

Then peg away, you river rats,
From sluiceway down to mill—
Each rock you clear will bring you near
The house upon the hill!

There's folks that like the good dry land, an' folks that like the sea,
But rock an' river, shoal an' sand, are good enough for me.
There's folks that like the ocean crest, an' folks that like the town—
But when I really feel the best is when the drive goes down!

## THE ZEBRA DUN [2]

### A Cowboy's Story

*Author Unknown*

We were camped on the plains at the head of the Cimarron
When along came a stranger and stopped to arger some.
He looked so very foolish that we began to look around,
We thought he was a greenhorn that had just 'scaped from town.

We asked if he had been to breakfast; he hadn't had a smear,
So we opened up the chuck-box, and bade him have his share.
He took a cup of coffee and some biscuits and some beans,
And then began to talk and tell about foreign kings and queens.

Such an educated feller his thoughts just came in herds,
He astonished all them cowboys with them jaw-breaking words.

[1] Used by permission of Mrs. Douglas Malloch.
[2] From John A. and Alan Lomax, *Cowboy Songs and Other Frontier Ballads.*

He just kept on talking till he made the boys all sick,
And they began to look around just how to play a trick.

He said he had lost his job upon the Santa Fe
And was going across the plains to strike the 7-Bar-D.
He didn't say how come it, some trouble with the boss,
But said he'd like to borrow a nice fat saddle hoss.

This tickled all the boys to death, they laughed way down in their sleeves,
"We will lend you a horse just as fresh and fat as you please."
Shorty grabbed a lariat and roped the Zebra Dun
And turned him over to the stranger and waited for the fun.

Old Dunny was a rocky outlaw that had grown so awful wild
That he could paw the white out of the moon every jump for a mile.
Old Dunny stood right still—as if he didn't know,
Until he was saddled and ready for to go.

When the stranger hit the saddle, old Dunny quit the earth
And traveled right straight up for all that he was worth,
A-pitching and a-squealing, a-having wall-eyed fits,
His hind feet perpendicular, his front ones in the bits.

We could see the tops of the mountains under Dunny every jump,
But the stranger he was growed there just like the camel's hump;
The stranger sat upon him and curled his black mustache
Just like a summer boarder waiting for his hash.

He thumped him in the shoulders and spurred him when he whirled,
To show them flunky punchers that he was the wolf of the world.
When the stranger had dismounted once more upon the ground,
We knew he was a thoroughbred and not a gent from town.

The boss who was standing round watching of the show,
Walked right up to the stranger and told him he needn't go:
"If you can use the lasso like you rode old Zebra Dun,
You are the man I've been looking for ever since the year one."

Oh, he could twirl the lariat and he didn't do it slow,
He could catch them forefeet nine out of ten for any kind of dough.
And when the herd stampeded he was always on the spot
And set them to nothing, like the boiling of a pot.

There's one thing and a shore thing I've learned since I've been born,
That every educated feller ain't a plumb greenhorn.

## WHOOPEE TI YI YO, GIT ALONG LITTLE DOGIES [1]

### A Cowboy's Song

*Author Unknown*

As I walked out one morning for pleasure,
I spied a cow-puncher all riding alone;
His hat was throwed back and his spurs was a-jingling,
As he approached me a-singin' this song:
  Whoopee ti yi yo, git along little dogies,
  It's your misfortune, and none of my own.
  Whoopee ti yi yo, git along little dogies,
  For you know Wyoming will be your new home.

[1] From John A. and Alan Lomax, *Cowboy Songs and Other Frontier Ballads.*

Early in the spring we round up the dogies,
Mark and brand and bob off their tails;
Round up our horses, load up the chuck-wagon,
Then throw the dogies upon the trail.

It's whooping and yelling and driving the dogies;
Oh, how I wish you would go on;
It's whooping and punching and go on little dogies,
For you know Wyoming will be your new home.

Some boys goes up the trail for pleasure,
But that's where you get it most awfully wrong;
For you haven't an idea the trouble they give us
While we go driving them all along.

When the night comes on and we hold them on the bedground,
These little dogies that roll on so slow;
Roll up the herd and cut out the strays,
And roll the little dogies that never rolled before.

Your mother she was raised way down in Texas,
Where the jimson weed and sand-burrs grow;
Now we'll fill you up on prickly pear and cholla
Till you are ready for the trail to Idaho.

Oh, you'll be soup for Uncle Sam's Injuns;
"It's beef, heap beef," I hear them cry.
Git along, git along, git along little dogies
You're going to be beef steers by and by.

## THE CLINKER

*Author Unknown*

When the ship drives on through the tumbling sea,
And speeds through the darkest night,
With the steady wash of turning screws,
That drive her in her flight;
And you, in your bunk or up on deck,
Have naught to do but ride,
Do you ever think of the watch below,
Have you ever thought what drives her so,
Or have you never tried?

Do you ever picture the turning wheels
Or flashing rods of steel,
Or hissing steam or scorching heat,
Way down there near the keel;
Do you ever think of the black stoke-hold,
And its sweating, straining crew;
Do you ever think of the flaming bed,
In that gaping maw that must be fed,
Or is it strange to you?

Do you ever picture the dusty "Heave"
Who toils in the bunkers' gloom,
Where the air is dead and clogged with dust,
Mid silence of the tomb?
Do you pity the clinker who struggles alone
With no complaining sound?
Well, if you do, don't say it aloud,
He wants no pity—the boy is proud,
He's making the wheels go 'round.

## GOETHALS, THE PROPHET ENGINEER [1]

*Percy MacKaye*

A man went down to Panama,
Where many a man had died,
To slit the sliding mountains
And lift the eternal tide;
A man stood up in Panama,
And the mountains stood aside.

For a poet wrought in Panama
With a continent for his theme,
And he wrote with flood and fire
To forge a planet's dream,
And the derricks rang his dithyrambs
And his stanzas roared in steam.

[1] From Percy MacKaye, *The Present Hour.*

Where old Balboa bent his gaze
He leads the liners through,
And the Horn that tossed Magellan
Bellows a far halloo,
For where the navies never sailed
Steamed Goethals and his crew;

So nevermore the tropic routes
Need poleward warp and veer,
But on through the Gates of Goethals
The steady keels shall steer,
Where the tribes of man are led toward peace
By the prophet-engineer.

## THE SECRET OF THE MACHINES[1]

*Rudyard Kipling*

We were taken from the ore-bed and the mine,
We were melted in the furnace and the pit—
We were cast and wrought and hammered to design,
We were cut and filed and tooled and gauged to fit.
Some water, coal, and oil is all we ask,
And a thousandth of an inch to give us play;
And now if you will set us to our task,
We will serve you four and twenty hours a day!

We can pull and haul and push and lift and drive,
We can print and plough and weave and heat and light,
We can run and dig and swim and fly and dive,
We can see and hear and count and read and write!

Would you call a friend from half across the world?
If you'll let us have his name and town and state,
You shall see and hear your crackling question hurled
Across the arch of heaven while you wait.
Has he answered? Does he need you at his side?
You can start this very evening if you choose,
And take the western ocean in the stride
Of seventy thousand horses and some screws!

The boat-express is waiting your command!
You will find the *Mauretania* at the quay,
Till her captain turns the lever 'neath his hand,
And the monstrous nine-decked city goes to sea.

Do you wish to make the mountains bare their head,
And lay their new-cut forests at your feet?
Do you want to turn a river in its bed,
Or plant a barren wilderness with wheat?
Shall we pipe aloft and bring you water down
From the never-failing cisterns of the snows,
To work the mills and tramways in your town,
And irrigate your orchard as it flows?

It is easy! Give us dynamite and drills!
Watch the iron-shouldered rocks lie down and quake
As the thirsty desert-level floods and fills,
And the valley we have dammed becomes a lake.

But remember, please, the law by which we live.
We are not built to comprehend a lie.
We can neither love nor pity nor forgive.
If you make a slip in handling us you die!
We are greater than the peoples or the kings—
Be humble, as you crawl beneath our rods!—
Our touch can alter all created things,
We are everything on earth—except the gods!

[1] From Rudyard Kipling, *Songs for Youth.*

*Though our smoke may hide the heavens from your eyes,*
*It will vanish and the stars will shine again,*
*Because, for all our power and weight and size,*
*We are nothing more than children of your brain!*

## THE THINKER [1]

*Berton Braley*

Back of the beating hammer
By which the steel is wrought,
Back of the workshop's clamor
The seeker may find the thought;
The thought that is ever master
Of iron and steam and steel,
That rises above disaster
And tramples it under heel!

The drudge may fret and tinker,
Or labor with lusty blows,
But back of him stands the thinker,
The clear-eyed man who knows;
For into each plow or sabre,
Each piece and part and whole,
Must go the brains of labor
Which give the work a soul!

Back of the motor's humming,
Back of the belts that sing,
Back of the hammer's drumming,
Back of the cranes that swing,
There is the eye which scans them,
Watching through stress and strain,
There is the mind which plans them—
Back of the brawn, the brain!

Might of the roaring boiler,
Force of the engine's thrust,
Strength of the sweating toiler,
Greatly in these we trust.
But back of them stands the schemer,
The thinker who drives things through;
Back of the job—the dreamer,
Who's making the dream come true!

# *The Day's Work: Suggested Grades*

*Grade Two*
Busy Carpenters

*Grade Three*
Carpenter

*Grade Four*
Psalm of Those Who Go Forth before Daylight
Evening at the Farm

*Grade Five*
Plowing: A Memory
The Plowman of Today

*Grade Six*
The Village Blacksmith
I Hear America Singing
When the Drive Goes Down

[1] Used by permission of the author.

The Zebra Dun
The Clinker

*Grade Seven*
Whoopee Ti Yi Yo, Git Along Little Dogies

*Grade Eight*
Goethals, the Prophet Engineer
The Secret of the Machines
The Thinker

# Our Country

## DEAR LAND OF ALL MY LOVE [1]

*Sidney Lanier*

Long as thine Art shall love true love,
Long as thy Science truth shall know,
Long as thine Eagle harms no Dove,
Long as thy Law by law shall grow,
Long as thy God is God above,
Thy brother every man below,
So long, dear Land of all my love,
Thy name shall shine, thy fame shall glow!

## INDIAN CHILDREN [2]

*Annette Wynne*

Where we walk to school each day
Indian children used to play—
All about our native land,
Where the shops and houses stand.

And the trees were very tall,
And there were no streets at all,
Not a church and not a steeple—
Only woods and Indian people.

Only wigwams on the ground,
And at night bears prowling round.
What a different place today
Where we live and work and play!

## THE WILDERNESS IS TAMED [3]

*Elizabeth Coatsworth*

The axe has cut the forest down,
The laboring ox has smoothed all clear,
Apples now grow where pine trees stood,
And slow cows graze instead of deer.

Where Indian fires once raised their smoke
The chimneys of a farmhouse stand,
And cocks crow barnyard challenges
To dawns that once saw savage land.

The axe, the plow, the binding wall,
By these the wilderness is tamed,
By these the white man's will is wrought,
The rivers bridged, the new towns named

[1] From Sidney Lanier, *Centennial Ode*.
[2] From Annette Wynne, *For Days and Days*.
[3] From Elizabeth Coatsworth, *Away Goes Sally*.

## COLUMBUS

*Joaquin Miller*

Behind him lay the gray Azores,
  Behind, the Gates of Hercules;
Before him not the ghost of shores,
  Before him only shoreless seas.
The good mate said: "Now must we pray,
  For, lo! the very stars are gone.
Brave Admiral, speak; what shall I say?"
  "Why, say: 'Sail on! sail on! and on!' "

"My men grow mutinous day by day;
  My men grow ghastly wan and weak."
The stout mate thought of home, a spray
  Of salt wave washed his swarthy cheek.
"What shall I say, brave Admiral, say,
  If we sight naught but seas at dawn?"
"Why, you shall say, at break of day:
  'Sail on! sail on! sail on! and on!' "

They sailed and sailed, as winds might blow,
  Until at last the blanched mate said:
"Why, now not even God would know
  Should I and all my men fall dead.
These very winds forget their way,
  For God from these dread seas is gone.
Now speak, brave Admiral; speak and say—"
  He said: "Sail on! sail on! and on!"

They sailed. They sailed. Then spake the
  mate:
  "This mad sea shows his teeth tonight.
He curls his lips, he lies in wait,
  With lifted teeth, as if to bite!
Brave Admiral, say but one good word:
  What shall we do when hope is gone?"
The words leapt like a leaping sword:
  "Sail on! sail on! sail on! and on!"

Then, pale and worn, he kept his deck,
  And peered through darkness. Ah, that
  night
Of all dark nights! And then a speck—
  A light! A light! At last a light!
It grew, a starlit flag unfurled!
  It grew to be Time's burst of dawn.
He gained a world; he gave that world
  Its grandest lesson: "On, sail on!"

## CONCORD HYMN

*Ralph Waldo Emerson*

By the rude bridge that arched the flood,
  Their flag to April's breeze unfurled,
Here once the embattled farmers stood,
  And fired the shot heard round the world.

The foe long since in silence slept;
  Alike the conqueror silent sleeps;
And Time the ruined bridge has swept
  Down the dark stream which seaward
  creeps.

On this green bank, by this soft stream,
  We set today a votive stone;
That memory may their deed redeem,
  When, like our sires, our sons are gone.

Spirit, that made those heroes dare
  To die, and leave their children free,
Bid Time and Nature gently spare
  The shaft we raise to them and thee.

## PAUL REVERE'S RIDE[1]

*Henry Wadsworth Longfellow*

Listen, my children, and you shall hear
Of the midnight ride of Paul Revere,
On the eighteenth of April, in Seventy-five;
Hardly a man is now alive
Who remembers that famous day and year.

He said to his friend, "If the British march
By land or sea from the town tonight,
Hang a lantern aloft in the belfry arch
Of the North Church tower, as a signal
  light—
One, if by land, and two, if by sea;
And I on the opposite shore will be,
Ready to ride and spread the alarm
Through every Middlesex village and farm,
For the country folk to be up and to arm."

Then he said "Good night!" and with muf-
  fled oar
Silently rowed to the Charlestown shore,
Just as the moon rose over the bay,
Where, swinging wide at her moorings, lay

[1] From Henry Wadsworth Longfellow, *Tales of a Wayside Inn.*

The *Somerset,* British man-of-war—
A phantom ship, with each mast and spar
Across the moon, like a prison bar,
And a huge black hulk, that was magnified
By its own reflection in the tide.

Meanwhile, his friend, through alley and street,
Wanders and watches with eager ears,
Till in the silence around him he hears
The muster of men at the barrack door,
The sound of arms, and the tramp of feet,
And the measured tread of the grenadiers,
Marching down to their boats on the shore.

Then he climbed to the tower of the Old North Church,
By the wooden stairs, with stealthy tread,
To the belfry-chamber overhead,
And startled the pigeons from their perch
On the somber rafters, that round him made
Masses and moving shapes of shade—
By the trembling ladder, steep and tall,
To the highest window in the wall,
Where he paused to listen and look down
A moment on the roofs of the town,
And the moonlight flowing over all.

Beneath, in the churchyard, lay the dead
In their night-encampment on the hill,
Wrapped in silence so deep and still
That he could hear, like a sentinel's tread,
The watchful night-wind, as it went
Creeping along from tent to tent,
And seeming to whisper, "All is well!"
A moment only he feels the spell
Of the place and the hour, the secret dread
Of the lonely belfry and the dead;
For suddenly all his thoughts are bent
On a shadowy something far away,
Where the river widens to meet the bay—
A line of black that bends and floats
On the rising tide, like a bridge of boats.

Meanwhile, impatient to mount and ride,
Booted and spurred, with a heavy stride
On the opposite shore walked Paul Revere.
Now he patted his horse's side,
Now gazed at the landscape far and near,
Then, impetuous, stamped the earth,
And turned and tightened his saddle-girth;
But mostly he watched with eager search
The belfry-tower of the Old North Church,
As it rose above the graves on the hill,
Lonely and spectral and somber and still.
And lo! as he looks, on the belfry's height
A glimmer, and then a gleam of light!
He springs to the saddle, the bridle he turns,
But lingers and gazes, till full on his sight
A second lamp in the belfry burns!

A hurry of hoofs in a village street,
A shape in the moonlight, a bulk in the dark,
And beneath, from the pebbles, in passing, a spark
Struck out by a steed flying fearless and fleet—
That was all! And yet, through the gloom and the light,
The fate of a nation was riding that night;
And the spark struck out by that steed, in his flight,
Kindled the land into flame with its heat.

He has left the village and mounted the steep,
And beneath him, tranquil and broad and deep,
Is the Mystic, meeting the ocean tides;
And under the alders that skirt its edge,
Now soft on the sand, now loud on the ledge,
Is heard the tramp of his steed as he rides.

It was twelve by the village clock,
When he crossed the bridge into Medford town.
He heard the crowing of the cock,
And the barking of the farmer's dog,
And felt the damp of the river fog,
That rises after the sun goes down.

It was one by the village clock,
When he galloped into Lexington.
He saw the gilded weathercock
Swim in the moonlight as he passed,
And the meeting-house windows, blank and bare,
Gazed at him with a spectral glare,
As if they already stood aghast
At the bloody work they would look upon.

It was two by the village clock,
When he came to the bridge in Concord
town.
He heard the bleating of the flock,
And the twitter of birds among the trees,
And felt the breath of the morning breeze
Blowing over the meadows brown.
And one was safe and asleep in his bed
Who at the bridge would be first to fall,
Who that day would be lying dead,
Pierced by a British musket-ball.

You know the rest. In the books you have
read
How the British Regulars fired and fled,
How the farmers gave them ball for ball,
From behind each fence and farmyard wall,
Chasing the red-coats down the lane,
Then crossing the fields to emerge again
Under the trees at the turn of the road,
And only pausing to fire and load.

So through the night rode Paul Revere;
And so through the night went his cry of
alarm
To every Middlesex village and farm—
A cry of defiance and not of fear,
A voice in the darkness, a knock at the door,
And a word that shall echo forevermore!
For, borne on the night-wind of the Past,
Through all our history, to the last,
In the hour of darkness and peril and need,
The people will waken and listen to hear
The hurrying hoof-beats of that steed,
And the midnight message of Paul Revere.

## IN PRAISE OF JOHNNY APPLESEED[1]

*Vachel Lindsay*

A boy
Blew west,
And with prayers and incantations,
And with "Yankee Doodle Dandy,"
Crossed the Appalachians,
And was "young John Chapman,"
Then
"Johnny Appleseed, Johnny Appleseed,"
Chief of the fastnesses, dappled and vast.
In a pack on his back,
In a deer-hide sack,
The beautiful orchards of the past,
The ghosts of all the forests and the groves—
In that pack on his back,
In that talisman sack;
Tomorrow's peaches, pears, and cherries,
Tomorrow's grapes and red raspberries,
Seeds and tree-souls, precious things,
Feathered with microscopic wings;
All the outdoors the child heart knows,
And the apple, green, red, and white,
Sun of his day and his night—
The apple allied to the thorn,
Child of the rose.
Porches untrod of forest houses
All before him, all day long,
"Yankee Doodle" his marching song;
And the evening breeze
Joined his psalms of praise
As he sang the ways
Of the Ancient of Days.
Leaving behind august Virginia,
Proud Massachusetts, and proud Maine.
Planting the trees that would march and
train
On, in his name to the great Pacific,
Like Birnam wood to Dunsinane,
Johnny Appleseed swept on,
Every shackle gone,
Loving every sloshy brake,
Loving every skunk and snake,
Loving every leathery weed;
Johnny Appleseed, Johnny Appleseed,
Master and ruler of the unicorn-ramping
forest,
The tiger-mewing forest,
The rooster-trumpeting, boar-foaming, wolf-
ravening forest,
The spirit-haunted, fairy-enchanted forest,
Stupendous and endless,
Searching its perilous ways
In the name of the Ancient of Days.

Painted Kings in the midst of the clearing
Heard him asking his friends the eagles
To guard each planted seed and seedling.
Then he was a god, to the red man's dream-
ing;

[1] From Vachel Lindsay, *Johnny Appleseed, and Other Poems.*

Then the chiefs brought treasures grotesque and fair—
Magical trinkets and pipes and guns,
Beads and furs from their medicine-lair—
Stuck holy feathers in his hair.
Hailed him with austere delight.
The orchard god was their guest through the night.
While the late snow blew from bleak Lake Erie,
Scourging rock and river and reed,
All night long they made great medicine
For Jonathan Chapman,
Johnny Appleseed,
Johnny Appleseed;
And as though his heart were a wind-blown wheat-sheaf,
As though his heart were a new-built nest,
As though their heaven house were his breast,
In swept the snowbirds singing glory.
And I hear his bird heart beat its story,
Hear yet how the ghost of the forest shivers,
Hear yet the cry of the gray, old orchards,
Dim and decaying by the rivers,
And the timid wings of the bird-ghosts beating,
And the ghosts of the tom-toms beating, beating.

But he left their wigwams and their love.
By the hour of dawn he was proud and stark,
Kissed the Indian babes with a sigh,
Went forth to live on roots and bark,
Sleep in the trees, while the years howled by.
Calling the catamounts by name,
And buffalo bulls no hand could tame.
Slaying never a living creature,
Joining the birds in every game,
With the gorgeous turkey gobblers mocking,
With the lean-necked eagles boxing and shouting;
Sticking their feathers in his hair—
Turkey feathers,
Eagle feathers,
Trading hearts with all beasts and weathers
He swept on, winged and wonder-crested,
Bare-armed, barefooted, and bare-breasted.
The maples, shedding their spinning seeds,
Called to his appleseeds in the ground,
Vast chestnut-trees, with their butterfly nations,
Called to his seeds without a sound.
And the chipmunk turned a "summerset;"
And the foxes danced the Virginia reel;
Hawthorn and crab-thorn bent, rain-wet,
And dropped their flowers in his night-black hair;
And the soft fawns stopped for his perorations;
And his black eyes shone through the forest-gleam,
And he plunged young hands into new-turned earth,
And prayed dear orchard boughs into birth;
And he ran with the rabbit and slept with the stream,
And he ran with the rabbit and slept with the stream,
And he ran with the rabbit and slept with the stream.
And so for us he made great medicine,
And so for us he made great medicine,
And so for us he made great medicine.
In the days of President Washington.

## THE PASSING OF THE BUFFALO [1]

*Hamlin Garland*

Going, the wild things of our land.
Passing, the antelope and the buffalo.
They have gone with the sunny sweep
Of the untracked plain!
They have passed away with the untrammeled
Current of our streams!

With the falling trees they fell,
With the autumn grasses they rotted,
And their bones
Lie white on the flame-charred sod,
Mixed with the antlers of the elk.

[1] Used by permission of the author.

For centuries they lay down and rose
In peace and calm content.
They were fed by the rich grass
And watered by sunny streams.
The plover called to them
Out of the shimmering air,
The hawk swooped above them,
The blackbirds sat on their backs
In the still afternoons;
In the cool mud they wallowed,
Rolling in noisy sport.

They lived through centuries of struggle—
In swarming millions—till the white man came.
The snows of winter were terrible!
The dry wind was hard to bear,
But the breath of man, the smoke
Of his gun were more fatal.

They fell by the thousands.
They melted away like smoke!
Mile by mile they retreated westward;
Year by year they moved north and south
In dust-brown clouds;
Each year they descended upon the plains
In endless floods;
Each winter they retreated to the hills
Of the south.
Their going was like the ocean current,
But each spring they stopped a little short—
They were like an ebbing tide!
They came at last to meager little bands
That never left the hills—
Crawling in somber files from canyon to canyon—
Now, they are gone!

## THE PRAIRIE SCHOONER [1]

*Edwin Ford Piper*

The meadow larks rejoice, as the bright sun
Drinks up the burdening dew from slender grass,
From flower cups, purple, yellow, white, and blue,
On the green hill-slopes where the dusty trail
Lies like a loose gray ribbon. Westward creeps
The jolting prairie schooner, and its wheels
Talk on the axle while the sweating bays
Draw sturdily, nodding their patient heads.
Humping between spring seat and canvas roof
The bearded, weather-beaten driver guides
With slackened line. An eager boy and girl—
The lass with yellow curls, the lad well tanned—
Peer close beside him. From the hidden depths
Comes the low crooning of a lullaby.
The meadow larks rejoice, the wild flowers blow—
He eyes the dusty margin of the trail
Communing with his vision of a home.

## THE OREGON TRAIL: 1851 [2]

*Jim Marshall*

Out they came from Liberty, out across the plains,
Two-stepping, single-footing, hard-boiled and easy-shooting,
Whips cracking; oaths snapping . . .
Hear those banjos wail—
Emigratin' westward on the Oregon Trail.

Squishing through the mudholes, drunken with the rain;
Turn your face to heaven, boy—and punch those bulls again;
Onward to the sunset;
Hallelujah! Sing!
Don't let nothing stop yuh! Not a con-sarned thing!
White sails of schooners, snapping in the wind,
Oregon ahead of us—good-by, to them be-hind!
Free land in Oregon!
Through the prairie gale
Emigratin' westward on the free land trail.

[1] From Edwin Ford Piper, *Barbed Wire and Wayfarers.*
[2] From H. G. Merriam, *Northwest Verse.*

The blasted heathens, Rickarees and Sioux!
Aim across the wagon wheel and drill the varmints through.
Line 'em up, line 'em out,
  Pray the tugs'll hold,
Wheels a-screeching glory through the sunset's gold;
Keep y'r musket handy, trigger on the cock,
Peel y'r eyes, kid, if you'd see old Independence Rock!
Took our luck right in our hands;
  Can't afford to fail—
Hittin' f'r the westward on the bone-strewed trail.

Put y'r faith in God, friends, and conquer everything!
Line them millin' leaders out, get the bulls a-going—
Got to get to Oregon!
  West winds blowing
Bitter from the Stonies, looming blue ahead,
Wagons bogged in prairie mud, teams stuck fast;
Heave the tumbled baggage off, clean the wagon bed,
Sweat and curse and on again, freed at last,
On again and face the rain,
  Buck the wind and hail—
Emigratin' westward on the Oregon Trail.

Onward through the mountains, lifting to the blue,
Up and through the rock cuts, weaving to the pass;
Old Ezra stopped here, where his spirit flew,
Left his little gran'child, such a pretty lass;
Ben's a-goin' to take her; that'll make him eight—
God sure'll bless him for his kindly thought.
Hitch up and roll again. Hi, 's getting late
And this old defile ain't no place t'be caught;
No time for sorrowing,
  Tear-eyed and pale—
Got to keep a-movin' on the Oregon Trail.

Can't see the wagon tracks; trail's pinched out;
Nothing but the snow peaks and shale-rock slopes;
Outspan the bull-teams; we'll heave them wagons
Upside and over with the rawhide ropes—
Pounding through the chill wind, shirts sweat-black,
Oh! But I wisht I was back down in Liberty!
Pull there, you quitter! for y'u can't turn back—
Top of the mountains now, keen in the starlight,
Sunup's a-comin' on the western sea,
Yellow beams of glory-glow,
  Floodin' the snow peaks—
There lies Oregon! Glory to Thee!

Punch up the bull-teams, tune up the banjo,
Hallelujah! Praise God, kneeling in the snow;
Land of the dripping fir, land of the homestead,
Oregon! Oregon! Beckoning below—
All out from Liberty, out across the ranges,
Two-stepping, single-footing, hard-boiled and glory-singing,
Whips cracking, oats snapping, bull-teams slogging on,
Babes a-borning, men a-dying, trail shouts ringing—
Here come the conquerors
  (And there lie the frail),
Roaring to the sunset on the Oregon Trail!

## BARBARA FRIETCHIE

*John Greenleaf Whittier*

Up from the meadows rich with corn,
Clear in the cool September morn,

The clustered spires of Frederick stand
Green-walled by the hills of Maryland.

Round about them orchards sweep,
Apple and peach tree fruited deep,

Fair as the garden of the Lord
To the eyes of the famished rebel horde,

On that pleasant morn of the early fall
When Lee marched over the mountain-
wall;

Over the mountains winding down,
Horse and foot, into Frederick town.

Forty flags with their silver stars,
Forty flags with their crimson bars,

Flapped in the morning wind; the sun
Of noon looked down, and saw not one.

Up rose old Barbara Frietchie then,
Bowed with her fourscore years and ten;

Bravest of all in Frederick town,
She took up the flag the men hauled down;

In her attic window the staff she set,
To show that one heart was loyal yet.

Up the street came the rebel tread,
Stonewall Jackson riding ahead.

Under his slouched hat left and right
He glanced; the old flag met his sight.

"Halt!"—the dust-brown ranks stood fast.
"Fire!"—out blazed the rifle-blast.

It shivered the window, pane and sash;
It rent the banner with seam and gash.

Quick as it fell, from the broken staff
Dame Barbara snatched the silken scarf.

She leaned far out on the window-sill,
And shook it forth with a royal will.

"Shoot, if you must, this old gray head,
But spare your country's flag," she said.

A shade of sadness, a blush of shame,
Over the face of the leader came;

The nobler nature within him stirred
To life at that woman's deed and word;

"Who touches a hair of yon gray head
Dies like a dog! March on!" he said.

All day long through Frederick street
Sounded the tread of marching feet.

All day long that free flag tost
Over the heads of the rebel host.

Ever its torn folds rose and fell
On the loyal winds that loved it well;

And through the hill-gaps, sunset light
Shone over it with a warm good-night.

Barbara Frietchie's work is o'er,
And the Rebel rides on his raids no more.

Honor to her! and let a tear
Fall, for her sake, on Stonewall's bier.

Over Barbara Frietchie's grave,
Flag of Freedom and Union, wave!

Peace and order and beauty draw
Round thy symbol of light and law;

And ever the stars above look down
On thy stars below in Frederick town!

## O CAPTAIN! MY CAPTAIN! [1]

*Walt Whitman*

O Captain! my Captain! our fearful trip is
done;
The ship has weather'd every rack, the prize
we sought is won;
The port is near, the bells I hear, the peo-
ple all exulting,
While follow eyes the steady keel, the vessel
grim and daring;
But O heart! heart! heart!
O the bleeding drops of red,
Where on the deck my Captain lies,
Fallen cold and dead.

[1] From Walt Whitman, *Leaves of Grass.*

O Captain! my Captain! rise up and hear the bells;
Rise up—for you the flag is flung—for you the bugle trills;
For you bouquets and ribbon'd wreaths—for you the shores a-crowding;
For you they call, the swaying mass, their eager faces turning;
Here Captain, dear father!
This arm beneath your head!
It is some dream that on the deck,
You've fallen cold and dead.

My Captain does not answer, his lips are pale and still;
My father does not feel my arm, he has no pulse nor will;
The ship is anchor'd safe and sound, its voyage closed and done;
From fearful trip the victor ship comes in with object won;
Exult, O shores, and ring, O bells!
But I with mournful tread,
Walk the deck my Captain lies,
Fallen cold and dead.

## IN FLANDERS FIELDS[1]

*John McCrae*

In Flanders fields the poppies blow
Between the crosses, row on row,
That mark our place; and in the sky
The larks, still bravely singing, fly
Scarce heard amid the guns below.

We are the dead. Short days ago
We lived, felt dawn, saw sunset glow,
Loved and were loved, and now we lie
In Flanders fields.

Take up our quarrel with the foe;
To you from failing hands we throw
The torch; be yours to hold it high.
If ye break faith with us who die,
We shall not sleep, though poppies grow
In Flanders fields.

## MY OWN, MY NATIVE LAND[2]

*Sir Walter Scott*

Breathes there the man with soul so dead,
Who never to himself hath said,
This is my own, my native land?
Whose heart hath ne'er within him burned,
As home his footsteps he hath turned,
From wandering on a foreign strand?
If such there breathe, go, mark him well!
For him no minstrel raptures swell;
High though his titles, proud his name,
Boundless his wealth as wish can claim;
Despite those titles, power, and pelf,
The wretch, concentred all in self,
Living, shall forfeit fair renown,
And, doubly dying, shall go down
To the vile dust from whence he sprung,
Unwept, unhonored, and unsung.

# *Our Country: Suggested Grades*

*Grade Two*
Indian Children

*Grade Four*
The Wilderness Is Tamed

[1] From John McCrae, *In Flanders Fields, and Other Poems.*
[2] From Sir Walter Scott, *The Lay of the Last Minstrel.*

*Grade Five*

Paul Revere's Ride
Barbara Frietchie

*Grade Six*

Dear Land of All My Love
Columbus
Concord Hymn
O Captain! My Captain!
In Flanders Fields

*Grade Seven*

In Praise of Johnny Appleseed
The Prairie Schooner

*Grade Eight*

The Passing of the Buffalo
The Oregon Trail: 1851
My Own, My Native Land

# Guideposts

## MOTHER TO SON [1]

*Langston Hughes*

Well, son, I'll tell you:
Life for me ain't been no crystal stair.
It's had tacks in it,
And splinters,
And boards torn up,
And places with no carpet on the floor—
Bare.
But all the time
I'se been a-climbin' on,
And reachin' landin's,
And turnin' corners,
And sometimes goin' in the dark
Where there ain't been no light.
So, boy, don't you turn back.
Don't you set down on the steps
'Cause you finds it kinder hard.
Don't you fall now—
For I'se still goin', honey,
I'se still climbin',
And life for me ain't been no crystal stair.

## PRIMER LESSON [2]

*Carl Sandburg*

Look out how you use proud words,
When you let proud words go, it is not easy to call them back.
They wear long boots, hard boots; they walk off proud; they can't hear you calling—
Look out how you use proud words.

## A CHILD'S GRACE

*Robert Burns*

Some hae meat and canna eat,
And some wad eat that want it;
But we hae meat and we can eat,
And sae the Lord be thankit.

## HE PRAYETH BEST [3]

*Samuel Taylor Coleridge*

He prayeth best, who loveth best
All things both great and small;
For the dear God who loveth us,
He made and loveth all.

[1] From Langston Hughes, *The Dream Keeper, and Other Poems.*
[2] From Carl Sandburg, *Slabs of the Sunburnt West.*
[3] From Samuel Taylor Coleridge, *The Rime of the Ancient Mariner.*

## ALL THINGS BRIGHT AND BEAUTIFUL

*Cecil Frances Alexander*

All things bright and beautiful,
  All creatures great and small,
All things wise and wonderful,
  The Lord God made them all.

Each little flower that opens,
  Each little bird that sings,
He made their glowing colors,
  He made their tiny wings.

The purple-headed mountain,
  The river running by,
The sunset and the morning,
  That brightens up the sky;

The cold wind in the winter,
  The pleasant summer sun,
The ripe fruits in the garden,
  He made them every one;

The tall trees in the greenwood,
  The meadows where we play,
The rushes by the water
  We gather every day;

He gave us eyes to see them,
  And lips that we might tell
How great is God Almighty,
  Who has made all things well.

## CRADLE HYMN

*Martin Luther*

Away in a manger, no crib for a bed,
The little Lord Jesus laid down his sweet
  head.
The stars in the bright sky looked down
  where he lay—
The little Lord Jesus asleep on the hay.
The cattle are lowing, the baby awakes,
But little Lord Jesus, no crying he makes.
I love thee, Lord Jesus! look down from the
  sky,
And stay by my cradle till morning is nigh.

## AS JOSEPH WAS A-WALKING

OLD CAROL

As Joseph was a-walking,
  He heard an angel sing,
"This night shall be the birthnight
  Of Christ our heavenly King.

"His birth-bed shall be neither
  In housen nor in hall,
Nor in the place of paradise,
  But in the oxen's stall.

"He neither shall be rockèd
  In silver nor in gold,
But in the wooden manger
  That lieth in the mould.

"He neither shall be washen
  With white wine nor with red,
But with the fair spring water
  That on you shall be shed.

"He neither shall be clothèd
  In purple nor in pall,
But in the fair, white linen
  That usen babies all."

As Joseph was a-walking,
  Thus did the angel sing,
And Mary's son at midnight
  Was born to be our King.

Then be you glad, good people,
  At this time of the year;
And light you up your candles,
  For His star it shineth clear.

## THE LAMB[1]

*William Blake*

  Little lamb, who made thee,
  Dost thou know who made thee,
Gave thee life and bade thee feed
By the stream and o'er the mead;

[1] From William Blake, *Songs of Innocence*.

Gave thee clothing of delight,
Softest clothing, woolly, bright;
Gave thee such a tender voice,
Making all the vales rejoice?
  Little lamb, who made thee?
  Dost thou know who made thee?

  Little lamb, I'll tell thee;
  Little lamb, I'll tell thee:
He is callèd by thy name,
For He calls Himself a Lamb.
He is meek, and He is mild,
He became a little child.
I a child and thou a lamb,
We are callèd by His name.
  Little lamb, God bless thee!
  Little lamb, God bless thee!

## THE OLD WOMAN OF THE ROADS [1]

*Padraic Colum*

Oh, to have a little house!
To own the hearth and stool and all!
The heaped-up sods upon the fire,
The pile of turf against the wall!

To have a clock with weights and chains,
And pendulum swinging up and down!
A dresser filled with shining delf,
Speckled with white and blue and brown!

I could be busy all the day
Cleaning and sweeping hearth and floor,
And fixing on their shelf again
My white and blue and speckled store!

I could be quiet there at night
Beside the fire, and by myself,
Sure of a bed and loth to leave
The ticking clock and shining delf!

Och! but I'm weary of mist and dark,
And roads where there's never a house or bush,
And tired I am of bog and road,
And the crying wind and the lonesome hush!

And I'm praying to God on high,
And I'm praying Him night and day,
For a little house—a house of my own,
Out of the wind's and rain's way.

## SONG FOR A LITTLE HOUSE [2]

*Christopher Morley*

I'm glad our house is a little house,
Not too tall nor too wide;
I'm glad the hovering butterflies
Feel free to come inside.

Our little house is a friendly house,
It is not shy or vain;
It gossips with the talking trees.
And makes friends with the rain.

And quick leaves cast a shimmer of green
Against our whited walls,
And in the phlox, the courteous bees
Are paying duty calls.

## THE HOUSE WITH NOBODY IN IT [3]

*Joyce Kilmer*

Whenever I walk to Suffern along the Erie track,
I go by a poor old farmhouse with its shingles broken and black.
I suppose I've passed it a hundred times, but I always stop for a minute,
And look at the house, the tragic house, the house with nobody in it.

I never have seen a haunted house, but I hear there are such things;
That they hold the talk of spirits, their mirth and sorrowings.
I know this house isn't haunted, and I wish it were, I do;
For it wouldn't be so lonely if it had a ghost or two.

[1] From Padraic Colum, *Wild Earth, and Other Poems.*
[2] From Christopher Morley, *Chimney Smoke.*
[3] From Joyce Kilmer, *Poems, Essays and Letters.*

This house on the road to Suffern needs a dozen panes of glass,
And somebody ought to weed the walk and take a scythe to the grass.
It needs new paint and shingles, and the vines should be rimmed and tied;
But what it needs the most of all is some people living inside.

If I had a lot of money and all my debts were paid,
I'd put a gang of men to work with brush and saw and spade.
I'd buy that place and fix it up the way it used to be,
And I'd find some people who wanted a home and give it to them free.

Now, a new house standing empty, with staring window and door,
Looks idle, perhaps, and foolish, like a hat on its block in the store.
But there's nothing mournful about it; it cannot be sad and lone
For the lack of something within it that it has never known.

But a house that has done what a house should do, a house that has sheltered life,
That has put its loving wooden arms around a man and his wife,
A house that has echoed a baby's laugh and held up his stumbling feet,
Is the saddest sight, when it's left alone, that ever your eyes could meet.

So whenever I go to Suffern along the Erie track
I never go by the empty house without stopping and looking back,
Yet it hurts me to look at the crumbling roof and the shutters fallen apart,
For I can't help thinking the poor old house is a house with a broken heart.

## A THING OF BEAUTY [1]

*John Keats*

A thing of beauty is a joy for ever;
Its loveliness increases; it will never
Pass into nothingness; but still will keep
A bower quiet for us, and a sleep
Full of sweet dreams, and health, and quiet breathing.

## A PRAYER [2]

*Edwin Markham*

Teach me, Father, how to go
Softly as the grasses grow;
Hush my soul to meet the shock
Of the wild world as a rock;
But my spirit propt with power
Make as simple as a flower.
Let the dry heart fill its cup,
Like a poppy looking up;
Let life lightly wear her crown,
Like a poppy looking down,
When its heart is filled with dew,
And its life begins anew.

Teach me, Father, how to be
Kind and patient as a tree.
Joyfully the crickets croon
Under shady oak at noon;
Beetle, on his mission bent,
Tarries in that cooling tent.
Let me also cheer a spot,
Hidden field or garden grot—
Place where passing souls can rest
On the way and be their best.

## NAVAHO PRAYER [3]

*Edward S. Yeomans*

Lord of the Mountain
Reared within the Mountain,
Young man, Chieftain,
Hear a young man's prayer!
Hear a prayer for cleanness.

[1] From John Keats, *Endymion*.
[2] From Edwin Markham, *The Man with the Hoe, and Other Poems*.
[3] From Edward S. Yeomans, *Shackled Youth*.

Keeper of the strong rain,
Drumming on the mountain;
Lord of the small rain,
That restores the earth in newness;
Keeper of the clean rain,
Hear a prayer for wholeness.

Young man, Chieftain,
Hear a prayer for fleetness.
Keeper of the deer's way,
Reared among the eagles,
Clear my feet of slothness.
Keeper of the paths of men
Hear a prayer for straightness.
Hear a prayer for courage.
Lord of the thin peaks
Reared among the thunders,
Keeper of the headlands
Holding up the harvest,
Keeper of the strong rocks,
Hear a prayer for staunchness.

Young man, Chieftain,
Spirit of the Mountain!

## ABOU BEN ADHEM

*Leigh Hunt*

Abou Ben Adhem (may his tribe increase!)
Awoke one night from a deep dream of peace,
And saw, within the moonlight of his room,
Making it rich and like a lily in bloom,
An angel writing in a book of gold.
Exceeding peace had made Ben Adhem bold,
And to the Presence in the room he said,
"What writest thou?" The vision raised its head,
And, with a look made of all sweet accord,
Answered, "The names of those who love the Lord."
"And is mine one?" said Abou. "Nay, not so,"
Replied the angel. Abou spoke more low,
But cheerly still; and said, "I pray thee, then,
Write me as one that loves his fellowmen."
The Angel wrote, and vanished. The next night
It came again, with a great wakening light,
And showed the names whom love of God had blessed;
And lo! Ben Adhem's name led all the rest.

## THE LORD IS MY SHEPHERD

THE BIBLE: PSALM 23

The Lord is my shepherd;
I shall not want.

He maketh me to lie down in green pastures;
He leadeth me beside the still waters.

He restoreth my soul;
He leadeth me in the paths of righteousness for his name's sake.

Yea, though I walk through the valley of the shadow of death,
I will fear no evil;
For thou art with me;
Thy rod and thy staff, they comfort me.

Thou preparest a table before me in the presence of mine enemies;
Thou anointest my head with oil;
My cup runneth over.

Surely goodness and mercy shall follow me all the days of my life;
And I will dwell in the house of the Lord for ever.

## THANKSGIVING

THE BIBLE: PSALM 100

Make a joyful noise unto the Lord, all ye lands.
Serve the Lord with gladness;
Come before his presence with singing.

Know ye that the Lord he is God;
It is he that hath made us, and not we ourselves;
We are his people, and the sheep of his pasture.

Enter into his gates with thanksgiving,
And into his courts with praise;
Be thankful unto him, and bless his name.

For the Lord is good;
His mercy is everlasting;
And his truth endureth to all generations.

## A MERRY HEART

THE BIBLE: PROVERBS 15

A soft answer turneth away wrath;
But grievous words stir up anger.

A merry heart maketh a cheerful countenance;
But by sorrow of the heart the spirit is broken.

All the days of the afflicted are evil;
But he that is of a merry heart hath a continual feast.

Better is little with the fear of the Lord
Than great treasure and trouble therewith;

Better is a dinner of herbs where love is
Than a stalled ox and hatred therewith.

## CHARITY

THE BIBLE: I CORINTHIANS 13

Though I speak with the tongues of men and of angels,
And have not charity,
I am become as sounding brass or a tinkling cymbal.

And though I have the gift of prophecy,
And understand all mysteries and all knowledge,
And though I have all faith so that I could remove mountains,
And have not charity,
I am nothing.
And though I bestow all my goods to feed the poor,
And though I give my body to be burned,
And have not charity,
It profiteth me nothing.

Charity suffereth long and is kind;
Charity envieth not;
Charity vaunteth not itself, is not puffed up;
Doth not behave itself unseemly,
Seeketh not her own,
Is not easily provoked,
Thinketh no evil;
Rejoiceth not in iniquity but rejoiceth in the truth;
Beareth all things, believeth all things, hopeth all things, endureth all things.

Charity never faileth;
But whether there be prophecies, they shall fail;
Whether there be tongues, they shall cease;
Whether there be knowledge, it shall vanish away
For we know in part and we prophesy in part;
But when that which is perfect is come,
Then that which is in part shall be done away.

When I was a child, I spake as a child,
I understood as a child, I thought as a child;
But when I became a man, I put away childish things.
For now we see through a glass darkly,
But then face to face;
Now I know in part,
But then shall I know even as also I am known.

And now abideth faith, hope, charity—
These three,
But the greatest of these is charity.

## *Guideposts: Suggested Grades*

*Grade Two*

All Things Bright and Beautiful
Cradle Hymn

*Grade Three*

A Child's Grace
As Joseph Was A-Walking
The Lamb
The Lord Is My Shepherd

*Grade Four*

He Prayeth Best
The Old Woman of the Roads
Thanksgiving

*Grade Five*

Mother to Son
Song for a Little House
A Merry Heart

*Grade Six*

Primer Lesson
The House with Nobody in It

*Grade Seven*

A Thing of Beauty
A Prayer
Navaho Prayer

*Grade Eight*

Abou Ben Adhem
Charity

# Stories in Verse

## THE THREE LITTLE KITTENS

*Eliza Lee Follen*

Three little kittens lost their mittens;
And they began to cry,
"Oh, mother dear,
We very much fear
That we have lost our mittens."
"Lost your mittens!
You naughty kittens!
Then you shall have no pie!"
"Mee-ow, mee-ow, mee-ow."
"No, you shall have no pie."

The three little kittens found their mittens;
And they began to cry,
"Oh, mother dear,
See here, see here!
See, we have found our mittens!"
"Put on your mittens,
You silly kittens,
And you may have some pie."
"Purr-r, purr-r, purr-r,
Oh, let us have the pie!
Purr-r, purr-r, purr-r."

The three little kittens put on their mittens,
And soon ate up the pie;
"Oh, mother dear,
We greatly fear
That we have soiled our mittens!"
"Soiled your mittens!
You naughty kittens!"
Then they began to sigh,
"Mee-ow, mee-ow, mee-ow."
Then they began to sigh,
"Mee-ow, mee-ow, mee-ow."

The three little kittens washed their mittens,
And hung them out to dry;
"Oh, mother dear,
Do not you hear
That we have washed our mittens?"
"Washed your mittens!
Oh, you're good kittens!
But I smell a rat close by,
Hush, hush! Mee-ow, mee-ow."
"We smell a rat close by,
Mee-ow, mee-ow, mee-ow."

## A VISIT FROM MR. FOX

*Old Folk Rhyme*

The Fox set out in hungry plight,
And begged the moon to give him light,
For he'd many a mile to travel that night,
Before he could reach his den, O!

First he came to a farmer's yard,
Where the ducks and geese declared it was hard
That their nerves should be shaken, and their rest be marred
By a visit from Mr. Fox, O!

He seized the gray goose by the sleeve,
Says he, "Madam Gray Goose, by your leave,
I'll carry you off without reprieve,
And take you away to my den, O!"

He seized the gray duck by the neck,
And flung her over across his back,
While the old duck cried out, "Quack, quack, quack,"
With her legs dangling down behind, O!

Then old Mrs. Flipper Flapper jumped out of bed,
And out of the window she popped her head,
Crying, "John, John, John, the gray goose is gone,
And the Fox is off to his den, O!"

Then John went up to the top of the hill,
And he blew a blast both loud and shrill.
Says the Fox, "That is fine music, still
I'd rather be off to my den, O!"

So the Fox he hurried home to his den,
To his dear little foxes eight, nine, ten.
"We're in luck, here's a big fat duck
With her legs dangling down behind, O!"

The Fox sat down with his hungry wife,
And they made a good meal without fork or knife.
They never had a better time in all their life,
And the little ones picked the bones, O!

## HIAWATHA'S CHILDHOOD[1]

*Henry Wadsworth Longfellow*

By the shores of Gitche Gumee,
By the shining Big-Sea-Water,
Stood the wigwam of Nokomis,
Daughter of the Moon, Nokomis.
Dark behind it rose the forest,
Rose the black and gloomy pine-trees,
Rose the firs with cones upon them;
Bright before it beat the water,
Beat the clear and sunny water,
Beat the shining Big-Sea-Water.
There the wrinkled old Nokomis
Nursed the little Hiawatha,
Rocked him in his linden cradle,
Bedded soft in moss and rushes,
Safely bound with reindeer sinews;
Stilled his fretful wail by saying,
"Hush! the Naked Bear will hear thee!"
Lulled him into slumber, singing,
"Ewa-yea! my little owlet!
Who is this, that lights the wigwam?
With his great eyes lights the wigwam?
Ewa-yea! my little owlet!"
Many things Nokomis taught him
Of the stars that shine in heaven;
Showed him Ishkoodah, the comet,
Ishkoodah, with fiery tresses;
Showed the Death-Dance of the spirits,
Warriors with their plumes and war-clubs,
Flaring far away to northward
In the frosty nights of winter;
Showed the broad white road in heaven,
Pathway of the ghosts, the shadows,
Running straight across the heavens,
Crowded with the ghosts, the shadows.
At the door on summer evenings,
Sat the little Hiawatha;
Heard the whispering of the pine-trees,
Heard the lapping of the waters,
Sounds of music, words of wonder;
"Minne-wawa!" said the pine-trees,
"Mudway-aushka!" said the water.
Saw the fire-fly, Wah-wah-taysee,
Flitting through the dusk of evening,
With the twinkle of its candle
Lighting up the brakes and bushes,
And he sang the song of children,
Sang the song Nokomis taught him:
"Wah-wah-taysee, little fire-fly,
Little, flitting, white-fire insect,
Little, dancing, white-fire creature,
Light me with your little candle,
Ere upon my bed I lay me,
Ere in sleep I close my eyelids!"
Saw the moon rise from the water,

[1] From Henry Wadsworth Longfellow, *The Song of Hiawatha.*

Rippling, rounding from the water,
Saw the flecks and shadows on it,
Whispered, "What is that, Nokomis?"
And the good Nokomis answered:
"Once a warrior, very angry,
Seized his grandmother, and threw her
Up into the sky at midnight;
Right against the moon he threw her;
'Tis her body that you see there."
Saw the rainbow in the heaven,
In the eastern sky, the rainbow,
Whispered, "What is that, Nokomis?"
And the good Nokomis answered:
"'Tis the heaven of flowers you see there;
All the wild-flowers of the forest,
All the lilies of the prairie,
When on earth they fade and perish,
Blossom in that heaven above us."
When he heard the owls at midnight,
Hooting, laughing in the forest,
"What is that?" he cried in terror;
"What is that," he said, "Nokomis?"
And the good Nokomis answered:
"That is but the owl and owlet,
Talking in their native language,
Talking, scolding at each other."
Then the little Hiawatha
Learned of every bird its language,
Learned their names and all their secrets,
How they built their nests in summer,
Where they hid themselves in winter,
Talked with them whene'er he met them,
Called them "Hiawatha's Chickens."
Of all beasts he learnéd the language,
Learned their names and all their secrets,
How the beavers built their lodges,
Where the squirrels hid their acorns,
How the reindeer ran so swiftly,
Why the rabbit was so timid,
Talked with them whene'er he met them,
Called them "Hiawatha's Brothers."

## THE LEAK IN THE DIKE

*Phoebe Cary*

The good dame looked from her cottage
At the close of the pleasant day,
And cheerily called to her little son
Outside the door at play:
"Come, Peter, come! I want you to go,
While there is light to see,
To the hut of the blind old man who lives
Across the dike, for me,
And take these cakes I made for him—
They are hot and smoking yet;
You have time enough to go and come
Before the sun is set."

Then the good wife turned to her labor,
Humming a simple song,
And thought of her husband, working hard
At the sluices all day long;
And set the turf a-blazing,
And brought the coarse black bread,
That he might find a fire at night,
And find the table spread.

And Peter left the brother
With whom all day he had played,
And the sister who had watched their sports
In the willow's tender shade,
And told them they'd see him back before
They saw a star in sight,
Though he wouldn't be afraid to go
In the very darkest night!

For he was a brave, bright fellow,
With eye and conscience clear;
He could do whatever a boy might do,
And he had not learned to fear.
Why, he wouldn't have robbed a bird's nest,
Nor brought a stork to harm,
Though never a law in Holland
Had stood to stay his arm!

And now, with his face all glowing
And eyes as bright as the day
With the thoughts of his pleasant errand,
He trudged along the way,
And soon his joyous prattle
Made glad a lonesome place—
Alas! if only the blind old man
Could have seen that happy face!
Yet he somehow caught the brightness
Which his voice and presence lent,
And he felt the sunshine come and go
As Peter came and went.

And now, as the day was sinking,
  And the winds began to rise,
The mother looked from her door again,
  Shading her anxious eyes;
And saw the shadows deepen
  And birds to their homes come back,
But never a sign of Peter
  Along the level track.
But she said: "He will come at morning,
  So I need not fret or grieve—
Though it isn't like my boy at all
  To stay without my leave."

But where was the child delaying?
  On the homeward way was he,
And across the dike while the sun was up
  An hour above the sea.
He was stopping now to gather flowers,
  Now listening to the sound
As the angry waters dashed themselves
  Against their narrow bound.
"Ah! well for us," said Peter,
  "That the gates are good and strong,
And my father tends them carefully,
  Or they would not hold you long!
You're a wicked sea," said Peter;
  "I know why you fret and chafe,
You would like to spoil our lands and
    homes;
  But our sluices keep you safe!"

But hark! Through the noise of waters
  Comes a low, clear, trickling sound;
And the child's face pales with terror,
  And his blossoms drop to the ground.
He is up the bank in a moment,
  And stealing through the sand
He sees a stream not yet so large
  As his slender, childish hand.
*'Tis a leak in the dike!* He is but a boy,
  Unused to fearful scenes;
But, young as he is, he has learned to know
  The dreadful thing that means.
*A leak in the dike!* The stoutest heart
  Grows faint that cry to hear,
And the bravest man in all the land
  Turns white with mortal fear.
For he knows the smallest leak may grow
  To a flood in a single night,
And he knows the strength of the cruel sea
  When loosed in its angry might.

And the boy! He has seen the danger,
  And, shouting a wild alarm,
He forces back the weight of the sea
  With the strength of his single arm!
He listens for the joyful sound
  Of a footstep passing nigh,
And lays his ear to the ground, to catch
  The answer to his cry.
And he hears the rough winds blowing,
  And the waters rise and fall,
But never an answer comes to him
  Save the echo of his call.
He sees no hope, no succor,
  His feeble voice is lost,
Yet what shall he do but watch and wait,
  Though he perish at his post!

So, faintly calling and crying
  Till the sun is under the sea,
Crying and moaning till the stars
  Come out for company,
He thinks of his brother and sister
  Asleep in their safe warm bed,
He thinks of his father and mother,
  Of himself as dying—and dead,
And of how, when the night is over,
  They must come and find him at last,
But he never thinks he can leave the place
  Where duty holds him fast.

The good dame in the cottage
  Is up and astir with the light,
For the thought of her little Peter
  Has been with her all night.
And now she watches the pathway,
  As yester eve she had done;
But what does she see so strange and black
  Against the rising sun?
Her neighbors are bearing between them
  Something straight to her door;
Her child is coming home, but not
  As he ever came before!

"He is dead!" she cries; "My darling!"
  And the startled father hears,
And comes and looks the way she looks,
  And fears the thing she fears;

Till a glad shout from the bearers
  Thrills the stricken man and wife—
"Give thanks, for your son has saved our land,
  And God has saved his life!"
So, there in the morning sunshine
  They knelt about the boy,
And every head was bared and bent
  In tearful, reverent joy.

'Tis many a year since then; but still,
  When the sea roars like a flood,
Their boys are taught what a boy can do
  Who is brave and true and good.
For every man in that country
  Takes his son by the hand,
And tells him of little Peter,
  Whose courage saved the land.

They have many a valiant hero,
  Remembered through the years,
But never one whose name so oft
  Is named with loving tears.
And his deed shall be sung by the cradles
  And told to the child on the knee,
So long as the dikes of Holland
  Divide the land from the sea!

## THE RAGGLE, TAGGLE GYPSIES

*Old Folk Song*

There were three gypsies a-come to my door,
  And downstairs ran this lady, O.
One sang high and another sang low,
  And the other sang "Bonnie, Bonnie Biskay, O."

Then she pulled off her silken gown,
  And put on hose of leather, O.
With the ragged, ragged rags about her door
  She's off with the Raggle, Taggle Gypsies, O.

'Twas late last night when my lord came home,
  Inquiring for his lady, O.
The servants said on every hand,
  "She's gone with the Raggle, Taggle, Gypsies, O."

"Oh, saddle for me my milk-white steed,
  Oh, saddle for me my pony, O,
That I may ride and seek my bride
  Who's gone with the Raggle, Taggle Gypsies, O."

Oh, he rode high and he rode low,
  He rode through woods and copses, O,
Until he came to an open field,
  And there he espied his lady, O.

"What makes you leave your house and lands?
  What makes you leave your money, O?
What makes you leave your new-wedded lord
  To go with the Raggle, Taggle Gypsies, O?"

"What care I for my house and lands?
  What care I for my money, O?
What care I for my new-wedded lord?
  I'm off with the Raggle, Taggle Gypsies, O."

"Last night you slept on a goose-feather bed,
  With the sheet turned down so bravely, O.
Tonight you will sleep in the cold, open field,
  Along with the Raggle, Taggle Gypsies, O."

"What care I for your goose-feather bed,
  With the sheet turned down so bravely, O?
For tonight I shall sleep in a cold, open field,
  Along with the Raggle, Taggle Gypsies, O."

## KING BRUCE AND THE SPIDER

*Eliza Cook*

King Bruce of Scotland flung himself down
  In a lonely mood to think;
'Tis true he was monarch, and wore a crown,
  But his heart was beginning to sink.

For he had been trying to do a great deed,
  To make his people glad;
He had tried and tried, but couldn't succeed;
  And so he became quite sad.

He flung himself down in low despair,
  As grieved as man could be;
And after a while as he pondered there,
  "I'll give it all up," said he.

Now, just at that moment, a spider dropped,
  With its silken, filmy clue;
And the King, in the midst of his thinking, stopped
  To see what the spider would do.

'Twas a long way up to the ceiling dome,
  And it hung by a rope so fine,
That how it would get to its cobweb home
  King Bruce could not divine.

It soon began to cling and crawl
  Straight up, with strong endeavor;
But down it came with a slippery sprawl,
  As near to the ground as ever.

Up, up it ran, not a second to stay
  To utter the least complaint,
Till it fell still lower, and there it lay,
  A little dizzy and faint.

Its head grew steady—again it went,
  And traveled a half yard higher;
'Twas a delicate thread it had to tread,
  And a road where its feet would tire.

Again it fell and swung below,
  But again it quickly mounted;
Till up and down, now fast, now slow,
  Nine brave attempts were counted.

"Sure," cried the King, "that foolish thing
  Will strive no more to climb;
When it toils so hard to reach and cling,
  And tumbles every time."

But up the insect went once more;
  Ah me! 'tis an anxious minute;
He's only a foot from his cobweb door,
  Oh, say, will he lose or win it?

Steadily, steadily, inch by inch,
  Higher and higher he got;
And a bold little run at the very last pinch
  Put him into his native cot.

"Bravo, bravo!" the King cried out;
  "All honor to those who *try;*
The spider up there, defied despair;
  He conquered, and why shouldn't I?"

And Bruce of Scotland braced his mind,
  And gossips tell the tale,
That he tried once more as he tried before,
  And that time did not fail.

## HOW THEY BROUGHT THE GOOD NEWS FROM GHENT TO AIX

*Robert Browning*

I sprang to the stirrup, and Joris, and he;
I galloped, Dirck galloped, we galloped all three;
"Good speed!" cried the watch, as the gatebolts undrew;
"Speed!" echoed the wall to us galloping through;
Behind shut the postern, the lights sank to rest,
And into the midnight we galloped abreast.

Not a word to each other; we kept the great pace
Neck by neck, stride by stride, never changing our place;
I turned in my saddle and made its girths tight,
Then shortened each stirrup, and set the pique right,
Rebuckled the cheek strap, chained slacker the bit,
Nor galloped less steadily Roland a whit.

'Twas moonset at starting; but while we drew near
Lokeren, the cocks crew and twilight dawned clear;
At Boom, a great yellow star came out to see;
At Düffeld, 'twas morning as plain as could be;
And from Mecheln church steeple we heard the half-chime,
So Joris broke silence with, "Yet there is time!"

At Aershot, up leaped of a sudden the sun,
And against him the cattle stood black every one,
To stare through the mist at us galloping past,
And I saw my stout galloper Roland at last,
With resolute shoulders, each butting away
The haze, as some bluff river headland its spray;

And his low head and crest, just one sharp ear bent back
For my voice, and the other pricked out on his track;
And one eye's black intelligence—ever that glance
O'er its white edge at me, his own master, askance!
And the thick heavy spume-flakes which aye and anon
His fierce lips shook upwards in galloping on.

By Hasselt, Dirck groaned; and cried Joris, "Stay spur!
Your Roos galloped bravely, the fault's not in her,
We'll remember at Aix"—for one heard the quick wheeze
Of her chest, saw the stretched neck and staggering knees,
And sunk tail, and horrible heave of the flank,
As down on her haunches she shuddered and sank.

So, we were left galloping, Joris and I,
Past Looz and past Tongres, no cloud in the sky;
The broad sun above laughed a pitiless laugh,
'Neath our feet broke the brittle bright stubble like chaff;
Till over by Dalhem a dome spire sprang white,
And "Gallop," gasped Joris, "for Aix is in sight!"

"How they'll greet us!"—and all in a moment his roan
Rolled neck and croup over, lay dead as a stone;
And there was my Roland to bear the whole weight
Of the news which alone could save Aix from her fate,
With his nostrils like pits full of blood to the brim,
And with circles of red for his eye sockets' rim.

Then I cast loose my buffcoat, each holster let fall,
Shook off both my jack boots, let go belt and all,
Stood up in the stirrup, leaned, patted his ear,
Called my Roland his pet name, my horse without peer;
Clapped my hands, laughed and sang, any noise, bad or good,
Till at length into Aix Roland galloped and stood.

And all I remember is—friends flocking round
As I sat with his head 'twixt my knees on the ground;
And no voice but was praising this Roland of mine,
As I poured down his throat our last measure of wine,
Which (the burgesses voted by common consent)
Was no more than his due who brought good news from Ghent.

## THE BLIND MEN AND THE ELEPHANT

*John Godfrey Saxe*

It was six men of Indostan,
To learning much inclined,
Who went to see the Elephant
(Though all of them were blind),
That each by observation
Might satisfy his mind.

The *First* approached the Elephant,
And happening to fall
Against his broad and sturdy side,
At once began to bawl:
"God bless me! but the Elephant
Is very like a wall!"

The *Second,* feeling of the tusk,
Cried, "Ho! what have we here
So very round and smooth and sharp?
To me 'tis mighty clear
This wonder of an Elephant
Is very like a spear!"

The *Third* approached the animal,
And happening to take
The squirming trunk within his hands,
Thus boldly up and spake:
"I see," quoth he, "the Elephant
Is very like a snake!"

The *Fourth* reached out his eager hand,
And felt about the knee.
"What most this wondrous beast is like,
Is mighty plain," quoth he;
" 'Tis clear enough the Elephant
Is very like a tree!"

The *Fifth,* who chanced to touch the ear,
Said: "E'en the blindest man
Can tell what this resembles most;
Deny the fact who can,
This marvel of an Elephant
Is very like a fan!"

The *Sixth* no sooner had begun
About the beast to grope,
Than, seizing on the swinging tail
That fell within his scope,
"I see," quoth he, "the Elephant
Is very like a rope!"

And so these men of Indostan
Disputed loud and long,
Each in his own opinion
Exceeding stiff and strong,
Though each was partly in the right,
And all were in the wrong!

## THE BATTLE OF BLENHEIM

*Robert Southey*

It was a summer's evening,
Old Kaspar's work was done,
And he before his cottage door
Was sitting in the sun;
And by him sported on the green
His little grandchild Wilhelmine.

She saw her brother Peterkin
Roll something large and round,
Which he, beside the rivulet,
In playing there, had found.
He came to ask what he had found,
That was so large, and smooth, and round.

Old Kaspar took it from the boy,
Who stood expectant by;
And then the old man shook his head,
And, with a natural sigh,
" 'Tis some poor fellow's skull," said he,
"Who fell in the great victory!

"I find them in the garden,
For there's many here about;
And often when I go to plough,
The ploughshare turns them out;
For many thousand men," said he,
"Were slain in that great victory!"

"Now tell us what 'twas all about,"
Young Peterkin he cries;
And little Wilhelmine looks up
With wonder-waiting eyes;
"Now tell us all about the war,
And what they fought each other for."

"It was the English," Kaspar cried,
"Who put the French to rout;
But what they fought each other for
I could not well make out;
But everybody said," quoth he,
"That 'twas a famous victory!

"My father lived at Blenheim then,
  Yon little stream hard by.
They burned his dwelling to the ground,
  And he was forced to fly;
So with his wife and child he fled,
Nor had he where to rest his head.

"With fire and sword the country round
  Was wasted far and wide;
And many a childing mother then
  And new-born baby died.
But things like that, you know, must be
At every famous victory.

"They say it was a shocking sight
  After the field was won;
For many thousand bodies here
  Lay rotting in the sun.
But things like that, you know, must be
After a famous victory.

"Great praise the Duke of Marlbro' won,
  And our good Prince Eugene."
"Why, 'twas a very wicked thing!"
  Said little Wilhelmine.
"Nay, nay, my little girl," quoth he,
"It was a famous victory!

"And everybody praised the Duke
  Who this great fight did win."
"But what good came of it at last?"
  Quoth little Peterkin.
"Why that I cannot tell," said he,
"But 'twas a famous victory."

## THREE KINGS CAME RIDING

*Henry Wadsworth Longfellow*

Three Kings came riding from far away,
  Melchoir and Gaspar and Baltasar;
Three Wise Men out of the East were they,
And they travelled by night and they slept by day,
  For their guide was a beautiful, wonderful star.

The star was so beautiful, large, and clear,
  That all the other stars of the sky
Became a white mist in the atmosphere,
And by this they knew that the coming was near
  Of the Prince foretold in the prophecy.

Three caskets they bore on their saddle-bows,
  Three caskets of gold with golden keys;
Their robes were of crimson silk with rows
Of bells and pomegranates and furbelows,
  Their turbans like blossoming almond-trees.

And so the Three Kings rode into the West,
  Through the dusk of night, over hill and dell,
And sometimes they nodded with head on breast,
And sometimes talked, as they paused to rest,
  With the people they met at some wayside well.

"Of the child that is born," said Baltasar,
  "Good people, I pray you, tell us the news;
For we in the East have seen his star,
And have ridden fast, and have ridden far,
  To find and worship the King of the Jews."

And the people answered, "You ask in vain;
  We know of no king but Herod the Great!"
They thought the Wise Men were men insane,
As they spurred their horses across the plain,
  Like riders in haste, and who cannot wait.

And when they came to Jerusalem,
  Herod the Great, who had heard this thing,
Sent for the Wise Men and questioned them;
And said, "Go down unto Bethlehem,
  And bring me tidings of this new king."

So they rode away; and the star stood still,
The only one in the gray of morn;
Yes, it stopped—it stood still of its own free will,
Right over Bethlehem on the hill,
The city of David, where Christ was born.

And the Three Kings rode through the gate and the guard,
Through the silent street, till their horses turned
And neighed as they entered the great inn yard;
But the windows were closed, and the doors were barred,
And only a light in the stable burned.

And cradled there in the scented hay,
In the air made sweet by the breath of kine,
The little child in the manger lay,
The child, that would be king one day
Of a kingdom not human but divine.

His mother Mary of Nazareth
Sat watching beside his place of rest,
Watching the even flow of his breath,
For the joy of life and the terror of death
Were mingled together in her breast.

They laid their offerings at his feet:
The gold was their tribute to a King,
The frankincense, with its odor sweet,
Was for the Priest, the Paraclete,
The myrrh for the body's burying.

And the mother wondered and bowed her head,
And sat as still as a statue of stone;
Her heart was troubled, yet comforted,
Remembering what the angel had said
Of an endless reign and of David's throne.

Then the Kings rode out of the city gate,
With a clatter of hoofs in proud array;
But they went not back to Herod the Great,
For they knew his malice and feared his hate,
And returned to their homes by another way.

## HIAWATHA'S CANOE [1]

*Henry Wadsworth Longfellow*

"Give me of your bark, O Birch-Tree!
Of your yellow bark, O Birch-Tree!
Growing by the rushing river,
Tall and stately in the valley!
I a light canoe will build me,
Build a swift Cheemaun for sailing,
That shall float upon the river,
Like a yellow leaf in Autumn,
Like a yellow water lily!
"Lay aside your cloak, O Birch-Tree!
Lay aside your white-skin wrapper,
For the Summertime is coming,
And the sun is warm in heaven,
And you need no white-skin wrapper!"
Thus aloud cried Hiawatha
In the solitary forest,
By the rushing Taqaumenaw,
While the birds were singing gayly,
In the Moon of Leaves were singing;
And the sun, from sleep awaking,
Started up and said, "Behold me!
Geezis, the great Sun, behold me!"
And the tree with all its branches
Rustled in the breeze of morning,
Saying, with a sigh of patience,
"Take my cloak, O Hiawatha!"
With his knife the tree he girdled;
Just beneath its lowest branches,
Just above the roots, he cut it,
Till the sap came oozing outward;
Down the trunk from top to bottom,
Sheer he cleft the bark asunder,
With a wooden wedge he raised it,
Stripped it from the trunk unbroken.
"Give me of your boughs, O Cedar!
Of your strong and pliant branches,
My canoe to make more steady,
Make more strong and firm beneath me!"
Through the summit of the Cedar
Went a sound, a cry of horror,
Went a murmur of resistance;
But it whispered, bending downward,
"Take my boughs, O Hiawatha!"

[1] From Henry Wadsworth Longfellow, *The Song of Hiawatha.*

Down he hewed the boughs of Cedar,
Shaped them straightway to a framework,
Like two bows he formed and shaped them,
Like two bended bows together.
"Give me of your roots, O Tamarack!
Of your fibrous roots, O Larch-Tree!
My canoe to bind together,
So to bind the ends together
That the water may not enter,
That the river may not wet me!"
And the Larch, with all its fibres,
Shivered in the air of morning,
Touched his forehead with its tassels,
Said, with one long sigh of sorrow,
"Take them all, O Hiawatha!"
From the earth he tore the fibres,
Tore the tough roots of the Larch-Tree,
Closely sewed the bark together,
Bound it closely to the framework.
"Give me of your balm, O Fir-Tree!
Of your balsam and your resin,
So to close the seams together
That the water may not enter,
That the river may not wet me!"
And the Fir-Tree, tall and sombre,
Sobbed through all its robes of darkness,
Rattled like a shore with pebbles,
Answered wailing, answered weeping,
"Take my balm, O Hiawatha!"
And he took the tears of balsam,
Took the resin of the Fir-Tree,
Smeared therewith each seam and fissure,
Made each crevice safe from water.
"Give me of your quills, O Hedgehog!
All your quills, O Kagh, the Hedgehog!
I will make a necklace of them,
Make a girdle for my beauty,
And two stars to deck her bosom!"
From the hollow tree the Hedgehog
With his sleepy eyes looked at him,
Shot his shining quills, like arrows,
Saying, with a drowsy murmur,
Through the tangle of his whiskers,
"Take my quills, O Hiawatha!"
From the ground the quills he gathered,
All the little shining arrows,
Stained them red and blue and yellow,
With the juice of roots and berries;
Into his canoe he wrought them,
Round its waist a shining girdle,
Round its bows a gleaming necklace,
On its breast two stars resplendent.
Thus the Birch Canoe was builded
In the valley, by the river,
In the bosom of the forest;
And the forest's life was in it,
All its mystery and its magic,
All the lightness of the birch-tree,
All the toughness of the cedar,
All the larch's supple sinews;
And it floated on the river
Like a yellow leaf in Autumn,
Like a yellow water lily.

## ROBIN HOOD AND THE RANGER

*Old Ballad*

When Phoebus had melted the sickles of ice,
And likewise the mountains of snow,
Bold Robin Hood he would ramble to see,
To frolic abroad with his bow.

He left all his merry men waiting behind,
Whilst through the green valleys he passed;
There did he behold a forester bold,
Who cried out, "Friend, whither so fast?"

"I'm going," quoth Robin, "to kill a fat buck,
For me and my merry men all;
Besides, e'er I go, I'll have a fat doe,
Or else it shall cost me a fall."

"You'd best have a care," said the forester then,
"For these are His Majesty's deer;
Before you shall shoot the thing I'll dispute,
For I am head-forester here."

"These thirteen long summers," quoth Robin, "I'm sure,
My arrows I here have let fly,
Where freely I range; methinks it is strange,
You should have more power than I."

"This forest," quoth Robin, "I think is my own,
And so are the nimble deer, too;
Therefore I declare, and solemnly swear,
I won't be affronted by you."

The forester he had a long quarter-staff,
Likewise a broad sword by his side;
Without more ado, he presently drew,
Declaring the truth should be tried.

Bold Robin Hood had a sword of the best,
Thus, e'er he would take any wrong,
His courage was flush, he'd venture a brush,
And thus they fell to it ding-dong.

The very first blow that the forester gave,
He made his broad weapon cry twang;
'Twas over the head, he fell down for dead,
O, that was a terrible bang!

But Robin he soon did recover himself,
And bravely fell to it again;
The very next stroke their weapons were broke,
Yet never a man there was slain.

At quarter-staff then they resolved to play,
Because they would have t'other bout;
And brave Robin Hood right valiantly stood,
Unwilling he was to give out.

Bold Robin he gave him very hard blows,
The other returned them as fast;
At every stroke their jackets did smoke,
Three hours the combat did last.

At length in a rage the bold forester grew,
And cudgeled bold Robin so sore
That he could not stand, so shaking his hand,
He said, "Let us freely give o'er."

"Thou art a brave fellow, I needs must confess
I never knew any so good;
Thou'rt fitting to be a yeoman for me,
And range in the merry green wood.

"I'll give thee this ring as a token of love,
For bravely thou'st acted thy part;
That man that can fight, in him I delight,
And love him with all my whole heart."

Then Robin Hood setting his horn to his mouth,
A blast he merrily blows;
His yeomen did hear and straight did appear,
A hundred with trusty long bows.

Now Little John came at the head of them all,
Clothed in a rich mantle of green;
And likewise the rest were gloriously drest,
A right gallant sight to be seen.

"Lo, these are my yeomen," said Robin Hood,
"And thou shalt be one of the train;
A mantle and bow, a quiver also,
I give them whom I entertain."

The forester willingly entered the list,
They were such a beautiful sight;
Then with a long bow they shot a fat doe,
And made a rich supper that night.

What singing and dancing was in the green wood,
For joy of another new mate!
With mirth and delight they spent the long night,
And lived at a plentiful rate.

Then Robin Hood gave him a mantle of green,
Broad arrows and a very long bow;
This done, the next day, so gallant and gay,
He marched them all in a row.

Quoth he, "My brave yeomen, be true to your trust,
And then we may range the woods wide";
They all did declare and solemnly swear,
They'd conquer, or die by his side.

## ROBIN HOOD AND LITTLE JOHN

*Old Ballad*

When Robin Hood was about twenty years old,
*With a hey down, down, and a down;*
He happened to meet Little John,
A jolly, brisk blade, right fit for the trade,
For he was a lusty young man.

Though he was called Little, his limbs they were large,
And his stature was seven foot high;
Wherever he came, they quaked at his name,
For soon he would make them fly.

How they came acquainted, I'll tell you in brief,
If you would but listen awhile;
For this very jest, among all the rest,
I think it may cause you to smile.

They happened to meet on a long, narrow bridge,
And neither of them would give way;
Quoth bold Robin Hood, and sturdily stood,
"I'll show you right Nottingham play."

"Thou talkest like a coward," the stranger replied;
"Well armed with a long bow you stand,
To shoot at my breast, while I, I protest.
Have naught but a staff in my hand."

"The name of a coward," quoth Robin, "I scorn,
Wherefore my long bow I'll lay by,
And now, for thy sake, a staff will I take,
The truth of thy manhood to try."

Then Robin stept to a thicket of trees,
And chose him a staff of ground oak;
Now this being done, away he did run
To the stranger, and merrily spoke:

"Lo! see my staff is lusty and tough,
Now here on the bridge we will play;
Whoever falls in, the other shall win
The battle, and so we'll away."

"With all my whole heart," the stranger replied;
"I scorn in the least to give out";
This said, they fell to't without more dispute,
And their staffs they did flourish about.

At first Robin he gave the stranger a bang,
So hard that he made his bones ring;
The stranger he said, "This must be repaid,
I'll give you as good as you bring.

"So long as I am able to handle a staff,
To die in your debt, friend, I scorn."
Then to it each goes, and followed their blows,
As if they had been threshing of corn.

The stranger gave Robin a crack on the crown,
Which caused the blood to appear;
Then Robin, enraged, more fiercely engaged,
And followed his blows more severe.

So thick and so fast did he lay it on him,
With a passionate fury and ire;
At every stroke he made him to smoke,
As if he had been all on fire.

O, then into fury the stranger he grew,
And gave him a furious look,
And with it a blow, that laid him full low,
And tumbled him into the brook.

"I prithee, good fellow, where art thou now?"
The stranger, in laughter, he cried.
Quoth bold Robin Hood, "Good faith, in the flood,
And floating along with the tide.

"I needs must acknowledge thou art a brave soul,
With thee I'll no longer contend;
For needs must I say, thou hast got the day,
Our battle shall be at an end."

Then unto the bank he did presently wade,
And pulled himself out by a thorn;
Which done, at the last he blew a loud blast
Straightway on his fine bugle horn;

The echo of which through the valleys did fly,
At which his stout bowmen appeared,
All clothed in green, most gay to be seen,
So up to their master they steered.

"O, what is the matter?" quoth William Stutly,
"Good master, you are wet to the skin."
"No matter," quoth he, "the lad which you see
In fighting hath tumbled me in."

"He shall not go scot free," the others replied.
So straightway they were seizing him there,
To duck him likewise; but Robin Hood cries,
"He is a stout fellow, forbear.

"There's no one shall wrong thee, friend, be not afraid;
These bowmen upon me do wait;
There's three score and nine; if thou wilt be mine,
Thou shalt have my livery straight,

"And other accouterments fit for a man;
Speak up, jolly blade, never fear;
I'll teach you also the use of the bow,
To shoot at the fat fallow deer."

"O, here is my hand," the stranger replied,
"I'll serve you with all my whole heart;
My name is John Little, a man of good mettle;
Ne'er doubt me, for I'll play my part."

"His name shall be altered," quoth William Stutly,
"And I will his godfather be;
Prepare, then, a feast, and none of the least,
For we will be merry," quoth he.

He was, I must tell you, but seven foot high
And may be an ell in the waist—
A sweet pretty lad; much feasting they had;
Bold Robin the christening graced,

With all his bowmen, which stood in a ring,
And were of the Nottingham breed;
Brave Stutly came then, with seven yeomen,
And did in this manner proceed:

"This infant was called John Little," quoth he;
"Which name shall be changed anon;
The words we'll transpose, so wherever he goes,
His name shall be called Little John."

Then Robin took the pretty sweet babe,
And clothed him from top to toe,
In garments of green, most gay to be seen,
And gave him a curious long bow.

"Thou shalt be an archer as well as the best,
And range in the green wood with us;
Where we'll not want gold nor silver, behold,
While others have aught in their purse."

Then music and dancing did finish the day;
At length, when the sun waxed low,
Then all the whole train the grove did refrain,
And unto their caves they did go.

And so, ever after, as long as he lived,
Although he was proper and tall,
Yet, nevertheless, the truth to express,
Still Little John they did him call.

## ROBIN HOOD AND ALLEN-A-DALE

*Old Ballad*

Come listen to me, you gallants so free,
All you that love mirth for to hear,
And I will tell you of a bold outlaw,
That lived in Nottinghamshire.

As Robin Hood in the forest stood,
All under the greenwood tree,
There was he ware of a brave young man,
As fine as fine might be.

The youngster was clothed in scarlet red,
In scarlet fine and gay,
And he did frisk it over the plain,
And chanted a roundelay.

As Robin Hood next morning stood,
Amongst the leaves so gay,
There did he spy the same young man
Come drooping along the way.

The scarlet he wore the day before,
It was clean cast away;
And every step he fetched a sigh,
"Alack! and well-a-day!"

Then stepped forth brave Little John,
And Nick, the miller's son,
Which made the young man bend his bow,
When as he saw them come.

"Stand off! stand off!" the young man said;
"What is your will with me?"
"You must come before our master straight
Under yon greenwood tree."

And when he came bold Robin before,
Robin asked him courteously,
"O, hast thou any money to spare
For my merry men and me?"

"I have no money," the young man said,
"But five shillings and a ring;
And that I have kept this seven long years,
To have it at my wedding.

"Yesterday I should have married a maid,
But she is now from me ta'en,
And chosen to be an old knight's delight,
Whereby my poor heart is slain."

"What is thy name?" then said Robin Hood;
"Come tell me without any fail."
"By the faith of my body," then said the young man,
"My name it is Allen-a-Dale."

"What wilt thou give me," said Robin Hood,
"In ready gold or fee,
To help thee to thy truelove again,
And deliver her unto thee?"

"I have no money," then quoth the young man,
"No ready gold nor fee,
But I will swear upon a book
Thy true servant for to be."

"How many miles is it to thy truelove?
Come tell me without any guile."
"By the faith of my body," then said the young man,
"It is but five little mile."

Then Robin he hasted over the plain,
He did neither stint nor lin,
Until he came unto the church
Where Allen should keep his wedding.

"What dost thou here?" the bishop he said,
"I prithee now tell to me."
"I am a bold harper," quoth Robin Hood,
"And the best in the north country."

"O, welcome, O, welcome," the bishop he said,
"That music best pleaseth me."
"You shall have no music," quoth Robin Hood,
"Till the bride and bridegroom I see."

With that came in a wealthy knight,
Which was both grave and old,
And after him a finikin lass,
Did shine like glistering gold.

"This is no fit match," quoth bold Robin Hood,
"That you do seem to make here;
But since we are come unto the church,
The bride she shall choose her own dear."

Then Robin Hood put his horn to his mouth,
And blew blasts two or three;
When four and twenty bowmen bold
Came leaping over the lea.

And when they came into the churchyard,
 Marching all in a row,
The first man was Allen-a-Dale,
 To give bold Robin his bow.

"This is thy truelove," Robin he said,
 "Young Allen, as I hear say;
And you shall be married at this same time,
 Before we depart away."

"That shall not be," the bishop he said,
 "For thy word shall not stand;
They shall be three times asked in the church,
 As the law is of our land."

Robin Hood pulled off the bishop's coat,
 And put it upon Little John;
"By the faith of my body," then Robin said,
 "This cloth doth make thee a man."

When Little John went into the choir,
 The people began for to laugh;
He asked them seven times in the church,
 Lest three times should not be enough.

"Who gives me this maid?" then said Little John;
 Quoth Robin, "That do I,
And he that doth take her from Allen-a-Dale
 Full dearly he shall her buy."

And thus having ended this merry wedding,
 The bride looked as fresh as a queen,
And so they returned to the merry green wood,
 Amongst the leaves so green.

## MEG MERRILIES

*John Keats*

Old Meg she was a gypsy,
 And lived upon the moors;
Her bed it was the brown heath turf,
 And her house was out of doors.

Her apples were sweet blackberries,
 Her currants pods o' broom;
Her wine was dew of the wild white rose,
 Her book a churchyard tomb.

Her brothers were the craggy hills,
 Her sisters larchen trees—
Alone with her great family
 She lived as she did please.

No breakfast had she many a morn,
 No dinner many a noon,
And 'stead of supper she would stare
 Full hard against the moon.

And every morn of woodbine fresh
 She made her garlanding,
And every night the dark glen yew
 She wove, and she would sing.

And with her fingers old and brown
 She plaited mats o' rushes,
And gave them to the cottagers
 She met among the bushes.

Old Meg was brave as Margaret Queen
 And tall as Amazon;
An old red blanket cloak she wore;
 A chip hat had she on.
God rest her aged bones somewhere—
 She died full long agone!

## THE DISCOVERER OF THE NORTH CAPE [1]

*Henry Wadsworth Longfellow*

Othere, the old sea-captain,
 Who dwelt in Helgoland,
To King Alfred, the Lover of Truth,
Brought a snow-white walrus tooth,
 Which he held in his brown right hand.

His figure was tall and stately,
 Like a boy's his eye appeared;
His hair was yellow as hay,
But threads of a silvery gray
 Gleamed in his tawny beard.

[1] From Henry Wadsworth Longfellow, *Birds of Passage.*

Hearty and hale was Othere,
  His cheek had the color of oak;
With a kind of a laugh in his speech,
Like the sea tide on a beach,
  As unto the King he spoke.

And Alfred, King of the Saxons,
  Had a book upon his knees,
And wrote down the wondrous tale
Of him who was first to sail
  Into the Arctic seas.

"So far I live to the northward,
  No man lives north of me;
To the east are wild mountain chains,
And beyond them meres and plains;
  To the westward all is sea.

"So far I live to the northward,
  From the harbor of Skeringes-hale,
If you only sailed by day,
With a fair wind all the way,
  More than a month would you sail.

"I own six hundred reindeer,
  With sheep and swine beside;
I have tribute from the Finns,
Whalebone and reindeer skins,
  And robes of walrus hide.

"I ploughed the land with horses,
  But my heart was ill at ease,
For the old seafaring men
Came to me now and then,
  With their sagas of the seas—

"Of Iceland and of Greenland,
  And the stormy Hebrides,
And the undiscovered deep—
Oh, I could not eat nor sleep
  For thinking of those seas.

"To the northward stretched the desert,
  How far I fain would know;
So at last I sallied forth,
And three days sailed due north,
  As far as the whale ships go.

"To the west of me was the ocean,
  To the right the desolate shore,
But I did not slacken sail
For the walrus or the whale,
  Till after three days more.

"The days grew longer and longer,
  Till they became as one,
And northward through the haze
I saw the sullen blaze
  Of the red midnight sun.

"And then uprose before me,
  Upon the water's edge,
The huge and haggard shape
Of that unknown North Cape,
  Whose form is like a wedge.

"The sea was rough and stormy,
  The tempest howled and wailed,
And the sea fog like a ghost,
Haunted that dreary coast,
  But onward still I sailed.

"Four days I steered to eastward,
  Four days without a night;
Round in a fiery ring
Went the great sun, O King,
  With the red and lurid light."

Here Alfred, King of the Saxons,
  Ceased writing for a while;
And raised his eyes from his book,
With a strange and puzzled look,
  And an incredulous smile.

But Othere, the old sea-captain,
  He neither paused nor stirred,
Till the King listened, and then
Once more took up his pen,
  And wrote down every word.

"And now the land," said Othere,
  "Bent southward suddenly,
And I followed the curving shore
And ever southward bore
  Into a nameless sea.

"And there we hunted the walrus,
  The narwhale, and the seal;
Ha! 'twas a noble game!
And like the lightning's flame
  Flew our harpoons of steel.

"There were six of us all together,
  Norsemen of Helgoland;
In two days and no more
We killed of them three score,
  And dragged them to the strand!"

Here Alfred the Truth-teller
  Suddenly closed his book,
And lifted his blue eyes,
With doubt and strange surmise
  Depicted in their look.

And Othere the old sea-captain
  Stared at him wild and weird,
Then smiled, till his shining teeth
Gleamed white from underneath
  His tawny, quivering beard.

And to the King of the Saxons,
  In witness of the truth,
Raising his noble head,
He stretched his brown hand, and said,
  "Behold this walrus tooth!"

## IN SCHOOL DAYS

*John Greenleaf Whittier*

Still sits the schoolhouse by the road,
  A ragged beggar sleeping;
Around it still the sumacs grow,
  And blackberry vines are creeping.

Within, the master's desk is seen,
  Deep scarred by raps official;
The warping floor, the battered seats,
  The jackknife's carved initial;

The charcoal frescoes on its wall;
  Its door's worn sill, betraying
The feet that, creeping slow to school,
  Went storming out to playing!

Long years ago a winter sun
  Shone over it at setting;
Lit up its western windowpanes,
  And low eaves' icy fretting.

It touched the tangled golden curls,
  And brown eyes full of grieving,
Of one who still her steps delayed
  When all the school were leaving.

For near her stood the little boy
  Her childish favor singled,
His cap pulled low upon a face
  Where pride and shame were mingled.

Pushing with restless feet the snow
  To right and left, he lingered;
As restlessly her tiny hands
  The blue-checked apron fingered.

He saw her lift her eyes; he felt
  The soft hand's light caressing;
And heard the tremble of her voice,
  As if a fault confessing,

"I'm sorry that I spelt the word;
  I hate to go above you,
Because,"—the brown eyes lower fell—
  "Because, you see, I love you!"

Still memory to a gray-haired man
  That sweet child-face is showing.
Dear girl! the grasses on her grave
  Have forty years been growing!

He lives to learn, in life's hard school,
  How few who pass above him
Lament their triumph and his loss,
  Like her—because they love him.

## THE COURTIN' [1]

*James Russell Lowell*

God makes sech nights, all white an' still
  Fur 'z you can look or listen,
Moonshine an' snow on field an' hill,
  All silence an' all glisten.

Zekle crep' up quite unbeknown
  An' peeked in thru' the winder,
An' there sot Huldy all alone,
  'ith no one nigh to hender.

A fireplace filled the room's one side
  With half a cord o' wood in—
There warn't no stoves (tell comfort died)
  To bake ye to a puddin'.

[1] From James Russell Lowell, *The Biglow Papers.*

The wa'nut logs shot sparkles out
  Towards the pootiest, bless her,
An' leetle flames danced all about
  The chiny on the dresser.

Agin the chimbley crook-necks hung,
  And in amongst 'em rusted
The ole queen's-arm thet granther Young
  Fetched back from Concord busted.

The very room, coz she was in,
  Seemed warm from floor to ceilin',
An' she looked full ez rosy agin
  Ez the apples she was peelin'.

Twas kin' o' kingdom-come to look
  On such a blessed cretur.
A dogrose blushin' to a brook
  Ain't modester nor sweeter.

He was six foot o' man, A 1,
  Clear grit an' human natur;
None couldn't quicker pitch a ton
  Nor dror a furrer straighter.

He'd sparked it with full twenty gals,
  He'd squired 'em, danced 'em, druv 'em,
Fust this one, and then that, by spells—
  All is, he couldn't love 'em.

But 'long o' her his veins 'ould run
  All crinkly like curled maple,
The side she breshed felt full o' sun
  Ez a south slope in Ap'il.

She thought no v'ice had sech a swing
  Ez his'n in the choir;
My! when he made Ole Hunderd ring,
  She *know'd* the Lord was nigher.

An' she'd blush scarlit, right in prayer,
  When her new meetin'-bunnet
Felt somehow thru' its crown a pair
  O' blue eyes sot upon it.

Thet night, I tell ye, she looked *some!*
  She seem'd to've got a new soul,
For she felt sartin-sure he'd come,
  Down to her very shoe-sole.

She heered a foot, an' knowed it too,
  A-raspin on the scraper—
All ways to once her feelins flew
  Like sparks in burnt-up paper.

He kin' o' l'itered on the mat,
  Some doubtfle o' the sekle,
His heart kep' goin' pity-pat,
  But hern went pity Zekle.

An' yit she gin her cheer a jerk
  Ez though she wished him furder,
An' on her apples kep' to work,
  Parin' away like murder.

"You want to see my Pa, I s'pose?"
  "Wal, no . . . I come dasignin' . . ."
"To see my Ma? She's sprinklin' clo'es
  Agin tomorrer's i'nin'."

To say why gals acts so or so,
  Or don't, 'ould be presumin'.
Mebby to mean *yes* an' say *no*
  Comes nateral to women.

He stood a spell on one foot fust,
  Then stood a spell on t'other,
An' on which one he felt the wust
  He couldn't ha' told ye nuther.

Says he, "I'd better call agin";
  Says she, "Think likely, Mister!"
Thet last word pricked him like a pin,
  An' . . . wal, he up an' kissed her.

When Ma bimeby upon 'em slips,
  Huldy sot pale ez ashes,
All kin' o' smily roun' the lips,
  An' teary roun' the lashes.

For she was jes' the quiet kind
  Whose naturs never vary,
Like streams that keep a summer mind
  Snowhid in Jenooary.

The blood clost roun' her heart felt glued
  Too tight fer all expressin',
Tell mother see how matters stood,
  An gin' 'em both her blessin'.

Then her red come back like the tide
  Down to the Bay o' Fundy,
And all I know is they was cried
  In meetin' come nex' Sunday.

## LOCHINVAR[1]

*Sir Walter Scott*

Oh, young Lochinvar is come out of the west,
Through all the wide Border his steed was the best;
And save his good broadsword he weapons had none,
He rode all unarmed, and he rode all alone.
So faithful in love, and so dauntless in war,
There never was knight like the young Lochinvar.

He stayed not for brake, and he stopped not for stone,
He swam the Eske River where ford there was none;
But ere he alighted at Netherby gate
The bride had consented, the gallant came late;
For a laggard in love, and a dastard in war
Was to wed the fair Ellen of brave Lochinvar.

So boldly he entered the Netherby Hall
Among bridesmen and kinsmen and brothers and all;
Then spoke the bride's father, his hand on his sword
(For the poor craven bridegroom said never a word),
"Oh, come ye in peace here, or come ye in war,
Or to dance at our bridal, young Lord Lochinvar?"

"I long woo'd your daughter, my suit you denied—
Love swells like the Solway, but ebbs like its tide—
And now am I come, with this lost love of mine,
To lead but one measure, drink one cup of wine.
There are maidens in Scotland more lovely by far,
That would gladly be bride to the young Lochinvar."

The bride kissed the goblet; the knight took it up;
He quaffed of the wine, and he threw down the cup.
She looked down to blush, and she looked up to sigh,
With a smile on her lips and a tear in her eye.
He took her soft hand ere her mother could bar,
"Now tread we a measure!" said young Lochinvar.

So stately his form, and so lovely her face,
That never a hall such a galliard did grace;
While her mother did fret, and her father did fume,
And the bridegroom stood dangling his bonnet and plume,
And the bridemaidens whispered, " 'Twere better by far
To have matched our fair cousin with young Lochinvar."

One touch to her hand, and one word in her ear,
When they reached the hall door, and the charger stood near;
So light to the croupe the fair lady he swung,
So light to the saddle before her he sprung!
"She is won! we are gone, over bank, bush, and scaur;
They'll have fleet steeds that follow," quoth young Lochinvar.

There was mounting 'mong Græmes of the Netherby clan;
Forsters, Fenwicks, and Musgraves, they rode and they ran;

[1] From Sir Walter Scott, *Marmion.*

There was racing and chasing, on Cannobie Lee,
But the lost bride of Netherby ne'er did they see.
So daring in love, and so dauntless in war,
Have ye e'er heard of gallant like young Lochinvar?

## LADY CLARE

*Alfred Tennyson*

It was the time when lilies blow,
And clouds are highest up in air,
Lord Ronald brought a lily-white doe
To give his cousin, Lady Clare.

I trow they did not part in scorn—
Lovers long-betrothed were they;
They two will wed the morrow morn;
God's blessing on the day!

"He does not love me for my birth,
Nor for my lands so broad and fair;
He loves me for my own true worth,
And that is well," said Lady Clare.

In there came old Alice the nurse,
Said, "Who was this that went from thee?"
"It was my cousin," said Lady Clare,
"Tomorrow he weds with me."

"O God be thanked!" said Alice the nurse,
"That all comes round so just and fair;
Lord Ronald is heir of all your lands,
And you are not the Lady Clare."

"Are ye out of your mind, my nurse, my nurse,"
Said Lady Clare, "that ye speak so wild?"
"As God's above," said Alice the nurse,
"I speak the truth, you are my child.

"The old Earl's daughter died at my breast;
I speak the truth as I live by bread!
I buried her like my own sweet child,
And put my child in her stead."

"Falsely, falsely have ye done,
O mother," she said, "if this be true,
To keep the best man under the sun
So many years from his due."

"Nay now, my child," said Alice the nurse,
"But keep the secret for your life,
And all you have will be Lord Ronald's,
When you are man and wife."

"If I'm a beggar born," she said,
"I will speak out, for I dare not lie.
Pull off, pull off the brooch of gold,
And fling the diamond necklace by."

"Nay now, my child," said Alice the nurse,
"But keep the secret all ye can."
She said: "Not so, but I will know
If there be faith in man."

"Nay now, what faith?" said Alice the nurse;
"The man will cleave unto his right."
"And he shall have it," the lady replied,
"Though I should die tonight."

"Yet give one kiss to your mother dear!
Alas, my child, I sinned for thee."
"O mother, mother, mother," she said,
"So strange it seems to me.

"Yet here's a kiss for my mother dear,
My mother dear, if this be so,
And lay your hand upon my head,
And bless me, mother, ere I go."

She clad herself in a russet gown,
She was no longer Lady Clare;
She went by dale, she went by down,
With a single rose in her hair.

The lily-white doe Lord Ronald had brought
Leapt up from where she lay,
Dropt her head in the maiden's hand,
And followed her all the way.

Down stept Lord Ronald from his tower:
"O Lady Clare, you shame your worth!
Why come you drest like a village maid,
That are the flower of the earth?"

"If I come drest like a village maid,
  I am but as my fortunes are;
I am a beggar born," she said,
  "And not the Lady Clare."

"Play me no tricks," said Lord Ronald,
  "For I am yours in word and deed."
"Play me no tricks," said Lord Ronald,
  "Your riddle is hard to read."

O and proudly stood she up!
  Her heart within her did not fail;
She looked into Lord Ronald's eyes,
  And told him all her nurse's tale.

He laughed a laugh of merry scorn;
  He turned and kissed her where she stood.
"If you are not the heiress born,
  And I," said he, "the next in blood—

"If you are not the heiress born,
  And I," said he, "the lawful heir,
We two will wed tomorrow morn,
  And you will still be Lady Clare."

## THE SINGING LEAVES

*James Russell Lowell*

### I

"What fairings will ye that I bring?"
  Said the King to his daughters three;
"For I to Vanity Fair am boun',
  Now say what shall they be?"

Then up and spake the eldest daughter,
  That lady tall and grand:
"O, bring me pearls and diamonds great,
  And gold rings for my hand."

Thereafter spake the second daughter,
  That was both white and red:
"For me bring silks that will stand alone,
  And a gold comb for my head."

Then came the turn of the least daughter,
  That was whiter than thistledown,
And among the gold of her blithesome hair
  Dim shone the golden crown.

"There came a bird this morning,
  And sang 'neath my bower eaves,
Till I dreamed, as his music made me,
  'Ask thou for the Singing Leaves'."

Then the brow of the King swelled crimson
  With a flush of angry scorn:
"Well have ye spoken, my two eldest,
  And chosen as ye were born;

"But she, like a thing of peasant race,
  That is happy binding the sheaves";
Then he saw her dead mother in her face,
  And said, "Thou shalt have thy leaves."

### II

He mounted and rode three days and nights
  Till he came to Vanity Fair,
And 'twas easy to buy the gems and the silk,
  But no Singing Leaves were there.

Then deep in the greenwood rode he,
  And asked of every tree,
"O, if you have ever a Singing Leaf,
  I pray you give it me!"

But the trees all kept their counsel,
  And never a word said they,
Only there sighed from the pine tops
  A music of seas far away.

Only the pattering aspen
  Made a sound of growing rain,
That fell ever faster and faster,
  Then faltered to silence again.

"O, where shall I find a little foot-page
  That would win both hose and shoon,
And will bring to me the Singing Leaves
  If they grow under the moon?"

Then lightly turned him Walter the page,
  By the stirrup as he ran:
"Now pledge you me the truesome word
  Of a king and gentleman,

"That you will give me the first, first thing
 You meet at your castle gate,
And the Princess shall get the Singing
  Leaves,
 Or mine be a traitor's fate."

The King's head dropt upon his breast
 A moment, as it might be;
'T will be my dog, he thought, and said,
 "My faith I plight to thee."

Then Walter took from next his heart
 A packet small and thin,
"Now give you this to the Princess Anne,
 The Singing Leaves are therein."

III

As the King rode in at his castle gate,
 A maiden to meet him ran,
And "Welcome, Father!" she laughed and
  cried
 Together, the Princess Anne.

"Lo, here the Singing Leaves," quoth he,
 "And woe, but they cost me dear!"
She took the packet, and the smile
 Deepened down beneath the tear.

It deepened down till it reached her heart,
 And then gushed up again,
And lighted her tears as the sudden sun
 Transfigures the summer rain.

And the first Leaf, when it was opened,
 Sang: "I am Walter the page,
And the songs I sing 'neath thy window
 Are my only heritage."

And the second Leaf sang: "But in the
  land
 That is neither on earth or sea,
My lute and I are lords of more
 Than thrice this kingdom's fee."

And the third Leaf sang: "Be mine! Be
  mine!"
 And ever it sang, "Be mine!"
Then sweeter it sang and ever sweeter,
 And said, "I am thine, thine, thine!"

At the first Leaf she grew pale enough,
 At the second she turned aside,
At the third, 'twas as if a lily flushed
 With a rose's red heart's tide.

"Good counsel gave the bird," said she,
 "I have my hope thrice o'er,
For they sing to my very heart," she said,
 "And it sings to them evermore."

She brought to him her beauty and truth,
 But and broad earldoms three,
And he made her queen of the broader
  lands
 He held of his lute in fee.

## ANNABEL LEE

*Edgar Allan Poe*

It was many and many a year ago,
 In a kingdom by the sea,
That a maiden there lived whom you may
  know
 By the name of Annabel Lee;
And this maiden she lived with no other
  thought
 Than to love and be loved by me.

*I* was a child and *she* was a child,
 In this kingdom by the sea,
But we loved with a love that was more
  than love—
 I and my Annabel Lee;
With a love that the winged seraphs of
  heaven
 Coveted her and me.

And this was the reason that, long ago,
 In this kingdom by the sea,
A wind blew out of a cloud, chilling
 My beautiful Annabel Lee;
So that her high-born kinsmen came
 And bore her away from me,
To shut her up in a sepulchre
 In this kingdom by the sea.

The angels, not half so happy in heaven,
 Went envying her and me—
Yes!—that was the reason (as all men know,
 In this kingdom by the sea)

That the wind came out of the cloud by night,
  Chilling and killing my Annabel Lee.

But our love it was stronger by far than the love
  Of those who were older than we—
  Of many far wiser than we;
And neither the angels in heaven above,
  Nor the demons down under the sea,
Can ever dissever my soul from the soul
  Of the beautiful Annabel Lee.

For the moon never beams, without bringing me dreams
  Of the beautiful Annabel Lee;
And the stars never rise, but I feel the bright eyes
  Of the beautiful Annabel Lee;
And so, all the nighttide, I lie down by the side
Of my darling—my darling—my life and my bride,
  In the sepulchre there by the sea—
  In her tomb by the sounding sea.

## THE LEAP OF ROUSHAN BEG[1]

*Henry Wadsworth Longfellow*

Mounted on Kyrat strong and fleet,
His chestnut steed with four white feet,
  Roushan Beg, called Kurroglou,
Son of the road, and bandit chief,
Seeking refuge and relief,
  Up the mountain pathway flew.

Such was Kyrat's wondrous speed,
Never yet could any steed
  Reach the dust cloud in his course.
More than maiden, more than wife,
More than gold and next to life
  Roushan the Robber loved his horse.

In the land that lies beyond
Erzeroum and Trebizond,
  Garden-girt his fortress stood;
Plundered khan, or caravan
Journeying north from Koordistan,
  Gave him wealth and wine and food.

Seven hundred and fourscore
Men at arms his livery wore,
  Did his bidding night and day.
Now, through regions all unknown
He was wandering, lost, alone,
  Seeking without guide his way.

Suddenly the pathway ends,
Sheer the precipice descends,
  Loud the torrent roars unseen;
Thirty feet from side to side
Yawns the chasm; on air must ride
  He who crosses this ravine.

Following close in his pursuit,
At the precipice's foot,
  Reyhan the Arab of Orfah
Halted with his hundred men,
Shouting upward from the glen,
  "La Illáh illa Alláh!"

Gently Roushan Beg caressed
Kyrat's forehead, neck, and breast;
  Kissed him upon both his eyes;
Sang to him in his wild way,
As upon the topmost spray
  Sings a bird before it flies.

"O my Kyrat, O my steed,
Round and slender as a reed,
  Carry me this peril through!
Satin housings shall be thine,
Shoes of gold, O Kyrat mine,
  O thou soul of Kurroglou!

"Soft thy skin as silken skein,
Soft as woman's hair thy mane,
  Tender are thine eyes and true;
All thy hoofs like ivory shine,
Polished bright; O life of mine,
  Leap, and rescue Kurroglou!"

Kyrat, then, the strong and fleet,
Drew together his four white feet,
  Paused a moment on the verge,
Measured with his eye the space,
And into the air's embrace
  Leaped as leaps the ocean surge.

[1] From Henry Wadsworth Longfellow, *Birds of Passage.*

As the ocean surge o'er sand
Bears a swimmer safe to land,
  Kyrat safe his rider bore;
Rattling down the deep abyss
Fragments of the precipice
  Rolled like pebbles on a shore.

Roushan's tasselled cap of red
Trembled not upon his head,
  Careless sat he and upright;
Neither hand nor bridle shook,
Nor his head he turned to look,
  As he galloped out of sight.

Flash of harness in the air,
Seen a moment like the glare
  Of a sword drawn from its sheath;
Thus the phantom horseman passed,
And the shadow that he cast
  Leaped the cataract underneath.

Reyhan the Arab held his breath
While this vision of life and death
  Passed above him. "Allahu!"
Cried he. "In all Koordistan
Lives there not so brave a man
  As this Robber Kurroglou!"

## THE PIED PIPER OF HAMELIN

*Robert Browning*

Hamelin Town's in Brunswick,
  By famous Hanover city;
    The river Weser, deep and wide,
    Washes its wall on the southern side;
    A pleasanter spot you never spied;
  But, when begins my ditty,
    Almost five hundred years ago,
    To see the townsfolk suffer so
  From vermin, was a pity.

  Rats!
They fought the dogs and killed the cats,
  And bit the babies in the cradles,
And ate the cheeses out of the vats,
  And licked the soup from the cooks' own ladles,
Split open the kegs of salted sprats,
Made nests inside men's Sunday hats,
And even spoiled the women's chats,
  By drowning their speaking
  With shrieking and squeaking
In fifty different sharps and flats.

At last the people in a body
  To the Town Hall came flocking;
"'Tis clear," cried they, "our Mayor's a noddy;
  And as for our Corporation—shocking
To think we buy gowns lined with ermine
For dolts that can't or won't determine
What's best to rid us of our vermin!
You hope, because you're old and obese,
To find in the furry civic robe ease?
Rouse up, sirs! Give your brains a racking
To find the remedy we're lacking,
Or, sure as fate, we'll send you packing!"
At this the Mayor and Corporation
Quaked with a mighty consternation.

An hour they sat in council;
  At length the Mayor broke silence:
"For a guilder I'd my ermine gown sell,
  I wish I were a mile hence!
It's easy to bid one rack one's brain—
I'm sure my poor head aches again,
I've scratched it so, and all in vain.
Oh for a trap, a trap, a trap!"
Just as he said this what should hap
At the chamber door but a gentle tap?
"Bless us," cried the Mayor, "what's that?"
(With the Corporation as he sat,
Looking little though wondrous fat;
Nor brighter was his eye, nor moister
Than a too-long-opened oyster,
Save when at noon his paunch grew mutinous
For a plate of turtle green and glutinous)
"Only a scraping of shoes on the mat?
Anything like the sound of a rat
Makes my heart go pit-a-pat!"

"Come in!"—the Mayor cried, looking bigger,
And in did come the strangest figure!
His queer long coat from heel to head
Was half of yellow and half of red,
And he himself was tall and thin,
With sharp blue eyes, each like a pin,

And light loose hair, yet swarthy skin,
No tuft on cheek nor beard on chin,
But lips where smiles went out and in;
There was no guessing his kith and kin;
And nobody could enough admire
The tall man and his quaint attire.
Quoth one: "It's as if my great-grandsire,
Starting up at the Trump of Doom's tone,
Had walked this way from his painted tombstone!"

He advanced to the council table:
And, "Please, your honors," said he, "I'm able
By means of a secret charm, to draw
All creatures living beneath the sun,
That creep or swim or fly or run,
After me so as you never saw!
And I chiefly use my charm
On creatures that do people harm,
The mole and toad and newt and viper;
And people call me the Pied Piper."
(And here they noticed round his neck
A scarf of red and yellow stripe,
To match his coat of the self-same check;
And at the scarf's end hung a pipe;
And his fingers, they noticed, were ever straying
As if impatient to be playing
Upon this pipe, as low it dangled
Over his vesture so old-fangled.)
"Yet," said he, "poor piper as I am,
In Tartary I freed the Cham
Last June, from his huge swarm of gnats;
I eased in Asia the Nizam
Of a monstrous brood of vampire bats;
And as for what your brain bewilders,
If I can rid your town of rats
Will you give me a thousand guilders?"
"One? fifty thousand!"—was the exclamation
Of the astonished Mayor and Corporation.

Into the street the Piper stepped,
Smiling first a little smile,
As if he knew what magic slept
In his quiet pipe the while;
Then, like a musical adept,
To blow the pipe his lips he wrinkled,
And green and blue his sharp eyes twinkled,
Like a candle flame where salt is sprinkled;
And ere three shrill notes the pipe had uttered,
You heard as if an army muttered;
And the muttering grew to a grumbling;
And the grumbling grew to a mighty rumbling;
And out of the houses the rats came tumbling;
Great rats, small rats, lean rats, brawny rats,
Brown rats, black rats, gray rats, tawny rats,
Grave old plodders, gay young friskers,
Fathers, mothers, uncles, cousins,
Cocking tails and pricking whiskers,
Families by tens and dozens,
Brothers, sisters, husbands, wives—
Followed the Piper for their lives.
From street to street he piped advancing,
And step for step they followed dancing,
Until they came to the river Weser,
Wherein all plunged and perished!
—Save one who, stout as Julius Cæsar,
Swam across and lived to carry
(As he, the manuscript he cherished)
To Rat-land home his commentary,
Which was, "At the first shrill notes of the pipe,
I heard a sound as of scraping tripe,
And putting apples, wondrous ripe,
Into a cider press's gripe—
And a moving away of pickle-tub boards,
And a leaving ajar of conserve cupboards,
And a drawing the corks of train-oil flasks,
And a breaking the hoops of butter-casks;
And it seemed as if a voice
(Sweeter far than by harp or by psaltery
Is breathed) called out, 'O rats, rejoice!
The world is grown to one vast drysaltery!
So munch on, crunch on, take your nuncheon,
Breakfast, dinner, supper, luncheon!'
And just as a bulky sugar puncheon,
All ready staved, like a great sun shone
Glorious scarce an inch before me,
Just as methought it said, 'Come, bore me!'
—I found the Weser rolling o'er me."

You should have heard the Hamelin people
Ringing the bells till they rocked the steeple.

"Go," cried the Mayor, "and get long poles,
Poke out the nests and block up the holes!
Consult with carpenters and builders,
And leave in our town not even a trace
Of the rats!"—when suddenly, up the face
Of the Piper perked in the market place
With a "First, if you please, my thousand guilders!"

A thousand guilders! The Mayor looked blue;
So did the Corporation too.
For council dinners made rare havoc
With Claret, Moselle, Vin-de-Grave, Hock;
And half the money would replenish
Their cellar's biggest butt with Rhenish.
To pay this sum to a wandering fellow
With a gipsy coat of red and yellow!
"Beside," quoth the Mayor with a knowing wink,
"Our business was done at the river's brink;
We saw with our eyes the vermin sink,
And what's dead can't come to life, I think.
So, friend, we're not the folks to shrink
From the duty of giving you something for drink,
And a matter of money to put in your poke;
But as for the guilders, what we spoke
Of them, as you very well know, was in joke.
Beside, our losses have made us thrifty.
A thousand guilders! Come, take fifty!"

The Piper's face fell, and he cried,
"No trifling! I can't wait! beside
I've promised to visit by dinnertime
Bagdad, and accept the prime
Of the Head Cook's pottage, all he's rich in,
For having left, in the Caliph's kitchen,
Of a nest of scorpions no survivor;
With him I proved no bargain driver,
With you, don't think I'll bate a stiver!
And folks who put me in a passion
May find me pipe after another fashion."

"How?" cried the Mayor, "d'ye think I brook
Being worse treated than a Cook?
Insulted by a lazy ribald
With idle pipe and vesture piebald?
You threaten us, fellow? Do your worst,
Blow your pipe there till you burst!"

Once more he stept into the street,
And to his lips again
Laid his long pipe of smooth, straight cane;
And ere he blew three notes (such sweet,
Soft notes as yet musician's cunning
Never gave the enraptured air)
There was a rustling that seemed like a bustling
Of merry crowds justling at pitching and hustling;
Small feet were pattering, wooden shoes clattering,
Little hands clapping and little tongues chattering,
And, like fowls in a farmyard when barley is scattering,
Out came the children running.
All the little boys and girls,
With rosy cheeks and flaxen curls,
And sparkling eyes and teeth like pearls,
Tripping and skipping, ran merrily after
The wonderful music with shouting and laughter.

The Mayor was dumb, and the Council stood
As if they were changed into blocks of wood,
Unable to move a step, or cry
To the children merrily skipping by—
Could only follow with the eye
That joyous crowd at the Piper's back.
But how the Mayor was on the rack,
And the wretched Council's bosoms beat,
As the Piper turned from the High Street
To where the Weser rolled its waters
Right in the way of their sons and daughters!
However, he turned from south to west,
And to Koppelberg Hill his steps addressed,
And after him the children pressed;
Great was the joy in every breast.
"He never can cross that mighty top!
He's forced to let the piping drop,
And we shall see our children stop!"

When, lo, as they reached the mountain side,
A wondrous portal opened wide,
As if a cavern was suddenly hollowed;
And the Piper advanced and the children followed,
And when all were in to the very last,
The door in the mountain side shut fast.
Did I say, all? No! One was lame,
And could not dance the whole of the way;
And in after years, if you would blame
His sadness, he was used to say,
"It's dull in our town since my playmates left!
I can't forget that I'm bereft
Of all the pleasant sights they see,
Which the Piper also promised me.
For he led us, he said, to a joyous land,
Joining the town and just at hand,
Where waters gushed and fruit trees grew,
And flowers put forth a fairer hue,
And everything was strange and new;
The sparrows were brighter than peacocks here,
And their dogs outran our fallow deer,
And honeybees had lost their stings,
And horses were born with eagles' wings;
And just as I became assured
My lame foot would be speedily cured,
The music stopped and I stood still,
And found myself outside the hill,
Left alone against my will,
To go now limping as before,
And never hear of that country more!"

Alas, alas for Hamelin!
There came into many a burgher's pate
A text which says that heaven's gate
Opes to the rich at as easy rate
As the needle's eye takes a camel in!
The Mayor sent east, west, north, and south
To offer the Piper, by word of mouth,
Wherever it was men's lot to find him,
Silver and gold to his heart's content,
If he'd only return the way he went,
And bring the children behind him.
But when they saw 'twas a lost endeavor,
And Piper and dancers were gone forever,
They made a decree that lawyers never
Should think their records dated duly
If, after the day of the month and year,
These words did not as well appear,
"And so long after what happened here
On the Twenty-second of July,
Thirteen hundred and seventy-six;"
And the better in memory to fix
The place of the children's last retreat,
They called it, the Pied Piper's Street—
Where any one playing on pipe or tabor
Was sure for the future to lose his labor.
Nor suffered they hostelry or tavern
To shock with mirth a street so solemn;
But opposite the place of the cavern
They wrote the story on a column,
And on the great church window painted
The same, to make the world acquainted
How their children were stolen away,
And there it stands to this very day.
And I must not omit to say
That in Transylvania there's a tribe
Of alien people who ascribe
The outlandish ways and dress
On which their neighbors lay such stress,
To their fathers and mothers having risen
Out of some subterraneous prison
Into which they were trepanned
Long time ago in a mighty band
Out of Hamelin town in Brunswick land,
But how or why, they don't understand.

## SKIPPER IRESON'S RIDE

*John Greenleaf Whittier*

Of all the rides since the birth of time,
Told in story or sung in rhyme—
On Apuleius's Golden Ass,
Or one-eyed Calender's horse of brass,
Witch astride of a human back,
Islam's prophet on Al-Borák—
The strangest ride that ever was sped
Was Ireson's, out from Marblehead!
Old Floyd Ireson, for his hard heart,
Tarred and feathered and carried in a cart
By the women of Marblehead!

Body of turkey, head of owl,
Wings a-droop like a rained-on fowl,
Feathered and ruffled in every part,
Skipper Ireson stood in the cart.
Scores of women, old and young,
Strong of muscle, and glib of tongue,
Pushed and pulled up the rocky lane,
Shouting and singing the shrill refrain:
"Here's Flud Oirson, fur his horrd horrt,
Torr'd an' futherr'd an' corr'd in a corrt
By the women o' Morble'ead!"

Wrinkled scolds with hands on hips,
Girls in bloom of cheek and lips,
Wild-eyed, free-limbed, such as chase
Bacchus round some antique vase,
Brief of skirt, with ankles bare,
Loose of kerchief and loose of hair,
With conch-shells blowing and fish-horns' twang,
Over and over the Mænads sang:
"Here's Flud Oirson, fur his horrd horrt,
Torr'd an' futherr'd an' corr'd in a corrt
By the women o' Morble'ead!"

Small pity for him! He sailed away
From a leaking ship in Chaleur Bay,
Sailed away from a sinking wreck,
With his own town's people on her deck!
"Lay by! lay by!" they called to him.
Back he answered, "Sink or swim!
Brag of your catch of fish again!"
And off he sailed through the fog and rain!
Old Floyd Ireson, for his hard heart,
Tarred and feathered and carried in a cart
By the women of Marblehead!

Fathoms deep in dark Chaleur
That wreck shall lie forevermore.
Mother and sister, wife and maid,
Looked from the rocks of Marblehead
Over the moaning and rainy sea,
Looked for the coming that might not be!
What did the winds and the sea birds say
Of the cruel captain who sailed away?
Old Floyd Ireson, for his hard heart,
Tarred and feathered and carried in a cart
By the women of Marblehead!

Through the street, on either side,
Up flew windows, doors swung wide;
Sharp-tongued spinsters, old wives gray,
Treble lent the fish-horn's bray.
Sea-worn grandsires, cripple-bound,
Hulks of old sailors run aground,
Shook head, and fist, and hat, and cane,
And cracked with curses the hoarse refrain:
"Here's Flud Oirson, fur his horrd horrt,
Torr'd an' futherr'd an' corr'd in a corrt
By the women o' Morble-'ead!"

Sweetly along the Salem road
Bloom of orchard and lilac showed.
Little the wicked skipper knew
Of the fields so green and the sky so blue.
Riding there in his sorry trim,
Like an Indian idol glum and grim,
Scarcely he seemed the sound to hear
Of voices shouting, far and near:
"Here's Flud Oirson, fur his horrd horrt,
Torr'd an' futherr'd an' corr'd in a corrt
By the women o' Morble-'ead!"

"Hear me, neighbors!" at last he cried.
"What to me is this noisy ride?
What is the shame that clothes the skin
To the nameless horror that lives within?
Waking or sleeping, I see a wreck,
And hear a cry from a reeling deck!
Hate me and curse me—I only dread
The hand of God and the face of the dead!"
Said old Floyd Ireson, for his hard heart,
Tarred and feathered and carried in a cart
By the women of Marblehead!

Then the wife of the skipper lost at sea
Said, "God has touched him! Why should we?"
Said an old wife mourning her only son,
"Cut the rogue's tether and let him run!"
So with soft relentings and rude excuse,
Half scorn, half pity, they cut him loose,
And gave him a cloak to hide him in,
And left him alone with his shame and sin.
Poor Floyd Ireson, for his hard heart,
Tarred and feathered and carried in a cart
By the women of Marblehead!

## JOHN ANDERSON, MY JO

*Robert Burns*

John Anderson, my jo, John,
When we were first acquent,
Your locks were like the raven,
Your bonnie brow was brent;
But now your brow is beld, John,
Your locks are like the snaw:
But blessings on your frosty pow,
John Anderson, my jo.

John Anderson, my jo, John,
We clamb the hill thegither;
And monie a canty day, John,
We've had wi' ane anither:
Now we maun totter down, John,
But hand in hand we'll go,
And sleep thegither at the foot,
John Anderson, my jo.

## *Stories in Verse: Suggested Grades*

*Grade One*
- The Three Little Kittens

*Grade Two*
- A Visit from Mr. Fox
- Hiawatha's Childhood

*Grade Three*
- The Raggle, Taggle Gypsies
- King Bruce and the Spider

*Grade Four*
- The Leak in the Dike
- The Blind Men and the Elephant
- Robin Hood and the Ranger

*Grade Five*
- The Battle of Blenheim
- Three Kings Came Riding
- Hiawatha's Canoe
- Robin Hood and Little John
- Meg Merrilies

*Grade Six*
- How They Brought the Good News from Ghent to Aix
- Robin Hood and Allen-a-Dale
- Lochinvar
- Lady Clare

*Grade Seven*
- The Discoverer of the North Cape
- The Leap of Roushan Beg

*Grade Eight*

In School Days
The Courtin'
The Singing Leaves
Annabel Lee
The Pied Piper of Hamelin
Skipper Ireson's Ride
John Anderson, My Jo

## *Collections of Verse*

### *For Younger Children*

Barrows, Marjorie, *One Hundred Best Poems for Boys and Girls*. Whitman.

Brewton, John E., *Under the Tent of the Sky,* illus. by Robert Lawson. Macmillan.

Harrington, Mildred P., *Ring-a-Round,* illus. by Corydon Bell. Macmillan.

Hubbard, Alice, and Adeline Babbitt, *The Golden Flute*. John Day.

Huber, Miriam Blanton, Herbert B. Bruner, and Charles M. Curry, *The Poetry Book,* Vol. 1-4, illus. by Marjorie Hartwell. Rand McNally.

Hutchinson, Veronica, *Chimney Corner Poems,* illus. by Lois Lenski. Minton, Balch.

Johnson, Burges, *A Little Book of Necessary Nonsense,* illus. by Elizabeth MacKinstry. Harper.

Literature Committee of the Association for Childhood Education, *Sung under the Silver Umbrella,* illus. by Dorothy P. Lathrop. Macmillan.

Untermeyer, Louis, *Rainbow in the Sky,* illus. by Reginald Birch. Harcourt, Brace.

———, *This Singing World for Younger Children,* illus. by Decie Merwin and Clara M. Burd. Harcourt, Brace.

Wiggin, Kate Douglas, and Nora A. Smith, *The Posy Ring*. Doubleday, Doran.

### *For Older Children*

Auslander, Joseph, and Frank Ernest Hill, *The Winged Horse Anthology*. Doubleday, Doran.

Barnes, Ruth, *I Hear America Singing: An Anthology of Folk Poetry,* illus. by Robert Lawson. Winston.

Davis, Mary Gould, *The Girls' Book of Verse*. Stokes.

Fish, Helen Dean, *The Boys' Book of Verse*. Stokes.

Harper, Wilhelmina, *A Little Book of Necessary Ballads,* illus. by Helen B. Evers. Harper.

Huber, Miriam Blanton, Herbert B. Bruner, and Charles M. Curry, *The Poetry Book,* Vols. 5-9, illus. by Marjorie Hartwell. Rand McNally.

Huffard, Grace Thompson, Laura Mae Carlisle, and Helen Ferris, *My Poetry Book,* illus. by Willy Pogany. Winston.

Lomax, John A., and Alan Lomax, *Cowboy Songs and Other Frontier Ballads*. Macmillan.

Olcott, Frances Jenkins, *Story-Telling Ballads,* illus. by Milo Winter. Houghton Mifflin.

Stevenson, Burton E., *The Home Book of Verse for Young Folks,* illus. by Willy Pogany. Holt.

Teasdale, Sara, *Rainbow Gold,* illus. by Dugald Walker. Macmillan.

Thompson, Blanche J., *Silver Pennies,* illus. by Winifred Bromhall. Macmillan.

Untermeyer, Louis, *This Singing World,* illus. by Florence Wymand Ivins. Harcourt, Brace.

## *Books of Verse*

### *For Younger Children*

Aldis, Dorothy, *Everything and Anything,* illus. by Helen D. Jameson. Minton, Balch.

———, *Here, There and Everywhere,* illus. by Marjorie Flack. Minton, Balch.

———, *Hop, Skip and Jump,* illus. by Margaret Freeman. Minton, Balch.

Baruch, Dorothy W., *I Like Animals,* illus. by Corinne Pauli Waterall. Harper.

———, *I Like Machinery,* illus. by Corinne Pauli Waterall. Harper.

Chute, Marchette G., *Rhymes about Ourselves,* illus. by the author. Macmillan.

Conkling, Hilda, *Silverhorn,* illus. by Dorothy P. Lathrop. Stokes.

De la Mare, Walter, *A Child's Day,* illus. by Winifred Bromhall. Holt.

———, *Down-Adown-Derry,* illus. by Dorothy P. Lathrop. Holt.

———, *Peacock Pie,* illus. by Jocelyn Crowe. Holt.

Farjeon, Eleanor, *Come Christmas,* illus. by Rachel Field. Stokes.

———, *Over the Garden Wall,* illus. by Gwendolen Raverat. Stokes.

Field, Eugene, *Poems of Childhood,* illus. by Maxfield Parrish. Scribner.

Field, Rachel, *Branches Green,* illus. by Dorothy P. Lathrop. Macmillan.

———, *The Pointed People,* illus. by the author. Macmillan.

———, *Taxis and Toadstools,* illus. by the author. Doubleday, Doran.

Fyleman, Rose, *Fairies and Chimneys.* Doubleday, Doran.

———, *Gay Go Up,* illus. by Decie Merwin. Doubleday, Doran.

Howard, Winifred, *Out of the Everywhere,* illus. by Elizabeth Montgomery. Oxford.

Jackson, Leroy F., *The Peter Patter Book.* Rand McNally.

King, Edith, *Fifty New Poems for Children.* Appleton-Century.

Lear, Edward, *The Book of Nonsense and More Nonsense,* illus. by the author. Warne.

———, *Nonsense Songs,* illus. by L. Leslie Brooke. Warne.

Lofting, Hugh, *Porridge Poetry,* illus. by the author. Stokes.

Lucas, E. V., *Four and Twenty Toilers,* illus. by Francis D. Bedford. McDevitt-Wilson.

———, *Playtime and Company,* illus. by Ernest H. Shepard. Doubleday, Doran.

Milne, A. A., *When We Were Very Young,* illus. by Ernest H. Shepard. Dutton.

———, *Now We Are Six,* illus. by Ernest H. Shepard. Dutton.

Richards, Laura E., *Tirra Lirra: Rhymes Old and New,* illus. by Marguerite Davis. Little, Brown.

Riley, James Whitcomb, *Rhymes of Childhood.* Bobbs-Merrill.

Roberts, Elizabeth Madox, *Under the Tree,* illus. by Francis D. Bedford. Viking.

Rossetti, Christina G., *Sing-Song,* illus. by Marguerite Davis. Macmillan.

Sherman, Frank Dempster, *Little Folk Lyrics,* illus. by Genevieve Cowles. Houghton Mifflin.

Stevenson, Robert Louis, *A Child's Garden of Verses,* illus. by Marguerite Davis. Macmillan.

Tippett, James S., *Busy Carpenters,* illus. by Elizabeth T. Wolcott. World Book.

———, *I Go A-Traveling,* illus. by Elizabeth T. Wolcott. Harper.

———, *I Live in a City,* illus. by Elizabeth T. Wolcott. Harper.

Welles, Winifred, *Skipping Along Alone,* illus. by Marguerite Davis. Macmillan.

Wynne, Annette, *For Days and Days.* Stokes.

## *For Older Children*

Austin, Mary, *The Children Sing in the Far West,* illus. by Gerald Cassidy. Houghton Mifflin.

Carroll, Lewis, *Collected Verse of Lewis Carroll.* Dutton.

Dickinson, Emily, *Poems for Youth,* illus. by George and Doris Hauman. Little, Brown.

Hughes, Langston, *The Dream Keeper, and Other Poems for Young People,* edited by Effie Power, illus. by Helen Sewell. Knopf.

Kipling, Rudyard, *Songs for Youth.* Doubleday, Doran.

Lindsay, Vachel, *Johnny Appleseed, and Other Poems,* illus. by George M. Richards. Macmillan.

Millay, Edna St. Vincent, *Poems Selected for Young People,* illus. by Joseph Paget-Fredericks. Harper.

Sandburg, Carl, *Early Moon,* illus. by James Daugherty. Harcourt, Brace.

Teasdale, Sara, *Stars Tonight,* illus. by Dorothy P. Lathrop. Macmillan.

## *Student Activities*

1. Attitude toward poetry is the most significant factor in its enjoyment. Has your feeling toward poetry been a constant one, or have experiences with poetry produced changes in your feeling about it? Compare your experiences with those of other members of your class and analyze, if you can, the fortunate or unfortunate influences that have affected your enjoyment of poetry.

2. Verse to be read well should be read simply and unpretentiously. Select several poems and read them to a group of children. If a child audience is not available, perhaps your fellow students might like to hear them. Do not read verse as if it were prose, but at the same time avoid exaggerated rise and fall of syllables and monotonous similarity in inflection of rhyming words. Sustaining the end of the line and keeping it level in pitch, as well as giving full value to vowel sounds, will do much to make your reading pleasing.

3. Choral speaking of poetry holds interesting possibilities for group enjoyment among both children and adults. In *References for Students* are listed several articles and books which discuss verse-speaking choirs. Let groups of various sizes in your class experiment with this mode of expression. The old ballads are especially well suited for the purpose, as are many of Vachel Lindsay's poems.

4. Make a collection of verse written by children of the ages in which you are most interested. Not many years ago school children wrote little poetry; their present activity is interesting evidence of the change in attitude. Their school newspapers and magazines have many examples of delightful verse written by children of all ages. Many schools issue each year mimeographed or printed books of poetry written during the year.

5. Children and grownups find pleasure in compiling manuscript books of poems that they like. It is interesting to make such a collection for children of a certain age. A particular subject, such as the sea, birds, trees, mountains, the desert, the farm, the city, etc., will each yield an anthology of great charm. A prospective teacher will not only increase her acquaintance with children's verse through such an activity but will have at hand a collection of fine poems for future use.

6. Do you like to write verse? Perhaps you would like to write some simple verse for children, picturing something you have seen or experienced or imagined in a rhythmic form that children can understand and enjoy.

## *References for Students*

Auslander, Joseph, and Frank Ernest Hill, *The Winged Horse: The story of the Poets and Their Poetry*. Doubleday, Doran.

Barnes, Walter, *The Children's Poets*. World Book.

———, "Contemporary Poetry for Children," *Elementary English Review*, XIII: 3, 49, 135, 257, 298.

Dalgliesh, Alice, *First Experiences with Literature*, Chapter 3. Scribner.

Drew, Elizabeth, *Discovering Poetry*. Norton.

Drinkwater, John, *The Way of Poetry*, pp. xv-xxx. Houghton Mifflin.

Eastman, Max, *Enjoyment of Poetry*. Scribner.

Gillett, Odeyne, "Poetry as an Integrating Force," *Elementary English Review*, XIII:142.

Gullan, Marjorie, *Spoken Poetry in the Schools*. Methuen (London).

Hartman, Gertrude, and Ann Shumaker, *Creative Expression through Literature*. John Day.

Hill, May, "Unharnessing Pegasus," *Elementary English Review,* VIII:107.

Kaucher, Dorothy, "The Verse-Speaking Choir," *Quarterly Journal of Speech,* XVII:64.

Meader, Emma Grant, "Choral Speaking and Its Values," *Quarterly Journal of Speech,* XXII:235.

Mearns, Hughes, *Creative Youth*. Doubleday, Doran.

Moore, Annie E., *Literature Old and New for Children,* Chapters 9-10. Houghton Mifflin.

Ramsey, Eloise, "The Poetry Hour," *Childhood Education,* VIII:115.

Shepard, Loraine V., "There's Music in Their Speech," *Elementary English Review,* XVI:307.

Untermeyer, Louis, and Carter Davidson, *Poetry, Its Appreciation and Enjoyment*. Harcourt, Brace.

# *Old Tales and Legends*

# OLD TALES

## Folk Tales: Value and Origin

THE term folk tale is used to designate a very old story of unknown authorship that has been handed down orally from generation to generation. There are hundreds of such stories known in every country of the world and most of them were known long before books were made. These old stories are often called fairy tales because so many of them deal with fairies and magic. Not all of the old tales, however, have supernatural elements while many stories "made up" by modern writers are peopled with fairies, so for convenience the term folk tale has come to mean the story of traditional origin regardless of its content. To the great delight of children, the content is usually that of animals that talk, fairy godmothers that appear when needed, or heroes who overcome incredible obstacles and win rich rewards. It is to children a completely satisfying literature, which is one of the many strong reasons for including these fine old tales in children's reading.

Sometimes these stories are offered to children prematurely. The first literary fare should be stories of the real world in which they live, a world that is still new and strange and mysterious to them. The time for the folk tales and myths and legends, each in turn, is to come. A carefully told fairy story may fail to interest a young child or group of children who would listen eagerly to a story of everyday characters, children like themselves, in an everyday situation that has magic enough in its novelty. Later, when these same children are somewhat older, the fairy tale will come into its own and bring them pleasure of the highest order.

One of the most interesting facts that arises in a study of folk tales is the similarity in the stories handed down orally from generation to generation in different countries. Peoples in far-removed lands, and even in widely different periods of time, told the same stories. Details differ, but the essential plots are strikingly similar. For example, one scholar has identified three hundred and forty-five variants of the story of Cinderella. The version included here is from the French, but in Grimms' collection of German fairy tales, "Ashputtel" is the same story except that a friendly bird takes the place of the fairy godmother. In the interior of Brazil, stories are current among the natives who live in the mud huts under the palm trees that are identical in plot with the stories told by *Uncle Remus* on a Georgia plantation. Folklorists have found that hundreds of stories familiar in Europe and America are also known among primitive, savage peoples.

There are two theories concerning the origin and transmission of folk tales. One is that they all had a common origin in India in the sacred books of Buddhism and were transmitted by migrations of peoples, by Crusaders, Hebrews, and Gypsies. This theory undoubtedly explains the origin of some tales, but not all. Another, and to some scholars more acceptable, theory is that the tales (many of them at least) arose independently among peoples widely separated geographically and even historically. The universality of human experience and the sameness of human nature and human emotion may thus account for the similarity of the tales.

Each story in our collection has a long and interesting history of oral tradition extending back for hundreds and in some cases undoubtedly thousands of years. The history of which we can be sure begins at the point at which some storyteller, folklorist, or anthropologist set it down in print. The persistence with which these stories have retained their original plots is most interesting; of equal interest are the modifications that have taken place in some of the stories—modifications which reflect changing mores and changing circumstances in human living. In some cases the changes have continued to take place after the stories have reached print. For example, in the original version of "Little Red Riding Hood," the wolf eats both the grandmother and little Red Riding Hood, but later versions have contrived a happy ending either by rescuing the grandmother and little Red Riding Hood from the stomach of the wolf or by having the woodmen appear in time to save them.

"Little Red Riding Hood" first appeared in print in 1697 in a collection entitled *Contes de Ma Mère l'Oye* (*Tales of My Mother Goose*), one of the most famous collections of tales in all literature. It bore the name of Charles Perrault, a scholar and member of the French Academy, but in apology he said the stories were written by his little son who had learned them from his peasant nurse. Undoubtedly some such source was the true one, but Perrault, whose other scholarly achievements have been forgotten long ago, became immortal through his connection with these nursery tales. The frontispiece of the book showed three children listening to a tale told by an old woman spinning—*Mother Goose,* a name later to be associated more often with rhymes than with tales.[1]

As early as 1719 a translation of Perrault's tales was published in England. It instantly became popular and the many other translations and editions which followed gave these tales a secure place in the nursery lore of English-speaking children.

Perrault's volume was a slender one, with only eight tales in all. In addition to "Little Red Riding Hood," the stories were: "The Sleeping Beauty,"

[1] For discussion of *Mother Goose,* see pages 49, 50.

"Cinderella," "Puss in Boots," "Blue Beard," "Toads and Diamonds," "Riquet with the Tuft," and "Hop o' My Thumb." Nearly two hundred and fifty years have passed since these stories were first published, but in all that time, almost no general collection of fairy tales has appeared that does not contain some of them.

Just as these stories were not the invention of Perrault, neither were they the possession of France alone. When the Brothers Grimm made their extensive study of German folklore a century later, they found the same stories current in Germany. The form of the tales reported by the Grimms does not indicate that they were borrowed from France, for they are much cruder and more primitive and lack the details and embellishment of the Perrault stories, suggesting that they were well intrenched in German folklore before Perrault's tales were published. The Brothers Grimm published the results of their scientific researches in 1812–1815. Their purpose was not to entertain children but to record and preserve a national literature which they gathered orally, much of it from remote country districts. Children, however, appropriated the tales.

The first English translation of the Grimm *Hausmärchen* was made by Edgar Taylor and appeared with Cruikshank's inimitable drawings in 1823. An edition of Taylor's translation, published in 1868, carries an interesting introduction by John Ruskin which is a spirited defense of fairy tales.

A systematic collection of folk tales in England came somewhat later. James Orchard Halliwell's *Nursery Rhymes and Nursery Tales of England* appeared in 1849, and his work was followed by that of Joseph Jacobs, Andrew Lang, and others. At about the same time Asbjörnsen and Moe, working together much in the same way as the Grimms, gathered together an excellent collection of Norse folk tales which were delightfully translated into English by George Webbe Dasent and issued under the title, *Popular Tales from the Norse,* in 1859.

The middle of the nineteenth century found a very large body of folk material available in English. In 1840 Lane's translation of *The Arabian Nights' Entertainments* extended the audience for "Aladdin" and "Sinbad," though other translations had been available since 1704. Tales from India and the fables of Aesop had long been well known. Careful and authentic collections of folk tales from almost all civilized countries have been added, as well as many stories gathered by philologists and anthropologists from savage peoples, until now the amount of folk literature available to the general reader runs into hundreds of volumes.

The United States has made its own valuable contribution to folklore. In the sense that American folk tales have appeared in books comparatively recently, they are the latest contribution. There are at least three strains of folklore that are genuinely American. The most recent, and one not yet fully studied, consists of tales of Gargantuan heroes who have conquered the wilderness. Their exploits are on a grand scale and typify the American pioneer spirit. These stories, of which "Paul Bunyan" is a good example, are robust and abound in humor. The animal stories current among the slaves on the southern plantations before the Civil War, known to us as the tales of *Uncle Remus,* have many interesting parallels in the ancient beast tales from India but contain elements of humor that are peculiarly American. Since both types of stories just mentioned are so high in humor, they have been included in this volume in the group entitled *Stories for Fun* (pages 455-487). Children love these tales for their delightful humor; their American origins make them doubly interesting to adults.

A contribution to folklore from the United States is that of legends found among various tribes of Indians. This material also has not been completely collected. A great deal of the Indian lore is mystical, symbolic, and unsuited to children, but many fine animal and hero tales have come from the Indians and there are undoubtedly many more that have not yet appeared in a form that children can enjoy.

Many workers with children have questioned the value of fables and much less of this material is offered to children than was formerly the case. Until fairly recently children's books, especially school readers, were burdened with fables, many of them far beyond the understanding of children. The condensed form of the fable makes it difficult for children; the story develops so rapidly and so little detail is given that children hardly have time to feel the story until it is over. The presence of the moral at the end, especially if it be severe, seems to children unfair—they have been promised a story but another motive becomes suddenly apparent. Some of the fables, however, are in themselves good beast stories and as such are very interesting to children. Some of the simpler ones, embodying guides to conduct on the child's level of experience, may undoubtedly claim a place in children's reading.

On occasion, controversy has arisen as to the value of any "make-believe" in literature for children, and the old folk and fairy stories have been criticized on the ground that they give false and distorted pictures of life. Fortunately, the number of traditional stories is so large that we may choose among them and reject those that do not meet our standards of true worth. In fact, we shall reject all stories, whether fanciful or realistic, that give distorted views of life, but a distinction should be made between literal fact and eternal truth. Many of the fine old tales embody eternal truth in a form more convincing than any presentation of literal fact. In these tales of commonplace characters who solve the difficulties of daily living and of heroes who protect the weak and establish justice are distilled the wisdom and ideals of the ages. These stories are straightforward and honest, clear-cut in their issues, and free of sentimentality—high standards by which to measure any literature.

In many respects the tale of fairies, magic, or superhuman heroes plays a role in the emotional development of children that is not greatly different from its function among the folk who created it. The simple folk met the incongruous at every turn, and they saw in it the hand of helpers or of perverse peoples of earth or air. Man needed courage to face and gain some control over nature, and he was helped by making stories that peopled earth and air and water with creatures that came to his aid if right relationships were established. Formidable enemies of other clans met in reality were translated in retrospect into giants, and social inequalities became situations that a humble man might conquer. In his tales man allied himself with powerful forces at one time; at another, he laughed them out of countenance by making fun of the malevolent influences of trolls, by having the least of his own kind climb beanstalks into the heavens to defy giants, and by having a cinder girl win place with the mighty.

Among the folk, imagination was pitted against fear and the unknown, and courage and morale were built in the process. Tales told and retold set the folk standards of positive, confident attack upon life. Through the tales, imaginative capacities were released and turned to good account in stabilizing thoughts and efforts in constructive channels.

There are many parallels between the lives of children and of the folk of other days. To both, adjustments are complex; to both, the world about them is peopled with "big ones" who help or hinder; both must face difficulties that challenge imagination and ingenuity and call for a continuous bolstering of morale. Imagination, ingenuity, morale—these are as essential in present-day life as in the long ago. These tales, the simple tools of the folk, should have a welcome place in the reading of modern children, for these children also must develop courage and insight for living.

There are many kinds of happy experiences that children may have in their contacts with folk tales. One of the most delightful is hearing the stories told. The old tales and legends are more effective when told than when read to children. This is true of stories for the intermediate as well as for the primary grades. Storytelling is an art, but it is an exceedingly simple art that any teacher or mother can learn. Its secret lies in telling the story quietly with little embellishment and without the intrusion of the storyteller's personality. At the end of this section several references on storytelling are given.

Children get a great deal of pleasure from dramatizing stories that they like. The old tales are especially well adapted to play making because of their clearly defined plots and swift-moving action. The lines can be made up extemporaneously and such a play be free of the disadvantages and formality of the readymade play. A dramatization of a well-known story can be a creative experience for children that brings great satisfaction.

Many of the old tales, especially those with grotesque characters and situations, lend themselves to puppet shows—in fact, there is no material more suitable for the purpose than the old folk tales. Making a puppet theater, making the puppets, making and producing a puppet play is a cooperative activity for children of far-reaching social, literary, and artistic values. A list of references dealing with puppetry is given at the end of this section. Many of the books are simple enough to be read by children in the intermediate grades.

There is much that justifies the inclusion of the old tales in a literature program. They are ancient in origin and continue to evolve. They are universal in appeal and have challenged widespread scholarly effort in their preservation. The values of the tales are as old as the tales, and as new as the need for imagination, ingenuity, and courage in meeting the issues of life in a straightforward manner. The pleasure of children in the tales comes through varied avenues of experience to which they can give themselves whole-heartedly. The adult student can share that pleasure by reading the stories that follow for sheer enjoyment, forgetting for the moment the pressure of obligations and duties and escaping into the land of "faery" where life is ever fresh and new, and where things always turn out right in the end.

# Old Tales

## THE THREE BILLY GOATS GRUFF[1]

Once on a time there were three Billy Goats who were to go up to the hillside to make themselves fat, and the name of all the three was "Gruff."

On the way up was a bridge over a burn they had to cross; and under the bridge lived a great ugly Troll, with eyes as big as saucers and a nose as long as a poker.

So first of all came the youngest Billy Goat Gruff to cross the bridge.

"TRIP, TRAP! TRIP, TRAP!" went the bridge.

"WHO'S THAT tripping over my bridge?" roared the Troll.

"Oh! it is only I, the tiniest Billy Goat Gruff; and I'm going up to the hillside to make myself fat," said the Billy Goat, with such a small voice.

"Now, I'm coming to gobble you up," said the Troll.

"Oh, no! pray don't take me. I'm too little, that I am," said the Billy Goat. "Wait a bit till the second Billy Goat Gruff comes; he's much bigger."

"Well! be off with you," said the Troll.

A little while after, came the second Billy Goat Gruff to cross the bridge.

"TRIP, TRAP! TRIP, TRAP! TRIP, TRAP!" went the bridge.

"WHO'S THAT tripping over my bridge?" roared the Troll.

"Oh! it's the second Billy Goat Gruff, and I'm going up to the hillside to make myself fat," said the Billy Goat, who hadn't such a small voice.

"Now, I'm coming to gobble you up," said the Troll.

"Oh, no! don't take me. Wait a little till the big Billy Goat Gruff comes; he's much bigger."

"Very well! be off with you," said the Troll.

But just then up came the big Billy Goat Gruff.

"TRIP, TRAP! TRIP, TRAP! TRIP, TRAP! TRIP, TRAP!" went the bridge, for the Billy Goat was so heavy that the bridge creaked and groaned under him.

"WHO'S THAT tramping over my bridge?" roared the Troll.

"It's I! THE BIG BILLY GOAT GRUFF," said the Billy Goat, who had an ugly hoarse voice of his own.

"Now, I'm coming to gobble you up," roared the Troll.

"Well, come along! I've got two spears,
And I'll poke your eyeballs out at your ears;

[1] From George Webbe Dasent, *Popular Tales from the Norse.*

I've got besides two curling-stones,
And I'll crush you to bits, body and bones."

That was what the big Billy Goat said; and so he flew at the Troll and poked his eyes out with his horns, and crushed him to bits, body and bones, and tossed him out into the burn, and after that he went up to the hillside. There the Billy Goats got so fat they were scarce able to walk home again; and if the fat hasn't fallen off them, why they're still fat; and so—

"Snip, snap, snout,
This tale's told out."

## THE GINGERBREAD BOY[1]

There was once a little old man and a little old woman, who lived in a little old house in the edge of a wood. They would have been a very happy old couple but for one thing—they had no little child, and they wished for one very much. One day when the little old woman was baking gingerbread, she cut a cake in the shape of a little boy and put it into the oven.

Presently she went over to the oven to see if it was baked. As soon as the oven door was opened, the little gingerbread boy jumped out and began to run away as fast as he could go.

The little old woman called to her husband and they both ran after him. But they could not catch him.

Soon the gingerbread boy came to a barn full of threshers. He called out to them as he went by, saying:

"I've run away from a little old woman,
A little old man,
And I can run away from you, I can!"

Then the barn full of threshers set out to run after him. But, though they ran fast, they could not catch him.

He ran on till he came to a field full of mowers. He called out to them:

[1] From *St. Nicholas,* May, 1875.

"I've run away from a little old woman
A little old man,
A barn full of threshers,
And I can run away from you, I can!"

Then the mowers began to run after him, but they couldn't catch him.

He ran on till he came to a cow. He called out to her:

"I've run away from a little old woman,
A little old man,
A barn full of threshers,
A field full of mowers,
And I can run away from you, I can!"

But, though the cow started at once, she couldn't catch him.

Soon he came to a pig. He called out to the pig:

"I've run away from a little old woman,
A little old man,
A barn full of threshers,
A field full of mowers,
A cow—
And I can run away from you, I can!"

And the pig ran, but couldn't catch him.

He ran on till he came across a fox, and to him he called out:

"I've run away from a little old woman,
A little old man,
A barn full of threshers,
A field full of mowers,
A cow and a pig,
And I can run away from you, I can!"

Then the fox set out to run. Now foxes can run very fast, and so the fox soon caught the gingerbread boy and began to eat him up.

Presently the gingerbread boy said: "Oh, dear! I'm quarter gone!" And then: "Oh, I'm half gone!" And soon: "I'm three-quarters gone!" And at last: "I'm all gone!" And that was the end of the gingerbread boy.

## THE THREE BEARS[1]

Once upon a time there were three Bears, who lived together in a house of their own, in a wood. One of them was a Little Wee Bear, and one was a Middle-sized Bear, and the other was a Great Big Bear. They had each a bowl for their porridge; a little bowl for the Little Wee Bear; and a middle-sized bowl for the Middle-sized Bear; and a great bowl for the Great Big Bear. And they had each a chair to sit in; a little chair for the Little Wee Bear; and a middle-sized chair for the Middle-sized Bear; and a great chair for the Great Big Bear. And they had each a bed to sleep in; a little bed for the Little Wee Bear; and a middle-sized bed for the Middle-sized Bear; and a great bed for the Great Big Bear.

One day, after they had made the porridge for their breakfast, and poured it into their porridge bowls, they walked out into the wood while the porridge was cooling. And while they were away a little girl called Goldilocks, who lived at the other side of the wood and had been sent on an errand by her mother, passed by the house and looked in at the window. And then she peeped in at the keyhole. Then seeing nobody in the house she lifted the latch. The door was not fastened, so Goldilocks opened the door and went in; and well pleased was she when she saw the porridge on the table.

First she tasted the porridge of the Great Big Bear, and that was too hot for her. Next she tasted the porridge of the Middle-sized Bear, but that was too cold for her. And then she went to the porridge of the Little Wee Bear, and tasted it, and that was neither too hot nor too cold, but just right, and she liked it so well, that she ate it all up.

Then Goldilocks sat down in the chair of the Great Big Bear, but that was too hard for her. And then she sat down in the chair of the Middle-sized Bear, and that was too soft for her. But when she sat down in the chair of the Little Wee Bear, that was neither too hard, nor too soft, but just right. So she seated herself in it, and there she sat till the bottom of the chair came out, and down she came, plump! upon the ground.

Now Goldilocks went into the bedchamber in which the three Bears slept. And first she lay down upon the bed of the Great Big Bear, but that was too high at the head for her. And next she lay down upon the bed of the Middle-sized Bear, and that was too high at the foot for her. And then she lay down upon the bed of the Little Wee Bear, and that was neither too high at the head, nor at the foot, but just right. So she covered herself up, and lay there till she fell fast asleep.

By this time the Three Bears thought their porridge would be cool enough for them to eat it properly; so they came home to breakfast. Now Goldilocks had left the spoon of the Great Big Bear standing in his porridge.

"SOMEBODY HAS BEEN AT MY PORRIDGE!" said the Great Big Bear in his great, rough, gruff voice.

Then the Middle-sized Bear looked at his porridge and saw the spoon was standing in it too.

"SOMEBODY HAS AT BEEN AT MY PORRIDGE!" said the Middle-sized Bear in his middle-sized voice.

Then the Little Wee Bear looked at his, and there was the spoon in the porridge-bowl, but the porridge was all gone!

"SOMEBODY HAS BEEN AT MY PORRIDGE, AND HAS EATEN IT ALL UP!" said the Little Wee Bear in his little wee voice.

Upon this the Three Bears, seeing that some one had entered their house, and eaten up the Little Wee Bear's breakfast, began to look about them. Now Goldilocks had not put the cushion straight when she rose from the chair of the Great Big Bear.

"SOMEBODY HAS BEEN SITTING IN MY CHAIR!" said the Great Big Bear in his great, rough, gruff voice.

[1] From Flora Annie Steel, *English Fairy Tales.* For discussion of the origin of this story, see notes on Robert Southey in the Appendix of this book.

And Goldilocks had not put the cushion straight when she rose from the chair of the Middle-sized Bear.

"SOMEBODY HAS BEEN SITTING IN MY CHAIR!" said the Middle-sized Bear in his middle-sized voice.

"SOMEBODY HAS BEEN SITTING IN MY CHAIR, AND HAS SAT THE BOTTOM THROUGH!" said the Little Wee Bear in his little wee voice.

Then the Three Bears thought they had better look further, so they went into their bedchamber. Now Goldilocks had pulled the pillow of the Great Big Bear out of its place.

"SOMEBODY HAS BEEN LYING IN MY BED!" said the Great Big Bear in his great, rough, gruff voice.

And Goldilocks had pulled the pillow of the Middle-sized Bear out of its place.

"SOMEBODY HAS BEEN LYING IN MY BED!" said the Middle-sized Bear in his middle-sized voice.

But when the Little Wee Bear came to look at his bed, there was the pillow in its place!

And upon the pillow——?

There was Goldilocks' yellow head.

"SOMEBODY HAS BEEN LYING IN MY BED—AND HERE SHE IS STILL!" said the Little Wee Bear in his little wee voice.

Now Goldilocks had heard in her sleep the great, rough, gruff voice of the Great Big Bear; but she was so fast asleep that it was no more to her than the roaring of wind, or the rumbling of thunder. And she had heard the middle-sized voice of the Middle-sized Bear, but it was only as if she had heard some one speaking in a dream. But when she heard the little wee voice of the Little Wee Bear, it was so sharp, and so shrill, that it awakened her at once. Up she started, and when she saw the Three Bears on one side of the bed, she tumbled herself out at the other, and ran to the window. The window was open and out Goldilocks jumped; away she ran like the wind. The Three Bears never saw anything more of her.

## THE OLD WOMAN AND HER PIG [1]

An old woman was sweeping her house, and she found a little crooked sixpence. "What," said she, "shall I do with this little sixpence?"

"I know what I will do," she said to herself. "I will go to market, and buy me a little pig."

So off to market she went, and she bought a little pig and started home. On the way home she came to a stile, but piggy would not go over the stile.

She went a little further, and she met a dog. So she said,

"Dog! dog! bite pig;
Piggy won't get over the stile,
And I shan't get home tonight."
But the dog would not.

She went a little further, and she met a stick. So she said,

"Stick! stick! beat dog;
Dog won't bite pig;
Piggy won't get over the stile,
And I shan't get home tonight."
But the stick would not.

She went a little further, and she met a fire. So she said,

"Fire! fire! burn stick;
Stick won't beat dog;
Dog won't bite pig;
Piggy won't get over the stile,
And I shan't get home tonight."
But the fire would not.

She went a little further, and she met some water. So she said,

"Water! water! quench fire;
Fire won't burn stick;
Stick won't beat dog;
Dog won't bite pig;
Piggy won't get over the stile,
And I shan't get home tonight."
But the water would not.

[1] Adapted from James Orchard Halliwell, *Nursery Rhymes and Nursery Tales of England*.

She went a little further, and she met an ox. So she said,

"Ox! ox! drink water;
Water won't quench fire;
Fire won't burn stick;
Stick won't beat dog;
Dog won't bite pig;
Piggy won't get over the stile,
And I shan't get home tonight."
But the ox would not.

She went a little further, and she met a butcher. So she said,

"Butcher! butcher! kill ox;
Ox won't drink water;
Water won't quench fire;
Fire won't burn stick;
Stick won't beat dog;
Dog won't bite pig;
Piggy won't get over the stile,
And I shan't get home tonight."
But the butcher would not.

She went a little further, and she met a rope. So she said,

"Rope! rope! hang butcher;
Butcher won't kill ox;
Ox won't drink water;
Water won't quench fire;
Fire won't burn stick;
Stick won't beat dog;
Dog won't bite pig;
Piggy won't get over the stile,
And I shan't get home tonight."
But the rope would not.

She went a little further, and she met a rat. So she said,

"Rat! rat! gnaw rope;
Rope won't hang butcher;
Butcher won't kill ox;
Ox won't drink water;
Water won't quench fire;
Fire won't burn stick;
Stick won't beat dog;
Dog won't bite pig;
Piggy won't get over the stile,
And I shan't get home tonight."
But the rat would not.

She went a little further, and she met a cat. So she said,

"Cat! cat! kill rat;
Rat won't gnaw rope;
Rope won't hang butcher;
Butcher won't kill ox;
Ox won't drink water;
Water won't quench fire;
Fire won't burn stick;
Stick won't beat dog;
Dog won't bite pig;
Piggy won't get over the stile,
And I shan't get home tonight."

But the cat said to her,

"If you will go to yonder cow,
And fetch me a saucer of milk,
I will kill the rat."

Away went the old woman to the cow. But the cow said to her,

"If you will go to yonder haystack,
And fetch me a handful of hay,
I'll give you the milk."

Away went the woman to the haystack; and she brought the hay to the cow. As soon as the cow had eaten the hay, she gave the old woman the milk; and away she went with it in a saucer to the cat.

As soon as the cat had lapped up the milk,

The cat began to kill the rat;
The rat began to gnaw the rope;
The rope began to hang the butcher;
The butcher began to kill the ox;
The ox began to drink the water;
The water began to quench the fire;
The fire began to burn the stick;
The stick began to beat the dog;
The dog began to bite the pig.

The little piggy in a fright jumped over the stile; and so the old woman got home that night.

## THE STRAW OX[1]

There was once upon a time an old man and an old woman. The old man worked in the fields as a pitch-burner, while the old woman sat at home and spun flax. They were so poor that they could save nothing at all; all their earnings went for bare food, and when that was gone there was nothing left. At last the old woman had a good idea.

"Look now, husband," cried she, "make me a straw ox, and smear it all over with tar."

"Why, you foolish woman!" said he, "what's the good of an ox of that sort?"

"Never mind," said she, "you just make it. I know what I am about."

What was the poor man to do? He set to work and made the ox of straw, and smeared it all over with tar.

The night passed away, and at early dawn the old woman took her distaff, and drove the straw ox out into the steppe to graze, and she herself sat down behind a hillock, and began spinning her flax, and cried:

"Graze away, little ox, while I spin my flax. Graze away, little ox, while I spin my flax!" And while she spun, her head drooped down and she began to doze, and while she was dozing, from behind the dark wood and from the back of the huge pines a bear came rushing out upon the ox and said:

"Who are you? Speak, and tell me!"

And the ox said:

"A three-year-old heifer am I, made of straw and smeared with tar."

"Oh!" said the bear, "stuffed with straw and smeared with tar, are you? Then give me of your straw and tar, that I may patch up my ragged fur again!"

"Take some," said the ox, and the bear fell upon him and began to tear away at the tar.

He tore and tore, and buried his teeth in it till he found he couldn't let go again. He tugged and he tugged, but it was no good, and the ox dragged him gradually off, goodness knows where.

Then the old woman awoke, and there was no ox to be seen. "Alas!" cried she, "perchance it has gone home." Then she quickly caught up her distaff and spinning board, threw them over her shoulders, and hastened off home, and she saw that the ox had dragged the bear up to the fence, and in she went to her old man.

"Dad, dad," she cried, "look, look! The ox has brought us a bear. Come out and kill it!" Then the old man jumped up, tore off the bear, tied him up, and threw him in the cellar.

Next morning, between dark and dawn, the old woman took her distaff and drove the ox into the steppe to graze. She herself sat down by a mound, began spinning, and said:

"Graze, graze away, little ox, while I spin my flax! Graze, graze away, little ox, while I spin my flax!" And while she spun, her head drooped down and she dozed. And, lo! from behind the dark wood, from the back of the huge pines, a gray wolf came rushing out upon the ox and said:

"Who are you? Come, tell me!"

"I am a three-year-old heifer, stuffed with straw and trimmed with tar," said the ox.

"Oh! trimmed with tar, are you? Then give me of your tar to tar my sides, that the dogs and the sons of dogs tear me not!"

"Take some," said the ox. And with that the wolf fell upon him and tried to tear the tar off. He tugged and tugged, and tore with his teeth, but could get none off. Then he tried to let go, and couldn't; tug and worry as he might, it was no good. When the old woman woke, there was no heifer in sight. "Maybe my heifer has gone home!" she cried. "I'll go home and see." When she got there she was astonished, for by the paling stood the ox with the wolf still tugging at it. She ran and told her old man, and her old man came and threw the wolf into the cellar also.

[1] From R. Nisbet Bain, *Cossack Fairy Tales.*

On the third day the old woman again drove her ox into the pastures to graze, and sat down by a mound and dozed off. Then a fox came running up. "Who are you?" it asked the ox.

"I'm a three-year-old heifer, stuffed with straw and daubed with tar."

"Then give me some of your tar to daub my sides with, when those dogs and sons of dogs tear my hide!"

"Take some," said the ox. Then the fox fastened her teeth in him and couldn't draw them out again. The old woman told her old man, and he took and cast the fox into the cellar in the same way. And after that they caught a hare likewise.

So when he had got them all safely, the old man sat down on a bench before the cellar and began sharpening a knife. And the bear said to him:

"Tell me, daddy, what are you sharpening your knife for?"

"To flay your skin off, that I may make a leather jacket for myself and a pelisse for my old woman."

"Oh! don't flay me, daddy dear! Rather let me go, and I'll bring you a lot of honey."

"Very well, see you do it," and he unbound and let the bear go. Then he sat down on the bench and again began sharpening his knife. And the wolf asked him:

"Daddy, what are you sharpening your knife for?"

"To flay off your skin, that I may make me a warm cap against the winter."

"Oh! don't flay me, daddy dear, and I'll bring you a whole herd of little sheep."

"Well, see that you do it," and he let the wolf go.

Then he sat down, and began sharpening his knife again. The fox put out her little snout, and asked him:

"Be so kind, dear daddy, and tell me why you are sharpening your knife!"

"Little foxes," said the old man, "have nice skins that do capitally for collars and trimmings, and I want to skin you!"

"Oh! don't take my skin away, daddy dear, and I will bring you hens and geese."

"Very well, see that you do it!" and he let the fox go.

The hare now alone remained, and the old man began sharpening his knife on the hare's account.

"Why do you do that?" asked the hare, and he replied:

"Little hares have nice little, soft, warm skins, which will make me nice gloves and mittens against the winter!"

"Oh! daddy dear! Don't flay me, and I'll bring you kale and good cauliflower, if only you let me go!"

Then he let the hare go also.

Then they went to bed; but very early in the morning, when it was neither dark nor dawn, there was a noise in the doorway like "Durrrrrr!"

"Daddy!" cried the old woman, "there's some one scratching at the door; go and see who it is!"

The old man went out, and there was the bear carrying a whole hive full of honey. The old man took the honey from the bear; but no sooner did he lie down again than there was another "Durrrrr!" at the door. The old man looked out and saw the wolf driving a whole flock of sheep into the courtyard. Close on his heels came the fox, driving before him the geese and hens, and all manner of fowls; and last of all came the hare, bringing cabbage and kale, and all manner of good food.

And the old man was glad, and the old woman was glad. And the old man sold the sheep and oxen, and got so rich that he needed nothing more.

As for the straw-stuffed ox, it stood in the sun till it fell to pieces.

## LITTLE RED RIDING HOOD [1]

Once upon a time there was a little girl who was called little Red Riding Hood, because she was quite small and because she always wore a red cloak with a big red

[1] Adapted from Flora Annie Steel, *English Fairy Tales.*

hood to it, which her grandmother had made for her.

Now one day her mother, who had been churning and baking cakes, said to her:

"My dear, put on your red cloak with the hood to it, and take this cake, and this pot of butter to your Grannie, and ask how she is, for I hear she is ailing."

Now little Red Riding Hood was very fond of her grandmother who made her so many nice things, so she put on her cloak joyfully and started on her errand. But her grandmother lived some way off, and to reach the cottage little Red Riding Hood had to pass through a vast lonely forest. However, some wood-cutters were at work in it, so little Red Riding Hood was not so very much alarmed when she saw a great big wolf coming towards her.

And sure enough the wolf, though but for the wood-cutters he would surely have eaten little Red Riding Hood, only stopped and asked her politely where she was going.

"I am going to see Grannie, take her this cake and this pot of butter and ask how she is," said little Red Riding Hood.

"Does she live a very long way off?" asked the wolf craftily.

"Not so very far if you go by the straight road," replied little Red Riding Hood. "You only have to pass the mill and the first cottage on the right is Grannie's; but I am going by the wood-path because there are such a lot of nuts and flowers and butterflies."

"I wish you good luck," said the wolf politely. "Give my respects to your grandmother and tell her I hope she is quite well."

And with that he trotted off. But instead of going his way he turned back, took the straight road to the old woman's cottage and knocked at the door.

Rap! Rap! Rap!

But Grannie had gone to see the wood-cutters, so no one came to the door. The wolf knocked again and then walked in and shut the door. Then he put on Grannie's nightcap and her nightgown, and got into bed and rolled himself well up in the bedclothes.

By and by along came little Red Riding Hood, who had been amusing herself by gathering nuts, running after butterflies, and picking flowers.

So she knocked at the door.

Rap! Rap! Rap!

"Who's there?" said the wolf, making his voice as soft as he could.

Now little Red Riding Hood heard the voice and it was very gruff, but she thought her grandmother had a cold; so she said:

"Little Red Riding Hood with a pot of butter and a cake from Mother to ask how you are."

"Pull the bobbin and the latch will go up."

So little Red Riding Hood pulled the bobbin, the latch went up, and there, she thought, was her grandmother in the bed; for the cottage was so dark that she could not see well. Besides the crafty wolf turned his face to the wall at first. And he made his voice as soft as he could, when he said:

"Come and kiss me, my dear."

Then little Red Riding Hood took off her cloak and went to the bed.

"Oh, Grandmamma, Grandmamma," said she, "what big arms you've got!"

"All the better to hug you with," said he.

"Oh, Grandmamma, Grandmamma, what big ears you've got!"

"All the better to hear you with, my dear."

"But Grandmamma, Grandmamma, what big eyes you've got!"

"All the better to see you with, my dear!"

"Oh, Grandmamma, Grandmamma, what big teeth you've got!"

"All the better to eat you with, my dear!" said the wicked wolf. With that he jumped out of bed and chased little Red Riding Hood, who ran out of the house.

But that was the wolf's undoing, for there he met the wood-cutters, and they cut off his head before he could get out of Grannie's night clothes and run away.

## AIKEN-DRUM, THE BROWNIE[1]

Did you ever hear of Aiken-Drum, the brownie? And did you ever hear how he came one time and lived in a village?

It was on a fine warm evening in the fall that Aiken-Drum came to the village. The sun had gone down. The mothers came to the doors of the houses and called the children from play, for it was time to go to bed. The cows were in the barns for the night, and the men were bringing in the milk. It was then that the people of the village first heard Aiken-Drum.

The children heard the queer noise. They stopped and said, "Is that someone, or is it the wind?" They ran to their mothers and called to their fathers. They could all hear the queer noise now, but they did not know what it was.

Then they saw Aiken-Drum, and as he came along, he sang a queer song in a queer little voice,

"Have you work for Aiken-Drum?
Have you work for Aiken-Drum?"

As Aiken-Drum came nearer, the little children got behind their mothers. Even the mothers were a little afraid, and the fathers did not know what to think of this queer little man. They had never seen anyone like him. The men and the women said nothing, but the boys and the girls could not keep still.

One of them said, "See his long red beard! It comes down to his knees!"

"How little he is!" said another. "What is he? Is he a man, Mother?"

"His hands come nearly to his feet," said another.

"His knees knock together," said another.

"His clothes are made of long brown grass," said still another.

All the time Aiken-Drum was coming nearer and nearer, and as he came, he sang his song over and over again.

"Have you work for Aiken-Drum?
Have you work for Aiken-Drum?"

Then he came to a stop before them. They all looked at Aiken-Drum, and Aiken-Drum looked at them. And they were more afraid than he was.

Aiken-Drum stopped singing his song, and one of the men said to him, "Who are you, and why do you come here?"

This is what Aiken-Drum said,

"I am Aiken-Drum, Aiken-Drum.
To help you work is why I come."

"But where do you come from?" asked the man.

And Aiken-Drum said,

"I come from a land where work is play,
Where we like to work but take no pay."

The people could not believe this, and they said so. They thought it was silly for anyone to say that work was play. Why would anyone work and take no pay? They could not believe that this queer little man with a long beard and knees that knocked together could do much work. Why was he here?

Aiken-Drum heard all this and said in his queer high voice,

"You have work for Aiken Drum.
You have work, or I would not come.
I can watch your sheep by night,
Make your hay by the pale moonlight.
To your children, songs I'll sing,
And for my work take not a thing.
No gold, no clothes, may I take,
Or I'll be gone before you wake."

This is what Aiken-Drum said to the people of the village. Then he looked long at an old, old woman and said,

"One of you once I knew.
She can tell you this is true."

[1] From Miriam Blanton Huber, Frank Seely Salisbury, and Mabel O'Donnell, *After the Sun Sets* (*The Wonder-Story Books,* Book Three).

Then the old, old woman said, "Yes, it is true. He is a brownie. Brownies work and think it is play, and they never take any pay for their work. They like children, and children like them. They come when people need them most. They do their work at night when other people are asleep. They eat little and do much."

The people asked the old, old woman, "Where will he live? Who is to give him food? Where will he work?"

"Brownies know where there is work to do," said the old woman. "Aiken-Drum will work where he is needed. He will do his work while you are asleep. Say nothing to him of food to eat, but put a bowl of porridge by the fire. Where he lives no one knows."

When the people looked again, Aiken-Drum was not there.

"He has gone away," all the children said together.

"No," said the old, old woman. "He has not gone away. It is not often that brownies can be seen. He is near by. He has gone to find a place to live."

The children wondered where Aiken-Drum would find a place to live. They wondered where he would find his first work to do, and they wondered who would think to put some porridge by the fire for him.

But that all worked out as it should. That day the cream would not churn to butter for one woman, and it was still in the churn when evening came. Before the woman went to bed, she put a bowl of porridge by the fire, and beside the bowl she put a little spoon. In the morning anyone could see that Aiken-Drum had been there, for the cream was churned to butter and the porridge was gone from the bowl. The spoon was in the bowl, but the porridge was gone.

The next night a great wind came up and blew open the doors of many of the barns. The sheep and cows ran away. The men could not find them in the dark, and the wind blew so hard that no one wanted to be out of doors. But by morning the sheep and cows were back in the barns again. So who but Aiken-Drum could have put them in the barns?

There was another way to tell that Aiken-Drum had been working that night. In more than one house the children had asked their mothers to put a bowl of porridge by the fire. In the morning they found each bowl with the spoon in it, and some of the porridge gone.

One day the men could not put all the hay in the barns before night came. But in the morning they found none of the hay in the fields. They looked in the barns, and there it was. They could not believe that Aiken-Drum had done all this work. But who could have done it, if not Aiken-Drum?

The children knew that Aiken-Drum was still near, but they could not find where he lived. They looked here and they looked there, but they never found Aiken-Drum. They asked the old, old woman where he was, and she said, "I do not know. Some say that brownies live far down in the hay in the barns. Others say that they live in big holes in the trees. I have heard it said that they live in small woods at the top of hills. Some say that they live at the side of the road in the high grass."

So the children looked in the hay in the barns. They called to Aiken-Drum to come and play with them, but he never came. They looked in the big holes in all the trees, and they looked in the small woods at the top of the hill, but they did not find him.

They could almost believe that he lived in the high grass at the side of the road. One day the boys and girls were playing with their beanbags. One boy had a red beanbag. "It is just like Aiken-Drum's beard," he said.

Then he threw the beanbag as hard as he could, and it went over the heads of the others and fell in the high grass at the side of the road. They looked and looked for that beanbag, but they could not find it.

Then one of the children called out, "I believe Aiken-Drum took it away. He did not like to have you talk about him."

Their mothers called them to dinner, and when they came back to play, there was the beanbag right where they had looked for it before. Then they all said that Aiken-Drum must have been there in the high grass.

One day a little girl thought of the time that Aiken-Drum first came to the village. She said to the other children, "Aiken-Drum said he would sing songs to us. Why do we never hear him?"

They went to see the old, old woman and asked her why Aiken-Drum never sang to them. The old, old woman told them, "Aiken-Drum sings to you every day, but you do not hear him. I hear him. He has a queer little high voice that comes on the wind. You make so much noise at your play that you can not hear him. The very little children hear him, for he sings them to sleep."

So the days came and went. The children looked again and again for Aiken-Drum, but they never found him.

At times the children would stop in their play, and some of them were sure that they could hear the song of Aiken-Drum coming from the trees and from the high grass at the side of the road. Others said it was only the wind that made the noise.

The children were very sure that Aiken-Drum took their beanbags, for time after time they lost them and could not find them. Then they would come back, and there the beanbags would be, right where they had looked for them.

The fathers and mothers were sure that Aiken-Drum was still with them. Each morning they found some work done that had not been done the night before.

Aiken-Drum watched over the sheep when the nights were cold. He found the cows when they were lost.

On mornings when the mothers had much work to do, they would find the floors in their houses clean, the cream churned, and the butter put away in big bowls. They were very sure, too, that Aiken-Drum sang the little children to sleep.

The days and nights grew colder. The fall work was about over, and the wheat was all in the barns. In the mornings many a father found the wheat threshed on his barn floor. And a very fine piece of work it was that Aiken-Drum did, too. The wheat was threshed and cleaned and put in one place, and the straw in another. The barn floor was as clean as could be.

In all the houses the women were making warm clothes for the children. Many a time a mother came to the end of the day with the cloth cut for her children's clothes. In the morning there would be the clothes, all made.

One day a little girl said to her mother, "Mother, why not make Aiken-Drum some nice warm clothes? How can he keep warm in clothes made of long brown grass?"

"Very well," said the mother, "we will make Aiken-Drum some nice warm clothes. We will put the clothes beside his porridge, and then he will be sure to get them."

That day she made the clothes, and that night she put the little clothes beside the porridge.

But in the morning the clothes were right where the mother had put them, and all the porridge was in the bowl. In all the other houses the spoons were beside the porridge bowls, and all the porridge was in the bowls.

"Aiken-Drum is gone!" the people said. "Why did he go? Why did he go?"

They went to the old, old woman and told her all about it.

"Yes," said the old, old woman, "he is gone. Brownies go if you pay them."

"But it is cold, and he needs warm clothes," said the mother who had made the clothes.

"Brownies must make their own clothes of brown straw and grass. They can wear no other clothes and still be brownies."

"Will he come back?" they all asked.

"He may come back, and he may not," said the old, old woman. "Aiken-Drum has gone where there is more work to do, but he may come back again."

The little children of the village still put

out bowls of porridge for Aiken-Drum. Now and then the porridge is gone when morning comes, but the spoons are never in the bowls. "It must be the cat that eats the porridge," the mothers say.

When the little children go to sleep as soon as they are put to bed, the mothers say that Aiken-Drum is singing to them. When the work gets hard for the men, they say that it is time for Aiken-Drum to come back to help them.

At times the children say they hear Aiken-Drum singing in the trees, and they are sure that he finds their beanbags for them. "It must be true," they say, "for we come back to play and find them right where we have been looking for them."

And who knows, it may be Aiken-Drum who helps you find your beanbag, for is it not true that you come back and find it right where you have been looking for it?

## MR. VINEGAR [1]

Mr. and Mrs. Vinegar lived in a vinegar bottle. Now, one day when Mr. Vinegar was away from home and Mrs. Vinegar, who was a very good housewife, was busily sweeping her house, an unlucky thump of the broom brought the whole house clitter-clatter about her ears. In great grief she rushed forth to meet her husband. On seeing him she exclaimed,

"Oh, Mr. Vinegar, Mr. Vinegar, we are ruined, we are ruined! I have knocked the house down, and it is all to pieces!"

Mr. Vinegar then said:

"My dear, let us see what can be done. Here is the door; I will take it on my back, and we will go forth to seek our fortune."

They walked all that day and at nightfall entered a thick forest. They were both tired, and Mr. Vinegar said:

"My love, I will climb up into a tree, drag up the door, and you shall follow."

He did so, and they both stretched their weary limbs on the door, and fell fast asleep.

In the middle of the night Mr. Vinegar was disturbed by the sound of voices beneath, and to his dismay saw that a party of thieves were met to divide their booty.

"Here, Jack," said one, "here's five pounds for you; here, Bill, here's ten pounds for you; here, Bob, here's three pounds for you."

Mr. Vinegar could listen no longer; he was so afraid that he trembled violently and shook down the door on their heads. Away scampered the thieves, but Mr. Vinegar dared not come down till broad daylight. He then scrambled out of the tree and went to lift up the door. What did he see but a number of golden guineas!

"Come down, Mrs. Vinegar," he cried; "come down, I say; our fortune's made! Come down, I say."

Mrs. Vinegar got down as fast as she could and saw the money with equal delight.

"Now, my dear," said she, "I'll tell you what you shall do. There is a fair at the neighboring town; you shall take these forty guineas and buy a cow. I can make butter and cheese, which you shall sell at market, and we shall then be able to live very comfortably."

Mr. Vinegar agreed and took the money and went off to the fair. When he arrived, he walked up and down, and at length saw a beautiful red cow. It was an excellent milker and perfect in every respect.

"Oh," thought Mr. Vinegar, "if I had but that cow, I should be the happiest man alive."

So he offered the forty guineas for the cow, and the owner declaring that, as he was a friend, he'd oblige him, the bargain was made. Proud of his purchase, he drove the cow backwards and forwards to show it.

By and by Mr. Vinegar saw a man playing some bagpipes—*tweedle-dum, tweedle-dee*. The children followed him about, and he appeared to be pocketing money on all sides.

"Well," thought Mr. Vinegar, "if I had

[1] From James Orchard Halliwell, *Nursery Rhymes and Nursery Tales of England*.

that beautiful instrument, I should be the happiest man alive—my fortune would be made."

So he went up to the man.

"Friend," said he, "what a beautiful instrument that is, and what a deal of money you must make."

"Why, yes," said the man, "I make a great deal of money, to be sure, and it is a wonderful instrument."

"Oh!" cried Mr. Vinegar, "how I should like to possess it!"

"Well," said the man, "as you are a friend, I don't much mind parting with it; you shall have it for that red cow."

"Done!" said the delighted Mr. Vinegar. So the beautiful red cow was given for the bagpipes.

He walked up and down with his purchase; but in vain he attempted to play a tune, and instead of pocketing pence, the boys followed him hooting and laughing.

Poor Mr. Vinegar, his fingers grew very cold, and heartily ashamed and mortified, he was leaving the town, when he met a man with a fine thick pair of gloves.

"Oh, my fingers are so very cold," said Mr. Vinegar to himself. "If I had those beautiful gloves, I should be the happiest man alive."

He went up to the man, and said to him: "Friend, you seem to have a capital pair of gloves there."

"Yes, truly," cried the man; "and my hands are as warm as possible this cold November day."

"Well," said Mr. Vinegar, "I should like to have them."

"What will you give?" said the man. "As you are a friend, I don't much mind letting you have them for those bagpipes."

"Done!" cried Mr. Vinegar. He put on the gloves, and felt perfectly happy as he trudged homewards.

At last he grew very tired, when he saw a man coming towards him with a good stout stick in his hand.

"Oh," said Mr. Vinegar, "that I had that stick! I should then be the happiest man alive."

He said to the man: "Friend! what a rare good stick you have."

"Yes," said the man; "I have used it for many a long mile, and a good friend it has been; but if you have a fancy for it, as you are a friend, I don't mind giving it to you for that pair of gloves."

Mr. Vinegar's hands were so warm, and his legs so tired, that he gladly exchanged.

As he drew near to the wood where he had left his wife, he heard a parrot on a tree calling out his name:

"Mr. Vinegar, you foolish man! You went to the fair and laid out all your money in buying a cow. Not content with that, you changed it for bagpipes, on which you could not play and which were not worth one-tenth of the money. You had no sooner got the bagpipes than you changed them for the gloves, which were not worth one-quarter of the money. When you had got the gloves, you changed them for a poor miserable stick. Now for your forty guineas, cow, bagpipes, and gloves, you have nothing to show but that poor miserable stick, which you might have cut in any hedge."

At this the bird laughed, and Mr. Vinegar, falling into a violent rage, threw the stick at its head. The stick lodged in the tree. So Mr. Vinegar returned to his wife without money, cow, bagpipes, gloves, or stick.

## LAZY JACK[1]

Once upon a time there was a boy whose name was Jack, and he lived with his mother in an old house. They were very poor, and the mother made her living by spinning, but Jack was so lazy that he would do nothing but bask in the sun in the hot weather and sit by the corner of the hearth in the wintertime. His mother could not persuade him to do anything for her, and at last she told him he could

[1] From James Orchard Halliwell, *Nursery Rhymes and Nursery Tales of England.*

have nothing to eat unless he went to work.

This roused Jack, and he went out and hired himself for the day to a neighboring farmer for a penny. As he was coming home, never having had any money in his possession before, he lost it in passing over a brook.

"You foolish boy!" said his mother. "You should have put it in your pocket."

"I'll do so next time," said Jack.

The next day Jack went out again and hired himself to a cow-keeper, who gave him a jar of milk for his day's work. Jack took the jar and put it into the large pocket of his jacket, spilling it all long before he got home.

"You foolish boy!" said his mother. "You should have carried it on your head."

"I'll do so next time," said Jack.

The following day Jack hired himself again to a farmer, who agreed to give him a cream cheese for his services. In the evening Jack took the cheese and went home with it on his head. By the time he got home the cheese was completely spoilt, part of it being lost and part stuck in his hair.

"You foolish boy!" said his mother. "You should have carried it carefully in your hands."

"I'll do so next time," said Jack.

The day after this Jack again went out and hired himself to a baker, who would give him nothing for his work but a large cat. Jack took the cat and began carrying it very carefully in his hands, but in a short time the cat scratched him so that he had to let it go. When he got home, his mother said to him: "You foolish boy! You should have tied it with a string and dragged it along after you."

"I'll do so next time," said Jack.

The next day Jack hired himself to a butcher, who gave him a fine shoulder of mutton. Jack took the mutton, tied a string to it, and trailed it along after him in the dirt. By the time he had got home the meat was completely spoilt. His mother was this time quite out of patience with him, for the next day was Sunday, and she was obliged to content herself with cabbage for her dinner.

"You foolish boy!" she said. "You should have carried it on your shoulder."

"I'll do so next time," said Jack.

On Monday Jack went once more and hired himself to a cattle-keeper, who gave him a donkey for his trouble. Although Jack was very strong, he had some trouble getting the donkey on his shoulders, but at last he did and began walking slowly home with his prize.

Now it happened that in the course of his journey there lived a rich man with his only daughter, a beautiful girl, but unfortunately she could neither hear nor speak. She had never laughed in her life, and the doctors said she would never recover till somebody made her laugh. Many tried without success, and at last the father, in despair, promised her in marriage to the first man who could make her laugh.

This young lady happened to be looking out of the window when Jack was passing with the donkey on his shoulders, the legs sticking up in the air. The sight was so comical and strange that she burst out into a great fit of laughter, and immediately recovered her speech and hearing. Her father was overjoyed, and fulfilled his promise by marrying her to Jack, who was thus made a rich gentleman. They lived in a large house, and Jack's mother lived with them in great happiness until she died.

## THE THREE LITTLE PIGS [1]

Once upon a time there was an old mother pig who had three little pigs, and as she had not enough for them to eat, she said they had better go out into the world and seek their fortunes.

Now the oldest pig went first, and as he

[1] Adapted from Flora Annie Steel, *English Fairy Tales.*

trotted along the road he met a man carrying a bundle of straw. So he said very politely:

"If you please, sir, could you give me that straw to build me a house?"

And the man, seeing what good manners the little pig had, gave him the straw, and the little pig set to work and built a beautiful house with it.

Now, the next little pig met a man carrying a bundle of sticks, and, being very polite, he said to him:

"If you please, sir, could you give me those sticks to build me a house?"

And the man, seeing what good manners the little pig had, gave him the sticks, and the little pig set to work and built himself a beautiful house.

Then the next little pig met a man with a load of bricks and he was just as polite as the other little pigs, and he said to the man:

"If you please, sir, could you give me those bricks to build me a house?"

And the man, seeing what good manners the little pig had, gave him the bricks, and the little pig set to work and built himself a strong brick house.

Soon after the three houses were finished an old wolf happened to pass by the house of straw; first, he looked at the house, and then he smelt the pig inside.

So he knocked at the door and said:

"Little pig! Little pig! Let me come in!"

But the little pig saw the wolf's big paws through the keyhole, so he answered back:

"No! No! By the hair of my chinny chin chin!"

Then the wolf showed his teeth and said:

"Then I'll huff and I'll puff and I'll blow your house in!"

So he huffed and he puffed and he blew the house in. But the little pig was not there, for he had run out the back way, and had gone to the little pig that lived in the house of sticks.

But the old wolf could smell pigs a long way, and he went straight to the house of sticks and knocked on the door and said:

"Little pigs! Little pigs! Let me come in!"

But one little pig peeped through the keyhole, and the other peeped under the door, and one saw the wolf's big ears, and the other saw his long tail, and they both answered back in the same breath:

"No! No! By the hair of our chinny chin chins!"

Then the wolf showed his teeth and said:

"Then I'll huff and I'll puff and I'll blow your house in."

So he huffed and he puffed and he blew the house in.

But the old wolf did not get the two little pigs, for they ran away as fast as they could and went straight to the little pig that lived in the house of bricks. The old wolf got his breath and went right after them, and when he got to the house of bricks he was very angry and he knocked hard on the door and said:

"Little pigs! Little pigs! Let me come in!"

But the three little pigs answered right back, and said:

"No! No! By the hair of our chinny chin chins!"

"Then I'll huff and I'll puff and I'll blow your house in!" said the wolf, showing his teeth.

He huffed and he puffed. He puffed and he huffed. And he huffed, huffed, and he puffed, puffed; but he could not blow the house in. At last he was so out of breath that he couldn't huff and he couldn't puff any more. So he thought a bit. Then he said:

"Little pigs! I know where there is ever such a nice field of turnips."

"Do you?" said the little pigs. "And where may that be?"

"I'll show you," said the wolf; "if you will be ready at six o'clock tomorrow morning, I will call round for you, and we can go together to Farmer Smith's field and get turnips for dinner."

"Thank you kindly," said the little pigs,

"we will be ready at six o'clock sharp."

But, you see, the little pigs were not to be taken in so easily, so they got up at five, trotted off to Farmer Smith's field, rooted up the turnips, and were home eating them for breakfast when the wolf clattered at the door, and cried:

"Little pigs! Little pigs! Aren't you ready?"

"Ready?" said the little pigs. "Why! what a sluggard you are! We've been to the field and come back again; we are having a nice potful of turnips for breakfast."

Then the wolf grew red with rage; but he was determined to eat the little pigs, so he said, as if he didn't care:

"I'm glad you like them; but I know of something better than turnips."

"Indeed," said the little pigs, "and what may that be?"

"A nice apple tree down in Merry gardens with the juiciest, sweetest apples on it! So if you will be ready at five o'clock tomorrow morning I will come round for you and we can get the apples together."

"Thank you kindly," said the little pigs, "we will surely be ready at five o'clock sharp."

Now the next morning the pigs bustled up ever so early, and it wasn't four o'clock when they started to get the apples; but, you see, the wolf had been taken in once and wasn't going to be taken in again, so he also started at four o'clock, and the little pigs had just got their baskets half full of apples when they saw the wolf coming down the road licking his lips.

"Hullo!" said the wolf, "here already! You are early birds! Are the apples nice?"

"Very nice," said the little pigs. "We'll throw you down one to try."

But they threw it so far away, that when the wolf went to pick it up, the little pigs jumped down with their baskets and ran home.

Well, the wolf was angry; but he went next day to the little pigs' house and called through the door, as mild as milk:

"Little pigs! Little pigs! You are so clever, I should like to take you to the fair; so if you will come with me this afternoon you shall have a happy time."

"Thank you kindly," said the little pigs, "what time shall we start?"

"At three o'clock sharp," said the wolf, "so be sure to be ready."

"We'll be ready before three," sniggered the little pigs. And they were! They started early in the morning and went to the fair, and rode in a swing, and enjoyed themselves ever so much, and bought a great butter-churn, and trotted away towards home long before three o'clock. But just as they got to the top of the hill what should they see but the wolf coming up it, all panting and red with rage!

Well, there was no place to hide in but the butter-churn; so they jumped into it, and were just pulling down the cover when the churn started to roll down the hill—

Bumpety, bumpety, bump!

Of course the little pigs inside began to squeal, and when the wolf heard the noise, and saw the butter-churn rolling down on top of him—

Bumpety, bumpety, bump!

—he was so frightened that he turned tail and ran away.

But he was still determined to get the little pigs for his dinner; so he went next day to the house and told them how sorry he was not to have been able to keep his promise of going to the fair, because of an awful, dreadful, terrible Thing that had rushed at him, making a fearsome noise.

"Dear me!" said the little pigs, "that must have been us! We hid inside the butter-churn when we saw you coming, and it started to roll! We are sorry we frightened you!"

But this was too much. The wolf danced about with rage and swore he would come down the chimney and eat all the little pigs for his supper. But while he was climbing on to the roof one little pig made up a blazing fire, and one put on a big pot full of water to boil, and, just as the wolf was coming down the chimney, the other little pig took off the lid, and plump! in fell the wolf into the scalding water.

So the little pigs put on the cover again, boiled the wolf up, and ate *him* for supper.

## THE TRAVELING MUSICIANS[1]

A farmer had once a donkey that had been a faithful servant to him a great many years, but was now growing old and every day more and more unfit for work. His master therefore was tired of keeping him and began to think of putting an end to him. But the donkey who saw that some mischief was in the wind, took himself slyly off and began his journey towards the great city.

"For there," thought he, "I may turn musician."

After he had traveled a little way, he spied a dog lying by the roadside and panting as if he were very tired. "What makes you pant so, my friend?" said the donkey.

"Alas!" said the dog, "my master said he would not keep me because I am old and weak and can no longer make myself useful to him in hunting. So I ran away. But what can I do to earn my living?"

"Oh!" said the donkey, "I am going to the great city to turn musician. Suppose you go with me and try what you can do in the same way?"

The dog said he was willing, and they jogged on together.

Before they had gone far, they saw a cat sitting in the middle of the road and looking very sad.

"Pray, my good lady," said the donkey, "what's the matter with you? You look quite out of spirits!"

"Ah, me!" said the cat, "how can one be in good spirits when one's life is in danger? Because I am beginning to grow old and had rather lie at my ease by the fire than run about the house after mice, my mistress was going to drown me. Though I have been lucky enough to get away from her, I do not know what I am going to do."

[1] From Edgar Taylor, *Grimms' Popular Stories.*

"Oh!" said the donkey, "by all means go with us to the great city. You are a good night-singer and may make your fortune as a musician."

The cat was pleased with the thought and joined the party.

Soon afterwards, as they were passing by a farmyard, they saw a cock perched upon a gate, screaming out with all his might and main.

"Bravo!" said the donkey; "upon my word you make a famous noise. Pray what is all this about?"

"Why," said the cock, "I was just now saying that we should have fine weather for our washing-day. Yet my mistress and the cook don't thank me for my pains, but threaten to cut off my head tomorrow and make broth of me for the guests that are coming on Sunday."

"Well, then," said the donkey, "come with us. It will be better than staying here to have your head cut off! Besides, who knows? If we take care to sing in tune, we may get up some kind of a concert. So come along with us."

"With all my heart," said the cock.

So they all four went on together.

They could not, however, reach the great city the first day. When night came on they went into a wood to sleep. The donkey and the dog laid themselves down under a great tree, and the cat climbed up into the branches; while the cock, thinking that the higher he sat the safer he would be, flew up to the very top of the tree, and then, according to his custom, before he went to sleep, looked out on all sides of him to see that everything was well. In doing this, he saw afar off something bright and shining. Calling to his companions, he said, "There must be a house no great way off, for I see a light."

"If that is the case," said the donkey, "we had better change our quarters, for our lodging is not the best in the world!"

"Besides," added the dog, "I should not be the worse for a bone or two, or a bit of meat."

So they walked off together towards the spot where the cock had seen the light. As they drew near, it became larger and brighter, till they at last came close to a house.

The donkey, being the tallest of the company, marched up to the window and peeped in.

"Well, Donkey," said the cock, "what do you see?"

"What do I see?" replied the donkey. "Why, I see a table spread with all kinds of good things, and robbers sitting round it making merry."

"That would be a noble lodging for us," said the cock.

"Yes," said the donkey, "if we could only get in."

So they consulted together how they could get the robbers out, and at last they hit upon a plan. The donkey placed himself upright on his hind-legs, with his forefeet resting against the window. The dog got upon his back; the cat scrambled up to the dog's shoulders, and the cock flew up and sat upon the cat's head. When all was ready, a signal was given, and they began their music. The donkey brayed, the dog barked, the cat mewed, and the cock crowed. Then they all broke through the window at once and came tumbling into the room, amongst the broken glass, with a most hideous clatter!

The robbers, who had been not a little frightened by the opening concert, had now no doubt that some frightful hobgoblin had broken in upon them, and scampered away as fast as they could.

The coast once clear, our travelers soon sat down and ate what the robbers had left, with as much eagerness as if they did not expect to eat again for a month. Then they put out the lights and each once more sought out a resting place to his own liking. The donkey laid himself down upon a heap of straw in the yard; the dog stretched himself upon a mat behind the door; the cat rolled herself up on the hearth before the warm ashes; and the cock perched upon the roof of the house. As they were all rather tired from their journey, they soon fell asleep.

About midnight, the robbers saw from afar that the lights were out and that all seemed quiet, so they began to think that they had been in too great a hurry to run away; and one of them, who was bolder than the rest, went to see what was going on. Finding everything still, he marched into the kitchen and groped about till he found a match in order to light a candle; and then, seeing the glittering fiery eyes of the cat, he mistook them for live coals and held the match to them to light it. But the cat, not understanding this joke, sprang at his face, and spit, and scratched him. This frightened him dreadfully, and away he ran to the back door; but there the dog jumped up and bit him in the leg; and as he was crossing over the yard the donkey kicked him; and the cock, who had been awakened by the noise, crowed with all his might.

At this the robber ran back as fast as he could to his comrades and told the captain "how a horrid witch had got into the house, and had spit at him and scratched his face with her long bony fingers; how a man with a knife in his hand had hidden himself behind the door and stabbed him in the leg; how a black monster stood in the yard and struck him with a club, and how a ghost sat upon the top of the house and cried out, 'Throw the rascal up here!' "

After this the robbers never dared to go back to the house; but the musicians were so pleased with their quarters that they took up their home there; and there they are, I dare say, to this very day.

## WHY THE BEAR IS STUMPY-TAILED[1]

One day the Bear met the Fox, who came slinking along with a string of fish he had stolen.

[1] From George Webbe Dasent, *Popular Tales from the Norse.*

"Where did you get them?" asked the Bear.

"Oh! my Lord Bruin, I've been out fishing and caught them," said the Fox.

So the Bear had a mind to learn to fish too, and bade the Fox tell him how he was to set about it.

"Oh! it's easy," answered the Fox, "and soon learned. You've only got to go upon the ice, and cut a hole and stick your tail down into it. You must go on holding it there as long as you can. You're not to mind if your tail smarts a little; that's when the fish bite. The longer you hold it there the more fish you'll get; and then all at once out with it, with a cross pull sideways, and with a strong pull too."

Yes; the Bear did as the Fox had said, and held his tail a long, long time down in the hole, till it was fast frozen in. Then he pulled it out with a cross pull, and it snapped short off. That's why Bruin goes about with a stumpy tail to this very day.

## THE WOLF AND THE SEVEN YOUNG GOSLINGS [1]

There was once an old goose who had seven young goslings, and loved them as only a mother could love her children. One day she was going into the wood to seek for food, and before setting off she called all seven to her and said,

"Dear children, I am obliged to go into the wood, so be on your guard against the wolf; for if he gets in here he will eat you up, feathers, skin, and all. The villain often disguises himself, but you can easily recognize him by his rough voice and black paws."

The children answered, "Dear mother, we will take great care; you may go without any anxiety."

So the old lady was comforted, and set off cheerfully for the wood.

Before long some one knocked at the door, and cried, "Open, open, my dear children; your mother is here, and has brought something for each of you."

But the goslings knew, by the rough voice, that it was the wolf.

"We will not open," they said. "You are not our mother, for she has a sweet and lovely voice. Your voice is rough—you are the wolf."

Thereupon the wolf set off to a merchant and bought a large lump of chalk; he ate it, and it made his voice sweet.

Back he came, knocked at the door, and cried, "Open, open, my dear children; your mother is here, and has brought something for each of you."

But the wolf had laid his black paw on the window sill, and when the children saw it they cried, "We will not open; our mother has not black feet like you—you are the wolf."

So the wolf ran off to the baker, and said, "I have hurt my foot, put some dough on it."

And when the baker had plastered it with dough the wolf went to the miller and cried, "Strew some meal on my paws."

But the miller thought to himself, "The wolf wants to deceive some one," and he hesitated to do it.

Then the wolf said, "If you don't do it at once, I will eat you up." So the miller was afraid and made the paws white.

Now came the rogue back for the third time, knocked, and said, "Open the door, dear children; your mother has come home and has brought something for each of you."

The little goslings cried, "Show us your paws first, that we may see whether you are indeed our mother."

So the wolf laid his paws on the window sill, and when the goslings saw that they were white they believed it was all right, and opened the door; and who should come in but the wolf!

They screamed out and tried to hide themselves. One jumped under the table, another into the bed, the third into the oven, the fourth ran into the kitchen, the

[1] From Dinah Maria Mulock Craik, *The Fairy Book.*

fifth hopped into a chest, the sixth under the wash-tub, and the seventh got into the clock-case. But the wolf seized them; one after another he gobbled them all up, except the youngest, who being in the clock-case he couldn't find.

When the wolf had eaten his fill he strolled forth, laid himself down in the green meadow under a tree, and went fast asleep.

Not long after, back came the old goose home from the wood; but what, alas! did she see? The house door stood wide open; table, chairs, benches, were all overthrown; the wash-tub lay in the ashes; blankets and pillows were torn off the bed. She looked for her children, but nowhere could she find them; she called them each by name, but nobody answered.

At last, when she came to the youngest, a little squeaking voice answered, "Dear mother, I am in the clock-case." She pulled him out, and he told her how the wolf had come and eaten up all the others. You may think how she wept for her dear children.

At last, in grief, she went out, and the youngest gosling ran beside her. And when she came to the meadow there lay the wolf under the tree, snoring till the boughs shook. She walked round and examined him on all sides, till she saw that something was moving and kicking about inside him.

"Can it be," thought she, "that my poor children whom he has swallowed for his supper are yet alive?"

She sent the little gosling back to the house for scissors, needle, and thread, and began to slit up the monster's stomach. Scarcely had she given one snip when out came the head of a gosling, and when she had cut a little further the six jumped out one after another, not being the least hurt, because the greedy monster had swallowed them down whole. That was a joy! They embraced their mother tenderly, and skipped about as lively as a tailor at his wedding.

But the old goose said, "Now, go and find me six large stones, which we will put inside the greedy beast while he is still asleep."

The goslings got the stones in all haste, and they put them inside the wolf; and the old goose sewed him up again in a great hurry, while he never once moved nor took any notice.

Now, when the wolf at last woke up and got upon his legs he found he was very thirsty, and wished to go to drink. But as soon as he began to move, the stones began to shake and rattle inside him, till he cried:

"What's this rumbling and tumbling,
  What's this rattling like bones?
I thought I had eaten six little geese,
  But they've turn'd out only stones."

When he came to the spring and bent down his head to drink, the heavy stones overbalanced him, and in he went head over heels.

Now, when the seven goslings saw this they came running up, crying loudly, "The wolf is dead, the wolf is dead!" and danced for joy all round the spring, and their mother with them.

## THE LAD WHO WENT TO THE NORTH WIND [1]

Once on a time there was an old widow who had one son. As she was poorly and weak, her son had to go up into the safe to fetch meal for cooking; but when he got outside the safe, and was just going down the steps, there came the North Wind puffing and blowing, caught up the meal, and so away with it through the air. Then the Lad went back into the safe for more; but when he came out again on the steps, if the North Wind didn't come again and carry off the meal with a puff; and, more than that, he did so the third time. At this the Lad got very angry; and as he thought it hard that the North Wind should behave so, he decided he'd just look him up, and ask him to give back his meal.

[1] From George Webbe Dasent, *Popular Tales from the Norse.*

So off he went, but the way was long, and he walked and walked; but at last he came to the North Wind's house.

"Good day!" said the Lad, "and thank you for coming to see us yesterday."

"GOOD DAY!" answered the North Wind, for his voice was loud and gruff, "AND THANKS FOR COMING TO SEE ME. WHAT DO YOU WANT?"

"Oh!" answered the Lad, "I only wished to ask you to be so good as to let me have back that meal you took from me on the safe steps, for we haven't much to live on; and if you're to go on snapping up the morsel we have, there'll be nothing for it but to starve."

"I haven't got your meal," said the North Wind; "but if you are in such need, I'll give you a cloth which will get you everything you want, if you only say, 'Cloth, spread yourself, and serve up all kinds of good dishes!'"

With this the Lad was well content. But, as the way was so long, he couldn't get home in one day, so he turned into an inn on the way; and when they were going to sit down to supper he laid the cloth on a table which stood in the corner, and said: "Cloth, spread yourself, and serve up all kinds of good dishes!"

He had scarce said so before the cloth did as it was bid; and all who stood by thought it a fine thing, but most of all the landlord. So, when all were fast asleep at dead of night, he took the Lad's cloth, and put another in its stead, just like the one he had got from the North Wind, but which couldn't so much as serve up a bit of dry bread.

So, when the Lad woke, he took his cloth and went off with it, and that day he got home to his mother.

"Now," said he, "I've been to the North Wind's house, and a good fellow he is, for he gave me this cloth, and when I only say to it, 'Cloth, spread yourself, and serve up all kinds of good dishes,' I get any sort of food I please."

"All very true, I dare say," said his mother; "but seeing is believing, and I shan't believe it till I see it."

So the Lad made haste, drew out a table, laid the cloth on it, and said:

"Cloth, spread yourself, and serve up all kinds of good dishes!"

But never a bit of dry bread did the cloth serve up.

"Well," said the Lad, "there's no help for it but to go to the North Wind again"; and away he went.

So he came to where the North Wind lived late in the afternoon.

"Good evening!" said the Lad.

"Good evening!" said the North Wind.

"I want my rights for that meal of ours which you took," said the Lad. "As for the cloth I got, it isn't worth a penny."

"I've got no meal," said the North Wind; "but here is a ram which coins nothing but golden ducats as soon as you say to it: 'Ram, ram, make money!'"

So the Lad thought this a fine thing; but as it was too far to get home that day, he turned in for the night at the same inn where he had slept before.

Before he called for anything, he tried the truth of what the North Wind had said of the ram, and found it all right; but, when the landlord saw that, he thought it was a famous ram, and, when the Lad had fallen asleep, he took another which couldn't coin gold ducats, and changed the two.

Next morning off went the Lad; and when he got home to his mother, he said:

"After all, the North Wind is a jolly fellow; for now he has given me a ram which can coin golden ducats if I only say: 'Ram, ram, make money!'"

"All very true, I dare say," said his mother; "but I shan't believe any such stuff until I see the ducats made."

"Ram, ram, make money!" said the Lad; but the ram made no money.

So the Lad went back again to the North Wind, and said the ram was worth nothing, and he must have his rights for the meal.

"Well!" said the North Wind; "I've nothing else to give you but that old stick in the corner yonder; but it's a stick of the kind that if you say: 'Stick, stick, lay on!' it lays on till you say: 'Stick, stick, now stop!' "

The Lad took the stick, and as the way was long, he turned in this night, too, to the landlord; but as the Lad could pretty well guess how things stood as to the cloth and the ram, he lay down at once on the bench and began to snore as if he were asleep.

Now the landlord, who easily saw that the stick must be worth something, hunted up one which was like it, and when he heard the Lad snore, was going to change the two; but, just as the landlord was about to take it, the Lad cried out:

"Stick, stick, lay on!"

So the stick began to beat the landlord, till he jumped over chairs, and tables, and benches, and yelled and roared:

"Oh my! oh my! bid the stick be still, else it will beat me to death. You shall have back both your cloth and your ram."

When the Lad thought the landlord had got enough, he said:

"Stick, stick, now stop!"

Then he took the cloth and put it into his pocket, and went home with his stick in his hand, leading the ram by a cord round its horns.

The Lad's mother was very happy when the cloth spread the good dishes on the table, and when the ram coined golden ducats. As for the stick, she thought they might now need it to keep away robbers.

## JACK AND THE BEANSTALK [1]

There was once upon a time a poor widow who had an only son named Jack, and a cow named Milky-white. And all they had to live on was the milk the cow gave every morning, which they carried to the market and sold. But one morning Milky-white gave no milk, and they didn't know what to do.

"What shall we do, what shall we do?" said the widow, wringing her hands.

"Cheer up, Mother, I'll go and get work somewhere," said Jack.

[1] Adapted from Joseph Jacobs, *English Fairy Tales.*

"We've tried that before, and nobody would take you," said his mother; "we must sell Milky-white and with the money start a shop, or something."

"All right, Mother," said Jack; "it's market-day today, and I'll soon sell Milky-white, and then we'll see what we can do."

So he took the cow's halter in his hand, and off he started. He hadn't gone far when he met a funny looking old man, who said to him: "Good morning, Jack."

"Good morning to you," said Jack, and wondered how he knew his name.

"Well, Jack, and where are you off to?" said the man.

"I'm going to market to sell our cow."

"Oh, you look like you are the proper sort of chap to sell cows," said the man; "I wonder if you know how many beans make five."

"Two in each hand and one in your mouth," said Jack, as sharp as a needle.

"Right you are," said the man, "and here they are, the very beans themselves," he went on, pulling out of his pocket a number of strange looking beans. "As you are so sharp," said he, "I don't mind doing a swop with you—your cow for these beans."

"Go along," said Jack; "wouldn't you like it?"

"Ah! you don't know what these beans are," said the man; "if you plant them overnight, by morning they grow right up to the sky."

"Really?" said Jack. "You don't say so!"

"Yes, that is so, and if it doesn't turn out to be true, you can have your cow back."

"Right," said Jack, and handed him over Milky-white's halter and pocketed the beans.

Back home Jack went, and as he hadn't gone very far it wasn't dusk by the time he got to his door.

"Back already, Jack?" said his mother. "I see you haven't got Milky-white, so you've sold her. How much did you get for her?"

"You'll never guess, Mother," said Jack.

"Good boy! Five pounds, ten, fifteen? No, it can't be twenty!"

"I told you you couldn't guess. What do you say to these beans? They're magical, plant them overnight and—"

"What!" said Jack's mother. "Have you been such an idiot as to give away my Milky-white, the best milker in the parish, and prime beef to boot, for a set of paltry beans? Take that! And as for your precious beans, here they go out of the window. And now off with you to bed. Not a sup shall you drink, and not a bit shall you swallow this very night."

So Jack went upstairs to his little room in the attic, and sad and sorry he was, to be sure, as much for his mother's sake, as for the loss of his supper.

At last he dropped off to sleep.

When he woke up, the room looked so funny. The sun was shining into part of it, and yet all the rest was quite dark and shady. So Jack jumped up and dressed himself and went to the window. And what do you think he saw? Why, the beans his mother had thrown out of the window into the garden, had sprung up into a big beanstalk which went up and up and up till it reached the sky. So the man spoke truth after all.

The beanstalk grew up quite close past Jack's window, so all he had to do was to open it and give a jump on to the bean stalk which ran up just like a big ladder. So Jack climbed, and he climbed and he climbed and he climbed and he climbed. Up, up he went, far up over the housetops, and far up over the trees; up into the very sky he climbed. Here he found himself in another land, and before him stretched a long road which ran winding over the hills of the sky.

Jack had just started down the road when he heard his name called. He looked around and there at his side was a beautiful fairy.

"Where am I?" asked Jack.

"This is the Land of the Giants," said the fairy. "A great giant lives down the road who killed your father and took his money."

"I think I had better go back," said Jack. "But I wish I had the money the giant stole."

"I will help you," said the fairy. "Go down the road till you come to the giant's house. You will know what to do."

So he walked along, up hill and down, till he came to a great tall house, and on the doorstep there was a great big tall woman.

"Good morning, mum," said Jack, quite polite. "Could you be so kind as to give me some breakfast?" For he hadn't had anything to eat the night before and was as hungry as a hunter.

"It's breakfast you want, is it?" said the great big tall woman. "It's breakfast you'll be if you don't move off from here. My man is a giant and there's nothing he likes better than boys broiled on toast. You'd better be moving on or he'll soon be coming."

"Oh! please mum, do give me something to eat, mum. I've had nothing to eat since yesterday morning, really and truly, mum," said Jack. "I may as well be broiled as die of hunger."

Well, the giant's wife was not half so bad after all. So she took Jack into the kitchen, and gave him some bread and cheese and a jug of milk. But Jack hadn't half finished them when

Thump!
Thump!
Thump!

the whole house began to tremble with the noise of some one coming.

"Goodness gracious me! It's my old man," said the giant's wife. "What on earth shall I do? Come along quick and jump in here." And she bundled Jack into the oven just as the giant came in.

He was a big one, to be sure. At his belt he had three calves strung up by the heels, and he unhooked them and threw them down on the table and said: "Here, wife, broil me a couple of these for breakfast. Ah! what's this I smell?"

"Nonsense, dear," said his wife, "you're dreaming. Here you go and have a wash and tidy up, and by the time you come back your breakfast will be ready for you."

So off the giant went, and Jack was just going to jump out of the oven and run away when the woman told him not. "Wait till he's asleep," said she; "he always has a doze after breakfast."

Well, the giant had his breakfast, and after that he went to a big chest and took out of it a couple of bags of gold, and down he sat and counted till at last his head began to nod and he began to snore till the whole house shook again.

Then Jack crept out on tiptoe from the oven, and as he was passing the giant he took one of the bags of gold under his arm, and off he ran till he came to the beanstalk, and then he threw down the bag of gold, which of course fell into his mother's garden, and then he climbed down and climbed down till at last he got home and told his mother and showed her the gold and said: "Well, Mother, wasn't I right about the beans? They are really magical, you see."

So they lived on the bag of gold for some time, but at last they came to the end of it, and Jack made up his mind to try his luck once more up at the top of the beanstalk. So one fine morning he rose up early, and got on to the beanstalk, and he climbed and he climbed and he climbed and he climbed and he climbed and he climbed till at last he came out on the road again and up to the great tall house he had been to before. There, sure enough, was the great big tall woman standing on the doorstep.

"Good morning, mum," said Jack, as bold as brass, "could you be so good as to give me something to eat?"

"Go away, my boy," said the great big tall woman, "or my man will eat you up for breakfast. But aren't you the youngster who came here once before? Do you know, that very day, my man missed one of his bags of gold?"

"That's strange, mum," said Jack, "I dare say I could tell you something about that, but I'm so hungry I can't speak till I've had something to eat."

Well, the great big tall woman was so curious that she took him in and gave him something to eat. But he had scarcely begun munching it when

Thump!
Thump!
Thump!

they heard the giant's footstep, and his wife hid Jack away in the oven.

All happened as it did before. In came the giant as he did before, and had his breakfast off three broiled oxen. Then he said: "Wife, bring me the hen that lays the golden eggs." So she brought it, and the giant said: "Lay," and it laid an egg all of gold. And then the giant began to nod his head, and to snore till the house shook.

Then Jack crept out of the oven on tiptoe and caught hold of the golden hen, and was off before you could say "Jack Robinson." But this time the hen gave a cackle which woke the giant, and just as Jack got out of the house he heard him calling: "Wife, wife, what have you done with my golden hen?"

But that was all Jack heard, for he rushed off to the beanstalk and climbed down like a house on fire. And when he got home he showed his mother the wonderful hen, and said "Lay" to it; and it laid a golden egg every time he said "Lay."

Well, Jack was not content, and it wasn't very long before he determined to have another try at his luck up there at the top of the beanstalk. So one fine morning, he rose up early, and got on to the beanstalk, and he climbed and he climbed and he climbed and he climbed till he got to the top. But this time he knew better than to go straight to the giant's house. When he got near it, he waited behind a bush till he saw the giant's wife come out with a pail to get some water, and then he crept into the house and got into a great big pot. He hadn't been there long when he heard,

Thump!
Thump!
Thump!

as before, and in came the giant and his wife.

"Fee-fi-fo-fum," cried out the giant. "I smell an Englishman,"

"Do you, my dearie?" said the giant's wife. "Then, if it's that little rogue that stole your gold and the hen that laid the golden eggs, he's sure to have got into the oven." And they both rushed to the oven. But Jack wasn't there, luckily.

So the giant sat down to his breakfast and ate it, but every now and then he would mutter: "Well, I could have sworn—" and he'd get up and search the larder and the cupboards and everything, only, luckily, he didn't think of the great big pot.

After breakfast was over, the giant called out: "Wife, wife, bring me my golden harp." So she brought it and put it on the table before him. Then he said: "Sing!" and the golden harp sang most beautifully. And it went on singing till the giant fell asleep and commenced to snore like thunder.

Then Jack lifted up the lid of the pot very quietly and got down like a mouse and crept on hands and knees till he came to the table; then up he crawled, caught hold of the golden harp and dashed with it towards the door. But the harp called out quite loud: "Master! Master!" and the giant woke up just in time to see Jack running off with his harp.

Jack ran as fast as he could, and the giant came rushing after. Up hill and down hill they went, with the giant close behind at the top of the hills; but going down hill Jack ran away from the giant again. When he got to the beanstalk the giant was not more than twenty yards away. Suddenly he saw Jack disappear, and when he came to the end of the road he saw Jack underneath climbing down for dear life. Well, the giant didn't like trusting himself to such a ladder, and he stood and waited. But just then the harp cried out: "Master! Master!" and the giant swung himself down on to the beanstalk, which shook with his weight.

Down climbed Jack, and after him climbed the giant. By this time Jack had climbed down and climbed down and climbed down till he was very nearly home. So he called out: "Mother! Mother! bring me an axe, bring me an axe." And his mother came rushing out with the axe in her hand, but when she came to the beanstalk she stood stock still with fright for there she saw the giant with his legs just through the clouds.

But Jack jumped down and got hold of the axe and gave a chop at the beanstalk which cut it half in two. The giant felt the beanstalk shake and quiver so he stopped to see what was the matter. Then Jack gave another chop with the axe, and the beanstalk was cut in two and began to topple over. Then the giant fell down and broke his crown, and the beanstalk came toppling after.

Then Jack showed his mother his golden harp, and what with showing that and selling the golden eggs Jack and his mother became very rich, and they lived happy ever after.

## THE ELVES AND THE SHOEMAKER [1]

There was once a shoemaker who worked very hard and was very honest; but still he could not earn enough to live upon. At last all he had in the world was gone, except just leather enough to make one pair of shoes. Then he cut them all ready to make up the next day, meaning to get up early in the morning to work. His conscience was clear and his heart light amidst all his troubles; so he went peaceably to bed, and fell asleep.

In the morning, after he had said his prayers, he set himself down to his work, but to his great wonder, there stood the shoes, all ready made, upon the table. The good man knew not what to say or think of this strange event. He looked at the workmanship; there was not one false stitch in the whole job, and all was so neat and true that it was a complete masterpiece.

That same day a customer came in, and the shoes pleased him so well that he willingly paid a price higher than usual for them; and the poor shoemaker with the

[1] From Edgar Taylor, *Grimms' Popular Stories.*

money bought leather enough to make two pairs more. In the evening he cut out the work and went to bed early that he might get up and begin betimes next day. But he was saved all the trouble, for when he got up in the morning the work was finished ready to his hand.

Presently in came buyers, who paid him handsomely for his goods, so that he bought leather enough for four pairs more. He cut out the work again over night, and found it finished in the morning as before. So it went on for some time; what was got ready in the evening was always done by daybreak, and the good man soon became thriving and prosperous again.

One evening about Christmas time, as he and his wife were sitting over the fire chatting together, he said to her, "I should like to sit up and watch tonight, that we may see who it is that comes and does my work for me."

The wife liked the thought; so they left a light burning and hid themselves in the corner of the room behind a curtain and watched to see what would happen.

As soon as it was midnight, there came two little naked dwarfs; and they sat themselves upon the shoemaker's bench, took up all the work that was cut out, and began to ply with their little fingers, stitching and rapping and tapping away at such a rate that the shoemaker was all amazement and could not take his eyes off for a moment.

On they went till the job was quite finished, and the shoes stood ready for use upon the table. This was long before daybreak; and then they bustled away as quick as lightning.

The next day the wife said to the shoemaker, "These little wights have made us rich, and we ought to be thankful to them and do them a good office in return. I am quite vexed to see them run about as they do; they have nothing upon their backs to keep off the cold. I'll tell you what, I will make each of them a shirt, and a coat and waistcoat, and a pair of pantaloons into the bargain; do you make each of them a little pair of shoes."

The thought pleased the good shoemaker very much; and one evening, when all the things were ready, they laid them on the table instead of the work that they used to cut out, and then went and hid themselves to watch what the little elves would do.

About midnight the elves came in and were going to sit down to their work as usual; but when they saw the clothes lying for them, they laughed and were greatly delighted. Then they dressed themselves in the twinkling of an eye, and danced and capered and sprang about as merry as could be, till at last they danced out at the door and over the green.

The shoemaker saw them no more; but everything went well with him from that time forward, as long as he lived.

## DRAKESBILL [1]

Drakesbill was very little, that is why he was called Drakesbill; but tiny as he was he had brains, and he knew what he was about. Now the king of the country, who was very extravagant and never kept any money, having heard that Drakesbill had some, went one day to borrow his hoard.

Drakesbill was very proud to lend money to the king. But time went on and after the first and second year, seeing that the king never even dreamed of paying the interest, Drakesbill became uneasy, so much so that at last he resolved to go and see his majesty. So one fine morning Drakesbill, very spruce and fresh, went down the road, singing: "Quack, quack, quack, I must have my money back!"

He had not gone far when he met Friend Fox, out on his rounds.

"Good morning, neighbor," said Friend Fox, "where are you off to so early?"

"I am going to the king to get my money back."

"Oh! take me with you!"

[1] From Andrew Lang, *The Red Fairy Book*.

Drakesbill said to himself: "One can't have too many friends." Aloud he said, "I will, but going on all fours you will soon be tired. Make yourself small, get into my throat, and I will carry you."

"Happy thought!" said Friend Fox.

He took bag and baggage, and, presto! was gone like a letter into the post.

And Drakesbill was off again, all spruce and fresh, still singing: "Quack, quack, quack, I must have my money back!"

He had not gone far when he met his lady friend, Ladder, leaning on her wall.

"Good morning, my duckling," said the lady friend, "whither away so bold?"

"I am going to the king for what he owes me."

"Oh! take me with you!"

Drakesbill said to himself: "One can't have too many friends." Aloud he said, "I will, but with your wooden legs you will soon be tired. Make yourself small, get into my throat, and I will carry you."

"Happy thought!" said Friend Ladder, and nimble, bag and baggage, went to keep company with Friend Fox.

And "Quack, quack, quack," Drakesbill was off again, singing and as spruce as before. A little farther he met Friend River, wandering quietly in the sunshine.

"Well, my cherub," said she, "whither so lonesome, with arching tail, on this muddy road?"

"I am going to the king for what he owes me."

"Oh! take me with you!"

Drakesbill said to himself: "One can't have too many friends." Aloud he said, "I will, but you who sleep while you walk will soon get tired. Make yourself small, get into my throat, and I will carry you."

"Ah! happy thought!" said Friend River.

She took bag and baggage, and, glou, glou, glou! she took her place between Friend Fox and Friend Ladder.

And "Quack, quack, quack," Drakesbill was off again singing.

A little farther on he met Comrade Wasp's-nest with his wasps.

"Well, good morning, friend Drakesbill," said Comrade Wasps'-nest, "where are you bound for, so spruce and fresh?"

"I am going to the king for what he owes me."

"Oh! take me with you!"

Drakesbill said to himself, "One can't have too many friends." Aloud he said, "I will, but with all your wasps to carry, you will soon get tired. Make yourself small, get into my throat, and I will carry you."

"That's a good idea!" said Comrade Wasp's-nest.

And left file! he took the same road to join the others. There was not much room, but by closing up a bit they managed. And Drakesbill was off again singing.

He arrived in the city and went straight up High Street, still singing, "Quack, quack, quack, I must have my money back!" to the great astonishment of the good folks.

He came to the king's palace and knocked with the knocker: "Toc! toc!"

"Who is there?" asked the porter, putting his head out of the wicket.

"'Tis I, Drakesbill. I wish to speak to the king."

"Speak to the king! That's easily said. The king is dining, and will not be disturbed."

"Tell him that it is I, and I have come he well knows why."

The porter shut his wicket and went up to say it to the king, who was just sitting down to dinner with all his ministers.

"Good, good!" said the king, laughing. "I know what it is! Make him come in, and put him with the turkeys and chickens."

The porter went back.

"Have the goodness to enter."

"Good!" said Drakesbill to himself, "I shall now see how they eat at court."

"This way, this way," said the porter. "One step farther. There, there you are."

"How? what? in the poultry-yard?"

How vexed Drakesbill was!

"Ah! so that's it," said he. "Quack, quack, quack, I must have my money back!" But turkeys and chickens don't like people that are not like themselves. When they saw the newcomer and when they heard him crying too, they began to look black at him.

"What is it? What does he want?"

Finally they rushed at him all together, to overwhelm him with pecks.

"I am lost!" said Drakesbill to himself, when by good luck he remembered Friend Fox, and he cried,

"Reynard, Reynard, come out of your earth,
Or Drakesbill's life is of little worth."

Then Friend Fox, who was only waiting for these words, hastened out, threw himself on the wicked fowls, and quick! he tore them to pieces; so much so that at the end of five minutes there was not one left alive. And Drakesbill, quite content, began to sing again, "Quack, quack, quack, I must have my money back!"

When the king, who was still at table, heard this refrain, and the poultry-woman came to tell him what had been going on in the yard, he was terribly annoyed.

He ordered them to throw this drake into the well, to make an end of him.

And it was done as he commanded. Drakesbill could not think how to get himself out of such a deep hole, when he remembered his lady friend, Ladder.

"Ladder, Ladder, come out of thy hold,
Or Drakesbill's days will soon be told."

Ladder, who was only waiting for these words, hastened out and leaned her two arms on the edge of the well; then Drakesbill climbed nimbly on her back, and hop! he was in the yard, where he began to sing louder than ever.

When the king, who was still at table and laughing at the good trick he had played, heard Drakesbill again, he became livid with rage.

He commanded that the furnace should be heated, and this drake thrown into it.

The furnace was soon hot, but this time Drakesbill was not so afraid; he counted on his friend River.

"River, River, outward flow,
Or to death Drakesbill must go."

River hastened out, and threw herself into the furnace, which she flooded, with all the people who had lighted it; after which she flowed growling into the hall of the palace.

And Drakesbill, quite content, began to swim, singing deafeningly, "Quack, quack, quack, I must have my money back!"

The king was still at table, and thought himself quite sure of his game; but when he heard Drakesbill singing again, and when they told him all that had passed, he became furious and got up from the table brandishing his fists.

"Bring him here, and I'll cut his throat! Bring him here quick!" cried he.

And quickly two footmen ran to get Drakesbill.

"At last," said the poor chap, going up the great stairs, "they have decided to receive me."

Imagine his terror when on entering, he saw the king as red as a turkey cock, and all the ministers attending him standing sword in hand. He thought this time it was all up with him. Happily he remembered that there was still one remaining friend, and he cried:

"Wasp's-nest, Wasp's-nest, make a sally,
Or Drakesbill nevermore may rally."

Hereupon the scene changed.

The brave Wasp's-nest rushed out with all his wasps. They threw themselves on the king and his ministers, and stung them so fiercely in the face that they lost their heads, and not knowing where to hide themselves they all jumped pell-mell from the window.

Behold Drakesbill much astonished, all alone and master of the palace. He could not get over it.

Nevertheless, he remembered shortly what he had come for, and he set to work to hunt for his money. But in vain he rummaged in all the drawers; he found nothing; all had been spent.

From room to room he came at last to the one with the throne in it, and feeling fatigued, he sat himself down on it to think over his adventure. In the meanwhile the people had found their king and his ministers with their feet in the air on the pavement, and they had gone into the palace to find out how it had occurred. On entering the throne-room, when the crowd saw that there was already someone on the royal seat, they broke out in cries of surprise and joy:

"The King is dead, long live the King!
Heaven has sent us down this thing."

Drakesbill, who was no longer surprised at anything, received the people as if he had never done anything else all his life.

A few of them did not think that Drakesbill would make a fine king; those who knew him replied that Drakesbill was more worthy than a spendthrift. In short, they ran and took the crown off the head of the king, and placed it on that of Drakesbill, whom it fitted like wax.

Thus he became king.

"And now," said he after the ceremony, "ladies and gentlemen, let's all go to supper. I am so hungry!"

## BOOTS AND HIS BROTHERS[1]

Once on a time there was a man who had three sons, Peter, Paul, and John. John was Boots, of course, because he was the youngest.

I can't say the man had anything more than these three sons, for he hadn't one penny to rub against another. So he told his sons over and over again they must go out into the world and try to earn their bread, for there at home there was nothing to be looked for but starving to death.

Now, a bit off the man's cottage was the King's palace, and you must know, just against the King's windows a great oak had sprung up, which was so stout and big that it took away all the light from the palace. The King had said he would give many, many dollars to the man who could fell the oak, but no one was man enough for that, for as soon as ever one chip of the oak's trunk flew off, two grew in its stead.

A well, too, the King would have dug, which was to hold water for the whole year; for all his neighbors had wells, but he hadn't any, and that he thought a shame. So the King said he would give any one who could dig him a well that would hold water for a whole year round, both money and goods. But no one could do it, for the King's palace lay high, high up on a hill, and they hadn't dug a few inches before they came upon the living rock.

But as the King had set his heart on having these two things done, he had it given out far and wide, in all parts of his kingdom, that he who could fell the big oak in the king's courtyard, and get him a well that would hold water the whole year round, should have the Princess and half the kingdom. Well! you may easily know there was many a man who came to try his luck; but for all their hacking and hewing, and all their digging and delving, it was no good. The oak got bigger and stouter at every stroke, and the rock didn't get softer either.

So one day the three brothers thought they'd set off and try too, and their father hadn't a word against it. Even if they didn't get the Princess and half the kingdom, they might get a place somewhere with a good master; and that was all he wanted. So when the brothers said they thought of going to the palace, their father said "yes" at once. So the three brothers started out.

Well! they hadn't gone far before they came to a fir wood, and up along one side of it rose a steep hillside, and as they went, they heard something hewing and hacking away up on the hill among the trees.

"I wonder now what it is that is hewing away up yonder?" said Boots.

"You're always so clever with your wonderings," said his brothers both at once.

[1] From George Webbe Dasent, *Popular Tales from the Norse.*

"What wonder is it, pray, that a woodcutter should stand and hack on a hillside?"

"Still, I'd like to see what it is, after all," said Boots; and up he went.

"Oh, if you're such a child, 'twill do you good to go and take a lesson," bawled out his brothers after him.

But Boots didn't care for what they said; he climbed the steep hillside toward the noise, and when he reached the place, what do you think he saw? Why, an axe that stood there hacking and hewing, all of itself, at the trunk of a fir.

"Good day!" said Boots. "So you stand here all alone and hew, do you?"

"Yes; here I've stood and hewed and hacked a long, long time, waiting for you," said the Axe.

"Well, here I am at last," said Boots.

He took the axe, pulled it off its haft, and stuffed both head and haft into his wallet.

When he got down again to his brothers, they began to jeer and laugh at him.

"And now, what funny thing was it you saw up yonder on the hillside?" they said.

"Oh, it was only an axe we heard," said Boots.

When they had gone a bit farther, they came under a steep spur of rock, and up there they heard something digging and shoveling.

"I wonder now," said Boots, "what it is digging and shoveling up yonder at the top of the rock!"

"Ah, you're always so clever with your wonderings," said his brothers again, "as if you'd never heard a woodpecker hacking and pecking at a hollow tree."

"Well, well," said Boots, "I think it would be a piece of fun just to see what it really is."

And so off he set to climb the rock, while the others laughed and made game of him. But he didn't care a bit for that. Up he climbed, and when he got near the top, what do you think he saw? Why, a spade that stood there digging and delving.

"Good day!" said Boots. "So you stand here all alone, and dig and delve!"

"Yes, that's what I do," said the Spade, "and that's what I've done this many a long day, waiting for you."

"Well, here I am," said Boots.

He took the spade and knocked it off its handle, and put it into his wallet, and went down again to his brothers.

"Well, what was it, so rare and strange," said Peter and Paul, "that you saw up there at the top of the rock?"

"Oh," said Boots, "nothing more than a spade; that was what we heard."

So they went on again a good bit, till they came to a brook. They were thirsty, all three, after their long walk, and they lay down beside the brook to have a drink.

"I wonder now," said Boots, "where all this water comes from!"

"I wonder if you're right in your head," said Peter and Paul, in one breath. "If you're not mad already, you'll go mad very soon, with your wonderings. Where the brook comes from, indeed! Have you never heard how water rises from a spring in the earth?"

"Yes, but still I've a great fancy to see where this brook comes from," said Boots.

Up alongside the brook he went, in spite of all that his brothers bawled after him. Nothing could stop him.

On he went. As he went up and up, the brook got smaller and smaller, and at last, a little way farther on, what do you think he saw? Why, a great walnut, and out of that the water trickled.

"Good day!" said Boots. "So you lie here, and trickle and run down all alone?"

"Yes, I do," said the Walnut, "and here have I trickled and run this many a long day, waiting for you."

"Well, here I am," said Boots.

He took up a lump of moss, and plugged up the hole, that the water mightn't run out. Then he put the walnut into his wallet, and ran down to his brothers.

"Well, now," said Peter and Paul, "have you found out where the water comes from? A rare sight it must have been!"

"Oh, after all, it was only a hole it ran out of," said Boots; and so the others laughed and made game of him again, but Boots didn't mind that a bit.

"After all, I had the fun of seeing it," said he.

So when they had gone a bit farther, they came to the King's palace. As every one in the kingdom had heard how they might win the Princess and half the realm, if they could only fell the big oak and dig the King's well, so many had come to try their luck that the oak was now twice as stout and big as it had been at first, for two chips grew for everyone they hewed out with their axes.

The two brothers did not let themselves be scared by that; they were quite sure they could fell the oak. Peter, as he was eldest, was to try his hand first. But it went with him as with all the rest who had hewn at the oak; for every chip he cut out, two grew in its place.

Now Paul was to try his luck, but he fared just the same. When he had hewn two or three strokes, they began to see the oak grow and so the King's men seized him and made him stop.

So now Boots was to try.

"You might as well save yourself the bother," said the King, for he was angry with him because of his brothers.

"Well, I'd like just to try first," said Boots, and so he got leave. Then he took his axe out of his wallet and fitted it to its haft.

"Hew away!" said he to his axe.

Away it hewed, making the chips fly, so that it wasn't long before down came the oak.

When that was done, Boots pulled out his spade, and fitted it to its handle.

"Dig away!" said he to the spade.

The spade began to dig and delve till the earth and rock flew out in splinters, and he had the well soon dug.

And when he had got it as big and deep as he chose, Boots took out his walnut and laid it in one corner of the well, and pulled the plug of moss out.

"Trickle and run," said Boots.

The nut trickled and ran, till the water gushed out of the hole in a stream, and in a short time the well was brimful.

Then Boots had felled the oak which shaded the King's palace, and dug a well in the palace yard; so he got the Princess and half the kingdom, as the King had said.

Then Peter and Paul had to say, "Well, after all, Boots wasn't so much out of his mind when he took to wondering."

## SNOW-WHITE AND THE SEVEN DWARFS[1]

It was in the middle of winter, when the broad flakes of snow were falling around, that a certain queen sat working at a window, the frame of which was made of fine black ebony; and as she was looking out upon the snow, she pricked her finger, and three drops of blood fell upon it.

Then she gazed thoughtfully upon the red drops which sprinkled the white snow, and said, "Would that my little daughter may be as white as that snow, as red as the blood, and as black as the ebony window-frame!"

The little girl grew up so. Her skin was as white as snow, her cheeks as rosy as blood, and her hair as black as ebony; and she was called Snow-White.

But this queen died; and the king soon married another wife, who was very beautiful, but so proud that she could not bear to think that any one could surpass her. She had a magical looking glass, to which she used to go and gaze upon herself in it, and say,

"Tell me, glass, tell me true!
Of all the ladies in the land,
Who is the fairest? tell me who?"

The glass answered,

"Thou, queen, art fairest in the land."

But Snow-White grew more and more beautiful; and when she was seven years

[1] From Edgar Taylor, *Grimms' Popular Stories.*

old, she was as bright as the day, and fairer than the queen herself. Then the glass one day answered the queen, when she went to consult it as usual,

"Thou, queen, may'st fair and beauteous be,
But Snow-White is lovelier far than thee!"

When the queen heard this she turned pale with rage and envy; and called to one of her servants and said, "Take Snow-White away into the wide wood, that I may never see her more."

The servant led Snow-White away; but his heart melted when she begged him to spare her life, and he said, "I will not hurt thee, thou pretty child."

So he left her by herself. Though he thought it most likely that the wild beasts would tear her in pieces, he felt as if a great weight were taken off his heart when he had made up his mind not to kill her, but leave her to her fate.

Poor Snow-White wandered along through the wood in great fear; and the wild beasts were about her, but none did her any harm. In the evening she came to a little cottage, and went in there to rest herself, for her little feet would carry her no farther.

Every thing was spruce and neat in the cottage. On the table was spread a white cloth, and there were seven little plates with seven little loaves, and seven little glasses, and knives and forks laid in order; and by the wall stood seven little beds. Then as she was very hungry, she picked a little piece off each loaf, and drank a little from each glass; and after that she thought she would lie down and rest. So she tried all the little beds; and one was too long, and another was too short, till at last the seventh suited her; and there she laid herself down and went to sleep.

Presently in came the masters of the cottage, who were seven little dwarfs that lived among the mountains, and dug and searched about for gold. They lighted up their seven lamps, and saw directly that all was not right.

The first said, "Who has been sitting on my stool?" The second, "Who has been eating from my plate?" The third, "Who has been picking my bread?" The fourth, "Who has been meddling with my spoon?" The fifth, "Who has been handling my fork?" The sixth, "Who has been cutting with my knife?" The seventh, "Who has been drinking from my glass?"

Then the first looked round and said, "Who has been lying on my bed?" And the rest came running to him, and every one cried out that somebody had been upon his bed. But the seventh saw Snow-White, and called all his brethren to come and see her. They cried out with wonder and astonishment, and brought their lamps to look at her, and said, "What a lovely child she is!"

They were delighted to see her, and took care not to wake her. The seventh dwarf slept an hour with each of the other dwarfs in turn, till the night was gone.

In the morning Snow-White told them all her story. They pitied her, and said if she would keep all things in order, and cook and wash, and knit and spin for them, she might stay where she was, and they would take good care of her.

Then they went out all day long to their work, seeking for gold and silver in the mountains; and Snow-White remained at home. They warned her, and said, "The queen will soon find out where you are, so take care and let no one in."

The queen, now that she thought Snow-White was dead, believed that she was certainly the handsomest lady in the land; so she went to her glass and said,

"Tell me, glass, tell me true!
Of all the ladies in the land,
Who is the fairest? tell me who?"

The glass answered,

"Thou queen, art the fairest in all this land;
But over the hills, in the greenwood shade,
Where the seven dwarfs their dwelling have made,

There Snow-White is hiding her head, and
she
Is lovelier far, O queen, than thee."

The queen was very much alarmed; for she knew that the glass always spoke the truth, and was sure that the servant had betrayed her. She could not bear to think that any one lived who was more beautiful than she was; so she disguised herself as an old peddler and went her way over the hills to the place where the dwarfs dwelt.

She knocked at the door, and cried, "Fine wares to sell!"

Snow-White looked out at the window, and said, "Good day, good woman; what have you to sell?"

"Good wares, fine wares," said she; "laces and bobbins of all colors."

"I will let the old lady in; she seems to be a very good sort of body," thought Snow-White; so she ran down, and unbolted the door.

"Bless me!" said the old woman, "how badly your stays are laced! Let me lace them up with one of my nice new laces."

Snow-White did not dream of any mischief; so she stood up before the old woman, who she set to work so nimbly, and pulled the lace so tight, that Snow-White lost her breath, and fell down as if she were dead.

"There's an end of all thy beauty," said the spiteful queen, and went away home.

In the evening the seven dwarfs returned; and I need not say how grieved they they were to see their faithful Snow-White stretched upon the ground motionless, as if she were quite dead. However, they lifted her up, and when they found what was the matter, they cut the lace; and in a little time she began to breathe, and soon came to life again.

Then they said, "The old woman was the queen herself; take care another time, and let no one in when we are away."

When the queen got home, she went straight to her glass, and spoke to it as usual; but to her great surprise it still said,

"Thou, queen, art the fairest in all this land;
But over the hills, in the greenwood shade,
Where the seven dwarfs their dwelling have
made,
There Snow-White is hiding her head; and
she
Is lovelier far, O queen! than thee."

The blood ran cold in her heart with spite and malice to see that Snow-White still lived; and she dressed herself up again in a disguise, but very different from the one she wore before, and took with her a poisoned comb.

When she reached the dwarfs' cottage, she knocked at the door, and cried, "Fine wares to sell!"

But Snow-White said, "I dare not let any one in."

Then the queen said, "Only look at my beautiful combs;" and gave her the poisoned one.

It looked so pretty that Snow-White took it up and put it into her hair to try it. The moment it touched her head the poison was so powerful that she fell down senseless.

"There you may lie," said the queen, and went her way.

By good luck the dwarfs returned very early that evening. When they saw Snow-White lying on the ground, they guessed what had happened, and soon found the poisoned comb. When they took it away, she recovered, and told them all that had passed; and they warned her once more not to open the door to any one.

Meantime the queen went home to her glass, and trembled with rage when she received exactly the same answer as before; and she said, "Snow-White shall die, if it costs me my life."

So she went secretly into a chamber, and prepared a poisoned apple. The outside looked very rosy and tempting, but whoever tasted it was sure to die. Then she dressed herself up as a peasant's wife, and traveled over the hills to the dwarfs' cottage, and knocked at the door.

Snow-White put her head out of the window, and said, "I dare not let any one in, for the dwarfs have told me not."

"Do as you please," said the old woman, "but at any rate take this pretty apple; I will make you a present of it."

"No," said Snow-White, "I dare not take it."

"You silly girl!" answered, the other, "what are you afraid of? Do you think it is poisoned? Come! You eat one part, and I will eat the other."

Now the apple was so prepared that one side was good, though the other side was poisoned. Snow-White was very much tempted to taste, for the apple looked exceedingly nice. When she saw the old woman eat, she could refrain no longer, but she had scarcely put the piece into her mouth, when she fell down dead upon the ground.

"This time nothing will save you," said the queen; and she went home to her glass, and at last it said,

"Thou queen art the fairest of all the fair."

Then her envious heart was glad, and as happy as such an evil heart could be.

When evening came, and the dwarfs returned home, they found Snow-White lying on the ground. No breath passed her lips, and they were afraid that she was quite dead. They lifted her up, and combed her hair, and washed her face with water; but all was in vain, for the little girl seemed quite dead.

So they laid her down upon a bier, and all seven watched and bewailed her three whole days. Then they proposed to bury her; but her cheeks were still rosy, and her face looked just as it did while she was alive. So they said, "We will never bury her in the cold ground."

They made a coffin of glass so that they might still look at her, and wrote her name upon it, in golden letters, and that she was a king's daughter. And the coffin was placed upon the hill, and one of the dwarfs always sat by it and watched. And the birds of the air came too, and bemoaned Snow-White; first of all came an owl, and then a raven, and at last came a dove.

And thus Snow-White lay for a long, long time, and still looked as though she were only asleep; for she was even now as white as snow, and as red as blood, and as black as ebony.

At last a prince came and called at the dwarfs' house; and he saw Snow-White, and read what was written in golden letters. Then he offered the dwarfs money, and earnestly prayed them to let him take her away; but they said, "We will not part with her for all the gold in the world."

At last, however, they had pity on him, and gave him the coffin. The moment he lifted it up to carry it home with him, the piece of apple fell from between her lips, and Snow-White awoke, and said "Where am I?"

The prince answered, "Thou art safe with me." Then he told her all that had happened, and said, "I love you better than all the world. Come with me to my father's palace, and you shall be my wife."

Snow-White consented, and went home with the prince. And every thing was prepared with great pomp and splendor for their wedding.

To the feast was invited, among the rest, Snow-White's old enemy, the queen. As she was dressing herself in fine rich clothes, she looked in the glass and said,

"Tell me, glass, tell me true!
Of all the ladies in the land,
Who is fairest? tell me who?"

The glass answered,

"Thou, lady, art loveliest *here*, I ween;
But lovelier far is the new-made queen."

When she heard this, she started with rage. But her envy and curiosity were so great, that she could not help setting out to see the bride.

When she arrived, and saw that it was no other than Snow-White, who, as she thought, had been dead a long while, she choked with passion, and fell ill and died. But

Snow-White and the prince lived and reigned happily over that land many, many years.

## HANSEL AND GRETEL [1]

Near a great forest there lived a poor woodcutter and his wife, and his two children; the boy's name was Hansel and the girl's, Gretel. They had only a little to bite or to sup, and once, when there was great need in the land, the man could not even gain the daily bread.

As he lay in bed one night thinking of this, and turning and tossing, he sighed heavily, and said to his wife, who was the children's stepmother,

"What will become of us? We cannot even feed the children; there is nothing left for ourselves."

"I will tell you what, husband," answered the wife; "we will take the children early in the morning into the forest, where it is thickest; we will make them a fire, and we will give each of them a piece of bread, then we will go to our work and leave them alone; they will never find the way home again, and we shall be quit of them."

"No, wife," said the man, "I cannot do it; I cannot find it in my heart to take my children into the forest and to leave them there alone; the wild animals would soon come and devour them."

"O you fool," said she, "then we will all four starve," and she left him no peace until he consented.

"But I pity the poor children," said the man.

The two children had not been able to sleep for hunger, and had heard what their stepmother had said to their father. Gretel wept bitterly, and said to Hansel,

"It is all over with us."

"Do be quiet, Gretel," said Hansel, "and do not fret; I will manage something."

When the parents had gone to sleep, Hansel got up, put on his little coat, opened the back door, and slipped out. The moon was shining brightly, and the white pebbles that lay in front of the house glistened like pieces of silver. Hansel stooped and filled the little pocket of his coat as full as it would hold. Then he went back again, and said to Gretel,

"Be easy, dear little sister, and go to sleep quietly; God will not forsake us," and laid himself down again in his bed.

When the day was breaking, and before the sun had risen, the wife came and awakened the two children, saying,

"Get up, you lazy bones! We are going into the forest to cut wood."

Then she gave each of them a piece of bread, and said,

"That is for dinner, and you must not eat it before then, for you will get no more."

Gretel carried the bread under her apron, for Hansel had his pockets full of pebbles. Then they set off all together on their way to the forest.

When they had gone a little way Hansel stood still and looked back towards the house, and this he did again and again, till his father said to him,

"Hansel, what are you looking at? Take care not to forget your legs."

"O father," said Hansel, "I am looking at my little white kitten, who is sitting up on the roof to bid me good-by."

"You foolish boy," said the woman, "that is not your kitten, but the sunshine on the chimney pot."

Of course Hansel had not been looking at his kitten, but had been taking every now and then a pebble from his pocket and dropping it on the road.

When they reached the middle of the forest the father told the children to collect wood to make a fire to keep them warm. So Hansel and Gretel gathered brushwood enough for a little mountain; and it was set on fire, and when the flame was burning quite high the wife said,

"Now lie down by the fire and rest yourselves, you children, and we will go

[1] From Lucy Crane, *Household Stories from the Brothers Grimm.*

and cut wood; and when we are ready we will come and fetch you."

So Hansel and Gretel sat by the fire, and at noon they each ate their pieces of bread. They thought their father was in the wood all the time, as they seemed to hear the strokes of the axe. Really it was only a dry branch hanging to a withered tree that the wind moved to and fro. So when they had stayed there a long time their eyelids closed with weariness, and they fell fast asleep. When at last they woke it was night, and Gretel began to cry, and said,

"How shall we ever get out of this wood?"

But Hansel comforted her, saying,

"Wait a little while longer, until the moon rises, and then we can easily find the way home."

When the full moon came up, Hansel took his little sister by the hand, and followed the way where the little stones shone like silver and showed them the road. They walked on the whole night through, and at the break of day they came to their father's house.

They knocked at the door, and when their stepmother opened it and saw that it was Hansel and Gretel she said,

"You naughty children, why did you sleep so long in the wood? We thought you were never coming home again!"

But the father was glad, for it had gone to his heart to leave them both in the woods alone.

Not very long after that there was again great scarcity in those parts, and the children heard their stepmother say to their father,

"Everything is finished up; we have only half a loaf, and after that the tale comes to an end. The children must be off; we will take them farther into the wood this time, so that they shall not be able to find the way back again; there is no other way to manage."

The man felt sad at heart, and he thought,

"It would be better to share one's last morsel with one's children."

But the wife would listen to nothing that he said, but scolded and reproached him. When a man has given in once he has to do it a second time.

But the children were not asleep, and had heard all the talk. When the parents had gone to sleep, Hansel got up to go out and get more pebbles as he did before, but the stepmother had locked the door, and Hansel could not get out. But he comforted his little sister, and said,

"Don't cry, Gretel, and go to sleep quietly, and God will help us."

Early the next morning the wife came and pulled the children out of bed. She gave them each a little piece of bread—less than before; and on the way to the wood Hansel crumbled the bread in his pocket, and often stopped to throw a crumb on the ground.

"Hansel, what are you stopping behind and staring for?" said the father.

"I am looking at my little pigeon sitting on the roof, to say good-by to me," answered Hansel.

"No, boy," said the wife, "that is no pigeon, but the morning sun shining on the chimney pots."

Hansel went on as before, and strewed bread crumbs all along the road.

The woman led the children far into the wood, where they had never been before in all their lives. And again there was a large fire made, and she said,

"Sit still there, you children, and when you are tired you can go to sleep. We are going into the forest to cut wood, and in the evening, when we are ready to go home we will come and fetch you."

When noon came Gretel shared her bread with Hansel, who had strewed his along the road. Then they went to sleep, and the evening passed, and no one came for the poor children. When they awoke it was dark night, but Hansel comforted his little sister, and said,

"Wait a little, Gretel, until the moon gets up, then we shall be able to see our way home by the crumbs of bread that I have scattered along the road."

So when the moon rose they got up, but they could find no crumbs of bread, for the birds of the woods and of the fields had come and picked them up. Hansel thought they might find the way all the same, but they could not.

They went on all night, and the next day from the morning until the evening, but they could not find the way out of the wood. They were very hungry, for they had nothing to eat but the few berries they could pick up. And when they were so tired that they could no longer drag themselves along, they lay down under a tree and fell asleep.

It was now the third morning since they had left their father's house. They were always trying to get back to it, but instead of that they only found themselves farther in the wood; and if help had not soon come, they would have been starved. About noon they saw a pretty snow-white bird sitting on a bough, and singing so sweetly that they stopped to listen.

When he had finished, the bird spread his wings and flew before them, and they followed after him until they came to a little house, and the bird perched on the roof, and when they came nearer they saw that the house was built of gingerbread, and roofed with cakes; and the window was made of sugar.

"We will have some of this," said Hansel, "and make a fine meal. I will eat a piece of the roof, Gretel, and you can have some of the window—that will taste sweet."

So Hansel reached up and broke off a bit of the roof, just to see how it tasted, and Gretel stood by the window and gnawed at it. Then they heard a thin voice call out from inside,

"Nibble, nibble, like a mouse,
Who is nibbling at my house?"

The children answered,

"Never mind,
It is the wind."

They went on eating, never disturbing themselves. Hansel, who found that the roof tasted very nice, took down a great piece of it, and Gretel pulled out a large round windowpane, and sat down and began upon it.

Then the door opened, and an old woman came out, leaning upon a crutch. Hansel and Gretel felt very frightened, and let fall what they had in their hands. The old woman, however, nodded her head, and said,

"Ah, my dear children, how come you here? You must come indoors and stay with me, you will be no trouble."

So she took them each by the hand, and led them into her little house. There they found a good meal laid out, of milk and pancakes, with sugar, apples, and nuts. After that she showed them two little white beds, and Hansel and Gretel laid themselves down on them, and thought they were in heaven.

The old woman, although her behavior was so kind, was a wicked witch, who lay in wait for children, and had built the little house on purpose to entice them. When they were once inside she used to kill them, cook them, and eat them, and then it was a feast-day with her.

The witch's eyes were red, and she could not see very far, but she had a keen scent, like the beasts, and knew very well when human creatures were near. When she knew that Hansel and Gretel were coming, she had given a spiteful laugh, and said triumphantly,

"I have them, and they shall not escape me!"

Early in the morning, before the children were awake, she got up to look at them, and as they lay sleeping so peacefully with round rosy cheeks, she said to herself,

"What a fine feast I shall have!"

She grasped Hansel with her withered hand, and led him into a little stable, and shut him up behind a grating; and call and scream as he might, it was no good. Then she went back to Gretel and shook her, crying,

"Get up, lazy bones! Fetch water, and cook something nice for your brother; he is outside in the stable, and must be fattened up. And when he is fat enough, I will eat him."

Gretel began to weep bitterly, but it was of no use, she had to do what the wicked witch bade her.

So the best kind of victuals was cooked for poor Hansel, while Gretel got nothing but crab-shells. Each morning the old woman visited the little stable, and cried,

"Hansel, stretch out your finger, that I may tell if you will soon be fat enough."

Hansel, however, held out a little bone, and the old woman, who had weak eyes, could not see what it was, and supposing it to be Hansel's finger, wondered very much that it was not getting fatter. When four weeks had passed and Hansel seemed to remain so thin, she lost patience and could wait no longer.

"Now then, Gretel," she cried to the little girl, "be quick and draw water. Be Hansel fat or be he lean, tomorrow I must kill and cook him."

Oh, what a grief for the poor little sister to have to fetch the water, and how the tears flowed down over her cheeks!

"Dear God, pray help us!" cried she. "If we had been devoured by wild beasts in the wood, at least we should have died together."

"Spare me your lamentations," said the old woman. "They are of no avail."

Early next morning Gretel had to get up, make the fire, and fill the kettle.

"First we will do the baking," said the old woman. "I have heated the oven already, and kneaded the dough."

She pushed poor Gretel towards the oven, out of which the flames were already shining.

"Creep in," said the witch, "and see if it is properly hot so that the bread may be baked."

When Gretel was once in, she meant to shut the door upon her and let her be baked, and then she would have eaten her. But Gretel perceived her intention, and said,

"I don't know how to do it. How shall I get in?"

"Stupid goose," said the old woman, "the opening is big enough, do you see? I could get in myself!" and she stooped down and put her head in the oven's mouth.

Then Gretel gave her a push, so that she went in farther, and she shut the iron door upon her, and put up the bar. Oh, how frightfully she howled! But Gretel ran away, and left her in the oven. Then Gretel went straight to Hansel, opened the stable door, and cried,

"Hansel, we are free! The old witch is dead!"

Then out flew Hansel like a bird from its cage as soon as the door is opened. How rejoiced they both were! How they fell each on the other's neck! And danced about, and kissed each other! As they had nothing more to fear, they went over all the old witch's house, and in every corner there stood chests of pearls and precious stones.

"This is something better than little stones," said Hansel, as he filled his pockets. Gretel, thinking she also would like to carry something home with her, filled her apron full.

"Now, away we go," said Hansel, "if we only can get out of the witch's wood!"

When they had journeyed a few hours they came to a great piece of water.

"We can never get across this," said Hansel. "I see no stepping-stones and no bridge."

"There is no boat either," said Gretel. "But here comes a white duck; if I ask her, she will help us over." So she cried,

"Duck, duck, here we stand,
Hansel and Gretel, on the land,
Stepping-stones and bridge we lack,
Carry us over on your nice white back."

The duck came accordingly, and Hansel got on her back and told his sister to come too.

"No," answered Gretel, "that would be too hard upon the duck. We can go separately, one after the other."

That was how it was managed. After that they went on happily, until they came to the wood and the way grew more and more familiar. At last they saw in the distance their father's house. They ran till they came up to it, rushed in at the door, and fell on their father's neck.

The man had not had a quiet hour since he left his children in the wood; but now the stepmother was dead. When Gretel opened her apron, the pearls and precious stones scattered all over the room, and Hansel took one handful after another out of his pocket. Then was all care at an end, and they lived in great joy together.

## SNOW-WHITE AND ROSE-RED [1]

A poor widow lived alone in a little cottage, in front of which was a garden, where two little rose-trees stood; one bore white roses, the other red. The widow had two children, who resembled the two rose-trees; one was called Snow-White and the other Rose-Red.

They were two of the best children that ever lived; but Snow-White was quieter and more gentle than Rose-Red. Rose-Red liked best to jump about in the meadows, to look for flowers and catch butterflies; but Snow-White sat at home with her mother, helped her in the house, or read to her when there was nothing else to do.

The two children loved one another so much that they always walked hand in hand; and when Snow-White said, "We will not forsake one another," Rose-Red answered, "Never as long as we live;" and the mother added, "Yes, my children, whatever one has, let her divide with the other."

They often ran about in solitary places, and gathered red berries; and the wild creatures of the wood never hurt them, but came confidingly up to them. The little hare ate cabbage leaves out of their hands, the doe grazed at their side, the stag sprang merrily past them, and the birds remained sitting on the boughs, and never ceased their songs.

Snow-White and Rose-Red kept their mother's cottage so clean that it was a pleasure to look into it. In the summer Rose-Red managed the house. Every morning she gathered a nosegay in which was a rose from each tree, and set it by her mother's bed before she awoke.

In winter Snow-White lighted the fire, and hung the kettle on the hook; and though it was only copper, it shone like gold, it was rubbed so clean. In the evening, when the snow fell, the mother said, "Go, Snow-White, and bolt the door."

Then they seated themselves on the hearth, and the mother took her spectacles and read aloud out of a great big book, and the two girls listened, and sat and spun. Near them lay a lamb on the floor, and behind them, on a perch, sat a white dove, with its head under its wing.

One evening, as they were thus happy together, some one knocked to be let in. The mother said, "Quick, Rose-Red, open the door; perhaps it is a traveler who seeks shelter."

Rose-Red went to the door and pushed the bolt back. She thought it was a poor man, but a bear stretched his thick black head into the door. Rose-Red screamed and sprang back, the little lamb bleated, the little dove fluttered about, and Snow-White hid herself behind her mother.

But the bear began to speak, and said, "Do not be frightened, I will do you no harm. I am half frozen, and only want to warm myself a little."

"You poor bear," said the mother, "lay yourself down before the fire, only take care your fur does not burn." Then she called out, "Snow-White and Rose-Red,

[1] From Dinah Maria Mulock Craik, *The Fairy Book*.

come out; the bear will not hurt you—he means honestly by us."

Then they both came out, and, by degrees, the lamb and the dove also approached, and ceased to be afraid.

The bear said, "Children, knock the snow a little out of my fur;" and they fetched a broom, and swept the bear's skin clean; and he stretched himself before the fire and growled softly, like a bear that was happy and comfortable.

In a short time they all became quite friendly together, and the children played tricks with the awkward guest. They pulled his hair, set their feet on his back, and rolled him here and there; or took a hazel-rod and beat him, and when he growled they laughed. The bear was very much pleased with this frolic, only, when they became too mischievous, he called out: "Children, leave me alone—

"Little Snow-White and Rose-Red,
You will strike your lover dead."

When bedtime came, and the others went to sleep, the mother said to the bear, "You can lie there on the hearth, and then you will be sheltered from the cold and the bad weather."

At daybreak the two children let him out, and he trotted over the snow into the wood. Henceforward the bear came every evening at the same hour, laid himself on the hearth, and allowed the children to play with him as much as they liked. They became so used to him that the door was never bolted until their black companion had arrived.

When spring came, and everything was green out of doors, the bear said one morning to Snow-White, "Now I must go away, and may not come again the whole summer."

"Where are you going, dear Bear?" asked Snow-White.

"I must go into the wood, and guard my treasures from the bad dwarfs. In winter, when the ground is frozen hard, they have to stay underneath, and cannot work their way through; but now that the sun has thawed and warmed the earth they break through, come up, seek, and steal. What is once in their hands, and lies in their caverns, does not come so easily into daylight again."

Snow-White was quite sorrowful at parting. She unbolted the door for him, but as the bear ran out, the hook of the door caught him, and a piece of his skin tore off. It seemed to Snow-White that she saw gold shining through, but she was not sure. The bear ran quickly away, and soon disappeared behind the trees.

After some time their mother sent the children into the wood to collect faggots. They found there a large tree, which had been cut down and lay on the ground. By the trunk something was jumping up and down, but they could not tell what it was. As they came nearer they saw that it was a dwarf, with an old withered face and a snow-white beard a yard long. The end of the beard was stuck fast in a cleft in the tree, and the little fellow jumped about like a dog on a rope, and did not know how to help himself.

He stared at the girls with his fiery red eyes, and screamed out, "Why do you stand there? Can't you come and help me?"

"What is the matter with you, little man?" asked Rose-Red.

"Stupid little goose!" answered the dwarf; "I wanted to chop the tree, so as to have some small pieces of wood for the kitchen. We only want little bits for the small quantity of food that we cook for ourselves; we are not, like you, great greedy people. I had driven the wedge well in, and it was all going on right, but the detestable wood was too smooth, and the wedge sprang out and the tree closed up so quickly that I could not pull my beautiful white beard out. Now it is sticking there, and I can't get away. There, you foolish, soft milk-faces! You are laughing and thinking, 'How ugly you are! How ugly you are!' "

The children took a great deal of trouble, but they could not pull the beard out; it stuck too fast.

"I will run and fetch somebody," said Rose-Red.

"You great ninny!" snarled the dwarf, "to want to call more people; you are two too many for me now. Can't you think of anything better?"

"Don't be impatient," said Snow-White. "I have thought of something!"

She took her little scissors out of her pocket, and cut the end of the beard off. As soon as the dwarf felt himself free, he seized a sack filled with gold that was sticking between the roots of the tree. Pulling it out, he growled to himself, "You rude people, to cut off a piece of my beautiful beard! May evil reward you!"

Then he threw his sack over his shoulders and walked away, without once looking at the children.

Some time afterwards Snow-White and Rose-Red wished to catch some fish for dinner. As they came near to the stream they saw that something like a grasshopper was jumping towards the water, as if it were going to spring in. They ran on and recognized the dwarf.

"Where are you going?" asked Rose-Red. "You don't want to go into the water?"

"I am not such a fool as that," cried the dwarf. "Don't you see the detestable fish wants to pull me in?"

The little fellow had been sitting here fishing, and the wind had entangled his beard with the line. When directly afterwards a great fish bit at his hook, the weak creature could not pull him out, so the fish was pulling the dwarf into the water. It is true he caught hold of all the reeds and rushes, but that did not help him much. He had to follow the fish, and was in danger of being drowned.

The girls, coming at the right time, held him fast and tried to get the beard loose from the line, but in vain—beard and line were entangled fast together. There was nothing to do but to pull out the scissors and to cut off the beard. In doing so a little piece of it was lost.

When the dwarf saw what had happened, he cried out, "Is that manners, you goose! —to disfigure one's face so? Is it not enough that you once cut my beard shorter? But now you have cut the best part of it off, I dare not be seen by my people. I wish you had to run without any soles on your shoes!"

Then he fetched a sack of pearls that lay among the rushes, and, without saying a word more, he dragged it away and disappeared behind a stone.

Soon after, the mother sent the two girls to the town to buy cotton, needles, cord, and tape. The road led them by a field, which was scattered over with great rocks. There they saw a large bird hovering in the air; it flew round and round just above them, always sinking lower and lower, and at last it settled down by a rock not far distant.

Then they heard a piercing, wailing cry. They ran up, and saw with horror that the eagle had seized their old acquaintance the dwarf, and was going to carry him off. The children instantly seized hold of the little man, held him fast, and struggled so long that the eagle let him go.

When the dwarf had recovered from his first fright he called out, in his shrill voice, "Could you not deal rather more gently with me? You have torn my thin coat all in tatters, awkward, clumsy creatures that you are!"

Then he took a sack of precious stones, and slipped behind the rock again into his den. The girls, who were used to his ingratitude, went on their way and completed their business in the town.

As they were coming home again over the heath they surprised the dwarf, who had emptied his sack of precious stones on a little clean place, and had not thought that any one would come by there so late. The evening sun shone on the glittering stones, which looked so beautiful in all their colors that the children could not help standing still to gaze.

"Why do you stand there gaping?" cried the dwarf, his ash-colored face turning red with anger.

With these cross words he was going away, when he heard a loud roaring, and a black bear trotted out of the wood towards them. The dwarf sprang up terrified, but he could not get away—the bear was already close upon him. Then he called out in anguish:

"Dear Mr. Bear, spare me, and you shall have all my treasures; look at the beautiful precious stones that lie there. Give me my life! What do you want with a poor thin little fellow like me? You would scarcely feel me between your teeth. Rather take those two wicked girls; they will be tender morsels for you, as fat as young quails. Pray, eat them at once!"

The bear, without troubling himself to answer, gave the malicious creature one single stroke with his paw, and he did not move again.

The girls had run away, but the bear called after them, "Snow-White and Rose-Red, do not be frightened; wait, I will go with you."

Recognizing the voice of their old friend, they stood still. When the bear came up to them his skin suddenly fell off; and behold, he was not a bear, but a handsome young man dressed all in gold!

"I am a king's son," said he. "I was changed by the wicked dwarf, who had stolen all my treasures, into a wild bear, and obliged to run about in the wood until I should be freed by his death. Now he has received his well-deserved punishment."

So they all went home together to the widow's cottage, and Snow-White was married to the prince, and Rose-Red to his brother. They divided between them the dwarf's great treasures.

The old mother lived many quiet and happy years with her children; but when she left her cottage for the palace she took the two rose-trees with her, and they stood before her window and bore every year the most beautiful roses—one white and the other red.

## CINDERELLA, OR THE LITTLE GLASS SLIPPER [1]

There was once an honest gentleman who took for his second wife a lady, the proudest and most disagreeable in the whole country. She had two daughters exactly like herself in all things. He also had one little girl, who resembled her dead mother, the best woman in the world.

Scarcely had the second marriage taken place than the stepmother became jealous of the good qualities of the little girl, who was so great a contrast to her own two daughters. She gave her all the menial occupations of the house; compelled her to wash the floors and staircases, to dust the bedrooms and clean the grates.

While her sisters occupied carpeted chambers hung with mirrors, where they could see themselves from head to foot, this poor little damsel was sent to sleep in an attic, on an old straw mattress, with only one chair, and not a looking glass in the room.

She suffered all in silence, not daring to complain to her father, who was entirely ruled by his new wife. When her daily work was done, she used to sit down in the chimney corner among the ashes; from which the two sisters gave her the nickname of *Cinderella*. But Cinderella, however shabbilly clad, was handsomer than they were with all their fine clothes.

It happened that the king's son gave a series of balls, to which were invited all the rank and fashion of the city, and among the rest the two elder sisters. They were very proud and happy, and occupied their whole time in deciding what they should wear—a source of new trouble to Cinderella, whose duty it was to get up their fine linen and laces, and who never could please them, however much she tried. They talked of nothing but their clothes.

"I," said the elder, "shall wear my velvet gown and my trimmings of English lace."

"And I," added the younger, "will have

[1] From Dinah Maria Mulock Craik, *The Fairy Book*.

but my ordinary silk petticoat, but I shall adorn it with an upper skirt of flowered brocade, and shall put on my diamond tiara, which is a great deal finer than anything of yours."

Here the elder sister grew angry, and the dispute began to run so high that Cinderella, who was known to have excellent taste, was called upon to decide between them. She gave them the best advice she could, and gently and submissively offered to dress them herself, and especially to arrange their hair, an accomplishment in which she excelled many a noted coiffeur.

The important evening came, and she exercised all her skill to adorn the two young ladies. While she was combing out the elder's hair, this ill-natured girl said sharply, "Cinderella, do you not wish you were going to the ball?"

"Ah, madam" (they obliged her always to say madam), "you are only mocking me; it is not my fortune to have any such pleasure."

"You are right; people would only laugh to see a little cinder wench at a ball."

Any other than Cinderella would have dressed the hair all awry; but she was good, and dressed it perfectly even and smooth, and as prettily as she could.

The sisters had scarcely eaten for two days, and had broken a dozen stay-laces a day in trying to make themselves slender; but tonight they broke a dozen more, and lost their tempers over and over again before they had completed their toilette. When at last the happy moment arrived, Cinderella followed them to the coach; after it had whirled them away, she sat down by the kitchen fire and cried.

Immediately her godmother, who was a fairy, appeared beside her. "What are you crying for, my little maid?"

"Oh, I wish— I wish—" Her sobs stopped her.

"You wish to go to the ball. Isn't it so?"

Cinderella nodded.

"Well, then, be a good girl and you shall go. First run into the garden and fetch me the largest pumpkin you can find."

Cinderella did not comprehend what this had to do with her going to the ball, but, being obedient and obliging, she went. Her godmother took the pumpkin, and having scooped out all its inside, struck it with her wand; it became a splendid gilt coach lined with rose-colored satin.

"Now fetch me the mouse trap out of the pantry, my dear."

Cinderella brought it. It contained six of the fattest, sleekest mice. The fairy lifted up the wire door, and as each mouse ran out she struck it and changed it into a beautiful black horse.

"But what shall I do for your coachman, Cinderella?"

Cinderella suggested that she had seen a large black rat in the rat trap, and he might do for want of better.

"You are right. Go and look again for him."

He was found, and the fairy made him into a most respectable coachman, with the finest whiskers imaginable. She afterwards took six lizards from behind the pumpkin frame, and changed them into six footmen, all in splendid livery, who immediately jumped up behind the carriage, as if they had been footmen all their days. "Well, Cinderella," said the fairy godmother, "now you can go to the ball."

"What, in these clothes?" said Cinderella piteously, looking down on her ragged frock.

Her godmother laughed, and touched her also with the wand; at which her wretched threadbare jacket became stiff with gold and sparkling with jewels; her woolen petticoat lengthened into a gown of sweeping satin, from underneath which peeped out her little feet, no longer bare, but covered with silk stockings and the prettiest glass slippers in the world.

"Now, Cinderella, depart," said her godmother, "but remember, if you stay one instant after midnight your carriage will become a pumpkin, your coachman a rat, your horses mice, and your footmen lizards; while you yourself will be the little cinder wench you were an hour ago."

Cinderella promised without fear, her heart was so full of joy.

Arrived at the palace, the king's son, whom some one, probably the fairy, had told to await the coming of an uninvited princess whom nobody knew, was standing at the entrance, ready to receive her. He offered her his hand and led her with the utmost courtesy through the assembled guests, who stood aside to let her pass, whispering to one another, "Oh, how beautiful she is!" It might have turned the head of any one but poor Cinderella, who was so used to be despised that she took it all as if it were something happening in a dream.

Her triumph was complete; even the old king said to the queen that never since her majesty's young days had he seen so charming and elegant a person. All the court ladies scanned her eagerly, clothes and all, determining to have theirs made next day of exactly the same pattern. The king's son himself led her out to dance, and she danced so gracefully that he admired her more and more. Indeed, at supper, which was fortunately early, his admiration quite took away his appetite.

Cinderella with an involuntary shyness, sought out her sisters, placed herself beside them and offered them all sorts of civil attentions. This, coming as they supposed from a stranger and so magnificent a lady, almost overwhelmed them with delight.

While she was talking with them she heard the clock strike a quarter to twelve, and making a courteous adieu to the royal family she reentered her carriage, escorted tenderly by the king's son, and arrived in safety at her own door.

There she found her godmother, who smiled approval; and of whom she begged permission to go to a second ball the following night, to which the queen had earnestly invited her.

While she was talking, the two sisters were heard knocking at the gate, and the fairy godmother vanished, leaving Cinderella sitting in the chimney corner, rubbing her eyes and pretending to be very sleepy.

"Ah," cried the eldest sister maliciously, "it has been the most delightful ball, and there was present the most beautiful princess I ever saw, who was so exceedingly polite to us both."

"Was she?" said Cinderella indifferently, "and who might she be?"

"Nobody knows, though everybody would give their eyes to know, especially the king's son."

"Indeed!" replied Cinderella, a little more interested. "I should like to see her. Miss Javotte,"—that was the elder sister's name,—"will you not let me go tomorrow, and lend me your yellow gown that you wear on Sundays?"

"What, lend my yellow gown to a cinder wench! I am not so mad as that;" at which refusal Cinderella did not complain, for if her sister really had lent her the gown she would have been considerably embarrassed.

The next night came, and the two young ladies, richly dressed, went to the ball. Cinderella, more splendidly attired and beautiful than ever, followed them shortly after.

"Now remember twelve o'clock," was her godmother's parting speech; and she thought she certainly would. But the prince's attentions to her were greater even than the first evening, and in the delight of listening to his pleasant conversation time slipped by unperceived.

While she was sitting beside him in a lovely alcove, and looking at the moon from under a bower of orange blossoms, she heard a clock strike the first stroke of twelve. She started up and fled away as lightly as a deer.

Amazed, the prince followed, but could not catch her. Indeed, he missed his lovely princess altogether, and only saw running out of the palace doors a little dirty lass whom he had never beheld before, and of whom he certainly would never have taken the least notice.

Cinderella arrived at home breathless and weary, ragged and cold, without carriage, or footmen, or coachman; the only remnant of her past magnificence being one of her little glass slippers—the other she had dropped in the ballroom as she ran away.

When the two sisters returned they were full of this strange adventure, how the beautiful lady had appeared at the ball more beautiful than ever, and enchanted every one who looked at her; and how as the clock was striking twelve she had suddenly risen up and fled through the ballroom, disappearing no one knew how or where, and dropping one of her glass slippers behind her in her flight.

The sisters said the king's son had remained inconsolable until he chanced to pick up the little glass slipper, which he carried away in his pocket, and was seen to take it out continually and look at it affectionately, with the air of a man very much in love. In fact, from his behavior during the remainder of the evening, all the court and royal family were convinced that he had become desperately enamored of the wearer of the little glass slipper.

Cinderella listened in silence, turning her face to the kitchen fire, and perhaps it was that which made her look so rosy; but nobody ever noticed or admired her at home, so it did not signify, and next morning she went to her weary work again just as before.

A few days after, the whole city was attracted by the sight of the herald going round with a little glass slipper in his hand, publishing, with a flourish of trumpets, that the king's son ordered this to be fitted on the foot of every lady in the kingdom, and that he wished to marry the lady whom it fitted best, or to whom it and the fellow slipper belonged.

Princesses, duchesses, countesses, and simple gentlewomen all tried it on, but being a fairy slipper, it fitted nobody; and beside, nobody could produce its fellow slipper, which lay all the time safely in the pocket of Cinderella's old linsey gown.

At last the herald came to the house of the two sisters, and though they well knew neither of themselves was the beautiful lady, they made every attempt to get their clumsy feet into the glass slipper, but in vain.

"Let me try it on," said Cinderella from the chimney corner.

"What, you?" cried the others, bursting into shouts of laughter, but Cinderella only smiled and held out her hand.

Her sisters could not prevent her, since the command was that every young maiden in the city should try on the slipper, in order that no chance might be left untried, for the prince was nearly breaking his heart. His father and mother were afraid that, though a prince, he would actually die for love of the beautiful unknown lady.

The herald bade Cinderella sit down on a three-legged stool in the kitchen, and he, himself, put the slipper on her pretty little foot. It fitted exactly! She then drew from her pocket the fellow slipper, which she also put on, and stood up—for with the touch of the magic shoes all her dress was changed likewise—no longer the poor, despised cinder wench, but the beautiful lady whom the king's son loved.

Her sisters recognized her at once. Filled with astonishment, mingled with no little alarm, they threw themselves at her feet, begging her pardon for all their former unkindness. She raised and embraced them; told them she forgave them with all her heart, and only hoped they would love her always.

Then she departed with the herald to the king's palace, and told her whole story to his majesty and the royal family. They were not in the least surprised, for everybody believed in fairies, and everybody longed to have a fairy godmother.

The young prince found her more lovely and lovable than ever, and insisted upon marrying her immediately. Cinderella never went home again, but she sent for her two sisters to come to the palace, and with the consent of all parties married them shortly after to two rich gentlemen of the court.

## BRIER ROSE [1]

Once upon a time there lived a king and queen who had no children; and this they lamented very much. When at last the queen had a little girl, the king could not cease looking on it for joy, and determined to hold a great feast. So he invited not only his relations, friends, and neighbors, but also all the fairies, that they might be kind and good to his little daughter.

Now there were thirteen fairies in his kingdom, and he had only twelve golden dishes for them to eat out of, so he was obliged to leave one of the fairies without an invitation. The rest came, and after the feast was over they gave all their best gifts to the little princess: one gave her virtue, another beauty, another riches, and so on till she had all that was excellent in the world.

When eleven had done blessing her, the thirteenth, who had not been invited and was very angry on that account, came in and determined to take her revenge. So she cried out, "The king's daughter shall in her fifteenth year be wounded by a spindle, and fall down dead."

Then the twelfth, who had not yet given her gift, came forward and said that the bad wish must be fulfilled, but that she could soften it, and that the king's daughter should not die, but fall asleep for a hundred years.

But the king hoped to save his dear child from the threatened evil and ordered that all the spindles in the kingdom should be bought up and destroyed. All the fairies' gifts were in the meantime fulfilled, for the princess was so beautiful, and well behaved, and amiable, and wise that every one who knew her loved her.

Now it happened that on the very day she was fifteen years old the king and queen were not at home, and she was left alone in the palace. So she roved about by herself and looked at all the rooms and chambers till at last she came to an old tower, to which there was a narrow staircase ending with a little door. In the door there was a golden key, and when she turned it the door sprang open, and there sat an old lady spinning away very busily.

"Why, how now, good mother," said the princess, "what are you doing?"

"Spinning," said the old lady, and nodded her head.

"How prettily that little thing turns round!" said the princess, and took the spindle and began to spin. But scarcely had she touched it before the prophecy was fulfilled, and she fell down lifeless on the ground.

However, she was not dead, but had only fallen into a deep sleep; and the king and the queen, who just then came home, and all their court, fell asleep too; and the horses slept in the stables, and the dogs in the court, the pigeons on the housetop and the flies on the walls.

Even the fire on the hearth left off blazing and went to sleep; and the meat that was roasting stood still; and the cook, who was at that moment pulling the kitchenboy by the hair to give him a box on the ear for something he had done amiss, let him go, and both fell asleep; and so everything stood still, and slept soundly.

A large hedge of thorns soon grew round the palace, and every year it became higher and thicker till at last the whole palace was surrounded and hid, so that not even the roof or the chimneys could be seen.

But there went a report through all the land of the beautiful sleeping Brier Rose (for so was the king's daughter called); so that from time to time several kings' sons came and tried to break through the thicket into the palace. This they could never do, for the thorns and bushes laid hold of them as if with hands, and they could never break through.

After many many years there came a king's son into that land, and an old man told him the story of the thicket of thorns, and how a beautiful palace stood behind it, in which was a wondrous princess, called Brier Rose, asleep with all her court. He

[1] From Edgar Taylor, *Grimms' Popular Stories.*

told, too, how he had heard from his grandfather that many, many princes had come, and had tried to break through the thicket, but had always failed.

Then the young prince said, "All this shall not frighten me. I will go and see Brier Rose." The old man tried to dissuade him, but he persisted in going.

Now that very day were the hundred years completed, and as the prince came to the thicket, he saw nothing but beautiful flowering shrubs, through which he passed with ease, and they closed after him as firm as ever. He came at last to the palace, and there in the court lay the dogs asleep, and the horses in the stables, and on the roof sat the pigeons fast asleep with their heads under their wings. When he came into the palace, the flies slept on the walls, and the cook in the kitchen was still holding up her hand as if she would beat the boy, and the maid sat with a black fowl in her hand ready to be plucked.

Then he went on still further, and all was so still that he could hear every breath he drew. At last he came to the old tower and opened the door of the little room in which Brier Rose was.

There she lay fast asleep, and looked so beautiful that he could not take his eyes off, and he stooped down and gave her a kiss. But the moment he kissed her she opened her eyes and awoke and smiled upon him.

Then they went out together, and presently the king and queen also awoke, and all the court, and they gazed on one another with great wonder. And the horses got up and shook themselves, and the dogs jumped about and barked; the pigeons took their heads from under their wings and looked about and flew into the fields; the flies on the walls buzzed away; the fire in the kitchen blazed up and cooked the dinner, and the roast meat turned round again; the cook gave the boy the box on his ear so that he cried out, and the maid went on plucking the fowl.

And then was the wedding of the prince and Brier Rose celebrated, and they lived happily together all their lives long.

## THE PRINCESS ON THE GLASS HILL [1]

Once on a time there was a man who had a meadow, which lay high up on the hill-side, and in the meadow was a barn, which he had built to keep his hay in. Now, I must tell you, there hadn't been much in the barn for the last year or two, for every Midsummer Night, when the grass stood greenest and deepest, the meadow was eaten down to the very ground the next morning, just as if a whole drove of sheep had been there feeding on it overnight.

This happened once, and it happened twice; so at last the man grew weary of losing his crop of hay, and said to his sons—for he had three of them, and the youngest was nicknamed Boots, of course—that now one of them must go and sleep in the barn in the outlying field when Midsummer Night came, for it was too good a joke for his grass to be eaten, root and blade, this year, as it had been the last two years. So whichever of them went must keep a sharp lookout; that was what their father said.

Well, the eldest son was ready to go and watch the meadow; trust him for looking after the grass! It shouldn't be his fault if man or beast, or the fiend himself, got a blade of grass. So, when evening came, he set off to the barn, and lay down to sleep; but a little on in the night came such a clatter, and such an earthquake, that walls and roof shook, and groaned, and creaked; then up jumped the lad, and took to his heels as fast as ever he could; nor dared he once look around till he reached home; and as for the hay, why, it was eaten up this year just as it had been twice before.

The next Midsummer Night, the man said again it would never do to lose all the grass in the outlying field year after year in this way, so one of his sons must just

[1] From George Webbe Dasent, *Popular Tales from the Norse.*

trudge off to watch it, and watch it well too. Well, the next oldest son was ready to try his luck, so he set off, and lay down to sleep in the barn as his brother had done before him; but as the night wore on, there came on a rumbling and quaking of the earth, worse even than on the last Midsummer Night, and when the lad heard it, he got frightened, and took to his heels as though he were running a race.

Next year the turn came to Boots; but when he made ready to go, the other two began to laugh and to make game of him, saying:

"You're just the man to watch the hay, that you are; you, who have done nothing all your life but sit in the ashes and toast yourself by the fire."

But Boots did not care a pin for their chattering, and away he went as evening grew on, up the hillside to the outlying field. Then he went inside the barn and lay down; but in about an hour's time the barn began to groan and creak, so that it was dreadful to hear.

"Well," said Boots to himself, "if it isn't worse than this, I can stand it well enough."

A little while after came another creak and an earthquake, so that the litter in the barn flew about the lad's ears.

"Oh," said Boots to himself, "if it isn't worse than this, I dare say I can stand it out."

But just then came a third rumbling and a third earthquake, so that the lad thought walls and roof were coming down on his head; but it passed off, and all was still as death about him.

"It'll come again, I'll be bound," thought Boots; but no, it didn't come again; still it was, and still it stayed; but after he had lain a little while, he heard a noise as if a horse were standing just outside the barn door, and cropping the grass. He stole to the door, and peeped through a chink, and there stood a horse feeding away. So big, and fat, and grand a horse, Boots had never set eyes on; by his side on the grass lay a saddle and bridle, and a full set of armor for a knight, all of brass, so bright that the light gleamed from it.

"Ho, ho!" thought the lad; "it's you, is it, that eats up our hay? I'll soon put a spoke in your wheel, just see if I don't."

So he lost no time, but took the steel out of his tinder box, and threw it over the horse; then it had no power to stir from the spot, and became so tame that the lad could do what he liked with it. So he got on its back, and rode off with it to a place which no one knew of, and there he put up the horse. When he got home, his brothers laughed and asked how he had fared.

"You didn't lie long in the barn, even if you had the heart to go so far as the field."

"Well," said Boots, "all I can say is, I lay in the barn till the sun rose, and neither saw nor heard anything; I can't think what there was in the barn to make you both so afraid."

"A pretty story," said his brothers; "but we'll soon see how you have watched the meadow." So they set off; but when they reached it, there stood the grass as deep and thick as it had been overnight.

Well, the next Midsummer Night it was the same story over again; neither of the elder brothers dared to go out to the outlying field to watch the crop; but Boots, he had the heart to go, and everything happened just as it had happened the year before. First a clatter and an earthquake, then a greater clatter and another earthquake, and so on a third time; only this year the earthquakes were far worse than the year before. Then all at once everything was as still as death, and the lad heard how something was cropping the grass outside the barn door, so he stole to the door, and peeped through a chink; and what do you think he saw? Why, another horse standing right up against the wall, and chewing and champing with might and main. It was far finer and fatter than that which came the year before, and it had a saddle on its back, and a bridle on its neck, and a full suit of mail for a knight lay by its side, all of silver, and as grand as you would wish to see.

"Ho, ho!" said Boots to himself, "it's you that gobbles up our hay, is it? I'll soon put a spoke in your wheel"; and with that he took the steel out of his tinder box, and threw it over the horse, which stood as still as a lamb. Well, the lad rode this horse, too, to the hiding place where he kept the other one, and after that he went home.

"I suppose you'll tell us," said one of his brothers, "there's a fine crop this year too, up in the hayfield."

"Well, so there is," said Boots; and off ran the others to see, and there stood the grass thick and deep, as it was the year before; but they didn't give Boots softer words for all that.

Now, when the third Midsummer Night came the two elder brothers still hadn't the heart to lie out in the barn and watch the grass, for they had got so scared the nights they lay there before, that they couldn't get over the fright; but Boots, he dared to go; and, to make a very long story short, the very same thing happened this time as had happened twice before.

Three earthquakes came, one after the other, each worse than the one which went before, and when the last came, the lad danced about with the shock from one barn wall to the other; and after that, all at once, it was still as death. Now, when he had lain a little while, he heard something tugging away at the grass outside the barn, so he stole again to the door chink, and peeped out, and there stood a horse close outside—far, far bigger and fatter than the two which had come before. And it had a saddle and a bridle, and by its side lay a full suit of armor for a knight—all of the finest gold, and grander than you could ever hope to see.

"Ho, ho!" said the lad to himself; "it's you, is it, that comes here eating up our hay? I'll soon stop that—I'll soon put a spoke in your wheel."

So he caught up his steel and threw it over the horse's neck, and in a trice it stood as if it were nailed to the ground, and Boots could do as he pleased with it. Then he rode off with it to the hiding place where he kept the other two, and then went home. When he got home, his two brothers made game of him as they had done before, saying they could see he had watched the grass well, for he looked for all the world as if he were walking in his sleep, and many other spiteful things they said; but Boots gave no heed to them, only asking them to go and see for themselves; and when they went, there stood the grass as fine and deep this time as it had been twice before.

Now, you must know that the King of the country where Boots lived had a daughter, whom he would only give to the man who could ride up over the Hill of Glass, for there was a high, high hill, all of glass, as smooth and slippery as ice, close by the King's palace. Upon the tiptop of the hill the King's daughter was to sit, with three golden apples in her lap, and the man who could ride up and carry off the three golden apples was to have half the kingdom, and the Princess to wife. This the King had announced in all parts of his realm, and had given it out in many other kingdoms besides.

Now, this Princess was so lovely that all who set eyes on her fell over head and ears in love with her whether they would or no. So I needn't tell you how all the princes and knights who heard of her were eager to win her to wife, and half the kingdom beside; and how they came riding from all parts of the world on high prancing horses, and clad in the grandest clothes, for there wasn't one of them who hadn't made up his mind that he, and he alone, was to win the Princess.

So when the day of trial came, which the King had fixed, there was such a crowd of princes and knights under the Glass Hill that it made one's head whirl to look at them; and every one in the country who could even crawl along was off to the hill, for they were all eager to see the man who was to win the Princess. So the two elder brothers set off with the rest; but as for Boots, they said outright he shouldn't go with them, for if they were seen with such a dirty changeling, all begrimed with smut from cleaning their shoes and sifting cinders in the dust hole, they said folk would make game of them.

"Very well," said Boots to himself, "it's all one to me. I can go alone, and stand or fall by myself."

Now when the two brothers came to the Hill of Glass, the knights and princes were all hard at it, riding their horses till they were all in a foam; but it was no good, for as soon as ever the horses set foot on the hill, down they slipped, and there wasn't one who could get a yard or two up; and no wonder, for the hill was as smooth as a sheet of glass, and as steep as a house wall. But all were eager to have the Princess and half the kingdom. So they rode and slipped, and slipped and rode, and still it was the same story over again.

At last all their horses were so weary that they could scarce lift a leg, and in such a sweat that the lather dripped from them, and so the knights had to give up trying any more. So the King was just thinking that he would proclaim a new trial for the next day, to see if they would have better luck, when all at once a knight came riding up on so brave a steed that no one had ever seen the like of it in his born days, and the knight had mail of brass, and the horse a brass bit in his mouth, so bright that the sunbeams shone from it.

Then all the others called out to him he might just as well spare himself the trouble of riding at the hill, for it would lead to no good; but he gave no heed to them, and put his horse at the hill, and went up it like nothing for a good way, about a third of the height; and when he had got so far, he turned his horse round and rode down again. So lovely a knight the Princess thought she had never yet seen; and while he was riding, she sat and thought to herself:

"Would to heaven he might only come up, and down the other side."

And when she saw him turning back, she threw down one of the golden apples after him, and it rolled down into his shoe. But when he got to the bottom of the hill he rode off so fast that no one could tell what had become of him. That evening all the knights and princes were to go before the King, so that he who had ridden so far up the hill might show the apple which the Princess had thrown, but there was no one who had anything to show. One after the other they all came, but not a man of them could show the apple.

At evening the brothers of Boots came home, and had such a long story to tell about the riding up the hill.

"First of all," they said, "there was not one of the whole lot who could get so much as a stride up; but at last came one who had a suit of brass mail, and a brass bridle and saddle, all so bright that the sun shone from them a mile off. He was a chap to ride! He rode a third of the way up the Hill of Glass, and he could easily have ridden the whole way up, if he chose; but he turned round and rode down, thinking, maybe, that was enough for once."

"Oh! I should so like to have seen him, that I should," said Boots, who sat by the fireside, and stuck his feet into the cinders, as was his wont.

"Oh!" said his brothers, "you would, would you? You look fit to keep company with such high lords, nasty fellow that you are, sitting there amongst the ashes!"

Next day the brothers were all for setting off again, and Boots begged them this time, too, to let him go with them and see the riding; but no, they wouldn't have him at any price, he was too ugly and dirty, they said.

"Well, well!" said Boots to himself; "if I go at all, I must go by myself. I'm not afraid."

So when the brothers got to the Hill of Glass, all the princes and knights began to ride again, and you may fancy they had taken care to shoe their horses sharp; but it was no good—they rode and slipped, and slipped and rode, just as they had done the day before, and there was not one who could get so far as a yard up the hill.

When they had worn out their horses, so

that they could not stir a leg, they were all forced to give it up as a bad job. So the King thought he might as well proclaim that the riding should take place the day after for the last time, just to give them one chance more; but all at once it came across his mind that he might as well wait a little longer, to see if the knight in brass mail would come this day too.

Well, they saw nothing of him; but all at once came one riding on a steed far, far braver and finer than that on which the knight in brass had ridden, and he had silver mail, and a silver saddle and bridle, all so bright that the sunbeams gleamed and glanced from them far way. Then the others shouted out to him again, saying he might as well hold hard, and not try to ride up the hill, for all his trouble would be thrown away; but the knight paid no heed to them, and rode straight at the hill, and right up it, till he had gone two-thirds of the way, and then he wheeled his horse round and rode down again.

To tell the truth, the Princess liked him still better than the knight in brass, and she sat and wished he might only be able to come right up to the top, and down the other side; but when she saw him turning back, she threw the second apple after him, and it rolled down and fell into his shoe. But, as soon as ever he had come down from the Hill of Glass, he rode off so fast that no one could see what became of him.

At evening, when all were to go in before the King and the Princess, that he who had the golden apple might show it, in they went, one after the other; but there was no one who had any apple to show. And the two brothers, as they had done on the former day, went home and told how things had gone, and how all had ridden at the hill, and none got up.

"But, last of all," they said, "came one in a silver suit, and his horse had a silver saddle and a silver bridle. He was just the chap to ride; and he got two-thirds up the hill, and then turned back. He was a fine fellow, and no mistake; and the Princess threw the second golden apple to him."

"Oh!" said Boots, "I should so like to have seen him too, that I should."

"A pretty story," they said. "Perhaps you think his coat of mail was as bright as the ashes you are always poking about and sifting!"

The third day everything happened as it had happened the two days before. Boots begged to go and see the sight, but the two wouldn't hear of his going with them. When they got to the hill there was no one who could get so much as a yard up it; and now all waited for the knight in silver mail, but they neither saw nor heard of him.

At last came one riding on a steed, so brave that no one had ever seen his match; and the knight had a suit of golden mail, and a golden saddle and bridle, so wondrous bright that the sunbeams gleamed from them a mile off. The other knights and princes could not find time to call out to him not to try his luck, for they were amazed to see how grand he was. So he rode right at the hill, and tore up it like nothing, so that the Princess hadn't even time to wish that he might get up the whole way. As soon as ever he reached the top, he took the third golden apple from the Princess's lap, and then turned his horse and rode down again. As soon as he got down, he rode off at full speed, and was out of sight in no time.

Now, when the brothers got home at evening, you may fancy what long stories they told, how the riding had gone off that day; and amongst other things, they had a deal to say about the knight in golden mail.

"He just was a chap to ride!" they said; "so grand a knight isn't to be found in the wide world."

"Oh!" said Boots, "I should so like to have seen him, that I should."

"Ah!" said his brothers, "his mail shone a deal brighter than the glowing coals which you are always poking and digging at, dirty fellow that you are!"

Next day all the knights and princes were to pass before the King and the Princess—it was too late to do so the night before, I suppose—that he who had the golden apple might bring it forth; but one came after another, first the princes, and then the knights, and still no one could show the golden apple.

"Well," said the King, "some one must have it, for it was something we all saw with our own eyes, how a man came and rode up and bore it off."

So he commanded that every man who was in the kingdom should come up to the palace and sec if they could show the apple. Well, they all came one after another, but no one had the golden apple; and after a long time the two brothers of Boots came. They were the last of all, so the King asked them if there was no one else in the kingdom who hadn't come.

"Oh, yes," said they; "we have a brother, but he never carried off the golden apple. He hasn't stirred out of the dust hole at home on any of the three days."

"Never mind that," said the King; "he may as well come up to the palace like the rest."

So Boots had to go up to the palace.

"How now," said the King; "have you got the golden apple? Speak out!"

"Yes, I have," said Boots; "here is the first, and here is the second, and here is the third, too"; and with that he pulled all three golden apples out of his pocket, and at the same time threw off his sooty rags, and stood before them in his gleaming golden mail.

"Yes!" said the King; "you shall have my daughter, and half my kingdom, for you well deserve both her and it."

So they got ready for the wedding, and Boots got the Princess to wife, and there was great merrymaking at the bridal feast, you may fancy, for they could all be merry though they couldn't ride up the Hill of Glass; and all I can say is, if they haven't let off their merrymaking yet, why, they're still at it.

## EAST OF THE SUN AND WEST OF THE MOON [1]

Once on a time there was a poor husbandman who had so many children that he hadn't much of either food or clothing to give them. Pretty children they all were, but the prettiest was the youngest daughter, who was so lovely there was no end to her loveliness.

So one day—'twas on a Thursday evening late at the fall of the year—the weather was so wild and rough outside, and it was so cruelly dark, and rain fell and wind blew, till the very walls of the cottage shook. There they all sat round the fire, busy with this thing and that. But just then, all at once, something gave three taps on the windowpane. Then the father went out to see what was the matter; and, when he got out of doors, what should he see but a great big White Bear.

"Good evening to you!" said the White Bear.

"The same to you," said the man.

"Will you give me your youngest daughter? If you will, I'll make you as rich as you are now poor," said the Bear.

Well, the man would not be at all sorry to be so rich; but still he thought he must have a bit of a talk with his daughter first; so he went in and told them how there was a great White Bear waiting outside, who had given his word to make them so rich if he could only have the youngest daughter.

The lassie said "No!" outright. Nothing could get her to say anything else; so the man went out and settled it with the White Bear that he should come again the next Thursday evening and get an answer. Meantime he talked his daughter over, and kept on telling her of all the riches they would get, and how well off she would be herself; and so at last she thought better of it, and washed and mended her rags, made herself as smart as she could, and was ready to start. I can't say her packing gave her much trouble.

1 Adapted from George Webbe Dasent, *Popular Tales from the Norse.*

Next Thursday evening came the White Bear to fetch her, and she got upon his back with her bundle, and off they went. So, when they had gone a bit of the way, the White Bear said:

"Are you afraid?"

No, she wasn't.

"Well, mind and hold tight to my shaggy coat, and then there's nothing to fear," said the Bear.

So she rode a long, long way, till they came to a great steep hill. There, on the face of it, the White Bear gave a knock, and a door opened, and they came into a castle where there were many rooms all lit up; rooms gleaming with silver and gold; and there, too, was a table ready laid, and it was all as grand as grand could be. Then the White Bear gave her a silver bell; and when she wanted anything, she was only to ring it, and she would get it at once. Then the White Bear left her.

Well, after she had eaten and drunk, and evening wore on, she got sleepy after her journey, and thought she would like to go to bed, so she rang the bell; and she had scarce taken hold of it before she came into a chamber where there was a bed made, as fair and white as any one would wish to sleep in, with silken pillows and curtains and gold fringe. All that was in the room was gold or silver.

So things went on happily for a while. She thought of many fine things she wanted, and when she rang the bell she got them all—everything she liked to eat and all the fine clothes and jewels she could think of. But she never saw a living soul but the White Bear, and she didn't see much of him either, and never after the sun went down. Always when the sun set he vanished into another part of the castle and great doors shut behind him. She thought this was very queer, and at last she began to get silent and sorrowful; for there she went about almost all day alone, and she longed to go home to see her father and mother and brothers and sisters. So one day, when the White Bear asked what it was that she lacked, she said it was so dull and lonely there, and how she longed to go home to see her father and mother and brothers and sisters, and that was why she was so sad and sorrowful, because she couldn't get to see them.

"Well, well!" said the Bear, "perhaps there's a cure for all this; but you must promise me one thing, not to talk alone with your mother, but only when the rest are by to hear; for she'll take you by the hand and try to lead you into a room alone to talk; but you must mind and not do that, else you'll bring bad luck on both of us."

So one Sunday the White Bear came and said now they could set off to see her father and mother. Well, off they started, she sitting on his back; and they went far and long. At last they came to a grand house, and there her brothers and sisters were running about out of doors at play, and everything was so pretty, 'twas a joy to see.

"This is where your father and mother live now," said the White Bear, "but don't forget what I told you, else you'll make us both unlucky."

No! bless her, she'd not forget—and when she had reached the house, the White Bear turned right about and left her.

Then, when she went in to see her father and mother, there was such joy, there was no end to it. None of them thought they could thank her enough for all she had done for them. Now, they had everything they wished, as good as good could be, and they all wanted to know how she got on where she lived.

Well, she said, it was very good to live where she did; she had all she wished. What she said beside I don't know, but I don't think any of them got much out of her. But so, in the afternoon, after they had dinner, all happened as the White Bear had said. Her mother wanted to talk with her alone in her bedroom; but she minded what the White Bear had said.

"Oh, what we have to talk about will keep!" she said, and put her mother off.

But, somehow or other, her mother got round her at last, and she had to tell her the whole story. She saw no one but the Bear and she saw him only a very little each day. When night came he hurried away to another part of the castle. He was very good to her, but all day long she walked about there alone; and how dull and dreary and lonesome it was.

"My! my! my!" said her mother, "why should he be running away and hiding himself? Now I'll tell you how to find out what he is doing. I'll give you a bit of candle, which you can carry home in your bosom; just light that and take your little bell and find what he is doing hiding himself away."

Yes, she took the candle and hid it in her bosom, and as night drew on the Bear came and fetched her away.

But when they had gone a bit of the way, the White Bear asked if all hadn't happened as he had said.

Well, she couldn't say it hadn't.

"Now, mind," said he, "if you have listened to your mother's advice, you have brought bad luck on us both!"

No, she said, she hadn't listened to her mother's advice.

The sun began to set before they reached the palace, and the White Bear ran as fast as he could to be there before it was night. As soon as they were there, away he went to another part of the castle. Very queer, thought she, and before the night was over she would know what was beyond those doors. So instead of going to bed that night she took her little bell and with the piece of candle lighted she went into the other part of the castle. A ring of the bell and the doors opened at her wish. Into one room and then into another she went; and then she opened a door and saw that someone lay asleep in the room. She entered and let the light shine on the bed, and there she saw the loveliest Prince one ever set eyes on, and she fell so deep in love with him on the spot that she thought that she couldn't live if she didn't give him a kiss there and then. And so she did; but as she kissed him, she dropped three hot drops of tallow on his shirt, and he woke up.

"What have you done?" he cried. "Now you have made us both unlucky, for had you held out only this one year, I had been freed. For I have been bewitched, so that I am a White Bear by day and a man by night. But now all ties are snapped between us; now I must set off from you to the Witch. She lives in a castle which stands east of the sun and west of the moon, and there, too, is a Princess, the Witch's daughter, with a nose three ells long, and she's the wife I must have now."

She wept and took it ill, but there was no help for it; go he must.

Then she asked if she mightn't go with him.

No, she mightn't.

"Tell me the way, then," she said, "and I'll search you out; *that* surely I may get leave to do."

"Yes," she might do that, he said; but there was no way to that place. It lay east of the sun and west of the moon, and thither she'd never find her way.

Next morning, when she woke up, both Prince and castle were gone, and there she lay on a little green patch, in the midst of the gloomy thick wood, and by her side lay the same bundle of rags she had brought with her from her old home.

So when she had rubbed the sleep out of her eyes, and wept till she was tired, she set out on her way, and walked many, many days, till she came to a lofty crag. Under it sat an old hag, and played with a gold apple which she tossed about. The lassie asked her if she knew the way to the Prince, who was in the castle that lay east of the sun and west of the moon, and who was to marry the princess with a nose three ells long.

"How did you come to know about him?" asked the old hag; "but maybe you are the lassie who ought to have had him?"

Yes, she was.

"So, so; it's you, is it?" said the old hag. "Well, all I know about him is, that he is in the castle that lies east of the sun and west of the moon, and thither you'll come, late or never; but still you may have the loan of my horse, and on him you can ride to my next neighbor. Maybe she'll be able to tell you; and when you get there, just give the horse a switch under the left ear, and beg him to be off home; and, stay, this golden apple you may take with you."

So she got upon the horse, and rode a long, long time, till she came to another crag, under which sat another old hag, with a golden carding-comb. The lassie asked if she knew the way to the castle that lay east of the sun and west of the moon, and she answered, like the first old hag, that she knew nothing about it, except it was east of the sun and west of the moon.

"And thither you'll come, late or never, but you may have the loan of my horse to go to my next neighbor; maybe she'll tell you all about it; and when you get there, just switch the horse under the left ear, and beg him to be off home."

And this old hag gave her the golden carding-comb; it might be she'd find some use for it, she said. So the lassie got upon the horse, and rode a far, far way, and a weary time; and so at last she came to an other great crag, under which sat another old hag, spinning with a golden spinning wheel. Her, too, she asked if she knew the way to the Prince, and where the castle was that lay east of the sun and west of the moon. So it was the same thing over again.

"Maybe it's you who ought to have had the Prince?" said the old hag.

Yes, it was.

But she, too, didn't know the way a bit better than the other two. East of the sun and west of the moon it was, she knew—that was all.

"And thither you'll come, late or never; but I'll lend you my horse, and then I think you'd best ride to the East Wind and ask him; maybe he knows those parts, and can blow you thither. But when you get to him, you need only give the horse a switch under the left ear, and he'll trot home of himself."

And so, too, she gave her the golden spinning wheel. "Maybe you'll find a use for it," said the old hag.

Then on she rode many, many days, a weary time, before she got to the East Wind's house, but at last she did reach it, and then she asked the East Wind if he could tell her the way to the Prince who dwelt east of the sun and west of the moon. Yes, the East Wind had heard of it, the Prince and the castle, but he couldn't tell the way, for he had never blown so far.

"But, if you will, I'll go with you to my brother the West Wind; maybe he knows, for he's much stronger. So, if you will just get on my back, I'll carry you thither."

Yes, she got on his back, and away they went.

So when they got there, they went into the West Wind's house, and the East Wind said the lassie he had brought was the one who ought to have had the Prince who lived in the castle east of the sun and west of the moon; and so she had set out to seek him, and how he had come with her, and would be glad to know if the West Wind knew how to get to the castle.

"Nay," said the West Wind, "so far I've never blown; but if you will, I'll go with you to our brother the South Wind, for he's much stronger than either of us, and he has flapped his wings far and wide. Maybe he'll tell you. You can get on my back, and I'll carry you to him."

Yes, she got on his back, and so they traveled to the South Wind, and weren't so very long on the way, I can tell you.

When they got there, the West Wind asked him if he could tell her the way to the castle that lay east of the sun and west of the moon, for it was she who ought to have had the Prince who lived there.

"You don't say so! So you are the one?" said the South Wind. "Well, I have blustered about in most places in my time, but so far have I never blown; but if you will, I'll take you to my brother the North Wind; he is the oldest and strongest of the whole lot of us, and if he doesn't know where it is, you'll never find any one in the world to tell you. You can get on my back, and I'll carry you thither."

Yes, she got on his back, and away he went from his house at a fine rate. And this time, too, she wasn't long on her way.

So when they got to the North Wind's house, he was so wild and cross, cold puffs came from him a long way off.

"BLAST YOU BOTH, WHAT DO YOU WANT?" he roared out to them ever so far off, so that it struck them with an icy shiver.

"Well," said the South Wind, "you needn't be so very nasty, for here I am, your brother the South Wind, and here is the lassie who ought to have had the Prince who dwells in the castle that lies east of the sun and west of the moon, and now she wants to ask you if you ever were there, and can tell her the way, for she would be so glad to find him again."

"YES, I KNOW WELL ENOUGH WHERE IT IS," said the North Wind; "once in my life I blew an aspenleaf thither, but I was so tired I couldn't blow a puff for ever so many days after. But if you really wish to go there, and aren't afraid to come along with me, I'll take you on my back and see if I can blow you there.

Yes, with all her heart; she must and would get thither if it were possible in any way; and as for fear, however madly he went, she wouldn't be at all afraid.

"Very well, then," said the North Wind, "but you must sleep here tonight, for we must have the whole day before us, if we're to get there at all."

Early next morning the North Wind woke her, and puffed himself up, and blew himself out, and made himself so stout and big, 'twas gruesome to look at him; and so off they went high up through the air, as if they would never stop till they got to the world's end.

Down below there was such a storm; it threw down long tracts of wood and many houses, and when it swept over the great sea, ships foundered by hundreds.

So they tore on and on—no one can believe how far they went—and all the while they still went over the sea, and the North Wind got more and more weary, and so out of breath the could scarce bring out a puff, and his wings drooped and drooped, till at last he sank so low that the crests of the waves dashed over his heels.

"Are you afraid?" said the North Wind.

No, she wasn't.

But they weren't very far from land; and the North Wind had still enough strength left in him to throw her up on the shore under the windows of the castle which lay east of the sun and west of the moon; but then he was so weak and worn out, he had to stay there and rest many days before he could get home again.

Next morning the lassie sat down under the castle window, and began to play with the gold apple; and the first person she saw was the Princess Long-nose who was to marry the Prince.

"What do you want for your gold apple, you lassie?" said the Long-nose, as she threw open the window.

"It's not for sale, for gold or money," said the lassie.

"If it's not for sale for gold or money, what is it that you will sell it for? You may name your own price," said Long-nose.

"Well, if I may see the Prince, who lives here, you shall have it," said the lassie whom the North Wind had brought.

Yes, she might; that could be done. So the Princess got the gold apple; but when the lassie came up to the Prince's bedroom he was fast asleep; she called him and shook him, and between whiles she wept sore; but all she could do wouldn't wake him up. Then the Princess with the long nose came and drove her out again.

So the next day, she sat down under the castle windows again and began to card with her carding-comb, and the same thing happened. The Princess asked what she wanted for it; and she said it wasn't for sale for gold or money, but if she might get leave to go up to the Prince, the Princess should have it. When she went up she found him fast asleep again, and all she called, and all she shook, and wept, and prayed, she couldn't get life into him; but this time she tied some of her hair about one of the Prince's fingers before the Princess with the long nose came and chased her out again.

So on the third day, the lassie sat down outside under the castle window, and began to spin with her golden spinning wheel, and that, too, the Princess with the long nose wanted to have. So she threw up the window and asked what she wanted for it. The lassie said, as she had said twice before, it wasn't for sale for gold or money; but if she might go up to the Prince who was there, she should have it.

That morning when the Princess had come with her sleepy drink, the Prince made as if he drank, but threw it over his shoulder, for he had found the hair on his finger and he knew who had put it there. So when the lassie came in, she found the Prince wide awake; and then she told him the whole story how she had come thither.

"Ah," said the Prince, "you've just come in the nick of time, for tomorrow is to be my wedding day; but now I won't have to marry the Long-nose, for you are the only one in the world who can set me free. I'll say I want to see what my wife is fit for, and beg her to wash the shirt which has the three spots of tallow on it. She'll say yes, for she doesn't know 'tis you who put them there; but that's no work for witches, and I'll say that I won't have any other for my bride than the woman who can wash them out, and ask you to do it."

So there was great joy and love between them, and next day, when the wedding was to be, the Prince said:

"First of all, I'd like to see what my bride is fit for."

"Yes," said the old Witch, her mother, with all her heart.

"Well," said the Prince, "I've got a fine shirt which I'd like for my wedding shirt, but somehow or other it has got three spots of tallow on it, which I must have washed out; for I have sworn never to take any other bride than the woman who's able to do that. If she can't, she's not worth having for my wife."

Well, that was no great thing, they said, so they agreed; and she with the long nose began to wash away as hard as she could; but the more she rubbed and scrubbed, the bigger the spots grew.

"Ah!" said the old hag, her mother, "you can't wash; let me try."

But she hadn't long taken the shirt in hand before it got far worse than ever, and with all her rubbing, and wringing and scrubbing, the spots grew bigger and blacker, and the darker and uglier was the shirt.

Then all the trolls who were standing about began to wash; but the longer they washed, the blacker and uglier the shirt grew, till at last it was as black all over as if it had been up the chimney.

"Ah!" said the Prince, "you're none of you worth a straw; you can't wash. Why there, outside, sits a beggar lassie; I'll be bound she knows how to wash better than the whole lot of you. COME IN, LASSIE!" he shouted.

Well, in she came.

"Can you wash this shirt, lassie you?" said he.

"I don't know," she said, "but I think I can."

And almost before she had taken it and dipped it in the water, it was as white as driven snow, and whiter still.

"Yes; you are the lassie for me," said the prince.

At that the old Witch flew into such a rage, she burst on the spot, and the Princess with the long nose after her, and the whole pack of trolls after her—at least I have never heard a word about them since.

As for the Prince and the lassie, they took with them all the silver and gold that the old Witch had hoarded, and flitted away as far as they could from the castle that lay east of the sun and west of the moon, back to the kingdom from whence the Prince came.

## THE KING OF THE CROCODILES[1]

Once upon a time a farmer went out to look at his fields by the side of the river, and found to his dismay that all his young green wheat had been trodden down, and nearly destroyed, by a number of crocodiles, which were lying lazily amid the crops like great logs of wood. He flew into a great rage, bidding them go back to the water, but they only laughed at him.

Every day the same thing occurred—every day the farmer found the crocodiles lying in his young wheat, until one morning he completely lost his temper, and, when they refused to budge, began throwing stones at them. At this they rushed on him fiercely and he, quaking with fear, fell on his knees, begging them not to hurt him.

"We will hurt neither you nor your young wheat," said the biggest crocodile, "if you will give us your daughter in marriage; but if not, we will eat you for throwing stones at us."

The farmer, thinking of nothing but saving his own life, promised what the crocodiles required of him; but when, on his return home, he told his wife what he had done, she was very much vexed, for their daughter was as beautiful as the moon, and her betrothal into a very rich family had already taken place. So his wife persuaded the farmer to disregard the promise made to the crocodiles, and proceed with his daughter's marriage as if nothing had happened; but when the wedding-day drew near the bridegroom died, and there was an end to that business.

The farmer's daughter, however, was so beautiful that she was very soon asked in marriage again, but this time her suitor fell sick of a lingering illness; in short, so many misfortunes occurred to all concerned, that at last even the farmer's wife acknowledged the crocodiles must have something to do with the bad luck. By her advice the farmer went down to the river bank to try to induce the crocodiles to release him from his promise, but they would hear of no excuse, threatening fearful punishments if the agreement were not fulfilled at once.

So the farmer returned home to his wife, very sorrowful; she, however, was determined to resist to the uttermost, and refused to give up her daughter.

The very next day the poor girl fell down and broke her leg. Then the mother said, "These demons of crocodiles will certainly kill us all! Better to marry our daughter to a strange house than see her die."

Accordingly, the farmer went down to the river and informed the crocodiles they might send the bridal procession to fetch the bride as soon as they chose.

The next day a number of female crocodiles came to the bride's house with trays full of beautiful clothes. They behaved with the utmost politeness, and carried out all the proper ceremonies. Nevertheless the beautiful bride wept.

In due course the bridal procession arrived, and all the village was wonderstruck at the magnificence of the arrangements. Never was there such a retinue of crocodiles, some playing instruments of music, others bearing trays upon trays full of sweetmeats, garments, and jewels, and all dressed in the richest of stuffs. In the middle, a perfect blaze of gold and gems, sat the King of the Crocodiles.

The sight of so much magnificence somewhat comforted the beautiful bride, nevertheless she wept when she was put into the gorgeous bride's palanquin and borne off to the river bank. Lo and behold! no sooner had they reached the water than it divided before them, and, rising up on either side, showed a path leading to the bottom of the river, down which the bridal party disappeared, leaving the bride's father upon the bank, very much astonished at the marvelous sight.

Some months passed by without further news of the crocodiles. The farmer's wife wept because she had lost her daughter, declaring that the girl was drowned, and her husband's fine story about the stream dividing was not true.

[1] From Flora Annie Steel, *Tales of the Punjab*.

Now when the King of the Crocodiles was on the point of leaving with his bride, he had given a piece of brick to her father, with these words: "If ever you want to see your daughter, go down to the river, throw this brick as far as you can into the stream, and you will see what you will see!"

Remembering this, the farmer said to his wife, "Since you are so distressed, I will go myself and see if my daughter be alive or dead."

Then he went to the river bank, taking the brick, and threw it ever so far into the stream. Immediately the waters rolled back from before his feet, leaving a dry path to the bottom of the river. It looked so inviting, spread with clean sand, and bordered by flowers, that the farmer hastened along it without the least hesitation, until he came to a magnificent palace, with a golden roof, and shining, glittering walls. Lofty trees and gay gardens surrounded it, and a sentry paced up and down before the gateway.

"Whose palace is this?" asked the farmer of the sentry, who replied that it belonged to the King of the Crocodiles.

"My daughter has at least a splendid house to live in!" thought the farmer; "I only wish her husband were half as handsome!"

Then, turning to the sentry, he asked if his daughter were within.

"Your daughter!" returned the sentry, "what should she do here?"

"She married the King of the Crocodiles, and I want to see her."

At this the sentry burst out laughing. "A likely story, indeed!" he cried. "What! *my* master married to *your* daughter! Ha! ha! ha!"

Now the farmer's daughter was sitting beside an open window in the palace, waiting for her husband to return from hunting. She was as happy as the day was long, for you must know that in his own river kingdom the King of the Crocodiles was the handsomest young Prince anybody ever set eyes upon; it was only when he went on shore that he assumed the form of a crocodile.

With her magnificent palace and splendid young Prince, the farmer's daughter had been too happy even to think of her old home; but now, hearing a strange voice speaking to the sentry, her memory awakened, and she recognized her father's tones. Looking out, she saw him there, standing in his poor clothes, in the glittering court; she longed to run and fling her arms round his neck, but dared not disobey her husband, who had forbidden her to go out of, or to let any one into the palace without his permission. So all she could do was to lean out of the window, and call to him, saying, "Oh, dearest father! I am here! Only wait till my husband, the King of the Crocodiles, returns, and I will ask him to let you in. I dare not without his leave."

The father, though overjoyed to find his daughter alive, did not wonder she was afraid of her terrible husband, so he waited patiently.

In a short time a troop of horsemen entered the court. Every man was dressed from head to foot in armor made of glittering silver plates, but in the center of all rode a Prince clad in gold—bright burnished gold, from the crown of his head to the soles of his feet—the handsomest, most gallant young Prince that ever was seen.

Then the poor farmer fell at the gold-clad horseman's feet, and cried, "O King! cherish me! for I am a poor man whose daughter was carried off by the dreadful King of the Crocodiles!"

Then the gold-clad horseman smiled, saying, "*I* am the King of the Crocodiles! Your daughter is a good, obedient wife, and will be very glad to see you."

After this there were great rejoicings and merrymakings, but when a few days had passed away in feasting, the farmer became restless, and begged to be allowed to take his daughter home with him for a short visit, in order to convince his wife the girl was well and happy. But the Crocodile King refused, saying, "Not so! but if you like, I will give you a house and land here; then you can dwell with us."

The farmer said he must first ask his wife, and returned home, taking several bricks with him, to throw into the river and make the stream divide.

His wife would not at first agree to live in the Crocodile Kingdom, but she consented to go there on a visit, and afterwards became so fond of the beautiful river country that she was constantly going to see her daughter the Queen; till at length the old couple never returned to shore, but lived altogether in the Crocodile Kingdom with their son-in-law, the King of the Crocodiles.

## TOM THUMB [1]

One day Merlin, who was the great magician at the court of King Arthur, stopped at the home of a poor ploughman. The ploughman's wife brought him some milk in a wooden bowl and some brown bread on a wooden platter.

Merlin saw that everything within the little cottage was neat and clean and in good order and he wondered why the ploughman and his wife had such a sorrowful air. When he asked them about this, they told him that they were miserable because they had no children.

The poor woman declared with tears in her eyes that she should be the happiest creature in the world if she had a son, although he were no bigger than his father's thumb.

Merlin was much amused with the notion of a boy no bigger than a man's thumb, and as soon as he returned home he sent for the queen of the fairies (with whom he was very intimate) and related to her the desire of the ploughman and his wife to have a son the size of his father's thumb. She liked the plan exceedingly and declared their wish should be speedily granted. Accordingly the ploughman's wife had a son, who in a few minutes grew as tall as his father's thumb.

The queen of the fairies came in at the window as the mother was sitting up in bed admiring the child. Her majesty kissed the infant and, giving it the name of Tom Thumb, immediately summoned several fairies from Fairyland to clothe her new little favorite.

"An oak-leaf hat he had for his crown;
His shirt it was by spiders spun;
With doublet wove of thistledown,
His trousers up with points were done;
His stockings, of apple-rind, they tie
With eye-lash plucked from his mother's eye,
His shoes were made of a mouse's skin,
Nicely tann'd with hair within."

Tom was never any bigger than his father's thumb, which was not a large thumb either; but as he grew older he became very cunning, for which his mother did not sufficiently correct him, and by this ill quality he was often brought into difficulties. For instance, when he had learned to play with other boys for cherry-stones and had lost all his own, he used to creep into the boys' bags, fill his pockets, and come out again to play. But one day as he was getting out of a bag of cherry-stones, the boy to whom it belonged chanced to see him.

"Ah, ha, my little Tom Thumb!" said he, "have I caught you at your bad tricks at last?" Then he drew the string tight around Tom's neck and shook the bag. The cherry-stones bruised Tom Thumb's legs, thighs, and body sadly, which made him beg to be let out and promise never to be guilty of such things any more.

Shortly afterwards Tom's mother was making a batter-pudding, and that he might see how she mixed it, he climbed on the edge of the bowl; but his foot happening to slip, he fell over head and ears into the batter. His mother not observing him, stirred him into the pudding and popped him into the pot to boil. The hot water made Tom kick and struggle; and the mother, seeing the pudding jump up and down in such a

[1] Adapted from Dinah Maria Mulock Craik, *The Fairy Book*.

furious manner, thought it was bewitched; and a tinker coming by just at the time, she quickly gave him the pudding. He put it into his bag and walked on.

As soon as Tom could get the batter out of his mouth he began to cry aloud, and so frightened the poor tinker that he flung the pudding over the hedge and ran away from it as fast as he could. The pudding being broken to pieces by the fall, Tom was released, and walked home to his mother, who gave him a kiss and put him to bed.

Tom Thumb's mother once took him with her when she went to milk the cow; and it being a very windy day, she tied him with a needleful of thread to a thistle, that he might not be blown away. The cow, liking his oak-leaf hat, took him and the thistle up at one mouthful. While the cow chewed the thistle, Tom, terrified at her great teeth, which seemed ready to crush him to pieces, roared, "Mother, mother!" as loud as he could bawl.

"Where are you, Tommy, my dear Tommy?" said the mother.

"Here, mother, here in the red cow's mouth."

The mother began to cry and wring her hands; but the cow, surprised at such odd noises in her throat, opened her mouth and let him drop out. His mother clapped him into her apron and ran home with him.

Tom's father made him a whip of a barley straw to drive the cattle with, and one day when he was in the field he slipped into a deep furrow. A raven flying over picked him up with a grain of corn and flew with him to the top of a giant's castle by the seaside, where he left him; and old Grumbo, the giant, coming soon after to walk upon his terrace, swallowed Tom like a pill, clothes and all.

Tom presently made the giant very uncomfortable, and he threw him up into the sea. A great fish then swallowed Tom. The fish was soon after caught, and sent as a present to King Arthur. When it was cut open, everybody was delighted with little Tom Thumb. The king made him his dwarf; he was the favorite of the whole court, and by his merry pranks often amused the queen and the knights of the Round Table.

The king, when he rode on horseback, frequently took Tom in his hand; and if a shower of rain came on, he used to creep into the king's waistcoat pocket and sleep till the rain was over. The king also sometimes questioned Tom concerning his parents; and when Tom informed his majesty they were very poor people, the king led him into his treasury and told him he should pay his friends a visit and take with him as much money as he could carry. Tom procured a little purse, and putting a threepenny piece into it, with much labor and difficulty got it upon his back; and, after traveling two days and nights, arrived at his father's house.

When his mother met him at the door, he was almost tired to death, having in forty-eight hours traveled almost half a mile with a huge silver threepence upon his back. Both his parents were glad to see him, especially when he had brought such an amazing sum of money with him.

The next morning, when Tom was well rested, his mother took him in her hand and with one puff blew him back to King Arthur's court. But just as Tom should have alighted in the courtyard of the palace, the cook happened to pass along with the king's great bowl of furmenty and poor Tom Thumb fell plump into the middle of it and splashed the hot furmenty into the cook's eyes. Down went the bowl.

"Oh, dear! Oh, dear!" cried Tom.

"Murder! murder!" bellowed the cook; and away poured the king's nice furmenty into the kennel.

The cook was a red-faced, cross fellow, and swore to the king that Tom had done it out of mere mischief. The king loved furmenty so well that he had Tom taken up, tried, and sentenced to be beheaded. Tom hearing this dreadful sentence and seeing a miller stand by with his mouth wide open, he took a good spring and jumped down the miller's throat, unperceived by all, even the miller himself.

Tom being lost, the court broke up, and away went the miller to his mill. But Tom did not leave him long at rest; he began to roll and tumble about, so that the miller thought himself bewitched and sent for a doctor. When the doctor came, Tom began to dance and sing. The doctor was as much frightened as the miller and sent in great haste for five more doctors and twenty learnèd men.

While all these were debating upon the affair, the miller (for they were very tedious) happened to yawn, and Tom, taking the opportunity, made another jump and alighted on his feet in the middle of the table. The miller, provoked to be thus tormented by such a little creature, fell into a great passion, caught hold of Tom, and threw him out of the window into the river.

A large salmon swimming by snapped Tom up in a minute. The salmon was soon caught and sold in the market to a steward of a lord. The lord, thinking it an uncommonly fine fish, made a present of it to the king, who ordered it to be dressed immediately. When the cook cut open the salmon he found poor Tom and ran with him directly to the king; but the king, being busy with state affairs, desired that he might be brought another day.

The cook, resolving to keep him safe this time, as he had so lately given him the slip, clapped him into a mousetrap and left him to amuse himself by peeping through the wires for a whole week. When the king sent for him, he forgave him for throwing down the furmenty, ordered him new clothes, and knighted him.

"His shirt was made of butterflies' wings;
His boots were made of chicken skins,
His coat and breeches were made with pride,
A tailor's needle hung by his side;
A mouse for a horse he used to ride."

Thus dressed and mounted, he rode a-hunting with the king and nobility, who all laughed heartily at Tom and his prancing steed. As they rode by a farmhouse one day, a cat jumped from behind the door, seized the mouse and little Tom, and began to devour the mouse; however, Tom boldly drew his sword and attacked the cat, who then let him fall.

The king and his nobles, seeing Tom falling, went to his assistance, and one of the lords caught him in his hat; but poor Tom was sadly scratched, and his clothes were torn by the claws of the cat. In this condition he was carried home, and a bed of down was made for him in a little ivory cabinet.

The queen of the fairies came and took him to Fairyland, where she kept him for some years; and then, dressing him in bright green, sent him flying once more through the air to the earth, in the days of King Thunstone. The people flocked far and near to look at him; and the king, before whom he was carried, asked him who he was, whence he came, and where he lived? Tom answered:

"My name is Tom Thumb;
From the fairies I come;
When King Arthur shone,
This court was my home;
In me he delighted;
By him I was knighted.
Did you ever hear of
Sir Thomas Thumb?"

The king was so charmed with this address that he ordered a little chair to be made, in order that Tom might sit on his table, and also a palace of gold a span high with a door an inch wide, for little Tom to live in. He also gave him a coach drawn by six small mice. This made the queen angry, because she had not a new coach too; therefore, resolving to ruin Tom, she complained to the king that he had behaved very insolently to her. The king sent for him in a rage. Tom, to escape his fury, crept into an empty sea shell and there lay till he was almost starved.

One day Tom peeped out of the sea shell

and saw a fine butterfly settle on the ground. He then ventured out, and got astride the butterfly, which took wing and mounted into the air with little Tom on his back. Away he flew from field to field, from tree to tree, till at last he flew to the king's court. The king, queen, and nobles all strove to catch the butterfly, but could not. At length poor Tom, having neither bridle nor saddle, slipped from his seat and fell into a watering pot, where he was found almost drowned.

The queen vowed he should be guillotined; but while the guillotine was getting ready, he was secured once more in a mousetrap. The cat, seeing something stir and supposing it to be a mouse, patted the trap about till she broke it and set Tom at liberty.

Soon afterwards a spider, taking him for a fly, made at him. Tom drew his sword and fought valiantly, but the spider's poisonous breath overcame him:

"He fell dead on the ground where late he
 had stood,
And the spider suck'd up the last drop of
 his blood."

King Thunstone and his whole court went into mourning for little Tom Thumb. They buried him under a rosebush and raised a nice white marble monument over his grave, with the following epitaph:

"Here lies Tom Thumb, King Arthur's
 knight,
Who died by a spider's cruel bite.
He was well known in Arthur's court,
Where he afforded gallant sport;
He rode at tilt and tournament,
And on a mouse a-hunting went.
Alive he fill'd the court with mirth,
His death to sorrow soon gave birth.
Wipe, wipe your eyes, and shake your
 head,
And cry, 'Alas! Tom Thumb is dead.'"

## PUSS IN BOOTS [1]

A miller, dying, divided all his property among his three children. This was a very simple matter, as he had nothing to leave but his mill, his ass, and his cat; so he made no will, and he called in no lawyer, who would, probably, have taken a large slice out of these poor possessions. The eldest son took the mill, the second the ass, while the third was obliged to content himself with the cat, at which he grumbled very much.

"My brothers," said he, "by putting their property together may gain an honest livelihood, but there is nothing left for me except to die of hunger; unless, indeed, I were to kill my cat and eat him, and make a coat out of his skin, which would be very scanty clothing."

The cat, who heard the young man talking to himself, sat up and looking at him with a grave and wise air said, "Master, I think you had better not kill me; I shall be much more useful to you alive."

"How so?" asked his master.

"You have but to give me a sack and a pair of boots, such as gentlemen wear when they go shooting, and you will find you are not so ill off as you suppose."

Now, though the young miller did not much depend upon the cat's words, still he thought it rather surprising that a cat should speak at all. And he had before now seen him show so much adroitness and cleverness in catching rats and mice that it seemed advisable to trust him a little farther; especially as, poor young fellow! he had nobody else to trust.

When the cat got his boots he drew them on with a grand air, and slinging his sack over his shoulder, and drawing the cords of it round his neck, he marched bravely to a rabbit warren hard by, with which he was well acquainted. Then, putting some bran and lettuces into his bag, and stretching himself out beside it as if he were dead, he waited till some fine fat young rabbit, ig-

[1] From Dinah Maria Mulock Craik, *The Fairy Book*.

norant of the wickedness and deceit of the world, should peer into the sack to eat the food that was inside. This happened very shortly, for there are plenty of foolish young rabbits in every warren; and when one of them, who really was a splendid fat fellow, put his head inside, Master Puss drew the cords immediately, and took him and killed him without mercy. Then, very proud of his prey, he marched directly up to the palace, and begged to speak with the king. He was desired to ascend to the apartment of his majesty, where, making a low bow, he said:

"Sire, here is a magnificent rabbit, killed in the warren which belongs to my lord the Marquis of Carabas, and which he has desired me to offer humbly to your majesty."

"Tell your master," replied the king politely, "that I accept his present, and am very much obliged to him."

Another time Puss went and hid himself and his sack in a wheat field, and there caught two splendid fat partridges in the same manner as he had done the rabbit. When he presented them to the king, with a similar message as before, his majesty was so pleased that he ordered the cat to be taken down into the kitchen and given something to eat and drink; where, while enjoying himself, the faithful animal did not cease to talk in the most cunning way of the large preserves and abundant game which belonged to my lord the Marquis of Carabas.

One day, hearing that the king was intending to take a drive along the riverside with his daughter, the most beautiful princess in the world, Puss said to his master, "Sir, if you would only follow my advice, your fortune is made."

"Be it so," said the miller's son, who was growing very disconsolate, and cared little what he did. "Say your say, cat."

"It is but little," replied the Puss, looking wise, as cats can. "You have only to go and bathe in the river, at a place which I shall show you, and leave all the rest to me. Only remember that you are no longer yourself, but my lord the Marquis of Carabas."

"Just so," said the miller's son, "it's all the same to me"; but he did as the cat told him.

While he was bathing, the king and all the court passed by, and were startled to hear loud cries of "Help, help! My lord the Marquis of Carabas is drowning."

The king put his head out of the carriage, and saw nobody but the cat, who had, at different times, brought him so many presents of game; however, he ordered his guards to fly quickly to the succor of my lord the Marquis of Carabas. While they were pulling the unfortunate marquis out of the water the cat came up, bowing, to the side of the king's carriage, and told a long and pitiful story about some thieves, who, while his master was bathing, had come and carried away all his clothes, so that it could be impossible for him to appear before his majesty and the illustrious princess.

"Oh, we will soon remedy that!" answered the king kindly; and immediately ordered one of the first officers of the household to ride back to the palace with all speed, and bring back the most elegant supply of clothes for the young gentleman, who kept in the background until they arrived. Then, being handsome and well-made, his new clothes became him so well that he looked as if he had been a marquis all his days, and advanced with an air of respectful ease to offer his thanks to his majesty.

The king received him courteously, and the princess admired him very much. Indeed, so charming did he appear to her that she hinted to her father to invite him into the carriage with them, which, you may be sure, the young man did not refuse. The cat, delighted at the success of his scheme, went away as fast as he could, and ran so swiftly that he kept a long way ahead of the royal carriage. He went on and on, till he came to some peasants who were mowing in a meadow.

"Good people," said he, in a very firm voice, "the king is coming past here shortly, and if you do not say that the field you are mowing belongs to my lord the Marquis of Carabas, you shall all be chopped as small as mincemeat."

So when the king drove by, and asked whose meadow it was where there was such a splendid crop of hay, the mowers all answered, trembling, that it belonged to my lord the Marquis of Carabas.

"You have very fine land, Marquis," said his majesty to the miller's son, who bowed, and answered that it was "not a bad meadow, take it altogether."

Then the cat came to a wheat field, where the reapers were reaping with all their might. He bounced in upon them: "The king is coming past today, and if you do not tell him that this wheat belongs to my lord the Marquis of Carabas, I will have you every one chopped as small as mincemeat."

The reapers, very much alarmed, did as they were bid, and the king congratulated the Marquis upon possessing such beautiful fields, laden with such an abundant harvest.

They drove on—the cat always running before and saying the same thing to everybody he met, that they were to declare the whole country belonged to his master; so that even the king was astonished at the vast estate of my lord the Marquis of Carabas.

But now the cat arrived at a great castle where dwelt an Ogre, to whom belonged all the land through which the royal equipage had been driving. He was a cruel tyrant, and his tenants and servants were terribly afraid of him, which accounted for their being so ready to say whatever they were told to say by the cat, who had taken pains to inform himself all about the Ogre.

Putting on the boldest face he could assume, Puss marched up to the castle with his boots on, and asked to see the owner of it, saying that he was on his travels, but did not wish to pass so near the castle of such a noble gentleman without the paying of respects to him. When the Ogre heard this message he went to the door, received the cat as civilly as an Ogre can, and begged him to walk in and repose himself.

"Thank you, sir," said the cat; "but first I hope you will satisfy a traveler's curiosity. I have heard in far countries of your many remarkable qualities, and especially how you have the power to change yourself into any sort of beast you choose—a lion, for instance, or an elephant."

"That is quite true," replied the Ogre; "and lest you should doubt it I will immediately become a lion."

He did so; and the cat was so frightened that he sprang up to the roof of the castle and hid himself in the gutter—a proceeding rather inconvenient on account of his boots, which were not exactly fitted to walk with upon tiles. At length, perceiving that the Ogre had resumed his original form, he came down again stealthily, and confessed that he had been very much frightened.

"But, sir," said he, "it may be easy enough for such a big gentleman as you to change himself into a large animal; I do not suppose you can become a small one—a rat or mouse, for instance. I have heard that you can; still, for my part, I consider it quite impossible."

"Impossible?" cried the other indignantly. "You shall see!" and immediately the cat saw the Ogre no longer, but a little mouse running along the floor.

This was exactly what he wanted; and he did the very best a cat could do, and the most natural under the circumstances—he sprang upon the mouse and gobbled it up in a trice. So there was an end of the Ogre.

By this time the king had arrived opposite the castle, and was seized with a strong desire to enter it. The cat hearing the noise of the carriage wheels, ran forward in a great hurry, and, standing at the gate, said in a loud voice, "Welcome, sire, to the castle of my lord the Marquis of Carabas."

"What!" cried his majesty, very much surprised, "does the castle also belong to you? Truly, Marquis, you have kept your secret quite well up to the last minute. I have never seen anything finer than this courtyard and these battlements. Indeed, I have nothing like them in the whole of my dominions!"

The Marquis, without speaking, offered his hand to the princess to assist her to descend, and, standing aside that the king might enter first—for he had already acquired all the manners of a courtier—followed his majesty to the great hall, where a magnificent collation was laid out, and where, without more delay, they all sat down to feast.

Before the banquet was over the king, charmed with the good qualities of the Marquis of Carabas, said, bowing across the table at which the princess and the miller's son were talking very confidentially together, "It rests with you, Marquis, whether you will not become my son-in-law."

"I shall be only too happy," said the complaisant Marquis, and the princess's cast-down eyes declared the same.

So they were married the very next day, and took possession of the Ogre's castle and of everything that had belonged to him.

As for the cat, he became at once a grand personage, and had never more any need to run after mice, except for his own diversion.

## ALADDIN AND THE WONDERFUL LAMP [1]

There once lived a poor tailor, who had a son called Aladdin, a careless, idle boy who would do nothing but play all day long in the streets with little idle boys like himself. This so grieved the father that he died; yet, in spite of his mother's tears and prayers, Aladdin did not mend his ways. One day, when he was playing in the streets as usual, a stranger asked him his age, and if he was not the son of Mustapha the tailor. "I am, sir," replied Aladdin; "but he died a long while ago." On this the stranger, who was a famous African magician, fell on his neck and kissed him, saying: "I am your uncle, and knew you from your likeness to my brother. Go to your mother and tell her I am coming."

Aladdin ran home and told his mother of his newly found uncle. "Indeed, child," she said, "your father had a brother, but I always thought he was dead." However, she prepared supper, and bade Aladdin seek his uncle, who came laden with cake and fruit. He presently fell down and kissed the place where Mustapha used to sit, bidding Aladdin's mother not to be surprised at not having seen him before, as he had been forty years out of the country. He then turned to Aladdin, and asked him his trade, at which the boy hung his head, while his mother burst into tears.

On learning that Aladdin was idle and would learn no trade, he offered to take a shop for him and stock it with merchandise. Next day he bought Aladdin a fine suit of clothes and took him all over the city, showing him the sights, and brought him home at nightfall to his mother, who was overjoyed to see her son so fine.

Next day the magician led Aladdin into some beautiful gardens a long way outside the city gates. They sat down by a fountain and the magician pulled a cake from his girdle, which he divided between them. They then journeyed onwards till they almost reached the mountains. Aladdin was so tired that he begged to go back, but the magician beguiled him with pleasant stories, and led him on in spite of himself. At last they came to two mountains divided by a narrow valley, "We will go no farther," said the false uncle. "I will show you something wonderful; only do you gather up sticks while I kindle a fire."

When the fire was lit the magician threw on it a powder he had about him, at the same time saying some magical words. The earth trembled a little and opened in front of them, disclosing a square flat stone with a brass ring in the middle to raise it by. Aladdin tried to run away, but the magician caught him and gave him a blow that knocked him down.

"What have I done, uncle?" he said pite-

[1] From Andrew Lang, *Arabian Nights' Entertainments.*

ously; whereupon the magician said more kindly: "Fear nothing, but obey me. Beneath this stone lies a treasure which is to be yours, and no one else may touch it; so you must do exactly as I tell you."

At the word treasure Aladdin forgot his fears, and grasped the ring as he was told, saying the names of his father and grandfather. The stone came up quite easily, and some steps appeared.

"Go down," said the magician; "at the foot of those steps you will find an open door leading into three large halls. Tuck up your gown and go through them without touching anything, or you will die instantly. These halls lead into a garden of fine fruit trees. Walk on till you come to a niche in a terrace where stands a lighted lamp. Pour out the oil it contains, and bring it me." He drew a ring from his finger and gave it to Aladdin, bidding him prosper.

Aladdin, finding everything as the magician had said, gathered some fruit off the trees, and having got the lamp, arrived at the mouth of the cave. The magician cried out in a great hurry: "Make haste and give me the lamp."

This Aladdin refused to do until he was out of the cave. The magician flew into a terrible passion, and throwing some more powder on to the fire, he said something, and the stone rolled back into its place.

The magician left Persia forever, which plainly showed that he was no uncle of Aladdin's, but a cunning magician, who had read in his magic books of a wonderful lamp, which would make him the most powerful man in the world. Though he alone knew where to find it, he could only receive it from the hand of another. He had picked out the foolish Aladdin for this purpose, intending to get the lamp and kill him afterwards.

For two days Aladdin remained in the dark, crying and lamenting. At last he clasped his hands in prayer, and in so doing, rubbed the ring, which the magician had forgotten to take from him.

Immediately an enormous and frightful genie rose out of the earth, saying: "What wouldst thou with me? I am the Slave of the Ring, and will obey thee in all things."

Aladdin fearlessly replied: "Deliver me from this place!" whereupon the earth opened, and he found himself outside.

As soon as his eyes could bear the light he went home, but fainted on the threshold. When he came to himself, he told his mother what had passed, and showed her the lamp and the fruits he had gathered in the garden, which were in reality precious stones. He then asked for some food. "Alas! child," she said, "I have nothing in the house, but I have spun a little cotton and will go and sell it."

Aladdin bade his mother keep her cotton, for he would sell the lamp instead. As it was very dirty she began to rub it, that it might fetch a higher price. Instantly a hideous genie appeared and asked what she would have. She fainted away, but Aladdin, snatching the lamp, said boldly: "Fetch me something to eat!"

The genie returned with a silver bowl, twelve silver plates containing rich meats, two silver cups, and two bottles of wine. Aladdin's mother, when she came to herself, said: "Whence comes this splendid feast?"

"Ask not, but eat," replied Aladdin. So they sat at breakfast till it was dinner time and Aladdin told his mother about the lamp. She begged him to sell it, and have nothing to do with devils.

"No," said Aladdin, "since chance hath made us aware of its virtues, we will use it, and the ring likewise, which I shall always wear on my finger."

When they had eaten all the genie had brought, Aladdin sold one of the silver plates, and so on until none were left. He then had recourse to the genie, who gave him another set of plates, and thus they lived for many years.

One day Aladdin heard an order from the Sultan, proclaiming that everyone was to stay at home and close his shutters while the Princess, his daughter, went to and from the bath. Aladdin was seized by a desire to see her face, which was very difficult, as she always went veiled.

He hid himself behind the door of the bath and peeped through a chink. The Princess lifted her veil as she went in, and looked so beautiful that Aladdin fell in love with her at first sight. He went home so changed that his mother was frightened. He told her he loved the Princess so deeply that he could not live without her, and meant to ask her in marriage of her father.

His mother, on hearing this, burst out laughing; but Aladdin at last prevailed upon her to go before the Sultan and carry his request. She fetched a napkin and laid in it the magic fruits from the enchanted garden, which sparkled and shone like the most beautiful jewels. She took these with her to please the Sultan, and set out, trusting in the lamp.

The grand Vizier and the lords of council had just gone in as she entered the hall and placed herself in front of the Sultan. He took no notice of her. She went every day for a week, and stood in the same place. When the council broke up on the sixth day the Sultan said to his Vizier: "I see a certain woman in the audience chamber every day carrying something in a napkin. Call her next time, that I may find out what she wants."

Next day, at a sign from the Vizier, she went up to the foot of the throne and remained kneeling till the Sultan said to her: "Rise, good woman, and tell me what you want."

She hesitated, so the Sultan sent away all but the Vizier, and bade her speak freely, promising to forgive her beforehand for anything she might say. She then told him of her son's violent love for the Princess. "I prayed him to forget her," she said, "but in vain; he threatened to do some desperate deed if I refused to go and ask your Majesty for the hand of the Princess. Now I pray you to forgive not me alone, but my son Aladdin."

The Sultan asked her kindly what she had in the napkin, whereupon she unfolded the jewels and presented them. He was thunderstruck, and turning to the Vizier said: "What sayest thou? Ought I not to bestow the Princess on one who values her at such a price?"

The Vizier, who wanted her for his own son, begged the Sultan to withhold her for three months, in the course of which he hoped his son would contrive to make him a richer present. The Sultan granted this, and told Aladdin's mother that, though he consented to the marriage, she must not appear before him again for three months.

Aladdin waited patiently for nearly three months; but after two had elapsed, his mother, going into the city to buy oil, found everyone rejoicing, and asked what was going on. "Do you not know," was the answer, "that the son of the Grand Vizier is to marry the Sultan's daughter tonight?"

Breathless, she ran and told Aladdin, who was overwhelmed at first, but presently bethought him of the lamp. He rubbed it, and the genie appeared, saying: "What is thy will?"

Aladdin replied, "The Sultan, as thou knowest, has broken his promise to me, and the Vizier's son is to have the Princess. My command is that tonight you bring hither the bride and bridegroom."

"Master, I obey," said the genie.

Aladdin then went to his chamber, where, sure enough, at midnight the genie brought the Vizier's son and the Princess. "Take this man," he said, "and put him outside in the cold, and return at daybreak." Whereupon the genie took the Vizier's son, leaving Aladdin with the Princess.

"Fear nothing," Aladdin said to her; "you are my wife, promised to me by your unjust father, and no harm shall come to you."

The Princess was too frightened to speak, and passed the most miserable night of her life, while Aladdin lay down and slept soundly. At the appointed hour the genie fetched in the shivering bridegroom, and transported them back to the palace.

Presently the Sultan came to wish his daughter good-morning. The unhappy Vizier's son jumped up and hid himself, while the Princess would not say a word, and was very sorrowful. The Sultan sent her mother to her, who said: "How comes it, child, that you will not speak to your father? What has happened?"

The Princess sighed deeply, and at last told her mother how, during the night, she had been carried into a strange house, and what had passed there. Her mother did not believe her in the least, but bade her rise and consider it an idle dream.

The following night exactly the same thing happened, and next morning, on the Princess's refusing to speak, the Sultan threatened to cut off her head. She then confessed all, bidding him ask the Vizier's son if it were not so.

The Sultan told the Vizier to ask his son, who owned the truth, adding that, dearly as he loved the Princess, he had rather die than go through another such fearful night, and wished to be separated from her. His wish was granted, and there was an end of feasting and rejoicing.

When the three months were over, Aladdin sent his mother to remind the Sultan of his promise. She stood in the same place as before, and the Sultan, who had forgotten Aladdin, at once remembered him, and sent for her.

On seeing her poverty the Sultan felt less inclined than ever to keep his word, and asked his Vizier's advice, who counseled him to set so high a value on the Princess that no man living could come up to it. The Sultan then turned to Aladdin's mother, saying: "Good woman, a Sultan must remember his promises, and I will remember mine, but your son must first send me forty basins of gold, brimful of jewels, carried by forty black slaves, led by as many white ones, splendidly dressed. Tell him that I await his answer."

The mother of Aladdin bowed low and went home, thinking all was lost. She gave Aladdin the message, adding: "He may wait long enough for your answer!"

"Not so long, mother, as you think," her son replied. "I would do a great deal more than that for the princess." He summoned the genie, and in a few moments the eighty slaves arrived, and filled up the small house and garden. Aladdin made them set out to the palace, two and two, followed by his mother. They were so richly dressed, with such splendid jewels in their girdles, that everyone crowded to see them and the basins of gold they carried on their heads.

They entered the palace and, after kneeling before the Sultan, stood in a half-circle round the throne with their arms crossed, while Aladdin's mother presented them to the Sultan. He hesitated no longer, but said: "Good woman, return and tell your son that I wait for him with open arms."

She lost no time in telling Aladdin, bidding him make haste. But Aladdin first called the genie.

"I want a scented bath," he said, "a richly embroidered a habit, a horse surpassing the Sultan's, and twenty slaves to attend me. Besides this, six slaves, beautifully dressed, to wait on my mother; and lastly, ten thousand pieces of gold in ten purses." No sooner said than done.

Aladdin mounted his horse and passed through the streets, the slaves strewing gold as they went. Those who had played with him in his childhood knew him not, he had grown so handsome. When the Sultan saw him he came down from his throne, embraced him, and led him into a hall where a feast was spread, intending to marry him to the Princess that very day.

But Aladdin refused, saying, "I must build a palace fit for her," and took his leave.

Once home, he said to the genie: "Build me a palace of the finest marble, set with jasper, agate, and other precious stones. In the middle you shall build me a large hall with a dome, its four walls of heavy gold and silver, each side having six windows, whose lattices, all except one which is to be left unfinished, must be set with diamonds and rubies. There must be stables and horses and grooms and slaves; go and see about it!"

The palace was finished by next day, and the genie carried him there and showed him all his orders faithfully carried out, even to the laying of a velvet carpet from Aladdin's palace to the Sultan's.

Aladdin's mother then dressed herself carefully, and walked to the palace with her slaves. The Sultan sent musicians with trumpets and cymbals to meet them, so that the air resounded with music and cheers. She was taken to the Princess, who saluted her and treated her with great honor. At night the Princess said good-by to her father, and set out on the carpet for Aladdin's palace, with his mother at her side, and followed by the hundred slaves. She was charmed at the sight of Aladdin, who ran to receive her.

"Princess," he said, "blame your beauty for my boldness if I have displeased you."

She told him that, having seen him, she willingly obeyed her father in this matter.

After the wedding had taken place Aladdin led her into the hall, where a feast was spread, and she supped with him, after which they danced till midnight.

Next day Aladdin invited the Sultan to see the palace. On entering the hall with the four and twenty windows, with their rubies, diamonds, and emeralds, he cried: "It is a world's wonder! There is only one thing that surprises me. Was it by accident that one window was left unfinished?"

"No, sir, by design," returned Aladdin. "I wished your Majesty to have the glory of finishing this palace."

The Sultan was pleased, and sent for the best jewelers in the city. He showed them the unfinished window, and bade them fit it up like the others.

"Sir," replied their spokesman, "we cannot find jewels enough."

The Sultan had his own fetched, which they soon used, but to no purpose, for in a month's time the work was not half done.

Aladdin, knowing that their task was vain, bade them undo their work and carry the jewels back, and the genie finished the window at his command. The Sultan was surprised to receive his jewels again, and visited Aladdin, who showed him the window finished. The Sultan embraced him, the envious Vizier meanwhile hinting that it was the work of enchantment.

Aladdin had won the hearts of the people by his gentle bearing. He was made captain of the Sultan's armies, and won several battles for him; but remained modest and courteous as before and lived thus in peace and content for several years.

But far away in Africa the magician remembered Aladdin and by his magic arts discovered that Aladdin, instead of perishing miserably in the cave, had escaped and had married a Princess with whom he was living in great honor and wealth. He knew that the poor tailor's son could only have accomplished this by means of the lamp and traveled night and day till he reached the capital of China, bent on Aladdin's ruin. As he passed through the town he heard people talking everywhere about a marvelous palace.

"Forgive my ignorance," he said. "What is this palace you speak of?"

"Have you not heard of Prince Aladdin's palace," was the reply, "the greatest wonder of the world? I will direct you if you have a mind to see it."

The magician thanked him who spoke, and having seen the palace knew that it had been raised by the genie of the lamp and became half-mad with rage. He determined to get hold of the lamp and again plunge Aladdin into the deepest poverty.

Unluckily, Aladdin had gone hunting for eight days, which gave the magician plenty of time. He bought a dozen copper lamps, put them into a basket, and went to the palace, crying, "New lamps for old!" followed by a jeering crowd.

The Princess, sitting in the hall of twenty-four windows, sent a slave to find out what the noise was about, who came back laughing so, that the Princess scolded her.

"Madam," replied the slave, "who can help laughing to see an old fool offering to exchange fine new lamps for old ones?"

Another slave, hearing this, said: "There is an old one on the cornice there which he can have." Now, this was the magic lamp, which Aladdin had left there, as he could not take it out hunting with him.

The Princess, not knowing its value, laughingly bade the slave take it and make the exchange. She went and said to the magician: "Give me a new lamp for this."

He snatched it and bade the slave take her choice, amid the jeers of the crowd. Little he cared, but left off crying his lamps, and went out of the city gates to a lonely place, where he remained till nightfall, when he pulled out the lamp and rubbed it. The genie appeared, and at the magician's command carried him, together with the palace and the Princess in it, to a lonely place in Africa.

Next morning the Sultan looked out of the window toward Aladdin's palace and rubbed his eyes, for it was gone. He sent for the Vizier and asked what had become of the palace. The Vizier looked out too, and was lost in astonishment. He again put it down to enchantment, and this time the Sultan believed him, and sent thirty men on horseback to fetch Aladdin in chains.

They met Aladdin riding home, bound him, and forced him to go with them on foot. The people, however, who loved him, followed, armed, to see that he came to no harm.

Aladdin was carried before the Sultan, who ordered the executioner to cut off his head. The executioner made Aladdin kneel down, bandaged his eyes, and raised his scimitar to strike. At that instant the Vizier, who saw that the crowd had forced their way into the courtyard and were scaling the walls to rescue Aladdin, called to the executioner to stay his hand. The people, indeed, looked so threatening that the Sultan gave way and ordered Aladdin to be unbound, and pardoned him in the sight of the crowd. Aladdin now begged to know what he had done.

"False wretch!" said the Sultan, "come hither," and showed him from the window the place where his palace had stood. Aladdin was so amazed that he could not say a word.

"Where are the palace and my daughter?" demanded the Sultan. "For the first I am not so deeply concerned, but my daughter I must have, and you must find her or lose your head."

Aladdin begged for forty days in which to find her, promising if he failed, to return and suffer death at the Sultan's pleasure. His prayer was granted, and he went forth sadly from the Sultan's presence.

For three days Aladdin wandered about like a madman, asking everyone what had become of his palace, but they only laughed and pitied him. He came to the banks of a river, and knelt down to say his prayers before throwing himself in. In so doing he rubbed the magic ring he still wore. The genie he had seen in the cave appeared, and asked his will.

"Save my life, genie," said Aladdin, "and bring my palace back."

"That is not in my power," said the genie; "I am only the Slave of the Ring; you must ask him of the lamp."

"Even so," said Aladdin, "but thou canst take me to the palace, and set me down under my dear wife's window."

He at once found himself in Africa, under the window of the Princess, and fell asleep out of sheer weariness.

He was awakened by the singing of the birds, and his heart was lighter. He saw plainly that all his misfortunes were owing to the loss of the lamp, and vainly wondered who had robbed him of it.

That morning the Princess rose earlier than she had done since she had been carried into Africa by the magician, whose company she was forced to endure once a day. She, however, treated him so harshly that he dared not live there altogether. As she was dressing, one of her women looked out and saw Aladdin.

The Princess ran and opened the window, and at the noise she made Aladdin looked up. She called to him to come to her, and great was the joy of these lovers at seeing each other again.

After he had kissed her, Aladdin said: "I

beg of you, Princess, before we speak of anything else, for your own sake and mine, tell me what has become of an old lamp I left on the cornice in the hall of twenty-four windows when I went hunting."

"Alas!" she said, "I am the innocent cause of our sorrows," and told him of the exchange of the lamp.

"Now I know," cried Aladdin, "that we have to thank the African magician for this! Where is the lamp?"

"He carries it about with him," said the Princess. "I know, for he pulled it out of his breast to show me. He wishes me to break my faith with you and marry him, saying that you were beheaded by my father's command. He is forever speaking ill of you, but I only reply to him by my tears. If I persist, I doubt not but he will use violence."

Aladdin comforted her and left her for awhile. He changed clothes with the first person he met in the town and having bought a certain powder, returned to the Princess, who let him in by a little side door.

"Put on your most beautiful dress," he said, "and receive the magician with smiles, leading him to believe that you have forgotten me. Invite him up to sup with you and say you wish to taste the wine of his country. He will go for some and while he is gone, I will tell you what to do."

She listened carefully to Aladdin and when he left her, arrayed herself gayly. She put on a girdle and head-dress of diamonds, and, seeing in a glass that she was more beautiful than ever, received the magician, saying, to his great amazement: "I have made up my mind that Aladdin is dead, and that all my tears will not bring him back to me, so I am resolved to mourn no more, and have therefore invited you to sup with me; but I am tired of the wines of China, and would fain taste those of Africa."

The magician flew to his cellar, and the Princess put the powder Aladdin had given her in her cup. When he returned she asked him to drink her health in the wine of Africa, handing him her cup in exchange for his, as a sign she was reconciled to him. Before drinking the magician made her a speech in praise of her beauty, but the princess cut him short, saying: "Let us drink first, and you shall say what you will afterwards."

She set her cup to her lips and kept it there, while the magician drained his to the dregs and fell back lifeless.

The princess then opened the door to Aladdin, and flung her arms round his neck; but Aladdin put her away, bidding her leave him, as he had more to do. He then went to the dead magician, took the lamp out of his vest, and bade the genie carry the palace and all in it back to China. This was done, and the Princess in her chamber only felt two little shocks, and little thought she was at home again.

The Sultan, who was sitting in his hall, mourning for his lost daughter, happened to look up, and rubbed his eyes, for there stood the palace as before! He hastened thither, and Aladdin received him in the hall of the four and twenty windows, with the Princess at his side. Aladdin told him what had happened. A ten days' feast was proclaimed, and it seemed as if Aladdin might now live the rest of his life in peace; but it was not to be.

The African magician had a younger brother, who was, if possible, more wicked and more cunning than himself. He traveled to China to avenge his brother's death, and went to visit a pious woman called Fatima, thinking she might be of use to him. He entered her cell and clapped a dagger to her breast, telling her to rise and do his bidding on pain of death. He changed clothes with her, colored his face like hers, put on her veil, and murdered her, that she might tell no tales.

Then he went towards the palace of Aladdin, and all the people, thinking he was the holy woman, gathered round him, kissing his hands and begging his blessing. When he got to the palace there was such a noise going on round him that the Princess bade her slave look out of the window and ask what was the matter. The slave said it was the holy woman, curing people by her touch, whereupon the Princess, who had long desired to see Fatima, sent for her.

On coming to the Princess, the magician offered up a prayer for her health and prosperity. When he had done, the Princess made him sit by her, and begged him to stay with her always. The false Fatima, who wished for nothing better, consented, but kept his veil down for fear of discovery. The Princess showed him the hall, and asked him what he thought of it.

"It is truly beautiful," said the false Fatima.

"In my mind it wants but one thing."

"And what is that?" asked the Princess.

"If only a roc's egg," replied he, "were hung up from the middle of this dome, it would be the wonder of the world."

After this the Princess could think of nothing but the roc's egg, and when Aladdin returned from hunting he found her in a very ill humor. He begged to know what was amiss, and she told him that all her pleasure in the hall was spoilt for the want of a roc's egg hanging from the dome.

"If that is all," replied Aladdin, "you shall soon be happy." He left her and rubbed the lamp, and when the genie appeared commanded him to bring a roc's egg.

The genie gave such a loud and terrible shriek that the hall shook. "Wretch!" he cried, "is it not enough that I have done everything for you, but you must command me to bring my master and hang him up in the midst of this dome? You and your wife and your palace deserve to be burnt to ashes; but this request does not come from you, but from the brother of the African magician, whom you destroyed. He is now in your palace disguised as the holy woman —whom he murdered. He is was who put that wish into your wife's head. Take care of yourself, for he means to kill you." So saying, the genie disappeared.

Aladdin went back to the Princess, saying his head ached, and requesting that the holy Fatima should be fetched to lay her hands on it. But when the magician came near, Aladdin, seizing his dagger, pierced him to the heart.

"What have you done?" cried the Princess. "You have killed the holy woman!"

"Not so," replied Aladdin, "but a wicked magician," and told her of how she had been deceived.

After this Aladdin and his wife lived in peace. He succeeded the Sultan when he died, and reigned for many years, leaving behind him a long line of kings.

## THE PRINCE AND THE GIANT'S DAUGHTER [1]

All the wonderful events of which I am going to tell you arose from a very small beginning, when Jenny Wren tried to help a farmer thresh his wheat. This led to trouble with the mice that stole the grain Jenny threshed, and this trouble ended in a battle between the birds of the air and the beasts on the ground.

I have not time to tell you about the battle, but it was a fierce and bloody one, and it lasted far on into the night, and the noise of it was so great that it woke the young King of Tethertown, who was asleep in his mother's tumble-down castle, a little way down the hillside.

He got up and looked out of the window to see what the matter was, but the only thing visible was a great black raven which was engaged in deadly conflict with a snake. The snake had twined itself round the raven's neck, and the raven had seized the snake's throat in its beak, and they were both nearly choked for want of breath.

Now the young King hated serpents, so he took down a little dagger which was hanging on the wall, and ran out, and cut off the snake's head, and by doing so he saved the raven's life.

"Ah," said the bird, as soon as he could speak, "thou hast done me one good turn, I will do another to thee. It must be but a

[1] From Elizabeth W. Grierson, *The Book of Celtic Stories.*

dull life living day after day in that ruined castle. If thou wouldst get a glimpse of the world, thou hast only to climb on my back, and I will show thee things which thou hast never even dreamt of."

Now the young King had often found it very dull at home, so, nothing loath, he climbed on the raven's back, and took hold of the roots of the great bird's wings to steady himself, and they rose together into the air.

On and on they went, passing slowly over seven great mountains, and seven deep glens, and seven dreary, lonely moors.

At last, as it was drawing towards evening, the raven folded his wings, and sank slowly down to earth again.

"Dost see yon house?" he asked, pointing with his beak to a little cottage on the hillside. "If thou wouldst have shelter for the night, thou canst have it there, for my sister dwells within, and I warrant she will make thee right welcome for my sake. Only thou must tell her, if she asks thee, that thou wert at the Battle of the Birds, and that thou hast seen me. And hark'ee, be sure to meet me at this very spot tomorrow morning."

So the young King went up to the cottage door, and a comely young woman opened it to him.

She looked at him from head to foot in silence for a moment, then she asked him, "Wert thou at the Battle of the Birds, and didst thou see my likeness?"

This last part of the question puzzled the King, for there was certainly no likeness between the coal-black raven and this brown-haired, brown-eyed damsel; but he remembered what the bird had said to him, and he answered "Yes" to both questions.

Then the maiden welcomed him gladly, and made much of him.

Next morning she would fain have had him tarry a little longer with her, but he remembered his promise to the raven, and he would not be persuaded to remain.

The great bird was waiting for him at the trysting-place, and, as soon as he had mounted on his back again, the two set out on their travels.

Once again they passed slowly over seven great mountains, and seven deep glens, and seven dreary, lonely moors, and as evening drew on they once more came in sight of a little cottage.

"Another sister of mine dwells in that house," said the raven, "and, if thou wilt, she will entertain thee as willingly as did my other sister; only remember, she will ask thee the same questions, and thou must give her the same answers."

It all fell out as the raven said, and that night also the young King wanted for nothing.

Next day everything happened just the same. They journeyed over the seven mountains, and the seven glens, and the seven dreary, lonely moors, and at the end of the day there was another cottage and another of the raven's sisters awaiting the tired traveler.

He began to wonder if things would go on like this for ever, but the third morning brought a great surprise.

When he arrived at the trysting-place, what was his astonishment to find, instead of the raven, one of the handsomest young men he had ever seen, who carried a bundle in his hand.

The young King thought he was some traveler making his way over the hills, and he asked him if he had chanced to see a big black raven.

The stranger threw back his curly head and laughed. "Nay," said he, "but your Highness may look in vain for that bird. I am he. I was put under a spell from which I could not be loosed until I met a King. So thou hast been the means of freeing me, and restoring me to my true condition, and in return for that favor I will give thee this bundle. Carry it with thee, and guard it well, and retrace thy steps by the way we came, and, whatever else thou mayest be tempted to do, see that thou dost not open it until thou art come to the place where thou wouldst like most to dwell, else wilt thou rue thy haste."

The young King did as he was bid. He took the bundle and set out in the direction of his mother's castle, and after a long and weary journey he came in sight of it.

But he was very tired, and the bundle was very heavy, and, as he was passing through a thick wood, he felt that he must sit down and take a rest.

And as he sat he began to wonder what the mysterious bundle contained; and he wondered, and wondered, until at last his curiosity became so strong that he forgot the warning that the lad had given him, and he opened a corner of it, and peeped in.

He could scarcely believe his eyes. It was as though he had looked through a magic looking glass, for there, in front of him, was a magnificent castle, standing in the midst of a beautiful garden, in which grew every kind of fruit tree, and flower and shrub that you can think of.

In a moment he saw what a mistake he had made, for it was no use trying to put the castle back into the bundle again.

"What a fool I have been," he muttered ruefully to himself, "for although the castle is very beautiful, it must stand here in this dark wood, while I might have had it in the middle of the little green glen that I love so much, quite close to my mother's house."

Just then he chanced to lift his eyes, and whom should he spy coming towards him but a great Giant.

"A nice place thou hast chosen to build thy castle in," said the Giant. "This wood is so thick thou wilt never see the sun."

"By my troth, but thou never spake a truer word," said the young King mournfully; "and the worst of it is, I have only myself to blame, for I could have had it stand on the spot I love best, had it not been for my own impatience."

A nasty smile crossed the Giant's face, although the young King did not notice it.

"What wilt thou give me if I put thy castle back into the bundle again?" he asked slyly.

"Anything thou likest to ask," returned the other, only too glad to have a chance of setting his newly found dwelling-place in some better position.

"Wilt thou give me the first son thou hast, when he is seven years old?" asked the Giant.

"Ay, marry, that I will, if I ever chance to have a son," laughed the King, for seven years stretch a long way ahead, and the thought of taking a wife had not as yet even entered his mind.

Quick as lightning the Giant put the castle and the garden back into the bundle, and handed it to the young King. "Now," said he grimly, "each of us will go his own road; but remember, the promise stands. Thou mayest forget. I forget never!"

The young King swung the bundle over his shoulder, and hurried out of the wood, and in a short time he arrived at the little hollow where he would fain have his castle stand.

Here he opened the bundle once more, and the castle and the garden sprang up before his delighted eyes. He walked up to it and opened the door, and was about to enter, when, to his astonishment, he was met by the most beautiful maiden he had ever seen.

"Come in, come in, Your Highness," she said, "everything is ready for thee, and everything is thine; but on one condition only."

"And what is that?" asked the young King anxiously, for he felt that it would be very hard if he could not keep possession of his castle, after he had carried the magic bundle which had contained it, for so many miles.

"That thou wilt marry me, your Majesty," whispered the maiden coyly, and she blushed so rosy red, and looked so sweet, that the King fell in love with her at once, and very soon they were married.

The maiden turned out to be as good as she was beautiful, so they were very happy; and when, at the end of a year, a dear little son was born to them, their joy knew no bounds. They were so happy, in fact, that the King forgot all about his promise, and you may fancy what a shock it was to him when, at the end of seven years and one day, the Giant appeared at the door of the castle.

In great distress he sought the Queen's apartments, and told her the whole story, which she had never heard until now.

She sat in silence for a moment, then she sprang to her feet. "I have it," she cried, "go thou and talk to the Giant, and leave the matter to me."

Her husband obeyed her, and when he had gone down the front stairs to tell the Giant that the little Prince would be brought to him as soon as his mother had had time to dress him, she slipped down the back stairs, a bag of gold in her hand, to talk to the cook.

In a few moments she appeared at the front door, her kerchief to her eyes, and leading a little boy by the hand. She wept bitterly as she kissed him, and bade him farewell, but no sooner had the Giant disappeared round the corner with the child, than she turned to her husband, laughing merrily, and clapping her hands.

"Of course it is not our son," she cried in answer to his astonished looks. "Didst thou think I would let our child go, when the cook had a son just his age in the kitchen? The cook was glad enough to part with him in exchange for the bag of gold which I gave him, and as for the Giant, he will be none the wiser."

But she little knew how wily the Giant was. No sooner was he out of the castle than he cut a rod from a willow tree, and gave it to the little boy.

"If thy father had that rod, what would he do with it?" he asked.

"If my father had that rod, he would beat the dogs and the cats if they would be going near the King's meat," answered the child.

"Bah," said the Giant, "thou art the cook's son," and he threw him into the ditch.

Then he went back to the castle in a rage, and thundered at the door. "I will pull down every stone in the building, if thou bringest not thy son at once," he shouted.

Up in her chamber the Queen grew a little paler than was her wont, but she would not own herself vanquished.

"The butler hath a son who is the same age as ours," she whispered to the King, "and I have another bag of gold."

So once more she slipped down the back stairs, and once more she appeared in a few minutes, leading a little boy by the hand.

But once more the Giant was too clever for her. He cut a rod from a birch tree and gave it to the child.

"If thy father had that rod?" he asked, "what would he do with it?"

"If my father had that rod, he would beat the dogs and cats when they would be coming near the King's bottles and glasses," was the answer.

"Bah," said the Giant, "this time it is the son of the butler," and he threw him into the ditch beside the cook's son.

Then he went back to the castle stamping with rage, so that the earth shook as though there was an earthquake, and the castle rocked to its highest turrets.

"OUT WITH THY SON," he shouted, "ELSE SHALL EVERY STONE FALL ABOUT THINE EARS!" and this time the King and Queen saw that there was no escape, so they brought down their own little son, and the Giant carried him away.

The Giant was not cruel to the Prince, however, but brought him up in his house as if he had been his own son, and things went on smoothly enough until he had grown from a little boy into a fine young man.

Then it chanced one day that, as he was walking in the garden, he heard the most wonderful singing that ever he had heard in his life. It seemed to be coming from one of the upper windows of the Giant's house. As he stood looking up, wondering who the sweet singer could be, he saw a girl's face peeping down at him through the open casement.

She had auburn hair and blue eyes, and she was so beautiful that he fell in love with her at once, even though he had never spoken to her.

"Who art thou?" he cried in surprise.

The maiden beckoned to him to come nearer, and then laid her finger on her lips.

"Hush," she whispered, "I dare not speak to thee now, but if thou comest back at midnight, I will tell thee something that concerns both thee and me."

Needless to say, the Prince was back under the window as the clock struck twelve.

"I am the youngest daughter of the Giant, and my name is Mari Ruadh, which means 'Auburn Mary,' " began the maiden.

"The youngest daughter of the Giant?" repeated the Prince; "I thought he had but two daughters, and I have seen them both. They are as ugly as if some wicked fairy had bewitched them at their birth."

The girl laughed. "That is why thou hast never seen me, Prince," she whispered. "For my father intends thee to wed one of my elder sisters, and he fears that thou mightest take a fancy to me instead. He intends me to become the wife of the son of the King of the Green City, who squints like an ape, and, moreover, hath a club foot. 'Tis his wealth that my father wants me to marry, but money-bags will never make up for the want of a proper husband. Tomorrow my father will give thee the choice of my two sisters; refuse to marry either of them, and marry me."

Sure enough, the very next morning the Giant took the Prince into a chamber where all his three daughters were sitting. "Now," he said graciously, "I will prove to thee, Prince, that I had no ill-will against thee when I carried thee away from thine own people and from thine own house. I have given thee a good upbringing, and provided thee with food and raiment, and now thou art at liberty to go home again, provided that thou takest one of my two eldest daughters with thee as thy bride."

"Nay, but I will go home well content if thou wilt give me thy youngest daughter," said the Prince; "for now that I have seen her, I have made up my mind that no other maiden shall be my wife."

The Giant was very angry at these words, for he was determined that one of his plain-looking daughters should be the Princess of Tethertown; but he knew that it is not easy to force a man to marry against his will.

"The man that would wed my youngest daughter must first do three things," he said sharply.

"And what may they be?" asked the Prince.

"Come with me and I will show thee," said the Giant, with a sly smile, and he led the young man out to a barn.

"A hundred cattle stand here at nights," said he, "and it is seven years since last it was cleaned. I am going from home today, and if, when I return in the evening, thou hast made it so clean that a golden apple will run with ease from one end of it to the other, then thou mayest marry my youngest daughter, but if thou hast not done so, then all hopes of marriage will go out of thy head, for I will lift it from thy shoulders."

The Prince set to work right manfully, but he might as well have tried to drain the ocean as to clean that barn. By midday he was well-nigh exhausted, and he had not cleaned the twentieth part of it.

As he was leaning on his shovel in despair, who should appear at the door but the Giant's youngest daughter, Mari Ruadh.

" 'Tis hard work, King's son," said she.

"Ay, by my troth, 'tis hard work," answered the Prince, "and work which is like to prove too much for me."

The girl laughed. "Come and sit down and rest," she said, and the poor young man was so tired that, although he knew the Giant would keep his word, and put him to death when he got home, he sat down beside her and fell fast asleep.

When he awoke he was alone, but, wonder of wonders, the barn was so clean that anyone could roll a golden apple from end to end of it as easily as they could have rolled it on a polished floor.

The Prince could hardly believe his eyes,

and as he was rubbing them to make sure that it was not all a dream, the Giant came into the barn, and he too stared in astonishment.

"Hast thou cleaned the barn, King's son?" he asked suspiciously.

"Thou seest that I have cleaned it," answered the Prince, for he knew that Mari Ruadh must have had something to do with the marvel that had been wrought, and he did not want to get her into trouble.

"Humph," grunted the Giant, "somebody hath cleaned it at any rate, and if it wert thou who was clever enough to do it, thou wilt easily perform the next task which I will set thee. This barn needs thatching, and if by this time tomorrow thou hast thatched it with birds' feathers, my youngest daughter shall be thy bride. Only, hark'ee, no two of the feathers must be of the same color. Thou knowest the penalty if thou failest."

Next morning the Prince rose up early, and took his gun, and went out on to the heather moor, for he knew that no two feathers of the moorfowl are alike.

Alas, alas! by mid-day he had only shot two blackbirds, and all the world knows that the feathers of blackbirds are of one color.

He had thrown himself down on the grass in despair, feeling that the task was a hopeless one, when, lo and behold! Mari Ruadh came over the hill.

" 'Twill take the feathers of many birds to thatch the roof of my father's barn," she said.

"That will it," answered the Prince, "and as yet I have only shot two blackbirds."

"Leave the birds alone, and lie down on this little knoll and rest thyself," said she; and the Prince did so, for he felt that now that she had appeared, mayhap help would come on this day also.

Nor was he disappointed, for he went to sleep, and when he awoke the maiden was gone; but when he went down from the moor to the Giant's house he found the barn thatched most beautifully, and no two of the feathers with which it was covered were of the same color.

That evening the Giant came home in right good humor, for he was certain that the Prince must have failed to accomplish this second task. But the first thing that met his eye was the soft new thatch on the barn.

He sought the Prince at once. "Hast thou thatched the barn, King's son?" he asked, more suspiciously than ever, and when the Prince answered that he had done so (for again he feared that he would get the maiden into trouble if he answered otherwise), the Giant turned on his heel and walked straight into the house.

"Someone hath thatched it anyhow," he muttered; "but evil take me if that red-haired wench of mine hath not had a finger in the pie."

As soon as he was inside the house, he summoned the crooked old dame who acted as his housekeeper, "What hath Mari Ruadh been about all day?" he asked roughly. "Hath she been wasting her time, and wandering about out-of-doors?"

The wizened old woman cringed before him in terror. "An' it please thee, the maiden hath kept her chamber the livelong day, and busied herself with her seam," she answered; and as she always spoke the truth (at least so far as she knew it), the Giant was forced to be content.

He went back to the Prince. "Thou needest not think that thou wilt escape me yet," he said with a frown; "for, look ye, down by the loch there is a fir tree, and in the top branches of it there is a magpie's nest which holds four eggs. These eggs I will have for my breakfast tomorrow, and if one be lost or broken, off comes thy head."

To climb a tree and harry a magpie's nest sounded an easy task to the Prince, and he rose up early in the morning, with a light heart, to accomplish it. But his heart sank as he approached the fir tree, for there was no other tree like it in the wood. It was so high that one could measure five hundred feet from the ground to its lowest branch, and there was grip neither for hand nor foot on all its long straight trunk.

In vain he tried to scramble up; he bruised his knees and skinned his hands, but he never raised himself more than a couple of yards from the ground.

As he was gazing up at the nest, perched far out of his reach, he found his Love once more at his elbow.

"Thy hands are all bleeding," said she. "Little wonder," answered the Prince, "the bark of the tree is like a nutmeg grater, yet there is not so much as a twig on which a climber can rest his foot."

"It behoves thee to make haste," said the maiden, "for my father doth not like to wait for his breakfast. See!"—and with that she thrust her fingers, one after the other, into the trunk of the tree, thus making a ladder right up to the nest.

In less time than it takes to tell, the Prince ran up the ladder; but as he was lifting the eggs Mari Ruadh cried out anxiously from below, "Oh, haste thee, haste thee, my father suspects something, and his angry breath is burning my back."

In a moment the Prince was on the ground again, and they were speeding to the house; but poor Auburn Mary never noticed till she was on the doorstep, that, in her hurry, she had left her little finger sticking in the top of the tree.

"It matters not," she whispered cheerfully, "for this evening thou wilt get the chance of marrying me, if thou canst recognize me, which will be no easy task. For thou wilt see me with my sisters, and we shall all be dressed alike, and wear masks on our faces, *but be thou on the lookout for a hand that wants a little finger.*"

When the Giant came down stairs that morning, he was met by the Prince, who put a steaming dish of magpie's eggs in front of him. He grunted worse than ever, but never a word spoke he until he had finished his meal; then he said ungraciously, "Thou canst make thyself ready for thy wedding, King's son."

That night a splendid feast was prepared, and a great company was gathered together to celebrate the marriage of the Prince of Tethertown and one of the Giant's daughters.

There was music, and dancing, and rejoicings of all sorts, but the difficulty was to say which was the bride. For the three sisters were all dressed alike in beautiful white satin dresses, and each wore a string of priceless pearls, but each wore a silver mask as well, so that it was impossible to tell one from another.

At last the clock struck twelve, and the Giant held up his hand.

"It is time that we went to rest," he said; "so take thy bride, King's son, and we will bid thee goodnight."

He laughed as he spoke, for he was almost certain that the Prince would choose the wrong bride; but the young man went straight up to his youngest daughter, and put his arm round her. While the Giant had been speaking he had looked closely at all three maidens, and in the satin folds of Auburn Mary's gown he had seen a little hand held out so as to show that it wanted a finger.

"A good guess, by my troth," said the Giant in great disgust, while all the guests clapped their hands in delight; and he was so angry that he made up his mind that as soon as the household had gone to rest he would go stealthily upstairs and kill the Prince.

But his daughter was watching his face, and she knew what was in his mind. No sooner was she safe in her chamber than she seized her husband's hand. "We must fly, and that quickly," she whispered, "for my father means to kill thee, I can read it in his eye."

So together they stole down the stairs, and out to the stable, where stood a brown horse that was marvelously fleet of foot.

Just as they were mounting him, Mari Ruadh bethought herself of a trick which she could play, which would prevent her father discovering her absence as quickly as he might otherwise do.

So she plucked an apple from an apple tree which grew just outside the stable door, and cut it into nine parts; then she ran back to the house, and slipped upstairs into her room again. Two of the parts of the apple she placed at the head of the bed and two at the foot, two at the bedroom door, two at the front door, and one just outside the house.

"Now," she cried triumphantly, as she mounted behind her husband on the brown horse, "that will lead him a pretty dance, and gain us a little time; and in the meanwhile, good steed, lay legs to the ground as swiftly as thou canst."

The Giant had gone to sleep; but when he woke he remembered how he had intended to kill the Prince, so he arose, and took his club down from the wall, and went upstairs on the tips of his great clumsy toes, and listened at the back of the chamber door to hear, if he could, any noise.

"Art thou asleep?" he whispered.

"Not yet," answered the pieces of apple at the head of the bed.

So he waited a little while, then he asked again, "Art thou asleep?"

"Not yet," answered the pieces at the foot of the bed.

Once more the Giant waited, and once more he asked the same question, sharply this time, for he was growing impatient. "Not yet," said the pieces at the bedroom door.

The next time he asked, the voice seemed fainter, for it came from the apples at the front door; and next time it was fainter still, for it came from the single piece which lay outside.

"I cannot understand this at all," said the Giant in alarm; "my daughter's voice is running away from me," and he rushed into her room.

All that he found there was an empty bed, with two pieces of apple lying at its head and two pieces at its foot.

He kicked them aside in great wrath. "This is Mari Ruadh's work," he cried. "Fool that I was not to watch her more closely; but I will pursue them, and evil take me if I cannot catch them up."

The day was breaking, and the brown horse was flying swiftly over mountain, and moor, and glen, carrying the Prince of Tethertown and his bride home to his father's castle, when the Princess tightened her grasp of her husband's shoulder. "My father hath discovered our flight, and he is pursuing us," she said, "for his angry breath is burning my back."

"What shall we do?" asked the Prince, for his wife had helped him so often before, that he trusted entirely to her judgment.

"Put thy hand quickly into the right ear of the brown horse," she cried, "and throw whatever thou findest there behind thee."

He did as he was bid, and found a tiny branch of a sloe tree.

" 'Tis but a twig of sloe," he said doubtfully.

"It matters not, throw it behind thee, and that at once," she said, "for I can hear the tread of my father's horse."

Without wasting further words the Prince threw the twig over his shoulder, and in a moment a thicket of tangled sloe, seventy miles broad, stretched between the Giant and the lovers.

And, as if to help them further, the Giant's anger had so blinded his eyes, that he never saw the thicket until he was close upon it, and he fell headlong into it, and scratched himself terribly.

"May my daughter suffer for this," he groaned, as he tried to force his way through, but the sloe bushes were so thick that it was of no use, and he must needs go home and fetch his axe and his wood-knife, and cut a road for himself.

All this took time, but by midday he was in full pursuit again, and once more his daughter felt his breath burning her back.

"Put thy hand into the horse's right ear, and throw whatever thou findest there behind thee," she said again, and again the Prince obeyed her.

This time he found a splinter of grey stone, and as soon as it fell to the ground there were twenty miles of great grey rocks behind them.

When the Giant came to the rocks he found that he could not climb over them, and he fell into a fearful passion, and raged and stamped, and called his daughter all the names that he could think of, but of course that did not help him at all, and there was nothing for it but to go home and fetch his lever and mattock and hew a way through.

This took a long time, but just as night fell he was once more close to the fugitives, and once more his breath burned his daughter's back.

"Feel again in the horse's right ear," she cried, "else are we undone."

This time the Prince pulled out a drop of water, which, when he had thrown it over his shoulder, turned into a great loch, twenty miles in length and breadth, and the Giant was riding at such a pace that he could not stop, but went head over heels into the very middle of it, and no creature ever saw him rise again.

Now I wish I could tell you that the Prince and his bride, after having overcome so many difficulties, arrived safely at his father's castle, but, alas! their troubles were not yet over.

Next morning they arrived in sight of the castle, and the Prince's heart leaped with joy at the thought of the welcome he would receive after his long absence. He intended, of course, to take his bride straight home with him, but she refused to go.

"Nay," she said, "there is yet another trial which thou hast to go through ere thou be quit of my father's spells. Go thou and tell thy parents that thou art wedded, and that thou art bringing home a bride, but beware that thou art kissed by neither man nor beast, else will all remembrance of me pass from thy mind and heart."

The Prince obeyed her, as he always did, and left her sitting under a shady oak tree, beside a well, while he went alone to his father's house.

As you may imagine, his father and mother were overjoyed to see him, for they had not seen him since the Giant had carried him away, fourteen years before. They would have thrown their arms round him, and kissed him, had he not cried out to them not to do so; and he was just beginning to explain the reason, intending to tell them all about his wife, Mari Ruadh, when, as ill-luck would have it, an old greyhound, which had played with him when he was a baby, came into the room, and, at the long-forgotten sound of his voice, jumped up and kissed him in its own way.

In an instant all remembrance of his wife, or of his troubled wooing, passed from his mind, and strange as it may seem, he at once began to look about for a pretty girl whom he might wed.

Meanwhile Mari Ruadh sat waiting by the well, and as the day passed, and the Prince never came back, she was sure that the last spell which her wicked father had thrown over him had been successful, and that someone had kissed him, and that he had forgotten all about her. She felt very sad at the thought, and when night came, as she had nowhere else to go, she climbed up into the leafy oak tree, and went to sleep in its branches.

Now it chanced that near by there was a cobbler's hut, and next morning the cobbler happened to feel very thirsty, and he asked his wife if she would go to the well and fetch a drink of cool spring water.

Mari Ruadh heard her footsteps, and peeped down through the branches, to see who was coming; and in this way it came about that when the cobbler's wife was filling her pitcher she saw Mari Ruadh's lovely face reflected in the water.

The silly woman thought that it was her own face, and she was so delighted to think that she was so beautiful, that she let her pitcher fall, and, running indoors, haughtily told her husband, that with her good looks, she could not run his errands any longer.

Now she was a very plain-looking woman, and as her husband looked up at her from the shoe he was cobbling, he thought that she had suddenly gone crazy. As he was very thirsty, he did not waste time thinking about the matter, but asked his daughter if she would go to the well and bring him a drink. She did so, but in two minutes she was back again, without the water, and talking about her good looks in the same way that her mother had done.

"Drat it all," exclaimed the cobbler, "they have both taken leave of their senses. I'll go out myself, and see what is at the bottom of this." So out he went, but being more sensible than either his wife or daughter, when he saw the reflection of Mari Ruadh's face in the water, he looked up into the tree, and there he saw Mari Ruadh herself.

"Now," thought he, "folks say that a dog's bite can be cured by a hair of the dog that bit, and I will prove the truth of the saying. If I take this maiden home, my wife and daughter will surely see that it was not their faces that were reflected in the water, and the knowledge will cure their mad vanity."

So he took Mari Ruadh home, and gave her a share of all he had in his little cottage. She was so grateful to him for his kindness, that she began to look about for some way in which she could reward him, nor had she long to wait until she found it.

For in a very short time news went abroad that the King's son, who had so lately come home, was about to marry, and one day three fine young gentlemen came to the cobbler's cottage, and asked him to make each of them a pair of shoes to wear at the wedding.

As they were being measured for the shoes, Mari Ruadh chanced to pass through the little room, and straightway they all fell in love with her, and each of them offered the cobbler a hundred pounds to be allowed to marry her, for they thought that she was his daughter.

He, poor man, did not know what to do, for a hundred pounds seemed untold riches to him; yet there was something about his strange guest which made him feel that none of them was a fit match for her, gentlemen though they were.

So he gave them all one answer—that they should go home, and come to him next morning for his reply; then he went to Mari Ruadh, and told her the whole story.

She clapped her hands. "This puts me out of a difficulty," she cried; "tell them all to come, and to be sure to bring their purses with them."

"All three," exclaimed the astonished cobbler; "but thou canst not marry all three!"

"Thou canst not tell what I can do," she said mysteriously; "tell them all to come, but on different days."

The cobbler obeyed her, wondering greatly to himself; and the next evening the first young gentleman arrived, and paid his hundred pounds, and was introduced to his promised bride.

The only greeting she gave him was to ask him to go to the far end of the room, and to bring her a glass of water. Wishing to please her, he did so. But no sooner did his fingers touch the glass than they were glued to it, and his feet were glued to the floor, and in spite of all his efforts to get free, he had to stand there all night, holding the glass of water in his hand.

In the morning, as soon as the sun rose, Mari Ruadh let him go, but he was so frightened that he would be laughed at, that he went quietly home, and never told his two friends about his adventure.

On the second evening, the second gallant came with his hundred pieces of gold, and was introduced to Mari Ruadh. She promptly asked him to shut the door which he had left open, and no sooner had he touched it than his hand was glued to the latch, and there he had to stand until the sun rose next morning. He, too, went home, and told nobody.

The third night, the third young man appeared and paid his money, but he fared no better. Mari Ruadh made him stick fast to the floor in the middle of the room, and when the morning came he was only too glad to get back the power of walking, and to go home as fast as his legs would carry him.

When he was out of sight, Mari Ruadh danced for joy, and flung her arms round the old cobbler's neck.

"Now," she said, "I have been able to repay thee for thy kindness to me, for thou art three hundred pounds richer than thou wast when thou broughtest me hither, and gave me food and shelter. But there is one thing more that I am going to ask thee to do for me. Tomorrow is the Prince's wedding day, and I know that thou hast some new shoes to carry home to the castle. Wilt thou let me go with thee to help to carry them? For I have heard so much about this young Prince, that I should like well to catch a glimpse of him if it were possible."

"That request is easily granted," said the cobbler, "for I have friends among the servants, and if I speak them fair, they can give thee a chance of getting a peep at the Prince, and at all the other fine folk."

So Auburn Mary went up to the castle with the cobbler, and it fell out that as the couple were lingering in the courtyard among the servants, the eyes of some of the young nobles fell upon her, and they were so struck with her beauty, that nothing would satisfy them but that they should bring her into the banqueting-hall, where all the wedding guests were assembled, and pledge her in a glass of wine.

A murmur of admiration ran through the room when she entered, and everyone whispered that it was a pity that it was not she who was going to be their future Queen, instead of the black-browed damsel whom the Prince had chosen.

The murmurs of admiration changed to murmurs of astonishment, however, when she put the glass of wine, which the King had ordered to be filled for her, to her lips, for a little flame of fire sprang up out of the glass, and two pigeons, one golden, the other silver, jumped out of the flame.

They flew round and round the room, and everyone was trying to catch them, when suddenly a few grains of corn dropped down out of the air to the floor, right at the Prince's feet.

Down flew the silver pigeon, in a great hurry, and gobbled them up before the golden pigeon could reach them.

"If thou hadst minded when I cleaned the barn, thou wouldst not have eaten that without giving me a share," cooed the golden pigeon reproachfully.

No sooner were the words uttered than a few more grains of corn fell.

The silver pigeon did exactly as he had done before—gobbled them up without giving his neighbor a chance of having a share.

"If thou hadst minded when I thatched the barn, thou wouldst not have eaten that without giving me my share," cooed the golden pigeon still more reproachfully.

Once more some corn fell, and once more the greedy silver pigeon ate it.

This time the golden bird's voice sounded as if she were weeping.

"If thou hadst minded when I harried the magpie's nest, thou wouldst not have eaten that without giving me my share. I lost my little finger on that errand, and I want it still."

"Thou didst, thou didst," cried the King's son, and, springing from his seat, he threw his arms round Mari Ruadh's neck, and covered her face with kisses, while the wedding guests stared at him in astonishment, thinking he had gone mad.

But they did not think so long, for he took the maiden's hand and faced them all boldly, and told them the whole story, how she was his wife already, and how she had helped him to escape from the Giant, and how the old greyhound's kiss had wiped it all out of his mind. And when he had finished speaking, they all agreed that she was his rightful wife; and so at last they came to the end of their troubles, and lived a happy and peaceful life ever afterwards.

## RIQUET WITH THE TUFT[1]

Once upon a time a queen had a little son, who was so ugly and ill-made that for a long time the poor little baby was thought hardly human. However, a good fairy, who presided at his birth, assured his mother that, though ugly, he would never be disagreeable; moreover, she bestowed on him the power of communicating these gifts to the person he should love best in the world. At this the queen was a little comforted, and became still more so when, as soon as he could speak, the infant began to say such pretty and clever things that everybody was charmed with him. (I forgot to mention that his name was Riquet with the Tuft, because he was born with a curious tuft of hair on the top of his head.)

Seven or eight years after this the queen of a neighboring country had two little daughters, twins, at whose birth the same fairy presided. The elder twin was more beautiful than the day—the younger so extremely ugly that the mother's extravagant joy in the first was all turned to grief about the second. So, in order to calm her feelings, the fairy told her that the one daughter should be as stupid as she was pretty, while the other would grow up so clever and charming that nobody would miss her want of beauty.

"Heaven grant it!" sighed the queen; "but are there no means of giving a little sense to the one who is so beautiful?"

"I can do nothing for her, madam," returned the fairy, "nothing as regards her own fortunes; but I grant her the power of making the person who best pleases her as handsome as herself."

Accordingly, as the young princesses grew up, their perfections grew with them; and nothing was spoken of but the beauty of the elder and the wit of the younger. True, their faults increased equally; the one became uglier, and the other more stupid, day by day. Unlucky fair one! she never had a word to say for herself, or else it was the silliest word imaginable; and she was so awkward that she could not place four teacups in a row without breaking one of them, nor drink a glass of water without spilling half of it over her clothes.

Beauty is a great charm; yet, whenever the sisters went out together, those who were attracted by the elder's lovely face, in less than half an hour were sure to be seen at the side of the younger, laughing at her witty and pleasant sayings, and altogether deserting the poor beauty, who had just sense enough to find it out, and to feel that she would have given all her good looks for one-half of her sister's talents.

One day, when she had hid herself in a wood, and was crying over her hard fate, she saw coming towards her a little man, very ugly, but magnificently dressed. Who should this be but Prince Riquet with the Tuft! He had seen her portrait, had fallen desperately in love with her, and secretly quitted his father's kingdom that he might have the pleasure of meeting her. Delighted to find her alone, he came forward with all the respect and politeness imaginable. But he could not help noticing how very melancholy she was, and that all the elegant compliments he made her did not seem to affect her in the least.

"I cannot comprehend, madam," said he, "how so charming and lovely a lady can be so very sad. Never did I see anyone who could at all compare with you."

"That's all you know," said the princess, and stopped.

"Beauty," continued the prince, sighing, "is so great an advantage that, if one possessed it, one would never trouble one's self about anything else."

"I wish I were as ugly as you, and had some sense rather than be as handsome as I am and such a fool."

"Madam," said Riquet politely, though her speech was not exactly civil, "nothing shows intellect so much as the modesty of believing one does not possess it."

"I don't know that; but I know I am a

[1] From Dinah Maria Mulock Craik, *The Fairy Book*. This story first appeared in Charles Perrault, *Tales of My Mother Goose*.

great fool, and it vexes me so that I wish I were dead," cried the princess bitterly.

"If that is all, madam, I can easily put an end to your grief, for I have the power of making the person I love best as clever as I please. I will do it, provided you consent to marry me."

The princess stood dumb with astonishment. She—to marry that little frightful creature—scarcely a man at all!

"I see," said Riquet, "that my proposal offends and grieves you. Well, I will give you a year to consider it."

Now the young lady was so stupid that she thought a year's end was a long way off—so long that it seemed as if it might not come at all, or something might happen between whiles. And she had such a longing to be clever and admired that she thought at all risks she would accept the chance of becoming so. Accordingly, she promised Riquet to marry him that day twelvemonth.

No sooner had she said it than she felt herself quite another being. She found she could at once say anything she chose, and say it in the most graceful and brilliant way. She began a lively conversation with Prince Riquet, and chatted so fast and so wittily that he began to be afraid he had given her so much cleverness as to leave himself none.

When she returned to the palace, all the court was astonished at the change. She, who had annoyed everybody by the impertinent, tasteless, or downright foolish things she uttered, now charmed everybody by her wit, her pleasantness, and her exceeding good sense. The king himself began to come to her apartment, and ask her advice in state affairs. Her mother, and indeed the whole kingdom, were delighted; the only person to be pitied was the poor younger sister, of whom nobody now took the least notice.

Meantime, princes came in throngs to ask in marriage this wonderful princess, who was as clever as she was beautiful; but she found none to suit her, probably because the more sense a lady has, the more difficult she is to please. As for her promise to Riquet with the Tuft being given in the days when she was so dull and stupid, it now never once came into her head; until one day, being quite perplexed by her numerous suitors, she went to take a solitary walk and think the matter over, when by chance she came into the same wood where she had met the prince. There, all of a sudden, she thought she heard a queer running about and chatting underground. "Fetch me that spit," cried one; "Put some more wood on that fire," said another; and by and by the earth opened, showing a great kitchen filled with cooks, cooking a splendid banquet. They were all working merrily at their several duties, and singing together in the most lively chorus.

"What is all this about?" asked the amazed princess.

"If you please, madam," replied the head cook politely, "we are cooking the wedding dinner of Prince Riquet with the Tuft, who is to be married tomorrow."

"Tomorrow!" cried the princess, all at once recollecting her promise; at which she was so frightened that she thought she would have fallen to the earth. Greater still was her alarm when, at only a few steps' distance, she beheld Riquet dressed splendidly, like a prince and a bridegroom.

"You see me, princess, exact to my word; and I doubt not you are the same, come to make me the happiest of mankind."

"Prince," said the lady frankly, "I must confess that such was not my intention, and I fear I shall never be able to do as you desire."

"You surprise me, madam."

"I can well believe it; and if I had to do with a brute, instead of a gentleman of sense and feeling, I should be very uneasy," returned she; "but since I speak with the cleverest man in the world, I am sure he will hear reason, and will not bind me, now a sensible woman, to a promise I made when I was only a fool."

"If I were a fool myself, madam, I might well complain of your broken promise; and being, as you say, a man of sense, should I not complain of what takes away all the happiness of my life? Tell me candidly, is there anything in me, except my ugliness, which displeases you? Do you object to my birth, my temper, my manners?"

"No, truly," replied the princess; "I like everything in you, except"—and she hesitated courteously—"except your appearance."

"Then, madam, I need not lose my happiness; for if I have the gift of making clever whomsoever I love best, you also are able to make the person you prefer as handsome as ever you please. Could you love me enough to do that?"

"I think I could," said the princess; and her heart being greatly softened towards him she wished that he might become the handsomest prince in all the world. No sooner had she done so than Riquet with the Tuft appeared in her eyes the most elegant young man she had ever seen.

Ill-natured people have said that this was no fairy gift, but that love created the change. They declare that the princess, when she thought over her lover's perseverance, patience, good humor, and discretion, and counted his numerous fine qualities of mind and disposition, saw no longer the deformity of his body or the plainness of his features; that his hump was merely an exaggerated stoop, and his awkward movements became only an interesting eccentricity. Nay, even his eyes, which squinted terribly, seemed always looking on all sides for her, in token of his violent love, and his great red nose gave him an air very martial and heroic.

However this may be, it is certain that the princess married him; that either she retained her good sense, or he never felt the want of it; and he never again became ugly—or, at least, not in his wife's eyes; so they both lived very happy until they died.

## THE TIGER, THE BRAHMAN, AND THE JACKAL[1]

Once upon a time a tiger was caught in a trap. He tried in vain to get out through the bars, and rolled and bit with rage and grief when he failed.

By chance a poor Brahman came by. "Let me out of this cage, O pious one!" cried the tiger.

"Nay, my friend," replied the Brahman mildly; "you would probably eat me if I did."

"Not at all!" swore the tiger with many oaths; "on the contrary, I should be forever grateful, and serve you as a slave."

Now, when the tiger sobbed and sighed and wept, the pious Brahman's heart softened, and at last he consented to open the door of the cage. Out popped the tiger, and, seizing the poor man, cried, "What a fool you are! What is to prevent my eating you now, for after being cooped up so long I am just terribly hungry?"

In vain the Brahman pleaded for his life; the most he could gain was a promise to abide by the decision of the first three things he chose to question as to the justice of the tiger's action.

So the Brahman first asked a fig tree what it thought of the matter, but the fig tree only replied coldly, "What have you to complain about? Don't I give shade and shelter to every one who passes by, and don't they in return tear down my branches to feed their cattle? Don't whimper—be a man!"

Then the Brahman, sad at heart, went further afield till he saw a buffalo turning a well-wheel; but he fared no better from it, for it answered: "You are a fool to expect gratitude! Look at me! While I gave milk they fed me on cottonseed and oilcake, but now I am dry they yoke me here, and give me refuse as fodder!"

The Brahman, still more sad, asked the road to give him its opinion.

"My dear sir," said the road, "how foolish you are to expect anything else! Here

[1] From Flora Annie Steel, *Tales of the Punjab.*

am I, useful to everybody, yet all, rich and poor, great and small, trample on me as they go past, giving me nothing but the ashes of their pipes and the husks of their grain!"

On this the Brahman turned back sorrowfully, and on the way he met a jackal, who called out, "Why, what's the matter, Mr. Brahman? You look as miserable as a fish out of water!"

The Brahman told him all that had occurred. "How very confusing!" said the jackal, when the recital was ended; "would you mind telling me over again, for everything seems so mixed up?"

The Brahman told it all over again, but the jackal shook his head in a distracted sort of way, and still could not understand.

"It's very odd," said he sadly, "but it all seems to go in at one ear and out at the other! I will go to the place where it all happened, and then, perhaps, I shall be able to give a judgment."

So they returned to the cage, by which the tiger was waiting for the Brahman, and sharpening his teeth and claws.

"You've been away a long time!" growled the savage beast, "but now let us begin our dinner."

"*Our* dinner!" thought the wretched Brahman, as his knees knocked together with fright; "what a remarkably delicate way of putting it!"

"Give me five minutes, my lord!" he pleaded, "in order that I may explain matters to the jackal here, who is somewhat slow in his wits."

The tiger consented, and the Brahman began the whole story over again, not missing a single detail, and spinning as long a yarn as possible.

"Oh, my poor brain! oh, my poor brain!" cried the jackal, wringing its paws. "Let me see! How did it all begin? You were in the cage, and the tiger came walking by—"

"Pooh!" interrupted the tiger, "what a fool you are! *I* was in the cage."

"Of course!" cried the jackal, pretending to tremble with fright; "yes! I was in the cage—no, I wasn't—dear! dear! where are my wits? Let me see—the tiger was in the Brahman, and the cage came walking by —no, that's not it, either! Well, don't mind me, but begin your dinner, for I shall never understand!"

"Yes, you shall!" returned the tiger, in a rage at the jackal's stupidity; "I'll *make* you understand! Look here—I am the tiger—"

"Yes, my lord!"

"And that is the Brahman—"

"Yes, my lord!"

"And that is the cage—"

"Yes, my lord!"

"And I was in the cage—do you understand?"

"Yes—no—Please, my lord—"

"Well?" cried the tiger impatiently.

"Please, my lord! How did you get in?"

"How? Why in the usual way, of course!"

"Oh, dear me! my head is beginning to whirl again! Please don't be angry, my lord, but what is the usual way?"

At this the tiger lost patience, and jumping into the cage, cried, "This way! Now do you understand how it was?"

"Perfectly!" grinned the jackal, as he dexterously shut the door, "and if you will permit me to say so, I think matters will remain as they were!"

## THE FABLES OF AESOP[1]

### THE LION AND THE MOUSE

Once when a Lion was asleep a little Mouse began running up and down upon him; this soon wakened the Lion, who placed his huge paw upon him, and opened his big jaws to swallow him.

[1] From Joseph Jacobs, *The Fables of Aesop.* Aesop is said to have been a Greek slave of the sixth century B.C., who gained his freedom by his cleverness. Tradition has it that he used the fables associated with his name for political purposes. The fables are probably older than the era in which Aesop is supposed to have lived, and Aesop, himself, may be a legendary figure.

"Pardon, O King," cried the little Mouse; "forgive me this time, I shall never forget it. Who knows but what I may be able to do you a turn some of these days?"

The Lion was so tickled at the idea of the Mouse being able to help him, that he lifted up his paw and let him go.

Some time after the Lion was caught in a trap, and the hunters, who desired to carry him alive to the King, tied him to a tree while they went in search of a wagon to carry him in.

Just then the little Mouse happened to pass by, and seeing the sad plight in which the Lion was, went up to him and soon gnawed away the ropes that bound the King of the Beasts.

"Was I not right?" said the little Mouse. "Little friends may prove great friends."

## THE WIND AND THE SUN

The Wind and the Sun were disputing which was the stronger. Suddenly they saw a traveler coming down the road, and the Sun said: "I see a way to decide our dispute. Whichever of us can cause that traveler to take off his cloak shall be regarded as the stronger. You begin."

So the Sun retired behind a cloud, and the Wind began to blow as hard as he could upon the traveler. But the harder he blew the more closely did the traveler wrap his cloak round him, till at last the Wind had to give up in despair.

Then the Sun came out and shone in all his glory upon the traveler, who soon found it too hot to walk with his cloak on.

## THE FROG AND THE OX

"Oh, Father," said a little Frog to the big one sitting by the side of a pool, "I have seen such a terrible monster! It was as big as a mountain, with horns on its head, and a long tail, and it had hoofs divided in two."

"Tush, child, tush," said the old Frog, "that was only Farmer White's Ox. It isn't so big either; he may be a little bit taller than I, but I could easily make myself quite as broad; just you see."

So he blew himself out, and blew himself out, and blew himself out. "Was he as big as that?" asked he.

"Oh, much bigger than that," said the young Frog.

Again the old one blew himself out, and asked the young one if the Ox was as big as that.

"Bigger, Father, bigger," was the reply.

So the Frog took a deep breath, and blew and blew and blew, and swelled and swelled and swelled.

And then he said: "I'm sure the Ox is not as big as—" But at this moment he burst.

## THE HARE AND THE TORTOISE

The Hare was once boasting of his speed before the other animals. "I have never yet been beaten," said he, "when I put forth my full speed. I challenge any one here to race with me."

The Tortoise said quietly: "I accept your challenge."

"That is a good joke," said the Hare; "I could dance round you all the way."

"Keep your boasting till you've beaten," answered the Tortoise. "Shall we race?"

So a course was fixed and a start was made. The Hare darted almost out of sight at once, but soon stopped and, to show his contempt for the Tortoise, lay down to have a nap.

The Tortoise plodded on and plodded on, and when the Hare awoke from his nap, he saw the Tortoise just near the winning post and could not run up in time to save the race.

## THE CROW AND THE PITCHER

A Crow, half-dead with thirst, came upon a Pitcher which had once been full of water; but when the Crow put its beak into the mouth of the Pitcher he found that only very little water was left in it, and that he could not reach far enough down to get at it. He tried and he tried, but at last had to give up in despair.

Then a thought came to the Crow, and he took a pebble and dropped it into the Pitcher. Then he took another pebble and dropped it into the Pitcher. Then he took another pebble and dropped that into the Pitcher. Then he took another pebble and dropped that into the Pitcher. Then he took another pebble and dropped that into the Pitcher. Then he took another pebble and dropped that into the Pitcher.

At last, at last, he saw the water mount up near him; and after casting in a few more pebbles he was able to quench his thirst and save his life.

## THE ANT AND THE GRASSHOPPER

In a field one summer's day a Grasshopper was hopping about, chirping and singing to its heart's content. An Ant passed by, bearing along with great toil a grain of corn he was taking to the nest.

"Why not come and chat with me," said the Grasshopper, "instead of toiling and moiling in that way?"

"I am helping to lay up food for the winter," said the Ant," and recommend you to do the same."

"Why bother about winter?" said the Grasshopper. "We have got plenty of food at present." But the Ant went on its way and continued its toil.

When the winter came the Grasshopper had no food, and found itself dying of hunger, while it saw the ants distributing every day corn and grain from the stores they had collected in the summer.

## THE MICE IN COUNCIL

Long ago, the mice held a general council to consider what measures they could take to outwit their common enemy, the Cat. Some said this, and some said that; but at last a young mouse got up and said he had a proposal to make, which he thought would meet the case.

"You will all agree," said he, "that our chief danger consists in the sly and treacherous manner in which the enemy approaches us. Now, if we could receive some signal of her approach, we could easily escape from her. I venture, therefore, to propose that a small bell be procured, and attached by a ribbon round the neck of the Cat. By this means we should always know when she was about, and could easily retire while she was in the neighborhood."

This proposal met with general applause, until an old mouse got up and said: "That is all very well, but who is to bell the Cat?"

## THE DOG AND THE SHADOW

It happened that a Dog had got a piece of meat and was carrying it home in his mouth to eat it in peace. Now on his way home he had to cross a plank lying across a running brook. As he crossed, he looked down and saw his own shadow reflected in the water beneath. Thinking it was another dog with another piece of meat, he made up his mind to have that also. So he made a snap at the shadow in the water, but as he opened his mouth the piece of meat fell out, dropped into the water and was never seen more.

## THE FOX AND THE GRAPES

One hot summer's day a Fox was strolling through an orchard till he came to a bunch of Grapes just ripening on a vine which had been trained over a lofty branch.

"Just the thing to quench my thirst," quoth he.

Drawing back a few paces, he took a run and a jump, and just missed the bunch.

Turning round again with a *one, two, three!* he jumped up, but with no greater success.

Again and again he tried after the tempting morsel, but at last had to give it up, and walked away with his nose in the air, saying, "I am sure they are sour."

## THE TOWN MOUSE AND THE COUNTRY MOUSE

Now you must know that a Town Mouse once upon a time went on a visit to his cousin in the country. He was rough and ready, this cousin, but he loved his town friend and made him heartily welcome. Beans and bacon, cheese and bread, were all he had to offer, but he offered them freely.

The Town Mouse rather turned up his long nose at this country fare, and said: "I cannot understand, cousin, how you can put up with such poor food as this, but of course you cannot expect anything better in the country; come you with me and I will show you how to live. When you have been in town a week you will wonder how you could ever have stood a country life."

No sooner said than done. The two mice set off for the town and arrived at the Town Mouse's residence late at night.

"You will want some refreshment after our long journey," said the polite Town Mouse, and took his friend into the grand dining room.

There they found the remains of a fine feast, and soon the two mice were eating up jellies and cakes and all that was nice.

Suddenly they heard growling and barking. "What is that?" said the Country Mouse.

"It is only the dogs of the house," answered the other.

"Only!" said the Country Mouse. "I do not like that music at my dinner."

Just at that moment the door flew open, in came two huge mastiffs, and the two mice had to scamper down and run off.

"Good-by, my cousin," said the Country Mouse.

"What! going so soon?" said the other.

"Yes," he replied, "better beans and bacon in peace than cakes and ale in fear."

## HERCULES AND THE WAGONER

A Wagoner was once driving a heavy load along a very muddy way. At last he came to a part of the road where the wheels sank halfway into the mire, and the more the horses pulled, the deeper sank the wheels.

So the Wagoner threw down his whip, and knelt down and prayed to Hercules the Strong. "O Hercules, help me in this my hour of distress," quoth he.

But Hercules appeared to him, and said:

"Tut, man, don't sprawl there. Get up and put your shoulder to the wheel."

## THE MILKMAID AND HER PAIL

Patty, the Milkmaid, was going to market, carrying her milk in a Pail on her head. As she went along she began calculating what she could do with the money she would get for the milk.

"I'll buy some fowls from Farmer Brown," said she, "and they will lay eggs each morning, which I will sell to the parson's wife. With the money that I get from the sale of these eggs I'll buy myself a new dimity frock and a chip hat; and when I go to market, won't all the young men come up and speak to me! Polly Shaw will be that jealous; but I don't care. I shall just look at her and toss my head like this."

As she spoke, she tossed her head; the Pail fell off and all the milk was spilt. So she had to go home and tell her mother what had occurred.

"Ah, my child," said her mother, "do not count your chickens before they are hatched."

## Old Tales: Suggested Grades

*Grade One*

The Three Billy Goats Gruff
The Gingerbread Boy
The Three Bears
The Old Woman and Her Pig
The Straw Ox
Little Red Riding Hood
Aiken-Drum, the Brownie
Mr. Vinegar

*Grade Two*

Lazy Jack
The Three Little Pigs
The Traveling Musicians
Why the Bear Is Stumpy-Tailed
The Wolf and the Seven Young Goslings
The Lad Who Went to the North Wind
Jack and the Beanstalk
The Elves and the Shoemaker
Drakesbill
The Lion and the Mouse (Aesop)

*Grade Three*

Boots and His Brothers
Snow-White and the Seven Dwarfs
Hansel and Gretel
Snow-White and Rose-Red
Cinderella, or the Little Glass Slipper
Brier Rose
The Princess on the Glass Hill
East of the Sun and West of the Moon
The Wind and the Sun (Aesop)
The Crow and the Pitcher (Aesop)
The Town Mouse and the Country Mouse (Aesop)

*Grade Four*

The King of the Crocodiles
Puss in Boots
The Frog and the Ox (Aesop)
The Hare and the Tortoise (Aesop)
The Ant and the Grasshopper (Aesop)
The Mice in Council (Aesop)
The Dog and the Shadow (Aesop)

*Grade Five*

Tom Thumb
Aladdin and the Wonderful Lamp
The Tiger, the Brahman, and the Jackal
The Fox and the Grapes (Aesop)
Hercules and the Wagoner (Aesop)
The Milkmaid and Her Pail (Aesop)

*Grade Six*

The Prince and the Giant's Daughter
Riquet with the Tuft

## Books of Old Tales

### Primary Grades

Brooks, L. Leslie, *Golden Goose Book,* illus. by the author. Warne.

Carrick, Valery, *Picture Tales from the Russian* (trans. by Nevil Forbes), illus. by the author. Stokes.

Coolidge, Florence C., *Little Ugly Face,* illus. by Maud and Miska Petersham. Macmillan.

Dasent, George Webbe, *East of the Sun and West of the Moon,* illus. by Hedwig Collin. Macmillan.

———, *East of the Sun and West of the Moon,* illus. by Kay Nielsen. Doubleday, Doran.

Eells, Elsie Spicer, *Fairy Tales from Brazil,* illus. by Helen M. Barton. Dodd, Mead.

Gág, Wanda, *Tales from Grimm,* illus. by the author. Coward-McCann.

*Happy Hour Books,* illus. by Berta and Elmer Hader, Frank Dobias, and George Richards. Macmillan.

Huber, Miriam Blanton, Frank Seely Salisbury, and Mabel O'Donnell, *I Know a Story,* illus. by Florence and Margaret Hoopes. Row, Peterson.

———, *It Happened One Day,* illus. by Mary Royt. Row, Peterson.

———, *After the Sun Sets,* illus. by Nellie H. Farnam and Mary Royt. Row, Peterson.

Hutchinson, Veronica S., *Fireside Stories,* illus. by Lois Lenski. Putnam.

Jacobs, Joseph, *English Fairy Tales,* illus. by John D. Batten. Putnam.

Literature Committee of the Association for Childhood Education, *Told under the Green Umbrella,* illus. by Grace Gilkison. Macmillan.

Power, Effie L., *Blue Caravan Tales,* illus. by Pelagie Doane. Dutton.

Rickert, Edith, *The Bojabi Tree,* illus. by Gleb Botkin. Doubleday, Doran.

Skinner, Eleanor, and Ada Skinner, *Nursery Tales from Many Lands,* illus. by Blanche Fisher Wright. Scribner.

Steel, Flora Annie, *English Fairy Tales,* illus. by Arthur Rackham. Macmillan.

Wadsworth, Wallace, *The Real Story Book,* illus. by Margaret Evans Price. Rand McNally.

Wiggin, Kate Douglas, and Nora A. Smith, *Tales of Laughter,* illus. by Elizabeth MacKinstry. Doubleday, Doran.

## *Intermediate Grades*

Artzybasheff, Boris (editor and illustrator), *Aesop's Fables.* Viking.

Babbitt, Ellen C., *Jataka Tales,* illus. by Ellsworth Young. Appleton-Century.

Boggs, Ralph Steele, and Mary Gould Davis, *Three Golden Oranges,* illus. by Emma Brock. Longmans.

Bowman, James, and Margery Bianco, *Tales from a Finnish Tupa,* illus. by Laura Bannon. Whitman.

Borski, Lucia M., and Kate B. Miller, *The Jolly Tailor, and Other Polish Fairy Tales,* illus. by Kazimir Klepacki. Longmans.

Botsford, Florence H., *Picture Tales from the Italian,* illus. by Grace Gilkison. Stokes.

Carpenter, Frances, *Tales of a Chinese Grandmother,* illus. by Malthé Hasselriis. Doubleday, Doran.

———, *Tales of a Russian Grandmother,* illus. by I. Bilibine. Doubleday, Doran.

Capuana, Luigi, *Italian Fairy Tales,* illus. by Margaret Freeman. Dutton.

Cendrars, Blaise, *Little Black Stories for Little White Children* (trans. by Margery Bianco), illus. by Pierre Pinsard. Putnam.

Chamoud, Simone, *Picture Tales from the French,* illus. by Grace Gilkison. Stokes.

Craik, Dinah Maria Mulock, *The Fairy Book,* illus. by Warwick Goble. Macmillan.

Crane, Lucy, *Household Stories from the Brothers Grimm,* illus. by Walter Crane. Macmillan.

De Leeuw, Hendrik, *Java Jungle Tales,* illus. by Kurt Wiese. Doubleday, Doran.

Fillmore, Parker, *Czechoslovak Fairy Tales,* illus. by Jan Matulka. Harcourt, Brace.

———, *Mighty Mikko,* illus. by Jay Everen. Harcourt, Brace.

Jacobs, Joseph, *Fables of Aesop,* illus. by Richard Heighway. Macmillan.

———, *Indian Fairy Tales,* illus. by John D. Batten. Putnam.

Lang, Andrew, *The Blue Fairy Book,* illus. by H. J. Ford and G. P. J. Hood. Longmans.

———, *The Red Fairy Book,* illus. by H. J. Ford and Lancelot Speed. Longmans.

Lucas, Mrs. Edgar, *Grimms' Fairy Tales,* illus. by Arthur Rackham. Lippincott.

MacManus, Seumas, *Donegal Fairy Stories.* Doubleday, Doran.

Metzger, Berta, *Picture Tales from the Chinese,* illus. by Eleanor Frances Lattimore. Stokes.

Rasmussen, Knud, *The Eagle's Gift* (trans. by Isabel Hutchinson), illus. by Ernst Hansen. Doubleday, Doran.

Steel, Flora Annie, *Tales of the Punjab,* illus. by J. Lockwood Kipling. Macmillan.

Sugimoto, Chiyono, *Picture Tales from the Japanese,* illus. by Tekisui Tshii. Stokes.

Wheeler, Post, *Albanian Wonder Tales,* illus. by Maud and Miska Petersham. Doubleday, Doran.

## *Upper Grades*

Colum, Padraic, *The Forge in the Forest,* illus. by Boris Artzybasheff. Macmillan.

Finger, Charles J., *Tales from Silver Lands,* illus. by Paul Honoré. Doubleday, Doran.

Grierson, Elizabeth W., *The Book of Celtic Stories,* illus. by Allan Stewart. Macmillan.

Gunterman, Bertha L., *Castles in Spain,* illus. by Mahlon Blaine. Longmans.

James, Grace, *Green Willow,* illus. by Warwick Goble. Macmillan.

Lang, Andrew, *Arabian Nights' Entertainments,* illus. by H. J. Ford. Longmans.

McNeer, May, *Prince Bantam,* illus. by Lynd Ward. Macmillan.

Olcott, Frances Jankins, *The Arabian Nights' Entertainments,* illus. by Munro S. Orr. Holt.

Young, Ella, *The Wonder Smith and His Son,* illus. by Boris Artzybasheff. Longmans.

# LEGENDS AND HERO TALES

## Myths and Legends: Significance and Use

THE stories in this section are traditional tales and are very old. They are more complicated in plot and ideas than the stories commonly known as folk tales. Though their origins go back to great antiquity, these stories reflect less primitive conditions of living and thinking and picture more complex social situations and influences than do the folk tales. They are, therefore, better suited to the intermediate and upper grades than to the primary.

The terms legends, myths, and hero tales are often used to mean much the same thing and, like the term folk tale, refer to a large body of stories with no known authors. The term myth has usually a more specialized meaning and refers to stories in which gods, goddesses, and other pagan divinities play a part. Many of the world's greatest writers have taken the plots and themes of these tales and woven masterpieces about them, but the beginnings of the tales and the creators of the heroic characters are lost in dim antiquity.

A formal study of mythology with emphasis upon the names of the gods and the organizations of which they were believed to be a part has little place in the elementary school. Such procedure will do much to destroy the interest of children in these stories, which are, after all, tales of adventure and as such can give much pleasure. It is true that children often become absorbed in re-creating the life of ancient days, in imagination they become a boy or girl living in the Golden Age of Greece, and through dramatic and artistic activities the period becomes alive to them. Without such stimuli, the stories are still good stories and much liked by older children.

It is interesting to the student to note the similarities and differences in the Norse myths and those of Greece. Many teachers consider the Norse myths better suited to children than the Greek, but the Greek stories have had more frequent retelling with consequent refinement and clarifying of details that in some cases makes them more understandable to children.

Interesting parallels may be found in certain incidents in the myths and in folk tales. The achievement of Boots in "The Princess on the Glass Hill" is not greatly different from that of Meilanion in "The Winning of Atalanta," and the prince in "The Prince and the Giant's Daughter" accomplished tasks as difficult as the labors performed by Hercules. The idea of the long, living sleep is one that figures in simple folk tales as well as in myths; we find it in "Brier Rose," in "Snow-White and the Seven Dwarfs," and in the story of Sigurd and Brynhild. Some scholars have offered the explanation that old pagan stories were handed down among the folk long after pagan religions had been abandoned. To the folk, Boots being helped by unexplained magic was more satisfying than Boots being helped by the goddess Aphrodite and more fitting for the circumstances under which the story was told. Then, as now, good storytellers arranged their stories to give the greatest pleasure to the hearers.

Children, both boys and girls, in the early teens find the romantic stories of the era of chivalry very much to their liking. These were tales that the troubadours and minstrels sang in the medieval castles before books were made. A detailed study of national epics belongs to ages above the elementary school, but some of the simpler episodes from the great epics are high in interest to boys and girls if presented as heroic tales to be read and enjoyed.

It has not been possible to include in this section stories of all the well known legendary heroes, but the reading lists give sources of other tales. Since several ballads about Robin Hood have been given earlier, no prose stories appear. Robin Hood is one of the best-loved heroes, especially by children in the intermediate grades.

These tales of high exploits and brave deeds hold a favored place in the interests of children who have outgrown the simpler folk tales but find great satisfaction in heroes who overcome obstacles, redress wrongs, and help to make a better world.

# Legends and Hero Tales

## THE GHOST OF THE GREAT WHITE STAG[1]

*Arthur C. Parker*

There is a mighty mountain in the northlands. It rises from the placid waters of a beautiful lake and its summit catches the glint of the sun. On all sides but one are other towering peaks, but none rivals the mighty mountain, for here dwells the great white stag whom no hunter can kill.

In the valley of the lake there is yet another glimmering lake and beyond, a wooded slope where the forest-folk have their council grounds. It is a far-off retreat, but a safe one, and here all the fur-folk meet as friends.

In those dim days, Turtle was chief, and it was he who called the fur-folk and the feather-folk together. Turtle was chief because his shell was thick and he could draw in his head. A leader should be like that. A thick skin, ears that do not hear and a mouth that is shut in a shell are things that every chief needs. But Timber Wolf was envious, and *he* would be chief. So now comes the story.

The call had gone forth, and from far and wide the animals came to the council. Something had happened. What could it be?

All through the woodland there was motion—the deer were coming. All through the brushland there was a swaying—the muskrats and the raccoons were coming. All through the swampland there was a rustling—the beaver and the otter were coming. All through the waterways there was a splashing—the turtles and the lizards were coming. Above in the air were countless birds and above them, urging them on, was Sah-dah-gey-ah, the Great Blue Eagle, chief of all the feather-folk. All creatures had answered the call of Turtle.

Through the tangles slunk Timber Wolf, the envious one. Very sly was he, for he had a reason for keeping out of sight. His plan was a deep one, and if he could but succeed, he would be chief.

It is known to all that in the beginning of things, every animal and every bird had a magic pouch in which it kept its magical charms that gave power. This pouch every creature wore on its neck. While it possessed this, it had power over other beasts and could not be injured. Now it was the custom for the animals in coming to the council to place their magic pouches in a

[1] From Arthur C. Parker, *Skunny Wundy, and Other Indian Tales.*

great bark dish which Turtle kept by the council-fire. This meant that they had come for a council of peace and sat as equals.

Timber Wolf knew all this, and it was his plan to steal the basket of power and run with it to a secret cave where it might be hidden. This would weaken all the animals and they would have to look to him for favor. Oh, how they would beg to get even a little of that power back! Timber Wolf licked his chops at the thought of how he would make his brother beasts obey. The cowering things—more than one would slide down his throat before he got through!

Then Timber Wolf grew eager, and when night fell in the forest, he slunk about looking for sleepers that he might begin to steal their secret power even before the council was called.

He skulked around until he found Old Bear. Here was luck, indeed, for Old Bear was on his back, his paws over his eyes, and his pouch of secret power bulging from his neck. It took but a snap of Timber Wolf's sharp teeth to sever the thong that bound the pouch to Old Bear—just a snap. Timber Wolf gave a slight growl of satisfaction and bounded away to hide the magic in his own pouch. Old Bear was now in his power! The beginning was good.

Morning came and all the animals and birds started on their journey again—all save Old Bear who slept too long and arose weak and dazed. He did not know what had happened to him, but he knew that he felt sick. He shook himself and tried to amble along, but reeled from side to side. Still he made up his mind to keep on and never turn back, for Turtle had called a council and Turtle was chief. This being so, Old Bear would obey!

At length the great day came and Turtle saw around him a great host of tribesmen. Each sought its own group, its own corner, or its own side of the fire. Turtle stood upon a stump and looked over the throng.

"Are all here?" he shouted.

A great shout went up, "We're here!"

"I do not hear the voice of Old Bear," called out Turtle. "Who has seen Old Bear? Perhaps, like White Stag, some traitor has slain him."

No one answered, but all remembered the tragedy of White Stag.

"Those who fail shall be without the new power," said Turtle. "O all ye who are friends, place your magic power pouches in the great basket of friendship. Sit here as equals."

One by one the beasts and birds put their pouches into the basket. Even Timber Wolf put in a pouch—but kept one slyly hidden. It was his own, so that he could betray Turtle when the moment came.

Turtle surveyed the basket and spoke again. "I see the pouch of Old Bear but not of Timber Wolf," said Turtle. "Nevertheless, I see Timber Wolf here and do not see Old Bear. It appears that mischief has come upon us." You see, Turtle was very wise.

"How do you know that Old Bear's pouch is there and that mine is missing?" growled Timber Wolf, edging closely to the basket.

"Because Turtle is chief, and Turtle is wise," came the answer.

Timber Wolf gave a snarl and sprang at Turtle, tipping him over and throwing him upon his back on the ground. All the animals leaped toward Timber Wolf, who turned round and round, showing his fangs. Not one of the fur-folk or feather-folk could touch Timber Wolf, for all power to fight was in the basket of friendship.

"Stand back," growled Timber Wolf. "Behold your chief sprawling on his back, overthrown by a swish of my paw! A fine chief is he. His dignity is to be admired! O able leader of all the wood-folk, how neatly you spin upon your shiny shell! How yellow your breastplate, how beautifully marked! How your stubby hands and feet clutch at the air, appealing to the clouds to turn you over. Ho-ho, ho-ho!"

Timber Wolf now sprang to the stump and began to address the wood-folk. "Obey me," he shouted, "and I shall lead you forth to make war!"

There was a sudden sound behind him, and Timber Wolf gave one swift glance over his shoulders. He saw Turtle extend his head, dig his nose in the earth, give a twist of his neck and turn over with a flop. Timber Wolf's mouth opened and his tongue hung out, for Turtle now leaped into the air and came down upon the basket of friendship with a splash. As he landed, all the pouches of power popped out like seeds from a snapdragon pod, and flew back where they belonged, and one flew far, far into the forest, and struck the neck of poor Old Bear, limping along so slowly.

Immediately all the animals growled and rushed upon Timber Wolf, holding him prisoner in a circle of extended claws and sharp teeth. Timber Wolf was now in for it, and knew his time had come.

Turtle Chief now mounted the stump. "Hold the prisoner while I give you the great news," said he. "I have called this council to tell you that the *Ongwe* are coming, the mighty *Ongwe Oweh,*[1] who are wiser than all the wood-folk."

"Who are the *Ongwe* that we should consider their coming?" snapped Timber Wolf from the circle.

There was a rustle and a snort. Into the council square leaped Old Bear. "O Chief," shouted he, "I have been greatly wronged and by trickery delayed. My power was stolen, but by magic it came back to me. Still, my delay has shown me a great thing. The *Ongwe* are coming."

"The *Ongwe!*" shouted all the animals. "Who are the *Ongwe?*"

"I was about to tell you," shouted Turtle. "The *Ongwe* are *men-beings* and they are going to hunt, and there is one whom they shall hunt because they will hate him. He is Timber Wolf."

Timber Wolf snarled and with a sudden spring leaped high over the heads of the beasts around him, and dashed for the mighty mountains, swimming the lake, skulking the brushland and then scaling the peak. Here he found refuge in a dark cave—it was a den to his liking, for he could look down upon the council and lay his schemes against it.

"What shall we do now?" asked Turtle, when the excitement had died down.

"Let us hunt Timber Wolf and force him to run the gantlet," cried many voices.

"Let us catch him and leave none among us for the *Ongwe* to hate," cried others, planning to rend him limb from limb.

And so it was that all the birds and animals scattered in the forest looking for Timber Wolf, but when night had come not one had seen him, though Timber Wolf had seen them all.

Timber Wolf now crept into his dark cave, but drew back with a sharp cry. Before him in the darkness were two glowing eyes of evil. Someone was spying on him! He turned and fled to the mountain side, where he cowered behind a great rock, but here was a rustle, a constant rustle. Who could be here? Spies were everywhere!

Timber Wolf now slunk along with greater caution to an open space where the moonlight fell. Here he could see his foes if any appeared.

But what was that? A great black shadow waved over the ground. Timber Wolf's hair rose in a shaggy crest from his neck to his tail. The black shadow beckoned and swayed. Then there came a creak and a groan, "Djis-gaah, djis-gaah!"

So came the sound, and it was a word meaning *ghost!* Timber Wolf now looked up at the moon and gave a long despairing howl. His whole body trembled.

"Oh, to escape this awful place!" So thought Timber Wolf, as he crept away from the open and sought refuge behind a great pine. Here he heard a rattle and, looking down in the dim light, saw the bones of the great elk which he had stalked in the snow and slain only the winter before when the council had gathered.

The bones glinted a ghastly white in the dim light that filtered in through the branches. Timber Wolf felt a chill grip-

[1] *Indians.*

ping his very marrow, and with mincing steps he crawled out from the bone pile. Again he sought the open, but no sooner had he reached the clearing than he saw a great patch of white, like a cloud, slowly moving through the open spaces.

It seemed to grow large and then small, and a portion waved up and down. Timber Wolf grew cold with terror and stood as if frozen to the ground. The ghostly white thing came nearer and nearer.

Timber Wolf could not move now and his jaws grew hard. The ghost was upon him. There was a crash. He felt himself lifted high and borne away, nor could he even struggle now, for a great spear was thrust through his hind leg. Only a faint whimper escaped from his throat as he felt himself carried on and on and on.

Down in the council circle a great fire blazed and all about it were the faithful fur-folk discussing the coming of the *Ongwe*. Suddenly Turtle Chief raised his hand.

"Someone is coming," said he. "Be still."

There was a cracking of sticks and the dashing of swift feet. Then into the glare of the light leaped the great White Stag, Timber Wolf pinned on his antlers.

"I have come," began White Stag. "I have come with the culprit who disobeyed the laws of friendship and who sought power by theft."

"Deliver him to us," shouted all the fur-folk.

"I give him to you," answered White Stag. "Let him forever be despised and hunted. Know you that last year, when winter came, and we gathered in council, Timber Wolf took me as I slept and killed me. I am the ghost of him whom you once called the great White Stag. I am now the spirit of this mountain and watch over it. When the moon shines over the peak you will see me leaping through the clouds and now and again leaping down the mountain side into the water."

"O great White Stag," said Turtle, "you have done a good deed. Your slayer shall be punished. When the *Ongwe* come we shall suffer, perhaps, but Timber Wolf shall suffer more, for we shall call out to the *Ongwe* when Timber Wolf prowls 'round."

"Begone, Timber Wolf," called out Turtle. "Know that you are hated and despised."

"I go," snarled Timber Wolf, "and I go hating all of you."

"Farewell," called out the great White Stag, leaping into the air and up to the clouds.

The fur-folk and the feather-folk looked in amazement as their friend sped away, and as they watched, they saw him descend from the clouds and drop down upon the mountain he loved.

"He was the great White Stag," said Turtle Chief, "but henceforth we shall call him by a new name; it shall be White Face, for it is the law of the forest that, once gone to the spirit world, the earth-name may not be used."

And so, forever after, all the forest-folk looked up to the mountain and called out to their friend White Face, who dwelt there.

When the *Ongwe Oweh* came, they often saw White Face leaping from crag to crag, up in the air and down into the lake. Well did they know their arrows never could reach him, for White Face was a ghost.

In the days when wisdom came and Ha-yo-wen-tha brought the truth, the story of White Face came to men, and then all who were *Ongwe Oweh* went out to hunt timber wolves and to kill them.

The wolves have gone from the great forest and not one ever visits the mighty mountain now, but the spirit of the great White Stag may still be seen, for it is he who guards the mountain, the lake, and the valley and brings sweet peace.

Look on a starry night when the sky is bright and the moon is low—look above the mountain, and you, too, shall see the ghost of the great White Stag.

## FIN M'COUL AND THE GIANT[1]

*Joseph Jacobs*

What Irish man, woman, or child has not heard of our renowned Hibernian Hercules, the great and glorious Fin M'Coul? Not one, from Cape Clear to the Giant's Causeway, nor from that back again to Cape Clear. And, by the way, speaking of the Giant's Causeway brings me at once to the beginning of my story.

Well, it so happened that Fin and his men were all working at the Causeway, in order to make a bridge across to Scotland; when Fin, who was very fond of his wife Oonagh, took it into his head that he would go home and see how the poor woman got on in his absence. So, accordingly, he pulled up a fir tree, and, after lopping off the roots and branches, made a walking stick of it, and set out on his way to Oonagh.

Oonagh, or rather Fin, lived at this time on the very tiptop of Knockmany Hill, which faces a cousin of its own that rises up, half-hill, half-mountain, on the opposite side.

There was at that time another giant, named Cuhullin—some say he was Irish, and some say he was Scotch—but whether Scotch or Irish, no other giant of the day could stand before him. Such was his strength, that, when well-vexed, he could give a stamp that shook the country about him. The fame and name of him went far and near, and nothing in the shape of a man, it was said, had any chance with him in a fight. By one blow of his fists he flattened a thunderbolt and kept it in his pocket, in the shape of a pancake, to show to all his enemies when they were about to fight him.

Undoubtedly Cuhullin had given every giant in Ireland a considerable beating, barring Fin M'Coul himself. He swore that he would never rest, night or day, winter or summer, till he would serve Fin with the same sauce, if he could catch him. However, the short and long of it was that Fin heard Cuhullin was coming to the Causeway to have a trial of strength with him. So at once he was seized with a very warm and sudden fit of affection for his wife, poor woman, leading a very lonely life in his absence. He accordingly pulled up the fir tree, as I said before, and having made it into a walking stick, set out to see his wife on the top of Knockmany.

In truth, the people had wondered very much why it was that Fin selected such a windy spot for his dwelling-house, and they even went so far as to tell him as much.

"What can you mane, Mr. M'Coul," said they, "by pitching your tent upon the top of Knockmany, where you never are without a breeze, day or night, winter or summer, and where there's the sorrow's own want of water?"

"Why," said Fin, "ever since I was the height of a round tower, I was known to be fond of a good view; and where, neighbors, could I find a better spot for a good view than the top of Knockmany? As for water, I am sinking a pump, and, please goodness, as soon as the Causeway's made, I intend to finish it."

Of course the real state of the case was that he pitched upon the top of Knockmany in order that he might be able to see Cuhullin coming towards the house. All we have to say is, that if he wanted a spot from which to keep a sharp lookout—and, between ourselves, he did want it grievously—he could not have found a neater or more convenient situation for it.

"God save all here!" said Fin, good-humoredly, on putting his honest face into his own door.

"Fin, an' you're welcome home, you darlin' bully!" Here followed a smack that is said to have made the waters of the lake at the bottom of the hill curl, as it were, with kindness and sympathy.

Fin spent two or three happy days with Oonagh, and felt himself very comfortable considering the dread he had of Cuhullin.

[1] From Joseph Jacobs, *Celtic Fairy Tales.*

This, however, grew upon him so much that his wife could not but see there was something on his mind which he kept altogether to himself. Let a woman alone, and she will wheedle a secret out of her good man. Fin proved this.

"It's this Cuhullin," said he, "that's troubling me. When the fellow gets angry, and begins to stamp, he shakes a whole town; and it's well known that he can stop a thunderbolt, for he always carries one about him in the shape of a pancake, to show to any one that might misdoubt it."

As he spoke, he clapped his thumb in his mouth, which he always did when he wanted to find out something; and the wife asked him what he did it for.

"He's coming," said Fin; "I see him below Dungannon."

"An' who is it, dear?"

"That Cuhullin," replied Fin; "and how to manage I don't know. If I run away, I am disgraced; and I know that sooner or later I must meet him, for my thumb tells me so."

"When will he be here?" said she.

"Tomorrow, about two o'clock," replied Fin, with a groan.

"Well, my bully, don't be cast down," said Oonagh; "depend on me, and maybe I'll bring you better out of this scrape than ever you could bring yourself, by your rule o' thumb."

She then made a high smoke on the top of the hill, after which she put her finger in her mouth, and gave three whistles. By that Cuhullin knew he was invited to Knockmany—for this was the way that the Irish long ago gave a sign to all strangers and travelers, to let them know they were welcome to come and take share of whatever was going.

In the meantime, Fin was very melancholy, and did not know what to do, or how to act at all. Cuhullin was an ugly customer to meet with; and, the idea of the pancake flattened Fin's very heart. What chance could he have, strong and brave though he was, with a man who could, when put in a passion, walk the country into earthquakes and knock thunderbolts into pancakes? Fin knew not on what hand to turn. Right or left—backward or forward—where to go he could form no guess whatsoever.

"Oonagh," said he, "can you do nothing for me? Where's all your invention? Am I to be skivered like a rabbit before your eyes, and to have my name disgraced forever in the sight of all my tribe, and me the best man among them? How am I to fight this man-mountain—this huge cross between an earthquake and a thunderbolt?—with a pancake in his pocket that was once—"

"Be easy, Fin," replied Oonagh; "I'm ashamed of you. Talking of pancakes, maybe, we'll give him as good as any he brings with him—thunderbolt or otherwise. If I don't treat him to as smart feeding as he's got this many a day, never trust Oonagh again. Leave him to me, and do just as I bid you."

This relieved Fin very much; for, after all, he had great confidence in his wife, knowing, as he did, that she had got him out of many a difficulty before.

Then Oonagh sent round to the neighbors and borrowed one and twenty iron griddles, which she took and kneaded into the middle of one and twenty cakes of bread. She baked the cakes on the fire in the usual way, setting them aside in the cupboard as they were done. She then put down a large pot of new milk, which she made into curds and whey.

Having done all this, Oonagh sat down quite contented, waiting for Cuhullen's arrival on the next day about two o'clock. That was the hour at which he was expected—for Fin knew as much by his thumb. Now this was a curious property that Fin's thumb had.

At length, the next day, Cuhullin was seen coming across the valley, and Oonagh knew that it was time to commence operations. She immediately brought the cradle, and made Fin to lie down in it, and cover himself up with the clothes.

"You must pass for your own child,"

said she; "so just lie there snug, and say nothing, but be guided by me."

About two o'clock, as he had been expected, Cuhullin came in. "God save all here!" said he; "is this where the great Fin M'Coul lives?"

"Indeed it is, honest man," replied Oonagh; "won't you be sitting?"

"Thank you, ma'am," says he, sitting down; "you're Mrs. M'Coul, I suppose?"

"I am," said she; "and I have no reason, I hope, to be ashamed of my husband."

"No," said the other, "he has the name of being the strongest and bravest man in Ireland; but for all that, there's a man not far from you that's very desirous of taking a shake with him. Is he at home?"

"Why, no," she replied; "and if ever a man left his house in a fury he did. It appears that some one told him of a giant called Cuhullin being down at the Causeway to look for him, and so he set out to try if he could catch him. I hope, for the poor giant's sake, he won't meet with him, for if he does, Fin will make paste of him at once."

"Well," said the other, "I am Cuhullin, and I have been seeking him these twelve months, but he always kept clear of me; and I will never rest night or day till I lay my hands on him."

At this Oonagh set up a loud laugh of great contempt, and looked at him as if he were only a mere handful of a man.

"Did you ever see Fin?" said she, changing her manner all at once.

"How could I?" said he. "He always took care to keep his distance."

"I thought so," she replied. "I judged as much; and if you take my advice, you poor-looking creature, you'll pray night and day that you may never see him, for I tell you it will be a black day for you when you do. But, in the meantime, you see that the wind's blowing on the door, and as Fin himself is from home, maybe you'd be civil to turn the house, for it's always what Fin does when he's here."

This was a startler even to Culhullin; but he got up, however, went outside, and getting his arms about the house, turned it as she had wished. When Fin saw this, he felt the sweat of fear oozing out through every pore of his skin; but Oonagh, depending upon her woman's wit, felt not a whit daunted.

"When, then," said she, "as you are so civil, maybe you'd do another obliging turn for us, as Fin's not here to do it himself. You see, after this long stretch of dry weather we've had, we feel very badly off for want of water. Now, Fin says there's a fine spring-well somewhere under the rocks behind the hill here below, and it was his intention to pull them asunder; but having heard of you, he left the place in such a fury, that he never thought of it. Now, if you would try to find it, I'd feel it a kindness."

She brought Cuhullin down to see the place, which was then all one solid rock. After looking at it for some time, he stooped down and tore a cleft about four hundred feet deep and a quarter of a mile in length, which has since been christened by the name of Lumford's Glen

"You'll now come in," said she, "and eat a bit of such humble fare as we can give you. Fin, even although he and you are enemies, would scorn not to treat you kindly in his own house. Indeed, if I didn't do it even in his absence, he would not be pleased with me."

She accordingly brought him in, and placing half a dozen of the cakes before him, together with a can or two of butter, a side of boiled bacon, and a stack of cabbage, she desired him to help himself—for this, be it known, was long before the invention of potatoes. Cuhullin put one of the cakes in his mouth to take a huge whack out of it. Then he made a thundering noise, something between a growl and a yell. "Blood and fury," he shouted; "how is this? Here are two of my teeth out! What kind of bread is this you gave me."

"What's the matter?" said Oonagh coolly.

"Matter!" shouted the other again; "why here are the two best teeth in my head gone."

"Why," said she, "that's Fin's bread—the only bread he ever eats when at home; but, indeed, I forgot to tell you that nobody can eat it but himself and that child in the cradle there. I thought, however, that as you were reported to be rather a stout little fellow of your size, you might be able to manage it. I did not wish to affront a man that thinks himself able to fight Fin. Here's another cake—maybe it's not so hard as that.

Cuhullin at the moment was not only hungry, but ravenous, so he accordingly made a fresh set at the second cake, and immediately another yell was heard twice as loud as the first. "Thunder and gibbets!" he roared, "take your bread away, or I will not have a tooth in my head; there's another pair of them gone!"

"Well, honest man," replied Oonagh, "if you're not able to eat the bread, say so quietly, and don't be waking the child in the cradle there. There now, he's awake!"

Fin now gave a howl that startled the giant, as coming from such a youngster as he was supposed to be. "Mother," said he, "I'm hungry—get me something to eat." Oonagh went over, and putting into his hand a cake that had no griddle in it, Fin, whose appetite in the meantime had been sharpened by seeing eating going forward, soon swallowed it. Cuhullin was thunderstruck, and secretly thanked his stars that he had the good fortune to miss meeting Fin, for, as he said to himself, "I'd have no chance with a man who could eat such bread as that, which even his son that's but in his cradle can munch before my eyes."

"I'd like to take a glimpse at the lad in the cradle," said he to Oonagh; "for I can tell you that the infant who can manage that nutriment is no joke to look at."

"With all my heart," replied Oonagh. "Get up, dear, and show this decent little man something that won't be unworthy of your father, Fin M'Coul."

Fin, who was dressed for this occasion as much like a baby as possible, got up, and said to Cuhullin. "Are you strong?"

"Thunder an' 'ounds!" exclaimed the other, "what a voice in so small a chap!"

"Are you strong?" said Fin again. "Are you able to squeeze water out of that white stone?" he asked putting one into Cuhullin's hand. The latter squeezed and squeezed the stone, but in vain.

"Ah! you're a poor creature!" said Fin. "You a giant! Give me the stone here, and when I show what Fin's little son can do, you may judge of what my daddy himself is."

Fin then took the stone, and exchanging it for the curds, he squeezed the latter until the whey, as clear as water, oozed out in a little shower from his hand.

"I'll now go back," said he, "to my cradle; for I scorn to lose my time with any one that's not able to eat my daddy's bread, or squeeze water out of a stone. You had better be off before he comes back and catches you."

Cuhullin, seeing what he had seen, was of the same opinion himself. His knees knocked together with the terror of Fin's return. He accordingly hastened to bid Oonagh farewell, and to assure her, that from that day out, he never wished to hear of, much less to see, her husband. "I admit fairly that I'm not a match for him," said he, "strong as I am. Tell him I will avoid him as I would the plague, and that I will make myself scarce in this part of the country as long as I live."

Fin, in the meantime, had got back into the cradle, where he lay very quietly, his heart at his mouth with delight that Cuhullin was about to take his departure, without discovering the tricks that had been played on him.

"It's well for you," said Oonagh, "that he doesn't happen to be here, for it's nothing but hawk's meat he'd make of you."

"I know that," said Cuhullin; "never a thing else he'd make of me; so I'll be going."

Thus did Fin, through the wit and invention of Oonagh, his wife, succeed in overcoming his enemy by cunning, which he never could have done by force.

## THE FIRST HARP[1]

*Padraic Colum*

Upon a time that was neither your time nor my time, a man and his wife were living at the back of the hills yonder. They had been happy together when they were young, but now that they were getting aged they were not so happy. Misfortunes had come on them, and each misfortune left them less and less forbearing with each other.

So downcast did they become that they never went to a sport or a merrymaking; they got no new things to wear; they would look with surprise on people dressed in their best and going to amusements; they did not know when holidays came round: Hallowe'en would come, and they would have no apples to share with each other; Michaelmas would come, and they would kill no goose to feast themselves; May-day would come, and they would wonder to see the children going from door to door with flowers in their hands.

And if the goats strayed away and there was no milk for the supper, "It's because my husband doesn't mind what happens about the place that I've to eat dry bread tonight," the woman would say. And if she lost three halfpence out of the shilling she had got for something she sold in the market, the man would keep on blaming her for the rest of the day.

On times like these they would sit in the house remembering the miseries that had come on her or on him through the other. When they had been pleased with each other they had made no account of these miseries, but now when they were not pleased they remembered nothing else. One night as they sat in a house that had no fire they began going over the times when they had comforts and when they could do pleasant things together. In everything one remembered there was blame for the other. They lay down, each thinking they would clear the score by forsaking the other. And in the morning each put a hand in the cold ashes of their hearth and went away from the house.

They came to the seashore, the man not knowing that the woman was behind him, and the woman not knowing that the man was before her. This is what befell the man that morning. He saw how the beach stretched away without a rock breaking through its yellow sand, and he saw how the clouds sailed above, big and white, without even a gull stretching its wings under them. The waves could not be seen, for the tide was very far out. There was no mark to go towards, but the man went on. Then he heard a sound and he went towards where it came from. It was a long, strong, soughing sound, and then it became a soft, sighing, sinking sound, and between the sinking and the swelling there were other sounds—a whirring sound and a whispering sound, a lifting sound and a lulling sound. He went on and on, and at last he came to what they came from.

Lo and behold! there was a whale there, a great bulk upon the sands. But it was a whale that was only bones now; the flesh had been stripped off it, and the wind was going through its ribs and touching upon the slight bones that were like river-reeds inside the skeleton. And the sounds changing ever, never ceased—soughing, whirring, whispering, sighing. He stood listening to the music and forgetting everything that was upon his mind. And he saw his wife standing at the other end of the whale's bulk with wonder in her looks as she listened to the sinking and the swelling, the lifting and the lulling music that the wind made through the bones of the whale.

They went back talking about the wonder they had come upon. They had a meal in their house and still they talked about the wonder. Together they did the work that had to be done while they listened to the sounds that they thought they could hear.

One evening the man made a frame of

[1] From Padraic Colum, *The Big Tree of Bunlahy*.

pine-wood, strung strings loosely across it, and left it hanging in the doorway of the house. The wind made music on the strings. Then he had a dream; he knew that pieces of wood across the frame would make the sounds come stronger: he put two boards in the frame, and the wind upon the strings had a deeper sound.

Neighbors came to listen; the man was praised for the wonder he had made; rich people made gifts to the couple. Then the man made a frame on which the strings were drawn tightly; he made the sounds by striking his fingers across the strings—louder and more piercing sounds. He went from place to place playing this instrument, his wife going with him.

The King of the land heard about the instrument and the player; the man was brought to play before him. Sickness and sleeplessness left the King—so much did the music do for him. And the man and his wife were given riches so that they might stay always with him. They lived there content with themselves and content with each other. And the instrument that the man made was called a Harp, and the man himself was Cendfind, the first Harp-player in Ireland.

## THE HEROES OF ASGARD[1]

*A.* and *E. Keary*

In the beginning of ages there lived a cow, whose breath was sweet, and whose milk was bitter. This cow was called Audhumla, and she lived all by herself on a frosty, misty plain, where there was nothing to be seen but heaps of snow and ice piled strangely over one another. Far away to the north it was night, far away to the south it was day; but all around where Audhumla lay, a cold, grey twilight reigned. By and by a giant came out of the dark north, and lay down upon the ice near Audhumla. "You must let me drink of your milk," said the giant to the cow; and though her milk was bitter, he liked it well, and for him it was certainly good enough.

After a little while the cow looked all round her for something to eat, and she saw a very few grains of salt sprinkled over the ice; so she licked the salt, and breathed with her sweet breath, and then long golden locks rose out of the ice, and the southern day shone upon them, which made them look bright and glittering.

The giant frowned when he saw the glitter of the golden hair; but Audhumla licked the pure salt again, and a head of a man rose out of the ice. The head was more handsome than could be described, and a wonderful light beamed out of its clear blue eyes. The giant frowned still more when he saw the head; but Audhumla licked the salt a third time, and then an entire man arose—a hero majestic in strength and marvelous in beauty.

Now it happened that when the giant looked full in the face of that beautiful man, he hated him with his whole heart, and, what was still worse, he took a terrible oath, by all the snows of Ginnungagap, that he would never cease fighting until either he or Buri, the hero, should lie dead upon the ground. And he kept his vow; he did not cease fighting until Buri had fallen beneath his cruel blows. I cannot tell how it could be that one so wicked should be able to conquer one so majestic and so beautiful; but so it was, and afterwards, when the sons of the hero began to grow up, the giant and his sons fought against them too, and were very near conquering them many times.

But there was of the sons of the hero one of very great strength and wisdom, called Odin, who, after many combats, did at last slay the great giant, and pierced his body through with his keen spear, so that the blood swelled forth in a mighty torrent. And all the hideous giant brood were destroyed excepting one, who ran away panting and afraid.

After this Odin called round him his sons, brothers, and cousins, and spoke to

[1] From A. and E. Keary, *The Heroes of Asgard.*

them thus: "Heroes, we have won a great victory; our enemies are dead, or have run away from us. We cannot stay any longer here, where there is nothing evil for us to fight against."

The heroes looked round them at the words of Odin. North, south, east, and west there was no one to fight against them anywhere, and they called out with one voice, "It is well spoken, Odin; we follow you."

"Southward," answered Odin, "heat lies, and northward night. From the dim east the sun begins his journey westward home."

"Westward home!" shouted they all; and westward they went.

Odin rode in the midst of them, and they all paid to him reverence and homage as to a king and father. On his right hand rode Thor, Odin's strong, warlike, eldest son. On his left hand rode Baldur, the most beautiful and exalted of his children; for the very light of the sun itself shone forth from his pure and noble brow. After him came Tyr the Brave; the Silent Vidar; Hodur, who, alas! was born blind; Hermod, the Flying Word; Bragi, Haenir, and many more mighty lords and heroes; and then came a shell chariot, in which sat Frigga, the wife of Odin, with all her daughters, friends, and tirewomen.

Eleven months they journeyed westward, enlivening the way with cheerful songs and conversation, and at the twelfth new moon they pitched their tents upon a range of hills which stood near the borders of an inland sea. The greater part of one night they were disturbed by mysterious whisperings, which appeared to proceed from the seacoast, and creep up the mountain side; but as Tyr, who got up half a dozen times, and ran furiously about among the gorse and bushes, always returned saying that he could see no one, Frigga and her maidens at length resigned themselves to sleep, though they certainly trembled and started a good deal at intervals. Odin lay awake all night, however; for he felt certain that something unusual was going to happen. And such proved to be the case; for in the morning, before the tents were struck, a most terrific hurricane leveled the poles, and tore in pieces the damask coverings, swept from over the water furiously up the mountain gorges, round the base of the hills, and up again all along their steep sides right in the faces of the heroes.

Thor swung himself backwards and forwards, and threw stones in every possible direction. Tyr sat down on the top of a precipice, and defied the winds to displace him; whilst Baldur vainly endeavored to comfort his poor mother, Frigga. But Odin stepped forth calm and unruffled, spread his arms towards the sky, and called out to the spirits of the winds, "Cease, strange Vanir (for that was the name by which they were called), cease your rough play, and tell us in what manner we have offended you that you serve us thus."

The winds laughed in a whispered chorus at the words of the brave king, and, after a few low titterings, sank into silence. But each sound in dying grew into a shape; one by one the strange, loose-limbed, uncertain forms stepped forth from caves, from gorges, dropped from the tree-tops, or rose out of the grass—each wind-gust a separate Van.

Then Niörd, their leader, stood forward from the rest of them, and said, "We know, O mighty Odin, how you and your company are truly the Æsir—that is to say, the lords of the whole earth—since you slew the huge, wicked giant. We, too, are lords, not of the earth, but of the sea and air, and we thought to have had glorious sport in fighting one against another; but if such be not your pleasure, let us, instead of that, shake hands." And, as he spoke, Niörd held out his long, cold hand, which was like a windbag to the touch. Odin grasped it heartily, as did all the Æsir; for they liked the appearance of the good-natured, gusty chief, whom they begged to become one of their company, and live henceforth with them.

To this Niörd consented, whistled good-by to his kinsfolk, and strode cheerfully along amongst his new friends. After this they journeyed on and on steadily westward until they reached the summit of a lofty mountain, called the Meeting Hill. There they all sat round in a circle, and took a general survey of the surrounding neighborhood.

As they sat talking together Baldur looked up suddenly, and said, "Is it not strange, Father Odin, that we do not find any traces of that one giant who fled from us and escaped?"

"Perhaps he has perished," remarked Thor.

But Niörd pointed northward, where the troubled ocean rolled, and said, "Yonder, beyond that sea, lies the snowy region of Jötunheim. It is there the giant lives, and builds cities and castles, and brings up his children—a more hideous brood even than the old one."

"How do you know that, Niörd?" asked Odin.

"I have seen him many times," answered Niörd, "both before I came to live with you, and also since then, at night, when I have not been able to sleep, and have made little journeys to Jötunheim to pass the time away."

"This is, indeed, terrible news," said Frigga; "for the giants will come again out of Jötunheim, and devastate the earth."

"Not so," answered Odin, "not so, my dear Frigga; for here, upon this very hill, we will build for ourselves a city, from which we will keep guard over the poor earth, with its weak men and women, and from whence we will go forth to make war upon Jötunheim."

"That is remarkably well said, Father Odin," observed Thor, laughing amidst his red beard.

Tyr shouted, and Vidar smiled, but said nothing; and then all the Æsir set to work with their whole strength and industry to build for themselves a glorious city on the summit of the mountain. For days, and weeks, and months, and years they worked, and never wearied; so strong a purpose was in them, so determined and powerful were they to fulfill it. Even Frigga and her ladies did not disdain to fetch stones in their marble wheelbarrows, or to draw water from the well in golden buckets, and then, with delicate hands, to mix the mortar upon silver plates. And so that city rose by beautiful degrees, stone above stone, tower above tower, height above height, until it crowned the hill.

Then all the Æsir stood at a little distance, and looked at it, and sighed from their great happiness. Towering at a giddy height in the center of the city rose Odin's seat, called Air Throne, from whence he could see over the whole earth. On one side of Air Throne stood the Palace of Friends, where Frigga was to live; on the other rose the glittering Gladsheim, a palace roofed entirely with golden shields, and whose great hall, Valhalla, had a ceiling covered with spears, benches spread with coats of mail, and five hundred and forty entrance-gates, through each of which eight hundred men might ride abreast. There was also a large iron smithy, situated on the eastern side of the city, where the Æsir might forge their arms and shape their armor. That night they all supped in Valhalla, and drank to the health of their strong, new home, "The City of Asgard," Bragi, their chief orator, said it should be called.

## THE MAKING OF THE HAMMER[1]

*Emilie Kip Baker*

Among the gods there was one who was really unfit to be a god and to live in the shining city of Asgard. He was the cause of much trouble and mischief in his frequent journeys to the earth, and he brought evil upon even the gods themselves. But as Loki was the brother of Odin, he could not very well be banished from Asgard, so the gods endured his presence as best they could. Loki did many unkind things that the gods never heard of; but once he met with just punishment for his

[1] From Emilie Kip Baker, *Stories from Northern Myths.*

meanness. This was the time that he robbed Sif of her golden hair.

Sif was the wife of Thor, the god of Thunder. She had beautiful long hair which fell over her shoulders like a shower of gold, and of this she was very proud. One day Sif fell asleep on the steps of Thor's palace, and while she lay there sleeping Loki came walking by. There was nothing so dear to Loki as a chance to do mischief, and he never saw anything beautiful without wishing to spoil it; so when he found Sif fast asleep, he stole up softly behind her and cut off all her golden hair.

When Sif woke at last and saw what had happened, she began to cry bitterly, for her golden hair was the pride and joy of Thor, and she was afraid that he would never want to look at her again now that it was gone. So she got up from the steps where she was sitting, and went away to hide in the garden. When Thor came home, he looked for her all through the palace, and went from room to room calling her name. Not finding her in the house, he went out into the garden, and after searching for a long time finally found poor Sif behind a stone, sobbing bitterly. When he heard her story, he tried to comfort her the best he could, but Sif continued weeping and covered her shorn head with her arms.

"I know who did this shameful thing," cried Thor, wrathfully; "it was that mischief-maker Loki, but this time he shall pay dearly for his wickedness." And he strode out of the palace with a look so threatening that even the gods might have trembled before him. Now Loki was not expecting to be caught so soon, and he had not thought of seeking a hiding place; so when Thor came suddenly upon him he was too frightened to try to escape. He even forgot his ready lies, and when Thor shook him angrily and threatened to kill him for his wicked act, he made no denial, only begged for mercy and promised to restore to Sif the hair he had cut off. Thor therefore released him, after binding him by a solemn oath to fulfill his promise.

The real hair which Loki had cut off he had already lost, so to keep his word to Thor he must find something else which would resemble it closely enough to make Sif believe she had indeed her own hair again. As there was only one place where skillful and cunning work like this could be done, Loki crossed the rainbow bridge that spans the gulf between Asgard and the earth, and hurried to the tall mountain which hides, amid its rocks, the entrance to the lower world. No one but a god, or one of the swarthy elves themselves, could have found this hidden opening, but Loki knew it well.

He first looked for a tiny stream which flowed along at the foot of the mountain. This he followed to its source in a deep cave among the rocks, and when he came to the spot where it bubbled up from the ground, he raised a huge log that was lying, apparently by chance, close beside it. This disclosed a small passage leading down into the very center of the earth, and along this path Loki hastened, often stumbling about in the darkness, until he came to the underworld where lived the swarthy elves. They were busily engaged in their wonderful workshop, which was lighted only by the fires from the forge, but when they saw Loki they laid down their tools and asked him how they could serve him.

"I have a task," answered Loki, "which requires such great skill to perform that I hardly dare ask you to attempt it. It is nothing less than for you to make of your gold some locks of hair that will be as soft and fine and beautiful as the golden hair which adorns the head of Sif, the wife of Thor. You have heard, no doubt, of its beauty, so you know how difficult a task I have given you."

The dwarfs, nothing daunted, set at once to work, and selecting a bar of perfect gold, they pounded it very soft, then spun it into threads so fine that they looked like sunbeams, and so soft that they felt like silk. When the work was finished and placed in Loki's hand, it exceeded in beauty anything he had ever seen, and he felt sure that Thor could not complain of his gift.

Then he thanked the swarthy elves and hastened with his prize back to Asgard and to the palace of Thor, where all the gods had assembled to see the fulfillment of Loki's promise.

In spite of the success of his undertaking, the fear of Thor's hasty temper kept Loki somewhat humbled, for the Thunderer had been known to crush the object of his anger with his hammer when once his wrath was fully roused. His face was now dark and threatening as Loki approached, and beside him stood Sif, weeping bitterly, and trying to cover her head with her hands. But Loki came up boldly and placed upon her head the golden hair which the elves had made. To the astonishment of all, it immediately grew fast, and no one could have told that it was not her own golden hair. So Sif was proud and happy once again, and Loki was forgiven.

When Loki went to the underground home of the elves to find the golden hair for Sif, he thought that it would be as well to get two other gifts—one for Odin and one for Freyr—so that their anger would fall less heavily on him for his cruelty to Thor's beautiful wife. The dwarfs were always very glad to help Loki when he was in trouble, for they, too, delighted in mischief-making; so when he asked them for the two other gifts, they gladly set to work. The spun-gold hair they had already placed in Loki's hands; and now they hurried about, getting together a hundred different materials to use in their work—for things of earth, air, fire and water went into the making of the wonderful gifts that came from the hands of the dwarfs.

In a short time they handed to the waiting god a spear that would always hit the mark no matter how badly it was thrown, and a marvelous boat that would fold up into a tiny package, but could also expand large enough to hold all the gods and goddesses in Asgard. Loki was delighted with these gifts and hurried with them back to Odin's council hall where the gods had assembled to pass judgment on him for his cruel treatment of Sif.

Though the hair of spun gold proved to be so perfect that Loki had nothing to fear from Thor's anger, he saw that Odin was still displeased and was looking at him with stern brows. So the wily god produced his two other gifts, and handed the spear to Odin and the boat to Freyr. Both the gods were delighted with the clever workmanship of the elves; and all the company were so busy examining Loki's gifts that they did not notice the dwarf Brock, who had followed Loki to Asgard and was now standing in the shadow of Odin's throne.

When the gods grew loud in their approval of the magic spear and boat, Brock could contain his anger no longer and cried out: "Can you find nothing better than those petty toys to praise? My brother Sindri can make far more wonderful things than these." At this boastful interference Loki grew very angry and said: "Prove it, then; for I know that your brother is only a stupid workman. Let us make a wager that you cannot bring here three gifts better than those you scorn; and whichever of us loses in the contest shall pay for it with his head." Brock accepted the challenge and set off at once to the cave where Sindri kept his dwarfs at work night and day.

He told his brother of the wager he had made with Loki, and Sindri laughed. Then he made ready a huge fire, and as he worked busily over his tools he bade Brock keep the bellows going as hard as he could so that the flames would leap higher and higher. Then, when he thought the right moment had come, he threw into the fire a pigskin; and bidding Brock keep steadily at work on the bellows, he left the cave.

The dwarf blew hard at the fire, and the forge gleamed so brightly that the whole cave was lit up, and Brock could see the piles of gold and silver and glittering gems that lay all around. Then suddenly an enormous gadfly flew into the room; and, lighting on his hand, stung him so badly that he roared with pain. Still he did not take his hand from the bellows, for, with the cunning of his race, he knew that the gadfly was none other than Loki, who had taken this form, hoping to spoil Sindri's work.

When the master-smith returned, he looked eagerly at the forge and saw that the fire glowed as brightly as ever. So he muttered a few magic words over the flames and drew forth a golden boar. This he handed to his brother, saying that the boar had the power to fly through the air, and shed light from his golden bristles as he flew. Brock was so much pleased with this gift that he said nothing about his swollen hand; and when Sindri asked him to keep his place at the bellows, he willingly agreed.

The smith then threw a lump of gold into the flames; and bidding Brock keep the fire at white heat, he again left the cave. Brock began to work harder than ever at the bellows; and as the fire glowed so that it seemed like daylight in the room, the gadfly flew at him and stung him on the neck. He screamed with pain and tried to shake off his tormentor, but still he kept faithfully at his work and never lifted his hand a moment from the bellows. When Sindri returned, he found the fire glowing brightly, and, leaning over it, he pulled out of the flames a fine gold ring, which every ninth night would drop nine gold rings as wonderful as itself.

Brock was so delighted with this gift that he almost forgot about his wounded neck; and obediently kept his place at the bellows. Then Sindri threw a lump of iron into the fire, and bidding his brother work steadily at his task, for this was the most important gift of all—he went out of the cave. Brock grasped the bellows firmly, and began to work with all his might. Just as the flames were leaping fiercely and the room seemed lit by a million candles, the gadfly flew at Brock and stung him between the eyes.

The dwarf was almost frantic from the pain of the wound. But though dazed and blinded so that he could hardly see the fire, he kept doggedly at work on the bellows, only lifting one hand for a moment to wipe the blood from his eyes. The fire had been glowing like a furnace, but in that one instant the flames burned less brightly, and Sindri—who had just entered the room—began to berate his brother for his carelessness. Then the smith drew out of the fire a mighty hammer, perfect in every way except that the handle was too short, owing to Brock's having lifted his hand a moment from the bellows.

Sindri gave the three gifts to his brother, and bade him hasten to Asgard, and bring back the head of Loki as payment for the lost wager. When the dwarf reached Odin's council hall, the gods had assembled to decide the contest, for everyone was eager to see what gifts Sindri had sent. Brock handed the ring to Odin, who praised it highly and said, "Now, I shall never want for gold." Freyr was delighted with his gift of the golden boar and said that it would be much more entertaining to ride on its back than in Loki's magic boat. Lastly, Brock gave the strong, wonderful hammer to Thor, saying, "Here is a hammer which can crush mountains, can cause lightning and thunder when it swings through the air, and will always come back to your hand no matter how far you may throw it." Then the dwarf turned to Odin and said, "Decide now between Loki and me, O Wise One, and declare whose gifts are worth most to Asgard."

Though the gods were reluctant to condemn one of their number in favor of a dwarf, there was no disputing the fact that Thor's hammer was worth more than all of Loki's gifts, for it meant a sure protection to Asgard from the attacks of the frost-giants. So Odin declared that Brock had won the wager, and that Loki must pay the forfeit with his head. Now Loki had no intention of submitting to this decree, so he first offered the dwarf a huge sum of money as a ransom; but Brock angrily refused the gold, and insisted that the bargain should be kept. Then Loki cried out, "Well, you must catch me first," and sped off on his magic shoes, which could carry him through the air and over the water with wonderful swiftness. As Brock knew he could never catch the figitive, he grew black with rage, and turned upon Odin, crying, "Is this the way that the gods keep faith, or shall the word of Odin stand fast?" Now all the company knew well that a promise made by even the meanest among them must be held sacred; so Odin sent Thor after Loki. In his swift chariot, drawn by the snow-white goats, the Thunderer easily overtook the runaway and brought him back to Asgard. Then Loki saw that he must save his life by cunning, and he said to Brock, "You may take my head if you wish, but you must not touch my neck."

Now as this was obviously impossible, the dwarf knew that he was outwitted by the crafty Loki, so he went away fuming with rage and disappointment. But before he left Asgard, he took out of his pocket an awl and a thong, and sewed Loki's lips together so that, for a while at least, the tricky god could not do any more boasting.

## SIGURD THE VOLSUNG[1]

*Dorothy Hosford*

Of the race of the sons of Odin were born many brave heroes who performed mighty deeds. One was Sigurd, whose feats of valor are chronicled in song and story.

Now when the moon was full and the month of May had begun, Sigurd returned again to Regin. The King of the Dwarf Kind stood by his smithy and the light of the fire showed him dim-eyed and weary. And he spake to Sigurd:

"Hail, Son of the Volsungs! I have toiled as thou hast desired, and lo, there is the fateful blade."

Then Sigurd saw it lying on the grey ashes, and the hilt was ruddy and shining, and the edges pale and fine, and a gleam like the flame of lightning ran down to the very point of it and burned through the runes that were scored on its sides. No sound did Sigurd utter as he stooped down for his sword, but his lips moved as though the words of his desire spake within him. The blade leapt white over his head, then blazed like fire as he played it hither and thither, till he brought it down on the anvil with a fierce and mighty stroke. Then Sigurd cried aloud in his glory and held out the sword full length, as one who would show it to the world—for the edges were dulled no whit, but the anvil was cleft in twain.

Then turned the Volsung to Regin: "Now shall I work thy will. My father hath made me mighty, but I shall give thee the gold and the craft thou desirest, ere I wend my ways. For now thou hast failed me in nought, and the sword is a wondrous thing."

No word for a while spake Regin, and he looked down as a man that pondereth deeply. Then he spake, and his voice was no more weary:

"This Wrath of thine hath cleft what is hard and heavy. It shall shear the light and soft; come forth to the night and prove it."

So the twain went forth to the river, and the stream was swift and full, and the moon shone white upon it. Then Regin cast on the water a lock of fine-spun wool and held the sword in the water's edge. The wool spun round on the eddy, but when it met the blade's edge it was sheared in twain.

Then Regin spake: "It is good, this sword that I have wrought. And now thy work beginneth. Thy Wrath is alive and awake and the tale of thy deeds is begun."

Then the sword, which ever since has been called the Wrath of Sigurd, was laid in a golden sheath and the peace-strings were knit about it.

On the morrow after Sigurd had received his Wrath, he mounted Greyfell and rode toward the dwelling of Gripir, for he remembered the word of Gripir that he should return thence when he had won his sword and was girt and ready for the road that lay before him. So with the Wrath girded to his side, he wended his way across

[1] From Dorothy Hosford, *Sons of the Volsungs*. Adapted from William Morris, *Sigurd the Volsung*.

the wild heaths to the foot of the mountains. His grey eyes were bright and happy and he sang a song, for Sigurd's heart rejoiced that he had won his sword, and now should do the deeds of a man, yea, even the deeds of a Volsung.

When Sigurd reached his dwelling, Gripir greeted him with great friendliness, and they had talk together. And Sigurd asked of him how his life should go, because Gripir in his exceeding wisdom knew what things were to come, and what was fated to men. Gripir told Sigurd what his life should be, and the fate thereof, even as it afterwards came to pass. And Gripir gave Sigurd his blessing, and Sigurd departed and returned, as the sun set and the evening came on, to the dwelling of the kings.

On the day following, Sigurd the Volsung went forth again and by his side fared Regin, the Master of Masters. They left the dwelling of the kings and rode throughout the day, till in the evening they had left the plain behind and the hills were about them. They wended their way higher and higher, nor rested till it was midnight. When they awakened in the early dawning, far away they could see the land of the Helper, and the valleys and meadows, but before them rose the sheer wall of the mountains.

Then spake the Master of Masters: "We have come to the gate of the mountains. Behind thee there is youth and rest, and many a pleasure. And mayhap I could find rest and a peaceful end to my years. We have come to the gate of the mountains. Thinkest thou we should fare further?"

"Yea, and what else?" answered Sigurd. "Unless thy tale was but lies and mockeries."

"It was sooth, it was sooth," said Regin, "and more I might have told thee had I heart and space to remember."

But Regin hung his head as he spake these words, and there was fear in his face. Then he spake again:

"Thou art grown wise-hearted and thou knowest my thought. It were well if thine eyes were blinder, and we each were faring alone. But times I dream that thou hadst neither father nor mother; that I alone have wrought thee, a bright and glorious thing, to work my will. Then my hope riseth and I behold the day that is to come and the world moulded to my desires. But then I awake and remember that thou art the son of Sigmund and the Sword of the Branstock is in thy hand. Ah, if only the world might run backward to the days of the dwarfs!"

But Sigurd heeded not the words of Regin, nor answered him. He leapt aback of Greyfell, and the sun rose and the heavens glowed above him like the bowl of Baldur's cup. And the golden light streamed over him till he seemed himself the very heart of the sun. Then Sigurd cried to Greyfell and rode swift for the pass in the mountains, and Regin followed after.

Day-long they fared through the mountains, and the way was steep and treacherous. And when the moon rose up and the stars were shining, they slept on the ground. In the cold dawn they wakened, and Sigurd was fair and strong as he drew the girths of Greyfell's saddle. But Regin seemed old and like a ghost of that wan land, and his words were full of foreboding. But Sigurd was merry of heart and no fear of Regin's could turn him from the deed he had sworn to do. So for another day they rode and rode through the desolate mountains and slept again beneath the naked heavens. Again with the first light they arose, and on this morning Sigurd donned his war gear. And Regin asked of him:

"What is thine hope this morning, O Sigurd, that thou arrayest thyself in war gear to ride this world forlorn?"

"Who needeth hope," said Sigurd, "when the heart of the Volsungs turns to the Glittering Heath and the house of the serpent? I shall slay the foe of the gods, as thou didst bid me, and then with the gold and its curse shalt thou be left alone."

"O child," said the King of the Dwarf Kind, "when the last day comes and 'tis the end even of the gods, shalt thou praise thy hope and the gods that made this world?"

"Foe of the gods," said Sigurd, "now thou wouldst hide the evil thing, and the curse that is greater than thou, lest death should overtake thee. It is me, it is me thou fearest, if indeed I know thy thought; yea, me, who would light up all good and evil with the glare of the sword."

And Sigurd sprang aloft to the saddle as he spake these words, and the Wrath burned in its sheath by his side. The sun rose and the grey pass in the mountains was filled with the living light, and Regin turned from the glory with eyes that were blinded and dazed. But Sigurd, seated on Greyfell, gleamed in the light, and he spake in a great voice:

"O Regin, in good sooth, I have hearkened not nor heeded thy words of fear and of foreboding. Thou hast told thy tale and thy longing and to that I hearkened well. The deed shall be done tomorrow; let it lead thee up to heaven, or let it lead thee down to hell. Thou shalt have the measureless gold; with the blood and the might of thy brother thou shalt sate thy hunger, and this deed shall be mine and thine. But take heed for what followeth after! Let us each do after his kind! And for me, I shall do the deeds of men; to them shall I give my life days, and to the gods my glory to keep."

Then Sigurd shook the bridle reins of Greyfell and rode forth from the mountain pass and took his way to the westward. And Regin, little and dark, followed after. And now Regin forgot his fears and thought only of the gold that should be his. So they journeyed on and on, between high mountain walls, past dark fathomless lakes that held no fish, nor any sign of life. So they kept riding to the westward and the mountains were grown huge and their peaks reached to the very heavens. They rode through the noontide, and the sun grew low, nor even then did they tarry though the world was dark about them. On and on they rode, each man alone, through the night. And though the stars and the moon grew pale, no change came over the darkness, and no streak of dawn lit the sky.

In the blackness Sigurd felt for the walls of the pass, but though he rode first to one side and then the other, he found no wall before him. But lo, at last there came a glimmer in the sky, and the light grew, and a faint dawn came to the world. And Sigurd strained his eyes and all about him he saw a deserted land, barren and changeless as far as his eye could reach. Then his heart leapt up within him, for he knew that his journey was o'er, and here before him lay the first of the Glittering Heath. He drew the bridle and leaped down from Greyfell, and the Wrath burned in its sheath by his side, and on foot he wended his way through the grey light to meet the foe of the gods.

Sigurd saw nought of Regin, nor did he take any heed of him. He strode across the desert heath and Greyfell paced behind him. As he wended his way in that silence, a grey thing glimmered before him and became a mighty man, one-eyed and seeming ancient, and clad in cloud-grey raiment. A friendly man and glorious, and his face was smiling glad as he spake to Sigurd in a voice deep as the wind of winter:

"Hail, Sigurd! Give me thy greeting ere thou wendest thy ways alone!"

And Sigurd answered: "Hail! I greet thee, my friend and my fathers' friend."

"And whither," said the elder, "goest thou with the steed and the ancient sword?"

"To the house of the serpent, and the greedy king of the gold," said Sigurd.

"And wilt thou smite him, O Sigurd?" quoth the ancient grey-clad one.

"Yea, I shall smite," said the Volsung, "unless the gods be against me."

"And how," said the elder, "shalt thou smite, so that thou thyself be not devoured?"

"I have this sword," said Sigurd, "and the sword shall find a way."

"Be learned of me," said the Wise One, "for I was the first of thy folk."

And Sigurd answered: "I shall obey thy bidding, and for thee I shall do the deed."

Then spake the Wise One: "Thus shalt thou do when thou wendest again on thy way. Thou shalt come to a path, a road in this desert place that is smooth and deep and hollow. The rains have not made it, nor hath any wild wind worn that furrow, for it is Fafnir's track whereby he wends to the water and the ancient pool when he is athirst in the dawning. There remember the greatness of thy fathers, and bare thy sword, and dig a pit in that highway. Lie thou in it, O Sigurd, and be as dead for a time, and when the worm passeth over thee, then shalt thou thrust him through."

Said Sigurd: "I shall obey thy bidding, and for thee shall I do the deed. For I love thee, thou friend of my fathers, and wise heart of the holy folk."

So spake the son of Sigmund, but lo, no man was near. So Sigurd went on his way till he came to the path of Fafnir, and it was a mighty track. And Sigurd drew forth his Wrath and dug the pit as he had been told, and lay therein. Now the worm came on his way, and afar off Sigurd could hear him roaring, as he dragged him over the earth. And the roaring grew as he came nearer, and he snorted forth venom before him. Sigurd trembled not nor was afraid, but lay waiting in his path. Then the dark rolled over Sigurd and the blackness covered him, and he thought on the glory of his fathers, and gathered his strength and with a mighty upward thrust, drove his sword through the heart of the serpent. Then he leapt from the pit and the rushing river of blood.

But there lay Fafnir wounded with the death stroke, and the folds of the serpent lay huddled on the plain. And forth from the Face of Terror came the sound of speech:

"Child, who art thou that hast smitten me? And whence is thy birth?"

"I am called the Wild Thing Glorious, and alone I wend on the earth," answered Sigurd.

And Fafnir spake again: "Fierce child, and who was thy father?"

Quoth Sigurd: "Am I like to the sons of men folk that my father I should know?"

"Wert thou born of a nameless wonder?" asked Fafnir. "Come, speak me the truth on this, my death day."

"I am Sigurd the Volsung, the son of Sigmund the King."

Said Fafnir: "What matter hath taught thee of death? Hast thou not heard how all men feared me?"

"I desired the deed, and the bright sword learned the way."

And Fafnir answered: "Thou hast done it, thou child of Sigmund, but the gold and the red rings shall bring thee evil."

"But I shall cast them abroad," quoth Sigurd, "so that all men may gather again."

Said Fafnir: "Thou art great in thine anger, and the Norns thou heedest not."

Then Sigurd asked: "O Fafnir, speak to me of the Norns and the wisdom thou hast from ancient days."

Said Fafnir: "Few things wilt thou do after my counsel, but take heed that thou shalt be drowned if thou farest unwarily over the sea; so bide thou rather on the dry land, and wait the coming of the calm tide."

Sigurd cried: "O Fafnir, tell me of the Norns ere thou layest down thy life."

And Fafnir said: "Many there are—and who shall name them all?—and they rule the lives of men folk."

"O Fafnir, what of the isle, and what name hath it, where the gods shall mingle the swords with Surt and the Sons of Flame?"

Said Fafnir: "Unshapen yet is that end and destruction of all things."

"What then shall endure, to tell the tale of the world, O Fafnir?"

"I know not," answered Fafnir, "but I know that this rattling gold and these red rings shall bring evil unto thee."

"Yet mine hand shall scatter the gold, and the earth shall gather it," spake Sigurd.

"Woe, woe," cried Fafnir, "in the days that are past the hoarded gold and the Helm of Aweing were mine. I overcame and was mighty, till I met thine hand, O Sigurd. And I fought and fell in the morning, and I die far off from the gold."

Then Sigurd leaned on his sword, and a dreadful cry went by on the wind, and Fafnir died. Then all sank into silence and

Sigurd stood alone on the desert by the pool of Fafnir's blood and before him lay the serpent, grey and dead.

So Sigurd stood, and now was Greyfell beside him, and Regin came from afar. He came afoot over the desert, and when he stood before Sigurd he stared at him and at the Wrath yet bloody and unsheathed, and at the serpent lying dead at the feet of Sigurd. Then Regin lay on the ground and drank the blood of the serpent where it lay in a pool. And he cried:

"Now shall I be free from the yoke that binds my soul to a withered body; now shall I have again the wisdom and might of the dwarfs."

And Regin turned and saw how Sigurd wiped the blood from his sword, and how above him a flock of mountain eagles screamed in the sky. And his mood grew dark and he came to Sigurd and spake:

"Child, thou hast slain my brother."

"Yea," answered Sigurd, "the deed is mine and thine. But now our ways shall go asunder."

But Regin crouched before him and spake: "Fare on to the murder of men and the deeds of thy kindred. Surely of thee and of them the tale shall be speedily told. Thou hast slain thy master's brother, and what wouldst thou say thereto if thou wert judged for it?"

Then spake Sigurd as before: "The deed is mine and thine. And now our ways shall sunder, and into the world will I pass."

But Regin darkened before him and grew exceeding grim: "Thou hast slain my brother, and wherewith wilt thou atone?"

"Stand up, O Master," cried Sigurd, "and take the wealth I have won for thee, ere we go our ways. I have toiled and thou hast desired, and the treasure is surely near, and thou hast the wisdom to find it."

But Regin cried to Sigurd: "Thou hast slain my brother."

"Take thou the gold," quoth Sigurd, "for the ransom of my head."

Again Regin cried: "Thou hast slain my brother, and today shalt thou be my cook boy and this heath my cooking hall."

And Regin crept to the coils of the serpent and drew a glaive from his side and cut the heart from Fafnir. Overhead the flock of wild eagles circled about. Then Regin spake to Sigurd:

"Wilt thou be free of this slaying? Then build thou a fire and roast the heart for me, that I may eat it and live, and be thy master and more, for therein was might and wisdom. Or else, depart on thy ways afraid from the Glittering Heath."

Then Regin lay on the ground and slept, but his sword lay bare by his side with his hand on the hilt. He seemed a fearful thing as he lay and dreamed of the power that should be his.

So Sigurd took the heart. He found waste wood on the heath, and he built a hearth of stones and kindled a fire, and he sat before it and sang as he roasted the heart. The eagles flew low about him, but he little heeded their cries. After the heart had roasted for a space, Sigurd reached his hand to see if the cooking were enough. But the blood and fat seethed forth and scalded Sigurd's finger and he put it quick in his mouth to quench the smart. And thus he tasted the flesh of the serpent and the blood of Fafnir's heart. Then there came a change upon him, for he knew the speech of fowl, and grew as wise in the ways of the beast kind as were the dwarfs of old.

And he knit brows and hearkened and began to understand the cries of the eagles that circled above. And wrath rose in his heart for he saw the net of evil and death that Regin sought to draw about him. For the eagles cried out a warning to Sigurd that Regin would wake from his sleep all-powerful and cunning with the ancient craft of the dwarf kind and that he would destroy Sigurd. Thus, from the beginning, had he planned. For the eagles cried:

"He hath reared up a king for the slaying, that he alone might live."

With the eagles crying about him, Sigurd rose swiftly and the Wrath gleamed in his hand. Regin lay in sleep, but his eyes glared wide-open and his hand was on his sword. And his lips smiled as he slept, for he dreamt that Sigurd was no more and that he at last was master of the world. But Sigurd saw the evil in Regin's heart and cried aloud in his wrath:

"Thou wouldst betray me and keep me here for my destruction, that my death might serve thy need. It is for this thou feared me and my sword. Lo then, here is the sword and the stroke! Let the Norns judge betwixt us! But I will not die the death of a tame thing, nor yield my hope to thee!"

Then the Wrath of Sigurd flashed thin and white and the head of Regin was severed from his body. And there in that desert place lay Regin, lifeless by the side of his brother, Fafnir, the Serpent. But Sigurd cried in triumph:

"The blind heart of the dwarf kind shall not rule the world. Dead are the foes of the gods!"

Then Sigurd himself ate of the heart of Fafnir and grew wise in the ancient wisdom of the dwarf kind. Then he leapt aback of Greyfell and rode forth in search of the treasure of Andvari. Sigurd followed the track of Fafnir, and still the eagles flew above him, until at length he reached the dwelling of the serpent. It was builded of unwrought iron and it went high to the heavens and reached deep into the earth, and there was nought within it save the heaped-up piles of gold.

Sigurd entered and beheld the wealth of Andvari's treasure. There was coin of ancient cities and war gear and spoils from the battlefield; there was rich ore from the depths of the earth where none but the dwarfs had mined; and tawny gold from the sands of rivers no man had discovered. And in the midst of all these riches glittered the Helm of Aweing and beside it the War Coat of Gold, the like of which there was not anywhere in the heavens or the earth. Sigurd beheld, moreover, Andvari's Ring of Gain, which Loki had so coveted.

Then laughed the son of Sigmund and set the ring on his hand. Then he donned the Helm of Aweing and its fellow, the War Coat of Gold. Then he labored to bring forth that treasure and he toiled and loaded Greyfell, though it seemed more than one horse might bear. And as Sigurd went about the work the eagles sang above him:

"Bind the red rings, O Sigurd! let the gold shine free and clear!
For what hath the son of the Volsungs the ancient Curse to fear?

"Bind the red rings, O Sigurd! for thy tale is well begun,
And the world shall be good and gladdened by the gold lit up by the sun.

"Bind the red rings, O Sigurd! and gladden all thine heart!
For the world shall make thee merry ere thou and she depart.

"Bind the red rings, O Sigurd! for the ways go green below,
Go green to the dwelling of Kings, and the halls that the Queen-folk know.

"Bind the red rings, O Sigurd! for what is there bides by the way,
Save the joy of folk to awaken, and the dawn of the merry day?

"Bind the red rings, O Sigurd! for the strife awaits thine hand,
And a plenteous war-field's reaping, and the praise of many a land.

"Bind the red rings, O Sigurd! But how shall storehouse hold
That glory of thy winning and the tidings to be told?"

Now when the steed was fully laden it was well on in the night, and the stars shone. Then Sigurd took Greyfell's reins and turned toward the wall of the mountains, for he deemed that the way from the Glittering Heath lay hence. But Greyfell would move not a whit for aught that Sigurd might do. Then Sigurd pondered a space, till he knew the will of Greyfell, and then, clad all in his war gear, he leapt into the saddle; and with a proud and mirthful toss of his head Greyfell sprang unspurred over the desert plain. Light and swift he went and breasted the wall of the mountains and climbed the summit. And the Glittering Heath, that dread place where the Serpent had so long held sway, was left behind.

When Sigurd had passed beyond the Glittering Heath he found himself in a place of great crags and mountains. Greyfell went swift and light and Sigurd turned somewhat to the southward, for he longed to hear again the speech of men and to be with his own kind. But the desert still endured and he had ridden a long road when, early on a morning, he saw before him a mighty mountain. The clouds about its top were lit with flame as though a great torch burned there. Sigurd turned toward the mountain, for from thence he deemed that he might look over the world and see which way was best to take.

So he rode higher and higher, and a strange light shone about him from those flame-lit clouds on the mountain's crest. Toward noon the clouds grew darker and settled thickly, hiding the top of the mountain from Sigurd's sight, but he kept riding ever higher and higher toward it. In the late afternoon the winds blew up and the clouds were cleared away and again Sigurd saw the mountain. But the light that had seemed a torch from afar off was now a blazing river of fire, and the mountain was black above it and below it, and the head of Hindfell rose like an island in the sunset sky.

Night fell, but yet Sigurd rode on and on, and had no thought of rest, for he longed to climb that mighty rock and look forth over the world. As he came among the foothills he could see the light no more, but the stars were lovely and gleaming above him. He rode on through a dark pass in the mountain till the stars were dimmed and the world grew cold with the dawn. Then afar off he beheld a breach in the rock wall and forth from it poured a flood of light. Swiftly Sigurd rode thither and found the place. He drew up Greyfell and gazed in wonder on the marvel before him.

Lo, the side of Hindfell was enwrapped by a fervent blaze and there was nought betwixt earth and heaven save a shifting world of flame. Sigurd cried to Greyfell and they hastened up and nearer, until he drew rein in the dawning, for before him the flames wove a great wavering wall. No wind could drive it back, nor could rain drench it, nor was there any opening or pause in it for the wayfarer to pass through. A mammoth wall of fire, it flamed before Sigurd. Sigurd trembled not, but smiled as the breath of it lifted up his hair, and his eyes shone bright with its image and his coat of mail gleamed white and fair. In his war helm the heavens and the waning stars behind him were reflected. But Greyfell stretched his neck to snuff at the flame wall and his cloudy flanks heaved. In the great light the gold of Andvari heaped upon the steed was waxen wan and pale.

Then turned Sigurd in his saddle and drew the girths tighter and shifted the hilt of his Wrath. Gathering up the reins, he cried aloud to Greyfell and rode straight at the wildfire's heart. But the flame wall wavered before him and parted and rose o'er his head, roaring wild above him. But he rode through its roaring as a warrior rides through a field of waving rye. The white flame licked his raiment and swept through Greyfell's mane. It covered Sigurd's hands and the hilt of his sword and wound about his helmet and his hair. But the fervent fire hurt him not, neither was his raiment marred nor his war gear dimmed.

Then of a sudden the flames failed and faded and darkened, and a heavy murkiness spread over the earth. Sigurd rode further till all was calm about him; then he turned his eyes backward. The side of Hindfell blazed no longer, but behind him on the scorched earth lay a ring of pale slaked ashes. And beyond it the waste world of crags and mountains lay hushed and grey in the early dawn.

Then before him Sigurd saw a Shield-burg, a wall of many shields wrought clear without a flaw. Silver shields gleamed beside those of gold and ruddy shields beside the white, and all were carved and blazoned brightly. The wall rose high to the heavens and o'er the topmost shield rim there hung, like a banner, a glorious golden buckler. It swayed in the morning breeze and rang against the staff that held it.

Sigurd leapt down from Greyfell and stood before the wall. It rose above him as though 'twere the very dwelling of the gods and he looked but little beneath it. He drew not his sword from its scabbard as he wended his way round the rampart. All was silent; 'twas only the wind and Sigurd that wakened any sound.

Then lo, he came to the gate, and its doors were open wide. No warder withstood his way and no earls guarded the threshold. Sigurd stood a while and marveled at such strangeness. Then his Wrath gleamed bare in his hand as he wended his way inward, for he doubted some guile of the gods, or some dwarf king's snare, or perchance a mock of the giant people that should fade before his eyes. But he took his way in and he saw the wall of shields, with the ruddy by the white and the silver by the gold, but within that wall no work of man was set. There was nought but the utmost head of Hindfell rising high. Then, as Sigurd gazed, he beheld below in the very midmost a giant-fashioned mound that was builded as high as the topmost rim of the shield wall. And there, on that mound of the giants, with nought but wilderness about, a pale grey image lay and gleamed in the early morn.

So there was Sigurd alone in that desert of wonder; and he went forward with the Sword of the Branstock high in his hand. He set his face toward the earth mound and beheld the image, with the dawn growing light about it; and lo, he saw 'twas the shape of a man set forth in that desert place on the tower top of the world. So Sigurd climbed the mound to see if the man were living or dead, and who it was that lay there: some king of the days forgotten, or mayhap the frame of a god, or e'en some glorious heart beloved laid far from earthly strife.

He stood over the body and saw that it was shapen fair and clad from head to foot-sole in pale grey-glittering mail as closely wrought as though it were grown to the flesh. A war helm, girt with a golden crown, hid the face from view. Sigurd stooped and knelt beside the figure, and he felt a breath as sweet as a summer wind come forth from the sleeping one. Then spake Sigurd to himself that he would look on the face and see whether it bore him love or hate and who it might be that so strangely rested here. So he drew the helm from the head, and lo, Sigurd beheld the snow-white brow, and the smooth unfurrowed cheeks, and the lightly breathing lips of a woman. A woman fair beyond all dreaming. And Sigurd looked, and he loved her sore, and longed to move her spirit and waken her heart to the world.

Gently he touched her and spake softly: "Awake! I am Sigurd." But she moved not.

Then looked Sigurd on the bare blade beside him. The pale blue edges burned brightly as the sun began to rise. The rims of the Shield-burg glittered and the east grew exceeding clear. Sigurd took the Sword of the Branstock and set the edge to the dwarf-wrought coat of mail where the ring-knit collar constrained the woman's throat. The sharp Wrath bit and rended the rings, and lo, white linen gleamed softly beneath the armor.

Sigurd drove the blue steel onward through the coat and the skirt of the mail, till nought but the rippling linen was wrapping her about. Then he deemed her breath came quicker, and he turned the Wrath and cut down either sleeve. Her arms lay white in her raiment and glorious sun-bright hair fell shining across her shoulders.

Then a flush came over her visage, a sigh stirred her breast, her eyelids quivered and opened, and slowly she awakened. Wide-eyed she gazed on the dawning, too glad to change or smile; nor did she speak, and moved but little. Motionless beside her Sigurd knelt, waiting her first words, while the soft waves of the daylight sped over the starless heavens. The gleaming rims of the Shield-burg grew bright and yet brighter in the rising sun, and the thin moon hung her horns dead-white in the golden glow.

Then she turned and gazed on Sigurd and her eyes met the Volsung's eyes, and mighty and measureless within him now swelled the tide of his love. Their longing met and mingled, and he knew in his heart that she loved, as she spake softly to him:

"What is the thing so mighty that hath torn my weary sleep?"

Sigurd answered: "The hand of Sigurd and the Sword of Sigmund's son, and the heart that the Volsungs fashioned have done this deed for thee."

But she said: "Where then is Odin who hath laid me here? Long is the grief of the world, and mankind's tangled woe!"

"Odin dwelleth above," said Sigurd, "but I dwell on the earth. And I came from the Glittering Heath to ride the waves of thy fire."

Even as he spake the sun rose upward and lightened all the earth, and the light flashed back to the heavens from the glorious gleaming shields. The twain uprose together, and as the risen sun bathed them in the light of the new day, she lifted her arms with palms outspread and cried:

"All hail, O Day and thy Sons, and thy kin
of the colored things!
Hail, following Night, and thy Daughter
that leadeth thy wavering wings!
Look down with unangry eyes on us today
alive,
And give us the heart's victorious, and the
gain for which we strive!

"All hail, ye Lords of God-Home, and ye
Queens of the House of Gold!
Hail, thou dear Earth that bearest, and
thou Wealth of field and fold!
Give us, your noble children, the glory of
wisdom and speech,
And the hearts and the hands of healing,
and the mouths and the hands that
teach!"

They turned then and embraced, and gladness and rejoicing filled their hearts. Spake Sigurd:

"Thou art the fairest of the earth, and the wisest of the wise; oh, who art thou? I am Sigurd, e'en as I told thee. I have slain the Serpent Fafnir and gotten the ancient gold. Great indeed were the gift of my days if I should gain thy love and we twain, through all of life, should never part. Oh, who art thou that lovest, thou who art fairest of all things born? And what meaneth thy lonely slumber here?"

Said she: "I am she that loveth. I was born of earthly folk, but long ago Allfather took me from the home of the kings and he called me the Victory Wafter. I came and went and at Odin's will chose the victor on the battlefield, and the slain for his war host; and my days were glorious and good. But the thoughts of my heart overcame me and pride in my wisdom and power, and I deemed that I alone could choose the slain, and scorned the will of Allfather. For that came my punishment. Allfather decreed that I should return again among men, to be one of them. But I cried: 'If I must live and wed in the world, and gather grief on the earth, then the fearless heart shall I wed. E'en there shall I fashion a tale brave and fair, that shall give hope to the Earth.'

"Allfather smiled somewhat, but he spake: 'So let it be! Still thy doom abideth. Fare forth, and forget and be weary 'neath the Sting of the Sleepful Thorn, and long shall the time pass over e'er the day of thy waking come.'

"So I came to the head of Hindfell and there the sleep thorn pierced me and the slumber fell on me, from which none might wake me save him who would not turn back from the waving flames of the wildfire. And that is the tale. Now I am she that loveth; and the day is near when I, who have ridden the sea realm and the regions of the land and dwelt in the measureless mountains, shall live once more in the house of my fathers. There shall the days be joyous.

"Lo, now, I look on thine heart and behold thine inmost will and know that thou wouldst have me tell thee of the days that shall be ours. But restrain thy desire, as thou restrainest the steed in the beginning of the battle, lest toward its ending his limbs grow weary and fail thee. Ask me not of the future, lest thou ask of the thing thou shouldst not and the thing 'twere better not to know.

"Know thou, most mighty of men, that the Norns shall order all things, and yet without thy helping, their will cannot come to pass. 'Tis strange, and the fool and the blind believe it not, but I know; I have seen it writ in the heavens. The evil days of the world are born of the malice and cowardice of men, but the fair days of the earth, when the sun shines and good is brought forth, they are fashioned of daring deeds and the eager hearts of love. So loosen thy sword in the scabbard and settle thy war helm firm, for men betrayed are mighty, and great are the wrongfully dead."

Then spake the maiden: "I have spoken these words, beloved, but 'tis thy heart and mine were speaking."

Again spake the son of Sigmund: "Fairest, and most of worth, thou knowest the ways of men folk. Then speak yet more of wisdom; for meseems it is most meet that my soul be shapen to thy soul."

She took his hand and there on the side of Hindfell their glad eyes looked and loved. And she told of the hidden matters whereby the world is moved; she told of the framing of all things, the houses of the heaven, the star worlds' courses, and how the winds be driven. She told of the Norns and their names, and the fate that abideth the earth. She told of the ways of the king folk, of the love of women, of the fall of mighty houses, of the friend that falters and turns, and the grief that endureth for long.

"Aye," the maiden spake, "but man shall bear and forbear, and yet is each man wise to do bravely and well that thing that the gods have given him to do. Wise is the sower that sows, and wise is the reaper that reaps, and wise shalt thou be to deliver. And lo, a glorious tale shall be told of thee, of thy sword and the wakening fire.

"Hark now, how Greyfell neighs and the gold of Fafnir gleams upon him. Green go the roads to the children of men and the deeds that thou shalt do. Come now, O Sigurd, for now is the high noon come and the sun hangs over Hindfell and looks on the homes of the earth folk. Thy soul is great within thee and glorious are thine eyes. And I long that we twain may see men's dwellings and the house where we shall dwell, the place of our life's beginning."

So they climbed the burg of Hindfell. Hand in hand they fared till all about and above them was nought but the sunlit air. Far away beneath lay the kingdoms of the earth and the place of men folk's dwellings: the rich and plenteous acres, the silver ocean's hem, and the woodland wastes and the mountains.

Then spake the Victory Wafter: "O Sigurd, as a god thou beholdest thine heritage. But now I bid thee pause and look on the land 'twixt the wood and the silver sea; there near the swirling river is the house where I was born. Mine earthly sister and the king that she hath wed dwell there. There in days gone by I woke on a golden bed, and noon by noon I wandered and plucked the blossoming flowers, and eve by eve I tarried amid the speech and the lays of kings. Brynhild was I called in the days ere my father died. That is the land of Lymdale betwixt the woodland and the sea."

"I shall seek thee there," said Sigurd, "when the spring is come, ere we wend the world together in the season of the sun."

"I shall bide thee there," said Brynhild.

Then from his hand Sigurd drew Andvari's ancient gold. There was nought but the sky above them as together they held the ring, the shapen ancient token that hath no change nor end.

Then cried Sigurd: "O Brynhild, now hearken while I swear that the sun shall die in the heavens and the day no more be fair, if I seek thee not in Lymdale in the house that fostered thee!"

And Brynhild cried: "O Sigurd, Sigurd, now hearken while I swear that the day shall die for ever and the sun to blackness wear ere I forget thee, Sigurd, as I wait in the land of Lymdale in the house that fostered me!"

Then Sigurd set the ring on Brynhild's finger and their arms were about each other and their hearts were full and glad. The day grew old about them and eve and the sunset came. The twilight changed and died and the stars shone forth on the world, ere they turned and went the roads that go green to the dwellings of men.

More befell Sigurd in the days that were to come, both of grief and of joy, but these were the deeds of his youth.

## PANDORA [1]

*Emilie Kip Baker*

In the days of long, long ago when men built altars and worshiped their gods in temples of pure white marble, Jupiter, the greatest of the gods, sat upon his throne on high Olympus and looked down upon the doings of men. The topmost peak of Mount Olympus was covered with clouds—so high it was above all the hills of Greece—and its slopes were thickly wooded.

Just how high the mountain really was could only be guessed, for no man had dared to climb even as high as the first cloud line; though the story goes that once upon a time a wandering shepherd, looking for a strayed lamb, had ventured far up the mountain side and had soon lost his way. He groped about blindly, as the mists began to thicken all around him, and the sound of his own footsteps terrified him in the dreadful silence that seemed to be suddenly creeping over him. Then a mighty tempest broke over his head, and the mountain shook to its very base. From the hand of wrathful Jupiter fierce thunderbolts were hurled, while the lightning flashed and gleamed through the darkness of the forest, searching out the guilty mortal who had dared to climb too high.

No human eye had ever seen the glories of Olympus, no human foot had ever stepped within its sacred halls, where the ceiling was of gold and the pavement of pearl and the thrones of the gods shone with a thousand glittering jewels. Of the life that was lived among the dwellers on Olympus, not even the poets could claim to know; but sometimes a tired soldier dozing by his camp fire dreamed dreams of this wonderful country where the immortal gods walked by night and day; and sometimes a lonely fisherman, looking across the blue waters of the Mediterranean to the crimsoning sunset, saw visions of youth and beauty and life that lasted for ever and ever and ever.

It was long before the memory of man that the gods first came to live on Mount Olympus, and it was still longer ago that Jupiter conquered all his jealous enemies, and made himself ruler of the gods. From his throne on Mount Olympus, Jupiter looked down upon the kingdoms that he had portioned out to each of his brothers; and he saw Neptune, the god of the sea, driving through the waves his chariot drawn by huge, misshapen sea-beasts that beat up the thick white foam until it glistened on the sea-king's beard and on his crown of shells and seaweed. The other kingdom was so far away that even the all-seeing eyes of Jupiter were strained to catch any glimpse of the shapes that moved noiselessly there, for this was the realm of Pluto, god of the underworld, that dread country of darkness and unending gloom, where no

[1] From Emilie Kip Baker, *Stories of Old Greece and Rome.*

ray of sunlight ever came, and where the sad spirits of the dead wept for the lost world of love and light and laughter.

In the early days of man's life on the earth, there was no sickness anywhere, nor any pain, nor sorrow. Men lived to be very old and very wise.

Then at length, the gods fashioned a creature that they called woman. To her each of the gods gave a gift such as softness, or grace, or wonderful fairness; but Jupiter added one other quality, curiosity, and he gave the woman the name of Pandora. Then he bade Mercury, who is the messenger of the gods, take this new soft thing down to the earth and give her to Epimetheus for his wife.

For some time Epimetheus and Pandora lived happily, and every day Epimetheus thanked the gods for their last and best gift to man. He never tired of watching Pandora chasing butterflies through the tall meadow grass, or making cups out of broad leaves, that she and Epimetheus might drink from the clear, cool spring.

One day as they were resting under the trees and eating their simple meal of dates and wild honey, they saw a traveler coming toward them. He was walking very slowly and seemed heavily burdened with what appeared to be a large box. While he was yet some distance off, Pandora ran to meet him and asked him to come into the shade and rest. The stranger was old, and the chest that he carried bent his shoulders almost to the ground. He looked hungry and thirsty and tired, so Epimetheus urged him to stop and rest, and offered him some freshly gathered dates.

The traveler—who was none other than Mercury in disguise—replied that he could not tarry with them, for he had a long distance yet to go. He asked them, however, to take care of his great oak chest, for with that burden off his shoulders he could hurry on and reach his journey's end before nightfall. He promised to come back for the chest a few days later. Epimetheus and Pandora were delighted to be of service to a stranger, and promised to guard the chest with great care. The traveler thanked them and turned away; but just as they were saying good-by, he mysteriously disappeared, and whichever way they looked there was no trace of him to be seen.

Epimetheus was not at all eager to know what was in the mysterious chest; but as soon as they sat down again under the trees, Pandora began to ask a thousand questions as to who the traveler might be and what the chest contained. Epimetheus begged her not to think any more about it, as nothing could be learned of the old man or his burden; but Pandora refused to be silent, and talked still more of the probable treasure that they were guarding for the stranger. At last Epimetheus got up angrily and walked away, wearied with her insistence.

Pandora went over to the chest, and kneeling down beside it, examined the exquisitely carved figures that were on all four sides. Then she studied the fine golden cord that bound the chest. It looked soft enough, and yet it was very strong; for it was made of strands of twisted gold and was tied at the end with a curious knot. There was no lock to be seen, and apparently nothing to hinder eager fingers from opening the lid when once the knot was unfastened and the golden cord unwound. Pandora's fingers itched to try her skill on the knot, and she felt sure that if she worked at it long enough, she could finally loosen it.

The figures carved on the lid were groups of dancing children, and in the very center was one figure whose face was so strange that Pandora sat for a long time staring at it. Now and then she turned away, and when she looked at the face again, it had a different expression from the one she had seen on it before. She knew that this carved thing was not alive, and yet each time she gazed into the strange eyes of the wooden face they were quite unlike the eyes that had smiled or frowned or mocked at her before.

She went to see whether Epimetheus had come back, and finding that he was still away, she returned to the chest again, but would not let herself be tempted into so much as touching the golden cord. As she stood wondering what to do, she thought that she heard some little voices coming from inside the chest, and they seemed to say:

"Open, Pandora, please, please open and let us out."

Pandora looked quickly around to see whether Epimetheus were in sight, then she came a bit nearer to the chest and put one hand on the golden cord. Again she heard the small voices, this time very distinctly, and they said:

"Open, Pandora, please, please open and let us out."

Pandora's heart was now beating fast. What *could* be in the chest? What poor imprisoned creatures were calling to her, begging her to set them free? She put both hands on the golden cord, then she looked guiltily around; but no one was in sight, no one was watching her except some inquisitive squirrels who were peering down at her from the branches just above her head.

Swiftly and deftly she untied the knot, which yielded easily to her eager fingers; but even then she hesitated, fearing the anger of Epimetheus.

The little voices cried again:

"Open, Pandora, please, please open and let us out."

Still she hesitated, not daring to raise the lid. Just then she heard her husband calling to her, and she knew that there would be no chance now to explore the contents of the mysterious chest. She must wait for that pleasure until another time; meanwhile she would take just one peep inside to be sure that the voices were not mocking her. So she raised the lid very gently, but no sooner had she made the smallest opening than out poured a host of tiny creatures like brown-winged moths; and they swarmed all around her, biting and pinching and blistering her soft skin until she cried out in fear and pain.

She tried to fight them off, and rushed away to find Epimetheus; but the tormenting little sprites followed her, buzzing about her ears and stinging her again and again. In vain she strove to brush them away, for they clung to her dress, her hair, and her swollen skin. When she reached Epimetheus she was crying bitterly, and it did not need any questioning to find out the trouble, for the malicious little creatures were so numerous that hundreds of them encircled Epimetheus, and bit and stung him just as they had done Pandora. In the unhappy hour that followed, while husband and wife bound soothing herbs on their bruised skin, Pandora told Epimetheus how her fatal curiosity had led her to open the chest and set free the host of evil things.

It was not, however, until later that they realized the extent of Pandora's folly, for the little brown-winged creatures were the spirits of evil that had never before entered the world. Their names were Sickness and Pain and Sorrow; Envy and Pride and Jealousy; Hunger, Poverty, and Death. All these ills had Jupiter put into the oak chest, and bound it with only a golden cord. He knew that sooner or later Pandora would open the chest, and then man's life of untroubled happiness would be forever at an end. Evil things would take up their dwelling on earth, and they would stay for always and always and always, as long as the world should last.

When Epimetheus and Pandora saw the hateful winged creatures settling down on the leaves and flowers so as to be near at hand to torment them, they wept bitter tears and wished that the gods had never created them. In the midst of her sobbing Pandora had not, however, forgotten about the chest, and she was still wondering what else might be inside it, for she was sure that those mothlike things could never have wholly filled it. Suddenly she heard a soft whisper coming from within the chest, and it said:

"Open, Pandora, please, please open and let me out."

Pandora stared in surprise, for she

thought that all the evil sprites had rushed out in that moment when she raised the lid. Was there, then, another host of tormenting things still there; and if so, should she let them out to add to her misery and pain?

Again the little soft voice cried:

"Open, Pandora, please, please open and let me out."

Pandora now called to Epimetheus, and together they listened to the pleading voice which was so very soft and sweet that they were sure it could not belong to any evil thing. Still Epimetheus was unwilling to risk bringing any more trouble into the world; but in spite of her remorse, Pandora was curious to see what it was that was begging so plaintively for freedom. So with Epimetheus' consent she opened the lid once more, and out fluttered a tiny little creature with beautiful gauzy wings. She flew straight to Pandora, then to Epimetheus, and at her touch all their hurts were healed and all their pain forgotten.

The name of this gentle messenger was Hope; and she had been hidden in the chest secretly by one of the pitying gods, who grieved that Jupiter was sending so many ills to fret mankind. The host of evil beings, once set free, could never again be shut up in their narrow prison; but wherever they flew—even to the remotest corner of the earth—Hope followed them and brought healing in her wings; and when the world grew wicked, as it did in the days that came after, so that men neglected the altars of the gods, Hope was still remembered with votive offerings and her shrines kept garlanded with flowers.

## THE WINGED HORSE[1]

*Nathaniel Hawthorne*

Once, in the old, old times a fountain gushed out of a hillside, in the marvelous land of Greece. And, for aught I know, after so many thousand years, it is still gushing out of the very selfsame spot. At any rate, there was the pleasant fountain, welling freshly forth and sparkling adown the hillside, in the golden sunset, when a handsome young man named Bellerophon drew near its margin. In his hand he held a bridle, studded with brilliant gems, and adorned with a golden bit. Seeing an old man, and another of middle age, and a little boy, near the fountain, and likewise a maiden, who was dipping up some of the water in a pitcher, he paused, and begged that he might refresh himself with a draught.

"This is very delicious water," he said to the maiden as he rinsed and filled her pitcher, after drinking out of it. "Will you be kind enough to tell me whether the fountain has any name?"

"Yes; it is called the Fountain of Pirene," answered the maiden; and then she added, "My grandmother has told me that this clear fountain was once a beautiful woman; and when her son was killed by the arrows of the huntress Diana, she melted away into tears. And so the water, which you find so cool and sweet, is the sorrow of her heart!"

"I should not have dreamed," observed the young stranger, "that so clear a well spring, with its gush and gurgle, and its cheery dance out of the shade into the sunlight, had so much as one teardrop in its bosom! And this, then, is Pirene? I thank you, pretty maiden, for telling me its name. I have come from a far-away country to find this very spot."

A middle-aged country fellow (he had driven his cow to drink out of the spring) stared hard at young Bellerophon, and at the handsome bridle which he carried in his hand.

"The watercourses must be getting low, friend, in your part of the world," remarked he, "if you come so far only to find the Fountain of Pirene. But, pray, have you lost a horse? I see you carry the bridle in your hand, and a very pretty one it is with that double row of bright stones upon

[1] From Nathaniel Hawthorne, *A Wonder Book for Boys and Girls.*

it. If the horse was as fine as the bridle, you are much to be pitied for losing him."

"I have lost no horse," said Bellerophon, with a smile. "But I happen to be seeking a very famous one, which, as wise people have informed me, must be found hereabouts, if anywhere. Do you know whether the winged horse Pegasus still haunts the Fountain of Pirene, as he used to do, in your forefathers' days?"

Then the country fellow laughed.

As you have probably heard, this Pegasus was a snow-white steed, with beautiful silvery wings, who spent most of his time on the summit of Mount Helicon. He was as wild, and as swift, and as buoyant, in his flight through the air, as any eagle that ever soared into the clouds. There was nothing else like him in the world. He had no mate; he never had been backed or bridled by a master; and, for many a long year, he led a solitary and a happy life.

Sleeping at night, as he did, on a lofty mountain top, and passing the greater part of the day in the air, Pegasus seemed hardly to be a creature of the earth. Whenever he was seen, up very high above people's heads, with the sunshine on his silvery wings, you would have thought that he belonged to the sky, and that, skimming a little too low, he had got astray among our mists and vapors, and was seeking his way back again. It was very pretty to behold him plunge into the fleecy bosom of a bright cloud, and be lost in it, for a moment or two, and then break forth from the other side. Or, in a sullen rainstorm, when there was a gray pavement of clouds over the whole sky, it would sometimes happen that the winged horse descended right through it, and the glad light of the upper region would gleam after him. In another instant, it is true, both Pegasus and the pleasant light would be gone away together.

In the summertime, and in fine weather, Pegasus often alighted on the solid earth, and, closing his silvery wings, would gallop over hill and dale for pastime. Oftener than in any other place, he had been seen near the Fountain of Pirene, drinking the delicious water, or rolling himself upon the soft grass of the margin. Sometimes, too (but Pegasus was very dainty in his food), he would crop a few of the clover-blossoms that happened to be sweetest.

To the Fountain of Pirene, therefore, people's great-grandfathers had been in the habit of going in hopes of getting a glimpse at the beautiful Pegasus. But, of late years, he had been very seldom seen. Indeed, there were many of the country folks, dwelling within half an hour's walk of the fountain, who had never beheld Pegasus, and did not believe that there was any such creature in existence. The country fellow to whom Bellerophon was speaking chanced to be one of those incredulous persons.

And that was the reason why he laughed.

"Pegasus, indeed!" cried he, turning up his nose as high as such a flat nose could be turned up—"Pegasus, indeed! A winged horse, truly! Why, friend, are you in your senses? Of what use would wings be to a horse? Could he drag the plough so well, think you? To be sure, there might be a little saving in the expense of shoes; but then, how would a man like to see his horse flying out of the stable window?—yes; or whisking him up above the clouds, when he only wanted to ride to mill? No, no! I don't believe in Pegasus. There never was such a ridiculous kind of a horse-fowl made!"

"I have some reason to think otherwise," said Bellerophon, quietly.

And then he turned to an old, gray man, who was leaning on a staff, and listening very attentively, with his head stretched forward, and one hand at his ear, because, for the last twenty years, he had been getting rather deaf.

"And what say you, venerable sir?" inquired he. "In your younger days, I should imagine, you must frequently have seen the winged steed!"

"Ah, young stranger, my memory is very poor!" said the aged man. "When I was a lad, if I remember rightly, I used to believe there was such a horse, and so did everybody else. But, nowadays, I hardly know what to think, and very seldom think about the winged horse at all. If I ever saw the creature, it was a long, long while ago; and, to tell you the truth, I doubt whether I ever did see him. One day, to be sure, when I was quite a youth, I remember seeing some hoof-tramps round about the brink of the fountain. Pegasus might have made those hoof-marks; and so might some other horse."

"And have you ever seen him, my fair maiden?" asked Bellerophon of the girl, who stood with the pitcher on her head, while this talk went on. "You certainly could see Pegasus, if anybody can, for your eyes are very bright."

"Once I thought I saw him," replied the maiden, with a smile and a blush. "It was either Pegasus, or a large white bird, a very great way up in the air. And one other time, as I was coming to the fountain with my pitcher, I heard a neigh. Oh, such a brisk and melodious neigh as that was! My very heart leaped with delight at the sound. But it startled me, nevertheless; so that I ran home without filling my pitcher."

"That was truly a pity!" said Bellerophon.

And he turned to the child, whom I mentioned at the beginning of the story, and who was gazing at him, as children are apt to gaze at strangers, with his rosy mouth wide open.

"Well, my little fellow," cried Bellerophon, playfully pulling one of his curls, "I suppose you have often seen the winged horse."

"That I have," answered the child, very readily. "I saw him yesterday, and many times before."

"You are a fine little man!" said Bellerophon, drawing the child closer to him. "Come, tell me all about it."

"Why," replied the child, "I often come here to sail little boats in the fountain, and to gather pebbles out of its basin. And sometimes, when I look down into the water, I see the image of the winged horse, in the picture of the sky that is there. But, if I so much as stir to look at him, he flies far away out of sight."

And Bellerophon put his faith in the child, who had seen the image of Pegasus in the water, and in the maiden, who had heard him neigh so melodiously, rather than in the middle-aged clown, who believed only in carthorses, or in the old man who had forgotten the beautiful things of his youth.

Therefore, he stayed about the Fountain of Pirene for a great many days afterwards. He kept continually on the watch, looking upward at the sky, or else down into the water, hoping that he should see either the reflected image of the winged horse, or the marvelous reality. He held the bridle, with its bright gems and golden bit, always ready in his hand. The rustic people, who dwelt in the neighborhood, and drove their cattle to the fountain to drink, would laugh at Bellerophon, and sometimes take him pretty severely to task. They told him that an able-bodied young man, like himself, ought to have better business than to be wasting his time in such an idle pursuit. They offered to sell him a horse, if he wanted one; and when Bellerophon declined the purchase, they tried to drive a bargain with him for his fine bridle.

Now you will, perhaps, wish to be told why it was that Bellerophon had undertaken to catch the winged horse. If I were to relate the whole of Bellerophon's previous adventures, they might easily grow into a very long story. It will be quite enough to say, that, in a certain country of Asia, a terrible monster, called a Chimaera, had made its appearance, and was doing great mischief. According to the best accounts which I have been able to obtain, this Chimaera was nearly, if not quite, the ugliest and most poisonous creature, the strangest, and the hardest to fight with, and the most difficult to run away from, that ever came out of the earth's inside. It had a tail like a boa constrictor; and it had three separate heads, one of which was a lion's, the second a goat's, and the third a great snake's. And a hot blast of fire came flaming out of each of its three mouths! Being an earthly monster, I doubt whether it had any wings; but, wings or no, it ran like a goat, and a lion, and wriggled along like a serpent, and thus contrived to make as much speed as all three together.

With its flaming breath, the Chimaera could set a forest on fire, or burn up a field of grain, or, for that matter, a village, with all its fences and houses. It laid waste the whole country round about, and used to eat up people and animals alive, and cook them afterwards in the burning oven of its stomach.

While the hateful beast (if a beast we can anywise call it) was doing all these horrible things, it so chanced that Bellerophon came to that part of the world, on a visit to the king. The king's name was Iobates, and Lycia was the country which he ruled over. Bellerophon was one of the bravest youths in the world, and desired nothing so much as to do some valiant deed that would make all mankind admire and love him. In those days, the only way for a young man to distinguish himself was by fighting battles, either with the enemies of his country, or with wicked giants, or with troublesome dragons, or with wild beasts, when he could find nothing more dangerous to encounter. King Iobates, perceiving the courage of his youthful visitor, proposed to him to go and fight the Chimæra, which everybody else was afraid of, and which, unless it should be soon killed, was likely to convert Lycia into a desert. Bellerophon hesitated not a moment, but assured the king that he would either slay this dreaded Chimaera, or perish in the attempt.

But, in the first place, as the monster was so prodigiously swift, he bethought himself that he should never win the victory by fighting on foot. The wisest thing he could do, therefore, was to get the very best and fleetest horse that could anywhere be found. And what other horse, in all the world, was half so fleet as the marvelous horse Pegasus, who had wings as well as legs, and was even more active in air than on the earth? To be sure, a great many people denied that there was any such horse, but Bellerophon believed that Pegasus was a real steed, and hoped that he himself might be fortunate enough to find him; and, once fairly mounted on his back, he would be able to fight the Chimaera at better advantage.

And this was the purpose with which he had traveled from Lycia to Greece, and had brought the beautifully ornamented bridle in his hand. It was an enchanted bridle. If he could only succeed in putting the golden bit into the mouth of Pegasus, the winged horse would be submissive, and would own Bellerophon for his master, and fly whithersoever he might choose to turn the rein.

But, indeed, it was a weary and anxious time, while Bellerophon waited and waited for Pegasus, in hopes that he would come and drink at the Fountain of Pirene. He was afraid lest King Iobates should imagine that he had fled from the Chimaera. It pained him, too, to think how much mischief the monster was doing, while he himself, instead of fighting with it, was compelled to sit idly poring over the bright waters of Pirene, as they gushed out of the sparkling sand. And as Pegasus came thither so seldom, in these latter years, and scarcely alighted there more than once in a lifetime, Bellerophon feared that he might grow to be an old man, and have no strength left in his arms nor courage in his heart, before the winged horse would appear.

Day after day Bellerophon watched, and at last one afternoon he looked down into the dimpling mirror of the fountain, and saw what he took to be the reflection of a bird which seemed to be flying at a great height in the air, with a gleam of sunshine on its silvery wings.

Bellerophon's heart began to throb! He gazed keenly upward, but could not see the winged creature, whether bird or horse; because, just then, it had plunged into the fleecy depths of a summer cloud. It was but a moment, however, before the object reappeared, sinking lightly down out of the cloud, although still at a vast distance from the earth. Bellerophon shrank back until he was hidden among the thick shrubbery which grew all around the fountain.

Nearer and nearer came the aerial wonder, flying in great circles, as you may have seen a dove when about to alight. Downward came Pegasus, in those wide, sweeping circles, which grew narrower, and narrower still, as he gradually approached the earth. The nigher the view of him, the more beautiful he was, and the more marvelous the sweep of his silvery wings. At last, with so light a pressure as hardly to bend the grass about the fountain, he alighted, and, stooping his wild head, began to drink. He drew in the water, with long and pleasant sighs, and tranquil pauses of enjoyment; and then another draught, and another, and another.

After thus drinking to his heart's content, the winged horse began to caper to and fro and dance. There was never a more playful creature than this very Pegasus. He frisked, fluttering his great wings, half on earth and half in air. Bellerophon, meanwhile, peeped forth from the shrubbery, and thought that never was any sight so beautiful as this, nor ever a horse's eyes so wild and spirited as those of Pegasus. It seemed a sin to think of bridling him and riding on his back.

Once or twice, Pegasus stopped, and snuffed the air, pricking up his ears, tossing his head, and turning it on all sides, as if he partly suspected some mischief or other. Seeing nothing, however, and hearing no sound, he soon began his antics again.

At length—not that he was weary, but only idle and luxurious—Pegasus folded his wings, and lay down on the soft green turf. But, being too full of aerial life to remain quiet for many moments together, he soon rolled over on his back, with his four slender legs in the air. It was beautiful to see him, this one solitary creature, whose mate had never been created, but who needed no companion, and, living a great many hundred years, was as happy as the centuries were long. The more he did such things as mortal horses are accustomed to do, the less earthly and the more wonderful he seemed.

Finally, when he had had enough of rolling over and over, Pegasus turned himself about, and, indolently, like any other horse, put out his fore legs, in order to rise from the ground; and Bellerophon, who had guessed that he would do so, darted suddenly from the thicket, and leaped astride of his back.

But what a bound did Pegasus make, when, for the first time, he felt the weight of a mortal man upon his loins! Before he had time to draw a breath, Bellerophon found himself five hundred feet aloft, and still shooting upward, while the winged horse snorted and trembled with terror and anger. Upward he went, up, up, up, until he plunged into the cold, misty bosom of a cloud, at which, only a little while before, Bellerophon had been gazing. Then again, out of the heart of the cloud, Pegasus shot down like a thunderbolt, as if he meant to dash himself and his rider headlong against a rock. Then he went through about a thousand of the wildest caprioles that had ever been performed either by a bird or a horse.

I cannot tell you half that he did. He skimmed straight forward, and sideways, and backward. He reared himself erect, with his fore legs on a wreath of mist, and his hind legs on nothing at all. He flung out his heels behind, and put down his head between his legs, with his wings pointing upward. At about two miles' height above the earth, he turned a somerset, so that Bellerophon's heels were where his head should have been, and he seemed to look down into the sky, instead of up. Then Pegasus twisted his head about, and, looking Bellerophon in the face, with fire flashing from his eyes, made a terrible attempt to bite him.

But Bellerophon (who, as you may judge, was as good a horseman as ever galloped) had been watching his opportunity, and at last clapped the golden bit of the enchanted bridle between the winged steed's jaws. No sooner was this done, than Pegasus became as manageable as if he had taken food, all his life, out of Bellerophon's hand. He looked round to Bellerophon, with tears in his beautiful eyes, instead of the fire that so recently flashed from them. But when Bellerophon patted his head, and spoke a few authoritative, yet kind and soothing words, another look came into the eyes of Pegasus; for he was glad at heart, after so many lonely centuries, to have found a companion and a master.

While Pegasus had been doing his utmost to shake Bellerophon off his back, he had flown a very long distance; and they had come within sight of a lofty mountain by the time the bit was in his mouth. Bellerophon had seen this mountain before, and knew it to be Helicon, on the summit of which was the winged horse's abode. Thither (after looking gently into his rider's face, as if to ask leave) Pegasus now flew, and, alighting, waited patiently until Bellerophon should please to dismount. The young man, accordingly, leaped from his steed's back, but still held him fast by the bridle. Meeting the eyes of Pegasus, however, he was so affected by the gentleness of his aspect, and by his beauty, and by the thought of the free life which Pegasus had heretofore lived, that he could not bear to keep him a prisoner, if he really desired his liberty.

Obeying this generous impulse, he slipped the enchanted bridle off the head of Pegasus, and took the bit from his mouth. "Leave me, Pegasus!" said he. "Either leave me, or love me."

In an instant, the winged horse shot almost out of sight, soaring straight upward from the summit of Mount Helicon. Being long after sunset, it was now twilight on the mountain top, and dusky evening over all the country round about. But Pegasus flew so high that he overtook the departed day, and was bathed in the upper radiance of the sun. Ascending higher and higher, he looked like a bright speck, and, at last, could no longer be seen in the hollow waste of the sky. And Bellerophon was afraid that he should never behold him more. But, the bright speck reappeared, and drew nearer and nearer until it descended lower than the sunshine; and behold, Pegasus had come back! After this trial there was no more fear of the winged horse's making his escape. He and Bellerophon were friends, and put loving faith in one another.

That night they lay down and slept together, with Bellerophon's arm about the neck of Pegasus, not as a caution, but for kindness. And they awoke at peep of day, and bade one another good morning, each in his own language.

In this manner, Bellerophon and the wondrous steed spent several days, and grew better acquainted and fonder of each other, all the time. They went on long aerial journeys. They visited distant countries, and amazed the inhabitants, who thought that the beautiful young man, on the back of the winged horse, must have come down out of the sky. Bellerophon was delighted with this kind of life, and would have liked nothing better than to live always in the same way, aloft in the clear atmosphere. But he could not forget the horrible Chimaera, which he had promised King Iobates to slay. So, at last, when he had become well accustomed to feats of horsemanship in the air, and could manage Pegasus with the least motion of his hand and had taught him to obey his voice, he determined to attempt the performance of this perilous adventure.

At daybreak, therefore, as soon as he unclosed his eyes, he gently pinched the winged horse's ear, in order to arouse him. Pegasus immediately started from the ground, and pranced about a quarter of a mile aloft, and made a grand sweep around the mountain top, by way of showing that he was wide awake, and ready for any kind of an excursion. During the whole of this little flight, he uttered a loud, brisk, and melodious neigh, and finally came down at Bellerophon's side, as lightly as ever you saw a sparrow hop upon a twig.

"Well done, dear Pegasus! well done, my sky-skimmer!" cried Bellerophon, stroking the horse's neck. "And now, my fleet and beautiful friend, we must break our fast. Today we are to fight the terrible Chimaera."

As soon as they had eaten their morning meal and drunk some sparkling water from a spring, Pegasus held out his head, of his own accord, so that his master might put on the bridle. Then, with a great many playful leaps and airy caperings, he showed his impatience to be gone; while Bellerophon was girding on his sword, and hanging his shield about his neck, and preparing himself for battle. When everything was ready, the rider mounted, and (as was his custom, when going a long distance) ascended five miles perpendicularly, so as the better to see whither he was directing his course. He then turned the head of Pegasus towards the east and set out for Lycia. In their flight they overtook an eagle, and came so nigh him, before he could get out of their way, that Bellerophon might easily have caught him by the leg. Hastening onward at this rate, it was still early in the forenoon when they beheld the lofty mountains of Lycia, with their deep and shaggy valleys. If Bellerophon had been told truly, it was in one of those dismal valleys that the hideous Chimaera had taken up its abode.

Being now so near their journey's end, the winged horse gradually descended with his rider; and they took advantage of some clouds that were floating over the mountain tops, in order to conceal themselves. Hovering on the upper surface of a cloud, and peeping over its edge, Bellerophon had a distinct view of the mountainous part of Lycia, and could look into all its shadowy vales at once. At first there appeared to be nothing remarkable. It was a wild, savage, and rocky tract of high and precipitous hills. In the more level part of the country, there were the ruins of houses that have been burnt, and, here and there, the carcasses of dead cattle, strewn about the pastures where they had been feeding.

"The Chimaera must have done this mischief," thought Bellerophon. "But where can the monster be?"

As I have already said, there was nothing remarkable to be detected, at first sight, in any of the valleys and dells that lay among the precipitous heights of the mountains. Nothing at all; unless, indeed, it were three spires of black smoke, which issued from what seemed to be the mouth of a cavern, and clambered sullenly into the atmosphere. Before reaching the mountain top, these three black smoke-wreaths mingled themselves into one. The cavern was almost directly beneath the winged horse and his rider, at the distance of about a thousand feet. The smoke, as it crept heavily upward, had an ugly, sulphurous, stifling scent, which caused Pegasus to snort and Bellerophon to sneeze. So disagreeable was it to the marvelous steed (who was accustomed to breathe only the purest air), that he waved his wings, and shot half a mile out of the range of this offensive vapor.

But, on looking behind him, Bellerophon saw something that induced him first to draw the bridle, and then to turn Pegasus about. He made a sign; the winged horse understood and sank slowly through the air, until his hoofs were scarcely more than a man's height above the rocky bottom of the valley. In front, as far off as you could throw a stone, was the cavern's mouth, with the three smoke-wreaths oozing out of it.

There seemed to be a heap of strange and terrible creatures curled up within the cavern. Their bodies lay so close together, that Bellerophon could not distinguish them apart; but, judging by their heads, one of these creatures was a huge snake, the second a fierce lion, and the third an ugly goat. The lion and the goat were asleep; the snake was broad awake, and kept staring around him with a great pair of fiery eyes. The three spires of smoke evidently issued from the nostrils of these three heads! So strange was the spectacle, that, though Bellerophon had been all along expecting it, the truth did not immediately occur to him, that here was the terrible three-headed Chimaera. He had found out Chimaera's cavern. The snake, the lion, and the goat, as he supposed them to be, were not three separate creatures, but one monster!

All at once, Bellerophon started as from a dream and knew it to be the Chimaera. Pegasus seemed to know it, at the same instant, and sent forth a neigh, that sounded like the call of a trumpet to battle. At this sound the three heads reared themselves erect, and belched out great flashes of flame. Before Bellerophon had time to consider what to do next, the monster flung itself out of the cavern and sprang straight towards him, with its immense claws extended, and its snaky tail twisting itself venomously behind. If Pegasus had not been as nimble as a bird, both he and his rider would have been overthrown by the Chimaera's headlong rush, and thus the battle have been ended before it was well begun. But the winged horse was not to be caught so. In the twinkling of an eye he was up aloft, half-way to the clouds, snorting with anger.

The Chimaera, on the other hand, raised itself up so as to stand absolutely on the tip-end of its tail, with its talons pawing fiercely in the air, and its three heads spluttering fire at Pegasus and his rider. Bellerophon, meanwhile, was fitting his shield on his arm, and drawing his sword.

"Now, my beloved Pegasus," he whispered in the winged horse's ear, "thou must help me to slay this insufferable monster; or else thou shalt fly back to thy solitary mountain peak without thy friend Bellerophon. For either the Chimaera dies, or its three mouths shall gnaw this head of mine, which has slumbered upon thy neck!"

Pegasus whinnied, and, turning back his head, rubbed his nose tenderly against his rider's cheek.

"I thank you, Pegasus," answered Bellerophon. "Now, then, let us make a dash at the monster!"

He shook the bridle; and Pegasus darted down aslant, as swift as the flight of an arrow, right towards the Chimaera's threefold head, which, all this time, was poking itself as high as it could into the air. As he came within arm's-length, Bellerophon made a cut at the monster, but was carried onward by his steed, before he could see whether the blow had been successful. Pegasus continued his course, but soon wheeled round, at about the same distance from the Chimaera as before. Bellerophon then perceived that he had cut the goat's head of the monster off. But, to make amends, the snake's head and the lion's head had taken all the fierceness of the dead one into themselves, and spit flame, and hissed, and roared, with a vast deal more fury than before.

"Never mind, my brave Pegasus!" cried Bellerophon. "With another stroke like that, we will stop either its hissing or its roaring."

And again he shook the bridle. Dashing aslantwise, as before, the winged horse made another arrow-flight towards the Chimaera, and Bellerophon aimed another downright stroke at one of the two remaining heads, as he shot by. But, this time, neither he nor Pegasus escaped so well as at first. With one of its claws, the Chimaera had given the young man a deep scratch in his shoulder, and had slightly damaged the left wing of the flying steed with the other. On his part, Bellerophon had mortally wounded the lion's head of the monster, insomuch that it now hung downward, with its fire almost extinguished and sending out gasps of thick black smoke. The snake's head, however (which was the only one now left), was twice as fierce and venomous as ever before. It belched forth shoots of fire five hundred yards long, and emitted hisses so loud, so harsh, and so ear-piercing, that King Iobates heard them, fifty miles off, and trembled till the throne shook under him.

Meanwhile Pegasus had again paused in the air, and neighed angrily.

"Art thou wounded, my immortal horse?" cried the young man, caring less for his own hurt. "The execrable Chimaera shall pay for his mischief, with his last head!"

Then he shook the bridle, shouted loudly, and guided Pegasus, not aslantwise as before, but straight at the monster's hideous front. So rapid was the onset, that it seemed but a dazzle and a flash, before Bellerophan was at close grip with his enemy.

The Chimaera, by this time, after losing its second head, had got into a red-hot passion of pain and rage. It flounced about, half on earth and half in the air. It opened its snake jaws to such an abominable width, that Pegasus might have flown right down its throat, wings outspread, rider and all! At their approach it shot out a tremendous blast of its fiery breath, and enveloped Bellerophon and his steed in flame, singeing the wings of Pegasus, and scorching off one whole side of the young man's golden ringlets.

But this was nothing to what followed. When the airy rush of the winged horse had brought him within the distance of a hundred yards, the Chimaera gave a spring, and flung its huge, venomous carcass upon Pegasus and clung round him. Up flew the aerial steed, higher, higher, higher, above the mountain peaks, above the clouds, and almost out of sight of the earth. But still the earth-born monster kept its hold, and was borne upward, along with the creature of light and air. Bellerophon, meanwhile, turning about, found himself face to face with the ugly grimness of the Chimaera's visage, and could only avoid being scorched to death, or bitten right in twain, by holding up his shield. Over the upper edge of the shield, he looked sternly into the savage eyes of the monster.

But the Chimaera was so mad and wild with pain, that it did not guard itself well. In its efforts to stick its horrible iron claws into its enemy, the creature left its own breast quite exposed; and, perceiving this, Bellerophon thrust his sword up to the hilt into its cruel heart. Immediately the monster let go its hold of Pegasus, and fell from that vast height, downward; while the fire within its bosom, instead of being put out, burned fiercer than ever, and quickly began to consume the dead carcass. Thus it fell out of the sky, all aflame, and (it being nightfall before it reached the earth) was mistaken for a shooting star or a comet. But, at early sunrise, some cottagers were going to their day's labor, and saw, to their astonishment, that several acres of ground were strewn with black ashes. In the middle of a field, there was a heap of whitened bones, a great deal higher than a haystack. Nothing else was ever seen of the dreadful Chimaera!

And when Bellerophon had won the victory, he bent forward and kissed Pegasus, while the tears stood in his eyes.

"Back now, my beloved steed!" said he. "Back to the Fountain of Pirene!"

Pegasus skimmed through the air, quicker than ever he did before, and reached the fountain in a very short time.

Then Bellerophon slipt off the enchanted bridle from the head of the marvelous steed.

"Be free, forevermore, my Pegasus!" cried he, with a shade of sadness in his tone. "Be as free as thou art fleet!"

But Pegasus rested his head on Bellerophon's shoulder, and would not be persuaded to take flight.

"Well then," said Bellerophon, caressing the airy horse, "thou shalt be with me, as long as thou wilt; and we will go together, forthwith, and tell King Iobates that the Chimaera is destroyed."

## THE STORY OF ODYSSEUS[1]

*Padraic Colum*

Troy, the minstrel sang, was the greatest of the Cities of men; it had been built when

[1] From Padraic Colum, *The Children's Homer.*

the demi-gods walked the earth; its walls were so strong and so high that enemies could not break nor scale them; Troy had high towers and great gates; in its citadels there were strong men well armed and in its treasuries there were stores of gold and silver. And the King of Troy was Priam. He was old now, but he had sons that were good Captains. The chief of them all was Hector.

Hector, the minstrel sang, was a match for any warrior the nations could send against Troy. Because he was noble and generous as well as brave, the people were devoted to him. And Hector, Priam's son, was commander in the City.

But Priam had another son who was not counted amongst the Captains. Paris was his name. Now when Paris was in his infancy, a soothsayer told King Priam that he would bring trouble upon Troy. Then King Priam had the child sent away from the City. Paris was reared amongst country people, and when he was a youth he herded sheep.

Then the minstrel sang of Peleus, the King of Phthia, and of his marriage to the river nymph, Thetis. All the gods and goddesses came to their wedding feast. Only one of the immortals was not invited—Eris, who is Discord. She came, however. At the games that followed the wedding feast she threw a golden apple amongst the guests, and on the apple was written "For the fairest."

Each of the three goddesses there wished to be known as the fairest and each claimed the golden apple—Aphrodite, who inspired love; Athene, who gave wisdom; and Hera, who was the wife of Zeus, the greatest of the gods. But no one at the wedding would judge between the goddesses and say which was the fairest. And then the shepherd Paris came by, and him the guests asked to give judgment.

Said Hera to Paris, "Award the apple to me and I will give you a great kingship." Said Athene, "Award the golden apple to me and I will make you the wisest of men." And Aphrodite came to him and whispered, "Paris, dear Paris, let me be called the fairest and I will make you beautiful, and the fairest woman in the world will be your wife." Paris looked on Aphrodite and in his eyes she was the fairest. To her he gave the golden apple and ever afterwards she was his friend. But Hera and Athene departed from the company in wrath.

The minstrel sang how Paris went back to his father's City and was made a prince of Troy. Through the favor of Aphrodite he was the most beautiful of youths. Then Paris went out of the City again. Sent by his father he went to Tyre. And coming back to Troy from Tyre he went through Greece.

Now the fairest woman in the world was in Greece; she was Helen, and she was married to King Menelaus. Paris saw her and loved her for her beauty. And Aphrodite inspired Helen to fall in love with Paris. He stole her from the house of Menelaus and brought her into Troy.

King Menelaus sent to Troy and demanded that his wife be given back to him. But the people of Troy, thinking no King in the world could shake them, and wanting to boast that the fairest woman in the world was in their city, were not willing that Menelaus be given back his wife. Priam and his son, Hector, knew that a wrong had been done, and knew that Helen and all that she had brought with her should be given back. But in the council there were vain men who went against the word of Priam and Hector, declaring that for no little King of Greece would they give up Helen, the fairest woman in all the world.

Then the minstrel sang of Agamemnon. He was King of rich Mycenae, and his name was so high and his deeds were so renowned that all the Kings of Greece looked to him. Now Agamemnon, seeing Menelaus, his brother, flouted by the Trojans, vowed to injure Troy. And he spoke to the Kings and Princes of Greece, saying that if they all united their strength they would be able to take the great city of Troy and avenge the slight put upon Menelaus and win great glory and riches for themselves.

And when they had come together and had taken note of their strength, the Kings and Princes of Greece thought well of the word of Agamemnon and were eager to make war upon Troy. They bound themselves by a vow to take the City. Then Agamemnon sent messages to the heroes whose lands were far away, to Odysseus, and to Achilles, who was the son of Peleus and Thetis, bidding them also enter the war.

In two years the ships of all the Kings and Princes were gathered into Aulis and the Greeks, with their leaders, sailed for the coast of Troy. One hero after another subdued the cities and nations that were the allies of the Trojans, but Troy they did not take. And the minstrel sang of how year after year went by, and how the host of Greeks still remained between their ships and the walls of the City, and how in the ninth year there came a plague that smote with death more men than the Trojans killed.

Menelaus speaks:

"Odysseus devised the means by which we took Priam's city at last. He made us build a great Wooden Horse. We built it and left it upon the plain of Troy and the Trojans wondered at it greatly. And Odysseus had counselled us to bring our ships down to the water and to burn our stores and make it seem in every way that we were going to depart from Troy in weariness. This we did, and the Trojans saw the great host sail away from before their City. But they did not know that a company of the best of our warriors was within the hollow of the Wooden Horse, nor did they know that we had left a spy behind to make a signal for our return.

"The Trojans wondered why the great Wooden Horse had been left behind. And there were some who considered that it had been left there as an offering to the goddess, Pallas Athene, and they thought it should be brought within the city. Others were wiser and would have left the Wooden Horse alone. But those who considered that it should be brought within prevailed; and, as the Horse was too great to bring through the gate, they flung down part of the wall that they might bring it through. The Wooden Horse was brought within the walls and left upon the streets of the city, and the darkness of the night fell.

"Now Helen, my wife, came down to where the Wooden Horse was, and she, suspecting there were armed men within, walked around it three times, calling to every captain of the Greeks who might be within in his own wife's voice. And when the sound of a voice that had not been heard for so many years came to him each of the captains started up to answer. But Odysseus put his hands across the mouth of each and so prevented them from being discovered.

"We had left a spy hidden between the beach and the city. Now when the Wooden Horse had been brought within the walls and night had fallen, the spy lighted a great fire that was a signal to the ships that had sailed away. They returned with the host before the day broke. Then we who were within the Wooden Horse broke through the boards and came out on the City with our spears and swords in our hands. The guards beside the gates we slew and we made a citadel of the Wooden Horse and fought around it. The warriors from the ships crossed the wall where it was broken down, and we swept through the streets and came to the citadel of the King. Thus we took Priam's City and all its treasures, and thus I won back my own wife, the lovely Helen.

"But after we had taken and sacked King Priam's City, great troubles came upon us. Some of us sailed away, and some of us remained on the shore at the bidding of King Agamemnon, to make sacrifice to the gods. We separated, and the doom of death came to many of us.

"Of thy father, Telemachus, I have told thee what I know. Where he is now I do not know, but Odysseus was ever master of devices. And also he is favored greatly by the goddess, Pallas Athene. For these reasons, Telemachus, be hopeful that your father will yet reach his own home and country."

Odysseus speaks:

"O Alcinous, famous King, thou hast asked me to speak of my wanderings and my toils. Ah, where can I begin that tale? For the gods have given me more woes than man can speak of!

"But first of all I will declare to you my name and my country. I am ODYSSEUS, SON OF LAERTES, and my land is Ithaca, an island around which many islands lie. Ithaca is a rugged isle, but a good nurse of hardy men, and I, for one, have found that there is no place fairer than a man's own land. But now I will tell thee, King, and tell the Princes and Captains and Councilors of the Phaeacians, the tale of my wanderings.

"The wind bore my ships from the coast of Troy, and with our white sails hoisted we came to the cape that is called Malea. Now if we had been able to double this cape we should soon have come to our own country, all unhurt. But the north wind came and swept us from our course and drove us wandering past Cythera.

"Then for nine days we were borne onward by terrible winds, and away from all known lands. On the tenth day we came to a strange country. Many of my men landed there. The people of that land were harmless and friendly, but the land itself was most dangerous. For there grew there the honey-sweet fruit of the lotus that makes all men forgetful of their past and neglectful of their future. And those of my men who ate the lotus that the dwellers of that land offered them became forgetful of their country and of the way before them. They wanted to abide forever in the land of the lotus. They wept when they thought of all the toils before them and of all they had endured. I led them back to the ships, and I had to place them beneath the benches and leave them in bonds. And I commanded those who had not eaten of the lotus to go at once aboard the ships. Then, when I had got all my men upon the ships, we made haste to sail away.

"Later we came to the land of the Cyclôpes, a giant people. There is a waste island outside the harbor of their land, and on it there is a well of bright water that has poplars growing round it. We came to that empty island, and we beached our ships and took down our sails.

"As soon as the dawn came we went through the empty island, starting the wild goats that were there in flocks, and shooting them with our arrows. We killed so many wild goats there that we had nine for each ship. Afterwards we looked across to the land of the Cyclôpes, and we heard the sound of voices and saw the smoke of fires and heard the bleating of flocks of sheep and goats.

"I called my companions together and I said, 'It would be well for some of us to go to that other island. With my own ship and with the company that is on it I shall go there. The rest of you abide here. I will find out what manner of men live there, and whether they will treat us kindly and give us gifts that are due to strangers—gifts of provisions for our voyage.'

"We embarked and we came to the land. There was a cave near the sea, and round the cave there were mighty flocks of sheep and goats. I took twelve men with me and I left the rest to guard the ship. We went into the cave and found no man there. There were baskets filled with cheeses, and vessels of whey, and pails and bowls of milk. My men wanted me to take some of the cheeses and drive off some of the lambs and kids and come away. But this I would not do, for I would rather that he who owned the stores would give us of his own free will the offerings that were due to strangers.

"While we were in the cave, he whose dwelling it was, returned to it. He carried on his shoulder a great pile of wood for his fire. Never in our lives did we see a creature so frightful as this Cyclops was. He was a giant in size, and, what made him terrible to behold, he had but one eye, and that single eye was in his forehead. He cast down on the ground the pile of wood that he carried, making such a din that we fled in terror into the corners and recesses of the cave. Next he drove his flocks into the cave and began to milk his ewes and goats. And when he had the flocks within, he took up a stone that not all our strengths could move and set it as a door to the mouth of the cave.

"The Cyclops kindled his fire, and when it blazed up he saw us in the corners and recesses. He spoke to us. We knew not what he said, but our hearts were shaken with terror at the sound of his deep voice.

"I spoke to him saying that we were Agamemnon's men on our way home from the taking of Priam's City, and I begged him to deal with us kindly, for the sake of Zeus who is ever in the company of strangers and suppliants. But he answered me saying, 'We Cyclôpes pay no heed to Zeus, nor to any of thy gods. In our strength and our power we deem that we are mightier than they. I will not spare thee, neither will I give thee aught for the sake of Zeus, but only as my own spirit bids me. And first I would have thee tell me how you came to our land.'

"I knew it would be better not to let the Cyclops know that my ship and my companions were at the harbor of the island. Therefore I spoke to him guilefully, telling him that my ship had been broken on the rocks, and that I and the men with me were the only ones who had escaped utter doom.

"I begged again that he would deal with us as just men deal with strangers and suppliants, but he, without saying a word, laid hands upon two of my men, and, swinging them by the legs, dashed their brains out on the earth. He cut them to pieces and ate them before our very eyes. We wept and we prayed to Zeus as we witnessed a deed so terrible.

"Next the Cyclops stretched himself amongst his sheep and went to sleep beside the fire. Then I debated whether I should take my sharp sword in my hand, and feeling where his heart was, stab him there. But second thoughts held me back from doing this. I might be able to kill him as he slept, but not even with my companions could I roll away the great stone that closed the mouth of the cave.

"Dawn came, and the Cyclops awakened, kindled his fire, and milked his flocks. Then he seized two others of my men and devoured them for his morning meal. And now he rolled away the great stone and drove his flocks out of the cave.

"I had pondered on a way of escape, and I had thought of something that might be done to baffle the Cyclops. I had with me a great skin of sweet wine, and I thought that if I could make him drunken with wine, I and my companions might be able to escape. But there were other preparations to be made first. On the floor of the cave there was a great beam of olive wood which the Cyclops had cut to make a club when the wood should be seasoned. It was yet green. I and my companions went and cut off a fathom's length of the wood, and sharpened it to a point and took it to the fire and hardened it in the glow. Then I hid the beam in a recess of the cave.

"The Cyclops came back in the evening, and opening up the cave drove in his flocks. Then he closed the cave again with the stone and went and milked his ewes and his goats. Again he seized two of my companions. I went to the terrible creature with a bowl of wine in my hands. He took it and drank it and cried out, 'Give me another bowl of this, and tell me thy name that I may give thee gifts for bringing me this honey-tasting drink.'

"Again I spoke to him guilefully and said, 'Noman is my name. Noman my father and my mother call me.'

" 'Give me more of the drink, Noman,' he shouted. 'And the gift that I shall give to thee is that I shall make thee the last of thy fellows to be eaten.'

"I gave him wine again, and when he had taken the third bowl he sank backward with his face upturned, and sleep came upon him. Then I, with four companions, took that beam of olive wood, now made into a hard and pointed stake, and thrust it into the ashes of the fire. When the pointed end began to glow we drew it out of the flame. Then I and my companions laid hold on the great stake and, dashing at the Cyclops, thrust it into his eye. He raised a terrible cry that made the rocks ring and we dashed away into the recesses of the cave.

"His cries brought other Cyclôpes to the mouth of the cave, and they, naming him as Polyphemus, called out and asked him what ailed him to cry. 'Noman,' he shrieked out, 'Noman is slaying me by guile.' They answered him, saying, 'If no man is slaying thee, there is nothing we can do for thee, Polyphemus. What ails thee has been sent to thee by the gods.' Saying this, they went away from the mouth of the cave without attempting to move away the stone.

"Polyphemus then, groaning with pain, rolled away the stone and sat before the mouth of the cave with his hands outstretched, thinking that he would catch us as we dashed out. I showed my companions how we might pass by him. I laid hands on certain rams of the flock and I lashed three of them together with supple rods. Then under the middle ram I tied a man of my company. Thus every three rams carried a man. As soon as the dawn had come the rams hastened out to the pasture. As they passed, Polyphemus felt the backs of the fleecy rams, never dreaming that they carried his enemies under their bellies.

"For myself, I took a ram that was the strongest and fleeciest of the whole flock and I placed myself under him, clinging to the wool of his belly. As this ram, the best of all his flock, went by, Polyphemus, laying his hands upon him, said, 'Would that you, the best of my flock, were endowed with speech, so that you might tell me where Noman, who has blinded me, has hidden himself.' The ram went by him, and when he had gone a little way from the cave I loosed myself from him and went and set my companions free.

"We gathered together many of Polyphemus' sheep and we drove them down to our ship. The men we had left behind would have wept when they heard what had happened to six of their companions. But I bade them take on board the sheep we had brought and pull the ship away from that land. Then when we had drawn a certain distance from the shore I could not forbear to shout my taunts into the cave of Polyphemus. 'Cyclops,' I cried, 'you thought that you had the company of a fool and a weakling. But you have been worsted by me, and your evil deeds have been punished.'

"So I shouted, and Polyphemus came to the mouth of the cave with great anger in in heart. He took up rocks and cast them at the ship and they fell before the prow. The men bent to the oars and pulled the ship away or it would have been broken by the rocks he cast. And when we were further away I shouted to him:

" 'Cyclops, if any man should ask who it was set his mark upon you, say that he was Odysseus, the son of Laertes.'

"Then I heard Polyphemus cry out, 'I call upon Poseidon, the god of the sea, whose son I am, to avenge me upon you, Odysseus. I call upon Poseidon to grant that you, Odysseus, may never come to your home, or if the gods have ordained your return, that you come to it after much toil and suffering, in an evil plight and in a stranger's ship, to find sorrow in your home.'

"So Polyphemus prayed, and, to my evil fortune, Poseidon heard his prayers."

For twenty years Odysseus wandered and had many strange adventures. But through the help of Pallas Athene, as Menelaus had said, he came at last to the rugged isle of Ithaca, to his faithful wife, Penelope, and his brave son, Telemachus.

## THE WINNING OF ATALANTA [1]

*Elsie Finnimore Buckley*

Once upon a time, in ancient days, there ruled in Arcadia in Greece a proud-hearted

[1] From Elsie Finnimore Buckley, *Children of the Dawn.*

king named Schoenus. A tamer of horses was he, and a man mighty in the hunt and in battle. Above every other thing he loved danger and sport and all kinds of manly exercise. Indeed, these things were the passion of his life, and he despised all womenkind because they could take no part nor lot in them. And he wedded Clymene, a fair princess of a royal house, because he wished to raise up noble sons in his halls, who should ride and hunt with him, and carry on his name when he was dead. On his wedding-day he swore a great oath, and called upon all the gods to witness it.

"Never," he swore in his pride, "shall a maid child live in my halls. If a maid is born to me, she shall die ere her eyes see the light, and the honor of my house shall rest upon my sons alone."

When a man swears an oath in his pride, he repents full oft in humility, and so it fell out now. For many a long year no child was born to him, and when at last he had hopes of an heir, the babe that was born was a maid. When he saw the child his heart was cut in two, and the pride of a father and the pride of his oath did battle within him for victory. The pride of his oath conquered, for he was afraid to break his word in the face of all his people. He hardened his heart, though he had held the babe in his arms, and its little hand with a birthmark above the wrist had closed about his finger trustfully, and gave orders that the child should be cast out upon the mountains to die of hunger and cold. So the babe was given to a servant, who bore it forth and left it on the slope of bleak Parthenius. But Fate made a mock of Schoenus, of his pride and of his oath, for no other child, either man or maid, was born to him in his halls. All too late he repented of his folly, when he saw his hearth desolate and no children round his board, and knew that not only his name, but his race, was like to die with him, because of the rash oath which he had sworn.

Yet there was one who had pity on the babe, and whose heart was kinder than the heart of its own sire. When Artemis, the maiden goddess, saw the child cast forth to die, she was filled with anger against Schoenus, and swore that it should live. For it was a fair child, and a maid after her own heart, and no young life ever called to her in vain for mercy. Wherefore she sent a she-bear to the place where the child lay, and softened the heart of the beast, so that she lifted it gently in her mouth and bore it to the cave where her own cubs lay hid. There she suckled it with her own young ones, and tended it night and day, till it grew strong and could walk, and the cave rang with its laughter as it played and gamboled with the young bears. When Artemis knew that the child was old enough to live without its foster mother, she sent her nymphs to fetch it away, and when they bore it to her she was well pleased to find it fair and strong.

"Her name shall be Atalanta," she said to them. "She shall dwell on the mountains and in the woods of Arcadia, and be one of my band with you. A mighty huntress shall she be, and the swiftest of all mortals upon earth; and in time she shall return to her own folk and bring joy and sorrow to their hearts."

Thus it came to pass that Atalanta lived with the nymphs in the woodlands of Arcadia. They taught her to run and to hunt, and to shoot with bow and arrows, till soon the day came when she could do these things as well as any of their band. For the blood of her father ran in her veins; and not more easily does a young bird learn to fly than Atalanta learnt to love all manner of sport. So she came to womanhood in the heart of the hills, and as her form grew in height and strength, it grew too in beauty and grace. The light of the sunbeam lay hid in her hair, and the blue of the sky in her eyes. But she thought little of her beauty, or the power it might have over the hearts of men, for all her delight was in the hunt, and to follow Artemis, her mistress, over hill and over dale.

Artemis loved her, and delighted to do her honor; and when the land of Calydon cried to her for mercy, because of the boar she had sent to ravage it in her wrath, she decreed that none but Atalanta should have the glory of that hunt. By the fame of it her name was carried far and wide through Hellas, so that when she came to the games of Pelias there was no need to ask who she was. She ran in the foot race against the swiftest in the land, and won the prize so easily that when she reached the goal the first man had scarce passed the turning point, though he was no sluggard to make a mock of. When the games were over, she went back to Arcadia without a tear or a sigh, but her face and her memory lived in the heart of many a man whose very name she had not known.

One day, when King Schoenus held a great hunt in the forest on the edge of his domain, it chanced that Atalanta had come to those parts; and when she heard the blare of the bugles and the barking of the hounds, her heart leapt with joy. Full often had she joined in the hunt on the uplands of Arcadia, and run with the hounds; and when the hunt was over she had fled back into the forest, away from those who had been fain for her to stay. So now she joined in the chase as the stag broke loose from cover, and her white feet flashed in the sunlight as she followed the hounds across the open moorland. King Schoenus, when he saw her, was glad.

"It is Atalanta, the maiden huntress," he cried. "See that she be treated with due courtesy, for she is the only woman on earth who is fit to look a man in the face."

He rode eagerly after her. But the best horse in all that company was no match for Atalanta. Far ahead of them all she shot, like an arrow from the bow, and when at last the stag turned at bay in a pool, she was the first to reach him. When the rest had come up, and the huntsman had slain the stag, the king turned to her.

"Atalanta," he said, "the trophy of this chase is thine, and my huntsman shall bear the head of the stag whithersoever thou shalt bid him. In token of our esteem, I beg thee to accept this ring. When thou lookest upon it, think kindly of an old man whose heart is lonely, and who would fain have a daughter like thee."

As he spoke he drew off a gold ring from his finger and held it towards her; the tears stood in his eyes and his hand shook as he looked on her fair young form, and remembered the babe he had cast out on the mountains to die. If she had lived she would have been of an age with Atalanta, and perchance as fair and as strong as she; and his heart was bitter against himself for the folly of his oath.

When Atalanta heard his words, she had a mind at first to refuse his gift. Many a man before had offered her gifts, and she had refused them every one; for she had no wish to be beholden to any man. But when she saw the eyes of the old king dim with tears, and how his hand shook as he held out the ring, her heart was softened, and yearned with a strange yearning towards him. Coming forward, she knelt at his feet and took the ring, and held his hand and kissed it.

"May the gods grant the prayer of thy heart, sire," she said, "and give thee a daughter like unto me, but fairer and more wise than I!"

As he looked down on the hand that held his own the old king trembled more violently than before, for above the wrist was a birthmark like the birthmark above the wrist of the babe he had cast forth to die. And he knew that he made no mistake, for that mark had lived in his mind as though it had been branded with red-hot steel.

"Atalanta," he said, "the gods have heard thy prayer. This is not the first time thy fingers have closed about mine."

"What meanest thou, sire?" she asked.

"As many years ago as the span of thy young life," he said, "I held in my arms a newborn babe, the child that the gods had given me, and its little hand with a birthmark above the wrist closed about my finger trustfully. But because of my foolish pride I hardened my heart. I cast away the gift of the gods and sent the child to die upon the mountains. But the birthmark on its wrist was branded on my brain so that

I could not forget it. Never till this day have I seen that mark again, and now I see it on thy wrist, my child."

He bowed his head as he spoke, and the tears from his eyes fell upon her hand, which lay in his as she knelt before him.

"Oh, my father!" she cried, and bent forward and kissed his hand.

When he found that she did not turn from him, though she knew what he had done, he was more deeply moved than before.

"Atalanta," he said, "when I cast thee forth to die, I gave back to the gods the life they had given me, and now I have no right to claim it again. Yet would thy presence be as sunshine in my halls if thou wert to come back to me, my child."

Thus did the call come to Atalanta to return to her own folk, and the choice lay before her. On the one side was her free life in the forest, with Artemis and her nymphs, the hunt, the fresh air, and all the things that she loved; on the other was life within the walls of a city, and the need to bow her head to the customs and the ways of men. Her heart misgave her when she thought of it.

"My lord," she said, "will a young lion step into the cage of his own free will, think you?"

The old king bowed his head at her words.

"Alas! what other answer could I look for?" he said. "I thank the gods that they have shown me thy fair face this day. Perchance, when we hunt again in these parts, thou wilt join us for love of the chase. Till then, my child, farewell."

With trembling hands he raised her from her knees, and kissed her on the forehead. Then he signed to his men to lead forward his horse, and mounted and rode sadly home through the forest with his company. And Atalanta shaded her eyes and stood watching them till they disappeared from sight. When they had gone, she sighed, and turned and went upon her way. But her eyes were blind and her ears were deaf to the sights and sounds she loved so well, and that night she tossed restlessly upon her couch of moss. For before her eyes was the figure of an old man bowed with sorrow, and in her ear his voice pleaded, trembling with longing and love.

"Thy presence would be as sunshine in my halls if thou wert to come back to me, my child."

In the early dawn she rose up from her couch, and bathed in a stream close by, and gathered up her shining hair in a coil about her head. Then she put on her sandals and a fresh white tunic, slung her quiver about her shoulders, and bow in hand went forth through the forest. Looking neither to the right nor to the left, she went on her way till she came to the white road that led to the city. Then she turned and looked back at the forest.

"Dear trees and woods," she said, "farewell, and ye nymphs that dwell in the streams and dance on the greensward of the mountains. When I have trodden the white road and gone up to the city, I can live with you no more. As for thee, great Artemis, who saved me in the beginning, I will be thy servant for ever, and dwell a maiden all my days, and a lover of the hunt."

She stepped out bravely on the white highway, and went up into the city. The people as they saw her pass marveled greatly at her beauty, and whispered one to the other, "Surely it is Atalanta, the king's daughter. What doth she here?"

For the tale of how King Schoenus had found his child, and of how she had refused to come home with him, had spread like wildfire through the city; so that when they saw her, they knew full well who she must be. She took no heed of them at all, but went straight forward on her way till she came to the gate of the palace. The gate stood open, and without knocking or calling she passed in, and went across the echoing court and beneath the portico into the great hall, as one who comes by right. When she had entered the hall, she stopped and looked about her. At first all seemed silent and deserted, for the folk had gone their several ways for the work of the day; but at length she spied an old man sitting on a carved chair in one of the alcoves between the pillars. It was the king, her father. He sat with his head upon his hand and his eyes downcast upon the floor, and his face was sad and full of longing, as of one who dreams sweet dreams which he knows will not come true. Gently she drew near to him, and thanked the gods who had timed her coming so that she should find him alone. And she went and knelt at his feet. The old man gazed for a moment in her face, as though he did not see her; then he started from his chair and laid his hand upon her shoulder.

"Atalanta!" he cried.

"My father," she said, "I have come back to thee."

Then he gathered her up in his arms.

"Oh, my child, my child!" he said. "The gods are kind beyond my desert."

"Thy voice cried out to me in the night-time," she said, "and I could not shut my heart to thy pleading. The call of the free earth was strong, but the call of my blood was stronger."

Thus did Atalanta come back to her own fold and bring joy to the heart of her father and of the mother who had never held her in her arms. A great feast was held in the palace in her honor, and through all the city the people rejoiced because of her. For she was a fair princess of whom any land might be proud, and her fame had spread through the length and breadth of Hellas. Indeed, as soon as it was known who she was, and how she had left the mountains to come and live with her own kin, suitors flocked from far and wide to seek her hand in marriage. But she treated them one and all with scorn, and vowed that she would never wed.

At first her father smiled upon her, and looked on her refusal to wed as the sign of a noble nature, that was not to be won for the asking of the first chance-comers. So he gathered about him the noblest princes in the land in the hope that among them all there would be one who could win her heart. But the months passed by, and still she vowed that she would never wed. All her delight was in running and hunting, and to ride by her father's side. As for the young princes, she liked them full well for companions in sport, but as soon as they spoke of love and marriage she would turn her back upon them. At length the king grew anxious.

"Surely, my child," he said, "among all these princes there is one whom thou couldst love?"

"I shall never love any man but thee, my father," she replied. "When I left the forest and came back to thee I vowed a vow to Artemis, who saved me in the beginning. I said, 'I will be thy servant forever, and dwell a maiden all my days and a lover of the hunt.' "

"We vow rash vows in ignorance, Atalanta," said the king, as he remembered the oath he had sworn on his wedding-day, "and Fate makes a mock of us, and turns our nay to yea."

But Atalanta laughed at his words.

Nothing that he could say would persuade her to go back from her resolve. But still he reasoned with her night and day, till at length she grew so wearied of the matter that she bethought of a plan that would rid her of all her suitors.

"My father," she said, "I will wed any man who shall ask for my hand, if he will fulfill one condition."

"My child," cried her father, "I knew that in the end thou wouldst listen to reason. Tell me thy condition, that I may spread it abroad among those who are suing for thy hand."

"Tell them," she said, "that I will wed the first man among them who will run a race with me. If he win, I will be his bride, but if he lose, he must die."

The king's face fell when he heard her words.

"Surely thou speakest in mockery, Atalanta," he said. "No man in all the world can run as swiftly as thou canst, or if any be foolhardy enough to run with thee, they will run to a certain death."

"No man will run to a certain death, my father," she answered. "When they know that to sigh for me is to sigh for death, they will go back to their own folk, and I shall be troubled with suitors no more."

So her father published abroad among the suitors the condition she had made. When they heard it there was great consternation among them, and they consulted together as to what they should do, and some sent a deputation to her to find out the meaning of her words.

"Lady," they asked, "when thou speakest of death thou speakest perchance in parables. Those who run in the race with thee, and are outsripped must give up all hope of thee, and look upon thy face no more. And this would be death indeed to them that love thee."

But she laughed in their faces.

"If you would hear parables," she said, "go to the oracle at Delphi. I am no raving priestess to utter words that walk two ways at once. He who courts death may race with me at daybreak, and at sunset he shall drink the poison-cup without fail, and look neither on my face again nor the face of any living thing. Have I spoken plainly now?"

The next day there was great confusion in the halls of King Schoenus. There was shouting and bustling, and attendants ran this way and that. Chariots clattered through the gateway and drew up in the court, and baggage was piled high behind the horses. And Atalanta laughed aloud at the success of her scheme; for suitor after suitor came and kissed her hand and bade her farewell. They loved her much, but they loved life better, and were content to go home and find mates who, though less fair, were less ferocious, and were like to look upon their lords with eyes more lowly and obedient than Atalanta.

That night the gathering about the board of King Schoenus was scantier than it had been for many a long day. Yet a few of the suitors remained.

Then Atalanta herself pled with them.

"My friends," she said, "I pray you to be guided by me. Think not to win me in marriage."

But they replied, "Lady, thou hast given the condition of thy marrying, and we are waiting to fulfill it."

"But my condition means certain death," she cried.

"Nothing in this life is certain," they said, "save death in the end. If it come soon or late, what matter? For thy sake we are willing to face it now."

So now a time of darkness and mourning fell upon the land, and many a day in the year the city was hung with black for the sake of some noble suitor who had chosen death rather than life without Atalanta. And Atalanta's heart was sore within her, because of the rash condition she had made in her ignorance. When she would fain have recalled her words it was too late, for the suitors bound her to her promise.

"Either give thyself of thine own free will to one of us, or else let us take our chance of winning thee or death," they said.

And so she was forced to run with them. Thus were the words of Artemis fulfilled when she said, "In time she shall return to her own folk, and bring joy and sorrow to their hearts."

One day it chanced that a stranger came to the city on a morning that a race was to be run. The night before he had slept in a village near by, and the people had told him the tale of Atalanta, and how on the morrow another suitor was to run to his death. But he scoffed at their words.

"No man would run to certain death," he said, "were the maid as fair as Aphrodite."

"Go and see for thyself," they replied. "Soon we shall hear that thou too wilt run in the race."

"Never," he said; "no woman can cheat my life from me."

But they shook their heads unconvinced.

"Many before thee have spoken likewise," said they, "and yet they have run."

"If I run, I will run to win," he answered.

"Can a snail outstrip a deer?" they asked.

"It might so chance," said he.

"Thou art mad," they cried.

"Well, well," he said, with a laugh, "we shall see what we shall see."

The next morning he set forth early for the city, and, mingling with the crowd, he made his way to the racecourse, and found for himself a place where he could watch the whole sight with ease. The race was run, and ended as it always ended; and once again the city was hung with black. But in the mind of the stranger an image remained which had not been there before—the image of a maid whose white feet flashed in the sunlight.

"Great Hercules!" he thought within himself, "to run shoulder to shoulder with her for a moment, even in a race for death, might be worth the while after all. I will make myself known at the palace, and see what the gods will give me."

For some days he lay hid in the city, till he thought the time was ripe for him to go up to the palace of the king. Then he went for a walk along the highway, and when he was covered with dust and grime, he returned to the city and made his way at once to the palace. At the door of the gateway he knocked, and the old porter came out to ask his will.

"I am come from a distant land," he said, "and tomorrow I would journey yet further on my way. I pray thee to crave hospitality for one night for me from the steward of this house, whoe'er he be. I am a king's son, and worthy to sit at any man's table."

The porter cast a doubtful eye on the travel-worn clothes of the stranger. It seemed unlikely that a king's son would go on a distant journey with no body-servant and no horse or baggage. Then he looked in his clear blue eyes, and he saw that for all his sorry raiment he was by no means ill-favored, but held himself well and proudly. So he opened the door and led him across the court.

"Well, well," he muttered in his beard, "great folk have strange whims in these days. Our king must needs slay his daughter because she is a maid, and she must needs slay her suitors, because they are men. After that this fellow may well be, as he says, a king's son, who, because he has a palace and plenty, must needs tramp over the face of the earth and beg his bread. Praise be to the gods who put lowly blood in my veins and sense in my head, else had it been better for the gate to keep itself than to have me for a guardian."

Then he cast another look over his shoulder at the young man behind.

"At any rate, for one night he can do no harm," he muttered.

Thereupon he turned the young man over to the steward, who welcomed him sadly to the halls of King Schoenus. All strangers were looked upon askance in those days, lest they came as suitors for the hand of Atalanta, and wished to add to those who had run in the fatal race. When he heard that the young man would depart on the morrow on the journey he was glad, and gave him water to wash with and a change of raiment, and showed him his place at the board, without so much as asking his name.

When Atalanta saw a stranger at the board her heart sank within her, and she kept her eyes turned away, as though she had not seen him, for she made sure that he too had come to run in the race with her. It chanced that night that the company was scanty, and no man talked in private to his neighbor, but the conversation leapt from one end of the board to the other, as each one took his share in it and said his say. The stranger, too, took his part with the rest, in nowise abashed; and so shrewd were his words, and so full of wit, that soon he had a smile upon the face of each one at the table. For many a long day the talk had not been so merry nor the laughter so loud at the table of King Schoenus. Atalanta, too, forgot her constraint, and talked and laughed freely with the stranger; and he answered her back, as though it had been man to man, and showed no more deference to her than to the others of the company.

When the meal was over, the king approached the stranger, and Atalanta stood beside him.

"Sir," said the king, "thy name and country are still hid from us, but we are grateful for thy coming, and would be fain for thee to stay as long as it shall please thee."

"I thank thee, sire," said the stranger, "but I am bound by a strange vow. I may not reveal my name, nor accept hospitality for more than one night from any man, till I come to a house where none other than the king's daughter shall promise me her hand in marriage. From the tales I have heard in the neighboring country, I have learnt that I may not hope to end my vow beneath this roof—though indeed," he said, turning to Atalanta, "I would fain press my suit if there were any chance of success."

But Atalanta threw back her head at his words.

"Thou hast doubtless heard the condition," she said, "by the fulfillment of which alone a man may win my hand."

"Alas, sir!" said the king, "I would press no man to try his luck in that venture."

"Since that is so," said the stranger, "I will go forth once more upon my journey at break of day, and see what luck the gods will give me. I thank thee for thy kindly hospitality this night, and beg thee to excuse me. I have traveled far, and would fain rest now, as I must go a long distance ere I can rest again."

Thereupon he took his leave of King Schoenus and his daughter. But she, for all her pride, could not forget the man who seemed to bid her farewell with so light a heart. When she asked herself why she should remember one who by now had doubtless lost all memory of her, she could find no answer. As she tossed on her couch with a troubled mind, she determined that before he left the palace on the morrow she would have some speech with him.

"He thinks no more of me than of a stone upon the wayside," she said within herself, "wherefore I can do him no wrong by letting him speak with me again before he goes."

It was her custom to rise early in the morning, before the rest of the household was stirring, and to go forth alone into the woods; and it was the lot of one of the slaves to rouse himself betimes to give her food ere she went, so that when she appeared, as was her wont, he thought nothing of it. The stranger had risen even earlier than she, and the slave was waiting upon him. When Atalanta saw him, her heart gave a sudden thrill, for she had not looked to see him so soon.

"Good-morrow, sir," she said. "It is not often I have a companion when I break my fast."

Thereupon Atalanta sat down at the board beside the stranger, and they fell to with all the appetite of youth and health; and as they ate they laughed and joked, and talked of strange lands they both had seen and adventures that had befallen them. In the space of one half-hour they were as good friends as though they had known each other all their lives, and suitors who had sat at her father's board day after day were much more strangers to Atalanta than this man, who had craved but one night's hospitality.

When they had finished their meal the stranger rose.

"I must bid thee farewell, lady," he said.

"Nay, not yet," she replied; "I will set thee on thy way, and show thee a road through the forest that will bring thee to the city thou seekest. I know every track and path as well as the wild deer know them."

He tried to dissuade her, but she would not listen, and led him out from the palace by a side gate, which she unbarred with her own hands. Down through the sleeping streets they went, where the shadows of the houses lay long upon the ground, and out across the open downs into the shade of the forest. The dew gleamed like jewels on the leaves, as here and there the slanting rays of the sun shone through the trees, and above their heads the lark sang gaily in the bright summer sky. Yet they walked silently side by side, as though, in spite of the brightness of the day, sorrow and not joy were sitting in their hearts; and all their gay talk and laughter of the early morning was dead. At length they came to a broad track that crossed the path they were in, and Atalanta stopped short and pointed to the right.

"From here," she said, "thou canst not miss thy way. Follow the track till it lead thee to the high-road, and when thou strikest the highroad, turn to the left, and thou wilt come to the city thou seekest."

Then she held out her hand to him.

"I must bid thee farewell," she said, "and good luck to the ending of thy vow."

"Lady," he said, and took her hand in his, "if thou wilt, thou canst release me now from my vow."

But she drew her hand away sharply.

"Many kings have daughters besides King Schoenus," she said, "and any one of them could release thee from thy vow as well as I."

"Atalanta," he said, "no king's daughter save thee shall ever release me from my vow. That which all our laughter and our converse last night and this morning strove to hide, our silence, as we walked side by side, has revealed far better than I can tell thee. Thou knowest that I love thee. From the first moment that I saw thee, I have loved thee."

His words made her heart thrill with a strange joy. But she showed no sign of it. She was proud and wished to test him.

"Doubtless the floodgates of love are easily thrown open where a man would be released from a vow. Thou knowest how thou mayest win me. Art thou willing to run in the race?"

At this all his mirth returned to him, and his eyes shone with merriment as he answered:

"Much good would my love do me if I had to drink the poison cup perforce. Nay, nay," he said; "I love thee too well to put my death at thy door. When I have some chance of winning the race, I will come back and claim thee. In the meantime, lady, farewell."

And, bowing to her, he turned and went his way, without so much as looking back at her, as she stood trembling with astonishment and anger. It was not thus her other lovers had spoken. When he had gone from sight, she turned suddenly and went back by the path they had come. Her hands were clenched, and the tears sprang unbidden to her eyes, as she strode forward with long, angry strides that took no heed of where they went.

Then his form came back to her mind, as he had looked when they stood face to face at the parting of the ways, when the sun had glinted down upon them through the trees, and he had looked her straight in the face with his clear blue eyes, and said, "Thou knowest that I love thee. From the first moment I saw thee, I have loved thee."

A great sob rose in her throat as she remembered.

"Ah, he spoke the truth!" she said; "I know that he spoke the truth."

Moreover, her heart told her that long before he had spoken the words she had known that he loved her.

"If he would come back and run with me," she sighed, "my feet would be as heavy as lead against him."

But she sighed in vain. Day after day passed by, and he came not.

"He is a man of his word," she thought at last. "Till he has some chance of winning he will not come back. And he is no fool. He knows he can never run as I can run. He will never come back."

Yet for all this she watched for him night and day. When she went forth into the road, or into the forest, she looked for him at every turn of the way. When she entered the great hall of the place, she looked to see his face at the board. But always she looked in vain.

The weeks and months passed by, and still he returned not; winter came and went, and once again the dewdrops shone in the summer sunlight as Atalanta walked in the forest at break of day. She walked with her eyes upon the ground, thinking of the summer morning a long year ago when he had walked by her side in silence along that very path. When by chance she raised her eyes, there, at the parting of the ways, he stood, as though in answer to her thoughts. With a cry she stopped short and gazed at him, and he came forward and bowed to her.

"I have come back, lady," he said.

"Oh!" she cried from her heart, "I am glad thou hast come back."

Then he bent and kissed her hand. So once more they walked in silence side by side along the path they had walked before; and once again the bond of love was knit strong between them. As they drew near to the edge of the forest, Atalanta was the first to speak.

"And thy vow," she asked—"hast thou found release from it?"

"Not yet," he answered. "I am come back to run the race, that I may win release."

Once again the spirit of perversity came upon her.

"Where hast thou learnt to run like the wind? she asked.

"I have not learnt to run like the wind," he replied. "I have learnt something better than that."

"Few things are better in a race than swiftness," she said.

"True," he answered; "yet I have found the one thing better."

"What is this strange thing?" she asked.

"When we have run the race, thou wilt know," he said.

"I have grown no sluggard," she said, with a toss of her head, as though to warn him that her speed was not a thing to be despised.

"That I can see," he said, as he cast a glance at the easy grace of her bearing as she walked beside him. Then they talked of indifferent matters, and each knew that what they had nearest their hearts they were hiding from each other.

So they came to the palace, and from the lowest to the highest the inmates greeted the stranger with joy. For he had won the hearts of them all by his wit and his genial smile. But they sighed when they heard that he too had come to run in the fatal race.

"Alas!" said the old king, shaking his head, "I had rather not have looked upon thy face again than see thee back on such an errand."

The young man laughed. "He who runs with a fair hope of winning runs swiftly," he said. "The others were dragged down by the shackles of their own despair."

"Thou dost not know my daughter," said the king.

"Mayhap I know her better than thou thinkest, and better than thou knowest her thyself," said the stranger.

No arguments or entreaties would turn him from his purpose.

"I must win release from my vow," he said. "I cannot live all my life a nameless wanderer. Yet will I not wed any woman I love not, for the sake of my release. Atalanta alone can save me, for I love none other."

So the lists once again were prepared, and the course made smooth for the race. With trembling fingers Atalanta tied her girdle about her, and bound her sandals to her feet. Though her heart was crying out for the stranger to win, and praying that her feet might fail her at the last, yet her pride, too, lifted up its head.

Now the folk were gathered together round the course, and Atalanta and the stranger stood ready and waiting for the word to be given. She had made it a condition of the race that her rivals should have a good start of her, and she stood with her eyes upon the stranger's back, as he waited many paces before her. All too soon the word was given, and he sprang forward from his place. And Atalanta, too, sprang forward; but whereas the man ran like a hunted thing that strains every muscle to save its life, she ran with the swinging grace of the wild deer, and though she seemed to make no effort, she gained upon her rival at every step, and now she was running close behind him, and now she was almost shoulder to shoulder, and out of the corner of his eye he could see the gleam of her tunic. Then for a moment he slackened his pace, and it seemed that she would pass him, and on every side the people shouted out to him, "Run, run! Faster, faster! She will pass thee."

But he put his hand into the opening of his tunic, and drew forth something from his breast. Then his hand swung up above his head, and from it there flashed a dazzling fiery apple. Up and down through the air it flashed like a meteor, and rolled along the grass, till it stopped far away in the center of the course, and lay shining like a jewel in the rays of the sun.

Every eye was turned from the race to watch the flight of the gleaming apple, and Atalanta stopped short and watched it too. When she saw it stop still in the middle of the course, flashing and sparkling in the grass, a great desire sprang up in her heart to have it. And she darted aside out of the path of the race, and went and picked up the shining golden apple and put it in the bosom of her tunic.

Meanwhile the stranger had lost no time, and when Atalanta came back to the spot she had left, he was far ahead upon the course, and she had to run with a will if she wished to overtake him. But once again she gained upon him, and the space between them grew less and less, till they were running well-nigh shoulder to shoulder. And once again he saw the gleam of her tunic beside him; and again he slackened his speed for a moment, and sent a second gleaming apple into the air. Once more the mad, unreasoning desire sprang up in her heart, and, leaving the course, she picked up the second apple and put it in the bosom of her tunic beside the first.

By the time Atalanta had returned to the path, the stranger had rounded the turning point, and was well on his way towards the goal, and she put forth all her strength to overtake him. But the ease of her running was gone. She ran as one who runs bearing a burden, yet she would not cast away the golden apples in her bosom; for though they hampered her, she gained upon her rival, and for the third time they were running almost shoulder to shoulder. And again, the third time, the same thing happened, and Atalanta left the course to pick up the shining fruit. This time when she returned to her place the stranger was close upon the goal, and all around the people were shouting and waving their hands. Blindly she pulled herself together, and with all the strength that was left in her she made a great spurt to overtake him. If she would cast away the golden apples, she might yet win the race; but the desire which had spurred her to pick them up forbade her now to let them go.

As Atalanta ran, the apples seemed to grow heavier and heavier in her bosom; yet she struggled and panted on, and step by step did she gain upon him. On every side the people shouted louder than before, for they knew not now which of them would win. As they drew near to the goal they were again almost shoulder to shoulder, and the stranger saw once more the flash of Atalanta's tunic beside him, while there were yet some paces to run. Then he gave a great spurt forward, and leapt away from her side. She tried to do likewise, but her strength was gone. She had made her last effort before. Thus did it come to pass that the stranger ran in first to the goal, and, running close upon his heels, Atalanta fell breathless into his arms as he turned to catch her. The tears shone in her eyes, but he knew they were not tears of grief; and in the face of all the people he kissed her.

Thus was Atalanta, the swiftest of all mortals, beaten in the race by the stranger, and learnt from his lips what it was that he had found on his travels that had made speed of no avail in the race.

For after they had come back to the city, surrounded by the joyous folk, and had passed hand in hand beneath the gateway; after he had revealed to them all that he was Meilanion, the son of King Amphidamas, and the old king had fallen on his neck and given him his blessing, because he proved to be the son of his own boyhood friend, and the man of all others he would have chosen for his son-in-law—after all this, when the speeches and merrymaking were over, they two walked alone in the moonlit court of the palace. Atalanta had decked herself in the long saffron robes of a bride, and in her hands she bore the three shining apples. Meilanion's arm was about her, as they walked for a while in silence, but at length she spoke and held out the fruit in her hands.

"Tell me their secret," she said.

"Their secret lies in thy heart, Atalanta," he answered.

"What meanest thou?" she asked.

"I mean that if thou hadst not loved me, they would never have filled thy soul with longing to have them, and thou wouldst never have turned aside from the race."

"And, knowing this, thou didst stake thy life on my love?" she said.

"Knowing that, I staked my life on thy love," he answered.

"Then that was the one thing better than speed in the race?"

"Yes," he answered, "I learnt to trust in thy love."

There was silence for a moment between them, and then Atalanta spoke.

"And whence came the apples?" she asked him.

"When I left thee at the parting of the ways," he said, "I traveled many a weary league by land, and on the road I passed many a shrine of Aphrodite. At length I came to the seashore, and took ship for the pleasant isle of Cyprus, which is Aphrodite's home. There at last she came to me, walking on the waves of the sea. In her hand she bore three shining golden apples. She spoke to me in a voice that was soft and kind, and the melody of it touched my heart like the melody of music.

" 'Fear not, Meilanion,' she said; 'I have heard the cry of thy heart. Here are three apples from mine own apple tree. If she whom thou lovest, loves thee in return, she cannot resist the spell of their golden brightness. When thou runnest against her, cast them one by one into the middle of the course. If she love thee, she will turn aside to pick them up. For her they will be heavy as the gold they seem made of. For thee they will be light as the fruit whose form they wear. Farewell, and good luck to thy race.'

"Thereupon darkness came over my eyes, and I could find no words to thank her. When I awoke I thought it had been a dream, but lo! by my side upon the sand lay the apples."

"And thy vow?" asked Atalanta. "How camest thou to make such a vow?"

He laughed at her words.

"When a hare is hunted," he said, "thou knowest how he will double and turn, and take a line he has no mind to pursue to the end. So was it with me. Long ago in my father's house I heard of thee and of thy beauty, and how thou couldst cast such a spell upon the hearts of men that for thy sake they would fling away their lives. And a great desire came upon me to see this thing for myself, for I could scarce believe it. So I set forth alone to find thee, and hid my name from all men as I journeyed, for thus could I be more free to act as seemed best in mine own eyes. And I saw thee run in a race, and that glimpse was enough to tell me that I too one day must run with thee. Yet was I more wary than my rivals. I knew that to come as a suitor was the way to turn thy heart to stone. Wherefore I pretended to be bound by a vow, which would bring me as a passing stranger before thee."

She smiled into his face.

Such was the winning of Atalanta. As for the golden apples, she placed them in a precious casket, and guarded them jealously all her days, for a memorial of the race that she had failed to win.

## GARETH AND LYNETTE[1]

Gareth was the last of three tall sons at home. He was, in truth, taller than his brothers, Gawain and Modred. One day in spring he stood looking at the river swollen from the heavy rains. A young tree lost its hold upon the earth and was washed away.

"How it went down!" cried Gareth. "As a false knight or a bad king would fall before my sword—if a sword were mine to use. River, you are full only of water, while I am full of living blood. You do the will of Him who made you, and you do not know it. And I, who know and have fine strength, stay on at home here like a child. The queen, my mother, treats me as if I were still a child.

"I long to go to Arthur's court to fight with all my power against the wrongs of the world. I must not stay at home when I might serve King Arthur. Why, Gawain, when he came home here with Modred in in the summertime, asked me to try my strength against him in a joust with the spear. Modred was the judge. Gawain is a proved knight, and he said, 'You have half won against me.'

"But Modred, biting his thin lips, said nothing. I did not care, for Modred is never too pleased with me.

"I shall go to my mother and weary her ears, begging her to let me go to King Arthur's court."

So Gareth went, and waiting near her chair, asked, "Mother, though you think me still a child, do you love your child?"

She laughed. "You are foolish to ask."

"Then let me go to King Arthur's court."

The queen said, "Have you no pity for me? Your father is an old, old man. Both of your brothers are in Arthur's hall. I have loved you best of my three sons. Stay with me. The wars are hard, and you have never known even the pain of a broken arm or leg. Stay here at home and hunt the deer in our forests. You will grow stronger day by day, for hunting is fine pleasure. And some day I will find for you a fair, sweet wife. Stay, my son!"

"Follow the deer!" said Gareth. "I would follow Christ, and the King. I would live purely, speak truly, right all wrong, and follow the King! For what other reason was I born? I would walk through fire to serve the King."

The queen, his mother, saw that he would never turn from his purpose to go to Arthur's court. At last she answered, "Go, then, if you must. But I demand one promise of you before you ask the King to make you a knight."

Gareth cried, "If it is one hard promise or a hundred, yet will I go. Say quickly what it is that you demand of me."

His mother, looking at him, spoke slowly, "Prince, you shall not tell your name when you go to Arthur's hall. No one shall know that you are the son of a true king and queen. You shall ask for work in Arthur's kitchen and there serve up his meat and drink, among the kitchen-knaves, for twelve months and a day."

The queen believed that her own fine Gareth, when he saw that his only way to Arthur's Round Table was through kitchen service, would be too proud to go. She thought that he would then stay with her in her castle, far from wars and fighting.

Gareth waited for a moment, and then answered, "Even then I should be free in soul, and I should see the jousts. Since you are my mother, I must do the thing you ask. I will go and ask for work among the kitchen-knaves and tell my name to no one, not even to King Arthur."

Yet Gareth stayed at home a little while. His mother's eyes were always on him, full of fear that he would go. Then one morning early, before day brought full light, he rose and called two men that had served him all his young life. Before his mother heard him, he was gone.

[1] From Gertrude Moderow, Mary Yost Sandrus, Josephine Mitchell, and Ernest C. Noyes, *Six Great Stories*. This story, retold from Alfred Tennyson's "Idylls of the King," has been prepared especially for children in the upper grades who have difficulty in reading.

The three were dressed like common men. As they turned their faces to the south, the birds sang in the trees, and the hills were green and bright with flowers.

After many days they came to a wide plain. Before them they saw Camelot, the castle of King Arthur, standing upon a hill that rose between the field and forest. At times the top of the high city flashed through clouds. At times only the great gate that opened on the field was shining. And then again the whole fair city was not seen at all.

Those who went with Gareth were afraid at this strange thing. One cried, "Let us not go on, my lord. This is a magic city, built by fairy kings."

The second said, "Lord, we have heard from our wise man at home that this king is not the real king, but was made king by magic and has driven his enemies out by magic. Let us have nothing to do with such a king as this one."

Then the first one added, "Lord, there is no city here. This is a dream."

Gareth laughed at them, and they came on to the gate of Camelot. There was no gate like this under heaven. Upon it the Lady of the Lake was cut in stone, her dress flowing from her sides like water. From one hand a sword hung down, and from the other, a small lamp. To her right and to her left were pictures which told brave stories of Arthur's wars.

The two with Gareth looked so long upon the figures in the battles that the pictures seemed to move.

The men called to Gareth, "Lord, the gate has come alive!"

Then Gareth fixed his eyes long upon the gate, and even to him the figures seemed to move. Soon, out of the city, music sounded, and out of the gate there came an old, old man with a long beard.

"Who are you, my sons?" the old man asked.

Gareth answered, "We are farmers, sir. We have come to see the wonders of our King. But your city moved so strangely in the clouds that my men here doubt whether the King is king at all. They think he has come from fairyland and doubt whether the city is not built by magic, or whether there is any city. This music now has frightened them. Tell them the truth."

Then the old man answered, "My son, I have seen a good ship sail with bottom up and with sail down in the heavens. I have seen castles standing on their tops in air. Now this is truth. As you say, the city was built by magic. Fairy kings and queens came from the mountain, with harps in their hands, and built it to the music of their harps. It is a magic city where nothing is what it seems, except the King. And some men say that Arthur is not real, that only the city stands there truly.

"If you go within that gate, you will fall under Arthur's power. He will ask you for the highest promises. They will be hard to keep. Yet every man should promise them and live by them. If you are afraid, do not go in, but stay outside among the cows here in the field. If you heard music just now, perhaps they are still building, for the city is built to music. Therefore it is never built at all, and therefore built forever."

Gareth was angry. "Old man," he said, "why do you make fun of me? I spoke fairly to you."

"I am not making fun of you but you of me. For you are not the man you seem to be. But I know who you are. And you go to Arthur, seeming to be what you are not—to King Arthur who hates even the shadow of a lie."

So saying, the old man turned and went away across the field.

Then Gareth said, "My men, I do not like a lie. Our coming thus makes me ashamed. I did it out of love for my mother. And to good King Arthur I will make things right as early as I may."

Though Gareth did not know it, the old man was Merlin himself, master of magic in King Arthur's court—Merlin who knew all things.

Gareth and his men entered the gate of Camelot. All about the castle, pictures, cut in stone, told of the deeds of ancient kings.

Now and then a knight passed into the hall of Camelot, or out. His arms clashed and the sound was good in Gareth's ear. Out of the windows looked beautiful women, and everywhere the people walked as if before a great, good king.

When Gareth came into the hall, he heard a voice—the voice of Arthur. There sat the King far above the heads of others on his rich throne, judging the cases which his people brought before him. Gareth felt his young heart beat hard and turned his head away, thinking, "The King will see that I am not what I appear to be, and he will hate me for this half-shadow of a lie."

However, on he went. Though he feared that he would meet his brothers, Sir Gawain and Sir Modred, he did not see them. In the eyes of all the tall knights that stood about the throne, he saw honor shining like the morning star, and trust in their great King, with the light of glory they had won, and glory they would win.

Then a woman came crying to the King. "Grant me this favor, Sir King!" she said. "I am your enemy. With your hand you killed my lord in battle. I was against you, too. I have no right to ask a favor of you, but this I must ask. My husband's brother shut my son in the castle and gave him no food so that he died. Now this man has taken all my lands. Grant me some brave knight to do battle for me and give justice to the man who has killed my son and taken all I have."

A good knight stepped toward Arthur, crying, "A favor, Sir King! I am of this woman's family. Let me right her wrong."

Then Sir Kay, master of the food and drink, cried out, "A favor, Sir King! Grant this woman nothing, for she has lied. Send her away with nothing."

However, Arthur said, "We are the King to help those who have suffered wrong through all our land. Woman, you may go. You who offered to fight for her, go and lay low the man, yet do not kill him. Bring him here that I may judge the right, and if he has done these wrongs, so shall he die."

Next there came into the hall a man sent by King Mark. Mark was a king not honored in the land. The man put down a cloth of gold upon the floor before the throne and fell to his knees upon it. He said that Mark was on his way to Camelot to ask King Arthur to make him a knight. The cloth of gold Mark sent to Arthur as a gift.

Cried Arthur, "Take the cloth! Tear it to pieces! Throw it upon the fire, where the oak tree is burning there. Mark! Does he try to buy me with a gift? Shall the shield of false King Mark stand with these of my good knights?"

Gareth looked down the side of the long hall and saw three rows of shields cut in stone and under every shield the name of a knight. Some shields were colored, some were only cut, some had nothing on them. In Arthur's hall when a knight had done one noble deed, his arms were cut in the stone. When he had done two, his arms were colored. If he had done none, there was no sign upon the shield—only his name under it. Gareth saw that Gawain's shield was colored, rich and bright, but Modred's had nothing on it.

Arthur spoke again. "Mark is not fit to be a king, or fit to be my knight. Rise, man. Go back to Mark and tell him not to come to me. Sir Kay will give you food and find you what you need."

Then many others came, asking their favors.

Last Gareth came, leaning heavily upon his men as he knelt before the King. He asked, "A favor, Sir King!" His voice was ashamed. "I ask three gifts. Grant me to serve you just for my meat and drink, among your kitchen-knaves, for twelve months and a day. You see how weak I seem, and hungry. And do not ask my name. Later will I ask two other gifts."

The King said to him, "You look to be a good young man and to be worth a greater favor. Yet if this is what you ask, then Kay, master of the meat and drink, shall be your master."

Gareth rose and stepped away.

Then Kay said, "Look at the fellow! He must not have had enough to eat. If he works, I shall fill him up until he is as fat as any pig."

Sir Lancelot was standing near. "Sir Kay," he said, "you may know dogs. You may know horses. But you do not know a fine man when you see one. This boy is noble. He has not told all he knows. Be kind to him, for fear he will shame you for having judged him wrongly."

Kay answered, "If the boy were noble, he would have asked for horse and arms. You leave my man to me."

So Gareth took his place in Sir Kay's kitchen. He had his food with the young boys by the door and lay down at night with the kitchen-knaves.

Lancelot always spoke to him pleasantly. Kay, who did not like him, would hurry him and make him work much harder than the other boys at drawing water or cutting wood or heavier duties. However, Gareth did all that he was told the best he could. Even his least service seemed fine and good because he did it well. Gareth loved to hear the boys talk of King Arthur and of Sir Lancelot. They told him how Arthur had saved Lancelot's life two times, and Lancelot saved Arthur's once.

When the boys played at games, no one could throw a stone as far as Gareth. If there was a joust and Sir Kay would let him, Gareth hurried to see it. And when he saw the knight's arms shining in the light, he was beside himself with joy.

For one month he worked among the kitchen-knaves. Then his mother sent him his arms and freed him from his promise. Gareth went at once to Arthur. He found the King alone and told him all his story.

King Arthur said, "My son, your good mother let me know that you were here. Now I have promised you two other gifts. Tell me what you wish."

"First make me your knight," said Gareth, "and tell no one my name even yet. And the second gift I ask is that I may right the wrong for the first person that asks a favor of you."

"You ask to be my knight. My men promise to be strong and to be gentle, to be true in love, and to do as I command."

Gareth, kneeling, said, "I promise." Then King Arthur answered, "So be it. I take thee for my knight. We shall tell your name only to one, our noblest, truest Lancelot."

"As you wish, my King," said Gareth. "Let Lancelot know."

The great King smiled upon the boy. Then he called Lancelot where Gareth could not hear and told him, "I have promised Gareth to let him right the first wrong that we hear of. So listen in the hall, and when he starts away upon his horse, take your horse and follow him, far behind. Cover the lions on your shield so that he may not know you. See that he is not killed."

That same day a beautiful young girl came to the hall. She was as pretty as a flower.

Arthur asked, "What is your name? What is your need?"

"I am Lynette," she said. "I need a knight to battle for my sister Lyonors. She has been shut up in her own castle by four knights—all brothers. One guards her there. The other three watch at three places by the winding river where one must cross to bring help to her. Therefore I have come for Lancelot."

Arthur remembered Gareth. He asked, "Who are these four who keep your sister prisoner?"

"Their names," she said, "are Morning Star, Noonday Sun, Evening Star, and Night. But this last one is oftener called Death. They are all mighty men, and therefore I have come for Lancelot."

Sir Gareth rose. His eyes were shining. "A favor, Sir King!" he called. "Let me go. I have been your kitchen-knave, and I am strong through meat and drink. I can fight a hundred such as these. Let me go."

King Arthur said, "Go."

At this Lynette's fair face turned red in anger. "Sir King!" she cried. "I asked for your chief knight, and you have given me a kitchen-knave!"

Then before a man could stop her, she ran from the hall, took her horse, and went through the gate, saying to herself, "Kitchen-knave!"

As Gareth left the hall to follow her, he saw there by the door King Arthur's gift, worth half a town, a war horse of the best. And there were, too, a shield, a helmet, a spear, and a bright cloak. Gareth took the arms, got upon his horse, put the cloak about him, and passed out through the gate.

Lynette was riding now more slowly through the field. "Why did the King do this?" she asked herself. "If Lancelot could not come, could he not at least give me one of his proved knights rather than this, his kitchen-knave?"

Gareth came up to her. Few looked so strong and brave as this young knight in his new, shining arms. He said, "Lead, and I follow."

Lynette held her nose high. "Stay back," she said. "You smell of the kitchen. And look, knave! Your master comes behind to take you back with him."

There came Sir Kay. "We need you at your work, young kitchen-knave," called Kay. "Go back. I am your master."

"You are not my master now," replied Gareth.

"We shall fight to see," Kay answered.

They fought with swords, and Kay fell, cut deep in his shoulder.

Gareth cried to Lynette, "Lead, and I follow." Then she rode fast away before him. When the stones stopped flying from her horse's feet and her tired animal had slowed down, then Gareth came up to her.

Lynette spoke to him. "Why do you ride here beside me? Do you think I like you better since you have shown your strength against Sir Kay? You should be washing dishes. To me you smell of the kitchen as before."

"Lady," Sir Gareth answered gently, "say what you will. I will go on until I finish."

Gareth smiled, but she did not. Away she rode through the thick forest. Gareth followed, and again she called him "Kitchen-knave!" So they went along till evening.

As the sun set, they heard a man's voice calling. A serving man ran out of the dark wood, crying, "They have taken my master and tied his hands and feet to throw him into the lake."

"I should help this man," said Gareth, "but, fair lady, my first duty is to you."

"Lead, and I follow," said Lynette.

Gareth answered, "Follow! I lead!"

He rode into the forest. There six tall men were pulling another into the lake. A stone was tied about his neck. Gareth laid low three men with heavy blows, and the other three ran away. He took the stone from the man's neck and made free his hands and feet.

"You have saved my life," said the man. "What can I give you for this?"

Gareth said, "Nothing! I serve the King."

The man replied, "I well believe you are his knight." But Lynette laughed.

As night was coming on, the stranger took them to his castle and gave them food. He set Gareth down beside Lynette at table, but at once she rose. "No kitchen-knave shall sit with me," she cried.

The lord looked first at her and then at Gareth. Then taking Gareth to another place, he sat down beside him and began to eat. "Friend," he said, "whether you are a kitchen-knave or whether it is just her fancy, I ask not. However, you are strong and fine, and you have saved my life. Now you go on to fight alone with mighty men. Should you not turn back and ask that Lancelot come?"

Gareth answered, "I will go on, even to fight these mighty ones."

So in the morning the lord whose life he had saved sent the two on their way.

To Lynette, Gareth called, "Lead, and I follow!"

She replied proudly still, "I shall not ride in front. I shall allow you to ride by me a little while. But will you not go back? For we are near one who will surely kill you."

"I will go on," said he.

They came to the stream where the first enemy waited for them near the bridge. He was Sir Morning Star. His clothes were red and gold.

Gareth watched him make ready for the fight.

Then Lynette said to Sir Gareth, "There is yet time to run away down the valley before he charges. You need not care. You are not a knight but a knave."

Sir Gareth said, "You still speak badly of me, but I shall win in this."

The two men ran together on the bridge. Both their spears bent but did not break, and both men fell. Quickly they rose and drew their swords, and Gareth pushed his enemy back and down the bridge.

Then Lynette called out, "Well done! Well done, my kitchen-knave!"

Gareth's shield was cut in two, but Gareth laid him that cut it on the ground.

The enemy cried, "Take not my life."

Gareth answered, "If this lady ask it of me, I will not take your life."

Lynette's fair face grew red. "I ask of you? Never shall I ask one small thing of you!"

"Then, Sir Morning Star, shall you die!" cried Gareth.

But Lynette called, "Do not kill one higher than yourself, knave."

Gareth said, "Rise, fellow. Go to King Arthur's hall. Say that his kitchen-knave has sent you. Your shield is mine. Lady, lead, and I follow."

Fast away she went. When he came up with her, she said to him, "I thought, knave, when I watched you fighting on the bridge, that the kitchen smell was not so strong. Now the wind has changed, and it is twenty times as strong."

Then she sang a song which said, "My love has smiled on me."

After a while she spoke. "The second brother, whom we next meet, is stronger than the first. Turn back. You need not care. You are not a knight but a knave."

Gareth laughed and answered, "I will tell you a story of a knave. In my kitchen one boy had a cross dog to which he would throw his coat and say, 'Take care of that.' And no one dared to touch it. You are such a coat, which the king gave me to guard, and I am such a dog. If I am a knave but fight like a true knight, does that not serve as well to free your sister?"

"It makes me like you less," she said.

At the next river crossing they met the second brother, Noonday Sun. His arms were shining in the light. He pushed his horse to meet Sir Gareth in the middle of the stream. They fought with swords. So mighty were the blows against him Gareth feared that he would lose. But the other's horse drew back and fell, and Noonday Sun was carried away by the water. Gareth went into the stream after him, and helped him from the water; then he took his sword from him in fair fight and sent him to the King.

"Lead, and I follow," he said to fair Lynette.

Quietly she led.

"Has not the good wind changed again?" he asked. "Do I not seem a little better to you now?"

"No," she answered. "Not one bit. You did not win. His horse fell, for I saw it."

Then she sang another song which said, "Two times my love has smiled on me."

At length, evening came. Where they must cross the river again, they came to the third enemy, the one who called himself the Star of Evening.

Lynette cried to him, "Both of your brothers have fallen before this strong young man, and so will you, Sir Star, for you are old."

"I am old," said Sir Evening Star. "Old and hard, and strong as twenty boys."

Gareth said, "He who threw Sir Morning Star can throw Sir Evening Star."

They ran together in an awful battle on the bridge. Gareth threw the Star of Evening from his horse. They drew their swords. Sir Evening Star fell to his knees, and rose, and fell again, and rose. It seemed that Gareth could not win.

All the time Lynette was calling, "Well done, knave-knight! Well done, O good knight-knave! As fine as any knight! You are truly one of Arthur's best. The wind will never change again."

Gareth, hearing, had greater strength, and yet it seemed he could not win. Then at length he broke the other's sword in two. Sir Star then jumped upon him, his arms round Gareth's neck to choke him, but Gareth called up all his power and threw Sir Star of Evening from the bridge into the stream.

Again Gareth said, "Lead, and I follow."

Lynette replied, "I lead no longer. Ride by my side. You are the finest of all kitchen-knaves. I am ashamed that I have talked so to you."

"You did not know me," Sir Gareth said. "Now since your words to me are fair, there is no knight—not even Lancelot—who has the strength to throw me."

Then Lynette sang a song which said, "Three times my love has smiled on me."

Lynette knew that food for their supper, sent by her sister Lyonors, waited for them at a place near by. As they turned off the road, Lynette looked back, and cried, "Look! For someone rides behind!"

It was Lancelot who came, but the blue lions on his shield were covered as King Arthur had ordered. So Gareth did not know him. Lancelot, seeing the star on the shield which Gareth had taken from the fallen knight, thought him Sir Morning Star. "Stay!" he called. "I fight for my friend!"

They closed in fight, and before Lancelot's spear, which was the wonder of the world, Gareth fell. When he found the grass within his hands, he laughed.

Lynette said to him, "Why do you laugh? You have lost your fight. You are too proud."

Then Lancelot knew that it was Gareth, and he said, "Blessed be thou, Sir Gareth. Thou art a knight after the King's heart. I saw the star upon your shield and thought you were our enemy. I came to help you, not to hurt you. I am Lancelot, and glad to find you safe."

Gareth answered, "Lancelot! I knew yours was the spear that threw me! Therefore I laughed. Had I fallen before some other's strength, then I should be ashamed. But I am not sad to fall before your spear."

Still Lynette was not pleased with Gareth.

Then Lancelot said to her, "My lady, are you wise to call him shamed who has been thrown only once? I have been thrown, not once, but many times. By being thrown one learns to throw another."

Then to his young friend he spoke, "Sir Gareth, both you and your good horse are tired. Yet I felt you strong and brave. You have done well. You have freed the river of our enemies. You have answered the girl gently when she spoke badly of you. Prince and knight you are, and truly one of the Round Table of our King."

The three then found the food that had been left for them. And after supper Gareth fell into sleep.

Lynette said softly as she looked on him, "Sleep soundly. You have cause to sleep. Rise strong. Seem I not as gentle to him as any mother? But such a mother as has been not too gentle all day long and now blesses her child as he sleeps. How sweetly smells the honeysuckle in the night as if the world were one of peace and love!"

She said to Lancelot, "I am so glad to find that my good knave is both knight and noble. But I promised this last wicked brother, Sir Night, when he let me pass to come to Arthur's court, that I would bring you, Lancelot, back to fight with him. If you go with us, he will fight you first, and so Sir Gareth will not win completely."

Lancelot replied, "This fellow, Night, may know my shield. Let Gareth then change his shield for mine, if he will, and take my horse; for my brave animal is fresher and loves a battle as well as he that rides him."

"Lord Lancelot," she said, "how kind you are in this, as you are always kind."

Then Gareth woke. He took the shield with the blue lions. "O noble Lancelot," he cried, "I feel fire flow through me from this shield. I shall not shame you, Lancelot, wearing it. On! Let us go!"

On they went through the quiet field to Sir Night—or Death, as he was often called.

Suddenly Lynette, who was at Gareth's side, cried, "Let Lancelot do this battle. You have done wonders, but this time you will not win. Give Lancelot back his shield. I fear to see you hurt. You have thrown three, but you can never throw the fourth."

"Why not?" asked Gareth. "Tell me what you know of him. But still I will go."

"I have not seen him, Prince," she said. "He never rides abroad by day. Nor have I heard his voice; always he sent a page with his messages. But he is said to have the strength of ten. O Prince, I asked for Lancelot first. The quest is Lancelot's. Give him back the shield. Let Lancelot meet Sir Night."

But Gareth laughed and said, "Sir Night is mine!"

Lancelot gave him wise and cheering words to help him in the fight, while Lynette said, "Heaven keep you."

For a while they traveled on. Then Lynette lifted one arm and softly said, "There."

They stood before the castle of the Lady Lyonors. They watched, and all at once Lyonors came to a high window and waved her hand to them. Then out ran Night, upon a night-black horse, in night-black armor, with white bones painted on it. Ten steps he came in the half-light and then waited. He did not say a word.

Gareth called, "Why do you appear so terrible? Must you frighten men first so that you may win over them? Men say you have the strength of ten. Can you not trust the body which God gave you?"

Night did not answer.

Lady Lyonors cried out in fear, for she knew that if Gareth lost, Death would keep her always. Even Sir Lancelot feared for Gareth.

All at once Sir Lancelot's horse, bearing Gareth, lifted a foot quickly, and Death's dark war horse jumped forward, too. Together came Gareth and Night, spear on helmet—in a great cloud of dust. One was thrown to the ground. It was Sir Night. Quickly Gareth took his sword and cut Death's helmet wide open. Half fell to the right and half to the left, and there within appeared the face of a boy, fresh as a flower!

"Sir," he cried, "save me. My brothers did this wicked work. They made me stay to keep the Lady Lyonors. They never dreamed that you would have strength to pass them all and come to me."

Gareth answered kindly to one only a little younger then himself. "My fair child! Why were you wild enough to call for Lancelot, the chief knight of Arthur's hall, to come to fight you?"

"Fair sir, the others made me do it. They hate the King and they hate Lancelot, the King's friend. They hoped that Lancelot would come to save the Lady Lyonors and that they might kill him thus."

Then happy daylight came across the hills. Lady Lyonors and all her house made merry with song and dance. For they had been afraid of only a fair boy! So all was well, and Gareth won the quest.

He that told the story long ago said that Gareth took the Lady Lyonors to be his wife, but he that told it later said that Gareth took Lynette.

## THE FAIR JEHANE [1]

*Katharine Gibson*

The story of *The Fair Jehane* was first told far back in the days of good King Richard, the Lion-Hearted, and of that bold scamp, Robin Hood. It was sung by an old minstrel, viol in hand, who wandered from castle to castle in old France.

At twilight the good trouvère sang in some château of old Hainault, while ladies on velvet cushions sat listening. Little chil-

1 From Katharine Gibson, *The Golden Bird*. Adapted from William Morris, *Old French Romances*.

dren listened too, little children in fine wool gowns and doublets and long hosen. Little pages with scarlet caps and little scullery maids up from the kitchen listened with all their ears.

The day came when the troubadour's hand began to tremble from age, his voice grew weak, and his footsteps faltered. Then with much care and patience the old man taught his song to young singers, who, holding their heads high, caroled it merrily to their well-tuned instruments. They in turn wandered on the long roads, and through the fields of France, purple with fleurs-de-lis in the spring, golden with ash and linden in the fall. As they walked, they sang like a flock of gay young blackbirds.

The villagers welcomed these young trouvères and fed them. Ladies from the château gave them flagons of red wine and long loaves of crisp bread; the lords gave them roasted fowls and round white cheeses. In return they sang, and sang again. Their songs became known to rich and poor, great and lowly.

After many years these carolings were written down by some unknown pen, undoubtedly that of a monk, who sat at work in a quiet cell of his monastery and, in strange letters, placed the words of the singers upon fine parchment—leaving out their trills and folderols. Thus he turned their songs into stories. So it is that the tale of *The Fair Jehane* has come down the years still clothed in an old, old garb of quaint words, the speech of the days of good King Richard, and of that bold scamp, Robin Hood.

Long ago, near the marshes of Flanders and Hainault, there lived a knight, valiant and hardy and trusty. He had to wife a full fair dame, and for a daughter a much fair maid, who had to name Jehane and was then of the age of twelve years. Much word there was of this fair maiden, for in all the land was none so fair. Her mother spake often to her lord that he should give her in marriage. But so given up was he to the following of tourneys, that he was nowise thinking on the wedding of his daughter. Still his wife ever spake thereof when he came home from his journeying.

This knight had a squire, who had to name Robin and was the valiantest squire to be found in any land. By his prowess and his good fame oft he bore away the prize for his lord from the tourney. Now it befell that Jehane's mother, his lady, thus bespake him: "Robin, my lord is so given up to these tourneys that I know not how to speak with him, whereof I am sore at heart. I pray thee, for love of me, that thou say to him that he doth very ill and is sore blamed that he weddeth not his fair daughter. There is no knight in the land, how rich soever he be, who would not take her with a good will."

"Lady," said Robin, "thou hast said wisely. I will say it right well, for in many things doth my lord trust me, and so will he hereof, meseemeth. I will do all in my power herein."

"It is enough," said the lady.

No long while after, the knight betook him to wending to a tourney afar from his land; and the knight did so well by means of the good deeds of Robin, his squire, that he bore off the prize of the tourney from one party and the other. On the second day the knight betook him to wending to his own land, and Robin put him to reason many times and blamed him much in that he gave not his fair daughter in marriage. Many times he said it till at the last his lord said unto him: "Robin, thou and thy lady give me no peace about the marrying of my daughter, but as yet I know and see no man in my land unto whom I would give her."

"Ah, sir," said Robin, "there is not a knight in thy land who would not take her with a good will."

"Fair friend Robin, they are of no avail, all of them; and to none of them will I give her. To no one would I give her as now, save to one man only, and he forsooth is no knight."

"Sir, tell me of him," said Robin, "and I

shall speak so craftily to him that the marriage shall be made."

"Certes, Robin," said the knight, "from what I see of thee, thou willest well that my daughter should be wedded."

"Sir," said Robin, "thou sayest sooth, for it is well time."

"She shall be wedded right soon," quoth the knight, "if thou accord to the said wedding."

"Certes," said Robin, "of a good will shall I accord thereto."

"Wilt thou give me thy word herein?"

"Yea, sir," said Robin.

"Robin, thou hast served me exceeding well, and I have found thee a valiant man. Great gain have I gotten by thee; to wit, five hundred pounds of land. I tell thee that I owe much to thee; wherefore will I give my fair daughter unto thee, if thou wilt take her."

"Ha, sir!" said Robin. "God's mercy, what is this thou sayest! I am too poor a person to have so high a maiden or one so fair and so rich as my damsel is; I am not meet thereto."

"Robin," quoth the knight, "know that no man in this land shall have her, but I will give her to thee, if thou will it; and thereto will I give thee four hundred pounds."

"Ha, sir," said Robin, "I deem thou mockest me."

"Robin," said the knight, "wot thou surely that I mock thee not. Hold! Here is my glove. I invest thee with four hundred pounds of my land."

"Sir," said Robin, "I will naught naysay it; fair is the gift."

Then the knight delivered to him his glove and invested him with the land and his fair daughter. When the dame heard what her lord had done, she was much sorry and said that Robin should never have her fair daughter.

"Sir," said she, "Robin hath naught, and there is no knight so mighty in all the land but will take her with a good will."

"Nay, dame," said the lord, "have her he shall, wilt thou or wilt thou not; for even so have I made covenant, and I will hold to the same."

The knight sent for his chaplain and brought thither his fair daughter; and so was the fair Jehane betrothed to Robin, and a day was set for the wedding. The third day thereafter, Robin spake to his lord, and prayed him make him a knight, whereas it was naught meet that he should take to him so high a wife and so fair before he was made knight. His lord had great joy thereof; and the next day he was made knight, and the third day wedded the fair maiden with great feast and joyance.

But after Master Robin was made knight, before he wedded the fair Jehane, he spake thus to his lord: "Sir, thou hast made me knight; but true it is I vowed when but a page to go to the shrine of St. James on the morrow of my knighting, there to give thanks I were no longer a squire. On my life did I vow it. Wherefore, I pray, take it not in anger if tomorrow I must needs go my ways so soon as I shall have wedded thy fair daughter; whereas in nowise will I break mine oath."

Much against the will of the knight did Robin go his way. Ere he left, he did lay a wager on a matter with one Sir Raoul. Sir Raoul did declare that the fair Jehane loved him and not Sir Robin. In that Sir Raoul lied a false lie. Wherefore Robin did wager all his lands against Sir Raoul's, that by this he might prove Sir Raoul a lying coward.

. . . . . . .

Much array made the father of the fair lady against the coming of Sir Robin when he did wend his way home at last from the shrine of St. James. A feast was laid, which was great and grand with much of eating and drinking and of dancing and caroling thereto. But sad was Sir Robin, for when he returned from his journey, he found that by an evil craft had Sir Raoul made his lie seem not a lie but very truth. Thus did Sir Robin lose his lands and all that was his. On the morrow he went before his lord and said that he had lost his wager.

In nowise could Sir Robin meet Sir Raoul in combat, for that Sir Raoul was a knight strong and hardy, while Sir Robin was but a stripling, young and like a reed. Full sorrowful was he; in nowise could he bide with the fair Jehane in that she no longer loved him. Heavy of heart was he all day long, and when it was night he went to the stable, and set the saddle on his palfrey, and went forth from the house, bearing with him what he might get him of silver. So came he to Paris, and when he was at Paris he abode there three days.

Much sorrowful was his lady, the fair Jehane, when she called to mind how her lord must needs cast himself out of the house. Much she thought thereof and wept and made great dole. Then on the first hour of the night the lady arose, and took a nag and a harness thereto, and gat her to the road; and she let shear her fair locks, and was otherwise arrayed like an esquire. No man could say were she lad or wench. So much she went by her journeys that she came to Paris, and went after her lord; and she said and declared that she would never make an end before she found him. Thus she rode like to a squire. And on a morning she went forth out of Paris and wended the way toward Orleans until she came to the Tomb Isory, and there she fell in with her lord, Sir Robin. Full fain she was when she saw him, and she drew up to him and greeted him as a stranger. Yet said she not that she was the fair Jehane. Sir Robin gave her greeting back and said, "Fair friend, God give thee joy!"

"Sir," said she, "whence art thou?"

"Fair friend, I wot not right well whither I go, nor where I shall dwell. Forsooth needs must I where Fortune shall lead me, and she is contrary enough. I have lost the thing in the world that most I ever loved, and she hath lost me. Withal I have lost my land, which was great and fair enough. But what hast thou to name, and whither doth God lead thee?"

"Certes, sir," said Jehane, "I am minded for Marseilles-on-sea, where is war, I hope. There would I serve some valiant man, about whom I shall learn me arms if God will. For I am so undone in mine own country that therein for a while I may not have peace. But, sir, meseemeth that thou be a knight, and I would serve thee with a right good will if it please thee."

"Fair friend," said Robin, "a knight am I verily. And where I may look to find war, thitherward would I draw full willingly. But tell me what thou hast to name?"

"Sir," said she, "I have to name John."

"In a good hour," quoth the knight.

"And thou, sir, how art thou named?"

"John," said he, "I have to name Robin."

"Sir Robin, retain me as thine esquire, and I will serve thee to my power."

"John, so would I with a good will. But so little of money have I that I must needs sell my horse before three days are worn. Wherefore I cannot retain thee."

"Sir," said John, "be not dismayed thereof, for God will aid thee if it please Him. But tell me, where wilt thou eat thy dinner?"

"John, my dinner will soon be made; for not another penny have I than three sols of Paris."

"Sir," said John, "be naught dismayed thereof, for I have hard on ten pounds Tournais, whereof thou shalt not lack if thou hast not to spend at thy will."

"Fair friend John, have thou mickle thanks."

Then made they good speed to a town; there John bought him meat for his lord and they ate. When they had eaten, the knight slept in a bed and John at his feet. When they had slept, John did on the bridles; and they mounted and gat to the road. They went so far by their journeys that they came to Marseilles-on-sea. But of war they heard no word there, whereof they were much sorry, so Sir Robin said to John, "What do we? Thou hast lent me of thy moneys, whereof I thank thee; I will give them back to thee, for I will sell my steed and quit me toward thee."

"Sir," said John, "if it please thee, believe me; and I shall tell thee what we do. I have yet well an hundred sols of Tournais;

and if it please thee, I will sell our two horses and make money thereby. For I am the best of bakers that ye may wot of, and I will make French bread; and I doubt me not but I shall earn my spending well and bountifully."

"John," said Sir Robin, "I grant it thee to do all as thou wilt."

On the morrow John sold the two horses for ten pounds Tournais, and bought corn and let grind it, and bought baskets, and fell to making French bread, so good and so well made that he sold it for more than the best baker of the town might do. He did so much within two years that he had well an hundred pounds of chattels. Then said John to his lord, "Let us now buy a very great house, and buy us wine and take to harboring good folk. Let us set up an inn, an hostelry."

"John," said Sir Robin, "do according to thy will, for I grant it thee, and moreover I praise thee much."

So John bought a house, great and fair, and harbored good folk and earned plenteously. He arrayed his lord well and richly; and Sir Robin had his palfrey, and went to eat and drink with the most worthy of the town. And John sent him wine and victual, so that all the company marveled thereat. So much he gained that in three years' time he had gotten him more than three hundred pounds of garnishment. For four years more did Sir Robin and John dwell at Marseilles, and John did do marvelous well. So sweet he was and so debonair, that he made himself loved of all the neighbors; and he maintained his lord so nobly and so richly that it was a wonder to behold. When the end of seven years drew nigh, John fell to talk with his lord, Sir Robin, and spake thus: "Sir, we have now been a great while in this country, and so much have we gained that we have hard on six hundred pounds of chattels, what of money, what of silver."

"Forsooth, John," said Sir Robin, "they be not mine but thine; for it is thou hast earned them."

"Sir," said John, "saving thy grace, it is not so, but they are thine; for thou art my rightful lord, and never, if it please God, will I change."

"Gramercy, John, I hold thee not for servant but for companion and friend."

"Sir," said John, "all days have I kept thee loyal company and shall do from henceforth."

Then did John sell all their chattels and bought three horses: a palfrey for his lord, another for himself, and one to carry all their goods. They took leave of the neighbors and the most worthy of the town, who were sore grieved of their departure; and within fifteen days, they were journeying toward their own country.

In three weeks' space they came into their own land. Then did Robin make known to his lord, whose daughter he had wedded, that he was at hand. The lord was much joyful thereof, for he was deeming well that his daughter would be with him. And indeed she was, but in the guise of an esquire. Sir Robin was well received. When the Lord could have no tidings of his daughter, he was right sorrowful; nevertheless he made good feast to Sir Robin and bade thereto his knights and neighbors. Thither came Sir Raoul, the same who held the land of Sir Robin wrongfully. Great was the joy that day and the morrow. Then did Sir Robin tell John of the wager. Also did Sir Robin tell John how that he now believed Sir Raoul had lied a black lie and held his lands wrongfully.

"Sir," said John, "do thou accuse him of treason, and I will do the battle for thee."

"Nay, John," said Sir Robin, "thou shalt not do it. None shall do battle save me. Am I not now strong and full hardy? Nowise shalt thou hang shield on neck herein."

So were the pledges given, and the day of battle appointed, fifteen days from that day without naysay.

Now hear ye the marvels of what John did. John, who had to name my Lady Jehane, had in the house of her father a cousin of hers, who was a fair damsel of some five and twenty years. Jehane came to her and laid all the whole truth bare to her and told the whole business from point to point. The fair Jehane prayed her good cousin to hide all this matter until the time and the hour came when she should make herself known to her father.

Then in a chamber made ready by her cousin did the Lady Jehane take her ease the best she might. And she let cut and shape for her duly eight gowns, two of scarlet, two of green, which is called vair, two of blue, which is called perse, and two of cloth of silk. And she took so well her ease that she came back to her most beauty and was so fair and dainty as no lady might be more.

But when it came to the end of the fifteen days, then was Sir Robin sore grieving of John, his esquire, because he had lost him and knew not where he was. But still did he apparel him for the fight as one who had heart enough and hardihood.

On the morn of the day whenas the battle was appointed, came both the knights armed. They drew apart from one another, and then they fell on each other with the irons of their weapons and smote on each other with so great heat that they bore down each other's horses to the earth beneath their bodies. Sir Raoul was hurt a little on the left side. Sir Robin rose up the first and smote him a great stroke on the helm in such wise that he beat the mail and cut it all. But the mail was so strong that he wounded Sir Raoul not; howbeit he made him to stagger so that he caught hold of his saddle, and if he had not, he had fallen to earth. Then Sir Raoul, who was a mighty knight, smote Sir Robin so great a stroke upon the helm that it all astonied him but hurt him not.

Now were both knights come unto the skirmish on foot in that they had left their steeds. They hewed in pieces each other's shields and helms and hauberks and drew the blood from each other's bodies with their biting swords. Yet had neither of them fear of death or shame; nevertheless the nighness of them to each other called on them to bring the battle to an end. Sir Robin took his sword in both hands and smote Sir Raoul with all his might on the helm and sheared it amidst so that one half thereof fell upon each shoulder; and he sheared the steel coif and made him a great wound on the head.

Sir Raoul was so astonied of the stroke that he bent him to the earth on one knee; but he rose up straightway and was in great misease when he thus found his head naked, and great fear of death he had. But he came up to Sir Robin and fetched a stroke with all his might on what he had of a shield, and he sheared it asunder; and the stroke came on the helm and cut into it well three fingers so that the sword came on the mail, which was right good, and that the sword brake atwain.

When Sir Raoul saw his sword broken and his head naked, he doubted much the death. Nevertheless, he stooped down to earth and took up a great stone in his two hands and cast it after Sir Robin with all his might. But Sir Robin turned aside when he saw the stone coming and ran on Sir Raoul, who took to flight all over the field; and Sir Robin said to him that he would slay him not if he cried craven. Whereon Sir Raoul thus bespake him: "Have mercy on me, gentle knight; and lo, here my sword, so much as I have thereof, I render to thee and all of me therewith unto thy mercy. I pray thee have pity of me and beg of thy lord and mine to have mercy on me and that thou and he save my life. Then will I give thee both thy land and mine. For I have held it against right and against reason. And I am at thy feet with a black lie in my teeth, which thou hast proven false by the sword."

When Sir Robin heard this, he said that he had done enough, and he prayed his lord so much that he pardoned Sir Raoul of his misdeed in such wise that he was quit thereof on condition that he should go over seas and abide there lifelong.

Thuswise conquered Sir Robin his land and the land of Sir Raoul to boot for all his days. But he was sore grieving and sad at heart of his good dame and fair he had lost, that he could have no solace. On the other hand, he was sore grieving for John, his esquire, whom he had so lost that a marvel it was. And his lord was no less sad at heart for his fair daughter, whom he had thus lost and of whom he might have no tidings.

But dame Jehane, who was in the chamber of her cousin for fifteen days in good ease, when she wotted that her lord had vanquished the battle, was exceeding much at peace. Now she had let make for her four pairs of gowns, as is aforesaid, and clad herself with the richest of them, which was of silk banded of fine gold of Araby. Moreover, she was so fair of body and of visage, and so dainty withal, that naught in the world might be found fairer, so that her cousin all marveled at her great beauty. So she called to her cousin and said, "How deemest thou of me?"

"What, dame!" said her cousin. "Thou art the fairest lady of the world."

"I shall tell thee then, fair cousin, what thou shalt do. Go thou and tell my father that he need make dole no more but be glad and joyful; and that thou barest him good news of his daughter, who is whole and well; and that he come with thee and thou wilt show him. Then bring him hither, and meseemeth that he will see me with a good will."

The damsel did well the errand; and when the father saw his fair daughter, he had so great joy that scarce might he speak to her. Then did he send for his wife; and when she came into the chamber where was the fair Jehane and saw her and knew her, she swooned for joy; and then none might believe the great joy she made of her daughter.

Whilst they were in this joy, the father of the fair lady went to seek Sir Robin and bespake him thus: "Sir Robin, fair sweet son, tidings I can say thee exceeding joyous us between."

"Certes," said Sir Robin, "of joy have I great need, for none save God can make it whereby I may have my joy. For I have lost thy fair daughter, whereof have I sore grief at heart. And thereto have I lost my swain, who of all the world hath done me most good; to wit, John the Good, my esquire."

Then did the lord tell his knight tidings of the fair Jehane. When Sir Robin heard them, he trembled all with joy and said to his lord: "Ah, sir, for God's sake bring me where I may see if this be true."

"With a good will," said the lord. "Let us hasten."

The lord went before and he after, till they were come to the chamber where the mother was yet making great feast of her daughter, and they were weeping with joy one over the other. When they saw their rightful lords a-coming, they rose up; and so soon as Sir Robin knew his wife, he ran to her with his arms abroad, and they wept for joy and pity.

Then the lord commanded the tables to be laid for supper, and they supped and made great joy. After supper, when the feast had been right great, Sir Robin and the fair Jehane spoke of many things, and Sir Robin asked of her where she had been; and she said: "Sir, long were it to tell, but thou shalt know it well in time. Now tell me what thou couldst to do and where thou hast been so long a while."

"Lady," said Sir Robin, "that will I well tell thee."

So he fell to telling all that she well knew, and of John, his esquire, who had done him so much good, and said that he was so troubled whereas he had thus lost him that he would make never an end of wandering till he had found him, and that he would bestir himself thereto the morrow's morn.

"Sir," said the lady, "that were folly; and how should it be then? Wouldst thou leave me?"

"Forsooth, dame," said he "e'en so it behoveth me. For none did ever so much for another as did he for me."

"Sir," said the dame, "wherein he did for thee, he did but duly. Even so he was bound to do."

"Dame," said Sir Robin, "by what thou sayest thou shouldst know him."

"Forsooth," said the lady, "I should

ought to know him well, for never did he anything whereof I wotted not."

"Lady," said Sir Robin, "thou makest me to marvel at thy words."

"Sir," said the lady, "never marvel thou hereof. If I tell thee a word for sooth and for certain, wilt thou not believe me?"

"Dame," said he, "yea, verily."

"Well, then, believe me in this," said she; "for wot of a verity that I am the very same John whom thou wouldst go seek, and I will tell thee now."

Then did the fair Jehane tell her lord all; and greatly did he marvel and much. Thus did Sir Robin understand well that it was she that had served him and that John was in truth my Lady Jehane, and my Lady Jehane had been John, his esquire. So great joy he had that none could say it or think it; and much he wondered in his heart how she could think to do that which so turned to her great goodness. Wherefore he loved her the more all the days of his life.

Thus were these two persons together. Good life they led, as for young folks who loved dearly together. Long they lived upon their land, which was both fair and wide; and greatly did they get increase both in wealth and in honor.

## *Legends and Hero Tales: Suggested Grades*

*Grade Four*
The Ghost of the Great White Stag

*Grade Five*
Fin McCoul and the Giant
The First Harp

*Grade Six*
The Heroes of Asgard
The Making of the Hammer
Pandora
The Winged Horse

*Grade Seven*
The Story of Odysseus
The Winning of Atalanta
The Fair Jehane

*Grade Eight*
Sigurd the Volsung
Gareth and Lynette

## *Books of Legends and Hero Tales*

### *Grade Four*

Beston, Henry B., *The Sons of Kai,* illus. by Don Dickerman. Macmillan.

Brown, Abbie Farwell, *In the Days of the Giants,* illus. by E. Boyd Smith. Houghton Mifflin.

Creswick, Paul, *Robin Hood and His Adventures,* illus. by N. C. Wyeth. McKay.

DeHuff, Elizabeth, W., *Tay Tay's Tales,* illus. by Indian artists. Harcourt, Brace.

Parker, Arthur C., *Skunny Wundy, and Other Indian Tales,* illus. by Will Crawford. Doubleday, Doran.

Purnell, Idella, and John M. Weatherwax, *The Talking Bird: An Aztec Story Book,* illus. by Frances Purnell Dehlsen. Macmillan.

### *Grades Five and Six*

Baker, Emilie Kip, *Stories of Old Greece and Rome.* Macmillan.

———, *Stories from Northern Myths.* Macmillan.

Barbour, Harriot Buxton, *Old English Tales Retold,* illus. by Rodney Thomson. Macmillan.

Buckley, Elsie Finnimore, *Children of the Dawn,* illus. by Frank C. Pape. Stokes.

Chrisman, Arthur Bowie, *Shen of the Sea,* illus. by Else Hasselriis. Dutton.

Colum, Padraic, *The Big Tree of Bunlahy,* illus. by Jack Yeats. Macmillan.

———, *The Children of Odin,* illus. by Willy Pogány. Macmillan.

———, *The Golden Fleece,* illus. by Willy Pogány. Macmillan.

Eastman, Charles, and Elaine Eastman, *Wigwam Evenings,* illus. by E. W. Deming. Little, Brown.

Hall, Jennie, *Viking Tales,* illus. by Victor R. Lambkin. Rand McNally.

Hawthorne, Nathaniel, *A Wonder Book for Boys and Girls,* illus. by Arthur Rackham. Doubleday, Doran.

Hutchinson, W. M. L., *The Golden Porch,* illus. by Dugald Walker. Longmans.

Jacobs, Joseph, *Celtic Fairy Tales,* illus. by John D. Batten. Putnam.

Judd, Mary Catherine, *Wigwam Stories, Told by North American Indians,* illus. by Angel de Cora. Ginn.

Keary, A. and E., *The Heroes of Asgard,* illus. by C. E. Brock. Macmillan.

Lansing, Marian F., *Page, Esquire, and Knight.* Ginn.

Linderman, Frank B., *Old Man Coyote,* illus. by H. M. Stoops. Day.

Marshall, Henrietta E., *Stories of Beowulf.* Dutton.

Nusbaum, Aileen, *Zuni Indian Tales,* illus. by Margaret Finnan. Putnam.

Pogány, Nandor, *The Hungarian Fairy Book,* illus. by Willy Pogány. Stokes.

Pyle, Howard, *The Merry Adventures of Robin Hood,* illus. by the author. Scribner.

Rhead, Louis, *Bold Robin Hood and His Outlaw Band,* illus. by the author. Harper.

## Grades Seven and Eight

Baldwin, James, *The Story of Roland,* illus. by Peter Hurd. Scribner.

———, *The Story of Siegfried,* illus. by Peter Hurd. Scribner.

———, *The Sampo, a Wonder Tale of the Old North,* illus. by N. E. Wyeth. Scribner.

Collier, Virginia M., and Jeanette Eaton, *Roland the Warrior,* illus. by Frank Schoonover. Harcourt, Brace.

Colum, Padraic, *The Children's Homer,* illus. by Willy Pogány. Macmillan.

Crew, Helen Coale, *Singing Seaman.* Appleton-Century.

Gibson, Katherine, *The Golden Bird,* illus. by Edwin G. Sommers. Macmillan.

Higginson, Thomas Wentworth, *Tales of the Enchanted Islands of the Atlantic,* illus. by Albert Herter. Macmillan.

Hosford, Dorothy, *Sons of the Volsungs,* illus. by Frank Dobias. Macmillan.

Leighton, Robert, *Olaf the Glorious,* illus. by Henry C. Pitz. Macmillan.

MacLeod, Mary, *The Book of King Arthur and His Noble Knights,* illus. by A. G. Walker. Stokes.

Martin, John, *Wolf's Head and the Queen,* illus. by Nelson Grofé. Scribner.

Mukerji, Dhan Gopal, *Rama, the Hero of India,* illus. by Edgar Parin D'Aulaire. Dutton.

Pyle, Howard, *The Story of King Arthur and His Knights,* illus. by the author. Scribner.

Seredy, Kate, *The White Stag,* illus. by the author. Viking.

Sherwood, Merriam, *The Tale of the Warrior Lord,* illus. by Henry C. Pitz. Longmans.

Stephens, James, *Irish Fairy Tales,* illus. by Arthur Rackham. Macmillan.

Young, Ella, *The Tangle-Coated Horse,* illus. by Vera Brock. Longmans.

## *Student Activities*

1. Do the versions of the old tales given in this book differ from those heard in your childhood? Compare the American variant, "The Gingerbread Boy," with the English, "Johnny Cake," and the Scotch, "The Wee Bannock." (So far as is known, making the runaway of gingerbread is an American invention.)

2. Have you noticed how themes recur in the old tales? What stories besides "Cinderella" and "Boots" have the "youngest daughter or son" motif? What "noodles" have the same success as "Lazy Jack"? What "pourquoi" stories can you find—stories that explain the characteristics of animals or other phenomena of nature, such as "Why the Bear Is Stumpy-Tailed"? See how many other examples of recurring themes you can discover. It is interesting to note also that many of these same motifs and essential plots are the bases of most of our modern fiction.

3. What stories with accumulative plots ("The Old Woman and Her Pig" is an example) would you suggest for reading by young children who are learning to read? Can you see parallel reasons for the use of the accumulative tale in a folk society that had no written language?

4. Have you any evidence that myth-making continues in the present day? Have you encountered any examples of imaginary exploits being credited to famous people and popular heroes? Are these legends transmitted in ways at all similar to those in which the old folk tales were preserved? At not infrequent intervals stories of unusual and spectacular occurrences seem to spring up simultaneously in quite distant places. Their authenticity can never be proved nor their origin discovered. Do you know of any such stories? Do you think they represent folklore in the making?

5. Do you know any legends of local industrial heroes of the type of "Paul Bunyan" (page 478)? It is said that a body of such tales exists about a fabulous hero of the steel mills, a deep-sea fisherman, a stevedore on the Mississippi River, a cowboy of the plains, a desert prospector, and a harvester in the wheat fields of the northwest. There are probably others. Collect as many such unwritten tales as you can. Could they be retold to make suitable stories for children?

6. A class in children's literature sometimes finds it possible to produce a puppet play based on one of the old folk tales. The class working in groups may arrange the scenario, make the puppet theater and puppets, and play the parts. Perhaps you might take your show to a schoolroom and entertain the children, or invite them to your classroom to see it. The children in turn might invite you to see a play or show of theirs.

7. It is very fine training for a prospective teacher to get a repertory of stories he or she can tell. A story should not be memorized verbatim, but complete familiarity with it will give the teller assurance and permit flexibility in the telling. Impersonation, costume, or properties are unnecessary, though some individuals can use them effectively without spoiling a story. Usually simple and straightforward telling is best, and the only requirement to make a good

storyteller is a love of the story and the desire to share it with others. Perhaps you might volunteer your services for a story hour at a settlement house or institution for underprivileged children. You could give great pleasure to your hearers and you would yourself receive much satisfaction.

## *References for Students*

### *Folk Tales*

Curry, Charles M., and Erle E. Clippinger, *Children's Literature,* Section III. Rand McNally.

Darton, F. J. Harvey, *Children's Books in England,* Chapter 6. Macmillan.

Eastman, Mary H., *Index to Fairy Tales, Myths, and Legends.* Faxon.

Hansen, Harry, "The Brothers Grimm," *The Horn Book,* XV: 113.

Hartland, E. S., *The Science of Fairy Tales.* Stokes.

Hill, May, "The Place of the Folk Tale Today," *Childhood Education,* VIII: 123.

Jacobs, Joseph, *The Fables of Aesop.* Macmillan.

Keightley, Thomas, *Fairy Mythology.* Bell (London).

Kready, Laura F., *A Study of Fairy Tales.* Houghton Mifflin.

Lang, Andrew, *Custom and Myth,* pages 10-28. Longmans.

Lee, F. H., *Folk Tales of All Nations.* Coward-McCann.

Moore, Annie E., *Literature Old and New for Children,* Chapters 3-6, Houghton Mifflin.

Wittels, Fritz, "An Apology for Fairy Tales," *Child Study,* IX: 67.

### *Legends and Hero Tales*

Bulfinch, Thomas, *The Age of Chivalry.* McKay.

———, *The Golden Age of Myth and Legend.* Stokes.

———, *The Legends of Charlemagne.* McKay.

Carmer, Carl, *The Hurricane's Children.* Farrar and Rinehart.

Curtin, Jeremiah, *Hero Tales of Ireland.* Little, Brown.

Cushing, Hamilton, *Zuni Folk Tales.* Knopf.

Darton, F. J. Harvey, *Wonder Book of Old Romance,* illus. by Norman Ault. Stokes.

Fiske, John, *Myths and Myth-Makers.* Houghton Mifflin.

Gayley, Charles Mills, *Classic Myths in English Literature and in Art.* Ginn.

Henderson, Gertrude, *The Ring of the Nibelung.* Knopf.

Lang, Andrew, and S. H. Butcher, *The Odyssey.* Macmillan.

Mabie, Hamilton Wright, *Norse Stories Retold from the Eddas.* Dodd Mead.

Tatlock, Jessie M., *Greek and Roman Mythology.* Appleton-Century.

Verrill, A. H. *The American Indian, North, South, and Central America.* Appleton-Century.

Wilson, Calvin Dill, *The Story of the Cid.* Lothrop.

## Storytelling

Bone, Woutrina A., *Children's Stories and How to Tell Them.* Harcourt, Brace.

Bryant, Sara Cone, *How To Tell Stories to Children.* Houghton Mifflin.

Dalgliesh, Alice, *First Experiences with Literature,* Chapter 6. Scribner.

Nowlin, Clifford H., *The Story Teller and His Pack.* Bradley.

Shedlock, Marie L., *The Art of the Story-Teller.* Appleton-Century.

## Puppets and Plays

Ackley, Edith F., *Marionettes,* illus. by Marjorie Flack. Stokes.

Anderson, Madge, *Heroes of the Puppet Stage.* Harcourt, Brace.

Bufano, Remo, *Be a Puppet Showman,* Appleton-Century.

Brown, Corinne, *Creative Drama in the Lower School.* Appleton-Century.

Ficklen, Bessie A., *A Handbook of Fist Puppets.* Stokes.

Hoben, Alice M., *The Beginner's Puppet Show.* Noble.

Mackay, Constance D'Arcy, *Costumes and Scenery for Amateurs.* Holt.

Melcher, Marguerite Fellows, *Offstage,* illus. by Hilda Richman. Knopf.

Mills, Winifred H., and Louise M. Dunn, *Marionettes, Masks and Shadows,* illus. by Corydon Bell. Doubleday, Doran.

Murray, Josephine, and Effie G. Bathurst, *Creative Ways for Children's Programs.* Silver Burdett.

Rossback, C. Edmund, *Making Marionettes.* Harcourt, Brace.

Ward, Winifred, *Creative Dramatics.* Appleton-Century.

Warner, Frances L., *Ragamuffin Marionettes,* illus. by Margaret Freeman. Houghton Mifflin.

*Stories of Then and Now*

# STORIES OF THEN AND NOW

## Modern Literature for Children

BOOKS purposely written for children are limited almost entirely to the last two hundred years. Before 1744, when John Newbery opened his bookshop and publishing business in London, books intended for children received little attention. The few published before that time were lesson books and the so-called "Books of Courtesy"; the latter were guidebooks of conduct and manners for the youth of the upper classes. Books to be read for pleasure or information were almost unknown.

The earliest lesson book of which we have any knowledge was the *Hornbook,*[1] which was first printed in the latter part of the 1500's. It was made of a sheet of printed paper, mounted on wood and covered with transparent horn for protection. The edges were bound with various metals—copper, brass, and for the well-to-do, decorated silver. All of the hornbooks had handles, and often there was a hole in the handle, so the hornbook could be hung on a string about the child's neck. The surface was small, only about 3 by 4 inches, but it generally carried a cross, the alphabet in both capitals and small letters, the vowels, the combinations of vowels and consonants such as *ab, eb,* etc., the Roman numerals, and part of the Lord's Prayer. Hornbooks were widely used in both England and America throughout the seventeenth century and some were in use as late as the middle of the eighteenth century.

Between 1683 and 1691 appeared a book made especially for the children of the American colonies—*The New England Primer.*[2] It was probably first printed in England, but in 1691 an edition was issued in Boston. Its content was changed slightly from time to time, but throughout the colonial period it continued to be the standard lesson book in America. *The New England Primer* was a small book, about 3 by 4½ inches, had about 100 pages, and was literally bound in "boards," not pasteboard, but covers of oak about one-eighth of an inch thick. It contained the alphabet, words and syllables

1 An illustration showing the front and back of a *hornbook* made about 1649 appears on page 22.

2 Two pages of a *New England Primer* printed in 1727 are reproduced on page 23.

for spelling lessons, quotations from the Bible, the Lord's Prayer, the Catechism, several hymns and verses, and spiritual advice from Cotton Mather. There were rhymes for each letter of the alphabet, beginning

In Adam's Fall
We sinnéd all.

and ending

Zaccheus he
Did climb the Tree
His Lord to see.

There are a few copies of *The New England Primer* in museums and private collections and the crude woodcuts that illustrate each of the rhymes are most interesting. There is a larger woodcut that shows the martyrdom of John Rogers, a minister of London who was burned at the stake in 1554. In the picture his wife and ten children look on at his execution. There follow six pages of rhymed advice left by Rogers to his children, of which the following is an example:

Be never proud by any means,
Build not your house too high;
But always have before your eyes
That you were born to die.

The Puritan influence was strong in England and America throughout the 1600's and the first half of the 1700's; books for children, dominated by it, stressed religious instruction and preparation for death. Then as now, children appropriated adult books that interested them, and in *Pilgrim's Progress* (1678) they found satisfaction in John Bunyan's dignified prose and excellent narrative. Our judgment of the stern piousness of the literature of this period should not be too harsh; it was an era when living was hard, but it built strong men and women whom we can respect. It is pleasant to remember that children at this time found enjoyment in three other books not intended for them: *Robinson Crusoe* (1714), *Gulliver's Travels* (1726), and *Baron Munchausen* (1785).

Many books printed still earlier were undoubtedly read by children. William Caxton, the first English printer, published between 1477 and 1491 Malory's *Morte d' Arthur, Reynard the Fox,* and an excellent translation from the French of *Aesop's Fables*—all for adults, but some children must have read them. These books were expensive; the printing was expensive and the bindings, usually of leather, were expensive.

By the sixteenth century printing became cheaper and a great many *broadsides* were issued—single sheets of paper with printing on one side only. Well-known English ballads appeared on broadsides, especially the ballads of Robin Hood. By this time there was a large amount of literature for the common people being distributed in France in the form of a few leaves stitched together which carried farces and tales in prose and verse. Crude translations into English were made and became immensely popular. They were sold by itinerant peddlers called chapmen and soon the pamphlets came to be called *chapbooks.* Versions of English folk stories were added and though they were not intended for children at all, boys and girls of the sixteenth and seventeenth centuries could buy for a penny "Jack the Giant Killer," "Babes in the Wood," "Tom Thumb," or "Dick Whittington." After Perrault's *Tales of My Mother Goose* was translated into English early in the eighteenth century, the tales were issued separately as chapbooks. The same woodcuts were used over and over again in these books and often had little connection with the text. A picture of Queen Anne served to represent "Sleeping Beauty," and Henry VIII appeared as "Jack the Giant Killer." The printing was poor and trying on the eyes. Many of the pictures were in shockingly bad taste and the stories were interspersed with ribald jokes. In many cases the chapbooks were truly "penny dreadfuls."

It was into this scene that John Newbery came. Afterward Oliver Goldsmith was to characterize him in *The Vicar of Wakefield* as "the philanthropic bookseller in Saint Paul's Churchyard, who has written so many little books for children. He called himself their friend, but he was the friend of all mankind." Goldsmith's praise may have been extravagant, but there is no question that Newbery brought to children pleasure and happiness in books that had been almost entirely lacking before his time.

Actual information about John Newbery, the man, is meager, but in 1744 he moved his bookselling and publishing business from Reading to London and soon after published the *Little Pretty Pocket Book,* the subtitle of which read, "Intended for the Instruction and Amusement of Little Master Tommy and Pretty Miss Polly, with an agreeable Letter to read from Jack the Giant Killer." It is probable that Newbery wrote the *Little Pretty Pocket Book* himself, and while it had no literary significance it was frankly written to please children. There were alphabet rhymes, but this time the rhymes were about children's games and the pictures showed children playing games—something previously unknown except in the translation of the *Orbis Pictus.*[1] The *Little Pretty Pocket Book,* however, was free of the lessons in Latin which were a part of the *Orbis Pictus;* it was a book for pleasure.

The *Little Pretty Pocket Book* was the beginning of a long list of books that delighted children.[2] Newbery's books were well printed and well illustrated, and for the covers he imported paper from Holland, flowered gilt paper that made the books gay and charming. It is no wonder he found a ready market for the books he produced, many of which were reprinted in America. In 1922 when an annual award was instituted in the United States for

[1] See pages 23, 24.

[2] Charles Welsh, *A Bookseller of the Last Century.* Printed for Griffith, Farren, Okeden, and Welsh, successors to Newbery and Harris, at the sign of the Bible and Sun, in St. Paul's Churchyard, London, 1885.

First alph Bewick

the most distinguished book for children by an American author, it was fitting that the award be called the John Newbery Medal.

The most famous books published by Newbery were *Mother Goose's Melody* and *The History of Little Goody Two-Shoes.* Oliver Goldsmith was in Newbery's employ and had a hand in compiling the former and perhaps wrote the latter. *Little Goody Two-Shoes* appeared in 1765, ten years before Newbery's death, but it was singularly prophetic of the spirit that was to dominate children's literature for the next seventy-five years.

The publication of Rousseau's *Emile* in 1762 brought about a tremendous interest in the education of children. Rousseau advocated that classical methods of teaching be discarded and that children be taught about real things and the world in which they lived. This philosophy was reflected in three-quarters of a century of children's books devoted to *practical education.* An astonishing number of books were written by very serious people, but almost none of them can command even passing interest from children today; it is doubtful indeed that present-day children could be got to read them at all.

The first of the realistic books of this period was *The History of Sandford and Merton* by Thomas Day. It is hardly a story, though it centers around three characters—two little boys, Harry Sandford and Tommy Merton, and their schoolmaster, Mr. Barlow, with whom they lived. Mr. Barlow talks to them at great length about history and physical geography and proper conduct. He is ready with the answer to any question. Mr. Barlow is the forerunner of many uncles, aunts, parents, grandparents, and other adult characters still being introduced into children's books as devices for conveying information—characters that often have no other reason for being in the story.

*Sandford and Merton* was followed by a great supply of similar books for similar purposes in England; among them were *Evenings at Home,* by John Aiken and Anna Letitia Barbauld, and *The Parent's Assistant,* by Maria Edgeworth. In the latter is found the story, "Waste Not, Want Not," which was well known by our grandparents. The story hinges on a boy saving a piece of string which he produces at a crucial moment to string his bow and win the archery contest.

In point of number of books of this type by a single author, America led the field. S. G. Goodrich, under the pen name Peter Parley, published 116 books in a period of thirty years. The first, *The Tales of Peter Parley about America,* appeared in 1827, and there followed *The Tales of Peter Parley about Africa, about Great Britain,* about most of the countries of the world, about the figures of history, about the wonders of science, etc.—there was little that Peter Parley did not write "tales about." The books had no permanent value, but 7,000,000 copies were sold. Goodrich was accused of hiring other writers to produce his books for him, and it is clear that the name Peter Parley was pirated in both England and America, for books bearing the name continued to appear after Goodrich was dead.

Another American of the same period, Jacob Abbott, rivaled Peter Parley in output and popularity. His series of *Rollo* books ran to 28 volumes under such titles as *Rollo at Work, Rollo at Play, Rollo in Europe,* etc. There are also 10 volumes of his *Franconia Stories.* Abbott's stories give information and instruction, but at the same time they picture wholesome family life and his child characters go sleighing, pop corn, and have a good deal of fun. Of all the so-called "didactic" writers of the time, his books have longest endured. The *Franconia Stories* may still be found in libraries and continue to have some interest for children.

Few of the writers concerned with practical education had as kind and benign an attitude toward children as Jacob Abbott. On the contrary, they were severe; if the child characters in their stories at any time failed to use the judgment of adults in meeting difficult situations, they were made to appear foolish, usually by another child character who always did the right thing. As a result the reader can neither sympathize with the character in the wrong nor admire the one in the right, he can only feel embarrassed and confused—not a very good end result. The writers of this school were, most of them, "strong antidotes to hilarity," humor had little place in their scheme of living. They also rigidly banned all fancy and loudly condemned all the old fairy tales.

Before the middle of the nineteenth century a revolt had taken place. Earlier Charles Lamb, Coleridge, and Wordsworth had grieved at the banishment of the fairies. When Grimms' fairy tales were translated into English in 1823 there was an audience ready for them, but it was almost twenty years before the fairy tale, and with it romance and fantasy, regained a sure footing. It is perhaps not out of place to note here that within the last decade, in the twentieth century, a situation similar in children's reading arose; again in our day there was a movement to displace all fantasy and accept only realistic literature, but again, as a hundred years ago, the fairy tale has held its rightful place as a part of children's reading.

The German *Hausmärchen* were not the only fairy tales to be welcomed in England and America. In 1857, A. and E. Keary translated from the Norse, *The Heroes of Asgard,* and Dasent translated Asbjörnsen and Moe's *Popular Tales from the Norse;* both found eager readers. It was at about the same time, in 1846, that English speaking children were introduced to the work of one of the greatest writers of all time, Hans Christian Andersen. To children's literature were added "The Tinder Box," "The Wild Swans," "The Emperor's New Clothes," "The Nightingale," and Andersen's other immortal stories.

The question is sometimes asked, how far were Andersen's fairy tales original and how much did he draw upon folklore? Many of Andersen's plots and incidents were drawn from folklore, but he wove about them a wealth of imaginative detail in language so clear and beautiful that they became distinctly his own creations. A comparison of some of Andersen's stories with their counterparts in folk literature will make this point clear. For example, "The Tinder Box" parallels "The Blue Light" from Grimm, and a skeleton of "The Wild Swans" is found in "The Seven Ravens" from Grimm, but the reader will recognize the artistry with which Andersen has clothed the tales, at the same time preserving the straightforwardness of the originals.

We have a number of other examples in children's literature of outstanding stories based upon folklore into which the author has put so much of himself that a new story has resulted. The *Just So Stories* reflect the folklore of India, yet they are truly Kipling; Washington Irving embroidered the legends that he chose and made them his own; Joel Chandler Harris created the character of *Uncle Remus* and through that medium the animal tales of the plantations took new forms. It is sometimes difficult to distinguish between excellent retellings of traditional stories and the use of the same material by an author to create new wholes. When comparison with an early version from folk sources shows an author has contributed much that is new and original, we think of the story as the author's own. Our evaluation of it then is based upon the skill, artistry, and sincerity with which the story in its new form is presented.

Hans Christian Andersen has long been recognized as the master of the fanciful tale, but sometimes we are too hasty in offering his stories to children. They are not for young children. "The Tinder Box" is the simplest, but it will not find its best audience until the third and fourth grades. "The Nightingale" and several others are best suited to the upper grades. They are beautiful and absorbing stories, but the concepts are too mature for young children.

The year in which Andersen's *Fairy Tales* was translated from the Danish into English marked the appearance of Lear's *Book of Nonsense,* and humor as well as fantasy was restored as a desirable part of children's reading. With the publication of Lewis Carroll's *Alice in Wonderland* in 1865, the horizon of children's literature was widened still further. *Alice* taught no lessons, pointed no moral, its only purpose was pleasure. From that time on, children's stories offered enjoyment without apology, not to miniature adults but to children, who in their own right have interests that may be satisfied by literature. That these interests are varied we know to be true, and when children's books are freed of formal obligations, a wide range of subjects and plots may be utilized to present life and present it whole.

Close on the heels of *Alice in Wonderland* came *Little Women,* to be followed in a comparatively short time by *The Hoosier Schoolmaster, Tom Sawyer* and *Huckleberry Finn, Treasure Island,* and the host of fine books that join with the old to make a child's library today. In such a library may be found stories of boys and girls in a setting of simple home situations or in one of high adventure, stories of patriotism and devoted loyalty, stories of the wonders of nature and science, and stories of brave men and women who carry forward the work of the world in obscure and lonely positions and in high places. Paralleling the enduring stories is fine verse—verse of strength and force, of delicacy and charm, of rollicking good humor and fun. This stream of literature for children is constantly being fed. In our own day have appeared *Dr. Dolittle, Smoky, Hitty, When We Were Very Young, The Dark Frigate, Millions of Cats, The Good Master, Invincible Louisa,*

*Caddie Woodlawn,* and many others. Each year [1] sees the publication of some new books of such high quality that they will undoubtedly become a permanent part of literature for children.

Two hundred years ago John Newbery saw the significance and possibilities of such literature. He saw also the necessity of encouraging authors to write for children. He attracted not only Oliver Goldsmith but other well-known men of his day. In 1922 in the United States an impetus was given to writing for children by the establishment of the John Newbery Medal. In 1938 a second award was initiated, the Randolph Caldecott Medal,[2] for the finest picture book of the year. The selection in each case is made by the Children's Librarians' Section of the American Library Association. The donor of both medals is Frederic G. Melcher, editor of *Publishers' Weekly.*

We are indebted to Mr. Melcher for another service which has resulted in increased interest in children's books. In 1919 he inaugurated the first Children's Book Week.[3] Each year schools, libraries, booksellers, and various national and community organizations respond enthusiastically by celebrating a week in November in which special attention is given to children's books. In exhibits, school assemblies, plays, pageants, puppet shows, and various other interesting observances, children and adults join in paying tribute to good books. In many localities a Children's Book Festival is also held in the spring of each year.

An avenue of increased circulation for children's books, high in quality, has resulted from the organization in 1929 of the Junior Literary Guild, a book club for boys and girls, similar to book clubs for adults. Each subscriber receives a book each month, one of four selections for four different age groups, the selections made by a board of editors from manuscripts or proofs of unpublished books submitted by publishers. The selections are varied in content, and among them have been *Young Fu of the Upper Yangtze* by Elizabeth Foreman Lewis, *Down, Down the Mountain* by Ellis Credle, *Hansi* by Ludwig Bemelman, *A Day on Skates* by Hilda Van Stockum, *Young Americans* by Cornelia Meigs, *Seven Simeons* by Boris Artzybasheff, *The Clockwork Twin,* by Walter R. Brooks, *Roller Skates* bv Ruth Sawyer, and *The White Stag* by Kate Seredy.

History of the development of children's reading would not be complete without the inclusion of children's magazines. For some reason not easy to determine, such magazines have had a difficult existence both in the United States and England. Interesting and promising periodicals for young readers have been launched from time to time; some have survived, but the major-

[1] Excellent reviews and discussions of books for children at the time of their publication may be found in each issue of *The Horn Book,* a magazine devoted to books and reading for young people, published bi-monthly (Boston).

[2] Lists of the Newbery and Caldecott Medal Books are given on pages 779, 780.

[3] The exact date designated each year as Children's Book Week may be learned from the National Association of Book Publishers, New York, who also furnish posters and other material for carrying out the particular theme selected for each year's observance. The National Education Association and other educational organizations have helpful material and suggestions for celebrating Children's Book Week.

ity have had comparatively short lives. *St. Nicholas* was a notable exception From 1873 to 1905, under the editorship of Mary Mapes Dodge, *St. Nicholas* was eagerly awaited in American households. Its contributors included Louisa M. Alcott, Thomas Bailey Aldrich, Mark Twain, Palmer Cox, Sarah Orne Jewett, Frank R. Stockton, and Rudyard Kipling, who first published serially in *St. Nicholas* some of their most important stories for children. Drawings by Howard Pyle and Reginald Birch appeared in its pages. In recent years, *St. Nicholas* has changed editors and publishers a number of times with attending changes in policy and content.

*The Youth's Companion* also had a sturdy existence for a hundred years, from 1827 to 1929. It was a permanent part of the reading of many families from generation to generation, and its strong moral tone set a high standard of conduct. *The Youth's Companion* had a regular department of reviews of children's books, which was unique at the time it was started.

No other magazines for children have had such continued existence. *John Martin's Book,* which has not been published since 1933, was striking in appearance, and its illustration and printing did much to raise standards of format in children's periodicals. Today in the United States there are only five magazines of general circulation designed for children: *The American Boy, The American Girl, Boys' Life, Child Life,* and *Story Parade.* Compared to the large number of adult magazines, this is an astonishingly small number. Only the last two are simple enough for young children. It is a matter of regret that there is not more periodical literature for children, not only to build standards of taste that may carry over into adult life but to give the pleasure and satisfaction that come with the regular appearance of interesting material.

In contrast to the dearth of magazines, books for children have increased in great number in the last two decades—books in the main high in imaginative writing and abounding in genuine humor. Through them runs a spirit of well-balanced, wholesome confidence that life may be lived purposefully and constructively. Much of the present-day literature for adults is a literature of despair, of disillusionment, but such is not the spirit of present-day literature for children. It has assurance, proportion, and a sense of spiritual values. Parents and teachers are privileged to be the agents through which constructive experiences with books may become a part of the lives of boys and girls. Our opportunity is a rich one—to learn to know worthwhile books suited to the different ages and varied interests of children and to make such books available to them in as large number as possible. The enjoyment and satisfaction children receive will be shared by the adults who bring such happy experiences to them.

# Make-Believe Stories

## ASK MR. BEAR [1]

*Marjorie Flack*

Once there was a boy named Danny. One day Danny's mother had a birthday.

Danny said to himself, "What shall I give my mother for her birthday?"

So Danny started out to see what he could find.

He walked along, and he met a Hen.

"Good morning, Mrs. Hen," said Danny. "Can you give me something for my mother's birthday?"

"Cluck, cluck," said the Hen. "I can give you a nice fresh egg for your mother's birthday."

"Thank you," said Danny, "but she has an egg."

"Let's see what we can find then," said the Hen.

So Danny and the Hen skipped along until they met a Goose.

"Good morning, Mrs. Goose," said Danny. "Can you give me something for my mother's birthday?"

"Honk, honk," said the Goose. "I can give you some nice feathers to make a fine pillow for your mother's birthday."

"Thank you," said Danny, "but she has a pillow."

"Let's see what we can find then," said the Goose.

So Danny and the Hen and the Goose all hopped along until they met a Goat.

"Good morning, Mrs. Goat," said Danny. "Can you give me something for my mother's birthday?"

"Maa, maa," said the Goat. "I can give you milk for making cheese."

"Thank you," said Danny, "but she has some cheese."

"Let's see what we can find then," said the Goat.

So Danny and the Hen and the Goose and the Goat all galloped along until they met a Sheep.

"Good morning, Mrs. Sheep," said Danny. "Can you give me something for my mother's birthday?"

"Baa, baa," said the Sheep. "I can give you some wool to make a warm blanket for your mother's birthday."

"Thank you," said Danny, "but she has a blanket."

"Let's see what we can find then," said the Sheep.

So Danny and the Hen and the Goose

[1] From Marjorie Flack, *Ask Mr. Bear*.

and the Goat and the Sheep all trotted along until they met a Cow.

"Good morning, Mrs. Cow," said Danny. "Can you give me something for my mother's birthday?"

"Moo, Moo," said the Cow. "I can give you some milk and cream."

"Thank you," said Danny, "but she has some milk and cream."

"Then ask Mr. Bear," said the Cow. "He lives in the woods over the hill."

"All right," said Danny, "let's go and ask Mr. Bear."

"No," said the Hen.

"No," said the Goose.

"No," said the Goat.

"No," said the Sheep.

"No—no," said the Cow.

So Danny went alone to find Mr. Bear. He ran and he ran until he came to the hill, and he walked and he walked until he came to the woods and there he met—Mr. Bear.

"Good morning, Mr. Bear," said Danny. "Can you give me something for my mother's birthday?"

"Hum, hum," said the Bear. "I have nothing to give you for your mother's birthday, but I can tell you something you can give her."

So Mr. Bear whispered a secret in Danny's ear.

"Oh," said Danny. "Thank you, Mr. Bear!"

Then he ran through the woods and he skipped down the hill and he came to his house.

"Guess what I have for your birthday!" Danny said to his mother.

So his mother tried to guess.

"Is it an egg?"

"No, it isn't an egg," said Danny.

"Is it a pillow?"

"No, it isn't a pillow," said Danny.

"Is it a cheese?"

"No, it isn't a cheese," said Danny.

"Is it a blanket?"

"No, it isn't a blanket," said Danny.

"Is it milk or cream?"

"No, it isn't milk or cream," said Danny.

His mother could not guess at all. So—Danny gave his mother a Big Birthday Bear Hug!

## THE FIRST CHRISTMAS TREE[1]

*Rose Fyleman*

This story of the First Christmas Tree was told me by the Fairy Queen herself, so you may be quite sure it is a true one. Here it is.

Once upon a time there lived in the middle of a forest a poor woodcutter.

He had one little daughter called Annis, whom he loved dearly. Annis was a dear little girl, kind and gentle.

She was very fond of all the woodland creatures, and they in turn knew and loved her well. The fairies loved her also. They used to dance on the top of the low stone wall that went round the little garden in front of the cottage.

"Annis! Annis!" they would call to her while she was busy helping her mother in the kitchen. But she would shake her head.

"I can't come. I'm busy," she would answer.

But at nighttime, when she was fast asleep under her red quilt, they would come tapping at the little window.

"Annis! Annis!"

Then she would slip out of bed and run quickly downstairs in her bare feet, and off with the fairies into the moonshining woods.

But the next day she was never sure whether it had been a dream or reality.

That was in the summer.

It was winter now, and very cold. The sky was dark and heavy with coming snow.

Every evening, all through the winter, Annis would hang a little lantern with a candle in it on the small fir tree that grew just inside the garden gate. Her father could see it as he came home through the

[1] From Rose Fyleman, *A Little Christmas Book.*

trees. It was a little bright welcome for him even before he reached home.

On Christmas Eve he went to work as usual. He came home for his dinner at midday and started back early. He was at work quite a long way off.

"I shall finish there today," he said to his wife as he left the house. "Then I shall come nearer home. If the snow comes, it will be difficult to find the way in the dark evenings."

And that very day the snow began. All the afternoon it fell in great, soft flakes.

Down, down, down. . . . It seemed as if the whole sky were falling in little bits.

The woodcutter worked hard in the fading light.

It was quite dark by the time he had finished, and he had to keep shaking the snow from his shoulders and from his old hat.

The wood was all neatly stacked in the little shed which had been built up there to house it.

He started off home with a sigh of relief, smiling to himself as he thought of his warm hearth and the bowl of hot porridge waiting for him on the hob, and of little Annis knitting in the chimney corner.

But presently—how it happened I know not, for he knew the forest well, and the snow had almost stopped falling, and the moon was shining—he found that he had lost his way.

He was quite cheerful at first. "In a minute I shall find the path again," he said. But many minutes passed and he did not find it. A cloud came over the moon; the snow began to fall again more thickly. It was like a moving, whirling mist where the trees stood less close together.

The woodcutter began to lose heart.

Then, suddenly, he saw a light ahead of him on one of the fir trees.

"Can I be so near home?" he said, half-bewildered. But when he came near he found that it was not the fir tree in his own garden that was lit up, but an ordinary forest tree. Little lights twinkled and glittered on its branches, burning brightly and steadily in spite of the falling snow. The woodcutter rubbed his eyes. "Is this wicked magic?" he thought. But the lights burned more brightly than ever, and as he looked about he saw in the distance another tree lit up in the same way. Then he understood.

"It is the good fairies helping me," he said, and trudged off cheerily in the direction of the second tree.

And when he looked back, the first one had already grown dark again. But when he reached the second tree, another was shining ahead to show him the way.

And so he went on from tree to tree until at last he was guided safely home to Annis's little lantern in his own garden.

And always after that he used to put lights on a little fir tree on Christmas Eve in memory of the time when the fairies saved him from being lost in the forest. And so the custom began, and because it was such a pretty one, and because the fairies so willed it, it spread, and today the fairy Christmas tree is to be found all over the world in houses where there are children and where the fairies come. . . .

## THE TINDER BOX[1]

*Hans Christian Andersen*

A soldier was marching along the highroad; one, two! one, two! He had his knapsack on his back and his saber by his side, for he had been in the war and now he was going home. Then he met an old witch on the highroad; she was horrid, her lower lip hung right down on her breast. She said, "Good evening, soldier! What a nice saber you have and what a big knapsack; you are a regular soldier! Now you're going to get all the money you want!"

"Thank you, old witch," said the soldier.

"Do you see that big tree?" said the witch and pointed to a tree next to them. "It's all hollow inside. You're to climb up to

[1] From Hans Christian Andersen, *Fairy Tales and Stories,* translated by Signe Toksvig.

the top, and then you'll see a hole, and you can let yourself through that and far down into the tree. I'll tie a rope around you so that I can pull you up again when you call me."

"And what am I going to do down in the tree?" asked the soldier.

"Get money," said the witch, "you see, when you get down to the bottom of the tree you'll be in a big hall; it's very bright because there are more than a hundred lamps burning in it. Then you'll see three doors with the keys in, so you can open them. If you go into the first room, you'll see a big chest in the middle of the door, and there is a dog sitting on top of it; his eyes are as big as saucers, but don't you mind that! I'll give you my blue-checked apron, you can spread that out on the floor; then walk right up to the dog, take him, and put him on my apron, open the chest and take all the money you want. It's copper money, but if you'd rather have silver, then you must go into the next room. In there is a dog with eyes as big as mill wheels, but don't you mind that, put him on my apron and help yourself to the money! But if you want gold you can have that too, and just as much as you can carry, if you go into the third room. But the dog on the money chest in there has two eyes and each of them as big as a round tower. That's a regular dog, I tell you! But don't you mind that, just put him on my apron, then he won't hurt you, and take all the gold you want out of the chest!"

"That's not so bad!" said the soldier. "But what am I going to have to give you, old witch, because I suppose you'll want something too!"

"No," said the witch, "I don't want a single penny! All you have to bring me is an old tinder box that my grandmother forgot when she was down there last."

"Well! Tie the rope around me," said the soldier.

"Here it is," said the witch, "and here is my blue-checked apron."

Then the soldier climbed up in the tree, let himself drop through the hole, and there he was, as the witch had said, down in the big hall where the many hundred lamps were burning.

Now he opened the first door. Ugh! There sat the dog with eyes as big as saucers and glared at him.

"You're a nice fellow!" said the soldier, as he put him on the witch's apron and took all the copper money he could carry in his pockets. Then he shut the chest, put the dog up on it again, and went into the second room. Ugh! There sat the dog with eyes as big as mill wheels!

"You shouldn't look at me as much as that," said the soldier, "you might get a pain in the eye!" And then he put the dog on the witch's apron, but when he saw the heaps of the silver money in the chest, he threw away all the copper money he had; and filled his pockets and his knapsack with nothing but silver. Now he went into the third room. Oh, this was horrid! The dog in there really had two eyes as big as round towers and they turned in his head just like wheels!

"Good evening!" said the soldier and touched his cap, because he had never seen a dog like that before; but when he had looked at him a little while he thought, "That's enough now," and lifted him down on the floor. Then he opened the chest, and mercy on us, what a lot of gold! With that he could buy all of the cake women's sugar pigs, and all the tin soldiers, whips, and rocking horses in the world! That was certainly money! And now the soldier threw away all the silver coins he had filled his pockets and his knapsack with, and put in gold instead. He filled pockets, knapsack, and cap, and boots until he could hardly walk. Now he had money! He put the dog up on the chest, slammed the door, and shouted up through the tree:

"Pull me up, now, old witch!"

"Have you got the tinder box?" asked the witch.

"That's right," said the soldier, "I forgot all about that," and he went back and took it. The witch pulled him up, and there he was on the highroad again with pockets, boots, knapsack, and cap full of money.

"And what do you want that tinder box for?" asked the soldier.

"That's none of your business," said the witch, "you've got money now, just give me the tinder box!"

"Hoity-toity," said the soldier, "you tell me right away what you want it for, or I'll draw my saber and chop off your head!"

"No," said the wtich.

Then the soldier chopped off her head. There she lay! He tied all his money up in her apron, took it on his back like a bundle, put the tinder box in his pocket, and walked straight to the town.

It was a nice town, and he stopped at the nicest inn and asked for the very best rooms and his favorite dishes, because he was rich now with all that money. The servant who polished his boots did think that they were funny old boots for such a rich gentleman, but he hadn't bought new ones yet. Next day he got boots fit to be seen in, and lovely new clothes. The soldier was a fine gentleman now, and the people told him about all the grand things in their town, and about their king and how charming a princess his daughter was.

"Where can I see her?" asked the soldier.

"You can't see her at all!" everybody said. "She lives in a big copper castle with ever so many walls and towers around it! Only the king is allowed to go in and out, because it has been foretold that she is going to marry just a common soldier, and the king doesn't like that!"

"I'd certainly like to see her," thought the soldier, but that was the one thing he couldn't do.

Now he had a very good time; he went to the theater, he drove in the park, and he gave ever so much money to the poor, and that was kind of him. He knew well enough from former days how bad it is not to have one penny. He was rich now, and had nice clothes, and he had many friends who told him that he was all right, a real gentleman, and the soldier liked that. But since he spent money every day and didn't get any back at all, he had only two cents left at last and had to move away from the beautiful rooms where he had been living and up to a tiny little garret right under the roof. There he had to brush his own boots and mend them with a darning needle, and none of his friends came to see him, because there were so many stairs to climb.

One evening it was getting quite dark and he couldn't even buy a candle, but then he remembered that there was a little piece left in the tinder box which he had taken from the hollow tree that the witch had helped him down in. He got out the tinder box and the piece of candle, but just as he struck fire and the sparks flew from the flint, the door sprang open, and the dog with eyes as big as saucers stood before him and said, "What does my master command?"

"What's that!" said the soldier, "this is a funny tinder box. I wonder if I can get what I want? Get me some money," he said to the dog and pop, he was gone! Pop, he was back again, and with a big bag full of money in his mouth!

Now the soldier knew what a fine tinder box it was. If he struck it once, the dog came that sat on the chest with the copper money; if he struck it twice the one with the silver money came, and if he struck it three times the one with the gold came. And so the soldier moved down into the beautiful rooms again, put on his good clothes, and then all his friends knew him right away, and liked him ever so much.

Once he happened to think, "Isn't it a queer thing that nobody can get to see that princess? They all say she is so lovely, but what good does that do when she always has to sit in the big copper castle with the many towers? I wonder if I couldn't possibly get to see her? Where's my tinder box!" And then he struck fire, and pop, came the dog with eyes as big as saucers.

"I know that it's in the middle of the night," said the soldier, "but I would so very much like to see the princess for just one little moment!"

The dog was out of the door right away, and before the soldier had time to think he saw him again with the princess. She was asleep on the back of the dog, and she was so lovely that anybody could see she was a real princess. The soldier couldn't help it, he had to kiss her, because he was a regular soldier. Then the dog ran back with the princess, but when it was morning and the king and queen were pouring their tea, the princess said that she had had such a strange dream that night about a dog and a soldier. She had been riding on the dog and the soldier had kissed her.

"That's a pretty story, I must say!" said the queen.

The next night one of the old court ladies had to watch at the bed of the princess to see if it were a real dream, or what it might be. The soldier was so terribly anxious to see the beautiful princess again that the dog came at night and took her and ran as fast as he could, but the old court lady ran just as fast after him. When she saw them disappear into a large house, she thought, "Now I know where they are," and she made a big cross on the door with a piece of chalk. Then she went home and went to bed, and the dog came back again with the princess, but when he saw that cross on the door, he took a piece of chalk, too, and put crosses on all the doors in town, and that was a clever trick, because now of course the lady wouldn't be able to find the right door when they all had crosses on.

In the early morning the king and queen, the old court lady and all the officers came to see where it was that the princess had been.

"There it is!" said the king when he saw the first door with a cross on.

"No, my dear, there it is!" said the queen when she saw another door with a cross on.

"But there is one, and there is one!" they all said; wherever they looked there were crosses on the doors, and so they could see of course that searching wasn't of much use.

But the queen happened to be a very clever woman who could do more things than ride in a coach. She took her gold scissors and cut up a piece of silk; then she sewed a pretty little bag and filled it with tiny buckwheat grains and tied it to the back of the princess. Then she cut a little hole in the bag so that the grains could dribble out wherever the princess went.

At night the dog came again, took the princess on his back, and ran with her to the soldier, who loved her, and would have liked to have been a prince so that he could marry her. The dog didn't notice at all how the grains dribbled out right from the castle to the soldier's window where he ran up the wall with the princess. And in the morning the king and queen could see well enough where their daughter had been, and so they took the soldier and put him in prison.

There he was. Oh, how dark and dreary it was there! And then they said to him, "You'll be hanged tomorrow." That wasn't a pleasant thing to hear, and he had left his tinder box at the inn. Through the iron bars in his little window, he could see the next morning how people were hurrying out of the town to see him hanged. He could hear the drums and see the soldiers marching along. Everybody was running; there was a shoemaker's apprentice in his apron and slippers, he galloped so fast that one of his slippers flew off and hit the wall behind which the soldier sat and peered out through the bars.

"Hey, you shoemaker boy! You don't have to be in such a hurry," the soldier said to him, "they can't do anything until I come! Don't you want to run over to where I used to live and get me my tinder box, then I'll give you ten cents, but you'll have to skip!" The shoemaker's apprentice wanted the ten cents, so he rushed away for the tinder box, gave it to the soldier, and —well, now we'll hear what happened.

A big gallows had been raised outside the

town, and around it stood the soldiers and many hundreds of thousands of people. The king and queen sat on a beautiful throne right across from the judge and the whole council. The soldier was already standing on the ladder, but when they were going to put the rope around his neck he said that every sinner was allowed an innocent wish before he got his punishment, and he wanted so much to smoke a pipe of tobacco, it would be for the last time in this world.

The king didn't want to say no to this, and so the soldier took his tinder box and struck fire, one, two, three! And there stood all the dogs, the one with eyes as big as saucers, the one with eyes as big as mill wheels, and the one with eyes as big as round towers!

"Help me now, so that I won't be hanged!" said the soldier, and then the dogs jumped at the judges and all the council, took some by the legs and some by the nose and threw them many fathoms up in the air so that they fell down and broke into pieces.

"I won't!" said the king, but the biggest dog took both him and the queen and threw them after all the others, then the soldiers were frightened and the people shouted: "Little soldier, you shall be our king, and marry the lovely princess!"

Then they put the soldier in the royal coach, and all the three dogs danced in front of it and shouted, "Hurrah!" The boys whistled through their fingers and the soldiers presented arms. The princess came out of the copper castle and was queen, and she liked that very much! The wedding lasted eight days and the dogs sat at the table and opened their eyes wide.

## THE MIDNIGHT VOYAGE[1]

*John Masefield*

When the wheels of the fly had scrunched along the gravel out of the gate, the governess turned upon him.

"What a very impertinent little boy you are, Kay," she said; "not only to me this morning, but to your kind guardian, who has come here specially and solely to see how you are getting on. It would have done you good if he had boxed your ears soundly and sent you packing."

"I don't care," Kay said. "He oughtn't to have said that about Great-grandpapa Harker, because it isn't true."

"You are a wicked little boy, Kay," the governess said. "You will go straight to bed this minute, without your bread and milk."

Kay said nothing more. He knew the story better than the governess did. Long ago his Great-grandpapa Harker and his ship, the *Plunderer,* had been in tropic waters when a revolution broke out. The Archbishop asked the captain to take the gold and silver images and crosses and candlesticks from the churches on board for safety. Long after, Great-grandpapa Harker got back to England without his ship and without the treasure. He said he had been robbed by pirates. He had been dead many, many years, but some people still said he had kept the treasure and hidden it. Kay did not believe it.

The little boy went upstairs to his room, in the old part of the house. There were oak beams in the ceiling; the floor was all oak plank. The bed was big and old, valanced to the floor, and topped by a canopy. Kay was very much afraid of it at going-to-bed time because so many tigers could get underneath it, to wait till he was asleep; but tonight he did not mind, because it was still only sunset. He had two windows in his room. One looked out on a garden, where Nibbins, the black cat, was watching some birds; the other looked out over a field, where there was a sheep-trough. He did not like the look of the trough in the long grass, because it looked so like a puma, with its ears cocked. Beyond the field, he could see the stable, where Benjamin, the highwayman, had once lived.

[1] From John Masefield, *The Midnight Folk.*

In his room there were two doors, leading to different passages. On the wall were two colored prints, "The Meet," and "Full Cry," one on each side of the fireplace. Over the wash-hand-stand, as it was called, were two old pistols wired to nails. They were called Great-grandpapa Harker's pistols, and Kay was to be sure never to touch them, because they might go off. Then, on the other side of the room, there was the dressing-table, valanced to the floor, which made a very good secret room, where nobody ever looked for you. In the corner, near this, on a shelf on the wall, stood an old model of a ship, which Kay was never to touch, because boys are so destructive. This was the model of Great-grandpapa Harker's ship, the *Plunderer,* which had disappeared with the missing treasure so long before.

The sun was going down behind the wooded camp, known as King Arthur's Round Table, where King Arthur was supposed to ride at full moon. When the sun had gone, all the world glowed for a while; but it was not wise to wait till the glow had gone, because so soon the dusk began, when the owls would come, and the footsteps would begin, and the tigers would stir under the bed and put out their paws, and the scratchings would scrape under the floor. He got into bed with a leap, because then you dodged the paws. He got well under the clothes for a minute, to make sure that he was not pursued. Luckily none of the tigers had heard him. When Kay came from under the bedclothes he could not be sure that there was not a tiger lying in the canopy above him. It was sagged down, just as though a tiger were there. If it were to give way, the tiger would fall right on top of him. Or very likely it was not a tiger but a python, for that is what pythons do.

Footsteps passed, sometimes close to his door. Very strange creakings sounded in the house; there were scutterings to and fro, and scraping and scratchings. By and by he heard the governess, who had finished her supper, come to the room beneath him, the library, as she usually did in the evenings. He was cross with her for stopping his bread and milk, but glad that she was there. She opened the piano and began to play. Usually she played things without any tune, which she said he couldn't understand yet because they were classical. This night she played something that had a sort of tune, and then began to sing to it in a very beautiful voice, so that he was rapt away at once into joy. There were not any more tigers, or pythons; only a mouse gnawing in the wainscot; or was it someone playing on a guitar and humming some song about a treasure?

Now the sun was nearly down; a glow from it lit the wall opposite, so that the hunting men riding at the brook in "Full Cry" were made most vivid. A ray touched the model of the *Plunderer,* so that she glowed, too, and the green stripe upon her forecastle and the scarlet rims of her tops looked beautiful against her brown and black.

Just before he fell asleep he was almost sure that the water in the brook in "Full Cry" had eddies in it; eddies, and those little clouds of dissolving earth which the water rat makes when scared from a bank. "He must have been a jolly good painter," he thought, "to be able to do all that." He fell asleep soon after this, thinking that if he were a painter, he would paint, well, he did not know what he would paint; so much was always happening.

Then it seemed like broad daylight, although he could see the stars through the window. He was aware at once that something very odd was happening in the print of "Full Cry"; the hunting men, whose red coats were flapping, were turning from the brook. And what was the matter with the brook? It was very, very full of water, and coming with such a strong current that it swished against the loose alder root. He could see not only eddies, but bright ripples which ran into bubbles, and yes, yes, it was coming into the room, it was running on both sides of the bed, clear, swift, rushing water, carrying down petals and leaves and bits of twig. Then there came the water rats, who dived with a "phlumphing" noise when they caught sight of him. He was on an island in the midst of the stream; and the stream was so crystal clear that he could see the fish in the shallows.

But what on earth was happening to the model of the *Plunderer*? He could see that the water had reached her on the wall; she was afloat. She seemed to be alive with little tiny men, all busy with ropes. No, they were not men, they were little mice. "Water mice, I suppose," he thought. Now she was coming across the stream to him; and how big she was, or no, how little he was; he was no bigger than the water mice. There she came slowly to the edge of the bed. She had flags flying, a Blue Peter at the fore, a house-flag, with three oreilles couped proper, on the main, and a red ensign at the peak. But lovelier than the flags were the decks, with the little doors, each with a shiny brass handle and real lock and key, opening to the cabins. Then there were real lifeboats ready for use. He could see the barrels and lockers in them marked "Best Preserved Milk," "Corned Beef," "Ship's Bread," "Raisins," "Chocolate Cream," "Turkish Delight," "Split Peas," "Currants," "Mixed Biscuits," etc. No fear of starving in lifeboats like those. Then all the little brass cannon were shining in the sun, ready for use, with the little powder tubs all handy, and little men standing by them ready to fire them off in salute. Then as the ship came alongside the bed, each little gunner blew puff! upon his match, to make it glow (some of them had red-hot pokers instead of matches), and popped the glowing end of the touchholes. All the little brass cannon went bang! together in salute.

Then Kay saw that the Captain of the ship was his friend the Water Rat. He was standing on the poop, with his telescope in his hand, telling the mate to put the gangway over for Mr. Kay. Some of the little seamen at once thrust out a gangway on to the bed.

"Step on board, Mr. Kay," the Captain said.

"May I really and truly?"

"Yes, we're waiting for you."

Kay walked from his bed to the deck. He was amazed at the neatness of everything: all the rows of buckets, the sponges and rammers for the cannon, the capstans that worked, the compasses that pointed, the cask, painted red, for salt meat, and the other cask, painted blue, for fresh water; and all the rigging, with little ladders on it for going aloft. Then there was a ship's kitchen on the deck close to him, with a real little cook, with a wooden leg, making plum duff for dinner at a real fire.

"Welcome on board, Mr. Kay," the captain said. "I thought we might stand over to the westward to see what we can find of the old *Plunderer*. We've got a cabin prepared for you, with a hammock slung in it; and here are some nice long seaboots to pull over your pajamas, and a double-breasted pea jacket to keep out the seas and keep in the plum duff. And now, my hearties, cast loose forward, let go aft! The tug has got her. Hurry, lads, for the westward!"

Kay noticed now, what he had not noticed before, that on the other side of the *Plunderer* was a tugboat under steam. Long before, he had had a beautiful tugboat with a scarlet funnel. She had gone by real steam made by methylated spirit, which you lit under the boiler in a little lamp. But after two voyages, she set forth across the Squire's pond on a windy day, and in the draught of the gale she caught fire, blazed for a few minutes from stem to stern, and then went down head first in deep water. Yet now here she was, repainted, and with powerful new engines in her, which were thrashing the water as they towed the *Plunderer* clear of the bed.

Soon they had swung round clear of the sofa, and headed to the west, through the open window, into the night. Side lights and towing lights were lit; she plunged on beside her tug, casting streaks of colored light upon the water. Soon she was in the stream where Kay had so often seen the Water Rat. Someone in the *Plunderer* turned a strong searchlight on to the water ahead. Look-out men went aloft to watch the water; they called to the helmsmen from time to time to do this or that to dodge the rocks. "A bit anxious, this reach of the stream," the Water Rat said, "but there's lots of water tonight."

The ship went faster and faster over rapids and shallows; soon she was in the big, quiet pool where the stream entered the river. An otter looked out at them and wished them good luck. A moor hen came out and swam ahead of them to show them the best passage. Dawn was now breaking; but all the world of men was asleep. Kay saw the deserted quay of the river bank where he had so often watched people coming to hire skiffs. A light was burning there, although morning was growing everywhere. Kay saw the tug stand away from the *Plunderer's* side and cast loose the towropes. The *Plunderer's* men ran aloft and cast loose the sails. When Kay next looked back, the river wharf was far astern; the ship was running swiftly down the river under a press of sail.

"But come, Master Kay," the Captain said, "breakfast is on the table. Step down the ladder with me to the cabin."

He led the way down to a passage where there were a great many doors labeled "First Mate," "Second Mate, "Third Mate," "Captain's Stores," "Instrument Room," "Chart Room," "Steward's Pantry," "Bullion Room," "Captain's Bath," "Mates' Bath," "Jam Room," "Sardine Room," etc., as well as one big open door leading to the cabin, where the table was set for breakfast. They had for breakfast all the things that Kay was fondest of: very hot, little, round loaves of new white bread baked in the embers of a wood-fire, butter, a sardine with a lot of olive oil, some minced kidneys, a poached egg and frizzled bacon, a very fat sausage all bursting out of its skin, a home-made pork pie with jelly and yolk of egg beneath the crust, a bowl of strawberries and cream with sifted sugar, a bowl of raspberries and cream with blobs of sugar-candyish brown sugar that you could scrunch, some nice new mushrooms and chicken, a cup of coffee with crystals of white sugar candy, a yellow plum, a greengage, and then a ripe blue plum to finish off with.

"That's the way, Master Kay," the Captain said. "I always believe in a good breakfast—something to do your work on and start the day with. And now, if you've finished, as you haven't had much sleep lately, perhaps you'd like to keep the next watch in your hammock. Come up on deck for a moment first, though; we are now in the open sea."

The wonder of it was that they *were* in the open sea, out of sight of land, with the ship under full sail flying westward. One or two of the water mice were at work far aloft: others on deck were washing their clothes and hanging them out to dry on clotheslines, or fishing with hooks and lines, or feeding the sparrows (which they kept for the eggs) in the hen-coops, or polishing the brass on the ship's bells and railings. The sea was all blue and bright, the hot sun was shining, not a cloud could be seen. The ship was flying faster and faster.

Kay's cabin was a charming room, with mahogany lockers, and a porthole covered with red curtains. A telescope hung on a rack ready for use. A canvas hammock swung from hooks in the wall; it had a pillow, mattress, sheets, and blankets. The Captain showed him how to get in and tuck himself up. In a minute he was fast asleep.

He was wakened half an hour later by the ship anchoring in calm water. On going on deck he found that she was not far from a low, tropical shore, blindingly white, from the surf bursting on it. Palm trees grew here and there on the shore; there was no sign of man. The water, bright blue to seaward, with vivid green streaks, was clear as crystal.

"Now, Master Kay," the Captain said, "we will get into the diving bell and go down to see what we can see. We are now just over the wreck of the old *Plunderer*."

"How do you know?" Kay asked.

"We can always get directions about wrecks, we under-water folk, from mermaids and sirens, not to speak of dolphins and these other fellows. Some of them are very old and have astonishing memories. It was a mermaid who told Tom Otter about the *Plunderer,* and he told me."

The diving bell was a tight little room, just big enough for two nice comfortable armchairs. It was built of iron framing, with floor and side windows of strong clear glass. Air-pipes and speaking-tubes were let into the walls and through the roof. When Kay and the Captain had taken their seats in the armchairs, the crew closed the door very carefully so that no water could possibly squeeze in. Then they hoisted the bell up and began to lower it carefully into the water. Kay found that he could see quite clearly through the glass of the sides and the floor. The fish came to the windows and sucked at them with their mouths. Presently, when the Captain called through the speaking-tube to stop lowering, he turned on a searchlight which pointed through the floor. Kay could see the bottom of the sea, growing like a garden with white and red coral, weeds, anemones and sponges, all seeming to dilate in the light. Some gaily-colored fish came poking to the light, to find if it were good to eat; a few big fish, some of them like shadows, others like round collapsing bags with suckers waving from them, drifted or finned by, all noiseless; there was no whisper of sound, except a drumming in the ears. "There's what is left of the *Plunderer,*" the Captain said.

Lying on the bottom, partly on white sand, partly among coral and weed, was the wreck of an old wooden ship. All that remained in sight of her was her stern-post, her name-plate, marked *Plunderer,* a part of her keel, and a few ribs fallen out of place. All these timbers had been blackened by years under the sea. White and blue barnacles were growing on them; sprays of red and white coral had thrust up among them. The sunlight made all these things so glorious suddenly that the Captain turned out the light. Kay could see even the eyes of the lobsters peering into the crannies of the coral.

A mermaid floated to the side of the diving bell. She was young and merry-looking, with bright, big brown eyes and very white teeth. She wore a gold crown over her long brown hair. Her cheeks and lips were full of color. She put her mouth to the glass and smiled at them. "That's Sea-Flower," the Captain said. "Say good morning to her."

"Good morning, Miss Sea-Flower," Kay said. "Can you tell us how this ship came here?"

"Yes," she said. "She was upset in a squall, long ago, and all her men were drowned. They were making merry at the time. You can still see one of them: that scarlet coral is he. But open the door and come with me."

Three other mermaids had swum to the diving bell; together they opened the door. In an instant, Kay was swimming with them in the warm water that was so like green light. All the floor of the sea shone. Here and there were patches of a green plant which had flowers like flames, they were so bright. At first he thought that everything there was dead; but when he had been twenty seconds in that tingling water he knew that it was full of life. The white sand of the sea-floor was alive with tiny, scurrying, glittering creatures, little beings looked at him from the branches of the coral, flowers poked out eyes at him upon stalks like snails' horns, he could see the leaves of the seaweeds shine with joy at every good suck-in of light. All these living forms were swaying gently as the swell lifted and fell; a kind of drowsy song of delight moved through the water, everything was singing because life was so good.

Kay went up to a big scarlet fish that had pale goggle-eyes and a collapsing mouth; he tickled its throat; and others knew that he was liking it, because they, too, came to have their throats tickled, till Kay was surrounded by fish of all colors and shapes, scaled and slimy, finned, or legged, or feelered, all noiseless, most of them strange, many of them most beautiful.

"Come away, Kay," the mermaid said. "But first look at the lovely golden lad."

Lying among the coral, as though he were resting upon a bank of flowers, was a golden image of Saint George, still holding a white shield with a scarlet cross.

"We used to sing to him at first," Sea-Flower said, "hoping that he would wake. The ship was full of golden and silver people at one time. We loved them, they were so very beautiful; but they never answered when we spoke to them. Men came here searching for them in the old days, dragging anchors for them along the sea-floor. At last some Indian divers came down and carried them all away to a yacht, all except this one, which they would not touch, because we had so decked it with flowers.

"We do not know who it was who took those lovely things. He was going to take them to a city of evil men near here. We followed his yacht on his way thither, for we were sad to lose our lovely people. But come, Kay, you shall come with us as far as we can go on the way those golden people went."

They all set out together, Kay between Sea-Flower and Foam-Blossom, each of whom held one of his hands. Foam-Blossom was a golden-haired mermaid, with bright blue eyes and lovely rose cheeks; she was always laughing. "Is not this lovely?" she said, as they went swimming along.

"Oh, it *is* lovely," Kay said. Every stroke of their arms took them over some new kind of shellfish, or past some new anemone or waving weed.

"Come," Sea-Flower said, "let us go in on the tide, at the surface."

They rose up together to the air. There, on the shallow shore, long lines of rollers were always advancing to the beach, toppling as they went and at last shattering. A little river came out to the sea there; its little waves seemed to enjoy meeting the big waves.

"Come," Foam-Blossom said, "let us ride on this big roller that is just going in."

Together, they sat on the neck of the wave, with Kay between them. Kay felt the wave begin to run like a horse, and to gather speed and to lift. Soon the toppling water began to hiss and foam all about them; the shore seemed to rush nearer, and then they all rolled over and over in boiling bubbles into the cool pool of the river, where the sea shells looked as though they were all made of pearl.

Soon they were swimming up a river which flowed between banks of reed and bulrush. Giant flags grew among the reeds, with heavy blue, white and golden flowers. Little speckled birds with scarlet crests clung to the flowers. Waterfowl as big as swans, with orange bills and big black and white plumes on their heads, swam to them to be stroked. In the gloom and zebra striping of the light and shade of the reeds Kay saw long-legged water birds standing ankle-deep, fishing. Here and there, when they passed mudbanks, he saw the turtles enjoying themselves in the cool ooze.

Presently they left the river and swam up a backwater, where the reeds on both sides gave place to quince trees, which smelt like Arabia from the ripe fruit. At the end of the backwater there was a patch of red mud stamped down by the feet of cows that had come to drink there. Beyond the cows was a little roll of grassland.

"The man took the gold and silver things this way," Sea-Flower said. "In those days, the river ran this way, through all that grassy piece and for miles beyond it; we often used to swim there. We followed his yacht for a long way, further than we can see from here. He was a rosy-faced man, not old, but his hair was already grey; his eyes were very bright; and his mouth, when one could see it through the beard, was most cruel and evil. He had three Indians with him, who were his divers and sailors, whom he used to beat.

"When he was in a narrow part of the river, he heard guns, for his city of wickedness was being destroyed. He poled his yacht far into the reeds against the mud, and sent one of his Indians to find out what was happening. As the Indian did not come back, he sent a second Indian; and when the second did not come back he sent a third; but the third did not come back, either."

"What happened to the Indians?" Kay asked.

"They all went home to their village in the sea; they have houses there, built upon piles driven into the water. In the rainy seasons they keep very snug in their hammocks and tell each other stories."

"And what happened to the man, please?"

"He waited for the Indians to bring him news. When they did not come, he changed his yacht's hiding place, by driving her still further into the reeds, and then he set out by himself to find out what was happening. He was captured as a pirate that same night and sent far away.

"Nobody found his boat, she was too well-hidden, but there came great changes which hid her farther. At first we used to play in the water near her, hoping that she might soon fall to pieces, so that we might have her gold and silver people again; but then there came the earthquake, which raised the river-bed and buried the yacht in the mud. After the earthquake there came the great summer floods, which made a new channel for the river and altered all the coast. When the floods went down, the place where the yacht lay was five miles from the water and covered deep with flowers, so the birds told us.

"The man came back presently to look for his yacht; but with the land so changed he hardly knew where to begin. We used to see him digging sometimes, when we went up the streams. But he was evil, do not let us think of him; let us go to the sea, to play in the rollers as they burst."

In a few minutes they were in the shining shallow water across which the breaking rollers were marching. At first, Kay was frightened by the waves as they curled and toppled high over his head. Very soon he was wading to meet them, so that they could break all over him or carry him in to the sands.

"And now," the mermaids said, "let us all go down to look at the city under the sea."

They all swam for a few minutes; then Kay suddenly saw something very golden in the green of the under-water.

"Those are the walls," Foam-Blossom said. "And if you listen, you will hear the bells. Let us wait here."

They had paused at what had been the harbor. Three or four little ships had sunk with the city; they were there, still secured to the walls. Sponges like big yellow mushrooms covered one; another was starred all over with tiny white shells; another was thickly grown with a weed like many colored ribbons. The walls, which had once been of white marble, seemed golden in that dim light. As Kay looked he heard a sweet but muffled booming of the bells as the swell of the water surged and lapsed in the bell tower.

"Come, Kay," the Sea-Flower said, "the city gates have fallen open; we can go in."

They passed through the gates, which now drooped upon their hinges from the weight of the shells which grew upon them. Inside the gates was a guardhouse, with a rack of spears still standing against the wall. Beyond that was a street, with shops open, and fish slowly finning from shop to shop. At the end of the street there was a temple with a bell tower. No one was in that city. Kay went into two of the houses; in one, the kitchen was set out with pots and pans for dinner; two eggs were in a bowl and the bone of a leg of mutton was on a dish; in the other, the beds in the nursery were turned down ready for the children, and in one of the beds a child had set a doll, on which the little shells were growing. There were gaily painted carvings on some of the walls, showing the racing of children and romps and tugs-of-war.

"What is this city, please?" Kay asked, "I would love to go all over it, into every house. What is it called?"

"We call it the Golden City. But look, here come the merchildren, playing 'Touch and Tag'; let us play with them."

At that instant, about twenty little merchildren came darting down the street, at full speed, with streaming hair, bright eyes and laughter. They twisted about like eels, dived down chimneys and through windows, crying aloud from joy in the fun.

"I wonder," Kay said, "if we might play 'Hide and Seek?' This would be such a lovely place for it."

"Yes," Foam-Blossom said, "let us all play 'Hide and Seek'; Sea-Flower shall be 'It.' And Kay, you come with me, for I know a lovely place to hide."

She took him through one of the houses into what had been a garden. The fruit trees still stood, but were now crusted over with shells. Sponges, anemones, and corals, which were so covered with points of glitter that they seemed full of eyes, grew like mistletoe on the branches. There came a sort of cloud in swift movement across the golden light.

"Look," Foam-Blossom said, "there's a ship passing overhead. If you look up, you may see one of the crew looking down."

"That reminds me," Kay asked, "I meant to ask you before. Did you ever see another man taking away those golden and silver people? He may have taken them away in a big barge."

"Why, Kay," she answered, "that is the *Plunderer* passing. There is the Water-Rat Captain looking down. You must be quick; and oh, do look at the flying fish!"

Kay felt a sort of swirl as he rushed past a lot of green bubbles into the light. The billows burst all about him suddenly and the sun made him blink. Foam-Blossom, the lovely merchildren, the city, and its gardens, among which the beaked fishes had flitted like birds, were gone. He was sitting on the end of the *Plunderer's* jib-boom in the clouds of spray flung up as she sailed. Sheets of spray, as bright as snow, soared and flashed all around him. Then he saw that it was not spray, but a flight of flying fish, skimming and falling like darts, all glittering and quivering. "Oh, how lovely!" he cried.

As he cried, he heard his window creak; somebody rolled him into bed and the *Plunderer* went back to the wall. As for the sea, it was not there. When he opened his eyes, the maid, Ellen, was there, but no water at all.

"Where did it all run to?" he asked.

"Where did what all run to? Wake up," Ellen said. "You are such a one to sleep as I never did see."

"Well, it was here a moment ago," he said.

"I declare, you're dreaming still," she said. "Now don't go to sleep again. Breakfast will be in a quarter of an hour, and you're not to be late, the governess said; I was to tell you specially."

## THE PRINCESS AND THE PEA[1]

*Hans Christian Andersen*

There was once a prince who wanted to marry a princess; but she had to be a *real* princess. So he traveled all through the whole world to find a real one, but everywhere there was something the matter. There were plenty of princesses, but whether they were *real* princesses he couldn't quite make out; there was always something that didn't seem real enough. So he came home again, and was very sorry; for he wanted so much to have a real princess.

One evening a terrible storm came on. It lightened and thundered, the rain poured down; it was perfectly dreadful! Then there was a knocking at the town gate, and the old king went out to open it.

It was a princess who stood outside. But how the rain and the bad weather had made her look! The water ran down from her hair and her clothes; it ran in at the points of her shoes, and out at the heels; but she said that she was a real princess.

"Well, we'll soon find out," thought the

[1] From Hans Christian Andersen, *Fairy Tales and Stories,* translated by Signe Toksvig.

old queen. But she said nothing, only went into the bedroom, took all the bedclothes off, and put a pea on the bottom of the bedstead; then she took twenty mattresses and laid them on the pea, and then again twenty eider-down beds on the mattresses. On this the princess had to lie all night. In the morning they asked her how she had slept.

"Oh, horribly!" said the princess. "I hardly closed my eyes all night long. Goodness knows what was in my bed. I lay on something hard, so that I am black and blue all over."

Now they could see that she was a real princess, because she had felt the pea through the twenty mattresses and the twenty eider-down beds. Nobody but a real princess could be so delicate.

So the prince married her, because now he knew that he had a real princess; and the pea was put in the museum, and it is there now, unless somebody has taken it.

## THE WHITE CAT[1]

*Madame la Comtesse D'Aulnoy*

Once upon a time there was a King who had three sons. The day came when they were grown so big and strong that he began to fear they would be planning to rule in his place. This would cause trouble among themselves and his subjects. Now the King was not so young as he once had been, but nevertheless he had no notion of giving up his kingdom then and there. So after much thought he hit upon a scheme which should keep them too busily occupied to interfere in the affairs of state. Accordingly he called the three into his private apartments where he spoke to them with great kindliness and concern of his plans for their future.

"I am planning to retire from the affairs of state. But I do not wish my subjects to suffer from this change. Therefore, while I am still alive, I shall transfer my crown to one of you. I shall not follow the usual custom of leaving the crown to my eldest son, but whichever one of you shall bring me the handsomest and most intelligent little dog shall become my heir."

The Princes were greatly surprised by this strange request, but they could not very well refuse to humor their father's whim; and since there was luck in it for the two younger sons and the elder of the three was a timid, rather spiritless fellow, they agreed readily enough. The King then bade them farewell after first distributing jewels and money among them and adding that a year from that day at the same place and hour they should return to him with their little dogs.

Within sight of the city gates stood a castle where the three often spent many days in company with their young companions. Here they agreed to part and to meet again in a year before proceeding with their trophies to the King; and so having pledged their good faith, and changing their names that they might not be known, each set off upon a different road.

It would take far too long to recount the adventures of all three Princes so I shall tell only of those that befell the youngest, for a more gay and well-mannered Prince never lived, nor one so handsome and accomplished.

Scarcely a day passed that he did not buy a dog or two, greyhounds, mastiffs, bloodhounds, pointers, spaniels, water dogs, lapdogs; but the instant he found a handsomer one he let the first go and kept the new purchase, since it would have been impossible for him to carry them all on his journeyings. He went without fixed plan or purpose and so he continued for many days until at last darkness and a terrible storm overtook him at nightfall in a lonely forest. Thunder and lightning rumbled and flashed; rain fell in torrents; the trees seemed to close more densely about him, until at last he could no longer find his way.

[1] From Madame la Comtesse D'Aulnoy, *Tales of the Fairies,* arranged by Rachel Field in *The White Cat, and Other Old French Fairy Tales.*

When he had wandered for some time, he suddenly saw a glint of light between the tree trunks. Feeling certain that this must mean a shelter of some sort he pressed on till he found himself approaching the most magnificent castle he had ever seen. The gate was of gold and covered with jewels of such brilliance that it was their light which had guided him to the spot. In spite of the rain and storm he caught glimpses of walls of finest porcelain decorated with pictures of the most famous fairies from the beginning of the world up to that very day: Cinderella, Graciosa, Sleeping Beauty, and a hundred others.

As the young Prince admired all this magnificence he noticed a rabbit's foot fastened to the golden gates by a chain of diamonds. Marveling greatly at such a lavish display of precious gems, he pulled at the rabbit's foot and straightway an unseen bell of wonderful sweetness rang; the gate was opened by hundreds of tiny hands and others pushed him forward while he hesitated amazed upon the threshold. He moved on wonderingly, his hand on the hilt of his sword until he was reassured by two voices singing a welcome. Again he felt himself being pushed, this time toward a gate of coral, opening upon an apartment of mother-of-pearl from which he passed into others still more richly decorated and alight with wax candles and great chandeliers sparkling with a thousand rainbows.

He had passed through perhaps sixty such rooms when the hands that guided him made a sign for him to stop. He saw a large armchair moving by itself toward a fireplace at the same moment that the fire began to blaze, and the hands, which he now observed to be very small and white, carefully drew off his wet clothes and handed him others so fine and richly embroidered they seemed fit for a wedding day. The hands continued to dress him, until at last, powdered and attired more handsomely than he had ever been in his life before, the Prince was led into a banquet hall. Here the four walls were decorated solely with paintings representing famous cats, Puss-in-Boots and others whom he was quick to recognize. Even more astonishing than this was the table set for two with its gold service and crystal cups.

There was an orchestra composed entirely of cats. One held a music book with the strangest notes imaginable; another beat time with a little baton; and all the rest strummed tiny guitars.

While the Prince stared in amazement, each cat suddenly began to mew in a different key and to claw at the guitar strings. It was the strangest music ever heard! The Prince would have thought himself in bedlam had not the palace itself been so marvelously beautiful. So he stopped his ears and laughed heartily at the various poses and grimaces of these strange musicians. He was meditating upon the extraordinary sights he had already seen in the castle, when he beheld a little figure entering the hall. It was scarcely more than two feet in height and wrapped in a long gold crêpe veil. Before it walked two cats dressed in deep mourning and wearing cloaks and swords, while still others followed, some carrying rat-traps full of rats and mice in cages.

By this time the Prince was too astonished to think. But presently the tiny figure approached him and lifted its veil. He now beheld the most beautiful little white cat that ever was or ever will be. She had such a very youthful and melancholy air and a mewing so soft and sweet that it went straight to the young Prince's heart.

"Son of a King," she said to him, "thou art welcome; my mewing Majesty beholds thee with pleasure."

"Madam," responded the Prince, bowing as low as possible before her, "it is very gracious of you to receive me with so much attention, but you do not appear to me to be an ordinary little cat. The gift of speech which you have and this superb castle you inhabit are certainly evidence to the contrary."

"Son of a King," rejoined the White Cat, "I pray that you will cease to pay me compliments. I am plain in my speech and manners, but I have a kind heart. Come," she added, to her attendants, "let them serve supper and bid the concert cease, for the Prince does not understand what they are singing."

"And are they singing words, madam?" he asked incredulously.

"Certainly," she answered, "we have very gifted poets here, as you will see if you remain long enough."

Supper was then served to them by the same hands that had guided him there, and a very strange meal it was. There were two dishes of each course—one soup, for instance, being of savory pigeons while the other had been made of nicely fattened mice. The sight of this rather took away the Prince's appetite until his hostess, who seemed to guess what was passing in his mind, assured him that his own dishes had been specially prepared and contained no rats and mice of any kind. Her charming manners convinced the Prince that the little Cat had no wish to deceive him, so he began to eat and drink with great enjoyment.

During their meal the Prince happened to observe that on one paw the little Cat wore a tiny miniature set in a bracelet. This surprised him so that he begged her to let him examine it more closely. He had supposed it would be the picture of Master Puss, but what was his astonishment to find it the portrait of a handsome young man who bore a strange resemblance to himself! As he stared at it, the White Cat was heard to sigh so deeply and with such profound sadness that the Prince became even more curious; but he dared not question one so affected. Instead he entertained her with tales of court life, with which, to his surprise, he found her well acquainted.

After supper the White Cat led her guest into another hall, where upon a little stage twelve cats and twelve monkeys danced in the most fantastic costumes. So the evening ended in great merriment; and after the Cat had bade the Prince a gracious good night the same strange hands conducted him to his own apartment, where in spite of the softness of his bed he spent half the night trying to solve the mystery of the castle, the beautiful surroundings, and his extraordinary little hostess.

But when morning came he was no nearer to an answer to his questionings, so he allowed the pairs of hands to help him dress and lead him into the palace courtyard. Here a vast company of cats in hunting costume were gathering to the sound of the horn. A fête day indeed! The White Cat was going to hunt and wished the Prince to accompany her. Now the mysterious hands presented him with a wooden horse. He made some objection to mounting it, but it proved to be an excellent charger, and a tireless galloper. The White Cat rode beside him on a monkey, the handsomest and proudest that ever was seen. She had thrown off her long veil and wore a military cap which made her look so bold that she frightened all the mice in the neighborhood.

Never was there a more successful hunt. The cats outran all the rabbits and hares, and a thousand feats of skill were performed to the gratification of the entire company. Tiring of the hunt at last, the White Cat took up a horn no bigger than the Prince's little finger and blew upon it with so loud and clear a tone it could be heard ten leagues away. Scarcely had she sounded two or three flourishes when all the cats in the countryside seemed to appear. By land and sea and through the air they all came flocking to her call, dressed in every conceivable costume. So, followed by this extraordinary train, the Prince rode back with his hostess to the castle.

That night the White Cat put on her gold veil again and they dined together as before. Being very hungry the Prince ate and drank heartily, and this time the food had a strange effect upon him. All recollection of his father and the little dog he was to find for him slipped from his mind. He no longer thought of anything but of gossiping with the White Cat and enjoying her kind and gracious companionship.

So the days passed in pleasant sport and

amusement and the nights in feasting and conversation. There was scarcely one in which he did not discover some new charm of the little White Cat. Now he had forgotten even the land of his birth. The hands continued to wait upon him and supply every want till he began to regret that he could not become a cat himself to live forever in such pleasant company.

"Alas," he confessed to the White Cat at last, "how wretched it makes me even to think of leaving you! I have come to love you so dearly. Could you not become a woman or else make me a cat?"

But though she smiled at his wish, the look which she turned upon him was very strange.

A year passes away quickly when one has neither pain nor care, when one is merry and in good health. The Prince took no thought of time, but the White Cat was not so forgetful.

"There are only three days left to look for the little dog you were to bring to the King, your father," she reminded him. "Your two brothers have already found several very beautiful ones."

At her words the Prince's memory returned to him and he marveled at his strange forgetfulness.

"What spell could have made me forget what was most important to me in the whole world?" he cried in despair. "My honor and my fortune are lost unless I can find a dog that will win a kingdom for me and a horse swift enough to carry me home again in this short time!"

So, believing this to be impossible, he grew very sorrowful. Then the White Cat spoke to him with great reassurance.

"Son of a King," she said, "do not distress yourself so. I am your friend. Remain here another day, and though it is five hundred leagues from here to your country the good wooden horse will carry you there in less than twelve hours' time."

"But it is not enough for me to return to my father, dear Cat," said the Prince. "I must take him a little dog as well."

"And so you shall," replied she. "Here is a walnut which contains one more beautiful than the Dog Star."

"Your Majesty jests with me," he protested.

"Put the walnut to your ear then," insisted the Cat, "and you will hear it bark."

He obeyed her, and as he held the walnut to his ear a faint "Bow-wow" came from within, more tiny and shrill than a cricket on a winter night. The Prince could scarcely believe his ears or restrain his curiosity to see so diminutive a creature. But he was wise enough to follow the White Cat's advice not to open the walnut till he should reach his father's presence.

It was a sad leave-taking between the Prince and the White Cat. A thousand times he thanked her, but though he urged her to return to court with him, she only shook her head and sighed as deeply as upon the night of his arrival. So he galloped away at last on the wooden horse, which bore him more swiftly than the wind to the appointed place.

He reached the castle even before his two brothers and enjoyed the sight of their surprise at seeing a wooden horse champing at the bit in the courtyard. The two brothers were so busy telling of their various adventures that they took little note of their younger brother's silence concerning his, but when the time came to show one another their dogs the two were vastly amused at sight of an ugly cur which the young Prince had brought along, pretending to consider it a marvel of beauty. Needless to say the elder Princes smiled with secret satisfaction to think how far superior were their own dogs, for though they wished their brother no ill luck, they had no wish to see him ruling over the kingdom.

Next morning the three set out together in the same coach. The two eldest brothers carried baskets filled with little dogs too delicate and beautiful to be touched, while the youngest carried the poor cur as if it also was precious. By no outward sign did he betray the presence of the walnut with its precious occupant which was safely hidden in his pocket. No sooner did the three set foot in the palace than all the court crowded around to welcome the returned travelers and see the results of their journeyings. The King received them with great joy, professing delight over the little dogs his two elder sons brought out for his inspection. But the more he studied their merits, the more puzzled he became, so nearly were they alike in beauty and grace.

The two brothers were already beginning to dispute with one another as to which deserved the crown when the younger Brother stepped forward, holding upon the palm of his hand the walnut so lately presented to him by the White Cat. Opening it without more ado, he revealed a tiny dog lying upon cotton. So perfectly formed was it and so small that it could pass through a little finger ring without touching any part of it. It was more delicate than thistledown and its coat shone with colors of the rainbow. Nor was this all; immediately it was released from its kennel, the little creature arose on its hind legs and began to go through the steps of a tarantella, with tiny castanets and all the airs and graces of a Spanish dancer!

The King was dumfounded, and even the two brothers were forced to acknowledge that such a beautiful and gifted little dog had never been seen before. But their father was in no mood to give up his kingdom, so he announced that he had decided upon another test of their skill. This time he would give them a year to travel over land and sea in search of cloth so fine it would pass through the eye of the finest Venetian-point lace needle.

So the Prince remounted his wooden horse and set off at full speed, for now he knew exactly where he wanted to go. So great was his eagerness to see the beautiful White Cat once more that he could scarcely contain himself until her castle came into view. This time every window was alight to welcome him and the faithful pairs of hands which had waited on him so well before were ready to take the bridle of the wooden horse and lead it back to the stable while the Prince hurried to the White Cat's private apartments.

He found her lying on a little couch of blue satin with many pillows. Her expression was sad until she caught sight of him. Then she sprang up and began to caper about him delightedly.

"Oh, dear Prince," cried she, "I had scarcely dared to hope for your return. I am generally so unfortunate in matters that concern me."

A thousand times must the grateful Prince caress her and recount his adventures, which perhaps she knew more about than he guessed. And now he told her of his father's latest whim—how he had set his heart upon having a piece of cloth that could pass through the eye of the finest needle. For his own part he did not believe it was possible to find such a thing, but he believed that if any one could help him in this quest it would be his dear White Cat. She listened attentively to all he told her and finally explained with a thoughtful air that this was a matter demanding careful consideration. There were, it seemed, some cats in her castle who could spin with extraordinary skill, and she added that she would also put a paw to the work herself so that he need not trouble himself to search farther.

The Prince was only too delighted to accept this offer and he and his charming hostess sat down to supper together, after which a magnificent display of fireworks was set off in his honor. And once more the days passed in enchanted succession. The ingenious White Cat knew a thousand different ways of entertaining her guest, so that he never once thought of missing human society. Indeed, he was probably the first person in the world to spend a whole year of complete contentment with only cats for company.

The second year slipped away as pleasantly as the first. The Prince could scarcely think of anything that the tireless hands did not instantly supply, whether books, jewels, pictures, old things or new. In short, he had but to say, "I want a certain gem that is in the cabinet of the Great Mogul, or the King of Persia, or such and such a statue in Corinth or in any part of Greece," and he saw it instantly before him, without knowing how it came or who brought it. It is not unpleasant at all to find oneself able to possess any treasure in the world. No wonder our Prince was happy!

But the White Cat who was ever watchful of his welfare, warned him that the hour of departure was approaching and that he might make himself easy in his mind about the piece of cloth, for she had a most wonderful one for him. She added that it was her intention this time to furnish him with an equipage worthy of his high birth, and without waiting for his reply, beckoned him to the window overlooking the castle courtyard. Here he saw an open coach of gold and flame-color with a thousand gallant devices to please the mind and eye. It was drawn by twelve horses as white as snow, four-and-four abreast, with harnesses of flaming velvet embroidered with diamonds and gold. A hundred other coaches, each with eight horses and filled with superbly attired noblemen followed, escorted by a thousand bodyguards whose uniforms were so richly embroidered you could not see the material beneath. But the most remarkable part of this cavalcade was that a portrait of the White Cat was to be seen everywhere, in coach device, uniform, or worn as a decoration on the doublets of those who rode in the train, as if it were some newly created order that had been conferred upon them.

"Go now," said the White Cat to the Prince. "Appear at the court of the King, your father, in such magnificence that he cannot fail to be impressed and to bestow upon you the crown which you deserve. Here is another walnut. Crack it in his presence and you will find the piece of cloth you asked of me."

"Oh, dear White Cat," he answered tenderly, "I am so overcome by your goodness that I would gladly give up my hopes of power and future grandeur to stay here with you the rest of my life."

"Son of a King," she answered, "I am convinced of your kindness of heart. A kind heart is a rare thing among princes, who would be loved by all yet not love any one themselves. But you are proof that there is an exception to this rule. I give you credit for the affection you have shown to a little white cat that after all is good for nothing but to catch mice."

So the Prince kissed her paw and departed.

This time the two brothers arrived at their father's palace before him, congratulating themselves that their young brother must be dead or gone for good. They lost no time in displaying the cloths they had brought, which were indeed so fine that they could pass through the eye of a large needle but not through the small eye of the needle the King had already selected. At this there arose a great murmuring at court. The friends of the two Princes took sides among themselves as to which had fulfilled the bargain better. But this was interrupted by a flourish of trumpets announcing the arrival of their younger brother.

The magnificence of his train fairly took away the breath of the King and his court, but their astonishment grew even greater when, after saluting his father, the young Prince brought out the walnut. This he cracked with great ceremony only to find, instead of the promised piece of cloth, a cherry stone. At sight of this the King and the court exchanged sly smiles. Nothing daunted, the Prince cracked the cherry stone, only to find a kernel inside. Jeers and murmurs ran through the great apartment. The Prince must be a fool indeed!

He made no answer to them, but even he began to doubt the White Cat's words as he found next a grain of wheat and within that the smallest millet seed. "Oh, White Cat, White Cat! Have you betrayed me?" he muttered between his teeth. Even as he spoke he felt a little scratch upon his hand, so sharp that it drew blood. Taking this to be some sort of sign, the Prince proceeded to open the millet seed. Before the incredulous eyes of the whole court he drew out of it a piece of cloth four hundred yards long and marvelously embroidered with colored birds and beasts, with trees and fruits and flowers, with shells and jewels and even with suns and moons and countless stars. There were also portraits of Kings and Queens of the past upon it and of their children and children's children, not forgetting the smallest child, and each dressed perfectly in the habit of his century.

The sight of this was almost too much for the King. He could scarcely find the needle. Through its eye the wonderful piece of cloth was able to pass not only once but six times, before the jealous gaze of the two older Princes. But the King was still far from ready to give up his kingdom. Once more he turned to his sons.

"I am going to put your obedience to a new and final test," he told them. "Go and travel for another year and whichever one of you brings back with him the most beautiful Princess shall marry her and be crowned King on his wedding day. I pledge my honor that after this I shall ask no further favors of you."

So off the three went again, the youngest Prince still in a good humor although he had the least cause to be since he had twice been the acknowledged winner of the wager. But he was not one to dispute his father's will, so soon he and all his train were taking the road back to his dear White Cat. She knew the very day and hour of his arrival, and all along the way flowers had been strewn and perfume made the air sweet. Once more the castle gate was opened to him and the strange hands took him in charge while all the cats climbed into the trees to welcome their returning visitor.

"So, my Prince," said the White Cat when he reached her side at last, "once more you have returned without the crown. But no matter," she added as he opened his lips to explain, "I know that you are bound to take back the most beautiful Princess to court and I will find one for you, never fear. Meantime, let us amuse ourselves and be merry."

The third year passed for the young Prince as had the two others, and since nothing runs away faster than time passed without trouble or care, it is certain that he would have completely forgotten the day of his return to court had not the White Cat reminded him of it. This time, however, she told him that upon him alone depended his fate. He must promise to do whatever she asked of him. The Prince agreed readily enough until he heard her command him to cut off her head and tail and fling them into the fire.

"I!" cried the Prince, aghast, "I be so barbarous as to kill my dear White Cat! This is some trick to try my heart, but you should be sure of its gratitude."

"No, no, Son of a King," she answered, "I know your heart too well for that. But fate is stronger than either of us, and you must do as I bid you. It is the only way; and you must believe me, for I swear it on the honor of a Cat."

Tears came into the eyes of the Prince at the mere thought of cutting off the head of so amiable and pretty a creature. He tried to say all the most tender things he could think of, hoping to distract her. But she persisted that she wished to die by his hand because it was the only means of preventing his brothers from winning the crown. So piteously did she beg him that at last, all of a tremble, he drew his sword. With faltering hand he cut off the head and tail of his dear White Cat.

Next moment the most remarkable transformation took place before his very eyes. The body of the little White Cat suddenly changed into that of a young girl, the most graceful ever seen. But this was as nothing compared to the beauty and sweetness of her face, where only the shining brightness of the eyes gave any hint of the cat she had so recently been. The Prince was struck dumb with surprise and delight. He opened his eyes wider still to look at her, and what was his amazement to behold a troop of lords and ladies entering the apartment, each with a cat's skin flung over an arm. They advanced and, throwing themselves at the feet of their Queen, expressed their joy at seeing her once more restored to her natural form. She received them with great affection, but presently she desired them to leave her alone with the Prince.

"Behold, my dear Prince," she said as soon as they had done so, "I am released of a terrible enchantment, too long a tale to tell you now. Suffice it to say that this portrait which you saw upon my paw when I was a cat, was given to me by my guardian fairies during the time of my trial. I supposed it was of my first, unhappy love who was so cruelly taken from me and whose resemblance to you was so striking. Conceive my joy then, to find that it is of the Prince who has my entire heart and who was destined to rescue me from my enchantment."

And she bowed low before our Prince, who was so filled with joy and wonder that he would have remained there forever telling her of his love, had she not reminded him that the hour for his return to his father's court was almost upon them. Taking him by the hand, she led him into the courtyard to a chariot even more magnificent than the one she had provided before. The horses were shod with emeralds held in place by diamond nails, and there were such gold and jeweled trappings as were never seen before or since. But the young Prince had eyes for nothing beyond the beauty of his companion.

Just before they reached the outskirts of the city, they sighted the Prince's two brothers with their trains driving toward them from opposite directions. At this the Princess hid herself in a small throne of rock crystal and precious gems, while the Prince remained alone in the coach. His two brothers, each accompanied by a charming lady, greeted him warmly but expressed surprise and curiosity that he should be alone. To these questions he replied that he had been so unfortunate as not to have met with any lady of sufficient beauty to bring with him to court. He added, however, that he had instead a very rare and gifted White Cat. At this the brothers laughed loudly and exchanged pleased glances, for now they were convinced that he was indeed a simpleton and they need have no fears of his outwitting them a third time.

Through the streets of the city the two elder Princes rode with their ladies in open carriages, while the youngest Prince came last. Behind him was borne the great rock crystal, at which every one gazed in wonder.

The two Princes eagerly charged up the palace stairs with their Princesses, so anxious were they for their father's approval. The King received them graciously, but once more had difficulty in deciding which should have the prize. So he turned to his youngest son, who stood alone before him.

"Have you returned empty-handed this time?" he asked.

"In this rock your Majesty will find a little White Cat," he answered, "one which mews so sweetly and has such velvet paws that you cannot but be delighted with it."

But before the surprised King could reach the crystal, the Princess touched an inner spring. It flew open revealing her in all her beauty, more dazzling than the sun itself. Her hair fell in golden ringlets; she was crowned with flowers and she moved with incomparable grace in her gown of white and rose-colored gauze. Even the King himself could not resist such loveliness, but hastened to acknowledge her undisputed right to wear the crown.

"But I have not come to deprive your Majesty of a throne which you fill so admirably," she said, bowing before him graciously. "I was born the heiress to six kingdoms of my own, so permit me to offer one to you and to each of your elder sons. I ask no other favors of you than your friendship and that your youngest son shall be my husband. Three kingdoms will be quite enough for us."

And so in truth they found them.

## FAIRYFOOT [1]

*Frances Browne*

Once upon a time there stood far away in the west country a town called Stumpinghame. It contained seven windmills, a royal palace, a market place, and a prison with every other convenience befitting the capital of a kingdom. A capital city was Stumpinghame, and its inhabitants thought it the only one in the world.

It stood in the midst of a great plain, which for three leagues round its walls was covered with corn, flax, and orchards. Beyond that lay a great circle of pasture land, seven leagues in breadth, and it was bounded on all sides by a forest so thick and old that no man in Stumpinghame knew its extent; and the opinion of the learnèd was that it reached to the end of the world.

There were strong reasons for this opinion. First, that forest was known to be inhabited time out of mind by the fairies, and no hunter dared to go beyond its border—so all the west country believed it to be solidly full of trees. Secondly, the people of Stumpinghame were no travelers, for man, woman, and child—all had feet so large and heavy that it was by no means convenient to carry them far.

Whether it was the nature of the place or the people, I cannot tell, but great feet had been the fashion there from time immemorial, and the higher the family the larger their feet were.

Stumpinghame had a king of its own, and his name was Stiffstep; his family was very ancient and large-footed. His subjects called him Lord of the World, and he made a speech to them every year concerning the grandeur of his mighty empire.

His queen, Hammerheel, was the greatest beauty in Stumpinghame; her majesty's shoe was not much smaller than a fishing-boat. Their six children promised to be quite as handsome, and all went well with them till the birth of their seventh son.

For a long time nobody about the palace could understand what was the matter—the ladies-in-waiting looked so astonished, and the king so vexed. But at last it was whispered through the city that the queen's seventh child had been born with such miserably small feet that they resembled nothing ever seen or heard of in Stumpinghame, except the feet of the fairies.

All the relations of the king and queen assembled at the palace to mourn with them over their singular misfortune. The whole court and most of the citizens helped in this mourning, but when it had lasted seven days they all found out it was of no use. So the relations went to their homes, and the people back to their work. To cheer up the queen's spirits, the young prince was sent privately out to the pasture lands, to be nursed among the shepherds.

The chief man there was called Fleecefold, and his wife's name was Rough Ruddy. They lived in a snug cottage with their son Blackthorn and their daughter Brownberry, and were thought great people, because they kept the king's sheep. Moreover, Fleecefold's family were known to be ancient; and Rough Ruddy boasted that she had the largest feet in all the pastures.

The shepherds held them in high respect, and it grew still higher when the news spread that the king's seventh son had been sent to their cottage. People came from all quarters to see the young prince, and great were the lamentations over his misfortune in having such small feet.

The king and queen had given him fourteen names, beginning with Augustus—such being the fashion in that royal family. But the honest country people could not remember so many; besides, his feet were the most remarkable thing about the child, so with one accord they called him Fairyfoot. At first it was feared this might be high treason, but when no notice was taken by the king or his ministers, the shepherds concluded it was no harm, and the boy never had another name throughout the pastures.

[1] From Frances Browne, *Granny's Wonderful Chair*.

At court it was not thought polite to speak of him at all. They did not keep his birthday, and he was never sent for at Christmas, because the queen and her ladies could not bear the sight of him. Once a year the undermost scullion was sent to see how he did, with a bundle of his next brother's cast-off clothes; and, as the king grew old and cross, it was said he had thoughts of disowning him.

So Fairyfoot grew in Fleecefold's cottage. Perhaps the country air made him fair and rosy—for all agreed that he would have been a handsome boy but for his small feet. Nevertheless he learned to walk, and in time to run and to jump, thereby amazing everybody, for such doings were not known among the children of Stumpinghame.

The news of the court, however, traveled to the shepherds, and Fairyfoot was despised among them. The old people thought him unlucky; the children refused to play with him. Fleecefold was ashamed to have him in his cottage, but he dared not disobey the king's orders. Moreover, Blackthorn wore most of the clothes brought by the scullion.

At last, Rough Ruddy decided that the sight of such horrid jumping would make her children vulgar. So as soon as he was old enough, she sent Fairyfoot every day to watch some sickly sheep that grazed on a wild, weedy pasture, hard by the forest.

Poor Fairyfoot was often lonely and sorrowful; many a time he wished his feet would grow larger, or that people wouldn't notice them so much. All the comfort he had was running and jumping by himself in the wild pasture, and thinking that none of the shepherds' children could do the like, for all their pride in their great feet.

Tired of this sport, he was lying in the shadow of a mossy rock one warm summer's noon, with the sheep feeding round, when a robin, pursued by a great hawk, flew into the old velvet cap which lay on the ground beside him. Fairyfoot covered it up, and the hawk, frightened by his shout, flew away.

"Now you may go, poor robin!" he said, opening the cap.

Instead of the bird, out sprang a little man dressed in russet-brown, and looking as if he were a hundred years old. Fairyfoot could not speak for astonishment, but the little man said:

"Thank you for your shelter, and be sure I will do as much for you. Call on me if you are ever in trouble; my name is Robin Goodfellow"; and darting off, he was out of sight in an instant.

For days the boy wondered who that little man could be, but he told nobody, for the little man's feet were as small as his own, and it was clear he would be no favorite in Stumpinghame. Fairyfoot kept the story to himself, and at last midsummer came. That evening was a feast among the shepherds. There were bonfires on the hills, and fun in the villages. But Fairyfoot sat alone beside his sheepfold, for the children of his village had refused to let him play with them about the bonfire. Fairyfoot had never felt so lonely in all his life, and remembering the little man, he plucked up spirit, and cried—

"Ho! Robin Goodfellow!"

"Here I am," said a shrill voice at his elbow; and there stood the little man himself.

"I am very lonely, and no one will play with me, because my feet are not large enough," said Fairyfoot.

"Come then and play with us," said the little man. "We lead the merriest lives in the world, and care for nobody's feet. But all companies have their own manners, and there are two things you must mind among us: first, do as you see the rest doing; and secondly, never speak of anything you may hear or see, for we and the people of this country have had no friendship ever since large feet came in fashion."

"I will do that, and anything more you like," said Fairyfoot.

The little man, taking his hand, led him over the pasture into the forest and along a mossy path among old trees wreathed with ivy (he never knew how far), till they heard the sound of music and came upon a meadow where the moon shone as bright as day, and all the flowers of the year—snowdrops, violets, primroses, and cowslips—bloomed together in the thick grass.

There was a crowd of little men and women, some clad in russet color, but far more in green, dancing round a little well as clear as crystal. And under great rose-trees which grew here and there in the meadow, companies were sitting round low tables covered with cups of milk, dishes of honey, and carved wooden flagons filled with clear red wine. The little man led Fairyfoot up to the nearest table, handed him one of the flagons, and said:

"Drink to the good company."

Wine was not very common among the shepherds of Stumpinghame, and the boy had never tasted such a drink as that before. Scarcely had it gone down his throat when he forgot all his troubles; how Blackthorn and Brownberry wore his clothes, how Rough Ruddy sent him to keep the sickly sheep, how the children would not play with him—in short, he forgot the whole misfortune of his feet. It seemed to him now that he was really a king's son, and all was well with him.

All the little people about the well cried, "Welcome! welcome!" And every one said, "Come and dance with me!" So Fairyfoot was as happy as a prince. He danced, drank milk, and ate honey till the moon was low in the sky, and then the little man took him by the hand, and they neither stopped nor stayed till he was at his own bed of straw in the cottage corner.

Next morning Fairyfoot was not tired for all his dancing. Nobody in the cottage had missed him, and he went out with the sheep as usual. Every night all that summer, when the shepherds were safe in bed, the little man came and took him away to dance in the forest.

Now he did not care to play with the shepherds' children, nor grieve that his father and mother had forgotten him, but watched the sheep all day, singing to himself or braiding rushes; and when the sun went down, Fairyfoot's heart rejoiced at the thought of meeting that merry company.

The wonder was that he was never tired nor sleepy, but before the summer was ended Fairyfoot found out the reason. One night, when the moon was full, and the last of the ripe corn was rustling in the fields, Robin Goodfellow came for him as usual, and away they went to the flowery green. The fun there was high, and Robin was in haste. So he only pointed to the carved cup from which Fairyfoot every night drank the clear red wine.

"I am not thirsty. and there is no use losing time," thought the boy to himself, and he joined the dance; but never in all his life did Fairyfoot find such hard work as to keep pace with the company. Their feet seemed to move like lightning, the swallows did not fly so fast nor turn so quickly.

Fairyfoot did his best, for he never gave in easily, but at length, his breath and strength being spent, the boy was glad to steal away and sit down behind a mossy oak, where his eyes closed for very weariness. When he awoke the dance was nearly over, but two little ladies clad in green talked close beside him.

"What a beautiful boy!" said one of them. "He is worthy to be a king's son. Only see what handsome feet he has!"

"Yes," said the other, with a laugh that sounded spiteful. "They are just like the feet Princess Maybloom had before she washed them in the Growing Well. Her father has sent far and wide throughout the whole country searching for a doctor to make them small again, but nothing in this world can do it except the water of the Fair Fountain, and none but I and the nightingales know where it is."

"One would not care to let the like be known," said the first little lady. "There would come such crowds of these great coarse creatures of mankind, nobody would have peace for leagues round. But you will surely send word to the sweet princess! She was so kind to our birds and butterflies, and danced so like one of ourselves!"

"Not I, indeed!" said the spiteful fairy. "Her old skinflint of a father cut down the cedar which I loved best in the whole forest and made a chest of it to put his money in; besides, I never liked the princess—everybody praised her so. But come, we shall be too late for the last dance."

When they were gone, Fairyfoot could sleep no more from astonishment. He did not wonder at the fairies admiring his feet, because their own were much the same; but it amazed him that Princess Maybloom's father should be troubled at hers growing large. Moreover, he wished to see that same princess and her country, since there were really other places in the world than Stumpinghame.

When Robin Goodfellow came to take him home as usual he dared not let him know that he had overheard anything. But never was a boy so unwilling to get up as he on that morning, and all day he was so weary that in the afternoon he fell asleep, with his head on a clump of rushes.

It was seldom that any one thought of looking after him and the sickly sheep; but it so happened that towards evening the old shepherd, Fleecefold, thought he would see how things went in the pastures. The shepherd had a bad temper and a thick staff, and no sooner did he catch sight of Fairyfoot sleeping, and his flock straying away, than shouting all the ill names he could remember, in a voice which woke up the boy, he ran after him as fast as his great feet would allow. Fairyfoot, seeing no other shelter from his fury, fled into the forest, and neither stopped nor stayed till he reached the banks of a little stream.

Thinking it might lead him to the fairies' dancing-ground, he followed that stream for many an hour, but it wound away into the heart of the forest, flowing through dells, falling over mossy rocks, and at last leading Fairyfoot, when he was tired and the night had fallen, to a grove of great rose trees, with the moon shining on it as bright as day, and thousands of nightingales singing in the branches. In the midst of that grove was a clear spring, bordered with banks of lilies, and Fairyfoot sat down by it to rest himself and listen. The singing was so sweet he could have listened for ever, but as he sat the nightingales left off their songs, and began to talk together in the silence of the night.

"What boy is that," said one on a branch above him, "who sits so lonely by the Fair Fountain? He cannot have come from Stumpinghame with such small and handsome feet."

"No, I'll warrant you," said another, "he has come from the west country. How in the world did he find the way?"

"How simple you are!" said a third nightingale. "What had he to do but follow the ground ivy which grows from the lowest gate of the king's kitchen garden to the root of this rose tree? He looks a wise boy, and I hope he will keep the secret, or we shall have all the west country here, dabbling in our fountain, and leaving us no rest to either talk or sing."

Fairyfoot sat up in great astonishment. By and by, when the talk ceased and the songs began, he thought it might be as well for him to follow the ground ivy, and see the Princess Maybloom, not to speak of getting rid of Rough Ruddy, the sickly sheep, and the crusty old shepherd.

It was a long journey; but he went on, eating wild berries by day, sleeping in the hollows of old trees by night, and never losing sight of the ground ivy. It led him out of the forest, and along a noble highroad, with fields and villages on every side, to a great city, and a low old-fashioned gate of the king's kitchen garden, which was thought too mean for the scullions, and had not been opened for seven years.

There was no use knocking—the gate was overgrown with tall weeds and moss; so, being an active boy, he climbed over, and walked through the garden, till a white fawn came frisking by, and he heard a soft voice saying sorrowfully:

"Come back, come back, my fawn! I cannot run and play with you now, my feet have grown so heavy." Looking round, Fairyfoot saw the loveliest young princess in the world, dressed in snow-white, and wearing a wreath of roses on her golden hair; but walking slowly, as the great people did in Stumpinghame, for her feet were as large as the best of them.

After her came six young ladies, dressed in white and walking slowly, for they could not go before the princess. Fairyfoot was amazed to see that their feet were as small as his own. At once he guessed that this must be the Princess Maybloom, and made her a humble bow, saying:

"Royal princess, I have heard of your trouble because your feet have grown large; in my country that's all the fashion. For seven years past I have been wondering what would make mine grow, to no purpose. I know of a certain fountain that will make yours smaller and finer than ever they were, if the king, your father, gives you leave to come with me, accompanied by two of your maids that are the least given to talking and the most prudent officer in all his household. It would grievously offend the fairies and the nightingales to make that fountain known."

When the princess heard that, she danced for joy in spite of her large feet. She and her six maids brought Fairyfoot before the king and queen, where they sat in their palace hall, with all the courtiers paying their morning compliments. The lords were very much astonished to see a ragged, barefooted boy brought in among them, and all the ladies thought Princess Maybloom must have gone mad. Fairyfoot, making a humble bow, told his message to the king and queen, and offered to set out with the princess that very day.

At first the king could not believe that there could be any use in his offer, because so many great physicians had failed to help his daughter. The courtiers laughed Fairyfoot to scorn, the pages wanted to turn him out for an impudent imposter, and the prime minister said he ought to be put to death for high treason.

Fairyfoot wished himself safe in the forest again, or even keeping the sickly sheep; but the queen, being a prudent woman, said:

"I pray your majesty to notice what fine feet this boy has. There may be some truth in his story. For the sake of our only daughter, I will choose two maids, who talk the least of all our train, and my chamberlain, who is the most discreet officer in our household. Let them go with the princess; who knows but our sorrow may be lessened?"

After some persuasion the king consented, though all his councilors advised the contrary. So the two silent maids, the discreet chamberlain, and her fawn, which would not stay behind, were sent with Princess Maybloom, and they all set out after dinner.

Fairyfoot had hard work guiding them along the track of the ground ivy. The maids and the chamberlain did not like the brambles and rough roots of the forest, and they thought it hard to eat berries and sleep in hollow trees. But the princess went on with good courage, and at last they reached the grove of rose trees and the spring bordered with lilies.

The chamberlain washed and, though his hair had been grey, and his face wrinkled, the young courtiers envied his beauty for years after. The maids washed and from that day they were esteemed the fairest in all the palace.

Lastly, the princess washed also. It could make her no fairer, but the moment her feet touched the water they grew less, and when she had washed and dried them three times, they were as small and finely-shaped as Fairyfoot's own. There was great joy among them, but the boy said sorrowfully:

"Oh! if there had been a well in the world to make my feet large, my father and mother would not have cast me off, nor sent me to live among the shepherds."

"Cheer up," said the Princess Maybloom. "If you want large feet, there is a well in this forest that will do it. Last summer I came with my father and his foresters to see a great cedar cut down, from which he meant to make a money chest. While they were busy with the cedar, I saw a bramble branch covered with berries. Some were ripe and some were green, but it was the longest bramble that ever grew. For the sake of the berries, I went on and on to its root, which grew hard by a muddy-looking well, with banks of dark green moss, in the deepest part of the forest. The day was warm and dry and my feet were sore from the rough ground, so I took off my scarlet shoes and washed my feet in the well. As I washed they grew larger every minute, and nothing could ever make them less again. I have seen the bramble this day. It is not far off, and as you have shown me the Fair Fountain, I will show you the Growing Well."

Up rose Fairyfoot and Princess Maybloom, and went together till they found the bramble, and came to where its root grew, hard by the muddy-looking well, with banks of dark green moss in the deepest dell of the forest. Fairyfoot sat down to wash, but at that minute he heard a sound of music, and knew it was the fairies going to their dancing ground.

"If my feet grow large," said the boy to himself, "how shall I dance with them?"

Rising quickly, he took the Princess Maybloom by the hand. The fawn followed them; the maids and the chamberlain followed the fawn, and all followed the music through the forest.

At last they came to the flowery green. Robin Goodfellow welcomed the company for Fairyfoot's sake, and gave every one a drink of the fairies' wine. So they danced there from sunset till the grey morning, and nobody was tired. Before the lark sang, Robin Goodfellow took them all safe home as he used to take Fairyfoot.

There was great joy that day in the palace because Princess Maybloom's feet were made small again. The king gave Fairyfoot all manner of fine clothes and rich jewels; and when they heard his wonderful story, he and the queen asked him to live with them and be their son.

In time Fairyfoot and Princess Maybloom were married, and still live happily. When they go to visit at Stumpinghame, they always wash their feet in the Growing Well, lest the royal family think them a disgrace. When they come back, they make haste to the Fair Fountain. The fairies and the nightingales are great friends to them, as well as to the maids and the chamberlain, because they have told nobody about the fountain, and there is peace and quiet yet in the grove of rose trees.

## PINOCCHIO [1]

*C. Collodi*

Once upon a time there was a piece of wood. It was not an expensive piece of wood. Far from it. Just a common block of firewood, one of those thick, solid logs that are put on the fire in winter to make cold rooms cozy and warm.

I do not know how this really happened, yet the fact remains that one fine day this piece of wood found itself in the shop of an old carpenter. His real name was Antonio, but every one called him Cherry, for the tip of his nose was so round and red and shiny that it looked like a ripe cherry.

As soon as he saw that piece of wood, Cherry was filled with joy. Rubbing his hands together happily, he mumbled half to himself:

"This has come in the nick of time. I shall use it to make the leg of a table."

He grasped the hatchet quickly to peel off the bark and shape the wood. But as he was about to give it the first blow he stood still with arm uplifted, for he heard a little voice say in a beseeching tone:

"Please be careful! Do not hit me so hard!"

Cherry turned frightened eyes about the room to find out where that little voice came from, but he saw no one! He looked under the bench—no one! He peeped inside

[1] From C. Collodi (Carlo Lorenzini), *The Adventures of Pinocchio,* translated by Carol della Chiesa.

the closet—no one! He searched among the shavings—no one! He opened the door to look up and down the street—and still no one!

"Oh, I see!" he then said, laughing and scratching his wig. "It can easily be seen that I only thought I heard the tiny voice say the words! Well, well—to work once more."

He struck a most solemn blow upon the piece of wood.

"Oh, oh! You hurt!" cried the same faraway little voice.

Cherry grew dumb, his eyes almost popped out of his head, his mouth opened wide, and his tongue hung down on his chin.

As soon as he regained the use of his senses, he said, trembling and stuttering from fright:

"Where did that voice come from, when there is no one around? Might it be that this piece of wood has learned to weep and cry like a child? I can hardly believe it. Here it is—a piece of common firewood. Yet might some one be hidden in it? If so, the worse for him. I'll fix him!"

With these words, he grabbed the log with both hands and started to knock it about unmercifully. He threw it to the floor, against the walls of the room, and even up to the ceiling.

He listened for the tiny voice to moan and cry. He waited two minutes—nothing; five minutes—nothing; ten minutes—nothing.

"Oh, I see," he said, trying bravely to laugh and ruffling up his wig with his hand. "It can easily be seen I only imagined I heard the tiny voice! Well, well—to work once more!"

The poor fellow was scared half to death, so he tried to sing a gay song in order to gain courage.

He set aside the hatchet and picked up the plane to make the wood smooth and even, but as he drew it to and fro, he heard the same tiny voice. This time it giggled as it spoke:

"Stop it! Oh, stop it! Ha, ha, ha! You tickle my stomach."

This time poor Cherry fell as if shot. When he opened his eyes, he found himself sitting on the floor.

His face had changed; fright had turned even the tip of his nose from red to deepest purple.

In that very instant, a loud knock sounded on the door.

"Come in," said the carpenter, not having an atom of strength left with which to stand up.

At the words, the door opened and a dapper little old man came in. His name was Geppetto, and he always wore a wig that was just the color of yellow corn.

"Good day, Antonio," said Geppetto. "What are you doing on the floor?"

"I am teaching the ants their A B C's."

"Good luck to you!"

"What brought you here, friend Geppetto?"

"My legs. And it may flatter you to know, Antonio, that I have come to you to beg for a favor."

"Here I am, at your service," answered the carpenter, raising himself on to his knees.

"This morning a fine idea came to me."

"Let's hear it."

"I thought of making myself a beautiful wooden marionette. It must be wonderful, one that will be able to dance, fence, and turn somersaults. With it I intend to earn my way around the world."

"Well then, Geppetto," said the carpenter, "what is it you want?"

"I want a piece of wood to make a marionette. Will you give it to me?"

Then Antonio, very glad indeed, went immediately to his bench to get the piece of wood which had frightened him so much. But as he was about to give it to his friend, with a violent jerk it slipped out of his hands and hit against poor Geppetto's thin legs.

"Ah! Is this the gentle way, friend Antonio, in which you make your gifts? You have made me almost lame!"

"I swear to you I did not do it!"

"It was *I*, of course!"

"It's the fault of this piece of wood."

"You're right; but remember you were the one to throw it at my legs."

"I did not throw it!"

At this Geppetto lost his head with rage and threw himself upon the carpenter. Then and there they gave each other a sound thrashing.

After this fight, Antonio had two more scratches on his nose, and Geppetto had two buttons missing from his coat. Thus having settled their accounts, they shook hands and swore to be good friends for the rest of their lives.

Then Geppetto took the fine piece of wood, thanked Antonio, and limped away toward home.

Little as Geppetto's house was, it was neat and comfortable. It was a small room on the ground floor, with a tiny window under the stairway. The furniture could not have been much simpler: a very old chair, a rickety old bed, and a tumble-down table. A fireplace full of burning logs was painted on the wall opposite the door. Over the fire, there was painted a pot full of something which kept boiling happily away and sending up clouds of what looked like real steam.

As soon as he reached home, Geppetto took his tools and began to cut and shape the wood into a marionette.

"What shall I call him?" he said to himself. "I think I'll call him *Pinocchio*. This name will make his fortune. I knew a whole family of Pinocchi once—Pinocchio the father, Pinocchia the mother, and Pinocchi the children—and they were all lucky. The richest of them begged for his living."

After choosing the name for his marionette, Geppetto set seriously to work to make the hair, the forehead, the eyes. Fancy his surprise when he noticed that the eyes moved and then stared fixedly at him.

Geppetto, seeing this, felt insulted and said in a grieved tone:

"Ugly wooden eyes, why do you stare so?"

There was no answer.

After the eyes, Geppetto made the nose, which began to stretch as soon as finished. It stretched and stretched and stretched till it became so long, it seemed endless.

Poor Geppetto kept cutting it and cutting it, but the more he cut, the longer grew that impertinent nose. In despair he let it alone.

Next he made the mouth.

No sooner was it finished than it began to laugh and poke fun at him.

"Stop laughing!" said Geppetto angrily; but he might as well have spoken to the wall.

"Stop laughing, I say!" he roared in a voice of thunder.

The mouth stopped laughing, but it stuck out a long tongue.

Not wishing to start an argument, Geppetto made believe he saw nothing and went on with his work.

After the mouth, he made the chin, then the neck, the shoulders, the stomach, the arms, and the hands.

As he was about to put the last touches on the finger tips, Geppetto felt his wig being pulled off. He glanced up and what did he see? His yellow wig was in the marionette's hand.

"Pinocchio, give me my wig!"

But instead of giving it back, Pinocchio put it on his own head, which was half swallowed up in it.

At that unexpected trick, Geppetto became very sad and downcast, more so than he had ever been before.

"Pinocchio, you wicked boy!" he cried out. "You are not yet finished, and you start out by being impudent to your poor old father. Very bad, my son, very bad!"

And he wiped away a tear.

The legs and feet still had to be made. As soon as they were done, Geppetto felt a sharp kick on the tip of his nose.

"I deserve it!" he said to himself. "I should have thought of this before I made him. Now it's too late!"

He took hold of the marionette under the arms and put him on the floor to teach him to walk.

Pinocchio's legs were so stiff that he could not move them, and Geppetto held his hand and showed him how to put out one foot after the other.

When his legs were limbered up, Pinocchio started walking by himself and ran all around the room. He came to the open door, and with one leap he was out into the street. Away he flew!

Poor Geppetto ran after him but was unable to catch him, for Pinocchio ran in leaps and bounds, his two wooden feet, as they beat on the stones of the street, making as much noise as twenty peasants in wooden shoes.

"Catch him! Catch him!" Geppetto kept shouting. But the people in the street, seeing a wooden marionette running like the wind, stood still to stare and to laugh until they cried.

At last, by sheer luck, a policeman happened along who, hearing all that noise, thought that it might be a runaway colt, and stood bravely in the middle of the street, with legs wide apart, firmly resolved to stop it and prevent any trouble.

Pinocchio saw the policeman from afar and tried his best to escape between the legs of the big fellow, but in this he had little success.

The policeman grabbed him by the nose, for it was an extremely long one and seemed made on purpose for that very thing, and returned him to Geppetto.

The little old man wanted to pull Pinnocchio's ears. Think how he felt when, upon searching for them, he discovered that he had forgotten to make them!

All he could do was to seize Pinocchio by the back of the neck and take him home. As he was doing so, he shook him two or three times and said to him angrily:

"We're going home now. When we get home, then we'll settle this matter!"

Pinocchio, on hearing this, threw himself on the ground and refused to take another step. One person after another gathered around the two.

Some said one thing, some another.

"Poor marionette," called out a man. "I am not surprised he doesn't want to go home. Geppetto, no doubt, will beat him unmercifully."

"But Geppetto looks like a good man," added another.

They all had so much to say, that it grew tiresome to Pinocchio, so finally he got up and went home. What happened after that is a story that is really past all belief. Many strange adventures befell Pinocchio—so many that they fill an entire book!

## LITTLE DAYLIGHT [1]

*George MacDonald*

No house of any pretension to be called a palace is in the least worthy of the name, except it has a wood near it—very near it—and the nearer the better. Not all round it—I don't mean that, for a palace ought to be open to the sun and wind, and stand high and brave, with weathercocks glittering and flags flying; but on one side of every palace there must be a wood. And there was a very grand wood indeed beside the palace of the king who was going to be Daylight's father; such a grand wood, that nobody yet had ever got to the other end of it. Near the house it was kept very trim and nice, and it was free of brushwood for a long way in; but by degrees it got wild, and it grew wilder, and wilder, and wilder, until some said wild beasts did what they liked in it. The king and his courtiers often hunted, however, and this kept the wild beasts far away from the palace.

One glorious summer morning, when the wind and sun were out together, little Daylight made her appearance—a beautiful baby, with such bright eyes that she might have come from the sun, only by and by

[1] From George MacDonald, *At the Back of the North Wind.*

she showed such lively ways that she might equally well have come out of the wind. There was great jubilation in the palace, for this was the first baby the queen had had, and there is as much happiness over a new baby in a palace as in a cottage.

There is one disadvantage of living near a wood; you do not know quite who your neighbors may be. Everybody knew there were in it several fairies, living within a few miles of the palace, who always had had something to do with each new baby that came; for fairies live so much longer than we, that they can have business with a good many generations of human mortals. The curious houses they lived in were well known also—one, a hollow oak; another, a birch-tree, though nobody could ever find how that fairy made a house of it; another, a hut of growing trees intertwined, and patched up with turf and moss. But there was another fairy who had lately come to the place, an ugly swamp fairy, and nobody even knew she was a fairy except the other fairies. A wicked old thing she was, always concealing her power, and being as disagreeable as she could, in order to tempt people to give her offense, that she might have the pleasure of taking vengeance upon them. The people about thought she was a witch, and those who knew her by sight were careful to avoid offending her. She lived in a mud house, in a swampy part of the forest.

In all history we find that fairies give their remarkable gifts to prince or princess, or any child of sufficient importance in their eyes, always at the christening. Now this we can understand, because it is an ancient custom amongst human beings as well; and it is not hard to explain why wicked fairies should choose the same time to do unkind things; but it is difficult to understand how they should be able to do them, for you would fancy all wicked creatures would be powerless on such an occasion. But I never knew of any interference on the part of the wicked fairy that did not turn out a good thing in the end. What a good thing, for instance, it was that one princess should sleep for a hundred years! Was she not saved from all the plague of young men who were not worthy of her? And did she not come awake exactly at the right moment when the right prince kissed her?

Of course all the known fairies were invited to the christening. But the king and queen never thought of inviting the wicked fairy. The other fairies, however, knowing the danger run, provided as well as they could against accidents from her quarter. But they could neither render her powerless, nor could they arrange their gifts in reference to hers beforehand, for they could not tell what those might be.

Of course the old hag was there without being asked. Not to be asked was just what she wanted, that she might have a sort of reason for doing what she wished to do. For somehow even the wickedest of creatures likes a pretext for doing the wrong thing.

Five fairies had one after the other given the child such gifts as each counted best, and the fifth had just stepped back to her place in the surrounding splendor of ladies and gentlemen, when, mumbling a laugh between her toothless gums, the wicked swamp fairy hobbled out into the middle of the circle, and at the moment when the archbishop was handing the baby to the lady at the head of the nursery department of state affairs, addressed him thus, giving a bite or two to every word before she could part with it:

"Please your Grace, I'm very deaf; would your Grace mind repeating the princess's name?"

"With pleasure, my good woman," said the archbishop, stooping to shout in her ear, "the infant's name is little Daylight."

"And little Daylight it shall be," cried the fairy, in the tone of a dry axle, "and little good shall any of her gifts do her. For I bestow upon her the gift of sleeping all day long, whether she will or not. Ha, ha! He, he! Hi, hi!"

Then out started the sixth fairy, who, of course, the others had arranged should come after the wicked one, in order to undo as much as she might.

"If she sleep all day," she said, mournfully, "she shall, at least, wake all night."

"A nice prospect for her mother and me!" thought the poor king; for they loved her far too much to give her up to nurses, especially at night, as most kings and queens do.

"You spoke before I had done," said the wicked swamp fairy. "That's against the law. It gives me another chance."

"I beg your pardon," said the other fairies, all together.

"I hadn't done laughing," said the crone. "I had only got to Hi, hi! and I had to go through Ho, ho! and Hu, hu! So I decree that if she wakes all night she shall wax and wane with its mistress, the moon. And what that may mean I hope her royal parents will live to see. Ho, ho! Hu, hu!"

But out stepped another fairy, for they had been wise enough to keep two in reserve, because every fairy knew the trick of one.

"Until," said the seventh fairy, "a prince comes who shall kiss her without knowing it."

The wicked swamp fairy made a horrid noise like an angry cat, and hobbled away. She could not pretend that she had not finished her speech this time, for she had laughed Ho, ho! and Hu, hu!

"I don't know what that means," said the poor king to the seventh fairy.

"Don't be afraid. The meaning will come with the thing itself," said she.

The assembly broke up, miserable enough—the queen, at least, prepared for a good many sleepless nights, and the lady at the head of the nursery department anything but comfortable in the prospect before her, for of course the queen could not do it all.

I will not attempt to describe what they had to go through for some time. But at last the household settled into a regular system—a very irregular one in some respects. For at certain seasons the palace rang all night with bursts of laughter from little Daylight, whose heart the old fairy's curse could not reach; she was Daylight still, only a little in the wrong place, for she always dropped asleep at the first hint of dawn in the east. But her merriment was of short duration. When the moon was at the full, she was in glorious spirits, and as beautiful as it was possible for a child of her age to be. But as the moon waned, she faded, until at last she was wan and withered like the poorest, sickliest child any one ever saw. Then the night was quiet as the day, for the little creature lay in her gorgeous cradle night and day with hardly a motion, and indeed at last without even a moan.

At first they often thought she was dead, but at last they got used to it, and only consulted the almanac to find the moment when she would begin to revive, which, of course, was with the first appearance of the silver thread of the crescent moon. Then she would move her lips, and they would give her a little nourishment; and she would grow better and better and better, until for a few days she was splendidly well. When well, she was always merriest out in the moonlight; but even when near her worst, she seemed better when, in warm summer nights, they carried her cradle out into the light of the waning moon. Then in her sleep she would smile a faint, pitiful smile.

For a long time very few people ever saw her awake. As she grew older she became such a favorite, however, that about the palace there were always some who would contrive to keep awake at night, in order to be near her. But she soon began to take every chance of getting away from her nurses and enjoying her moonlight alone. And thus things went on until she was nearly seventeen years of age. Her father and mother had by that time got so used to the odd state of things that they had ceased to wonder at them. All their arrangements had reference to the Princess Daylight, and it is amazing how things contrive to accommodate themselves. But how any prince was ever to find and deliver her, appeared inconceivable.

As she grew older she had grown more and more beautiful, with the sunniest hair and the loveliest eyes of heavenly blue, brilliant and profound as the sky of a June day. But so much more painful and sad was the change as her bad time came on. The more beautiful she was in the full moon, the more withered and worn did she become as the moon waned. At the time at which my story has now arrived, she looked, when the moon was small or gone, like an old woman exhausted with suffering. Her wan face was drawn and wrinkled, and had an eager, hungry look. Her skinny hands moved as if wishing, but unable, to lay hold of something. Her shoulders were bent forward, her chest went in, and she stooped as if she were eighty years old. At last she had to be put to bed. But she grew to dislike being seen, during this season. One lovely summer evening, when the moon lay all but gone upon the verge of the horizon, she vanished from her attendants, and it was only after searching for her a long time in great terror, that they found her fast asleep in the forest, at the foot of a silver birch, and carried her home.

A little way from the palace there was a great open glade, covered with the greenest and softest grass. This was her favorite haunt; for here the full moon shone free and glorious. Here she had a little rustic house built for her, and here she mostly resided. None of the court might go there without leave, and her own attendants had learned by this time not to be officious in waiting upon her, so that she was very much at liberty. Whether the good fairies had anything to do with it or not I cannot tell, but at least she got into the way of retreating farther into the wood every night as the moon waned, so that sometimes they had great trouble in finding her; but as she was always very angry if she discovered they were watching her, they scarcely dared to do so. At length one night they thought they had lost her altogether. It was morning before they found her. Feeble as she was, she had wandered into a thicket a long way from the glade, and there she lay—fast asleep, of course.

Although the fame of her beauty and sweetness had gone abroad, yet as everybody knew she was under a bad spell, no king in the neighborhood had any desire to have her for a daughter-in-law.

About this time in a neighboring kingdom, in consequence of the wickedness of the nobles, an insurrection took place upon the death of the old king, and the young prince was compelled to flee for his life, disguised like a peasant. For some time, until he got out of the country, he suffered much from hunger and fatigue; but when he got into that ruled by the princess's father, and had no longer any fear of being recognized, he fared better, for the people were kind. He did not abandon his disguise, however. One reason was that he had no other clothes to put on, and another that he had very little money, and did not know where to get any more. There was no good telling everybody he met that he was a prince, for he felt that a prince ought to be able to get on like other pople.

For a day or two he had been walking through the palace wood, and had had next to nothing to eat, when he came upon a strange little house, inhabited by a very nice, tidy, motherly old woman. This was one of the good fairies. The moment she saw him she knew quite well who he was. She received him with the kindness she would have shown to any other traveler, and gave him bread and milk, which he thought the most delicious food he had ever tasted. The old woman pressed him to stay all night. When he awoke he was amazed to find how well and strong he felt. She would not take any of the money he offered, but begged him, if he found occasion of continuing in the neighborhood, to return and occupy the same quarters.

"Thank you much," answered the prince; "but there is little chance of that. The sooner I get out of this wood the better."

This did not offend the fairy. She stood at the door of her little house looking after him till the trees hid him quite. Then she said, "At last!" and went in.

The prince wandered and wandered, and got nowhere. The sun sank and sank and went out of sight, and he seemed no nearer the end of the wood than ever. He sat down on a fallen tree, ate a bit of bread the old woman had given him, and waited for the moon; for, although he was not much of an astronomer, he knew the moon would rise some time, because she had risen the night before. Up she came, slow and slow, but of a good size, pretty nearly round indeed; whereupon greatly refreshed with his piece of bread, he got up and went—he knew not whither.

After walking a considerable distance, he thought he was coming to the outside of the forest; but when he reached what he thought the last of it, he found himself only upon the edge of a great open space in it, covered with grass. The moon shone very bright, and he thought he had never seen a more lovely spot.

All at once he spied something in the middle of the grass. What could it be? It moved; it came nearer. Was it a human creature, gliding across—a girl dressed in white, gleaming in the moonshine? She came nearer and nearer. He crept behind a tree and watched, wondering. It must be some strange being of the wood—a nymph whom the moonlight and the warm dusky air had enticed from her tree. But when she came close to where he stood, he no longer doubted she was human—for he had caught sight of her sunny hair, and her clear blue eyes, and the loveliest face and form that he had ever seen.

All at once she began singing like a nightingale, and dancing to her own music, with her eyes turned towards the moon. She passed close to where he stood, dancing on by the edge of the trees and away in a great circle towards the other side, until he could see but a spot of white in the yellowish green of the moonlit grass. But when he feared it would vanish quite, the spot grew, and became a figure once more. She approached him again, singing and dancing, and waving her arms over her head, until she had completed the circle. Just opposite his tree she stood, ceased her song, dropped her arms, and broke out into a long clear laugh. Then, as if tired, she threw herself on the grass, and lay gazing at the moon. The prince was almost afraid to breathe lest he should startle her, and she should vanish from his sight. Then the prince, overcome with weariness, fell asleep; when he awoke it was broad daylight and the figure was nowhere to be seen.

But he could not leave the place. He walked round the glade to see if he could discover prints of her feet. But the grass was so short, and her steps had been so light, that she had not left a single trace behind her. Then he spied at one side a lovely little house, with thatched roof and low eaves, surrounded by an exquisite garden, with doves and peacocks walking in it. Of course this must be where the gracious lady who loved the moonlight lived.

Forgetting his appearance, he walked towards the door, determined to make inquiries, but as he passed a little pond full of gold and silver fishes, he caught sight of himself and turned to find the door to the kitchen. There he knocked, and asked for a piece of bread. The good-natured cook brought him in, and gave him an excellent breakfast. While he ate, he talked with his entertainer, and learned that this was the favorite retreat of the Princess Daylight. But he learned nothing more, both because he was afraid of seeming inquisitive, and because the cook did not choose to be heard talking about her mistress.

The prince remained in the forest, amusing himself as best he could, but waiting anxiously for the night, in the hope that the princess would again appear. Nor was he disappointed, for, directly the moon rose, he spied a glimmering shape far across the glade. As it drew nearer, he saw she was not dressed in white as before, but in pale blue like the sky. She looked lovelier still,

All night long he watched her, but dared not go near her. He would have been ashamed of watching her, too, had he not become almost incapable of thinking of anything but how beautiful she was. He watched the whole night long, and saw that as the moon went down she retreated in smaller and smaller circles, until at last he could see her no more.

Weary as he was, he set out for the old woman's cottage, where he arrived just in time for her breakfast, which she shared with him. He then went to bed, and slept for many hours. When he awoke the sun was down, and he departed in great anxiety lest he should lose a glimpse of the lovely vision. The moon was high in the heavens before he reached the glade. Then indeed his troubles vanished, for there was the princess coming dancing towards him, in a dress that shone like gold, and with shoes that glimmered through the grass like fireflies. Like a sunbeam she passed him, and danced away into the distance.

Before she had completed a circle, the clouds gathered, and there were growlings of distant thunder. Just as she passed the tree where he stood, a flash of lightning blinded him for a moment, and when he saw again, to his horror the princess lay on the ground. He darted to her, thinking she had been struck; but when she heard him coming, she was on her feet in a moment.

"What do you want?" she asked.

"I beg your pardon. I thought—the lightning—" said the prince, hesitating.

"There's nothing the matter," said the princess, waving him off rather haughtily.

The poor prince turned and walked towards the wood.

"Come back," said Daylight. "I like you. Tell me, will you, what is the sun like?"

"What's the good of asking what you already know?" he said.

"But I don't know," she rejoined.

"Why, everybody knows."

"That's the very thing; I'm not everybody. I've never seen the sun. Is the sun so very bright?"

"As bright as the lightning."

"But it doesn't go out like that, does it?"

"Oh, no. It shines like the moon, rises and sets like the moon, only so bright that you can't look at it for a moment."

"But I *would* look at it," said the princess.

"But you couldn't," said the prince.

"But I could," said the princess.

"Why don't you, then?"

"Because I can't."

"Why can't you?"

"Because I can't wake—"

Here the princess hid her face in her hands, turned away, and walked towards the house. The prince ventured to follow her at a little distance, but she turned and waved him back, and like a true gentleman-prince, he obeyed. He waited a long time, but as she did not come again, at last he set off for the old woman's cottage. It was long past midnight when he reached it, but, to his surprise, the old woman was paring potatoes at the door. Fairies are fond of doing odd things. Indeed, however they may dissemble, the night is always their day. And so it is with all who have fairy blood in them.

"Why, what are you doing, this time of the night, mother?" said the prince; for that was the kind way in which any young man in his country would address a woman who was much older than himself.

"Getting your supper ready, my son," she answered.

He asked the fairy many questions, but she answered none of them.

Now, all this time, the prince had stolen a march upon the swamp fairy who had made the wicked wish for Princess Daylight. She did not know he was in the neighborhood until after he had seen the princess three times. When she knew it, she set to work to do all the mischief she could.

She so contrived it by her deceitful spells, that the next night the prince could not find his way to the glade. He wandered about the forest till daylight, and then fell fast asleep. The same thing occurred for seven days following. After the third quarter of the moon, however, the bad fairy thought she might be at ease about the affair for a fortnight at least, for there was no chance of the prince wishing to kiss the princess when she was old and ugly.

So the first day of the fourth quarter he did find the cottage, and the next day he found the glade. For nearly another week he haunted it. But the princess never came. I have little doubt she was on the farther edge of it some part of every night, but at this period she always wore black, and, there being little or no light, the prince never saw her. He would not have known her if he had seen her. How could he have taken the worn decrepit creature she was now, for the glorious Princess Daylight?

At last, one night when there was no moon at all, he ventured near the house. There he heard voices talking, although it was past midnight; for her women were in considerable uneasiness, because the one whose turn it was to watch her had fallen asleep, and had not seen which way she went. When he understood from what they said that she had disappeared, he plunged at once into the wood to see if he could find her.

It was getting towards the dawn, but as yet there was no streak of light in the sky, when he came to a great birch tree, and sat down weary at the foot of it. While he sat—very miserable, you may be sure—full of fear for the princess, and wondering how her attendants could take it so quietly, he thought it would not be a bad plan to light a fire, which, if she were anywhere near, would attract her. This he managed with a tinder box, which the good fairy had given him. It was just beginning to blaze up, when he heard a moan, which seemed to come from the other side of the tree. He sprang to his feet. When he got round the tree, he saw a human form in a little dark heap on the earth. There was light enough from his fire to show that it was not the princess. He lifted it in his arms and carried it to the flame.

The countenance was that of an old woman, though she was hardly heavier than a child. A black hood concealed her hair, and her eyes were closed. He laid her down as comfortably as he could, chafed her hands, and took off his coat and wrapped it about her. In a little while she opened her eyes and looked at him. The tears rose and flowed down her grey wrinkled cheeks, but she said never a word. She closed her eyes again but the tears kept on flowing, and her whole appearance was so pitiful that the prince was near crying too. He begged her to tell him what was the matter, promising to do all he could to help her; but still she did not speak. He took her in his arms again to carry her to the princess's house, where he thought the good-natured cook might be able to do something for her. When he lifted her, the tears flowed yet faster, and she gave such a sad moan that it went to his very heart.

"Mother, mother!" he said. "Poor mother!" and kissed her on the withered lips.

She started, but he did not see, for it was still very dark, and he had enough to do to make his way through the trees towards the house.

Just as he approached the house, feeling more tired than he could have imagined possible—she was such a little thin old thing—she began to move, and became so restless that, unable to carry her a moment longer, he thought to lay her on the grass. But she stood upright on her feet. Her hood had dropped, and her hair fell about her. The first gleam of the morning was caught on her face, a face as bright as the dawn, and her eyes were lovely as the sky of darkest blue. The prince saw that it was Daylight herself whom he had brought from the forest! He fell on his knees before her, but she gave him her hand and bade him rise.

"You kissed me when I was an old woman. There, I kiss you when I am a young princess!" said Daylight. "Is that the sun coming?"

## THE UGLY DUCKLING [1]

*Hans Christian Andersen*

It was perfectly lovely out in the country; it was summer. The corn was yellow, the oats were green, the hay stood in stacks down in the green meadows, and there the stork was walking around on his long red legs and talking Egyptian, because he had learned that language from his mother. Around field and meadow were big woods, and deep lakes were in the middle of the woods; it was really lovely out in the country!

Right in the sunshine lay an old manor, surrounded by deep canals, and from the wall down to the water grew big burdock leaves, so high that little children could stand upright under the tallest of them. It was just as wild there as in the thickest wood. Here sat a duck on her nest, hatching out her little ducklings, but now she was almost tired of it, because it took such a long time; and then she so seldom had visitors. The other ducks liked better to swim around in the canals than to run up and sit down under a burdock, and gossip with her.

At last one eggshell after another began to crack. "Peep! peep!" it said in them; all the egg yolks were alive and stuck out their heads.

"Quack! quack!" she said; and they all came tumbling out as fast as they could, looking all round them under the green leaves; and the mother let them look as much as they wanted to, for green is good for the eyes.

"How big the world is!" said the young ones, for they certainly had much more room now than when they were in the eggs.

"Do you think this is all the world?" asked the mother. "It reaches away past the other side of the garden, right into the minister's field, but I have never been there. I hope you are all here now," and then she stood up. "No, I haven't got you all. The largest egg is still lying there. How long is that going to last? I am really tired of it." And she sat down again.

"Well, how goes it?" asked an old duck who had come to pay her a visit.

"It takes a long time with that one egg," said the duck. "It won't crack, but I'll show you the others now; they're the loveliest ducklings I ever saw."

"Let me see that egg that won't crack," said the old duck. "I tell you it's a turkey egg. I was fooled that way once too, and I had my troubles and trials with those young ones, because they're afraid of the water, let me tell you! I couldn't get them in. I quacked and snapped but it didn't help. Let me see the egg. Yes, that's a turkey egg! You just let that lie there, and teach the other children to swim."

"I think I will sit on it a little longer," said the duck. "I've sat so long now that I can sit a few days more."

"Just as you please," said the old duck; and she went away.

At last the big egg cracked. "Peep! peep!" said the little one, and rolled out. He was large and ugly. The duck looked at him.

"What a big duckling that is," she said. "None of the others look like that. I wonder could it really be a turkey chick? Well, we'll soon find that out. Into the water he must go, even if I have to push him in myself."

The next day the weather was lovely, and the sun shone on all the green burdocks. The mother duck went down to the water with her whole family. Splash, she jumped into the water. "Quack! quack!" she said, and one duckling after another plunged in. The water closed over their heads, but they came up in an instant, and floated beautifully; their legs went of themselves, and there they were all in the water, even the ugly gray one was swimming too.

"No, it's not a turkey," she said. "Look how well he uses his legs, and how straight he holds himself. He is my own child. On the whole he's quite pretty, if one really looks at him. Quack! quack! come with me, and I'll lead you out into the great world, and present you in the duck yard; but keep

[1] From Hans Christian Andersen, *Fairy Tales and Stories,* translated by Signe Toksvig.

close to me, so that nobody will step on you, and look out for the cat!"

And so they came into the duck yard. There was a terrible noise there, for two families were fighting about an eel's head, and the cat got it after all.

"Well, that's the way of the world!" said the mother duck; and she licked her beak, for she, too, wanted the eel's head. "Use your legs, now," she said. "Step lively and bow your necks to the old duck over there! She's the grandest person here, that's why she's fat, and do you see the red rag she's wearing round her leg? That's something very, very wonderful; it's the greatest distinction any duck can get; it means that people don't want to lose her and that she's to be recognized by man and beast. Step lively now—don't turn in your toes; a well-brought-up duck turns its toes way out, so! Now bend your necks and say 'Quack!' "

And they did so; but the other ducks round about looked at them, and said right out loud:

"Look there! now we're going to have that mob too, as if there weren't enough of us already. And pfui! what a funny looking duckling that one is; we won't stand him!" And one duck flew over at once, and bit him in the neck.

"Let him alone," said the mother, "he doesn't do anybody any harm."

"Yes, but he's too large and peculiar," said the duck who had bitten him, "and so we'll have to show him!"

"Mother has some pretty children there," said the old duck with the rag round her leg. "They're all pretty but that one; that was a failure. I wish she could make him over again."

"Can't be done, your Grace," said the mother duck; "he isn't pretty, but he has a lovely disposition and swims as well as any other; I may even say he swims better. I think he'll grow up pretty, and become smaller in time; he lay too long in the egg, and so he wasn't shaped right." And then she patted him on the neck, and smoothed his feathers. "Anyway, he's a drake," she said, "and so it doesn't make much difference. I think he will be very strong; he will make his way all right."

"The other ducklings are charming!" said the old duck. "Make yourselves at home; and if you find an eel's head, you may bring it to me."

And so they made themselves at home. But the poor Duckling who came out of the egg last, and looked so ugly, was bitten and pushed and made fun of, both by the ducks and by the chickens.

"He's too big!" they all said. And the turkey-cock, who had been born with spurs, and therefore thought he was an emperor, blew himself up like a ship in full sail, and went right up to him; then he gobbled, and got quite red in the face. The poor Duckling didn't know where to go; he was so sad because he looked ugly, and was made fun of by the whole yard.

That was how the first day went; and afterward it got worse and worse. The poor Duckling was chased by everybody; even his brothers and sisters were horrid to him and always said, "I hope the cat takes you, you awful sight!" And the mother said, "If you were only far away!" And the ducks bit him, and the chickens pecked at him, and the girl who had to feed the poultry kicked at him with her foot.

Then he ran and flew over the fence, and the little birds in the bushes flew up in fear.

"That is because I am so ugly!" thought the Duckling; and shut his eyes, but ran away anyhow, and he came out into the big marsh, where the wild ducks lived. Here he lay the whole night long, he was so tired.

Toward morning the wild ducks flew up, and looked at their new companion.

"What might you be?" they asked; and the Duckling turned in every direction, and bowed as well as he could. "You are remarkably ugly!" said the wild ducks. "But that's all the same to us, so long as you do not marry into our family."

Poor thing! he certainly wasn't thinking of marrying; all he wanted was to lie among the reeds and drink some of the swamp water.

He lay there two whole days; then two wild geese came, or, properly speaking, two wild ganders. They had come out of the egg only a little while ago, and that's why they were so lively.

"Listen, comrade," said one of them, "you're so ugly that I like you. Come along with us and be a bird of passage. Near here, in another marsh, there are some sweet, lovely wild geese. You've a chance of making your fortune, you're so ugly!"

"Piff! paff!" resounded through the air; and the two ganders fell down dead in the swamp. "Piff! paff!" it sounded again, and whole flocks of wild geese rose up from the reeds. And then there was another crash. A big hunt was going on. The hunters were lying in wait all around the marsh, and some were even sitting up in the branches of the trees, which spread far over the reeds. The blue smoke rose up like clouds among the dark trees, and hung far across the water; and the hunting dogs came—splash, splash!—into the mud, and the rushes and the reeds bent down on every side. It was a terrible scare for the poor Duckling! He turned his head to put it under his wing; but at that moment a dreadfully big dog stood close by. He put his jaws right down to the Duckling, showed his sharp teeth, and—splash, splash!—on he went, without seizing it.

"Oh, Heaven be thanked!" sighed the Duckling. "I am so ugly that even the dog doesn't want to bite me!"

And so he lay quite quiet, while the bullets rattled through the reeds and shot after shot crashed out. At last, late in the day, it was quiet; but the poor Duckling did not dare to get up; he waited several hours before he looked around, and then he hurried away from the marsh as fast as he could. He ran on over field and meadow; the wind blew so much he could hardly go against it.

Toward evening he came to a poor little farmhouse; it was such a wretched little house that it didn't know what side to fall on, and so it kept on standing. The storm whistled round the Duckling, so much that he had to sit right down on his tail to keep from falling, and it got worse and worse. Then he noticed that the door had slipped off one of its hinges and hung so crooked that he could slip into the room through the crack, and he did.

Here lived an old woman, with her cat and her hen. And the cat, whom she called "Sonnie," could arch his back and purr, he could even give out sparks; but for that one had to stroke his fur the wrong way. The hen had very little short legs, and therefore was called "Clucky-short-legs"; she laid good eggs, and the woman loved her as her own child.

The cat was master of the house, and the hen was the lady, and they always said, "We and the world!" for they thought they were half the world, and by far the better half. The Duckling thought one might have a different opinion, but the hen wouldn't stand for that.

"Can you lay eggs?" she asked.

"No."

"Then you'll please to hold your tongue."

And the cat said, "Can you curve your back, and purr, and sparkle?"

"No."

"Then you'd better not offer any opinions when sensible people are speaking."

And the Duckling sat in a corner feeling very badly; then he happened to think about fresh air and sunshine; and he was seized with such a strange longing to float on the water that at last he couldn't help himself, he had to tell the hen.

"What's the matter with you?" asked the hen. "You have nothing to do, that's why you get these notions."

"But it's so lovely to float on the water!" said the Duckling, "so lovely to let it close over your head, and to dive down to the bottom."

"Yes, that must certainly be a great pleasure!" said the hen. "I think you must have gone crazy. Ask the cat about it—he's the cleverest thing I know—ask him if he likes to float on the water, or to dive down; I won't speak about myself. Ask our mistress, the old woman; no one in the world is cleverer than she. Do you think she wants to float, and to get water over her head?"

"You don't understand me," said the Duckling.

"Well, if we don't understand you I'd like to know who does! You surely don't want to set yourself up to be wiser than the cat or the woman, not to mention myself! Don't put on airs, child! Didn't you get into a warm room, and into company from which you may learn something? But you're a chatterbox, and it is not pleasant to associate with you. You may believe me, I'm saying this for your own good. I tell you disagreeable things, and that's the only way of knowing one's true friends!"

"I think I will go out into the wide world," said the Duckling.

"Yes, do go," said the hen.

And the Duckling went away. He floated on the water, and dived, but he was looked down on by every animal because of his ugliness

Now came the autumn. The leaves in the forest turned yellow and brown; the wind sent them dancing around and there was a high chill in the air. The clouds hung heavy with hail and snowflakes, and on the fence stood the raven, screaming with the cold; it was enough to make one freeze to think of it. The poor little Duckling certainly had a very bad time. One evening, the sun was just setting most beautifully, a whole flock of big handsome birds came out of the bushes; the Duckling had never before seen anything so beautiful; they were dazzlingly white, with long flexible necks; they were swans. They uttered a very strange cry, spread their large, splendid wings, and flew away from that cold country to warmer lands, to open lakes. They mounted so high, so high, that the ugly little Duckling had a very strange sensation; he turned round and round in the water like a wheel, stretched out his neck toward them, and gave a cry so loud and queer that he frightened himself. Oh! he could not forget those lovely birds, those happy birds; and when he couldn't see them any more he dived down to the very bottom, and when he came up again he was quite beside himself. He didn't know the name of those birds, and didn't know where they were flying; but he loved them more than he had ever loved any one. He didn't envy them at all, he wouldn't have dared to think of wishing such beauty for himself.

The winter was so cold, so cold! The Duckling had to swim around in the water, to keep from freezing entirely; but every night the hole in which he swam became smaller and smaller. It froze so hard that the ice cracked; and the Duckling had to use his legs all the time to keep the hole from freezing up. At last he became too tired, and lay quite still, and froze fast in the ice.

Early in the morning a farmer came by, and when he saw what had happened, he took his wooden shoe, broke the ice crust to pieces, and carried the Duckling home to his wife. Then he came to himself again. The children wanted to play with him; but the Duckling was afraid, and in his terror fluttered up into the milk pan, so that the milk spurted into the room. The woman screamed and clapped her hands, at which the Duckling flew down into the butter tub, and then into the meal barrel and out again. Well, what a sight! The woman screamed, and struck at him with the fire tongs; the children tumbled over one another, trying to catch the Duckling; and they laughed and they screamed! It was a good thing that the door was open and he could rush out among the bushes in the newly-fallen snow; and there he lay quite exhausted.

But it would be too sad to tell all the want and misery the Duckling had to endure in the hard winter. . . . He was lying out on the swamp among the reeds, when the sun began to shine again. The larks sang—it was spring!

Then all at once the Duckling raised his wings; they beat the air more strongly than before, and bore him strongly away; and before he really knew how all this happened, he was in a large garden, where the apple trees stood in blossom, where the lilac flowers smelled sweet, and hung their long green branches down to the winding canals. Oh, it was so beautiful here, so fresh and springlike! And out from the thicket came three lovely white swans; they rustled their wings, and floated so lightly on the water. The Duckling knew the splendid creatures, and felt a strange sadness.

"I will fly over to them, the royal birds! And they will kill me, because I, that am so ugly, dare to come near them. But I don't care! Better to be killed by them than to be plucked at by the ducks and pecked at by the chickens and kicked around by the girl who takes care of the duck yard, and to suffer hardships in winter!" And he flew out into the water, and swam toward the splendid swans; they looked at him, and came sailing toward him, ruffling their wings.

"Kill me!" said the poor creature, and bent his head down to the water, and waited for death. But what was this that he saw in the clear water? Below him, he saw his own image, but he was no longer a clumsy dark gray bird, hideous and ugly; he was himself a swan!

To be born in a duck yard doesn't make any difference, if one has only lain in a swan's egg.

Some little children came into the garden; they threw bread and corn in the water; and the youngest cried, "There is a new one!" and the other children shouted joyously, "Yes, a new one has come!" And they clapped their hands and danced around, and ran to get their father and mother; and they threw bread and cake in the water; and they all said, "The new one is the most beautiful of all! so young and handsome!" and the old swans bowed their heads before him.

Then he felt quite shy, and at first hid his head under his wings. He thought of how he had been persecuted and mocked at, and now he heard everybody say that he was the loveliest of all lovely birds. Then he fluffed his feathers, lifted his slender neck, and from his heart came a cry of joy:

"I didn't dream of so much happiness, when I was the ugly Duckling!"

## THE EMPEROR'S NEW CLOTHES[1]

*Hans Christian Andersen*

Many years ago there lived an emperor who was so enormously fond of new clothes that he spent all his money for them. He didn't care for his soldiers, didn't care for the theater, didn't care for driving in the park except for the chance to show off his new clothes. He had a coat for every hour of the day, and just as people say about a king, "He is in council," so here they always said, "The emperor is in his dressing room."

The big city where he lived was a very gay place. Crowds of visitors came every day, and one day two swindlers came. They pretended they were weavers and said they knew how to weave the most gorgeous cloth you could imagine. Not only were their colors and patterns, they said, remarkably beautiful, but the clothes made of the stuff had the strange property that they became invisible to any one who was unfit for the office he held, or who was stupider than the law allowed.

"Those would be nice clothes!" thought the emperor. "If I wore them, I could find out what men in my empire are not fit for the places they have; I could tell the clever from the stupid. Yes, that cloth must be woven for me at once!"

And he gave the two swindlers a lot of money in advance to make them begin work.

And they did put up two looms, and pretended to be working; but they had nothing at all on their looms. They kept on demanding the finest silk and the costliest gold; this they put into their own pockets,

[1] From Hans Christian Andersen, *Fairy Tales and Stories,* translated by Signe Toksvig.

and worked at the empty looms till late into the night.

"Now I should really like to know how far they have got on with the stuff," thought the emperor. But he actually had a queer sensation in his heart when he thought that whoever was stupid or no good in his office couldn't see it. He believed, indeed, that he had nothing to fear for himself, but he wanted to send some one else first to see how matters stood. All the people in the whole city knew what peculiar power the stuff possessed, and all were anxious to see how bad or how stupid their neighbors were.

"I will send my honest old cabinet minister to the weavers," thought the emperor. "He can tell best what the stuff looks like, because he's a sensible man and nobody is better in his office than he is."

So the decent old minister went into the hall where the two swindlers sat working at the empty looms.

"Mercy on us!" thought the old minister, and he opened his eyes wide. "I can't see anything at all!" But he didn't say that.

Both the swindlers begged him to be kind enough to come nearer, and asked if he didn't think that was a lovely pattern and beautiful colors. Then they pointed to the empty loom, and the poor old minister went on opening his eyes; but he could see nothing, for there was nothing to see.

"Dear me!" he thought, "could it be that I am stupid? I never thought that, and not a soul must know it. Am I not fit for my office? No, it will never do for me to tell that I couldn't see the stuff."

"Well, haven't you anything to say about it?" said one of the weavers.

"Oh, it is charming!" said the old minister, as he peered through his spectacles. "What a fine pattern, and what colors! Yes, I shall tell the emperor that I am very much pleased with it."

"Well, we're very glad," said both the weavers; and then they named the colors, and explained the strange pattern. The old minister listened carefully, so that he could repeat it when he went back to the emperor. And so he did.

Now the swindlers asked for more money, and more silk and gold, which they said they wanted for weaving. They put everything into their own pockets, and not a thread was put on the loom; but they kept on working at the empty frames as before.

The emperor soon sent another official to see how the weaving was going on, and if the stuff would soon be ready. He had no better luck than the first; he looked and looked, but, as there was nothing to be seen but the empty looms, he could see nothing.

"Yes, isn't this a fine piece of cloth?" asked the two swindlers; and they pointed out and explained the handsome pattern which wasn't there at all.

"I know I am not stupid!" thought the man. "It must be my office, for which I am not fit. That's very queer, but I mustn't let anybody notice it." And so he praised the stuff he didn't see, and expressed his pleasure at the beautiful colors and the charming pattern. "Yes, it is beautiful," he said to the emperor.

All the people in the town were talking of the gorgeous stuff. The emperor now wanted to see it himself while it was still on the loom. With a whole crowd of chosen men, among whom were also the old officials who had already been there, he went to the two cunning swindlers, who were now weaving with might and main without fiber or thread.

"Isn't it magnificent?" said both the good officials, who had already been there once. "Will your majesty see what a pattern, what colors?" And then they pointed to the empty loom, for they thought that the others could probably see the stuff.

"What's this?" thought the emperor. "I can see nothing at all! That is terrible. Am I stupid? Am I unfit to be emperor? That would be the most dreadful thing that could happen to me. Oh, it is *very* pretty!" he said aloud. "It has our approval." And he nodded in a contented way, and gazed at the empty loom, for he wouldn't say that he couldn't see anything. His whole retinue looked and looked, and saw nothing, any more than the rest; but, like the emperor, they said, "That *is* pretty!" and counseled him to wear these splendid new clothes for the first time at the great procession soon to take place. "It is magnificent!" went from mouth to mouth, and they were all marvelously pleased. The emperor gave each of the swindlers a cross to hang at his buttonhole and the title of "Knight of the Loom."

The whole night before the morning on which the procession was to take place the swindlers were up, and had more than sixteen candles burning. The people could see that they were hard at work, finishing the emperor's new clothes. They pretended to take the stuff down from the looms; they made cuts in the air with big scissors; they sewed with needles without thread; and at last they said, "Now the clothes are ready!"

The emperor came himself with his noblest cavaliers; and the two swindlers lifted up one arm as if they were holding something, and said, "See, here are the trousers! here is the coat; here is the cloak!" and so on. "It is as light as a spider's web; one would think one had nothing on; but that is just the beauty of it."

"Yes," said all the cavaliers; but they couldn't see anything, for nothing was there.

"Will your imperial majesty please to condescend to undress?" said the swindlers, "then we shall put the new clothes on you here in front of the large mirror."

The emperor took off his clothes, and the swindlers pretended to put on him each of the new garments, and they took him round the waist, and seemed to fasten on something; that was the train; and the emperor turned round and round before the mirror.

"Oh, how well they look! How wonderfully they fit!" everybody said. "What a pattern! What colors! That *is* splendid!"

"They are standing outside with the canopy which is to be borne above your majesty in the procession!" announced the head master of the ceremonies.

"Well, I'm ready, of course," said the emperor. "Don't they fit me well?" And then he turned around again in front of the mirror because he wanted it to seem as if he were giving his fine clothes a good look.

The chamberlains, who were to carry the train, groped with their hands on the floor, just as if they were picking up the mantle; then they pretended to be holding something up in the air. They didn't dare to let anybody guess that they couldn't see anything.

So the emperor went in procession under the rich canopy, and every one in the streets said, "Look! See how matchless the emperor's new clothes are! What a lovely train his mantle has! What a miraculous fit!" No one would let it be known that he couldn't see anything, for that would have shown that he was not fit for his office, or was very stupid. Not any of the emperor's clothes had ever had such a success as these.

"But he has nothing on!" a little child cried out at last.

"Dear me, listen to what the innocent says," said the father, and people whispered to each other what the child had said.

"He has nothing on; a little child says that he has nothing on!"

"But he has nothing on!" everybody shouted at last. And the emperor shivered, for it seemed to him that they were right; but he thought within himself, "I must go through with the procession." And so he carried himself still more proudly, and the chamberlains walked along holding the train which wasn't there at all.

## RIP VAN WINKLE [1]

*Washington Irving*

Whoever has made a voyage up the Hudson must remember the Catskill Mountains. They are a dismembered branch of

[1] From Washington Irving, *The Sketch-Book.*

the great Appalachian family, and are seen away to the west of the river, swelling up to a noble height, and lording it over the surrounding country.

Every change of season, every change of weather, indeed every hour of the day, produces some change in the magical hues and shapes of these mountains; and they are regarded by all the good wives, far and near, as perfect barometers. When the weather is fair and settled, they are clothed in blue and purple, and print their bold outlines on the clear evening sky; but sometimes, when the rest of the landscape is cloudless, they will gather a hood of gray vapors about their summits, which, in the last rays of the setting sun, will glow and light up like a crown of glory.

At the foot of these fairy mountains the voyager may have descried the light smoke curling up from a village, whose shingle roofs gleam among the trees, just where the blue tints of the upland melt away into the fresh green of the nearer landscape. It is a little village, of great antiquity, having been founded by some of the Dutch colonists in the early times of the province, just about the beginning of the government of the good Peter Stuyvesant (may he rest in peace!); and there were some of the houses of the original settlers standing within a few years, built of small, yellow bricks brought from Holland, having latticed windows and gable fronts, surmounted with weathercocks.

In that same village, and in one of these very houses (which, to tell the precise truth, was sadly time-worn and weather-beaten), there lived many years since, while the country was yet a province of Great Britain, a simple, good-natured fellow of the name of Rip Van Winkle. He was a descendant of the Van Winkles who figured so gallantly in chivalrous days of Peter Stuyvesant, and accompanied him to the siege of Fort Christina.

He inherited, however, but little of the martial character of his ancestors. I have observed that he was a simple, good-natured man; he was, moreover, a kind neighbor, and an obedient, hen-pecked husband. Indeed, to the latter circumstance might be owing that meekness of spirit which gained him such universal popularity; for those men are most apt to be obsequious and conciliating abroad, who are under the discipline of shrews at home. Their tempers, doubtless, are rendered pliant and malleable in the fiery furnace of domestic tribulation; and a curtain lecture is worth all the sermons in the world for teaching the virtues of patience and long-suffering. A termagant wife may therefore, in some respects, be considered a tolerable blessing; and, if so, Rip Van Winkle was thrice blessed.

Certain it is, that he was a great favorite among all the good wives of the village, who, as usual with the amiable sex, took his part in all family squabbles, and never failed, whenever they talked those matters over in their evening gossipings, to lay all the blame on Dame Van Winkle. The children of the village, too, would shout with joy whenever he approached. He assisted at their sports, made their playthings, taught them to fly kites and shoot marbles, and told them long stories of ghosts, witches, and Indians. Whenever he went dodging about the village, he was surrounded by a troop of them, hanging on his skirts, clambering on his back, and playing a thousand tricks on him with impunity; and not a dog would bark at him throughout the neighborhood.

The great error in Rip's composition was an insuperable aversion to all kinds of profitable labor. It could not be from the want of assiduity or perseverance; for he would sit on a wet rock, with a rod as long and heavy as a Tartar's lance, and fish all day without a murmur, even though he should not be encouraged by a single nibble. He would carry a fowling-piece on his shoulder for hours together, trudging through woods and swamps, and up hill and down dale, to shoot a few squirrels or wild pigeons.

He would never refuse to assist a neighbor even in the roughest toil, and was a foremost man at all country frolics for husking Indian corn or building stone fences. The women of the village, too, used to employ him to run their errands, and to do such little odd jobs as their less obliging husbands would not do for them. In a word, Rip was ready to attend to anybody's business but his own; but as to doing family duty, and keeping his farm in order, he found it impossible.

In fact, he declared it was of no use to work on his farm. It was the most pestilent little piece of ground in the whole country. Everything about it went wrong, and would go wrong, in spite of him. His fences were continually falling to pieces; his cow would either go astray, or get among the cabbages; weeds were sure to grow quicker in his fields than anywhere else; the rain always made a point of setting in just as he had some outdoor work to do: so that, though his patrimonial estate had dwindled away under his management acre by acre, until there was little more left than a mere patch of Indian corn and potatoes, yet it was the worst-conditioned farm in the neighborhood.

His children, too, were as ragged and wild as if they belonged to nobody. His son Rip, an urchin begotten in his own likeness, promised to inherit the habits with the old clothes of his father. He was generally seen trooping like a colt at his mother's heels, equipped in a pair of his father's cast-off galligaskins; which he had much ado to hold up with one hand, as a fine lady does her train in bad weather.

Rip Van Winkle, however, was one of those happy mortals, of foolish, well-oiled dispositions, who take the world easy, eat white bread or brown, whichever can be got with least thought or trouble, and would rather starve on a penny than work for a pound. If left to himself, he would have whistled life away in perfect contentment; but his wife kept continually dinning in his ears about his idleness, his carelessness, and the ruin he was bringing on his family.

Morning, noon, and night, her tongue was incessantly going, and everything he said or did was sure to produce a torrent of household eloquence. Rip had but one way of replying to all lectures of the kind, and that, by frequent use, had grown into a habit. He shrugged his shoulders, shook his head, cast up his eyes, but said nothing. This, however, always provoked a fresh volley from his wife; so that he was fain to draw off his forces, and take to the outside of the house—the only side which, in truth, belongs to a hen-pecked husband.

Rip's sole domestic adherent was his dog Wolf, who was as much hen-pecked as his master; for Dame Van Winkle regarded them as companions in idleness, and even looked upon Wolf with an evil eye, as the cause of his master's going so often astray. True it is, in all points of spirit befitting an honorable dog, he was as courageous an animal as ever scoured the woods; but what courage can withstand the ever-during and all-besetting terrors of a woman's tongue? The moment Wolf entered the house, his crest fell; his tail drooped to the ground or curled between his legs; he sneaked about with a gallows air, casting many a sidelong glance at Dame Van Winkle; and, at the least flourish of a broomstick or ladle, he would fly to the door with yelping precipitation.

Times grew worse and worse with Rip Van Winkle as years of matrimony rolled on. A tart temper never mellows with age, and a sharp tongue is the only edged tool that grows keener with constant use. For a long while he used to console himself, when driven from home, by frequenting a kind of perpetual club of the sages, philosophers, and other idle personages of the village, which held its sessions on a bench before a small inn, designated by a rubicund portrait of his Majesty George III. Here they used to sit in the shade of a long, lazy, summer's day, talking listlessly over village gossip, or telling endless sleepy stories about nothing. But it would have been worth any statesman's money to have heard the profound discussions which sometimes took place, when by chance an old newspaper fell into their hands from some passing traveler. How solemnly they would listen to the contents, as drawled out by Derrick Van Bummel, the schoolmaster —a dapper, learned little man, who was not to be daunted by the most gigantic word in the dictionary! And how sagely they would deliberate upon public events some months after they had taken place!

The opinions of this junto were completely controlled by Nicholas Vedder, a patriarch of the village, and landlord of the inn, at the door of which he took his seat from morning till night, just moving sufficiently to avoid the sun, and keep in the shade of a large tree; so that the neighbors could tell the hour by his movements as accurately as by a sundial. It is true, he was rarely heard to speak, but smoked his pipe incessantly. His adherents, however (for every great man has his adherents), perfectly understood him, and knew how to gather his opinions. When anything that was read or related displeased him, he was observed to smoke his pipe vehemently, and to send forth short, frequent, and angry puffs; but, when pleased, he would inhale the smoke slowly and tranquilly, and emit it in light and placid clouds, and sometimes, taking the pipe from his mouth, and letting the fragrant vapor curl about his nose, would gravely nod his head in token of perfect approbation.

From even this stronghold the unlucky Rip was at length routed by his termagant wife, who would suddenly break in upon the tranquillity of the assemblage, and call the members all to naught; nor was that august personage, Nicholas Vedder himself, sacred from the daring tongue of this terrible virago, who charged him outright with encouraging her husband in habits of idleness.

Poor Rip was at last reduced almost to despair; and his only alternative, to escape from the labor of the farm and the clamor of his wife, was to take gun in hand and stroll away into the woods. Here he would sometimes seat himself at the foot of a tree, and share the contents of his wallet with Wolf, with whom he sympathized as a fellow-sufferer in persecution. "Poor Wolf," he would say, "thy mistress leads thee a dog's life of it; but never mind, my lad, whilst I live thou shalt never want a friend to stand by thee!" Wolf would wag his tail, look wistfully in his master's face, and, if dogs can feel pity, I verily believe he reciprocated the sentiment with all his heart.

In a long ramble of the kind on a fine autumnal day, Rip had unconsciously scrambled to one of the highest parts of the Catskill Mountains. He was after his favorite sport of squirrel shooting, and the still solitudes had echoed and re-echoed with the reports of his gun. Panting and fatigued, he threw himself, late in the afternoon, on a green knoll, covered with mountain herbage, that crowned the brow of a precipice. From an opening between the trees he could overlook all the lower country for many a mile of rich woodland. He saw at a distance the lordly Hudson, far, far below him, moving on its silent but majestic course, with the reflection of a purple cloud, or the sail of a lagging bark, here and there sleeping on its glassy bosom, and at last losing itself in the blue highlands.

On the other side he looked down into a deep mountain glen, wild, lonely, and shagged, the bottom filled with fragments from the impending cliffs, and scarcely lighted by the reflected rays of the setting sun. For some time Rip lay musing on this scene. Evening was gradually advancing; the mountains began to throw their long, blue shadows over the valleys; he saw that it would be dark long before he could reach the village, and he heaved a heavy sigh when he thought of encountering the terrors of Dame Van Winkle.

As he was about to descend, he heard a voice from a distance, hallooing, "Rip Van Winkle! Rip Van Winkle!" He looked around, but could see nothing but a crow winging its solitary flight across the mountain. He thought his fancy must have deceived him, and turned again to descend, when he heard the same cry ring through the still evening air, "Rip Van Winkle! Rip Van Winkle!" At the same time Wolf bristled up his back, and, giving a low growl, skulked to his master's side, looking fearfully down into the glen.

Rip now felt a vague apprehension stealing over him. He looked anxiously in the same direction, and perceived a strange figure slowly toiling up the rocks, and bending under the weight of something he carried on his back. He was surprised to see any human being in this lonely and unfrequented place, but, supposing it to be some one of the neighborhood in need of his assistance, he hastened down to yield it.

On nearer approach he was still more surprised at the singularity of the stranger's appearance. He was a short, square-built old fellow, with thick, bushy hair, and a grizzled beard. His dress was of the antique Dutch fashion—a cloth jerkin strapped round the waist, and several pairs of breeches, the outer one of ample volume, decorated with rows of buttons down the sides, and bunches at the knees. He bore on his shoulders a stout keg that seemed full of liquor, and made signs for Rip to approach and assist him with the load.

Though rather shy and distrustful of this new acquaintance, Rip complied with his usual alacrity; and, mutually relieving each other, they clambered up a narrow gully, apparently the dry bed of a mountain torrent. As they ascended, Rip every now and then heard long, rolling peals, like distant thunder, that seemed to issue out of a deep ravine, or rather cleft, between lofty rocks, toward which their rugged path conducted. He paused for an instant but, supposing it to be the muttering of one of those transient thunder-showers which often take place in mountain heights, he proceeded.

Passing through the ravine, they came to a hollow, like a small amphitheater, surrounded by perendicular precipices, over the brinks of which impending trees shot their branches, so that you only caught glimpses of the azure sky and the bright evening cloud. During the whole time, Rip and his companion had labored on in silence; for, though the former marveled greatly what could be the object of carrying a keg of liquor up this wild mountain, yet there was something strange and incomprehensible about the unknown that inspired awe and checked familiarity.

On entering the amphitheater, new objects of wonder presented themselves. On a level spot in the center was a company of odd-looking personages playing at nine-pins. They were dressed in a quaint, outlandish fashion. Some wore short doublets, others, jerkins, with long knives in their belts; and most of them had enormous breeches, of similar style with that of the guide's. Their visages, too, were peculiar. One had a large head, broad face, and small, piggish eyes. The face of another seemed to consist entirely of nose, and was surmounted by a white sugar-loaf hat, set off with a little red cock's tail. They all had beards of various shapes and colors.

There was one who seemed to be the commander. He was a stout old gentleman, with a weather-beaten countenance. He wore a lace doublet, broad belt and hanger, high-crowned hat and feather, red stockings, and high-heeled shoes with roses in them. The whole group reminded Rip of the figures in an old Flemish painting in the parlor of Dominie Van Schaick, the village parson, which had been brought over from Holland at the time of the settlement.

What seemed particularly odd to Rip was, that, though these folks were evidently amusing themselves, yet they maintained the gravest faces, the most mysterious silence, and were, withal, the most melancholy party of pleasure he had ever witnessed. Nothing interrupted the stillness of the scene but the noise of the balls, which, whenever they were rolled, echoed along the montains like rumbling peals of thunder.

As Rip and his companion approached them, they suddenly desisted from their play, and stared at him with such fixed, statue-like gaze, and such strange, uncouth, lack-luster countenances, that his heart turned within him, and his knees smote together. His companion now emptied the contents of the keg into large flagons, and made signs to him to wait upon the company. He obeyed with fear and trembling. They quaffed the liquor in profound silence, and then returned to their game.

By degrees Rip's awe and apprehension subsided. He even ventured, when no eye was fixed upon him, to taste the beverage, which he found had much of the flavor of excellent Hollands. He was naturally a thirsty soul, and was soon tempted to repeat the draught. One taste provoked another; and he reiterated his visits to the flagon so often, that at length his senses were overpowered, his eyes swam in his head, his head gradually declined, and he fell into a deep sleep.

On waking, he found himself on the green knoll whence he had first seen the old man of the glen. He rubbed his eyes. It was a bright, sunny morning. The birds were hopping and twittering among the bushes; and the eagle was wheeling aloft, and breasting the pure mountain breeze. "Surely," thought Rip, "I have not slept here all night." He recalled the occurrences before he fell asleep—the strange man with a keg of liquor, the mountain ravine, the wild retreat among the rocks, the woe-begone party at ninepins, the flagon. "Oh, that wicked flagon!" thought Rip. "What excuse shall I make to Dame Van Winkle?"

He looked round for his gun, but in place of the clean, well-oiled fowling-piece, he found an old firelock lying by him, the barrel incrusted with rust, the lock falling off, and the stock worm-eaten. He now suspected that the grave roisters of the mountain had put a trick upon him, and, having dosed him with liquor, had robbed him of his gun. Wolf, too, had disappeared; but he might have strayed away after a squirrel or partridge. He whistled after him, and shouted his name, but all in vain; the echoes repeated his whistle and shout, but no dog was to be seen.

He determined to revisit the scene of the last evening's gambol, and, if he met with any of the party, to demand his dog and gun. As he rose to walk, he found himself stiff in the joints, and wanting in his usual activity. "These mountain beds do not agree with me," thought Rip; "and, if this frolic should lay me up with a fit of the rheumatism, I shall have a blessed time with Dame Van Winkle."

With some difficulty he got down into the glen. He found the gully up which he and his companion had ascended the preceding evening; but, to his astonishment, a mountain stream was now foaming down it, leaping from rock to rock, and filling the glen with babbling murmurs. He, however, made shift to scramble up its sides, working his toilsome way through thickets of birch, sassafras, and witch-hazel, and sometimes tripped up or entangled by the wild grapevines that twisted their coils and tendrils from tree to tree, and spread a kind of network in his path.

At length he reached to where the ravine had opened through the cliffs to the amphitheater; but no trace of such opening remained. The rocks presented a high, impenetrable wall, over which the torrent came tumbling in a sheet of feathery foam, and fell into a broad, deep basin, black from the shadows of the surrounding forest. Here, then, poor Rip was brought to a stand. He again called and whistled after his dog. He was only answered by the cawing of a flock of idle crows, sporting high in air about a dry tree that overhung a sunny precipice, and who, secure in their elevation, seemed to look down and scoff at the poor man's perplexities.

What was to be done? The morning was passed away, and Rip felt famished for want of his breakfast. He grieved to give up his dog and gun, he dreaded to meet his wife; but it would not do to starve among the mountains. He shook his head, shouldered the rusty firelock, and, with a heart full of trouble and anxiety, turned his steps homeward.

As he approached the village, he met a number of people, but none whom he knew; which somewhat surprised him, for he had thought himself acquainted with every one in the country round. Their dress, too, was of a different fashion from that to which he was accustomed. They all stared at him with equal marks of surprise, and, whenever they cast their eyes upon him, invariably stroked their chins. The constant recurrence of this gesture induced Rip involuntarily to do the same, when, to his astonishment, he found his beard had grown a foot long.

He had now entered the skirts of the village. A troop of strange children ran at his heels, hooting after him and pointing at his gray beard. The dogs, too, not one of which he recognized for an old acquaintance, barked at him as he passed. The very village was altered; it was larger and more populous. There were rows of houses which he had never seen before, and those which had been his familiar haunts had disappeared. Strange names were over the doors, strange faces at the windows—everything was strange.

His mind now misgave him. He began to doubt whether both he and the world around him were not bewitched. Surely this was his native village, which he had left but the day before. There stood the Catskill Mountains; there ran the silver Hudson at a distance; there was every hill and dale precisely as it had always been. Rip was sorely perplexed. "That flagon last night," thought he, "has addled my poor head sadly."

It was with some difficulty that he found the way to his own house, which he approached with silent awe, expecting every moment to hear the shrill voice of Dame Van Winkle. He found the house gone to decay—the roof fallen in, the windows shattered, and the doors off the hinges. A half-starved dog that looked like Wolf was skulking about it. Rip called him by name; but the cur snarled, showed his teeth, and passed on. This was an unkind cut, indeed. "My very dog," sighed poor Rip, "has forgotten me!"

He entered the house, which, to tell the truth, Dame Van Winkle had always kept in neat order. It was empty, forlorn, and apparently abandoned. This desolateness overcame all his connubial fears. He called loudly for his wife and children; the lonely chambers rang for a moment with his voice, and then all again was silence.

He now hurried forth, and hastened to his old resort, the village inn; but it, too, was gone. A large, rickety, wooden building stood in its place, with great, gaping windows, some of them broken and mended with old hats and petticoats; and over the door was painted, "The Union Hotel, by Jonathan Doolittle." Instead of the great tree that used to shelter the quiet little Dutch inn of yore, there now was reared a tall, naked pole, with something on the top that looked like a red nightcap; and from it was fluttering a flag, on which was a singular assemblage of stars and stripes.

All this was strange and incomprehensible. He recognized on the sign, however, the ruby face of King George, under which he had smoked so many a peaceful pipe; but even this was singularly metamorphosed. The red coat was changed for one of blue and buff, a sword was held in the hand instead of a scepter, the head was decorated with a cocked hat, and underneath was painted in large characters, "General Washington."

There was, as usual, a crowd of folk about the door, but none that Rip recollected. The very character of the people seemed changed. There was a busy, bustling, disputatious tone about it, instead of the accustomed phlegm and drowsy tranquillity. He looked in vain for the sage Nicholas Vedder, with his broad face, double chin, and fair long pipe, uttering clouds of tobacco smoke instead of idle speeches; or Van Bummel, the schoolmaster, doling forth the contents of an ancient newspaper. In place of these, a lean, bilious-looking fellow, with his pockets full of handbills, was haranguing vehemently about the rights of citizens, election, members of Congress, liberty, Bunker's Hill, heroes of seventy-six, and other words, that were a perfect Babylonish jargon to the bewildered Van Winkle.

The appearance of Rip, with his long, grizzled beard, his rusty fowling-piece, his uncouth dress, and the army of women and children that had gathered at his heels, soon attracted the attention of the tavern politicians. They crowded round him, eyeing him from head to foot with great curiosity. The orator bustled up to him, and, drawing him partly aside, inquired on which side he voted. Rip stared in vacant stupidity.

Another short but busy little fellow pulled him by the arm, and, rising on tiptoe, inquired in his ear whether he was a Federal or a Democrat. Rip was equally at a loss to comprehend the question, when a knowing, self-important old gentleman in a sharp cocked hat made his way through the crowd, putting them to the right and left with his elbows as he passed, and, planting himself before Van Winkle, with one arm akimbo, the other resting on his cane, his keen eyes and sharp hat penetrating, as it were, into his very soul, demanded in an austere tone what brought him to the election with a gun on his shoulder and a mob at his heels, and whether he meant to breed a riot in the village.

"Alas! gentlemen," cried Rip, somewhat dismayed, "I am a poor, quiet man, a native of the place, and a loyal subject to the King, God bless him!"

Here a general shout burst from the bystanders: "A Tory, a Tory! A spy! A refugee! Hustle him! Away with him!" It was with great difficulty that the self-important man in the cocked hat restored order, and, having assumed a tenfold austerity of brow, demanded again of the unknown culprit what he came there for, and whom he was seeking. The poor man humbly assured him that he meant no harm, but merely came there in search of some of his neighbors, who used to keep about the tavern.

"Well, who are they? Name them."

Rip bethought himself a moment, and inquired, "Where's Nicholas Vedder?"

There was a silence for a little while, when an old man replied in a thin, piping voice, "Nicholas Vedder! Why, he is dead and gone these eighteen years! There was a wooden tombstone in the churchyard that used to tell all about him, but that's rotten and gone, too."

"Where's Brom Dutcher?"

"Oh, he went off to the army in the beginning of the war. Some say he was killed at the storming of Stony Point; others say he was drowned in the squall at the foot of Anthony's Nose. I don't know, he never came back again."

"Where's Van Bummel, the schoolmaster?"

"He went off to the wars, too, was a great militia general, and is now in Congress."

Rip's heart died away at hearing of these sad changes in his home and friends, and finding himself thus alone in the world. Every answer puzzled him, too, by treating of such enormous lapses of time, and of matters which he could not understand—war, Congress, Stony Point. He had no courage to ask after any more friends, but cried out in despair, "Does nobody here know Rip Van Winkle?"

"Oh, Rip Van Winkle!" exclaimed two or three. "Oh, to be sure! that's Rip Van Winkle yonder, leaning against the tree."

Rip looked, and beheld a precise counterpart of himself, as he went up the mountain, apparently as lazy, and certainly as ragged. The poor fellow was now completely confounded. He doubted his own identity, and whether he was himself or another man. In the midst of his bewilderment, the man in the cocked hat demanded who he was, and what was his name.

"God knows!" exclaimed he, at his wits' end. "I'm not myself; I'm somebody else.

That's me yonder. No, that's somebody else got into my shoes. I was myself last night, but I fell asleep on the mountain, and they've changed my gun; and everything's changed; and I'm changed; and I can't tell what's my name, or who I am!"

The bystanders began now to look at each other, nod, wink significantly, and tap their fingers against their foreheads. There was a whisper, also, about securing the gun, and keeping the old fellow from doing mischief, at the very suggestion of which the self-important man in the cocked hat retired with some precipitation. At this critical moment a fresh, comely woman pressed through the throng to get a peep at the gray-bearded man. She had a chubby child in her arms, which, frightened at his looks, began to cry.

"Hush, Rip!" cried she. "Hush, you little fool! The old man won't hurt you."

The name of the child, the air of the mother, the tone of her voice, all awakened a train of recollections in his mind. "What is your name, my good woman?" asked he.

"Judith Gardenier."

"And your father's name?"

"Ah, poor man, his name was Rip Van Winkle. It's twenty years since he went away from home with his gun, and never has been heard of since. His dog came home without him; but whether he shot himself, or was carried away by the Indians, nobody can tell. I was then but a little girl."

Rip had but one question more to ask, but he put it with a faltering voice:

"Where's your mother?"

"Oh, she too died but a short time since. She broke a blood-vessel in a fit of passion at a New England peddler."

There was a drop of comfort, at least, in this intelligence. The honest man could contain himself no longer. He caught his daughter and her child in his arms. "I am your father!" cried he. "Young Rip Van Winkle once, old Rip Van Winkle now! Does nobody know poor Rip Van Winkle?"

All stood amazed, until an old woman, tottering out from among the crowd, put her hand to her brow, and, peering under it in his face for a moment, exclaimed, "Sure enough! It is Rip Van Winkle! It is himself! Welcome home again, old neighbor! Why, where have you been these twenty long years?"

Rip's story was soon told, for the whole twenty years had been to him but as one night. The neighbors stared when they heard it. Some were seen to wink at each other, and put their tongues in their cheeks; and the self-important man in the cocked hat, who, when the alarm was over, had returned to the field, screwed down the corners of his mouth, and shook his head, upon which there was a general shaking of the head throughout the assemblage.

It was determined, however, to take the opinion of old Peter Vanderdonk, who was seen slowly advancing up the road. He was a descendant of the historian of that name, who wrote one of the earliest accounts of the province. Peter was the most ancient inhabitant of the village, and well versed in all the wonderful events and traditions of the neighborhood. He recollected Rip at once, and corroborated his story in the most satisfactory manner. He assured the company that it was a fact, handed down from his ancestor the historian, that the Catskill Mountains had always been haunted by strange beings; that it was affirmed that the great Hendrick Hudson, the first discoverer of the river and country, kept a kind of vigil there every twenty years, with his crew of the *Half Moon*, being permitted in this way to revisit the scenes of his enterprise, and keep a guardian eye upon the river, and the great city called by his name; that his father had once seen them in their old Dutch dresses, playing at ninepins in the hollow of the mountain; and that he himself had heard, one summer afternoon, the sound of their balls, like distant peals of thunder.

To make a long story short, the company broke up, and returned to the more important concerns of the election. Rip's daughter took him home to live with her. She had a snug, well-furnished house, and a stout, cheery farmer for a husband, whom Rip recollected for one of the urchins that used to climb upon his back. As to Rip's son and heir, who was the ditto of himself, seen leaning against the tree, he was employed to work on the farm, but evinced an hereditary disposition to attend to anything else but his business.

Rip now resumed his old walks and habits. He soon found many of his former cronies, though all rather the worse for the wear and tear of time, and preferred making friends among the rising generation, with whom he soon grew into great favor.

Having nothing to do at home, and being arrived at that happy age when a man can do nothing with impunity, he took his place once more on the bench at the inn door, and was reverenced as one of the patriarchs of the village, and a chronicle of the old times "before the war." It was some time before he could get into the regular track of gossip, or could be made to comprehend the strange events that had taken place during his torpor—how that there had been a revolutionary war, that the country had thrown off the yoke of old England, and that, instead of being a subject of His Majesty George III, he was now a free citizen of the United States.

Rip, in fact, was no politician; the changes of states and empire made but little impression on him, but there was one species of despotism under which he had long groaned, and that was—petticoat government. Happily, that was at an end. He had got his neck out of the yoke of matrimony, and could go in and out whenever he pleased, without dreading the tyranny of Dame Van Winkle. Whenever her name was mentioned, however, he shook his head, shrugged his shoulders, and cast up his eyes; which might pass either for an expression of resignation to his fate, or joy at his deliverance.

He used to tell his story to every stranger that arrived at Mr. Doolittle's hotel. He was observed at first to vary on some points every time he told it, which was doubtless owing to his having so recently awaked. It at last settled down precisely to the tale I have related; and not a man, woman, or child in the neighborhood but knew it by heart.

Some always pretended to doubt the reality of Rip's story, and insisted that he had been out of his head, and that this was one point on which he always remained flighty. The old Dutch inhabitants, however, almost universally gave it full credit. Even to this day they never hear a thunderstorm of a summer afternoon about the Catskills, but they say Hendrick Hudson and his crew are at their game of ninepins; and it is a common wish of all hen-pecked husbands in the neighborhood, when life hangs heavy on their hands, that they might have a quieting draught out of Rip Van Winkle's flagon.

## THE NIGHTINGALE[1]

*Hans Christian Andersen*

This story happened a good many years ago, but that's just why it's worthwhile to hear it, before it is forgotten.

The palace of the Emperor of China was the most splendid in the world; entirely and altogether made of porcelain, so costly, but so brittle, so difficult to handle that one had to be terribly careful. In the garden were to be seen the strangest flowers, and to the most splendid of them silver bells were tied, which tinkled so that nobody should pass by without noticing the flowers. The Emperor's garden extended so far that the gardener himself didn't know where the end was. If you went on and on, you came to the loveliest forest with high trees and deep lakes. The forest went right down to the sea, which was blue and deep; tall ships could sail right in under the branches of the trees; and in the trees lived a Nightingale, which sang so sweetly that even the poor fisherman, who

[1] From Hans Christian Andersen, *Fairy Tales and Stories,* translated by Signe Toksvig.

had many other things to do, stopped still and listened, when he had gone out at night to take up his nets, and then heard the Nightingale.

"How beautiful it is!" he said; but he had to attend to his business, and forgot the bird. But the next night when the bird sang again, and the fisherman heard it, he said again, "How beautiful it is!"

From all the countries of the world travelers came to the city of the Emperor, and admired it, and the palace and the garden, but when they heard the Nightingale, they said, "That is the best of all!"

And the travelers told about it when they came home; and the learned men wrote many books about the city, the palace, and the garden. But they did not forget the Nightingale; that was placed highest of all; and those who were poets wrote poems about the Nightingale in the forest by the sea.

The books went through all the world, and a few of them came to the Emperor. He sat in his golden chair, and read, and read; every moment he nodded his head, for it pleased him to read the splendid descriptions of the city, the palace, and the garden. "But the Nightingale is the best of all," it stood written there.

"What's that?" said the Emperor. "The Nightingale! I don't know that at all! Is there such a bird in my empire, and even in my own garden? I've never heard of that. I had to find it in a book!"

And then he called his cavalier. This cavalier was so grand that if any one lower in rank than himself dared to speak to him, or to ask him any question, he answered nothing but "P!"—and that doesn't mean anything.

"They tell me that we have here a highly remarkable bird called a Nightingale!" said the Emperor. "They say it is the best thing in all my great empire. Why haven't I ever been told about this?"

"I have never before heard anybody mention it," said the cavalier. "It has never been presented at court."

"I command that it shall appear this evening, and sing before me," said the Emperor. "It seems that all the world knows what I possess, except myself."

"I have never heard it mentioned," said the cavalier, "I will look for it. I will find it."

But where was it to be found? The cavalier ran up and down all the stairs, through halls and corridors, but no one among all those whom he met had ever heard of the Nightingale. And the cavalier ran back to the Emperor, and said that it must be a fable invented by the writers of books.

"Your Imperial Majesty mustn't believe the things people write!"

"But the book in which I read this," said the Emperor, "was sent to me by the high and mighty Emperor of Japan, and therefore it cannot be a lie. I *will* hear the Nightingale! It must be here this evening! It has my imperial favor; and if it does not come, the whole court will be punched on the stomach after the court has eaten its supper!"

"Tsing-pe!" said the cavalier; and again he ran up and down all the stairs, and through all the halls and corridors; and half the court ran with him, because they didn't want to be punched on the stomach.

Ever so many questions were asked about this remarkable Nightingale, which all the world knew excepting the people at court.

At last they met a poor little girl in the kitchen, who said:

"The Nightingale? I know it very well; yes, it certainly can sing! Every evening I am allowed to carry my poor sick mother the scraps from the table. She lives down by the shore, and when I walk back and am tired, and rest in the wood, then I hear the Nightingale sing. And then the tears come into my eyes, and it is just as if my mother kissed me!"

"Little kitchen maid," said the cavalier, "I will get you a permanent appointment in the kitchen, with permission to see the Emperor dine, if you will lead us to the Nightingale, for it is announced for this evening."

So they all went out into the wood where the Nightingale usually sang; half the court went along. When they were in the midst of their journey a cow began to low.

"Oh!" said all the court cavaliers, "there it is! That's really a remarkable power in so small a creature! I have certainly heard it before."

"No, those are cows lowing!" said the little kitchen maid. "We are a long way from the place yet."

Now the frogs began to croak in the pool.

"Glorious!" said the cavalier. "Now I can hear it—it sounds just like little church bells."

"No, those are frogs," said the little kitchen maid. "But now I think we shall soon hear it."

And then the Nightingale began to sing.

"That is it!" said the little girl. "Listen, listen, and it's sitting there!"

And she pointed to a little gray bird up in the boughs.

"Is it possible?" said the cavalier. "I should never have thought it looked like that! How plain it looks! I suppose it lost its color at seeing so many aristocratic visitors."

"Little Nightingale!" called the little kitchen maid, quite loudly, "our gracious Emperor would so like you to sing for him."

"With the greatest pleasure!" said the Nightingale, and began to sing most delightfully.

"It sounds just like glass bells!" said the cavalier. "And look at its little throat, how it's working! It's strange we've never heard it before. It will have a great success at court."

"Shall I sing once more for the Emperor?" asked the Nightingale, for it thought the Emperor was present.

"My excellent little Nightingale," said the cavalier, "I have great pleasure in inviting you to a court festival this evening, when you shall enchant His High and Imperial Majesty with your singing."

"My song sounds best in the green wood!" said the Nightingale; still it came willingly when it heard that the Emperor wanted it.

In the palace everything was brightly lighted. The walls and the flooring, which were of porcelain, gleamed in the rays of thousands of golden lamps. The loveliest flowers, those that tinkled best, had been placed in the passages. There was a running to and fro, and a draught, and then all the bells rang so loudly that one could not hear oneself speak.

In the midst of the great hall, where the Emperor sat, a golden perch had been placed, on which the Nightingale was to sit. The whole court was there, and the little kitchen maid had been allowed to stand behind the door, as she had now received the title of Regular Cook. All were in full dress, and all looked at the little gray bird, to which the Emperor nodded.

And the Nightingale sang so beautifully that the tears came into the Emperor's eyes, and the tears ran down over his cheeks; and then the Nightingale sang still more sweetly, so that its song went straight to the heart. The Emperor was so much pleased that he said the Nightingale should have his golden slipper to wear around its neck. But the Nightingale thanked him and said it had already had reward enough.

"I have seen tears in the Emperor's eyes —there is no richer treasure for me. An Emperor's tears have a strange power. I am rewarded enough!" And then it sang again with its marvelously sweet voice.

"Isn't it too darling?" said the ladies who stood around, and then they took water in their mouths to gurgle when any one spoke to them. Then they thought they were nightingales too. And the lackeys and chambermaids reported that they were satisfied too; and that was saying a good deal, for they are the most difficult to please. In short, the Nightingale had a real success.

It was now to remain at court, to have its own cage, with liberty to go out twice every day and once at night. Twelve servants came along when the Nightingale went out, each of whom had a silken string fastened to the bird's leg, which they held very tight. There was really no pleasure in an excursion of that kind.

The whole city spoke of the remarkable bird, and when two people met, one said nothing but "Nightin," and the other said "gale"; and then they sighed, and understood one another. Eleven grocers' children were named after the bird, but not one of them could sing a note.

One day the Emperor received a large parcel, on which was written "The Nightingale."

"Here we have a new book about this celebrated bird," said the Emperor.

But it was not a book, but a little work of art, lying in a box, an artificial nightingale, which was supposed to look like the living one, but it was decorated with diamonds, rubies, and sapphires. So soon as the artificial bird was wound up, it could sing one of the pieces that the real one sang, and then its tail moved up and down, and glittered with silver and gold. Round its neck hung a little ribbon, and on that was written, "The Emperor of Japan's nightingale is poor compared to that of the Emperor of China."

"Isn't that lovely?" they all said, and he who had brought the artificial bird immediately received the title, Imperial Head-Nightingale-Bringer.

"Now they must sing together; what a duet that will be!"

And so they had to sing together; but it did not sound very well, for the real Nightingale sang in its own way, and the artificial bird sang a waltz.

"That's not its fault," said the music master, "it keeps perfect time and very much in my style."

Now the artificial bird was to sing alone. It made just as much of a hit as the real one, and then it was much handsomer to look at—it shone like bracelets and breastpins.

Three and thirty times over it sang the same piece, still it was not tired. The people would gladly have heard it again, but the Emperor said that the living Nightingale ought to sing something now. But where was it? No one had noticed that it had flown away out of the open window, back to the green wood.

"But what in the world is this?" said the Emperor.

And all the courtiers scolded the Nightingale, and declared that it was a very ungrateful creature.

"We have the best bird, after all," they said.

And so the artificial bird had to sing again, and that was the thirty-fourth time that they listened to the same piece, but still they didn't know it quite by heart, for it was so very difficult. And the music master praised the bird very highly; yes, he declared that it was better than the real Nightingale, not only with regard to its plumage and the many beautiful diamonds, but inside as well.

"For you see, ladies and gentlemen, and above all, Your Imperial Majesty, with a real Nightingale one can never calculate what is coming, but in this artificial bird everything is settled. It is this way, and no other! One can explain it; one can open it and show where the music comes from and how it is made!"

"That's just what I was thinking," they all said.

And the speaker received permission to show the bird to the people on the next Sunday. The people were to hear it sing, too, the Emperor commanded; and they did hear it, and were so much pleased that they all said, "Oh!" and held up their forefingers and nodded. But the poor fisherman who had heard the real Nightingale said:

"It sounds pretty enough, but there's something missing; I don't know what it is."

The real Nightingale was banished from the country. The artificial bird had its place on a silken cushion close to the Emperor's bed; all the presents it had received, gold and precious stones, lay around it; in title it had advanced to be the High Imperial Night-Table-Singer, and in rank to number one on the left; for the Emperor considered that the most important on which the heart is placed, and even in an Emperor the heart is on the left side; and the music master wrote a work of five and twenty volumes about the artificial bird; it was very learned and very long, and full of the most difficult words; but still everybody said that they had read it and understood it.

So a whole year went by. The Emperor, the Court, and all the people knew every little gurgle in the artificial bird's song by heart. And that was just why they liked it; then they could sing it too, and they did. The street boys sang, "Tsi-tsi-tsi-glug-glug!" and the Emperor himself sang it too! Oh, it was certainly wonderful!

But one evening, when the artificial bird was singing its best, and the Emperor lay in bed listening to it, something inside the bird said, "Whizz!" Something cracked. "Whir-r!" All the wheels ran round, and then the music stopped.

The Emperor jumped out of bed right away and sent for his own doctor; but what could he do? Then they sent for a watchmaker, and after a good deal of talking and looking, the bird was put into something like order; but the watchmaker said that the bird must be carefully treated, for the pivots were worn, and it would be impossible to put new ones in in such a manner that the music would go. There was great lamentation; only once in a year was it permitted to let the bird sing, and that was almost too much. But then the music master made a little speech, full of difficult words, and said it was just as good as before—and so of course it was as good as before.

Now five years had gone by, and a real grief came to the whole nation. The people did, after all, like their Emperor very much, and now he was ill, and they said he couldn't live much longer. Already a new Emperor had been chosen, and the people stood out in the street and asked the cavalier how their old Emperor was.

"P!" he said, and shook his head.

Cold and pale the Emperor lay in his big gorgeous bed; the whole court thought him dead, and each one ran to bow to the new Emperor. Everywhere, in all the halls and passages, cloth had been laid down so that no footstep could be heard, and therefore it was so still, so still. But the Emperor was not dead, though he lay still and pale on the gorgeous bed with the long velvet curtains and the heavy gold tassels. High up, a window stood open, and the moon shone in on the Emperor and the artificial bird.

The poor Emperor could scarcely breathe; it was just as if something sat on his chest; he opened his eyes, and then he saw that it was Death who sat on his chest, and had put on his golden crown, and held in one hand the Emperor's gold sword, and in the other his beautiful banner. And all around, from the folds of the big velvet bed curtains, strange heads peered forth; some ugly, others lovely and mild. These were all the Emperor's bad and good deeds looking at him.

"Do you remember this?" whispered one after the other, "Do you remember that?" and then they told him so much that the sweat ran from his forehead.

"I never knew that!" said the Emperor. "Music! music! the big drum!" he called, "so that I won't hear what they say!"

But they kept on.

"Music! music!" cried the Emperor. "My blessed little golden bird, sing, sing! I have given you gold and costly presents; I have even hung my golden slipper around your neck—sing, now, sing!"

But the bird stood still; no one was there to wind it up, and it couldn't sing without that.

Just then the loveliest song sounded close by the window. It was the little live Nightingale, that sat outside on a spray. It had heard of the Emperor's danger, and had come to sing to him of comfort and hope. And as it sang, the specters grew paler and paler; the blood ran quicker and quicker through the Emperor's weak body; and even Death listened, and said:

"Go on, little Nightingale, go on!"

"But will you give me that splendid golden sword? Will you give me that rich banner? Will you give me the Emperor's crown?" said the Nightingale.

And Death gave up each treasure for a song. And the Nightingale sang on and on. Then Death felt a longing for his garden, and floated like a cold white mist out of the window.

"I thank you, thank you!" said the Emperor. "You heavenly little bird! I know you well. I drove you from my country, and yet you have sung away the evil faces from my bed, and taken Death from my heart! How can I reward you?"

"You have rewarded me!" said the Nightingale. "I have drawn tears from your eyes, when I sang the first time—I shall never forget that. Those are the jewels that do a singer's heart good. But now sleep and grow fresh and strong again. I will sing for you."

And it sang, and the Emperor fell into a sweet sleep. Ah, how mild and refreshing that sleep was! The sun shone on him through the windows when he woke up strong and well; not one of his servants had come back yet, for they all thought he was dead; only the Nightingale still sat beside him and sang.

"You must always stay with me," said the Emperor. "You shall sing only when you please; and I'll break the artificial bird into a thousand pieces."

"Don't do that," said the Nightingale. "It did as well as it could; keep it as you have done till now. I cannot live in the palace, but let me come when I want to; then I will sit in the evening on the branch there by the window, and sing you something, so that you may be glad and thoughtful at once. I will sing of those who are happy and of those who suffer. I will sing of the good and the evil that people hide around you. The little singing bird flies far around, to the poor fisherman, to the peasant's roof, to every one who dwells far away from you and your court. I will come, I will sing to you—but one thing you must promise me."

"Everything!" said the Emperor; and he stood there in his imperial robes, which he had put on himself, and pressed the sword which was heavy with gold to his heart.

"One thing I beg of you; tell no one that you have a little bird who tells you everything. Then things will be even better."

And the Nightingale flew away.

The servants came in to look at their dead Emperor, and—well, there they were, and the Emperor said "Good morning!"

## *Make-Believe Stories: Suggested Grades*

*Grade One*
Ask Mr. Bear

*Grade Two*
The First Christmas Tree

*Grade Three*
The Tinder Box

*Grade Four*
The Midnight Voyage

The Princess and the Pea
The White Cat

*Grade Five*
Fairyfoot
Pinocchio
The Ugly Duckling

*Grade Six*
Little Daylight
The Emperor's New Clothes

*Grade Seven*
Rip Van Winkle

*Grade Eight*
The Nightingale

## *Books of Make-Believe Stories*

### *Grades One and Two*

Beskow, Elsa, *Elf Children of the Woods* (trans. by Zita Beskow), illus. by the author. Harper.

———, *Olle's Ski Trip* (trans. by Siri Andrews), illus. by the author. Harper.

Bianco, Margery, *The Velveteen Rabbit,* illus. by William Nicholson. Doubleday, Doran.

Brock, Emma, *The Runaway Sardine,* illus. by the author. Knopf.

Flack, Marjorie, *Ask Mr. Bear,* illus. by the author. Macmillan.

Fyleman, Rose, *A Little Christmas Book,* illus. by Lisl Hummel. Doubleday, Doran.

Gág, Wanda, *Snippy and Snappy,* illus. by the author. Coward-McCann.

Grishina, N., *Gresha and His Clay Pig,* illus. by the author. Stokes.

La Rue, Mabel, *Zip, the Toy Mule,* illus. by Maud and Miska Petersham. Macmillan.

Literature Committee of the Association for Childhood Education, *Told under the Magic Umbrella,* illus. by Elizabeth Orton Jones. Macmillan.

Milne, A. A., *Winnie the Pooh,* illus. by Ernest H. Shepard. Dutton.

Newberry, Clare, *Herbert the Lion,* illus. by the author. Putnam.

Nicholson, William, *Clever Bill,* illus. by the author. Doubleday, Doran.

Potter, Beatrix, *The Tailor of Gloucester,* illus. by the author. Warne.

## *Grades Three and Four*

Alden, Raymond M., *Why the Chimes Rang, and Other Stories.* Bobbs-Merrill.

Baker, Margaret, *The Black Cats and the Tinker's Wife,* illus. by Mary Baker. Dodd Mead.

———, *The Pixies and the Silver Crown,* illus. by Mary Baker. Dodd Mead.

Barrie, James M., *Peter and Wendy,* illus. by Francis D. Bedford. Scribner.

Bianco, Margery, *The Little Wooden Doll,* illus. by Pamela Bianco. Macmillan.

Casserley, Anne, *Michael of Ireland,* illus. by the author. Harper.

Coatsworth, Elizabeth, *The Cat Who Went to Heaven,* illus. by Lynd Ward. Macmillan.

Colum, Padraic, *The Peep-Show Man,* illus. by Lois Lenski. Macmillan.

Craik, Dinah Maria Mulock, *The Adventures of a Brownie,* illus. by Mary Lott Seaman. Rand McNally.

Cregan, Mairin, *Old John,* illus. by Helen Sewell. Macmillan.

Dalgliesh, Alice, *Christmas: A Book of Stories Old and New,* illus. by Hildegard Woodward. Scribner.

Daugherty, James, *Andy and the Lion,* illus. by the author. Viking.

D'Aulnoy, Madame la Comtesse, *The White Cat, and Other Old French Fairy Tales* (ed. by Rachel Field), illus. by Elizabeth Mackinstry. Macmillan.

Field, Rachel, *The Bird Began to Sing,* illus. by Ilse Bischoff. Morrow.

Fyleman, Rose, *The Rainbow Cat, and Other Stories,* illus. by Thelma Cudlipp Grosvenor. Doubleday, Doran.

Harper, Wilhelmina, *A Merry Christmas to You!* illus. by Wilfred Jones. Dutton.

Hess, Fjeril, *The Magic Switch,* illus. by Neva Kanaga Brown. Macmillan.

Kingsley, Charles, *Water Babies: A Fairy Tale for a Land Baby,* illus. by Heath Robinson. Houghton Mifflin.

Lagerlöf, Selma, *The Wonderful Adventures of Nils* (trans. by V. S. Howard), illus. by Mary Hamilton Frye. Doubleday, Doran.

Lathrop, Dorothy P., *The Fairy Circus,* illus. by the author. Macmillan.

McCoy, Neely, *The Tale of the Good Cat Jupie,* illus. by the author. Macmillan.

MacDonald, George, *At the Back of the North Wind,* illus. by Francis D. Bedford. Macmillan.

———, *The Princess and the Goblin,* illus. by Elizabeth MacKinstry. Doubleday, Doran.

MacDonald, Greville, *Billy Barnicoat,* illus. by Francis D. Bedford. Dutton.

Masefield, John, *The Midnight Folk.* Macmillan.

Meigs, Cornelia, *The Wonderful Locomotive,* illus. by Berta and Elmer Hader. Macmillan.

Paine, Albert Bigelow, *The Hollow Tree and Deep Woods Book,* illus. by Reginald Birch. Harper.

Potter, Miriam Clark, *Sally Gabble and the Fairies,* illus. by Helen Sewell. Macmillan.

Pyle, Howard, *The Wonder Clock,* illus. by the author. Harper.

Stockton, Frank R., *The Poor Count's Christmas,* illus. by E. B. Bensell. Stokes.

## Grades Five and Six

Andersen, Hans Christian, *Fairy Tales and Stories* (trans. by Signe Toksvig), illus. by Eric Pape and Hans Christian Andersen. Macmillan.

——, *It's Perfectly True, and Other Stories* (trans. by Paul Leyssac), illus. by Richard Bennett. Harcourt, Brace.

Artzybasheff, Boris, *Seven Simeons,* illus. by the author. Viking.

Benson, E. F., *David Blaze and the Blue Door,* illus. by H. J. Ford. Doubleday, Doran.

Browne, Frances, *Granny's Wonderful Chair,* illus. by Katherine Pyle. Dutton.

Coatsworth, Elizabeth, *Knock at the Door,* illus. by Francis D. Bedford. Macmillan.

Collodi, C., *The Adventures of Pinocchio* (trans. by Carol della Chiesa), illus. by Attilio Mussino. Macmillan.

———, *Pinocchio, the Story of a Puppet,* illus. by Jack Tinker. Lippincott.

Farjeon, Eleanor, *Martin Pippin in the Daisy-Field,* illus. by J. Morton Sale. Stokes.

Grahame, Kenneth, *The Wind in the Willows,* illus. by Ernest H. Shepard. Scribner.

Harper, Wilhelmina (editor), *The Selfish Giant, and Other Stories,* illus. by Kate Seredy. McKay.

Kelly, Eric P., *The Christmas Nightingale,* illus. by Marguerite de Angeli. Macmillan.

Nesbit, E., *The Enchanted Castle,* illus. by H. R. Millar. Coward-McCann.

———, *The Wonderful Garden,* illus. by H. R. Millar. Coward-McCann.

Tolkien, J. R. R., *The Hobbit, or There Again and Back,* illus. by the author. Houghton Mifflin.

Travers, P. L., *Mary Poppins,* illus. by Mary Shepard. Reynal.

## Grades Seven and Eight

Colum, Padraic, *The King of Ireland's Son,* illus. by Willy Pogány. Macmillan.

De la Mare, Walter, *The Three Mulla Mulgars,* illus. by Dorothy P. Lathrop. Knopf.

Dickens, Charles, *A Christmas Carol,* illus. by Francis D. Bedford. Macmillan.

———, *The Cricket on the Hearth,* illus. by Francis D. Bedford. Harper.

Dumas, Alexander, *The Nutcracker of Nuremberg* (retold by Donald E. Cooke), illus. by Donald E. Cooke. Winston.

Hudson, William H., *A Little Boy Lost,* illus. by Dorothy P. Lathrop. Knopf.

Irving, Washington, *The Legend of Sleepy Hollow,* illus. by Arthur Rackham. McKay.

Irving, Washington, *Rip Van Winkle,* illus. by N. C. Wyeth. McKay.

Ruskin, John, *The King of the Golden River,* illus. by Mary Lott Seaman. Macmillan.

Stockton, Frank R., *The Queen's Museum, and Other Fanciful Tales,* illus. by Frederick Richardson. Scribner.

Swift, Jonathan, *Gulliver's Travels into Several Remote Nations of the World,* illus. by Charles Brock. Macmillan.

Tarn, W. W., *The Treasure of the Isle of Mist,* illus. by Robert Lawson. Putnam.

Verne, Jules, *Twenty Thousand Leagues under the Sea* (trans. by Philip Schuyler Allen), illus. by Milo Winter. Rand McNally.

Young, Ella, *The Unicorn with Silver Shoes,* illus. by Robert Lawson. Longmans.

# Stories for Fun

## THE TALE OF PETER RABBIT [1]

*Beatrix Potter*

Once upon a time there were four little Rabbits, and their names were Flopsy, Mopsy, Cotton-tail, and Peter.

They lived with their mother in a sand bank, underneath the root of a very big fir tree.

"Now, my dears," said old Mrs. Rabbit one morning, "you may go into the fields or down the lane, but don't go into Mr. McGregor's garden. Your father had an accident there; he was put in a pie by Mrs. McGregor. Now run along, and don't get into mischief. I am going out."

Then old Mrs. Rabbit took a basket and her umbrella, and went through the wood to the baker's. She bought a loaf of brown bread and five currant buns.

Flopsy, Mopsy, and Cotton-tail, who were good little bunnies, went down the lane to gather blackberries; but Peter, who was very naughty, ran straight to Mr. McGregor's garden, and squeezed under the gate.

First he ate some lettuces and some French beans; and then he ate some radishes; and then, feeling rather sick, he went to look for some parsley.

But round the end of a cucumber frame, whom should he meet but Mr. McGregor!

Mr. McGregor was on his hands and knees planting out young cabbages, but he jumped up and ran after Peter, waving a rake and calling out, "Stop, thief!"

Peter was most dreadfully frightened; he rushed all over the garden, for he had forgotten the way back to the gate.

He lost one of his shoes amongst the cabbages, and the other shoe amongst the potatoes.

After losing them, he ran on four legs and went faster, so that I think he might have got away altogether if he had not unfortunately run into a gooseberry net, and got caught by the large buttons on his jacket. It was a blue jacket with brass buttons, quite new.

Peter gave himself up for lost, and shed big tears; but his sobs were overheard by some friendly sparrows, who flew to him in great excitement, and implored him to exert himself.

Mr. McGregor came up with a sieve, which he intended to pop upon the top of Peter; but Peter wriggled out just in time, leaving his jacket behind him, and rushed

[1] From Beatrix Potter, *The Tale of Peter Rabbit.*

into the tool shed, and jumped into a can. It would have been a beautiful thing to hide in, if it had not had so much water in it.

Mr. McGregor was quite sure that Peter was somewhere in the tool shed, perhaps hidden underneath a flower pot. He began to turn them over carefully, looking under each.

Presently Peter sneezed—"Kerty-schoo!" Mr. McGregor was after him in no time, and tried to put his foot upon Peter, who jumped out of a window, upsetting three plants. The window was too small for Mr. McGregor, and he was tired of running after Peter. He went back to his work.

Peter sat down to rest; he was out of breath and trembling with fright, and he had not the least idea which way to go. Also he was very damp with sitting in that can.

After a time he began to wander about, going lippity—lippity—not very fast, and looking all around.

He found a door in a wall; but it was locked, and there was no room for a fat little rabbit to squeeze underneath.

An old mouse was running in and out over the stone doorstep, carrying peas and beans to her family in the wood. Peter asked her the way to the gate, but she had such a large pea in her mouth that she could not answer. She only shook her head at him. Peter began to cry.

Then he tried to find his way straight across the garden, but he became more and more puzzled. Presently, he came to a pond where Mr. McGregor filled his water cans. A white cat was staring at some goldfish; she sat very, very still, but now and then the tip of her tail twitched as if it were alive. Peter thought it best to go away without speaking to her; he had heard about cats from his cousin, little Benjamin Bunny.

He went back towards the tool shed, but suddenly, quite close to him, he heard the noise of a hoe—scr-r-ritch scratch, scratch, scritch. Peter scuttered underneath the bushes. But presently, as nothing happened, he came out, and climbed upon a wheelbarrow and peeped over. The first thing he saw was Mr. McGregor hoeing onions. His back was turned towards Peter, and beyond him was the gate!

Peter got down very quietly off the wheelbarrow, and started running as fast as he could go, along a straight walk behind some black-currant bushes.

Mr. McGregor caught sight of him at the corner, but Peter did not care. He slipped underneath the gate, and was safe at last in the wood outside the garden.

Mr. McGregor hung up the little jacket and the shoes for a scarecrow to frighten the blackbirds.

Peter never stopped running or looked behind him till he got home to the big fir tree.

He was so tired that he flopped down upon the nice soft sand on the floor of the rabbit-hole, and shut his eyes. His mother was busy cooking; she wondered what he had done with his clothes. It was the second little jacket and a pair of shoes that Peter had lost in a fortnight!

I am sorry to say that Peter was not very well during the evening.

His mother put him to bed, and made some camomile tea; and she gave a dose of it to Peter!

"One tablespoonful to be taken at bedtime."

But Flopsy, Mopsy, and Cotton-tail had bread and milk and blackberries for supper.

## LITTLE BLACK SAMBO[1]

*Helen Bannerman*

Once upon a time there was a little boy and his name was Little Black Sambo. His mother was called Black Mumbo. His father was called Black Jumbo.

Black Mumbo made him a beautiful little red coat, and beautiful blue trousers, and a beautiful little green umbrella and

[1] From Helen Bannerman, *The Story of Little Black Sambo.*

a lovely pair of purple shoes with crimson soles and crimson linings.

And then wasn't Little Black Sambo grand!

He put on his fine clothes and went for a walk in the jungle. By and by he met a Tiger.

The Tiger growled at him and said, "Little Black Sambo, I'm going to eat you up!"

Little Black Sambo said, "Oh, please, Mr. Tiger, don't eat me up, and I'll give you my beautiful little red coat."

So the Tiger said, "Very well, I won't eat you this time, but you must give me your beautiful red coat."

Little Black Sambo took off his beautiful red coat and the Tiger put it on, and off he went with his head in the air, saying, "Now I'm the grandest Tiger in the jungle."

Little Black Sambo went still farther and he met another Tiger.

The Tiger growled at him and said, "Little Black Sambo, I'm going to eat you up!"

Little Black Sambo said, "Oh, please, Mr. Tiger, don't eat me up, and I'll give you my beautiful blue trousers."

Then the Tiger said, "Very well, I won't eat you up this time, but you must give me your beautiful blue trousers."

Little Black Sambo took off his beautiful blue trousers, and the Tiger put them on, and off he went with his head in the air, saying, "Now I'm the grandest Tiger in the jungle."

Little Black Sambo went farther and he met another Tiger.

The Tiger growled at him and said, "Little Black Sambo, I'm going to eat you up!"

Little Black Sambo said, "Oh, please, Mr. Tiger, don't eat me up, and I'll give you my lovely purple shoes with the crimson soles and crimson lining."

But the Tiger said, "Oh no; your shoes wouldn't do me any good, I have four feet and you have only two. I'm going to eat you up."

Then Little Black Sambo said, "You could put them on your ears."

"So I could," said the Tiger, "that's a very good idea. Very well, I won't eat you up this time."

Little Black Sambo took off his lovely purple shoes with the crimson soles and crimson lining and the Tiger put one on each ear, and off he went with his head in the air, saying, "Now I'm the grandest Tiger in the jungle."

Little Black Sambo went still farther and he met another Tiger.

The Tiger growled at him and said, "Little Black Sambo, I'm going to eat you up!"

Little Black Sambo said, "Oh, please, Mr. Tiger, don't eat me up, and I'll give you my beautiful green umbrella."

The Tiger said, "Oh, no; your umbrella wouldn't do me any good, I couldn't carry it. You see I have to use my four feet to walk on. I'm going to eat you up."

"Oh," said Little Black Sambo, "I know what you could do. You could tie a knot in your tail and carry it that way."

"So I could," said the Tiger. "Very well, I won't eat you up this time."

So he tied a knot in his tail and slipped the beautiful green umbrella through it, and off he went with his head in the air, saying, "Now I'm the grandest Tiger in the jungle."

Poor Little Black Sambo had lost all his fine clothes and he started home, crying.

By and by he heard a terrible noise that sounded like:

"Gr-r-r-r-r-rrrrrrr!"

It grew louder and louder.

"Oh, dear," said Little Black Sambo, "what shall I do? Here come the Tigers to eat me up!"

He ran and hid behind a palm tree. After a while he peeped round it to see what the Tigers were doing.

There were all the Tigers fighting. Each said that he was the grandest Tiger in the jungle. At last they grew so angry that they took off their fine clothes and began to fight still harder.

They came rolling and tumbling right to the foot of the tree where Little Black Sambo was hiding. Little Black Sambo jumped quickly and hid behind his little green umbrella. The Tigers went round and round the tree, one Tiger with another Tiger's tail in his mouth.

Little Black Sambo called out, "Tigers, don't you want your fine clothes any more? If you don't want them, say so, and I'll take them back."

But the Tigers wouldn't let go of each other's tails. All that they said was:

"Gr-r-r-r-r-rrrrrrr!"

Then Little Black Sambo put on all his fine clothes again and walked off.

When the Tigers saw this, they were very, very angry, but they wouldn't let go of each other's tails. They ran round and round the tree, faster and faster, trying to eat each other up. Finally they ran so fast that they just melted away, and there was nothing left of them but melted butter round the foot of the tree.

That evening Black Jumbo was coming home from work with a big brass pot in his arms. When he saw what was left of the Tigers, he said:

"Oh, what nice melted butter! I'll take some home for Black Mumbo to cook with."

So he filled up the big brass pot and carried it home to Black Mumbo.

When Black Mumbo saw the melted butter, wasn't she pleased!

"Now," she said, "we will have pancakes for supper!"

So she mixed up some flour and eggs and milk and sugar and the butter, and made a huge platter of lovely pancakes.

Then they all sat down to supper. Black Mumbo ate twenty-seven pancakes because she made them.

Black Jumbo ate fifty-five pancakes because he brought the butter home.

But Little Black Sambo ate one hundred and sixty-nine pancakes because he was so hungry.

## THE LION-HEARTED KITTEN[1]

*Peggy Bacon*

Once there was a striped kitten with yellow eyes and a black nose. He was only a very little kitten, but he had the heart of a lion. He was as brave as he could be, and one day he started out to conquer the world. The path he took led through a big black wood, and down this path the kitten stalked very proudly, with his head held high as possible.

Pretty soon, along came a big gray wolf.

"Grumble, tumble in the jungle, I'm hungry!" growled the wolf, for this is what the wolves say when they are going to eat you up.

Now it is all very well to be brave in a crisis, but it is even better to be clever too. This the kitten knew, so without showing any fear he said boldly:

"O Mr. Wolf, I was just looking for you. My great-aunt the tigress told me to ask you the way to roast lamb. She says you know so much more about such things than she."

The wolf was impressed and a little flattered. But he was also a bit suspicious of this small kitten, and so he said:

"Tell your great-aunt the tigress that I roast lamb the same way that I roast kitten."

This really frightened the kitten, but he pretended great unconcern and retorted:

"Of course, Mr. Wolf, if you really wish me to tell her that, I will do so; but my great-aunt the tigress is rather short of temper and she might take offense at what you say; she has some kittens of her own and a great many little nieces and nephews."

"Hmmm," murmured the wolf gazing thoughtfully at the kitten who had begun to wash its face, "you may tell her that roast lamb tastes nice with sage and onions." He turned and ran into the wood.

The kitten trotted on along the path and suddenly around a corner he came face to face with a great big enormous snake who

[1] From Peggy Bacon, *The Lion-Hearted Kitten, and Other Stories.*

was hanging from the branch of a tree just over the path.

"Hiss, swish, wish a dish for dinner!" hissed the snake, for that is what the snakes say when they are going to eat you up.

"O Miss Boa Constrictor," cried the kitten (for that was the snake's name), "I have been looking for you everywhere. My great-aunt the tigress wishes to know the best way to catch birds. She says that you are so clever at it, and she would be much obliged for some advice on the subject."

Now snakes catch little creatures by staring in their eyes till they are so frightened they dare not move; so the boa constrictor said:

"Watch me and I'll show you," for she thought the little kitten looked quite fat and delicious.

But the kitten was far too wise for that, so he simply looked hard beyond the snake and called out:

"Well, I do declare, if that isn't my great-aunt the tigress herself coming this way now!"

The snake whipped round quickly for fear the tigress was creeping up behind her, and while she looked back, the kitten escaped into the wood.

The brave little kitten ran on and on till by and by, very suddenly, round a big tree he came face to face with the tigress herself.

This time the kitten for all his courage was much alarmed. His breath came fast and his heart beat rapidly, but his wits did not forsake him.

"O Aunty Tigress," he gasped, "I have been hunting and hunting for you till I am all out of breath. My mother, the golden tigress of the next forest but one, wishes to know what it is your kittens eat which makes them so big and fat. She is worried about me because I am so very small." After this speech the kitten held his breath, waiting for the tigress to reply.

For a long time the tigress looked at the kitten and sniffed at the kitten, and put her head on one side and considered the kitten. And after a while she came to the conclusion that this kitten certainly did look quite like her kittens save for size; and since her own children had grown up and left home she decided it would be nice to adopt another; so giving the kitten a motherly lick of a large kind she said:

"You certainly are much too small, and if you will come home with me I will feed you up and fatten you up and see what I can do."

Away they walked together, the kitten not without misgivings, going through the big black wood till they came to the tigress' cave. There the tigress gave the kitten all kinds of meat and bones; and sure enough the kitten began to grow, and he grew and grew and grew until he got to be about as big as a cat.

The tigress was then well satisfied, for she said: "You are now exactly the size of my own kittens; this diet has agreed with you."

And so the kitten continued to live happily in the cave, cared for and protected by the tigress, but he never grew to be any bigger than a cat.

## THE MAGIC FISH-BONE[1]

*Charles Dickens*

There was once a king, and he had a queen; and he was the manliest of his sex, and she was the loveliest of hers. The king was, in his private profession, under government. The queen's father had been a medical man out of town.

They had nineteen children, and were always having more. Seventeen of these children took care of the baby; and Alicia, the eldest, took care of them all. Their ages varied from seven years to seven months.

Let us now resume our story.

One day the king was going to the office, when he stopped at the fishmonger's to buy a pound and a half of salmon not too near the tail, which the queen (who was a careful housekeeper) had requested him to

[1] From Charles Dickens, *A Holiday Romance.*

send home. Mr. Pickles, the fishmonger, said, "Certainly, sir; is there any other article? Good morning."

The king went on towards the office in a melancholy mood; for quarter day was such a long way off, and several of the dear children were growing out of their clothes. He had not proceeded far, when Mr. Pickles's errand boy came running after him, and said, "Sir, you didn't notice the old lady in our shop."

"What old lady?" inquired the king. "I saw none."

Now the king had not seen any old lady, because this old lady had been invisible to him, though visible to Mr. Pickles's boy. Probably because he messed and splashed the water about to that degree, and flopped the pairs of soles down in that violent manner, that, if she had not been visible to him, he would have spoilt her clothes.

Just then the old lady came trotting up. She was dressed in shot-silk of the richest quality, smelling of dried lavender.

"King Watkins the First, I believe?" said the old lady.

"Watkins," replied the king, "is my name."

"Papa, if I am not mistaken, of the beautiful Princess Alicia?" said the old lady.

"And of eighteen other darlings," replied the king.

"Listen. You are going to the office," said the old lady. It instantly flashed upon the king that she must be a fairy, or how could she know that?

"You are right," said the old lady, answering his thoughts. "I am the good Fairy Grandmarina. Attend! When you return home to dinner, politely invite the Princess Alicia to have some of the salmon you bought just now."

"It may disagree with her," said the king.

The old lady became so very angry at this absurd idea that the king was quite alarmed, and humbly begged her pardon.

"We hear a great deal too much about this thing disagreeing, and that thing disagreeing," said the old lady, with the greatest contempt it was possible to express. "Don't be greedy. I think you want it all yourself."

The king hung his head under this reproof, and said he wouldn't talk about things disagreeing any more.

"Be good, then," said the Fairy Grandmarina, "and don't! When the beautiful Princess Alicia consents to partake of the salmon—as I think she will—you will find she will leave a fish-bone on her plate. Tell her to dry it, and to rub it, and to polish it, till it shines like mother-of-pearl, and to take care of it as a present from me."

"Is that all?" asked the king.

"Don't be impatient, sir," returned the Fairy Grandmarina, scolding him severely. "Don't catch people short, before they have done speaking. Just the way with you grown-up persons. You are always doing it."

The king again hung his head, and said he wouldn't do so any more.

"Be good, then," said the Fairy Grandmarina, "and don't. Tell the Princess Alicia, with my love, that the fish-bone is a magic present which can only be used once; but that it will bring her, that once, whatever she wishes for, *provided she wishes for it at the right time*. That is the message. Take care of it." The king was beginning, "Might I ask the reason?" when the fairy became absolutely furious.

"*Will* you be good, sir?" she exclaimed, stamping her foot on the ground. "The reason for this, and the reason for that, indeed! You are always wanting the reason. No reason. There! Hoity, toity me! I am sick of your grown-up reasons."

The king was extremely frightened by the old lady's flying into such a passion, and said he was very sorry to have offended her, and he wouldn't ask for reasons any more.

"Be good, then," said the old lady, "and don't!"

With those words, Grandmarina vanished, and the king went on and on and on, till he came to the office. There he wrote and wrote and wrote, till it was time to go home again. Then he politely invited the Princess Alicia, as the fairy had directed him, to partake of the salmon. And when she had enjoyed it very much, he saw the fish-bone on her plate, as the fairy had told him he would, and he delivered the fairy's message, and the Princess Alicia took care to DRY the bone, and to RUB it, and to POLISH it, till it shone like mother-of-pearl.

And so, when the queen was going to get up in the morning, she said, "Oh dear me, dear me; my head, my head!" and then she fainted away.

The Princess Alicia, who happened to be looking in at the chamber door, asking about breakfast, was very much alarmed when she saw her royal mamma in this state, and she rang the bell for Peggy, which was the name of the lord chamberlain. But remembering where the smelling-bottle was, she climbed on a chair and got it; and after that she climbed on another chair by the bedside, and held the smelling-bottle to the queen's nose; and after that she jumped down and got some water; and after that she jumped up again and wetted the queen's forehead; and, in short, when the lord chamberlain came in, that dear old woman said to the little princess, "What a trot you are! I couldn't have done it better myself!"

But that was not the worst of the good queen's illness. Oh, no! She was very ill indeed, for a long time. The Princess Alicia kept the seventeen young princes and princesses quiet, and dressed and undressed and danced the baby, and made the kettle boil, and heated the soup, and swept the hearth, and poured out the medicine, and nursed the queen, and did all that ever she could, and was as busy, busy, busy as busy could be; for there were not many servants at that palace for three reasons: because the king was short of money, because a rise in his office never seemed to come, and because quarter day was so far off that it looked almost as far off and as little as one of the stars.

But on the morning when the queen fainted away, where was the magic fish-bone? Why, there it was in the Princess Alicia's pocket! She had almost taken it out to bring the queen to life again, when she put it back, and looked for the smelling-bottle.

After the queen had come out of her swoon that morning, and was dozing, the Princess Alicia hurried upstairs to tell a most particular secret to a most particularly confidential friend of hers, who was a duchess. People did suppose her to be a doll; but she was really a duchess, though nobody knew it except the princess.

This most particular secret was the secret about the magic fish-bone, the history of which was well-known to the duchess, because the princess told her everything. The princess kneeled down by the bed on which the duchess was lying, full-dressed and wide-awake, and whispered the secret to her. The duchess smiled and nodded. People might have supposed that she never smiled and nodded; but she often did, though nobody knew it except the princess.

Then the Princess Alicia hurried downstairs again to keep watch in the queen's room. She often kept watch by herself in the queen's room; but every evening, while the illness lasted, she sat there watching with the king. And every evening the king sat looking at her with a cross look, wondering why she never brought out the magic fish-bone. As often as she noticed this, she ran upstairs, whispered the secret to the duchess over again, and said to the duchess besides, "They think we children never have a reason or a meaning!" And the duchess, though the most fashionable duchess that ever was heard of, winked her eye.

"Alicia," said the king, one evening, when she wished him good-night, "What has become of the magic fish-bone?"

"In my pocket, papa."

"I thought you had lost it?"

"Oh, no, papa!"

"Or forgotten it?"

"No, indeed, papa."

And so another time the dreadful little snapping pug dog, next door, made a rush at one of the young princes as he stood on the steps coming home from school, and terrified him out of his wits; and he put his hand through a pane of glass, and bled, bled, bled. When the seventeen other young princes and princesses saw him bleed, bleed, bleed, they screamed themselves black in their seventeen faces all at once. But the Princess Alicia put her hands over all their seventeen mouths, one after another, and persuaded them to be quiet because of the sick queen. And then she put the wounded prince's hand in a basin of fresh cold water, while they stared with their twice seventeen are thirty-four, put down four and carry three, eyes, and then she looked in the hand for bits of glass, and there were fortunately no bits of glass there. And then she said to two chubby-legged princes, who were sturdy though small, "Bring me in the royal rag-bag: I must snip and stitch and cut and contrive." So these two young princes tugged at the royal rag-bag, and lugged it in; and the Princess Alicia sat down on the floor, with a large pair of scissors and a needle and thread, and snipped and stitched and cut and contrived, and made a bandage, and put it on, and it fitted beautifully; and so when it was all done, she saw the king her papa looking on by the door.

"Alicia."

"Yes, papa."

"What have you been doing?"

"Snipping, stitching, cutting, and contriving, papa."

"Where is the magic fish-bone?"

"In my pocket, papa."

"I thought you had lost it?"

"Oh, no, papa!"

"Or forgotten it?"

"No, indeed, papa."

After that, she ran upstairs to the duchess, and told her what had passed, and told her the secret over again; and the duchess shook her flaxen curls, and laughed with rosy lips.

Well! and so another time the baby fell under the grate. The seventeen young princes and princesses were used to it; for they were almost always falling under the grate or down the stairs; but the baby was not used to it yet, and it gave him a swelled face and a black eye. The way the poor little darling came to tumble was, that he was not in the Princess Alicia's lap just then, as she was sitting, in a great coarse apron that quite smothered her, in front of the kitchen fire, beginning to peel the turnips for the broth for dinner. And the way she came to be doing that was, that the king's cook had run away that morning with her own true love, who was a very tall but very tipsy soldier. Then the seventeen young princes and princesses, who cried at everything that happened, cried and roared. But the Princess Alicia (who couldn't help crying a little herself) quietly called to them to be still, on account of not throwing back the queen upstairs, who was fast getting well, and said, "Hold your tongues, you wicked little monkeys, every one of you, while I examine baby."

Then she examined baby, and found that he hadn't broken anything; and she held cold iron to his poor dear eye, and smoothed his poor dear face, and he presently fell asleep in her arms. Then she said to the seventeen princes and princesses, "I am afraid to let him down yet, lest he should wake and feel pain; be good, and you shall all be cooks." They jumped for joy when they heard that, and began making themselves cooks' caps out of old newspapers. So to one she gave the salt-box, and to one she gave the barley, and to one she gave the herbs, and to one she gave the turnips, and to one she gave the carrots, and to one she gave the onions, and to one she gave the spice-box, till they were all cooks, and all running about at work, she sitting in the middle, smothered in the great coarse apron, nursing baby.

By and by the broth was done; and the baby woke up, smiling like an angel, and was trusted to the sedatest princess to hold, while the other princes and princesses were squeezed into a far-off corner to look at the Princess Alicia turning out the saucepanful of broth, for fear (as they were always getting into trouble) they should get splashed and scalded. When the broth came tumbling out, steaming beautifully, and smelling like a nosegay good to eat, they clapped their hands. That made the baby clap his hands; and that, and his looking as if he had a comic toothache, made all the princes and princesses laugh.

So the Princess Alicia said, "Laugh and be good; and after dinner we will make him a nest on the floor in a corner, and he shall sit in his nest and see a dance of eighteen cooks." That delighted the young princes and princesses, and they ate up all the broth, and washed up all the plates and dishes, and cleared away, and pushed the table into a corner; and then they in their cooks' caps, and the Princess Alicia in the smothering coarse apron that belonged to the cook that had run away with her own true love that was the very tall but very tipsy soldier, danced a dance of eighteen cooks before the angelic baby, who forgot his swelled face and his black eye, and crowed with joy.

And so then, once more the Princess Alicia saw King Watkins the First, her father, standing in the doorway looking on, and he said, "What have you been doing, Alicia?"

"Cooking and contriving, papa."

"What else have you been doing, Alicia?"

"Keeping the children lighthearted, papa."

"Where is the magic fish-bone, Alicia?"

"In my pocket, papa."

"I thought you had lost it?"

"Oh, no, papa!"

"Or forgotten it?"

"No, indeed, papa."

The king then sighed so heavily, and seemed so low-spirited, and sat down so miserably, leaning his head upon his hand, and his elbow upon the kitchen table pushed in the corner, that the seventeen princes and princesses crept softly out of the kitchen, and left him alone with the Princess Alicia and the angelic baby.

"What is the matter, papa?"

"I am dreadfully poor, my child."

"Have you no money at all, papa?"

"None, my child."

"Is there no way of getting any, papa?"

"No way," said the king. "I have tried very hard, and I have tried all ways." When she heard those last words, the Princess Alicia began to put her hand into the pocket where she kept the magic fish-bone.

"Papa," said she, "when we have tried very hard, and tried all ways, we must have done our very, very best?"

"No doubt, Alicia."

"When we have done our very, very best, papa, and that is not enough, then I think the right time must have come for asking help of others." This was the very secret connected with the magic fish-bone, which she had found out for herself from the good Fairy Grandmarina's words, and which she had so often whispered to her beautiful and fashionable friend, the duchess.

So she took out of her pocket the magic fish-bone, that had been dried and rubbed and polished till it shone like mother-of-pearl; and she gave it one little kiss, and wished it was quarter day. And immediately it was quarter day; and the king's quarter's salary came rattling down the chimney, and bounced into the middle of the floor.

But this was not half of what happened —no, not a quarter; for immediately afterwards the good Fairy Grandmarina came riding in, in a carriage and four peacocks, with Mr. Pickles's boy up behind, dressed in silver and gold, with a cocked hat, powdered hair, pink silk stockings, a jewelled cane, and a nosegay. Down jumped Mr. Pickles's boy, with his cocked hat in his hand, and wonderfully polite (being entirely changed by enchantment), and handed Grandmarina out; and there she stood, in her rich shot-silk smelling of dried lavender, fanning herself with a sparkling fan.

"Alicia, my dear," said this charming old fairy, "how do you do? I hope I see you pretty well? Give me a kiss."

The Princess Alicia embraced her; and then Grandmarina turned to the king, and said rather sharply, "Are you good?"

The king said he hoped so.

"I suppose you know the reason now, why my goddaughter here," kissing the princess again, "did not apply to the fish-bone sooner?" said the fairy.

The king made a shy bow.

"Ah! but you didn't then?" said the fairy.

The king made a shyer bow.

"Any more reasons to ask for?" said the fairy.

The king said, "No," and he was very sorry.

"Be good, then," said the fairy, "and live happy ever afterwards."

Then Grandmarina waved her fan, and the queen came in most splendidly dressed; and the seventeen young princes and princesses, no longer grown out of their clothes, came in, newly fitted out from top to toe, with tucks in everything to admit of its being let out. After that, the fairy tapped the Princess Alicia with her fan; and the smothering coarse apron flew away, and she appeared exquisitely dressed, like a little bride, with a wreath of orange flowers and a silver veil. After that, the kitchen dresser changed of itself into a wardrobe, made of beautiful woods and gold and looking glass, which was full of dresses of all sorts, all for her and all exactly fitting her. After that, the angelic baby came in running alone, with his face and eye not a bit worse, but much the better. Then Grandmarina begged to be introduced to the duchess; and, when the duchess was brought down, many compliments passed between them.

A little whispering took place between the fairy and the duchess; and then the fairy said out loud, "Yes, I thought she would have told you." Grandmarina then turned to the king and queen, and said, "We are going in search of Prince Certainpersonio. The pleasure of your company is requested at church in half an hour precisely." So she and the Princess Alicia got into the carriage; and Mr. Pickles's boy handed in the duchess, who sat by herself on the opposite seat; and then Mr. Pickles's boy put up the steps and got up behind, and the peacocks flew away with their tails behind.

Prince Certainpersonio was sitting by himself, eating barley sugar. When he saw the peacocks, followed by the carriage, coming in at the window, it immediately occurred to him that something uncommon was going to happen.

"Prince," said Grandmarina, "I bring you your bride."

The moment the fairy said those words, Prince Certainpersonio's face left off being sticky, and his jacket and corduroys changed to peach-bloom velvet, and his hair curled, and a cap and feather flew in like a bird and settled on his head. He got into the carriage by the fairy's invitation; and there he renewed his acquaintance with the duchess, whom he had seen before.

In the church were the prince's relations and friends, and the seventeen princes and princesses, and the baby, and a crowd of the neighbors. The marriage was beautiful beyond expression. The duchess was bridesmaid, and beheld the ceremony from the pulpit, where she was supported by the cushion of the desk.

Grandmarina gave a magnificent wedding-feast afterwards in which there was everything and more to eat. The wedding-cake was delicately ornamented with white satin ribbons, frosted silver, and white lilies, and was forty-two yards round.

When Grandmarina had drunk her love to the young couple, and Prince Certainpersonio had made a speech and everybody had cried, "Hip, hip, hip, hurrah!" Grandmarina announced to the king and queen that in future there would be eight quarter days in every year, except in leap year, when there would be ten. She then turned to Certainpersonio and Alicia, and said, "My dears, you will have thirty-five children, and they will all be good and beautiful. Seventeen of your children will be boys, and eighteen will be girls. The hair of the whole of your children will curl naturally. They will never have the measles and will have recovered from the whooping cough before being born."

On hearing such good news, everybody cried out "Hip, hip, hip, hurrah!" again.

"It only remains," said Grandmarina in conclusion, "to make an end of the fishbone."

So she took it from the hand of the Princess Alicia, and it instantly flew down the throat of the dreadful little snapping pug dog, next door, and choked him.

## THE TAR BABY[1]

*Joel Chandler Harris*

One day, after Brer Rabbit fool him about dat calamus root, Brer Fox went to work and got some tar, and mix it with some turpentine, and fix up a contraption what he call a Tar Baby. He took this here Tar Baby and set her in de big road. Then he lay off in de bushes for to see what de news gwine to be.

He didn't have to wait long neither. By and by, here come Brer Rabbit pacing down de road—

lippity-clippity,
clippity-lippity—

jest as sassy as a jay bird. Brer Fox, he lay low. Brer Rabbit come prancing along till he spy de Tar Baby, and then he sat up on his behind legs like he was astonished. De Tar Baby she sat there she did, and Brer Fox he lay low.

"Morning," says Brer Rabbit.

Tar Baby ain't say nothing, and Brer Fox he lay low.

"Nice weather this morning," says Brer Rabbit.

Brer Fox he wink his eye slow and lay low, and de Tar Baby she ain't say nothing.

"How you come on, then? Is you deaf?" says Brer Rabbit. "Because if you is, I can holler louder."

Tar Baby stay still, and Brer Fox he lay low.

"You're stuck up, dat's what you is," says Brer Rabbit, "and I'm gwine to cure you, dat's what I'm gwine to do."

Brer Fox, off in de bushes, sort of chuckle in his stomach, but Tar Baby ain't say nothing.

"I'm gwine to learn you how to talk to respectable folks if it's de last act I ever do," says Brer Rabbit. "If you don't take off dat hat and tell me howdy, I'm gwine to bust you wide open."

Tar Baby stay still, and Brer Fox he lay low.

Brer Rabbit keep on asking him, and de Tar Baby she keep on saying nothing. Presently Brer Rabbit draw back with his fist, and blip! he took her side of de head. Right there is where he broke his molasses jug! His fist stuck and he can't pull it loose. De tar held him. But Tar Baby she stay still, and Brer Fox he lay low.

"If you don't let me loose, I'll knock you again," says Brer Rabbit. With dat he give her a wipe with de other hand, and dat stuck. Tar Baby she ain't say nothing, and Brer Fox he lay low.

"Turn me loose, before I kick de stuffing out of you," says Brer Rabbit, but de Tar Baby she ain't say nothing. She jest held on. Then Brer Rabbit lose de use of his feet in de same way.

Brer Fox he lay low.

Then Brer Rabbit squall out dat if de Tar Baby don't turn him loose, he gwine to butt her. He butted, and his head stuck. About dat time Brer Fox walk out, looking jest as innocent as one of your mammy's mocking birds.

"Howdy, Brer Rabbit," says Brer Fox. "You look sort of stuck up this morning." Then he rolled on de ground, and laughed and laughed till he couldn't laugh no more.

"I expect you'll take dinner with me this time, Brer Rabbit, and I done laid in some calamus root. I expect I got you this time. Maybe I ain't, but I expect I is. You been running around here, sassin' me a mighty

[1] From Miriam Blanton Huber, *The Uncle Remus Book, Retold from Joel Chandler Harris.*

long time, but I expect you done come to de end of de row.

"You been cutting up your capers and bouncing around in this neighborhood till you come to believe yourself de boss of de whole gang. Then you're always somewhere you got no business. Who asked you to come and strike up an acquaintance with this here Tar Baby?

"Who stuck you up where you is? Nobody in the round world. You jest took and jam yourself on dat Tar Baby! And there you is, and there you'll stay till I fixes up a brush pile and fires her up. I'm gwine to barbecue you this day, sho'," says Brer Fox.

Then Brer Rabbit talk mighty humble:

"I don't care what you do with me, Brer Fox, so you don't fling me in dat brier patch. Roast me, Brer Fox, but don't fling me in dat brier patch."

"It's so much trouble to kindle a fire," says Brer Fox, "dat I expect I'll have to hang you."

"Hang me jest as high as you please, Brer Fox, but for de Lord's sake don't fling me in dat brier patch."

"I ain't got no string," says Brer Fox. "I expect I'll have to drown you."

"Drown me jest as deep as you please, Brer Fox, but don't fling me in dat brier patch."

"There ain't no water nigh," says Brer Fox. "I expect I'll have to skin you."

"Skin me, Brer Fox, snatch out my eyeballs, tear out my ears by de roots, and cut off my legs, but please, Brer Fox, don't fling me in dat brier patch."

Of course Brer Fox want to hurt Brer Rabbit jest as bad as he can, so he catch him by the behind legs and slung him right in de middle of de brier patch. There was a considerable flutter where Brer Rabbit hit de bushes, and Brer Fox hang around to see what gwine to happen.

By and by, he hear somebody call him. Away up de hill he see Brer Rabbit sitting cross legged on a log combing de pitch out of his hair with a chip. Then Brer Fox know he been swop off mighty cheap.

Brer Rabbit was obliged to fling back some of his sass, and he holler out:

"Bred and born in a brier patch, Brer Fox—bred and born in a brier patch!"

With dat he skip out jest as lively as a cricket in de embers.

## THE WELL STORY[1]

*Joel Chandler Harris*

One day Brer Rabbit, and Brer Fox, and Brer Coon, and Brer Bear, and a whole lot of 'em was clearing up a new ground to plant a roasting-ear patch. De sun begun to git sort of hot, and Brer Rabbit got tired; but he didn't let on, 'cause he feared de balance of 'em would call him lazy. He kept on toting off trash and piling up brush. By and by, he hollered out dat he got a brier in his hand. Then he take and slip off and hunt for a cool place to rest.

After a while, he come across a well with a bucket hanging in it. It was one of them wells like dat one down on your grandmammy's plantation, with a bucket on this end of de rope and another bucket on de other end of de rope, what works with a pulley at de top. You remembers about dat well, don't you, honey?

Brer Rabbit come along and he see dat bucket hanging there, and he say:

"Dat looks like a cool place to rest, and cool I expect she is. I'll jest about git in there and take a nap."

In he jump, he did, and he ain't no sooner fix himself than de bucket begun to go down! There ain't been no worse scared beast since de world begin than this here same Brer Rabbit. He know where he come from, but he don't know where he gwine.

Directly de bucket hit de water and there she sit. Brer Rabbit keep mighty still, 'cause he don't know what minute gwine to be de next. He jest lay there and shook and shiver.

Brer Fox always got one eye on Brer Rabbit, and when he see him slip off from de new ground, he sneak after him. He

[1] From Miriam Blanton Huber, *The Uncle Remus Book, Retold from Joel Chandler Harris.*

know Brer Rabbit up to something or other, and he take and creep off and watch him. Brer Fox see Brer Rabbit come to de well and stop, and he see him jump in de bucket. Then, lo and behold, he see him go down out of sight!

Brer Fox was de most astonished Fox dat you ever laid eyes on. He sit off there in de bushes and study and study, but he don't make heads nor tails to this kind of business. He says to himself, says he:

"Well, if this don't bang my times, then Joe's dead and Sal's a widow! Right down there in dat well Brer Rabbit keeps his money hid. If it ain't dat, then he gone and discovered a gold mine. If it ain't dat—well, I gwine to see what's in there."

Brer Fox creep up a little nigher and listen. He don't hear no fuss. He keep on gittin' nigher, but he don't hear nothing. By and by, he git up close and peep down, but he don't see nothing and he don't hear nothing.

All this time Brer Rabbit mighty nigh scared out of his skin. He feared to move 'cause de bucket might keel over and spill him out in de water. While he was saying his prayers over like a train of cars running, old Brer Fox holler out:

"Heyo, Brer Rabbit! Who you visiting down there?"

"Who? Me? Oh, I'm jest a-fishing, Brer Fox," says Brer Rabbit. "I jest say to myself dat I sort of surprise you all with a mess of fishes for dinner, I says. So here I is, and there's de fishes. I'm fishing for suckers, Brer Fox."

"Is there many of 'em down there, Brer Rabbit?"

"Scores and scores of 'em. Come on down and help me haul 'em in, Brer Fox," says Brer Rabbit.

"How I gwine to git down, Brer Rabbit?"

"Jump into de bucket, Brer Fox. It will fetch you down all safe and sound."

Brer Rabbit talk so happy and talk so sweet dat Brer Fox jump in de bucket, and as he went down of course his weight pull Brer Rabbit up. When they pass one another on de halfway ground, Brer Rabbit sing out:

"Good-by, Brer Fox, take care your clothes,
For this is de way de wor-rild goes;
Some goes up and some goes down,
You'll git to de bottom all safe and sound."

When Brer Rabbit got out, he gallop off and told de folks what de well belong to, dat Brer Fox was down in there muddying up de drinking water. Then he gallop back to de well and holler down to Brer Fox:

"Here come a man with a great big gun—
When he haul you up, you jump and run."

In jest about half an hour, honey, both of 'em was back in de new ground working jest like they never heard tell of no well. Every now and then Brer Rabbit would bust out in a big laugh, and old Brer Fox, he would git a spell of de dry grins.

## THE ELEPHANT'S CHILD [1]

*Rudyard Kipling*

In the High and Far-Off Times the Elephant, O Best Beloved, had no trunk. He had only a blackish, bulgy nose, as big as a boot, that he could wriggle about from side to side; but he couldn't pick up things with it. But there was one Elephant—a new Elephant—an Elephant's Child—who was full of 'satiable curiosity, and that means he asked ever so many questions. *And* he lived in Africa, and he filled all Africa with his 'satiable curiosities. He asked his tall aunt, the Ostrich, why her tail-feathers grew just so, and his tall aunt, the Ostrich, spanked him with her hard, hard claw. He asked his tall uncle, the Giraffe, what made his skin spotty, and his tall uncle, the Giraffe, spanked him with his hard,

[1] From Rudyard Kipling, *Just So Stories.*

hard hoof. And still he was full of 'satiable curiosity! He asked his broad aunt, the Hippopotamus, why her eyes were red, and his broad aunt, the Hippopotamus, spanked him with her broad, broad hoof; and he asked his hairy uncle, the Baboon, why melons tasted just so, and his hairy uncle, the Baboon, spanked him with his hairy, hairy paw. And *still* he was full of 'satiable curiosity! He asked questions about everything that he saw, or heard, or felt, or smelt, or touched, and all his uncles and his aunts spanked him. And still he was full of 'satiable curiosity!

One fine morning in the middle of the Precession of the Equinoxes, this 'satiable Elephant's Child asked a new fine question that he had never asked before. He asked, "What does the Crocodile have for dinner?" Then everybody said, "Hush!" in a loud and dretful tone, and they spanked him immediately and directly, without stopping, for a long time.

By and by, when that was finished, he came upon Kolokolo Bird sitting in the middle of a wait-a-bit thorn-bush, and he said, "My father has spanked me, and my mother has spanked me; all my aunts and uncles have spanked me for my 'satiable curiosity; and *still* I want to know what the Crocodile has for dinner!"

Then Kolokolo Bird said, with a mournful cry, "Go to the banks of the great grey-green, greasy Limpopo River, all set about with fever-trees, and find out."

That very next morning, when there was nothing left of the Equinoxes, because the Precession had preceded according to precedent, this 'satiable Elephant's Child took a hundred pounds of bananas (the little short red kind), and a hundred pounds of sugar-cane (the long purple kind), and seventeen melons (the greeny-crackly kind), and said to all his dear families, "Good-by. I am going to the great grey-green, greasy Limpopo River, all set about with fever-trees, to find out what the Crocodile has for dinner." And they all spanked him once more for luck, though he asked them most politely to stop.

Then he went away, a little warm, but not at all astonished, eating melons, and throwing the rind about, because he could not pick it up.

He went from Graham's Town to Kimberley, and from Kimberley to Khama's Country, and from Khama's Country he went east by north, eating melons all the time, till at last he came to the banks of the great grey-green, greasy Limpopo River, all set about with fever-trees, precisely as Kolokolo Bird had said.

Now you must know and understand, O Best Beloved, that till that very week, and day, and hour, and minute, this 'satiable Elephant's Child had never seen a Crocodile, and did not know what one was like. It was all his 'satiable curiosity.

The first thing that he found was a Bi-Colored-Python-Rock-Snake curled round a rock.

" 'Scuse me," said the Elephant's Child most politely, "but have you seen such a thing as a Crocodile in these promiscuous parts?"

"*Have* I seen a Crocodile?" said the Bi-Colored-Python-Rock-Snake, in a voice of dretful scorn. "What will you ask me next?"

" 'Scuse me," said the Elephant's Child, "but could you kindly tell me what he has for dinner?"

Then the Bi-Colored-Python-Rock-Snake uncoiled himself very quickly from the rock, and spanked the Elephant's Child with his scalesome, flailsome tail.

"That is odd," said the Elephant's Child, "because my father and my mother, and my uncle and my aunt, not to mention my other aunt, the Hippopotamus, and my other uncle, the Baboon, have all spanked me for my 'satiable curiosity—and I suppose this is the same thing."

So he said good-bye very politely to the Bi-Colored-Python-Rock-Snake, and helped to coil him up on the rock again, and went on, a little warm, but not at all astonished, eating melons, and throwing the rind about, because he could not pick it up, till he trod on what he thought was a log of wood at the very edge of the great grey-green, greasy Limpopo River, all set about with fever-trees.

But it was really the Crocodile, O Best Beloved, and the Crocodile winked one eye—like this!

"'Scuse me," said the Elephant's Child most politely, "but do you happen to have seen a Crocodile in these promiscuous parts?"

Then the Crocodile winked the other eye, and lifted half his tail out of the mud; and the Elephant's Child stepped back most politely, because he did not wish to be spanked again.

"Come hither, Little One," said the Crocodile. "Why do you ask such things?"

"'Scuse me," said the Elephant's Child most politely, "but my father has spanked me, my mother has spanked me, not to mention my tall aunt, the Ostrich, and my tall uncle, the Giraffe, who can kick ever so hard, as well as my broad aunt, the Hippopotamus, and my hairy uncle, the Baboon, *and* including the Bi-Colored-Python-Rock-Snake, with the scalesome, flailsome tail, just up the bank, who spanks harder than any of them; and *so,* if it's quite all the same to you, I don't want to be spanked any more."

"Come hither, Little One," said the Crocodile, "for I am the Crocodile," and he wept crocodile-tears to show it was quite true.

Then the Elephant's Child grew all breathless, and panted, and kneeled down on the bank and said, "You are the very person I have been looking for all these long days. Will you please tell me what you have for dinner?"

"Come hither, Little One," said the Crocodile, "and I'll whisper."

Then the Elephant's Child put his head down close to the Crocodile's musky, tusky mouth, and the Crocodile caught him by his little nose, which up to that very week, day, hour, and minute, had been no bigger than a boot, though much more useful.

"I think," said the Crocodile—and he said it between his teeth, like this—"I think today I will begin with Elephant's Child!"

At this, O Best Beloved, the Elephant's Child was much annoyed, and he said, speaking through his nose, like this, "Led go! You are hurtig be!"

Then the Bi-Colored-Python-Rock-Snake scuffled down from the bank and said, "My young friend, if you do not now, immediately and instantly, pull as hard as ever you can, it is my opinion that your acquaintance in the large-pattern leather ulster" (and by this he meant the Crocodile) "will jerk you into yonder limpid stream before you can say Jack Robinson."

This is the way Bi-Colored-Python-Rock-Snakes always talk.

Then the Elephant's Child sat back on his little haunches, and pulled, and pulled, and pulled, and his nose began to stretch. And the Crocodile floundered into the water, making it all creamy with great sweeps of his tail, and *he* pulled, and pulled, and pulled.

And the Elephant's Child's nose kept on stretching, and the Elephant's Child spread all his little four legs and pulled, and pulled, and pulled, and his nose kept on stretching; and the Crocodile threshed his tail like an oar, and *he* pulled, and pulled, and pulled, and at each pull the Elephant's Child's nose grew longer and longer—and it hurt him hijjus!

Then the Elephant's Child felt his legs slipping, and he said through his nose, which was now nearly five feet long, "This is too butch for be!"

Then the Bi-Colored-Python-Rock-Snake came down from the bank, and knotted himself in a double-clove-hitch, round the Elephant's Child's hind legs, and said, "Rash and inexperienced traveler, we will now seriously devote ourselves to a little high tension, because if we do not, it is my impression that yonder self-propelling man-of-war with the armor-plated upper deck" (and by this, O Best Beloved, he meant the Crocodile), "will permanently vitiate your future career."

That is the way all Bi-Colored-Python-Rock-Snakes always talk.

So he pulled, and the Elephant's Child pulled, and the Crocodile pulled; but the Elephant's Child and the Bi-Colored-Python-Rock-Snake pulled hardest; and at last the Crocodile let go of the Elephant's Child's nose with a plop that you could hear all up and down the Limpopo.

Then the Elephant's Child sat down most hard and sudden; but first he was careful to say "Thank you" to the Bi-Colored-Python-Rock-Snake; and next he was kind to his poor pulled nose, and wrapped it all up in cool banana leaves, and hung it in the great grey-green, greasy Limpopo to cool.

"What are you doing that for?" said the Bi-Colored-Python-Rock-Snake.

" 'Scuse me," said the Elephant's Child, "but my nose is badly out of shape, and I am waiting for it to shrink."

"Then you will have to wait a long time," said the Bi-Colored-Python-Rock-Snake. "Some people do not know what is good for them."

The Elephant's Child sat there for three days waiting for his nose to shrink. But it never grew any shorter, and, besides, it made him squint. For, O Best Beloved, you will see and understand that the Crocodile had pulled it out into a really truly trunk same as all Elephants have today.

At the end of the third day a fly came and stung him on the shoulder, and before he knew what he was doing he lifted up his trunk and hit that fly dead with the end of it.

" 'Vantage number one!" said the Bi-Colored-Python-Rock-Snake. "You couldn't have done that with a mere-smear nose. Try and eat a little, now."

Before he thought what he was doing the Elephant's Child put out his trunk and plucked a large bundle of grass, dusted it clean against his forelegs, and stuffed it into his own mouth.

" 'Vantage number two!" said the Bi-Colored-Python-Rock-Snake. "You couldn't have done that with a mere-smear nose. Don't you think the sun is very hot here?"

"It is," said the Elephant's Child, and before he thought what he was doing he schlooped up a schloop of mud from the banks of the great grey-green, greasy Limpopo, and slapped it on his head, where it made a cool schloopy-sloshy mud-cap all trickly behind his ears.

" 'Vantage number three!" said the Bi-Colored-Python-Rock-Snake. "You couldn't have done that with a mere-smear nose. Now how do you feel about being spanked again?"

" 'Scuse me," said the Elephant's Child, "but I should not like it at all."

"How would you like to spank somebody?" said the Bi-Colored-Python-Rock-Snake.

"I should like it very much indeed," said the Elephant's Child.

"Well," said the Bi-Colored-Python-Rock-Snake, "you will find that new nose of yours very useful to spank people with."

"Thank you," said the Elephant's Child, "I'll remember that; and now I think I'll go home to all my dear families and try."

So the Elephant's Child went home across Africa frisking and whisking his trunk. When he wanted fruit to eat he pulled fruit down from a tree, instead of waiting for it to fall as he used to do. When he wanted grass he plucked grass up from the ground, instead of going on his knees as he used to do. When the flies bit him he broke off the branch of a tree and used it as a fly-whisk; and he made himself a new, cool, slushy-squshy mud-cap whenever the sun was hot. When he felt lonely walking through Africa he sang to himself down his trunk, and the noise was louder than several brass bands. He went especially out of his way to find a broad Hippopotamus (she was no relation of his), and he spanked her very hard, to make sure that the Bi-Colored-Python-Rock-Snake had spoken the truth about his new trunk. The rest of the time he picked up the melon rinds that he had dropped on his way to the Limpopo—for he was a Tidy Pachyderm.

One dark evening he came back to all his dear families, and he coiled up his trunk and said, "How do you do?" They were very glad to see him, and immediately said, "Come here and be spanked for your 'satiable curiosity."

"Pooh," said the Elephant's Child. "I don't think you peoples know anything about spanking; but *I* do, and I'll show you."

Then he uncurled his trunk and knocked two of his dear brothers head over heels.

"O Bananas!" said they, "where did you learn that trick, and what have you done to your nose?"

"I got a new one from the Crocodile on the banks of the great, grey-green, greasy Limpopo River," said the Elephant's Child. "I asked him what he had for dinner, and he gave me this to keep."

"It looks very ugly," said his hairy uncle, the Baboon.

"It does," said the Elephant's Child. "But it's very useful," and he picked up his hairy uncle, the Baboon, by one hairy leg, and hove him into a hornets' nest.

Then that bad Elephant's Child spanked all his dear families for a long time, till they were very warm and greatly astonished. He pulled out his tall Ostrich aunt's tail-feathers; and he caught his tall uncle, the Giraffe, by the hind leg, and dragged him through a thorn-bush; and he shouted at his broad aunt, the Hippopotamus, and blew bubbles into her ear when she was sleeping in the water after meals; but he never let any one touch Kolokolo Bird.

At last things grew so exciting that his dear families went off one by one in a hurry to the banks of the great grey-green, greasy Limpopo River, all set about with fever-trees, to borrow new noses from the Crocodile. When they came back nobody spanked anybody any more; and ever since that day, O Best Beloved, all the Elephants you will ever see, besides all those that you won't, have trunks precisely like the trunk of the 'satiable Elephant's Child.

## DOCTOR DOLITTLE AND THE PUSHMI-PULLYU [1]

*Hugh Lofting*

Pushmi-pullyus are now extinct. That means, there aren't any more. But long ago, when Doctor Dolittle was alive, there were some of them still left in the deepest jungles of Africa; and even then they were very, very scarce. They had no tail, but a head at each end, and sharp horns on each head. They were very shy and terribly hard to catch. The black men get most of their animals by sneaking up behind them while they are not looking. But you could not do this with the pushmi-pullyu—because, no matter which way you came towards him, he was always facing you. And besides, only one half of him slept at a time. The other head was always awake—and watching. This was why they were never caught and never seen in Zoos. Though many of the greatest huntsmen and the cleverest menagerie-keepers spent years of their lives searching through the jungles in all weathers for pushmi-pullyus, not a single one had ever been caught. Even then, years ago, he was the only animal in the world with two heads.

Well, the monkeys set out hunting for this animal through the forest. And after they had gone a good many miles, one of them found peculiar footprints near the edge of a river; and they knew that a pushmi-pullyu must be very near that spot.

Then they went along the bank of the river a little way and they saw a place where the grass was high and thick; and they guessed that he was in there.

So they all joined hands and made a great circle round the high grass. The pushmi-pullyu heard them coming; and he tried hard to break through the ring of monkeys. But he couldn't do it. When he saw that it was no use trying to escape, he sat down and waited to see what they wanted.

They asked him if he would go with Doctor Dolittle and be put on show in the Land of the White Men.

[1] From Hugh Lofting, *The Story of Doctor Dolittle.*

But he shook both his heads hard and said, "Certainly not!"

They explained to him that he would not be shut up in a menagerie but would just be looked at. They told him that the Doctor was a very kind man but hadn't any money; and people would pay to see a two-headed animal and the Doctor would get rich and could pay for the boat he had borrowed to come to Africa in.

But he answered, "No. You know how shy I am—I hate being stared at." And he almost began to cry.

Then for three days they tried to persuade him.

And at the end of the third day he said he would come with them and see what kind of a man the Doctor was first.

So the monkeys traveled back with the pushmi-pullyu. And when they came to where the Doctor's little house of grass was, they knocked on the door.

The duck, who was packing the trunk, said, "Come in!"

And Chee-Chee, the monkey, very proudly took the animal inside and showed him to the Doctor.

"What in the world is it?" asked John Dolittle, gazing at the strange creature.

"Lord save us!" cried the duck. "How does it make up its mind?"

"It doesn't look to me as though it had any," said Jip, the dog.

"This, Doctor," said Chee-Chee, "is the pushmi-pullyu—the rarest animal of the African jungles, the only two-headed beast in the world! Take him home with you and your fortune's made. People will pay any money to see him."

"But I don't want any money," said the Doctor.

"Yes, you do," said Dab-Dab, the duck. "Don't you remember how we had to pinch and scrape to pay the butcher's bill in Puddleby? And how are you going to get the sailor the new boat you spoke of—unless we have the money to buy it?"

"I was going to make him one," said the Doctor.

"Oh, do be sensible!" cried Dab-Dab. "Where would you get all the wood and the nails to make one with? And besides, what are we going to live on? We shall be poorer than ever when we get back. Chee-Chee's perfectly right! Take the funny-looking thing along, do!"

"Well, perhaps there is something in what you say," murmured the Doctor. "It certainly would make a nice new kind of pet. But does the—er—what-do-you-call-it really want to go abroad?"

"Yes, I'll go," said the pushmi-pullyu who saw at once, from the Doctor's face, that he was a man to be trusted. "You have been so kind to the animals here—and the monkeys tell me that I am the only one who will do. But you must promise me that if I do not like it in the Land of the White Men you will send me back."

"Why, certainly—of course, of course," said the Doctor. "Excuse me, surely you are related to the Deer Family, are you not?"

"Yes," said the pushmi-pullyu—"to the Abyssinian Gazelles and the Asiatic Chamois—on my mother's side. My father's great-grandfather was the last of the Unicorns."

"Most interesting!" murmured the Doctor; and he took a book out of the trunk which Dab-Dab was packing and began turning the pages. "Let us see if Buffon says anything—"

"I notice," said the duck, "that you only talk with one of your mouths. Can't the other head talk as well?"

"Oh, yes," said the pushmi-pullyu. "But I keep the other mouth for eating—mostly. In that way I can talk while I am eating without being rude. Our people have always been very polite."

When the packing was finished and everything was ready to start, the monkeys gave a grand party for the Doctor, and all the animals of the jungle came. And they had pineapples and mangoes and honey and all sorts of good things to eat and drink.

After they had all finished eating, the Doctor got up and said,

"My friends, I am not clever at speaking long words after dinner, like some men;

and I have just eaten many fruits and much honey. But I wish to tell you that I am very sad at leaving your beautiful country. Because I have things to do in the Land of the White Men, I must go. After I have gone, remember never to let the flies settle on your food before you eat it; and do not sleep on the ground when the rains are coming. I—er—er—I hope you will all live happily ever after."

When the Doctor stopped speaking and sat down, all the monkeys clapped their hands a long time and said to one another, "Let it be remembered always among our people that he sat and ate with us, here, under the trees. For surely he is the Greatest of Men!"

And the Grand Gorilla, who had the strength of seven horses in his hairy arms, rolled a great rock up to the head of the table and said,

"This stone for all time shall mark the spot."

And even to this day, in the heart of the jungle, that stone still is there. And monkey-mothers, passing through the forest with their families, still point down at it from the branches and whisper to their children, "Sh! There it is—look—where the Good White Man sat and ate food with us in the Year of the Great Sickness!"

Then, when the party was over, the Doctor and his pets started out to go back to the seashore. And all the monkeys went with him as far as the edge of their country, carrying his trunk and bags, to see him off.

## ALICE GOES DOWN THE RABBIT-HOLE[1]

*Lewis Carroll*

Alice was beginning to get very tired of sitting by her sister on the bank, and of having nothing to do; once or twice she had peeped into the book her sister was reading, but it had no pictures or conversations in it, "and what is the use of a book," thought Alice, "without pictures or conversations?"

So she was considering in her own mind (as well as she could, for the hot day made her feel very sleepy and stupid) whether the pleasure of making a daisy-chain would be worth the trouble of getting up and picking the daisies, when suddenly a white rabbit with pink eyes ran close by her.

There was nothing so *very* remarkable in that; nor did Alice think it so *very* much out of the way to hear the Rabbit say to itself, "Oh, dear! Oh, dear! I shall be too late!" (When she thought it over afterward, it occurred to her that she ought to have wondered at this, but at the time it all seemed quite natural.) But when the Rabbit actually *took a watch out of its waistcoat pocket,* and looked at it, and then hurried on, Alice started to her feet; for it flashed across her mind that she had never before seen a Rabbit with either a waistcoat pocket or a watch to take out of it, and, burning with curiosity, she ran across the field after it, and was just in time to see it pop down a large rabbit-hole under the hedge.

In another moment down went Alice after it, never once considering how in the world she was to get out again.

The rabbit-hole went straight on like a tunnel for some way, and then dipped suddenly down, so suddenly that Alice had not a moment to think about stopping herself, before she found herself falling down what seemed to be a very deep well.

Either the well was very deep, or she fell very slowly; for she had plenty of time as she went down to look about her, and to wonder what was going to happen next. First, she tried to look down and make out what she was coming to, but it was too dark to see anything; then she looked at the sides of the well, and noticed that they were filled with cupboards and bookshelves; here and there she saw maps and pictures hung upon pegs. She took down a jar from one of the shelves as she passed; it was labelled "ORANGE MARMALADE," but

[1] From Lewis Carroll, *Alice's Adventures in Wonderland.*

to her great disappointment it was empty; she did not like to drop the jar for fear of killing somebody underneath, so managed to put it into one of the cupboards as she fell past it.

"Well," thought Alice to herself, "after such a fall as this, I shall think nothing of tumbling downstairs. How brave they'll all think me at home! Why, I wouldn't say anything about it, even if I fell off the top of the house." (Which was very likely true.)

Down, down, down. Would the fall *never* come to an end? "I wonder how many miles I've fallen by this time?" she said aloud. "I must be getting somewhere near the centre of the earth. Let me see, that would be four thousand miles down, I think" (for, you see, Alice had learned several things of this sort in her lessons in the schoolroom; and though this was not a *very* good opportunity for showing off her knowledge, as there was no one to listen to her, still it was good practice to say it over); "yes, that's about the right distance—but then I wonder what latitude or longitude I've got to?" (Alice had not the slightest idea what latitude was or longitude either, but she thought they were nice grand words to say.)

Presently she began again. "I wonder if I shall fall right *through* the earth! How funny it'll seem to come out among the people that walk with their heads downward! The Antipathies, I think" (she was rather glad there *was* no one listening this time, as it didn't sound at all the right word); "but I shall have to ask them what the name of the country is, you know. Please, ma'am, is this New Zealand or Australia?" (And she tried to curtsey as she spoke—fancy *curtseying* as you're falling through the air! Do you think you could manage it?) "And what an ignorant little girl she'll think me for asking! No, it'll never do to ask; perhaps I shall see it written up somewhere."

Down, down, down. There was nothing else to do, so Alice soon began talking again. "Dinah'll miss me very much to-night, I should think!" (Dinah was the cat.) "I hope they'll remember her saucer of milk at tea time. Dinah, my dear! I wish you were down here with me! There are no mice in the air, I'm afraid, but you might catch a bat, and that's very like a mouse, you know. But do cats eat bats, I wonder?" And here Alice began to get rather sleepy, and went on saying to herself, in a dreamy sort of way, "Do cats eat bats? Do cats eat bats?" and sometimes, "Do bats eat cats?" for, you see, as she couldn't answer either question, it didn't much matter which way she put it. She felt that she was dozing off, and had just begun to dream that she was walking hand in hand with Dinah, and was saying to her very earnestly, "Now, Dinah, tell me the truth; did you ever eat a bat?" when suddenly, thump! thump! down she came upon a heap of sticks and dry leaves, and the fall was over.

Alice was not a bit hurt, and she jumped up on to her feet in a moment. She looked up, but it was all dark overhead; before her was another long passage, and the white rabbit was still in sight, hurrying down it. There was not a moment to be lost; away went Alice like the wind, and was just in time to hear it say, as it turned a corner, "Oh, my ears and whiskers, how late it's getting!" She was close behind it when she turned the corner, but the Rabbit was no longer to be seen; she found herself in a long, low hall, which was lit up by a row of lamps hanging from the roof.

There were doors all round the hall, but they were all locked, and when Alice had been all the way down one side and up the other, trying every door, she walked sadly down the middle, wondering how she was ever to get out again. Suddenly she came upon a little three-legged table, all made of solid glass; there was nothing on it but a tiny golden key, and Alice's first idea was that this might belong to one of the doors of the hall; but alas! either the locks were too large, or the key was too small, but at any rate it would not open any of them. However, on the second time round, she came upon a low curtain that she had not noticed before, and behind it was a little door about fifteen inches high; she tried the little golden key in the lock, and to her great delight it fitted!

Alice opened the door and found that it led into a small passage, not much larger than a rat-hole; she knelt down, and looked along the passage into the loveliest garden you ever saw. How she longed to get out of that dark hall, and wander about among those beds of bright flowers and those cool fountains, but she could not even get her head through the doorway; "and even if my head would go through," thought poor Alice, "it would be of very little use without my shoulders. Oh, how I wish I could shut up like a telescope! I think I could, if I only knew how to begin." For, you see, so many out-of-the-way things had happened lately that Alice had begun to think that very few things indeed were really impossible.

There seemed to be no use in waiting by the little door; so she went back to the table, half hoping she might find another key on it, or at any rate a book of rules for shutting people up like telescopes. This time she found a little bottle on it ("Which certainly was not here before," said Alice), and tied round the neck of the bottle was a paper label with the words "DRINK ME" beautifully printed on it in large letters.

It was all very well to say "Drink me," but the wise little Alice was not going to do *that* in a hurry. "No, I'll look first," she said, "and see whether it's marked '*poison*' or not;" for she had read several nice little stories about children who had got burned, and eaten up by wild beasts, and other unpleasant things, all because they *would* not remember the simple rules their friends had taught them; such as, that a red-hot poker will burn you if you hold it too long; and that if you cut your finger *very* deeply with a knife, it usually bleeds; and she had never forgotten that, if you drink much from a bottle marked "poison," it is almost certain to disagree with you, sooner or later.

However, this bottle was *not* marked "poison," so Alice ventured to taste it; and finding it very nice (it had, in fact, a sort of mixed flavor of cherry tart, custard, pineapple, roast turkey, toffy, and hot buttered toast), she very soon finished it off.

"What a curious feeling!" said Alice; "I must be shutting up like a telescope."

And so it was indeed; she was now only ten inches high, and her face brightened up at the thought that she was now the right size for going through the little door into that lovely garden. First, however, she waited for a few minutes to see if she was going to shrink any further; she felt a little nervous about this, "for it might end, you know," said Alice to herself, "in my going out altogether, like a candle. I wonder what I should be like then?" And she tried to fancy what the flame of a candle looks like after the candle is blown out, for she could not remember ever having seen such a thing.

After a while, finding that nothing more happened, she decided on going into the garden at once, but, alas for poor Alice! when she got to the door, she found she had forgotten the little golden key, and when she went back to the table for it, she found she could not possibly reach it; she could see it quite plainly through the glass, and she tried her best to climb up one of the legs of the table, but it was too slippery; and when she had tired herself out with trying, the poor little thing sat down and cried.

"Come, there's no use in crying like that!" said Alice to herself, rather sharply; "I advise you to leave off this minute!" She generally gave herself very good advice (though she very seldom followed it), and sometimes she scolded herself so severely as to bring tears into her eyes; and once she remembered trying to box her own ears for having cheated herself in a game of croquet she was playing against herself, for this curious child was very fond of pretending to be two people. "But it's no use now," thought poor Alice, "to pretend to be two people! Why, there's hardly enough of me left to make *one* respectable person!"

Soon her eye fell on a little glass box that was lying under the table; she opened it, and found in it a very small cake, on which the words "EAT ME" were beautifully marked in currants. "Well, I'll eat it," said Alice; "and if it makes me grow larger, I can reach the key; and if it makes me grow smaller, I can creep under the door; so either way I'll get into the garden, and I don't care which happens."

She ate a little bit, and said anxiously to herself, "Which way? Which way?" holding her hand on the top of her head to feel which way it was growing, and she was quite surprised to find that she remained the same size; to be sure, this is what generally happens when one eats cake, but Alice had got so much into the way of expecting nothing but out-of-the-way things to happen, that it seemed quite dull and stupid for life to go on in the common way.

So she set to work, and very soon finished off the cake.

"Curiouser and curiouser," cried Alice (she was so much surprised that for the moment she quite forgot how to speak good English); "now I'm opening out like the largest telescope that ever was! Good-by, feet" (for when she looked down at her feet, they seemed to be almost out of sight, they were getting so far off). "Oh, my poor little feet, I wonder who will put on your shoes and stockings for you now, dears? I'm sure I shan't be able! I shall be a great deal too far off to trouble myself about you; you must manage the best way you can. But I must be kind to them," thought Alice, "or perhaps they won't walk the way I want to go! Let me see; I'll give them a new pair of boots every Christmas."

And she went on planning to herself how she would manage it. "They must go by the carrier," she thought; "and how funny it'll seem, sending presents to one's own feet. And how odd the directions will look:

Alice's Right Foot, Esq.
Hearthrug,
near the Fender,
(with Alice's love).

Oh, dear, what nonsense I'm talking!"

Just at this moment her head struck against the roof of the hall; in fact, she was now rather more than nine feet high, and she at once took up the little golden key and hurried off to the garden door.

Poor Alice! It was as much as she could do, lying down on one side, to look through into the garden with one eye; but to get through was more hopeless than ever: she sat down and began to cry again.

"You ought to be ashamed of yourself," said Alice, "a great girl like you" (she might well say this), "to go on crying in this way! Stop, this moment, I tell you!" But she went on all the same shedding gallons of tears, until there was a large pool all round her, about four inches deep, and reaching half down the hall.

After a time she heard a little pattering of feet in the distance, and she hastily dried her eyes to see what was coming. It was the White Rabbit returning, splendidly dressed, with a pair of white kid gloves in one hand and a large fan in the other. He came trotting along in a great hurry, muttering to himself as he came, "Oh! the Duchess, the Duchess! Oh! won't she be savage if I've kept her waiting?" Alice felt so desperate that she was ready to ask help of any one; so, when the Rabbit came near her, she began, in a low, timid voice, "If you please, sir——" The Rabbit started violently, dropped the white kid gloves and the fan, and scurried away into the darkness as hard as he could go.

Alice took up the fan and gloves, and, as the hall was very hot, she kept fanning herself all the time she went on talking. "Dear, dear! How queer everything is today! And yesterday things went on just as usual. I wonder if I've been changed in the night? Let me think; was I the same when I got up this morning? I almost think I can remember feeling a little different. But if I'm not the same, the next question is, who in the world am I? Ah, *that's* the great puzzle!" And she began thinking over all the children she knew that were of the same age as herself, to see if she could have been changed for any of them.

"I'm sure I'm not Ada," she said, "for her hair goes in such long ringlets, and mine doesn't go in ringlets at all; and I'm sure I can't be Mabel, for I know all sorts of things, and she, oh! she knows such a very little! Besides, *she's* she, and *I'm* I, and—oh, dear, how puzzling it all is! I'll try if I know all the things I used to know. Let me see; four times five is twelve, and four times six is thirteen, and four times seven is—oh, dear! I shall never get twenty at that rate! However, the multiplication table doesn't signify; let's try geography. London is the capital of Paris, and Paris is the capital of Rome, and Rome—no, *that's* all wrong, I'm certain! I must have been changed for Mabel! I'll try and say, *'How doth the little'* "—and she crossed her hands on her lap, as if she were saying lessons, and began to repeat it; but her voice sounded hoarse and strange, and the words did not come the same as they used to do:

"How doth the little crocodile
  Improve his shining tail,
And pour the waters of the Nile
  On every golden scale!

How cheerfully he seems to grin,
  How neatly spreads his claws,
And welcomes little fishes in
  With gently smiling jaws!"

"I'm sure those are not the right words," said poor Alice; and her eyes filled with tears again as she went on, "I must be Mabel after all, and I shall have to go and live in that poky little house, and have next to no toys to play with, and oh, ever so many lessons to learn! No, I've made up my mind about it; if I'm Mabel, I'll stay down here! It'll be no use their putting their heads down and saying, 'Come up again, dear!' I shall only look up and say, 'Who am I, then? Tell me that first, and then, if I like being that person, I'll come up; if not, I'll stay down here till I'm somebody else'—but, oh, dear!" cried Alice, with a sudden burst of tears, "I do wish they *would* put their heads down! I am so *very* tired of being all alone here!"

As she said this, she looked down at her hands, and was surprised to see that she had put on one of the Rabbit's little white kid gloves while she was talking. "How *can* I have done that?" she thought. "I must be growing small again." She got up and went to the table to measure herself by it, and found that, as nearly as she could guess, she was now about two feet high, and was going on shrinking rapidly; she soon found out that the cause of this was the fan she was holding, and she dropped it hastily, just in time to save herself from shrinking away altogether.

"That *was* a narrow escape!" said Alice, a good deal frightened at the sudden change, but very glad to find herself still in existence; "and now for the garden," and she ran with all her speed back to the little door; but alas! the little door was shut again, and the little golden key was lying on the glass table as before, "and things are worse than ever," thought the poor child, "for I never was so small as this before, never! And I declare it's too bad, that it is!"

As she said these words her foot slipped, and in another moment, splash! she was up to her chin in salt water. Her first idea was that she had somehow fallen into the sea, "and in that case I can go back by railway," she said to herself. (Alice had been at the seaside once in her life, and had come to the general conclusion that wherever you go to on the English coast, you find a number of bathing-machines in the sea, some children digging in the sand with wooden spades, then a row of lodging houses, and behind them a railway station.) However, she soon made out that she was in the pool of tears which she had wept when she was nine feet high.

"I wish I hadn't cried so much!" said Alice as she swam about, trying to find her way out. "I shall be punished for it now, I suppose, by being drowned in my own tears. That *will* be a queer thing, to be sure! However, everything is queer to-day."

Just then she heard something splashing about in the pool a little way off, and she swam nearer to make out what it was; at first she thought it must be a walrus or hippopotamus; but then she remembered how small she was now, and she soon made out that it was only a mouse that had slipped in like herself.

It was not long before the pool was quite crowded with the birds and animals that had fallen into it; there was a Duck and a Dodo, a Lory and an Eaglet, and several other curious creatures. So Alice led the way, and the whole party swam to the shore.

This was only the beginning of many strange adventures that befell Alice in that strangest of all countries, Wonderland.

## PAUL BUNYAN[1]

*Wallace Wadsworth*

In the lumber woods the winter night has settled down over the snowy forest land. The trees crackle with the cold, the ice of the lakes booms and creaks harshly in the rending grip of the frost, and far to the north those ever restless dancers, the Northern Lights, leap and climb the sky in flickering waves of green and purple and crimson. The air stings the skin and prickles the nostrils, and no creature braves its chill save the fur-clad forest animals that slip hungrily along, restless and unseen shadows, among the trees.

Only in the big lumber camp is there sign of warmth and comfort. There, in bunkhouse and shanty, the men have gathered together after their hard labors of the day, enjoying the companionship of one another and perhaps playing crude jokes, boasting of past deeds, or looking on laughingly while one of their number tests the mettle of another in some feat of strength. But most likely they are doing what they like best to do on a night like this, when the wind groans and whistles around the buildings and the frost noises crackle and jeer, and that is to sit back and listen while the old-timers tell over again the wonderful tales of Paul Bunyan and his marvelous deeds.

Paul Bunyan! the mightiest man that ever came into the woods! Never do woodsmen tire of hearing of him. Never do the stories of his tremendous labors grow old to them, for not only was he the first one of all their kind, but he was also the greatest lumberjack that ever lived, the hero of them all.

Paul Bunyan! the first and greatest logger! He is really the father of logging as it is today, for all the best methods for logging off timber were developed by him, and have been in use ever since. Not only that, but he also invented all the tools that are used by lumberjacks even today: the double-bitted ax, the grindstone, the crosscut saw, the peavy, and all the others. A very great genius was Paul, a remarkable man in every way and one well fit to be the hero of all woodsmen who have come after him.

It has been long since any one has seen him face to face, though now and then some old-time lumberjack will admit that he has worked for Paul in one or another of his smaller camps, or that he has a friend who once knew Paul personally. It is from such men as these that the stories of the great logger's exploits have come, and since these tales of him are firsthand so to speak, they are therefore of unquestionable truth.

Paul Bunyan was of tremendous size and strength, the strongest man that ever swung an ax. Now a lumberjack always measures things by ax-handles instead of by feet or yards—a thing will be so many ax-handles long or so many ax-handles high—and the various estimates as to Paul's size are given in this way. Accordingly, the estimate which seems most nearly correct is that Paul was so big that ninety-seven ax-handles would

[1] From Wallace Wadsworth, *Paul Bunyan and His Great Blue Ox*.

just barely measure him from hip to hip. This estimate is a little misleading, however, as no one is sure whether the ordinary ax-handle is meant, or one of Paul's, which was seven—or perhaps it was seventy—times as long as the ordinary one. At any rate, it can easily be seen that he was no little fellow.

He had curly black hair which his loving wife used to comb for him every morning with a great crosscut saw, after first parting it nicely with a broadax, and a big black beard that was as long as it was wide and as wide as it was long. He was rather proud of this beard, and took great care of it. Several times every day he would pull up a young pine tree by the roots and use its stiff branches in combing and brushing it smooth.

Paul was so strong that he never did things as other men did them. That is what Joe Mufraw discovered once when he came looking for Paul, intending to get into a fight with him. Joe also was a very big man, and a great bully, always looking for a fight. One by one he had whipped the best fighters in all the logging camps around, until by the time the big drive was over in the spring he claimed to be the boss bully and the mightiest fighter in the woods. It was then that some one told him about Paul Bunyan, and Joe straightway set off to find him. As he went along he kept boasting more and more, telling every one he met of all the fearful things he would do to Paul when finally he found him.

The winter's logging work being done, Paul was at his farm, getting his land ready for spring planting, and when Joe discovered him he was plowing a piece of recently cleared land with five yokes of oxen. Joe threw off his coat and watched the plow come nearer and nearer, its share cutting and slicing its way through great stumps and mighty boulders as if they were not there. When Paul reached the end of the field, instead of letting his oxen take the time to turn themselves around he just picked them up, all ten of them, and set them down again headed in the other direction without any delay or trouble. It was not until then that he noticed Joe.

"Well, stranger," he hailed in a mighty voice that made Joe's ears ring, "what can I do for you?"

But Joe didn't answer. With a stunned expression on his face, he backed away from the field, and turned and stumbled along the path he had come. "Ox an' all!" he kept muttering to himself, shaking his head as if the very thought made him dizzy. "He picks up ox an' all! No, no! No fights with that man for Joe!" And so it happened that the big contest never did occur, and Joe Mufraw was never heard of again.

It is pretty hard to give a definite date to any of the mighty deeds which Paul Bunyan performed, as only one guidepost as to time is given in all the stories that have been told of him and his exploits. This guidepost, as one may call it, is the definite mention of the winter of the Blue Snow. The snow that fell during that winter was a bright, glistening blue in color, very interesting and attractive at first, but soon growing so tiresome to the eyes that every one was longing for the sight of some common, old-fashioned white snow again.

Now it is certain that all that the great logger ever did took place either before or after the falling of the Blue Snow, and so if it were only possible to discover the exact year during which the Blue Snowstorm occurred—all the things he did could be dated forward or backward from that time, and the definite date of their occurrence established in that way.

It is thought quite probable that the Blue Snow fell during the Year of the Two Winters, when it grew so cold that it didn't start to thaw until after it began to freeze again. They had winter all summer that year, and then in the fall it turned colder. It was so cold that one night when Paul set the coffeepot out of doors to cool, the coffee froze so quickly that the ice was hot.

At any rate, one thing is sure, and that is that Paul Bunyan did all the mighty deeds which are told of him. It is not nearly so important to know *when* he did them as to know that they actually did happen.

Mrs. Paul was about of a size to match her husband. It took forty-seven grizzly bear skins to make her a fur coat—that is, one of these short ones—and one of her skirts used up more canvas than a full-rigged ship. She was affectionate and lovable, and every one said that Paul was mighty lucky to get such a wife. The only difference between her and other women was that of size—with her the measurements were yards or rods instead of inches.

As for Babe, the Great Blue Ox, just where Paul got him has never been learned. It is thought that he secured him when but a calf, being attracted by his strange blue color, and reared him from calfhood with great care. The Ox well repaid the kindness of his master, for he was with him through all his logging operations and was continually performing labors that could not have been done in any other way. The Great Blue Ox was so strong that he could pull anything that had two ends and some things that had no ends at all, which made him very valuable at times, as one can easily understand.

Babe was remarkable in a number of ways besides that of his color, which was a bright blue. His size is rather a matter of doubt, some people holding that he was twenty-four ax-handles and a plug of tobacco wide between the eyes, and others saying that he was forty-two ax-handles across the forehead. It may be that both are wrong, for the story goes that Jim, the pet crow, who always roosted on Babe's left horn, one day decided to fly across to the tip of the other horn. He got lost on the way, and didn't get to the other horn until after the spring thaw, and he had started in the dead of winter.

The Great Blue Ox was so long in the body that an ordinary person, standing at his head, would have had to use a pair of field glasses in order to see what the animal was doing with his hind feet.

Babe had a great love for Paul, and a peculiar way of showing it which discovered the great logger's only weakness. Paul was ticklish, especially around the neck, and the Ox had a strong passion for licking him there with his tongue. His master good-naturedly avoided such outbursts of affection from his pet whenever possible.

Paul Bunyan was puzzled greatly over the problem of getting enough flapjacks for his men, and finally he ordered Big Ole, his blacksmith, to make him a huge griddle. So big was this griddle that the cookees greased it with telephone poles on the end of which were tied great bunches of gunny sacks for swabs. As Paul kept on hiring more men all the time, however, it was not very long before it became far too small, and he had his problem to settle all over again.

Some one at last told him where he could get a much bigger griddle to take the place of the one that was now outgrown, but it was so large that he couldn't at first figure out how to get it to camp. Luckily it was perfectly round in shape, and though it was so thick when it was stood on edge that it made a track as wide as a wagon road and was terribly hard to lift, Paul soon thought out a way to get it to the place where he wanted it.

Being so hard pressed by the need of more flapjacks in camp, he started working the inventive side of his brain, and it was at this time that he invented the electro magnet. He and Ole made two enormous big ones so strong that when they were tested out for the first time they pulled all the axes and saws and others tools out of the hands of the men in the woods within five miles of the camp. Seeing the trouble they had caused, Paul shut off the magnets at once, but it was worse than a jig-saw puzzle, sorting out all the things that had been pulled into camp. He was quite pleased, however, with such a demonstration by the magnets, for he knew that they were just the things to help him get the big griddle to where he wanted it.

Shortly before this he had bought a team of mules, Jerry and Jinny, intending to use them occasionally while he gave Babe a rest. This mule team could travel so fast, after they had had their regular feed of ten bushels of wheat apiece, that no one else could hold them in, and so Paul always had to drive them himself. He used them hitched to a big flat-bottomed wagon without wheels.

So now he harnessed his mules up, fixed his new magnets in the back of the wagon, and drove off to where the griddle was. He swung the magnets around until their strength drew the griddle right up on its edge, and then he drove off lippity-cut towards the camp. The pull of the magnets got the griddle going around so fast and following him at such a great rate of speed that he hardly knew how to stop it, for the faster the mules went, just that much faster did the griddle roll along behind trying to catch up. It was clearly impossible for him to run away from it.

When he at last passed over the spot where he wanted it, he just dropped the magnets out of the wagon and pulled up to one side to watch what would happen. It rolled around and around, like a big pie pan circling about on the floor as it loses its speed after some one spins it, getting nearer and nearer to where the magnets lay. It kept rolling weaker and weaker, until finally it twisted around a couple of times more just at the place where he wanted it, and gouged out a big hole in the ground as it turned. Then it settled down, as nice as you please, right flat over the hole it had dug, and there it was at last, all ready for use and with a place for the fire underneath.

Paul then built a high fence around the griddle, and right beside it he put a couple of big buildings to hold his pancake flour. So perfectly did he have these buildings arranged that others just like them are used today as elevators for storing grain. He also invented a machine for mixing up the hot-cake batter, and had Ole make eight or ten of them, which were placed in position by the griddle. These machines of Paul's are also copied today, and any one may see many small models of them being used by paving contractors for mixing concrete.

"There now," said Paul to Sourdough Sam, the head baker of the camp, who also had charge of all the flapjack making, "there is a griddle to be proud of—a griddle which it should be a pleasure to work with. Everything is nice and handy, there is plenty of room to insure the best of results, and from now on you should find the subject of flapjacks as interesting as that of your sourdough bread."

Sam was doubtful at first, but it was not long until he was turning out his giant hot cakes with all the artistry which he had hitherto reserved exclusively for his first love, sourdough bread. From that time on his flapjacks were so wonderful that men still talk about them, and no other griddle expert has ever been able to equal him in the preparation of this supreme delicacy.

Everything was worked out on a very definite schedule, and it was truly a wonderful sight to see the big griddle being put to its daily use. Along in the afternoon every day a gang of three hundred flapjack cooks would start getting down the flour and fixin's from the elevators, start the mixers going, and stir up the batter under the careful supervision of the boss baker. Meanwhile, as the batter was being mixed, the cook boys would have to grease the griddle. This they did by strapping whole hams or sides of bacon on their feet and skating around over the hot surface. When the batter was all ready and the greasing done, a cook would trip the chute from the mixers, and out would roll a wave of flapjack batter ten feet high.

Paul had a hard time at first figuring out how to flip the flapjack over onto its other side so that both sides of it would be cooked the same. Every one has, of course, seen flapjacks flipped up in the air out of a skillet, so that when they come down again they have turned completely over and the undone side has a chance to get browned in its turn. Of course the big griddle and the flapjack on it were far too heavy for any wrist to flip in the ordinary manner, and so for a while everybody had to eat flapjack that was done only on one side.

Paul tried rigging a block-and-tackle arrangement for turning the big hot cake over, but that did not work very well, and the plan was abandoned.

At last he hit on the scheme of flipping it over with dynamite, which plan worked out so well that it was used from that time on. Whenever one side of the flapjack became done, he would explode a ton or so of dynamite under it, and away up in the air the big cake would sail until it was almost out of sight. By putting a few more sticks under one side than under the other, he made sure that it would turn over while in the air, and so nicely did he calculate the exact amount of explosive to use each time that when the flapjack came down again it landed exactly on the griddle with the brown side uppermost.

After this, Paul's men never had any cause for kicking about the flapjacks.

## THE BOLD DRAGOON[1]

*Washington Irving*

My grandfather was a bold dragoon, for it's a profession, d'ye see, that has run in the family. All my forefathers have been dragoons, and died on the field of honor, except myself, and I hope my posterity may be able to say the same; however, I don't mean to be vainglorious. Well, my grandfather, as I said, was a bold dragoon, and had served in the Low Countries. In fact, he was one of that very army, which, according to my uncle Toby, swore so terribly in Flanders.

Well, gentlemen, my grandfather was on his way to England, for which he intended to embark from Ostend. So one evening, towards nightfall, he rode jollily into Bruges. —Very like you all know Bruges; a queer, old-fashioned Flemish town, once, they say, a great place for trade and money-making in old times, when the Mynheers were in their glory; but almost as large and as empty as an Irishman's pocket at the present day.—Well, gentlemen, it was at the time of the annual fair. All Bruges was crowded; and the canals swarmed with Dutch boats, and the streets swarmed with Dutch merchants; and there was hardly any getting along for goods, wares, and merchandises, and peasants in big breeches, and women in half a score of petticoats.

My grandfather rode jollily along, in his easy, slashing way, for he was a saucy, sunshiny fellow—staring about him at the motley crowd, and the old houses with gable ends to the street, and storks' nests on the chimneys; winking at the young women who showed their faces at the windows, and joking right and left in the street. All the people laughed, and took it in amazing good part; for though he did not know a word of the language, yet he had always a knack of making himself understood.

Well, gentlemen, it being the time of the annual fair, all the town was crowded, every inn and tavern full, and my grandfather applied in vain from one to the other for admittance. At length he rode up to an old rickety inn, that looked ready to fall to pieces, and which all the rats would have run away from, if they could have found room in any other house to put their heads. It was just such a queer building as you see in Dutch pictures, with a tall roof that reached up into the clouds, and as many garrets, one over the other, as the seven heavens of Mahomet. Nothing had saved it from tumbling down but a stork's nest on the chimney, which always brings good luck to a house in the Low Countries; and at the very time of my grandfather's arrival, there were two of these long-legged birds of grace standing like ghosts on the chimney-top. Faith, but they've kept the house on its legs to this very day, for you may see it any time you pass through Bruges, as it stands there yet—at least it was so when I came that way after the battle of Waterloo. My grandfather eyed the house curiously as he approached. "This is the house for me," said he, stopping short before the door.

The sudden appearance of a dashing dragoon was an event in an old inn fre-

[1] From Washington Irving, *Tales of a Traveller*.

quented only by the peaceful sons of traffic. A rich burgher of Antwerp, a stately, ample man in a broad Flemish hat, and who was the great man and great patron of the establishment, sat smoking a clean long pipe on one side of the door; a fat little distiller, from Schiedam, sat smoking on the other; and the bottle-nosed host stood in the door, and the comely hostess, in crimped cap, beside him; and the hostess's daughter, a plump Flanders lass, with long gold pendants in her ears, was at a side window.

The landlord saw, with the quick glance of a publican, that the new guest was not at all to the taste of the old ones; and, to tell the truth, he did not like my grandfather's saucy eye. He shook his head. "Not a garret in the house but is full."

"Not a garret!" echoed the landlady.

"Not a garret!" echoed the daughter.

The burgher of Antwerp and the little distiller of Schiedam smoked their pipes sullenly, eyeing the enemy askance from under their broad hats, but said nothing.

My grandfather was not a man to be browbeaten. He threw the reins on his horse's neck, cocked his head on one side, stuck one arm akimbo—"Faith and troth!" said he, "but I'll sleep in this house this very night." As he said this he gave a slap of his thigh, by way of emphasis.

He followed up the vow by jumping off his horse, and making his way past the staring Mynheers into the public room. Maybe you've been in the barroom of an old Flemish inn—faith, but a handsome chamber it was as you'd wish to see; with a brick floor, and a great fireplace, with glazed tiles, and then the mantelpiece, pitching itself head foremost out of the wall, with a whole regiment of cracked teapots and earthen jugs paraded on it; not to mention half a dozen great Delft platters, hung about the room by way of pictures; and the little bar in one corner, and the bouncing barmaid inside of it, with a red calico cap, and yellow eardrops.

My grandfather snapped his fingers over his head, as he cast an eye round the room. "Faith, this is the very house I've been looking after," said he.

There was some further show of resistance on the part of the garrison; but my grandfather was an old soldier, and an Irishman to boot, and not easily repulsed, especially after he had got into the fortress. So he blarneyed the landlord, and the landlord's wife, and the landlord's daughter, and the barmaid; and it was agreed on all hands that it would be a thousand pities, and a burning shame into the bargain, to turn such a bold dragoon into the streets. So they laid their heads together, and it was at length agreed to accommodate him with an old chamber that had been for some time shut up.

"Some say it's haunted," whispered the landlord's daughter; "but you are a bold dragoon, and I dare say don't fear ghosts."

"Never a bit!" said my grandfather. "I'll never be troubled by ghosts, my darling."

In a little while, as was his usual way, he took complete possession of the house, swaggering all over it; into the stable to look after his horse, into the kitchen to look after his supper. He had something to say or do with every one; smoked with the Dutchmen, drank with the Germans, slapped the landlord on the shoulder, romped with his daughter and the barmaid—never, since the days of Alley Croaker, had such a rattling blade been seen. The landlord stared at him with astonishment; the landlord's daughter hung her head and giggled whenever he came near; and as he swaggered along the corridor, with his sword trailing by his side, the maids looked after him, and whispered to one another, "What a proper man!"

At supper, my grandfather took command of the table-d'hote as though he had been at home; helped everybody, not forgetting himself; talked with everyone, whether he understood his language or not; and made his way into the intimacy of the rich burgher of Antwerp, who had never been known to be sociable with any one during his life. In fact, he revolutionized the whole establishment, and gave it such a rouse, that the very house reeled with it. He outsat every one at table, excepting the little fat distiller of Schiedam, who sat soaking a long time before he broke forth; but when he did, he took a violent affection for my grandfather. They sat smoking, and telling stories, and singing Dutch and Irish songs, without understanding a word each other said, until the little Hollander went off to bed, trolling the burden of a Low Dutch love song.

Well, gentlemen, my grandfather was shown to his quarters up a large staircase, composed of loads of hewn timber, and through long rigmarole passages, hung with blackened paintings of fish, and fruit, and game, and country frolics, and huge kitchens, and portly burgomasters, such as you see about old-fashioned Flemish inns, till at length he arrived at his room.

An old-time chamber it was, sure enough, and crowded with all kinds of trumpery. It looked like an infirmary for decayed and superannuated furniture, where everything diseased or disabled was sent. No two chairs were alike. Such high backs and low backs, and leather bottoms, and worsted bottoms, and straw bottoms, and no bottoms; and cracked marble tables with curiously carved legs, holding balls in their claws, as though they were going to play ninepins.

My grandfather made a bow to the motley assemblage as he entered, and, having undressed himself, placed his light in the fireplace. The rest of the guests were by this time sound asleep, for your Mynheers are huge sleepers. The housemaids, one by one, crept up yawning to their attics; and not a female head in the inn was laid on a pillow that night without dreaming of the bold dragoon.

My grandfather, for his part, got into bed, and drew over him one of those great bags of down, under which they smother a man in the Low Countries; and there he lay, melting between two feather beds, like an anchovy sandwich between two slices of toast and butter.

Soon the house grew quiet, excepting the snoring of the Mynheers from the different chambers; who answered one another in all kinds of tones and cadences, like so many bullfrogs in a swamp. The quieter the house became, the more unquiet became my grandfather. He waxed warmer and warmer, until at length he jumped out of bed, and went for a stroll in the passage.

Well, my grandfather had been for a short time absent from his room, and was returning, perfectly cool, when just as he reached the door, he heard a strange noise within. He paused and listened. It seemed as if some one were trying to hum a tune in defiance of the asthma. He recollected the report of the room being haunted; but he was no believer in ghosts, so he pushed the door gently open and peeped in.

Gentlemen, there was a gambol carrying on within, enough to have astonished anybody. By the light of the fire he saw a pale weazen-faced fellow, in a long flannel gown and a tall white nightcap with a tassel to it, who sat by the fire with a bellows under his arm by way of bagpipe, from which he forced the asthmatical music that had bothered my grandfather. As he played, too, he kept twitching about with a thousand queer contortions, nodding his head, and bobbring about his tasseled nightcap.

My grandfather thought this very odd and mighty presumptuous, and was about to demand what business he had to play his wind instrument in another gentleman's quarters, when a new cause of astonishment met his eye. From the opposite side of the room a long-backed, bandy-legged chair, covered with leather, and studded all over with little brass nails, got suddenly into motion, thrust out first a claw foot, then a crooked arm, and at length went gracefully up to an easy chair of tarnished brocade, and led it gallantly out in a ghostly minuet about the floor.

The musician now played fiercer and fiercer, and bobbed his head and his nightcap about like mad. By degrees the dancing mania seemed to seize upon all other pieces of furniture. The antique, long-bodied chairs paired off in couples and led down a country-dance; a three-legged stool danced a hornpipe, though horribly puzzled by its supernumerary limb; while the tongs seized the shovel round the waist, and whirled it about the room in a German waltz. In short, all the movables got in motion, pirouetting hands across, right and left; all except a great clothespress, which kept curtseying and curtseying in a corner, like a dowager, in exquisite time to the music, being rather too corpulent to dance, or perhaps at a loss for a partner.

My grandfather concluded the latter to be the reason; so being, like a true Irishman, devoted to the sex, and at all times ready for a frolic, he bounced into the room, called to the musician to strike up Paddy O'Rafferty, capered up to the clothespress, and seized upon the two handles to lead her out—when—whirr! the whole revel was at an end. The chairs, tables, tongs, and shovel slunk in an instant as quietly into their places as if nothing had happened, and the musician vanished up the chimney, leaving the bellows behind him in his hurry. My grandfather found himself seated in the middle of the floor with the clothespress sprawling before him, and the two handles jerked off, and in his hands.

Well, gentlemen, as the clothespress was a mighty heavy body, and my grandfather likewise, you may easily suppose that two such heavy bodies coming to the ground would make a bit of a noise. Faith, the old mansion shook as though it had mistaken it for an earthquake. The whole garrison was alarmed. The landlord, who slept below, hurried up with a candle to inquire the cause, and with all haste his daughter arrived at the scene of uproar. The landlord was followed by the landlady, who was followed by the bouncing barmaid, who was followed by the simpering chambermaids, all in a terrible hurry to see what the deuce was to pay in the chamber of the bold dragoon.

My grandfather related the marvelous scene he had witnessed, and the broken handles of the prostrate clothespress bore testimony to the fact. There was no contesting such evidence; particularly with a lad of my grandfather's complexion, who seemed able to make good every word either with sword or shillelah. So the landlord scratched his head and looked silly, as he was apt to do when puzzled. But the landlord's daughter corroborated it by recollecting that the last person who had dwelt in that chamber was a famous juggler who died, and had no doubt infected all the furniture.

This set all things to rights, particularly when the chambermaids declared that they had all witnessed strange carryings on in that room; and as they declared this "upon their honors," there could not remain a doubt upon this subject.

Well, gentlemen, as to whether my grandfather went to bed in that room again is more than I can tell. He never disclosed it, if he did. But he always believed in ghosts. And so do I.

## BARON MUNCHAUSEN GOES TO THE MOON[1]

*Rudolph Erich Raspe*

I, Baron Munchausen, believe that braggarts deserve no consideration; therefore let us be modest in our words and deeds. Thus may we deserve respect and achieve greatness. All my narrow escapes were chances turned to advantage by the presence of mind and vigorous exertion which went hand in hand with the wisdom of a gentleman and a soldier.

But let me add that you would be blamable and imprudent sportsmen, admirals, or generals, if you allowed yourselves to depend upon fortune, without troubling about the instruments of success, such as the proper arms, that ensure a happy ending to all adventures. I have always been remarkable for the excellency of my horses, dogs, guns, and swords, and for the proper manner of using and managing them. Upon the whole, I may hope to be remembered in the forest, upon the turf, and in the field.

[1] From John Martin, *The Children's Munchausen,* retold from *Adventures of Baron Munchausen,* by Rudolph Erich Raspe.

I was not always as fortunate, however, as some of my narratives may lead you to suppose. Once I had the misfortune to be overpowered by numbers, and to be made a prisoner of war by the Turks. In that state of humiliation my daily task was neither hard nor laborious, but rather singular and irksome. My work was to drive the Sultan's bees to their pasture grounds, to attend to them all the day long, and to drive them back to their hives before sunset.

One evening I missed a bee, and soon observed that two ferocious bears had fallen upon her to tear her to pieces for the honey she carried. I had no weapon about me but a small silver hatchet, which is the badge of the Sultan's gardeners and farmers. I threw this at the bears with the intention of frightening them away and setting the poor bee at liberty; but, by an unlucky turn of my arm, the hatchet flew upwards and continued rising till it reached the moon. How should I recover it? Fortunately, I recollected that the Turkey-bean grows with great rapidity and climbs to an astonishing height. I planted a bean immediately, and it grew until it actually fastened itself to one of the horns of the new moon. I had no more to do now but climb up by the beanstalk into the moon, where I arrived safely. It was a troublesome piece of business to find my silver hatchet in a place where everything has the brightness of silver. At last, however, I laid hold of it in a heap of chaff and chopped straw.

I was now for returning, but, alas! the heat of the sun had dried up my beanstalk. It was entirely useless for my descent, but I fell to work and twisted me a long rope of that chopped straw (an easy matter for one of my deftness and intelligence). This I fastened to one of the moon's horns and slid down to the end of it. Here I held myself fast with the left hand, and, with the hatchet in my right, I cut the long and now useless end of the upper part which, when tied to the lower end of the upper part, brought me a good deal nearer my journey's end. This repeated cutting and splicing and tying of the rope did not improve its quality, or bring me down to the Sultan's farm. I was still at least four or five miles from the earth when the rope broke, and I fell to the ground with such amazing violence that I found myself stunned, and in a hole fully fifty-four feet deep! Of course, this hole was made by the weight of my body falling from so great a height. I recovered, however, but did not know how to get out of the hole my unfortunate accident had made. After some careful thought and wise planning, I dug steps in the earth with my fingernails, which were fortunately both long and strong, and easily succeeded in reaching the surface of the earth.

Peace was soon after concluded with the Turks, and, having gained my liberty, I left immediately for Saint Petersburg. The winter was then so uncommonly severe all over Europe that ever since the sun has seemed frostbitten.

My journey was made by post, and, finding myself in a narrow lane, I bid the postilion give a signal with his horn so that other travelers might not meet us in the narrow passage. He blew with all his might, but in vain; he could not make the horn sound. What could this silence mean, for French horns are noted for their ready willingness on all occasions? It was most unfortunate, for the moment after we found ourselves facing another coach coming in our direction. There was no proceeding. However, I got out of my carriage, and, being rather muscular, placed it, wheels and all, upon my head. I then jumped a hedge about nine feet high, which, considering the weight of the coach, was somewhat difficult. But with little trouble I landed in a field and came out again by another jump into the road beyond the other carriage. I then went back for the horses, and, placing one upon my head and the other under my left arm, I brought them to my coach, and proceeded to an inn at the end of our day's run.

I should have told you that the horse under my left arm was very spirited, being not over four years old. In making my second jump over the hedge, he showed great dislike to that violent kind of motion by kicking and snorting. However, I tucked his hind legs into my coat pocket, and this settled his uneasiness completely.

After we arrived at the inn, my postilion and I refreshed ourselves, and he hung his horn on a peg by the kitchen fire, near which I sat. Suddenly we heard a *tereng! tereng! teng! teng!* We looked around and now found the reason why the postilion had not been able to sound his horn. His tunes were frozen up in the instrument, and came out now by thawing! All were plain, and much to the credit of my driver, who could give us various fashionable airs without further strain or effort to himself. A little of this music, however, was sufficient, for too frequent repetition of this sort would become a great nuisance, especially if frozen music were of the common sort.

In conclusion of this portion of my narrative, I wish to state that some travelers are inclined to tell more than is perhaps strictly true. If you have the slightest doubt of my veracity, I can only say that I pity your lack of faith.

## *Stories for Fun: Suggested Grades*

*Grade One*
The Tale of Peter Rabbit

*Grade Two*
Little Black Sambo

*Grade Three*
The Lion-Hearted Kitten

*Grade Four*
The Magic Fish-Bone
The Tar Baby
The Well Story

*Grade Five*
The Elephant's Child
Doctor Dolittle and the Pushmi-Pullyu

*Grade Six*
Alice Goes Down the Rabbit-Hole
Paul Bunyan

*Grade Seven*
The Bold Dragoon

*Grade Eight*
Baron Munchausen Goes to the Moon

## *Books for Fun*

### *Primary Grades*

Bannerman, Helen, *The Story of Little Black Sambo,* illus. by the author. Stokes.

Bechdolt, Jack, and Decie Merwin, *John's Dragon,* illus. by the authors. Oxford.

Brock, Emma L., *To Market! To Market!* illus. by the author. Knopf.

Bryant, Sara Cone, *Epaminondas and His Auntie,* illus. by Inez Hogan. Houghton Mifflin.

Flack, Marjorie, *Wait for William,* illus. by the author. Houghton Mifflin.

Fyleman, Rose, *Forty Good-Morning Tales.* Doubleday, Doran.

Gág, Wanda, *The Funny Thing,* illus. by the author. Coward-McCann.

———, *Millions of Cats,* illus. by the author. Coward-McCann.

Harper, Wilhelmina, *The Gunniwolf, and Other Merry Tales,* illus. by Kate Seredy. McKay.

Hogan, Inez, *Nicodemus and the Little Black Pig,* illus. by the author. Dutton.

Kunhardt, Dorothy, *Junket Is Nice,* illus. by the author. Harcourt, Brace.

Lenski, Lois, *Sugarplum House,* illus. by the author. Harper.

Lofting, Hugh, *The Story of Mrs. Tubbs,* illus. by the author. Stokes.

Potter, Beatrix, *The Tale of Jemima Puddle-Duck,* illus. by the author. Warne.

———, *The Tale of Peter Rabbit,* illus. by the author. Warne.

———, *The Tale of Squirrel Nutkin,* illus. by the author. Warne.

### *Intermediate Grades*

Atwater, Richard, and Florence Atwater, *Mr. Popper's Penguins,* illus. by Robert Lawson. Little Brown.

Bacon, Peggy, *The Lion-Hearted Kitten,* illus. by the author. Macmillan.

———, *Mercy and the Mouse,* illus. by the author. Macmillan.

Bemelmans, Ludwig, *The Castle No. 9,* illus. by the author. Viking.

Brooks, Walter R. *The Clockwork Twin,* illus. by Kurt Wiese. Knopf.

———, *Freddy, the Detective,* illus. by Kurt Wiese. Knopf.

———, *To and Again,* illus. by Adolfo Best-Maugard. Knopf.

De Brunhoff, Jean, *The Story of Babar, the Little Elephant* (trans. by Merle Haas), illus. by the author. Random House.

———, *The Travels of Babar* (trans. by Merle Haas), illus. by the author. Random House.

Canfield, Dorothy, *Made-to-Order Stories,* illus. by Dorothy P. Lathrop. Harcourt, Brace.

Davis, Mary Gould, *With Cap and Bells,* illus. by Richard Bennett. Harcourt, Brace.

Dickens, Charles, *The Magic Fish-Bone,* illus. by Francis D. Bedford. Warne.

Dr. Seuss, *And To Think That I Saw It on Mulberry Street,* illus. by the author. Vanguard.

Dr. Seuss, *The 500 Hats of Bartholomew Cubbins,* illus. by the author. Vanguard.

Duplaix, Georges, *Gaston and Josephine,* illus. by the author. Oxford.

Emerson, Caroline, *A Hat-Tub Tale,* illus. by Lois Lenski. Dutton.

Hale, Lucretia P., *The Peterkin Papers,* illus. by Harold Brett. Houghton Mifflin.

Harper, Wilhelmina, *Ghosts and Goblins: Stories for Hallowe'en,* illus. by Wilfred Jones. Dutton.

Harris, Joel Chandler, *Little Mr. Thimblefinger and His Queer Country,* illus. by Oliver Herford. Houghton Mifflin.

Huber, Miriam Blanton, *The Uncle Remus Book, Retold from Joel Chandler Harris,* illus. by A. B. Frost. Appleton-Century.

Kipling, Rudyard, *Just So Stories,* illus. by the author. Doubleday, Doran.

Lofting, Hugh, *Doctor Dolittle's Post Office,* illus. by the author. Stokes.

———, *The Story of Doctor Dolittle,* illus. by the author. Stokes.

———, *The Voyages of Doctor Dolittle,* illus. by the author. Stokes.

Parrish, Anne, *Floating Island,* illus. by the author. Harper.

Sandburg, Carl, *Rootabaga Stories,* illus. by Maud and Miska Petersham. Harcourt, Brace.

Stong, Phil, *The Hired Man's Elephant,* illus. by Doris Lee. Dodd Mead.

———, *Honk the Moose,* illus. by Kurt Wiese. Dodd Mead.

## *Upper Grades*

Bowman, James Cloyd, *Pecos Bill: The Greatest Cowboy of All Time,* illus. by Laura Bannon. Whitman

Carroll, Lewis, *Alice's Adventures in Wonderland,* illus. by John Tenniel. Macmillan.

———, *Through the Looking Glass and What Alice Found There,* illus. by John Tenniel. Macmillan.

Harris, Joel Chandler, *Nights with Uncle Remus,* illus. by Milo Winter. Houghton Mifflin.

———, *Uncle Remus: His Songs and Sayings,* illus. by A. B. Frost. Appleton-Century.

Irving, Washington, *The Bold Dragoon, and Other Ghostly Tales* (ed. by Anne Carroll Moore), illus. by James Daugherty. Knopf.

Leaf, Munro, *The Story of Ferdinand,* illus. by Robert Lawson. Viking.

Martin, John, *The Children's Munchausen* (retold from *Adventures of Baron Munchausen,* by Rudolph Erich Raspe), illus. by Gordon Ross. Houghton Mifflin.

Rounds, Glen, *Ol' Paul, the Mighty Logger,* illus. by the author. Holiday House.

Stockton, Frank R., *The Casting Away of Mrs. Lecks and Mrs. Aleshine,* illus. by F. D. Steele. Appleton-Century.

Wadsworth, Wallace, *Paul Bunyan and His Great Blue Ox,* illus. by Will Crawford. Doubleday, Doran.

# The World and Its Creatures

## BLUE BARNS [1]

*Helen Sewell*

Once upon a time there were two big white geese, named Andrew and Martha.

They lived at Blue Barns farm. It was a famous place, because most farmers paint their barns red, but on this farm the barns were all painted blue.

I know Blue Barns very well. It is a real farm, where I met Andrew and Martha, and I watched this story happen to them. It is all true!

Andrew was the gander of the family, Martha was the goose.

Andrew was very busy and important. He liked to go around the world at Blue Barns, and to know everything that happened.

But Martha just cared about eating. She ate and ate, all day long, and Andrew scolded her.

"Martha," he said, "you mark my words! You'd better not eat so much! Soon you'll be so fat you won't be able to walk."

"Oh, nonsense!" said Martha.

One day the farmer came home to Blue Barns with seven eggs.

He put them in the incubator to keep them warm.

[1] From Helen Sewell, *Blue Barns.*

Andrew and Martha knew nothing about them.

Day after day the eggs stayed there, until, one morning, one of them went crack! One little yellow bill poked out.

Crack, crack! Another and another.

Out of each egg came a little yellow duck.

Seven little yellow ducks!

They were very lonesome, because an incubator is not a very kind mother.

Meanwhile, Martha just ate and ate. She was so fat, she could hardly waddle. Andrew's scolding did no good.

Poor Andrew had to go about Blue Barns all alone.

When the seven little ducks saw Andrew, they quacked with joy, and gathered close around him.

Andrew was delighted. "What a lot of company!" he said. For the first time in weeks he was happy.

Blue Barns seemed a good home again.

Andrew raised his long neck. "Follow me, one by one," he said, "and I will show you all the sights of Blue Barns."

He started off, out of the barnyard. The seven little ducks followed, one by one. The smallest duck was lame in her right leg, so she came last in the line.

"Moo-o!" A big brown creature stood rolling her eyes at them. Her big head came down, and her warm breath came out like a wind on the little ducks.

"That's only Maud, the cow. She's friendly, but just a little careless. Keep away from her big hooves, and you'll be all right."

Next they met the turkey.

"Gobble, gobble, gobble," he said, and looked very cross.

"What a terrible bird!" said the seven little ducks.

"He talks a good deal, but he's nothing to be afraid of," said Andrew.

"Woof, woof!"

Blix, the farm dog of Blue Barns, caught sight of the parade. He made a rush at the little ducks, and they fled under the bushes.

Andrew hissed loudly, Blix ran away, and the ducks came out.

"Don't mind him," said Andrew proudly. "See, he wouldn't dare touch you."

Evalina, the pig, and her babies were rooting in the mud inside their pen.

"Quack, quack!" The little ducks peeked in.

But the baby pigs just grunted, "Don't bother us, we're busy."

"*Those* are pigs," said Andrew. "Now let's go to the pond."

All in line, the big white gander and the seven little ducks went down the farm road.

Past the blue barns, through the fields, under the willow trees—there was the pond!

When the little ducks saw the water, they didn't need to be told what to do. They waddled down to the edge, and floated off like little boats.

Andrew sailed along ahead, like a big boat.

The little ducks paddled with their feet, and stood on their heads in the water.

Snap! the smallest duck almost caught a dragonfly.

"That's right," said Andrew. "You'll learn."

Back to the barnyard they waddled.

"Listen to that door," said Andrew. "When it goes slam, the farmer's wife comes out."

Slam! went the kitchen door. The farmer's wife came out and sat on the grass with her sewing.

Andrew stretched out his long neck and pecked at her bright beads. Then he pecked at her thimble.

The seven little ducks tried to get into her lap.

"Goodness!" said the farmer's wife, "you're the friendliest little ducks I ever did see."

After that, they always listened for the kitchen door to slam. Sometimes the farmer's wife came out and walked down the path and out the gate. Then Andrew and the ducks waddled after her.

They followed her up the road to the village store, and waited outside. When she came out, they followed her home again. Waddle, waddle, waddle, down the dusty road and in at the gate.

At night, the little ducks all tried to crowd in under Andrew's big wings.

But soon they grew too big for that. So Andrew spread out his wings, and they just tucked their heads underneath.

It wasn't very comfortable, but the little ducks were happy. They slept soundly every night.

Poor Andrew had to stand up, so he just dozed now and then.

All summer, Andrew took care of the seven little ducks.

He did not care now how greedy Martha was. He had the seven little ducks.

"What a lot of company!" he said.

## PLOUF, THE LITTLE WILD DUCK[1]

*Lida*

Quack! Quack! Quack!

Plumette, the mother duck, tenderly looked at her eggs. There were eight of them lying in the bottom of the big nest which she had built among the reeds. They

[1] From Lida, *Plouf, the Little Wild Duck,* translated by Georges Duplaix,

shone under the light April sun like large green pears. How beautiful they were!

Plumette remembered the moon was full when she started to sit on her nest. Since then the moon had changed her face four times, and tonight she appeared again round and full over the swamp. Plumette knew that soon her babies would break through their shells. She settled herself on her eggs, covering them with her wings and fluffing out her feathers to keep them warm. She murmured softly, "Quack-quack," and fell asleep.

With the first light of dawn Plumette felt something stir under her. Something tickled her. Quickly she jumped up—and what did she see? Eight little yellow beaks, eight little pairs of black eyes, eight little ducklings squirming and peeping. The smallest one still had a piece of shell attached to his tail and it was he who made the most noise. "Wek . . . wek . . . wek!" said Plumette, very happy.

"Wek . . . wek . . . wek!" answered the little ducks in their squeaky voices.

Eight babies! That is a large family!

They squirmed about, bumping into one another, and calling with squeaking little voices, tried to get out of the big nest which had suddenly become too small.

"What a rumpus!" thought the mother duck. "Nothing but a soft down on their backs and they want to explore the world!"

She caressed all her ducklings and said in a very wise voice:

"Now, now, my darlings! You must stay here all day long and keep warm."

It seemed to them that this first day would never end. But at last the day faded, the night came, and the little brood cuddled under their mother's wings to go to sleep. From time to time there was a muffled little "wek-wek." Plumette could not sleep very well. She was too excited. She had dreams of large juicy frogs and watercress shoots as big as trees.

Next day, as soon as they opened their eyes, the little family was on the water.

"Wek . . . wek . . . wek! My darlings, be careful and follow me. We are going to take a turn around the pond. Topple and Plouf, hurry up. Numps, hold your head up! Flash, push your feet well back. Be quiet, Cackle!

"We are going along the edge of the swamp.

"Now we are following the long line of rushes which separates us from the lake. There you must hide in case of danger, every time you hear me cry. Listen, and remember what I say!

"We are approaching the pool of water lilies. It is a quiet spot where you can come to catch frogs when you are bigger. Now we are skirting the wood. Never come here alone, my ducklets. Listen, and remember what I say!"

Plumette and her little brood continued the promenade around the pond. The ducklings would have liked to play among the rocks and venture as far as the little stream flowing in the middle of the reeds, but Plumette saw they were tired and took them all back to the nest.

The days passed. The little ducks grew round and tall. From morning until night they stayed on the pond with their mother. They did everything she did. When she dove, they dove. When she smoothed her feathers, they passed their tiny beaks over their fine soft down. When she was motionless on the water, the ducklings stayed perfectly still. And every weed their mother pulled, they pulled also.

But they did not understand why they couldn't fly like their mother.

"It must be so much fun to swim in the air," they thought.

They flapped their little bits of wings, but nothing happened.

Plumette watched them and laughed. The ducklings gathered round her:

"Wek . . . wek . . . wek! We want to fly, too."

Their mother caressed them with her beak.

"Quack . . . quack! Wait, your time will come. One day you will spread your wings and fly away."

"But tell us when, when, when?"

"Watch the Queen Anne's lace. When it begins to bloom you will start to fly."

The ducklings looked each day to see when the Queen Anne's lace would blossom into white flowers. Then the days went by, and so many things happened that they forgot about the Queen Anne's lace. They were so busy with swimming and eating and growing that it was July before something happened to Plouf to make them remember.

One morning in July he was playing hide and seek with Topple, when all of a sudden he stopped, dazzled. No more grass, no more rushes, only water, a great expanse of water. It was the lake, the honest-to-goodness big lake! And he completely forgot the game of hide and seek, the warnings of Plumette, everything. He had only one idea—to swim to the other side of the lake.

The crossing was quickly made. He came out of the water, shook his feathers, and could not believe his eyes. Before him lay a vast prairie and, as far as one could see, fields, woods, and hills. Never would he have believed the earth so big! He went on very gravely, looking right and left, stopping to nibble a plant, to gobble a slug in passing, or to chase a grasshopper. It was all delightful.

"One can also live on the ground," he thought, "Too bad it's so hard. Ouf! My feet!"

Hippity-hopping, he reached a field of wheat. He thought they were reeds of the ground and hid among them to rest awhile. His head dropped wearily and his eyes were already closed when he heard, all of a sudden, a muffled growl, and then a deafening "Bow-wow-wow!" Between the stalks, Plouf saw an enormous body without any wings, a great big head without any beak, four paws, and a funny looking tail. It was a dog.

Plouf's heart was in his mouth. He would have given all the slugs in the world to be home in his pond. He didn't even have enough strength to cry.

Then, all of a sudden, silence. The enemy was gone!

Plouf cautiously left his hiding place and cloppety-clop, went for the lake. Alas! The same awful voice rang out behind him, "Bow-wow-wow!" The dog was at his heels. Plouf forgot he wasn't on the water and tried to dive—and hit the hard ground. The dog was not two feet away.

Then, much to Plouf's surprise, a miracle happened. His little wings spread out all by themselves. He flapped them with all his strength. His feet were no longer on the ground. He was flying! Wonder of all wonders! He went higher and higher over the prairie and then over the lake. How beautiful it was! How good to feel the air caressing his feathers and to find he could go faster than anything that swims or runs on the ground!

But already he was over the pond. He saw his mother encircled by his anxious little brothers, and saluted them with such a mighty "Quack . . . quack!" that Plumette was completely overcome.

"It is he! He is flying . . . flying!" clamored the young ducks. And the moment Plouf came down beside them, Cackle cried at the top of his lungs:

"The Queen Anne's lace is blooming! The Queen Anne's lace is blooming!"

The young ducks started off in all directions, flapping their wings in the hope that they too, could fly. But it wasn't until three days later that Topple succeeded in raising himself above the pond. Then, in turn, Flash and Gobble, and the others.

And just as their mother had said, when the Queen Anne's lace blossomed into white flowers, all the little wild ducks spread their wings and flew away.

## THE GENTLEMAN IN BROWN[1]

*Margery Bianco*

There are some animals that no one seems to like. The woodchuck is one of them. There are many who admire the

[1] From Margery Bianco, *More about Animals.*

skunk, in spite of his drawbacks; charming poems have been written about the mole whom gardeners so detest. But I have seldom found anyone to say a good word for woodchucks.

It is true that the woodchuck is clumsy, impudent, and homely. His walk is a waddle; he is snub nosed, with bristles on his face, and in figure a portly woodchuck—and most woodchucks are portly—resembles nothing so much as a shabby brown plush sofa cushion with a leg at each corner.

Perhaps if he were more graceful, with a slender nose and a feathery tail, people would be less inclined to give him such a bad character!

Only once a year does the woodchuck get any sort of recognition, and then he is usually referred to as the "ground hog." On the second of February, he is supposed to come out blinking from his winter sleep to look for his shadow, and if he sees it, then winter will last another six weeks. So once a year, at least, he has his picture in the papers, and that should make up a little for the mean things that are said about him during the rest of the twelve months, especially in early summer, when everyone's thoughts are on the vegetable garden.

Year after year I had heard so much about woodchucks, how greedy they were and how much damage they did among the peas and beans and young cauliflowers, that it almost discouraged me from ever attempting to have a garden at all. Everyone had her tale of woe; everyone had new plans each spring for outwitting the woodchucks, and none of them, it seemed, was successful!

It was all the worse because, this particular summer, we had rented an old farmhouse that had stood empty for several years. And during that time, of course, the wild creatures had been having it all their own way.

Neighbors said cheerfully: "Why, you'll never make a garden there! The place is just *running* over with woodchucks! They'll eat you out of house and home!"

And woodchucks there were, in plenty, though it was some time before I actually saw one. Meantime I dug and raked and planted my beans and carrots recklessly. If woodchucks were going to come, let them come. There should be plenty for me and them, too!

For I have long held a private theory—which friends make fun of—that as long as you let other creatures alone, they will let you alone. Complain, and they will give you something to complain about. Of course I have never had a chance to try this out with anything of a really fierce nature, but it certainly seems to work with the smaller beings.

But to return to the woodchucks.

One side of the garden was bounded by an old stone wall, and near this stood a small unused building that had once been a blacksmith shop. One morning I needed a bit of old iron for some purpose or other, and thought of looking in this little shed. No sooner had I opened the door than I was startled by a sudden shrill whistle—much like the sound boys produce by blowing on two fingers, only louder and shriller. Somewhere under the broken flooring one of the many Mrs. Woodchucks had made her home, and this police-like whistle was just her warning to keep away.

Anyone who for the first time hears an angry woodchuck whistle, close at hand, will receive just such a shock as I did, and that is exactly what the woodchuck intends. Coming so unexpectedly on the stillness, it is really quite a startling sound, and it carries a long distance. Woodchucks use it not only to scare off intruders, but also as a danger signal to one another. If ever you come upon a group of them on some old pasture slope on a sunny morning, sitting up outside their burrows as they love to do, just try whistling sharply on your fingers, and you will see them all fly to cover.

I soon learned to know that sound very well, for I heard it quite often, nearly every time I approached the stone wall, and although it didn't startle me again so much as the first time, still I never quite got used to it.

Inquisitive eyes must have watched my planting and raking, though my brown neighbors were at first very shy about showing themselves. Early morning was the time they chose for their inspection. Looking from my bedroom window I would see a fat brown figure hoist himself carefully from some hole in the stone wall, waddle down the path, and examine those tiny green seedlings with the utmost interest. Up and down the rows he would go, sniffing and twitching his whiskers, with very much the air of a stout elderly gentleman out early to see how his garden was getting on. Sometimes Mrs. Woodchuck would join him, and they would have a consultation, sitting up solemnly and glancing now and then towards the house.

By and by I caught glimpses of the young ones too, stealing in and out the thicket of goldenglow, or trotting over to the apple tree by the kitchen door to see if there were an apple or two for the picking up.

But except for the fallen apples, which later in the summer they gathered greedily, not one thing in the garden did those woodchucks touch!

Either they had too much of their natural wild food, whatever it may be, or else they decided that I was such an amateur gardener that it wasn't even sport to rob me.

Not so the cutworms and other insects. They did their best to ruin everything. But then, as I waged war on them, it was quite fair on both sides.

One other person besides myself took great interest in the woodchucks, and that was Trotty, the little Scotch terrier who shared our home.

Her first sight of the woodchucks was almost disastrous. She was staring out from an upper window early one morning, and in her eagerness to discover just what that fat brown creature was, wandering about the vegetable garden, she overbalanced and tumbled straight out on her little black nose, much to the woodchuck's amazement. For though he probably kept an eye trained for possible dogs on the ground, he could scarcely have expected to see one fall from the skies like that. Luckily no harm was done, but Trotty was just as astonished as the woodchuck at her own mishap.

I can't say that they ever became good friends, but Trotty learned not to interfere with them within the garden limits, at least. She did a good deal of fussy patrolling, as little dogs will, and would often lie out there in the blazing sun, when she would have been far more comfortable in the shade, just to show those impudent creatures that she had as much right to the garden as they had. But it never came to an actual encounter.

Certain plans, however, must have been brewing all the while inside her little black head, only waiting a chance to be put into practice.

On the pasture slope leading down to the brook, some distance from the house, lived another colony of woodchucks, who had made their burrows in the middle of a brier patch. Trotty, very likely because I had discouraged her from worrying their cousins who lived in the garden, was very inquisitive about this particular woodchuck family. Whenever we neared the brier patch she always tried either to rush on ahead, or to lag behind us unnoticed, and one day she succeeded. I heard a scuffle and a frightened squeal, and realized to my dismay that Trotty had actually caught one of the babies, who had wandered too far from the burrow.

Now woodchucks will fight very savagely in defense of their young ones, and Trotty might have had a very unpleasant surprise in another moment, when Mrs. Woodchuck came to the rescue, but luckily as I came up the baby managed to wriggle from between Trotty's paws and scamper home, more scared than hurt. I thought, however, that a little explanation would be good, so I haled the young lady to the mouth of the burrow, pointed to it, and scolded her well.

"Bad dog!" I said, and immediately a gruff voice from inside the burrow added: "*Bobble*-bobble-bobble!"

It was Mrs. Woodchuck, very indignant, and determined to have her own little say in the matter too.

I was rather surprised, and so was Trotty. She looked in a puzzled way at the burrow, and then at me.

We waited a moment. Silence from the woodchuck hole. Then I said firmly and distinctly: "Very naughty, unpleasant little dog!"

And again Mrs. Woodchuck added: "*Bobble*-bobble-bobble!" this time less angrily, but as if she were saying: "Just what I think! I told you so!"

Being scolded by two people at once was just too much for one little dog. Trotty hung her ears, and it was my turn to call into the burrow: "Look here, you've said quite enough, now. Don't be so unpleasant about it!"

"Gr-rr!" returned Mrs. Woodchuck promptly.

We felt, like Alice in Wonderland, that this last piece of rudeness was more than we could bear. We turned our backs on the woodchuck hole. Little dogs may sometimes act hastily but, after all, manners are man ners!

## HIDE AND GO SEEK [1]

*Dorothy P. Lathrop*

"I spy! I spy!"

It was Barney who had first thought of playing hide and go seek in the woods. And he lay, still safely hidden, flat on his stomach on the hemlock needles. Thick branches spread down all around him like a green tent.

"I spy!"

But the cry was faint in the distance.

Dead sticks broke under running feet. Far away there was a shout and a scuffle in the dry leaves.

Someone had been caught. But they'd never find *him!*

Suddenly he held his breath and listened. Who was tiptoeing through the leaves? He lay very still and waited.

All at once the leaves rose in a flurry. And with a rush, a gray squirrel sprang to a branch above and stared down at Barney.

"Aeeeeee! Aeeeeee!" said the squirrel through his long, sharp nose, pointing Barney out for everyone in the woods to see.

"Aeeeeeeeee!" he scolded, flicking his tail into angry waves.

"Ssssh!" whispered Barney imploringly. For now they would see him. Now they would surely know where he was hiding.

How many other creatures, he wondered, were playing hide and go seek in the woods, lying just as still as he was, hoping no sharp eyes would find them?

"Barney! Barrr-neeeeey!"

They hadn't found him. Now they were giving up and going away.

He sat up, shivering a little in his cool, dark tent, for evening was coming. The last sunlight lay flat along the floor of the woods. And at the edge of the pond, tiny spring peepers were already puffing out their throats into white bubbles and sending their sweet, shrill call all through the woods.

For it was still April. Ferns pushed tightly curled heads up out of the ground. And spring beauties opened frail petals where budding leaves cast no shade.

Had spring come?

Chipmunks popped out of their holes to see. Perhaps, even down in their deep burrows, the singing of the peepers had waked them from their light sleep.

Was that the gray squirrel's hole far up the trunk of that tree?

No, for as suddenly as a wooden cuckoo bobs out of his clock and in again, so quickly did a little head appear from the hole's blackness, gaze silently down at Barney—and was gone.

It wasn't a gray squirrel, with head so small. Nor a chipmunk, with nose so blunt and eyes so enormous. *Was* it a flying squirrel?

But, though Barney sat as still as a rock, watching until the hole was lost in shadows, no face peered again from that small

[1] From Dorothy P. Lathrop, *Hide and Go Seek.*

round doorway. No wonder, for in a nest at the bottom of the hole, the flying squirrel had four babies.

They weren't nearly as pretty as she was. They were blind, and pink, and perfectly naked, but she was very proud of them. She had had them only three days.

Blindly they nuzzled close to her as she lay down and spread herself over them like a soft, warm blanket.

And Barney didn't even guess that they were there!

Day after day he came back to the woods and stared up at that hole, hoping to see a small, gray head blot out its darkness.

But the woods were warm and bright with sun. And what flying squirrel who loved the night would willingly look out into such a glare of daylight?

The gray squirrel lay flat along a limb, warming his back. Red ones frisked through the barest, sunniest branches. And when it was hottest, chipmunks sat toasting their stripes, and little dusty snakes crawled out of the ground and basked on sun-warmed rocks.

The turtle felt its warmth right through his shell. It limbered his chilled legs and made him dreadfully hungry. He hadn't eaten anything all winter!

What a long, delicious worm lay there half out of the ground! He lurched toward it. But with a slip, and a slide, and a flip of its head, the worm was gone before those sharp jaws could open. Slowly the turtle uncrooked his neck, and plodded off to his meadow.

Every day the four tiny squirrels were growing bigger.

But even when they were ten days old, they couldn't see a bit more than on the day they were born.

Their heavy heads wobbled when they tried to walk. Their legs wobbled too, and they sprawled flat on their tight little stomachs with webs outspread as if already they longed to sail through space. But over their pink backs was creeping a dark sheen of fur.

A few more days and their whiskers sprouted. Could such stubs ever grow long like their mother's? And their tails, which had been so short they stuck out straight, sprouted, too, and curved downward.

Then the little squirrels grew so fast they stretched the wrinkles right out of their skins. They no longer looked like grubs. But still their eyes were sealed fast shut, and all their world was dark, and soft, and warm. What was there to do but to eat and sleep?

Even yet Barney didn't know what was hidden in the heart of the tree. And sometimes he wondered if that hollow trunk wasn't just as empty as its little round entrance.

Two chickadees hoped that it was. They stood still in the air with fast beating wings and looked at the hole. They wanted a house so badly! Could it really be that they were the first to find it?

No, oh no! For the poor bird had no sooner thrust her head inside than she nearly tumbled out backward.

The flying squirrel, usually so gentle, was furious. She hung out of her doorway. And though she made no sound, she made a face so frightful that the terrified birds took to their wings and never came back.

And then, when the little squirrels were just four weeks old their eyes opened, not wide and round, but gently till a new world grew less strange.

They saw their mother, and they saw one another. They were no longer fumbling in darkness.

They saw their own fur and they washed it—the smooth, mouse-gray fur on their sides, and the downy white fur on their stomachs. They had to sit on their tails to do that.

They spied bits of seeds their mother had left uneaten and, balancing shakily on their small haunches, nibbled them with teeth no bigger than pin points.

And if any little squirrel had no piece of his own, he stole one right out of another's mouth.

All but one of them. He was so little and timid that they all stole from *him*.

They even crowded him away from his dinner and he didn't grow quite as strong as the rest.

Where did their mother go when she climbed up over their heads and left them? They dug in their sharp little nails, and jerkily scrambled up to see. But no matter how hard they squeezed, only two could look out of the hole at the same time.

One night the boldest crept all the way out. But in no time at all his mother came back and caught him. She wasn't very gentle, for she didn't want to drop him. How sharp her teeth were! How they pinched his tender stomach! He squealed and curled up like a worm. And back into the hole she stuffed him headfirst.

Soon she couldn't keep any of them in bed after twilight, or get them back in before dawn. Though she pushed them in firmly, out they popped time and again to chase one another around the tree trunk and along big branches and little. If they ever sat still to rest, they were up and away in a twinkling.

And their mother kept a sharp watch for owls.

But one little squirrel often looked timidly down from a branch above them, and never ran as hard as the rest. For his feet didn't grip as tightly as theirs did. He had gone without too many dinners.

Sometimes he sat by himself in the nest, or curled himself into a furry ball and slept while the others played outside in the starlight.

And then one night Barney saw them.

Just as the sun was going down, he had crept through the cool, dim woods. And sitting down at the foot of their tree, he had watched and waited.

Now he knew what the squirrel had kept hidden all the while the fern fronds were uncurling. For, at the first pale gleam of a star, out they slipped, one by one, all four and their mother. Quietly, like small shadows, for darkness had not yet come to hide them.

Then all of a sudden the littlest one slipped!

For a moment he hung by one leg. He dangled there over nothing.

Even then, if he had been strong like the others, he could have climbed back. But his weak foot loosened.

Catching at twigs and bark, tumbling, gliding, tumbling again, he fell through space. And he landed, shaken and dazed, and with hardly a puff of breath in his body, right on a pile of brown leaves.

Oh, no, not leaves at all, but a brood of little grouse chicks, who scattered swiftly with a patter of feet like rain, and hid themselves under real leaves!

And there he lay without stirring. Oh, was he *hurt?*

But before Barney could reach him, he had picked himself up and crept behind the biggest lady-slipper leaf. Very carefully Barney peered over it. No squirrel was there.

He looked under dried leaves, under maple leaves and beech. But nothing was hidden there, not even a grouse chick.

The little squirrel was frightened. He wasn't really hurt. But how he wished he could find his mother!

He would run and burrow under her warm, comforting body and hide there forever!

But he could find only cold, brittle leaves and thin sticks to hide him. And when he tried to burrow under stones, he hurt his head. *Here* was one that was softer! He dug under it frantically.

It leaped away! And the little squirrel leaped the other way in a panic.

It was a toad, but when the toad saw Barney, he sat down hastily and dug himself into the leaf mold. He dug himself in backward.

By now the little squirrel had run so far he was lost. He no longer knew up which tree he lived.

He had run past two lady-slippers, five trilliums, and over any number of tiny white violets. And he had scuttled under little bushes all hung with white bells. Of course he didn't know what anything was.

He was so little he didn't even know blueberries.

Something was coming around a big fern!

He made himself very small and wrapped his tail tightly around his neck for comfort. Then fearfully he peeped over it and waited.

A wood duck waddled toward him, waggling his tail from side to side, and whispering softly to himself as he came—for he never quacked like other ducks.

Even in that dim light, blue and green and all sorts of colors glinted from his polished feathers.

What was that in his path? His flat feet stopped side by side.

The feathers rose on his head until it looked twice the size it had been. He cocked a red eye down at the small gray ball before him. It didn't look good to eat. Bugs were much better.

He snapped at a black fly and missed it. He was very embarrassed! So he clattered his bill, and waggled his tail even faster.

But the poor little squirrel hid his head in his tail and shivered, for he thought that the duck meant to eat *him*.

But all the duck wanted was a good tree to sleep in. So away he went through the woods, waddling, waggling, and whispering to himself.

Up in the tree tops two of the other little squirrels were playing hide and go seek. And no matter where one of them hid, behind a branch, or under a new, crumpled leaf, the other could find him. Something always stuck out—a tail, or a few whiskers.

But Barney in all the time he had been searching could find only a snail, moving slowly with all four horns waving and all his ruffles outspread.

Once more the little squirrel was all alone in the woods. He peered out from behind his tail to make sure.

Where was his mother? He wanted to get up where she was, up where his nest was, up away from the ground where strange things ran, and jumped, and waddled, and scared him.

He must get *up!*

And there was nothing to climb. The trees were so far apart he couldn't find them. Ferns bent under his weight. And the bushes with bells were so short that his tail still dragged on the ground when he had climbed them. He scrambled hopefully up the side of a rock.

But over its top like a dark, swift shadow, a weasel was noiselessly sliding!

For an instant, the little squirrel clung there, his eyes round and staring with fright. Then, as never before, he leaped!

And the weasel bent his long neck and fixed his bright, greedy eyes on the leaf under which the squirrel lay flattened.

Then Barney shouted. He saw the leap. He saw the weasel.

He shouted and ran.

And the shadow vanished. Without a sound, or a stirring of leaf or twig, or a flicker of brown, the weasel was gone. But Barney didn't care where he was if only the little squirrel was safe.

The little squirrel was too frightened to move. How he hoped he was hidden under the leaf!

Barney picked him up in his cupped hands. And in that warm, dark, comforting refuge, the squirrel forgot, at last, to tremble.

Above in the tree, one of his sisters was singing. The tree toad started it. All day, a gray bump on a gray twig, he had clung there with the round tips of his toes. But now he sat up, puffed his throat into a big bubble, and out into the dusk sent a loud trilling.

The little squirrel opened her mouth, her ears rose high on her head, her whiskers shot forward, and "Eeeeeeeeeee-eeeeeeeeee," she sang, with a sound like the long-drawn peep of a very small bird.

Then they sang together, "Br-r-r-r-r-br-r-r-r," "Eeeeeeeeeep—eeeeeeeeeep—eeeeeeeeep."

At the squirrel's own tree, Barney opened his hands. But tiny feet clung fast to his fingers and wouldn't let go.

He smoothed the deep fur with one finger tip. Not even milkweed silk was softer! How big the eyes were! How long the whiskers that quivered with every heart beat! (Barney had never seen a big squirrel's whiskers!) And here, stretched between leg and leg, were the little sails with which some day he would glide through the tree tops.

The little squirrel's mother had missed him. Around and around the tree trunk she ran, head downward. And all at once she saw him.

Then suddenly she sprang down to Barney's shoulder, seized her baby, and was back up the tree and stuffing him into the hole before Barney could draw his breath.

She poked and she pushed, but he wouldn't go in. How could he when she was trying to cram him in backward? He didn't fit that way!

How he squealed! Hadn't he had trials enough for one night? He squealed louder and louder until she pushed him in the right way.

After that night, Barney brought nuts in his pockets, and all kinds of seeds. The nuts were cracked, for such tiny teeth as his squirrel's could never gnaw through shells.

Then he reached up and tucked them, after red squirrels and gray had gone off to bed, into any crevice of bark and branch that would hold them. And the flying squirrels smelled them.

They dashed down from their tree tops, tasted this nut and that seed, then hurried back to play through the branches. But Barney's little squirrel, hungrier than all the rest, just sat there and ate.

So each day he grew stronger and bigger, and could run with the others. *Now* when they tried to steal his best squash seed, he hung by his toes down out of their reach until not a crumb was left. And at last he could even gnaw into whole nuts bigger than his own head.

Now the little squirrels were beginning to fly. Of course it wasn't *really* flying, because they had no wings to flap.

First they hopped a few inches.

Then they gathered their courage and their legs and hopped a bit farther.

At last they grew bold. They sprang into the air, spread their legs so wide that the sails stretched tightly between them, and swooped down to a branch.

Barney counted them anxiously. One, two, three, and the mother. She was browner than they were. And she sailed from one tree to another, while they sailed only from branch to branch.

Where was *his* squirrel? Wasn't he strong enough yet to fly?

For now it was summer, and the young squirrels were almost as big as their mother. Now when daylight was fading, it was no longer the peepers who sang in the pond, but frogs with voices that boomed. And the long, warm dusk was sweet with the singing of thrushes.

But still the one little squirrel was afraid to fly. No matter how fast he ran along branches, he dared only the smallest of hops. Once he had fallen all the way down to the ground.

But one night he woke up just at dusk. And while he was yawning and stretching to wake himself up, his brother came dashing headlong, bumped into him, and knocked him right off the branch.

Oh, he was falling! Frantically he spread out his legs, and his sails caught the air. Why no, he was *flying!*

On and on he glided through empty space, steering with his flat tail like a rudder. Then he soared, and, as gently as a feather, he landed on the trunk of a tree through whose branches he had never run.

What fun to fly!

His eyes popped with excitement.

Why, he had sailed farther than all the rest!

Darkness soon stilled the thrushes' singing. But under their tent of leaves, through which the bright stars shone, the four little squirrels and their mother, silent as shadows, ran and flew until dawn.

## SKUNKS[1]

*Edith M. Patch*

Did you ever see a skunk? People do not think that "skunk" is a pretty name, but the animal the name belongs to is very handsome indeed.

One day I saw some little skunk kittens in an oak grove, and they were so playful that it was fun to watch them. Once in a forest I saw a grown skunk hunting. He ran to a soft old stump and tore it to bits with his front paws. He looked very quickly to see what insects he could find, and then hurried away to another stump.

One morning about sunrise I saw some skunks hunting on a prairie field. The grass on the prairie was brown and dry. Some underground insects had chewed off the roots, so of course the grass died. But the skunks came into the field and ate the insects before they could go into another field and kill any more grass. These skunks had a good way of hunting, and they were funny to watch. They ripped places in the dry sod with their claws and then rolled it back out of the way like strips of rolled carpet. That made it easy for them to find the juicy insects in the ground.

Skunks like grass-eating insects better than they do chickens. In some states the farmers know this and have laws to prevent men from killing skunks. It is easier and cheaper for men to build good hen-houses to keep out skunks and rats and foxes than it is for them to kill some of the insects that eat valuable crops. Since skunks help the farmers take care of their crops, it is only fair for men to make laws to protect the skunks.

Skunks are not timid. Even the wild ones are not. The reason they are not timid is that they have a very good way of taking care of themselves. There are two scent glands in their bodies under the skin, one on each side, near the base of the tail. These scent glands are little sacs filled with liquid. When skunks are attacked or badly frightened, they squirt out the liquid from their scent sacs in two streams of fine spray. It is not a pleasant-smelling scent. In fact it smells bad enough to make people or dogs or other animals feel sick if they try to bother skunks.

Since a skunk can make animals sick if they try to harm it, it does not need to be timid. It does not need to run to its home like a fox. It does not need to hide at all. It can walk about slowly and show its pretty black and white coat plainly.

Early one morning I met a skunk in a path. He was not a tame skunk, but he was not afraid. I walked up the path until I was not far from the skunk. He did not run away. He patted the ground with his front paws and then he lifted his tail. His tail was a signal of danger when he lifted it like that. He was not horrid about it. He was quite polite. He gave me a chance to stop where I was. I stopped. Then I went backwards very slowly until I was far enough away to suit the pretty black and white animal. In a minute he lowered his tail and went on with his walk up the path. I sniffed the air and there was not even one little bit of skunk scent. All he wanted was a chance to go walking without having anyone come too near.

Since skunks are not naturally timid, they are easy to tame. In fact, even the wild ones like being near places where people live. They like to stay under barns and sheds. They like such places for shelter for themselves and their young. There is another reason why they come to barns and sheds. They are glad to eat rats and mice and are pleased to come where they can find them. People who know about this sometimes have tame skunks for mouse-catchers. Some people get young skunks and take out the scent sacs, and then let them run about the house as much as they like. It is not necessary to take out these sacs, since tame skunks soon learn to know their friends. But most people feel safer to have the scent glands out of the way, so that there may be no bad-smelling accident

[1] From Edith M. Patch, *First Lessons in Nature Study*.

if a stranger should come into the house and be rude to the skunks.

A girl once told me about a pet skunk she had. She found it caught with its foot in a trap and she felt sorry. So she took it out of the trap and put it into an empty henhouse. She knew how to hold it so that it could not spray her. She gave it good food and fresh water and kept it shut up until it knew her and liked to be handled. This pet soon found that it was fun to climb up and take a ride on the girl's shoulders. The henhouse was a lonesome place and the little animal was very happy when the girl would let it go into the house for a visit. When the girl's father was resting on the sofa, the skunk would climb up and curl down cosily beside him and have a nap, too. The scent glands of this skunk were not removed, but the pet never did any harm about the house and was not bad-smelling at all.

The fur of skunks is warm and good and people wear it. You may think that, since skunks are easily tamed, they can be kept on a fur farm. So they can. They are less work to care for than foxes are, but their fur does not sell for so much money.

## ROCKY BILLY GOES VISITING[1]

*Holling Clancy Holling*

Rocky Billy was a kid, a little billy goat, a Rocky Mountain goat. Rocky Billy was born among the rocks far up on Squaw Asleep Peak above the timber line. His home was under a shelf of rock with a patch of curly grass as a front yard, and near by was one lone pine tree—the first tree when you looked down the mountain, the last tree when you went up.

His life was adventure from the start. First he fell over a cliff; that was at the first bounce given him by his little hind legs. Then he started an avalanche and his mother gave him his name, Rocky Billy, because of the rocks he started down the mountain. Then his mother barely saved him from an eagle that grabbed him in its cruel talons.

Many days came and went, as days do, and nothing in particular happened. The sun came out more often and kept its smile longer. The white clouds puffed whiter and larger, and the blue sky brushed itself with snowy peaks and spruce tree brooms and washed itself with spring rains and hung itself out to dry much bluer than before.

Rocky Billy hadn't done a great deal since his escape from the eagle, except grow. And he had grown! He stayed within the shelter of the cave opening most of the time and never far from the first tree. Mamma Nan's white coat was always a light spot in the corner of his eye. He learned to use his machinery much better, too. His shoulder had healed from the eagle's claws and didn't hurt when he walked. He could step out with ease and confidence, and his nose didn't run into things any more. He could stand on his hind legs without falling over, and scratch his ear with a hind foot without losing his balance. This didn't mean much to any one else, but it meant a great deal to him. It gave him a sense of importance and well-being. It made him feel that, after all, he was getting to be a big goat, and he said so out loud a couple of times to prove it. Mamma Nan went right on eating, and if she smiled to herself, he didn't see, and there was no one else to say he wasn't a big goat, so that settled it. He was the biggest goat in sight except his mother, and of course she didn't count.

To prove it, one day he made a decision. He had watched for days and days the far green scraggly edge that was timber line. He would go down the slopes for himself, and find out what it all meant. So, with one eye on Mamma Nan and one on the blue sky for eagles, he went. Mamma Nan saw him going, and made a start in his direction, but changed her mind.

"He's growing all the time," she said to herself, "and he must begin to learn things.

[1] From Holling Clancy Holling, *Rocky Billy: The Story of a Rocky Mountain Goat.*

If I don't go with him, he will feel more self-reliant and will be a stronger kid for it." Which was wise, for goats can't be always tied to their mother's apron strings.

So Rocky Billy wandered far out into the world and he found the most interesting things! There was a pocket of snow here and there, hiding from the sun beneath rocks, and across the snow he saw odd little tracks. They waddled in irregular rows, three-cornered. Rocky Billy followed one of these to a boulder, and all of a sudden, with a flutter and a scuffle, out from behind it walked a bird. It was almost a slate-brown, with white speckles. It was a ptarmigan, a bird of the grouse family, but Rocky Billy did not know that. As he watched it, astonished, it flew away with a whirring sound.

"Eagle!" gasped the little goat and trembled all over. But he didn't run. Instead, he backed up under a rock shelf, resolved to show as little of his body as possible for the attack; but, strange to say, the bird flew away down the slope and didn't come back. It didn't return to grasp him in the middle and take him away.

"That's odd," he thought. "Then all things that fly aren't eagles? How amusing!"

This fact made him feel better. This bird flew, and it made tracks in snow, but it didn't take you away. He must be quite a big goat to have things fly away from him. He said that he was a big goat, out loud, and that made him feel better. As there was no one to say differently, he went on.

The rocks on the broad, rounded slope of Squaw Asleep were long and flat and came out in layers like huge bricks along the mountain. Some were small, and if you stepped on these at the wrong end, they came out and you almost fell. But early the little goat learned how to pick his way. When there was a doubtful rock he avoided it, and patted the others with a front foot now and then to see if they teetered or were solid. He still remembered, back in his little head, the fall and slide of his first few days. He didn't want to do that again, although it had been exciting. Down he went among the slide rock, zigzag, and the stones grew in size. At one place they had fallen into a small canyon and lay there all jumbled like huge loaves of bread in a basket. He went from one to another and found that he could leap one or two feet without anything coming loose.

This was great fun! He jumped here and he jumped there and he jumped the other place. He felt as though he were flying! Bound, bound, bound he went, and back again. He squealed with delight and stood on the highest rock to look out over the valley.

"Mba-a!" he shouted. "What a big goat I am!"

"Oh, rock dust!" sputtered a shrill, small voice right below him, and he almost fell off. It was the first voice he had heard in a long while.

"You're not so big!" went on the little voice in a shrill key, "but you're big enough to shake my house with your jumping and your leaping and your clambering, and I won't have it, that's all. I won't have it!"

Rocky Billy came to his senses and looked down. There sat Little Chief, the rock rabbit, or cony. Altogether he was about the size of his Mamma Nan's muzzle and looked nothing more than a bump of gray moss. He was a round, cozy-looking little fellow, like a very tiny rabbit with large, round ears. But of course Rocky Billy hadn't seen a rabbit before. Little Chief sat on a rock top and scolded the goat in a high, short squeak. Rocky Billy wanted to laugh, but he didn't.

"Mba!" he said instead. "Excuse me, I was just finding my springs. You know, I am comparatively new and I never did any jumping before, and it's great fun, don't you think? I mean, to jump. And besides, I find that I am quite a big goat."

"Oh, hayseed!" said Little Chief. "If you're big, I live in a tree. You? Say! I may not be large myself, but I have seen hundreds of goats in my day, and some of 'em were *really* big! You may grow to be big some day, but you're a pretty small affair as it is!"

At this Rocky Billy felt rather ashamed. However, he was larger than Little Chief, and he said so. But that didn't help matters any. Little Chief talked right back to him, until finally in disgust he wandered away.

In a crevice of the rocks he found a pile of nice long grass. It was quite an armful, and perfectly cured by the sun, and dry. He nibbled at it, although he couldn't eat grass, for of course he was mostly on a milk diet these days. But just the moment he nibbled at it, he realized he had made a mistake. Little Chief came scuttling over the slide rock like an animated moss bump and scolded Rocky Billy very much.

"You meddlesome creature, you!" he sputtered. "Eat my hay, will you? Eat my hay! Don't you know that that's my private and particular hay? Don't you know that I slaved and labored last fall to gather that hay and cure it in the sun and store it away for food? Don't you know that I have all the rights and privileges of this vicinity, and that each year I have a regular haying bee with all of my relatives, and that we tuck hay into every hole and cranny possible to provide for a hard winter?"

Of course Rocky Billy was dumfounded. He didn't know about any of this and he said so in very good goat. He did not see why he should be scolded for something he did not know about. And besides, he couldn't eat the hay anyway. But he was learning. It was the first scolding he had ever had. So he backed away and kept saying "yes" and "no" and "yes" again, until he was out of hearing of the squeaky voice. Then he went racing down hill. He didn't want to get mixed up any more.

This racing was more fun than jumping from one rock to another, anyhow. It really was exhilarating and, besides, it got one somewhere. The green edge of timber line came up toward him at every leap, and before he knew it, he had come so close that he saw what it was. It wasn't a jagged green line at all. It was merely a lot of trees like the first tree, all jumbled together.

He went from one to another and sniffed at each and nothing happened. He went past the first few scraggly ones to others taller and greener. Here was more fun. A lot of trees to butt your head against! Nobody seemed to care.

And another thing. There weren't so many rocks in sight. They were covered up with moss and lichens, sunny little tufts that clung to them like dried-up tongues, and underfoot there were brown pine needles and long grasses. Here and there were dead trees, trees that had lived long lives battling with the winds and had finally lost and lain down on the long slope. These could be jumped. Farther down were more of them, and more living trees, with little green trees between, and all so fascinating that it made a wonderful game of hide and seek to chase yourself around among them. And then there was young grass of brilliant green coming up in small spurts. Oh, how good it was to be alive! He had never known that anything could be so interesting as timber line! And notwithstanding what Little Chief had said, he just knew that he was a big goat! He leaped a fallen tree and climbed on top of another and said so out loud rapidly.

By this time there was some one else interested. It was Slinker, the coyote. He did not come to timber line as a rule, and he was far from home. But there was a bone somewhere on the slope that he remembered, and he was taking a short cut this way rather than go around the ridge by way of Elk Creek. He hadn't hoped for a meal up here, unless he could surprise a ptarmigan, but those birds knew him from long ago and were very prudent. Yet here he was, and right before him, bleating to the blue sky, was one of the tenderest, juiciest, plumpest little dinners any respectable coyote could ever wish for. And what a terrible appetite he had had all day!

Then Rocky Billy saw Slinker. He took one look. He didn't need any more. This time Mamma Nan was not there to tell him that there was danger, that here was a yawning abyss on four legs more dangerous than any rock slide. Immediately he felt that his playing was over and, whatever the charms of timber line, it was just about time he was going home. He went.

But not so fast as that. He took one spasmodic bound that carried him a little way up the slope. Then another. Slinker had been running until he saw Rocky Billy, and so he started out without much surplus wind, but that seemed to make no difference. He was as swift as lightning. Up and after the little kid he went.

There were two streaks up from timber line, going fast and furious toward the slide rock pile of Little Chief, one gray, one white. The gray one almost caught the white one, but, suddenly, the white streak made a zigzag to one side. From side to side and straight up, Rocky Billy was bounding. The coyote, not used to such large rocks and slippery shale lost a good deal of footing, but Rocky Billy's hoofs held every time. When they struck rock they seemed to freeze to it until he made another bound.

And now they had come to the jumbled heap where Little Chief had his home. Here there was trouble for Slinker. Try as he might, he couldn't leap as fast or as sure-footedly as the small kid. The rocks had slippery sides, and he fell several times. One fall jarred him quite a lot, and what breath there was left by this time was jarred loose from his lungs. When he had recovered, he saw that his fresh meal was a small white spot moving up the crag at a gallop.

He started again with a lunge, but the utter folly of ever getting a dinner in that direction came home to him forcibly, so he turned and went off limping and panting into the timber. It didn't help his vanity any to have Little Chief and a dozen relatives squeal laughingly at him from the rock slide, but he knew better than to attempt chasing these moss bumps. He might dig out a rabbit or marmot, but he couldn't pry the big boulders loose which housed that family. And so he went back to the valley much chagrined.

Rocky Billy never stopped until he reached the base of the first tree and Mamma Nan. She had seen him coming, and knew what it was all about. She had worried a great deal at first, but when she saw him bounding along at top speed, she nodded her head and chewed her whiskers.

"A real goat," she said. "A remarkable goat, even if he is my son!"

And Rocky Billy? He was frightened, but he came home intact. And after lying down in the cave and wheezing and grunting, blowing and panting, he told Mamma Nan all about it.

"Yes," said she, licking him tenderly and nosing him all over to make sure he was not hurt, "Slinker is a very bad person for little goats to meet. He's even worse than an eagle, and the only way to keep out of his mouth is to run among the high rocks. But Little Chief, although he scolded you, is your friend. When you are older and learn to eat grass, you will find that you can feed near his hayfields unafraid. He may scold a lot, but he always tells you when there is danger."

"Whew!" said Rocky Billy, at last in possession of his breath, "I have learned a lot for one day. Maybe Little Chief was right. Maybe I am not so big, after all; but then I was able to get away from Slinker. Say, Mamma Nan, I must be quite a big goat, at that!" And he went to sleep in the warm sun, dreaming of all that had happened during the day.

## KEEPING STILL IN THE WOODS[1]

*Charles G. D. Roberts*

The Boy was beginning to feel that if he could not move very soon he'd burst.

Of course, under Uncle Andy's precise instructions, he had settled himself in the most comfortable position possible before starting upon the tremendous undertaking

[1] From Charles G. D. Roberts, *Children of the Wild.*

of keeping perfectly still for a long time. To hold oneself perfectly still and to keep the position as tirelessly as the most patient of the wild creatures themselves—this, he had been taught by Uncle Andy, was one of the first essentials to the acquirement of true woodcraft, as only such stillness and such patience could admit one to anything like a real view of the secrets of the wild.

Even the least shy of the wilderness folk are averse to going about their private and personal affairs under the eyes of strangers, and what the Boy aspired to was the knowledge of how to catch them off their guard. He would learn to see for himself how the rabbits and the partridges, the woodchucks and the weasels, the red deer, the porcupines, and all the other furtive folk who had their habitations around the tranquil shores of Lake Silverwater, were accustomed to behave when they felt quite sure no one was looking.

Before consenting to the Boy's initiation, Uncle Andy had impressed upon him with the greatest care the enormity of breaking the spell of stillness by even the slightest and most innocent-seeming movement.

"You see," said Uncle Andy, "it's this way! When we get to the place where we are going to hide and watch, you may think that we're quite alone. But not so. From almost every bush, from surely every thicket, there'll be at least one pair of bright eyes staring at us—maybe several pairs. They'll be wondering what we've come for; they'll be disliking us for being so clumsy and making such a racket, and they'll be keeping just as still as so many stones in the hope that we won't see them—except, of course, certain of the birds, which fly in the open and are used to being seen, and don't care a hang for us because they think us such poor creatures in not being able to fly.

"But it's a curious thing about the wild creatures, or at least about a great many of them, that for all their keenness they don't seem to distinguish things as sharply as we do. The very slightest movement they detect, sometimes at an astonishing distance. But when a person is perfectly motionless for a long time, they seem to confuse him with the stumps and stones and bushes. If you go on the way you're beginning (and I'm bound to say you're doing very well indeed, considering that you're not *very* big), you'll often have occasion to observe that some of the wild creatures, otherwise no fools, are more afraid of a bit of colored rag fluttering in the wind than of an able-bodied man who sits staring right at them, if only he doesn't stir a finger. But only let him wiggle that finger, his very littlest one, and off they'll go."

The Boy put his hand behind his back and wiggled his little finger gently, smiling to think what sharp eyes it would take to see that motion. But his Uncle went on to say:

"It's not as if those sly, shy watchers were all in front of you, you know. The suspicious eyes will be all around you. Perhaps it may be a tiny wood-mouse peering from under a root two or three steps behind you. You have been perfectly still, say, for ten minutes, and the mouse is just beginning to think that you may be something quite harmless. She rubs her whiskers, and is just about to come out when, as likely as not, you move your fingers a little, behind your back"—here the Boy blushed guiltily, and thrust both his fists well to the front—"feeling quite safe because you don't see the movement yourself.

"Well, the mouse sees it. She realizes at once that you aren't dead, after all. She whisks indignantly back into her hole. Somebody else sees her alarm, and follows her example, and in two seconds it's gone all about the place that you're not a stump or a stone or a harmless dead thing waiting to be nibbled at, but a terrible enemy lying in wait for them all. So you see how important it is to keep still."

The Boy winked his eyes rapidly. "But I can't keep from winking, Uncle Andy," he protested. "I'll promise not to wiggle my fingers or wrinkle my nose. But if I don't wink my eyes sometimes they'll begin to smart and get full of tears, and then I won't be able to see anything—and then all the keeping still will be just wasted."

"Of course, you won't be able to keep from winking," agreed Uncle Andy. "And, of course, you won't be able to keep from breathing. But you mustn't make a noise about either process."

"How can I make a noise winking?" demanded the Boy in a voice of eager surprise. If such a thing were possible he wanted to learn how at once.

"Oh, nonsense!" returned Uncle Andy. "Now, listen to me! We're nearly there, and I don't want to have to do any more talking, because the quieter we are now the sooner the wild folk will get over their first suspiciousness. Now, after we once get fixed, you won't move a muscle, not even if two or three mosquitoes alight on you at once and begin to help themselves?"

"No!" agreed the Boy confidently.

"Well, we'll hope there won't be any mosquitoes!" said Uncle Andy reassuringly. "And if a yellow jacket lights on your sock and starts to crawl up under the leg of your knickers, you won't stir?"

"N-no!" agreed the Boy, with somewhat less confidence. He had had such an experience before, and remembered it with a pang. Then he remembered that he had enough string in his pockets to tie up both legs so securely that not the most enterprising of wasps could get under. His confidence returned. "No, Uncle Andy!" he repeated, with earnest resolution.

"Umph! We'll see," grunted Uncle Andy doubtfully, not guessing what the Boy had in mind. But when he saw him fish out two bits of string from his pocket, he grinned appreciatively.

The place for watching had been well chosen by Uncle Andy—a big log to lean their backs against, a cushion of deep, dry moss to sit upon, and a tiny sapling of silver poplar twinkling its leaves just before their faces, to screen them a little without interfering with their view. Their legs, to be sure, stuck out beyond the screen of the poplar sapling, in plain sight of every forest wayfarer. But legs were of little consequence so long as they did not move.

For just about a minute the Boy found it easy to keep still. In the second minute his nose itched, and he began to wonder how long they had been there. In the third minute he realized that there was a hard little stick in the moss that he was sitting on. In the fourth minute it became a big stick, and terribly sharp, so that he began to wonder if it would pierce right through him and make him a cripple for life. By the ninth minute, both legs began to fill up with pins and needles. But he remembered his promise. His grit was good, and he determined to keep his promise at all costs, no matter at what fatal consequences to his legs.

Then, as the tenth minute dragged its trailing length along, came that terrible feeling that he must either move or burst. But, fortunately for him, before he felt himself obliged to come to any final decision, something happened, and his pain and doubts were forgotten.

Two big yellow-gray snowshoe rabbits came hopping lazily past, one just ahead of the other. One jumped clean over Uncle Andy's outstretched feet, as if they were of no account or interest whatever to a rabbit. The other stopped and thumped vigorously on the ground with his strong hind foot. At this signal the first one also stopped. They both sat up on their haunches, ears thrust forward in intense questioning, and gazed at the two motionless figures behind the poplar sapling.

The one immediately in front of him absorbed all the Boy's attention. Its great, bulging eyes surveyed him from head to foot, at first with some alarm, then with half-contemptuous curiosity. Its immensely long ears see-sawed meditatively, and its queer three-cornered mouth twinkled incessantly as if it were talking to itself. At last, apparently having decided that the Boy was nothing worth taking further notice of, it dropped on all fours, nibbled at a leaf, discarded it, and hopped off to find more tasty food. Its companion, having "sized up" Uncle Andy in the same way, presently followed. But being of a more suspicious disposition, it stopped from time to time to glance back and assure itself that the strange, motionless things behind the poplar sapling were not attempting to follow it.

The Boy was immensely interested. He thought of a lot of questions to ask as soon as he should be allowed to speak, and he resolved to remember every one of them. But just as he was getting them arranged a small, low, long-bodied, snaky-slim, yellowish beast came gliding by and drove them all out of his head. It was a weasel. It almost bumped into the Boy's feet before it noticed them. Then it jumped back, showing its keen teeth in a soundless snarl, and surveyed the Boy with the cruellest little eyes that he had ever imagined. The savage eyes stared him full in the face, a red light like a deep-buried spark coming into them, till he thought the creature was going to spring at his throat. Then gradually the spark died out, as the little furry creature reassured itself. The triangular face turned aside. The working, restless nose sniffed sharply and caught the fresh scent of the two rabbits; in the next instant the creature was off, in long, noiseless bounds, upon the hot trail. The Boy knew enough of woodcraft to realize at once the meaning of its sudden departure, and he thought to himself, "Oh, I do hope he won't catch them!"

All thoughts of the weasel and the rabbits, however, were speedily driven from his mind, for at this moment he noticed a fat, yellowish grub, with a chestnut-colored head, crawling up his sleeve. He hated grubs, and wondered anxiously if it had any unpleasant design of crawling down his neck. He squirmed inwardly at the idea. But just as he was coming to the conclusion that that was something he'd never be able to stand, a most unexpected ally came to his rescue. With a blow that almost made him jump out of his jacket, something lit on the fat grub.

It was a big black hornet, with white bands across its shining body. She gave the grub a tiny prick with the tip of her envenomed sting, which caused it to roll up into a tight ball and lie still. Then straddling it, and holding it in place with her front pair of legs, she cut into it with her powerful mandibles and began to suck its juices. The Boy's nose wrinkled in spite of himself at sight of this unalluring banquet, but he stared with all his eyes. There was something terrifying to him in the swiftness and efficiency of the great hornet.

Presently the grub, not having received quite a big enough dose of its captor's anesthetic, came to under the devouring jaws and began to lash out convulsively. Another touch of the medicine in the hornet's tail, however, promptly put a stop to that, and once more it tightened up into an unresisting ball. Then straddling it again firmly, and handling it cleverly with her front legs as a raccoon might handle a big apple, the hornet bit into it here and there, sucking eagerly with a quick, pumping motion of her body. The fat ball got smaller and smaller, till soon it was no bigger than an ordinary pea. The hornet turned it over and over impatiently, to see if anything more was to be got out of it; then she spurned it aside, and bounced into the air with a deep hum.

When the hornet was gone, the Boy began once more to remember that little stick in the soft moss beneath him. He decided that he must have been sitting on it for hours and hours. But just as it was beginning to burn its way into his flesh, a queer little rushing sound close at his side brought his heart into his throat. It was such a vicious, menacing little sound. Glancing down, he saw that a tiny woodmouse had darted upon a big brown-winged butterfly and captured it. The butterfly's big wings flapped for a few seconds; but the mouse bit them off, to save herself the bother of lugging useless material home to her burrow. She was so near that the Boy could have touched her by reaching out his hand. But she took no more notice of him than if he had been a rotten stump.

Less, in fact, for she might have tried to gnaw into him if he had been a rotten stump, in the hope of finding some wood-grubs.

The mouse dragged away the velvety body of the butterfly to her hole under the roots. She was no more than just in time, for no sooner was she out of sight than along came a fierce-eyed little shrew-mouse, the most audacious and pugnacious of the mouse tribe, who would undoubtedly have robbed her of her prey, and perhaps made a meal of her at the same time. He nosed at the wings of the butterfly, nibbled at them, decided they were no good, and then came ambling over to the Boy's feet.

Shoe leather! That was something quite new to him. He nibbled at it, didn't seem to think much of it, crept along up to the top of the shoe, sniffed at the sock, and came at last plump upon the Boy's bare leg. "Was he going to try a nibble at that, too?" wondered the Boy anxiously. But no. This live, human flesh—unmistakably alive—and the startling Man smell of it, were too much for him. With a squeak of indignation and alarm, he sprang backward and scurried off among the weed stalks.

"There, now!" thought the Boy, in intense vexation. "He's gone and given the alarm!" But, as good luck would have it, he had done nothing of the kind. For a red fox, trotting past just then at a distance of not more than ten or a dozen feet, served to all observers as a more than ample explanation of the shrew's abrupt departure. The fox turned his head at the sound of the scurry and squeak, and very naturally attributed it to his own appearance on the scene. But at the same time he caught sight of those two motionless human shapes sitting rigid behind the poplar sapling. They were so near that his nerves received a shock. He jumped about ten feet; and then, recovering himself with immense self-possession, he sat up on his haunches to investigate.

Of course, he was quite familiar with human beings and their ways, and he knew that they never kept still in that unnatural fashion unless they were either asleep or dead. After a searching scrutiny—head sagely to one side and mouth engagingly half open—he decided that they might be either dead or asleep for all he cared. He rose to his feet and trotted off with great deliberation, leaving on the still air a faint, half-musky odor which the Boy's nostrils were keen enough to detect. As he went a bluejay, which had been sitting on the top of a near-by tree, caught sight of him, darted down, and flew along after him, uttering harsh screeches of warning to the rest of the small folk of the wilderness. It is not pleasant even in the wilderness, to have "Stop thief! Stop thief! Thief! Thief! Thief!" screeched after you by a bluejay. The fox glanced up at the noisy bird as if he were willing to give two fat geese and a whole litter of rabbits for the pleasure of crunching her impudent neck.

All this while there had been other birds in view besides the bluejay—chick-a-dees and nut-hatches hunting their tiny prey among the dark branches of the fir-trees, Canada sparrows fluting their clear call from the tree tops, flycatchers darting and tumbling in their zigzag, erratic flights, and sometimes a big golden-wing woodpecker running up and down a tall, dead trunk which stood close by, and *rat-tat-tat-tat-ing* in a most businesslike and determined manner.

The Boy was not, as a rule, as interested in birds as in the four-footed animals. Just now, however, a bird came on the scene which interested him extremely. It was a birch-partridge (or ruffled grouse) hen, accompanied by a big brood of her tiny, nimble chicks. They looked no bigger than chestnuts as they swarmed about her, crowding to snatch the dainties which she kept turning up for them. The Boy watched them with fascinated eyes, not understanding how things so tiny and so frail as these chicks could be so amazingly quick and strong in their movements. Suddenly, at a little distance through the bushes, he caught sight of the red fox coming back, with an air of having forgotten something.

The Boy longed to warn the little partridge mother, but, realizing that he must not, he waited with thumping heart for a tragedy to be enacted before him.

He had no need to worry, however. The little mother saw the fox before he caught sight of her. The Boy saw her stiffen herself suddenly, with a low *chit* of warning which sounded as if it might have come from anywhere. On the instant every chick had vanished. The Boy realized that it was impossible for even such active creatures as they were to have run away so quickly as all that. So he knew that they had just made themselves invisible by squatting absolutely motionless among the twigs and moss which they so exactly resembled in coloring.

The fox, meanwhile, had been gazing around in every direction but the right one, to try and see where that partridge cry had come from. He liked partridge, and it was some time since he had had any. All at once he was surprised and pleased to see a hen partridge, apparently badly wounded, drop fluttering on the moss almost under his nose. He sprang forward to seize her, but she managed to flutter feebly out of his reach. It was obviously her last effort, and he was not in the least discouraged. She proved, however, to have many such last efforts, and the last the Boy saw of the fox he was still hopefully jumping at her, as he disappeared from view in the underbrush.

About three minutes later there was a hard *whirr* of wings, and the triumphant little mother reappeared. She alighted on the very spot where she had first caught sight of the fox, stood for a moment stiffly erect while she stared about her with keen, bright eyes, and then she gave a soft little call. Instantly the chicks were all about her, apparently springing up out of the ground. And proudly she led them away to another feeding ground.

What more the Boy might have seen will never be known, for now the session was interrupted. He was hoping for a porcupine to come by, or a deer, or a moose. He was half-hoping, half-fearing that it might be a bear, or a big Canadian lynx with dreadful eyes and tufted ears. But before any of these more formidable creatures arrived he heard a sound of rushing, of eager, desperate flight. Then a rabbit came into view—he felt sure it was one of the two who had appeared at the beginning of his watch. The poor beast was in terror, running violently, but aimlessly, and every now and then stopping short, all a-tremble, as if in despair. It ran straight past the poplar sapling, swerved to the right, and disappeared; but the Boy could hear the sound of its going and perceived that it was making a circle. A couple of seconds later came the weasel, running with its nose in the air, as if catching the scent from the air rather than from the fugitive's tracks.

The weasel did not seem to be in any hurry at all. And the Boy hated it savagely. Just opposite the poplar sapling it paused, seeming to listen. Then it bounded into the bushes on a short circle, saving itself unnecessary effort, as if it had accurately estimated the tactics of its panic-stricken quarry. A few moments later the rabbit reappeared, running frantically. Just as it came once more before the poplar sapling —not more than a couple of yards from the Boy's feet, out from under a neighboring bush sprang the weasel. With a scream the rabbit stopped short and crouched in its tracks, quivering, to receive its doom.

The weasel leaped straight at its victim's throat. But it never arrived. For at that moment the Boy gave vent to a shrill yell of indignation and jumped at the slayer with hands, eyes, and mouth wide open. He made such a picture that Uncle Andy broke out laughing. The astonished weasel vanished. The rabbit, shocked back into its senses, vanished also, but in another direction. And the Boy, pulling himself together, turned to his uncle with a very red face.

"I'm sorry!" he said sheepishly. "I'm so sorry, Uncle Andy, but I just couldn't help it."

"Oh, well!" said Uncle Andy, getting up and stretching, and rubbing his stiffened legs, "I can't say that I blame you. I came mighty near doing the same thing myself."

## THE HORNY ONES[1]

*Edith M. Patch*
and
*Carroll Lane Fenton*

### CORNU

Cornu was lucky. It was now October, and no one had taken him away from his desert home. A great many things had happened to him since he awoke from his winter's sleep last March, but all had ended pleasantly for him.

One day early in the spring of that year, a boy called Bob had picked him up near a road and carried him to his father.

"Daddy," Bob said, "look at the Texas horned toad I found. When he tries to get out of my hands, I just tickle him on top of his head or under his chin, and then he stays as quiet as if he were tamed!"

Was the queer little creature that Bob cuddled in his hands really a toad, as many people call him? Did you ever see a toad with scales on his body and claws on his feet? Well, Cornu had scales and claws. Then, too, when Cornu had been quite young, even on his very first day, he looked about like his father and mother except that he was tiny. He never had a tadpole babyhood, such as frogs and toads have—with a shape quite different from those of his parents. No, Cornu was not a toad. He was a *lizard*.

Bob played with Cornu for a while and then said, "I like him. He's comical. Shall we take him home for a pet?"

"If you like him well *enough,* Bob," answered Father, "you will let him stay in the desert. Horned lizards can be kept alive in zoos where they are given all they need—just the right temperature and plenty of proper food. But in people's homes, like ours, they usually die after a few weeks or months."

Bob decided that he liked Cornu "well enough" to let him live in the desert where he belonged. But he did not think that the little lizard was safe near a road where many travelers passed. Perhaps someone would find him there and take him away from the hot climate that agreed so well with him. So Bob carried Cornu to a place where few people cared to go, and put him down in the sand beside some tall yucca plants.

The next morning Cornu waited a while where Bob had hidden him, blinking in the sunshine. The sun would need to warm his body before he could move quickly enough to catch any insects for his breakfast.

Cornu had not had many breakfasts that spring. Indeed, only a few days before, he was lying in a dark hole, where he had been since sometime in November. The hole had been started by a mouse, but Cornu made it bigger and deeper to fit his own body. Then he lay still and went to sleep. His eyes shut, his body grew stiff, and his legs stuck out awkwardly. Now and then, but not often, he took short, jerky breaths which showed that he was still alive.

At last the spring sunshine warmed Cornu's hole. His body stopped being cold and stiff, and his eyes began to open. One afternoon he wriggled his legs and crawled to the surface of the ground. Soon he was spry enough to walk and to catch a small black beetle that ran across the brown sand near him.

If you were as small as that beetle, Cornu would look very big to you—big and very, very fierce. Yet he measured only about four inches from his nose to the tip of his tail. His tail was stubby, and his body was wide. His short legs could run quickly for a dash of a yard or so, but they could not go fast very far.

Why did he look so very fierce? Because he had a great many horny spines. Some of them stuck out behind his head, others were arranged in two rows on his sides,

[1] From Edith M. Patch and Carroll Lane Fenton, *Desert Neighbors.*

while many covered his back and tail. They made his brown and buff skin rough. They also helped him to look like the bare ground as long as he kept still. Of course, nothing can look like ground while it moves its head or wriggles or runs.

There were some brownish-red ants near the yuccas where Bob had left Cornu. After eating a few of these, he rambled about until he came to a regular ant path which ran among small clumps of grass. This path was used by harvesting ants, and Cornu stopped beside it and waited for something to come.

Soon he saw two ants, each carrying a grass seed. First Cornu stood almost on tiptoe, head high and tail twitching. As the ants came near, down went Cornu's head and out shot his sticky tongue. He swallowed the first ant with a gulp and hurried to catch the second. Then he returned to watch the path. Cornu caught fifty or sixty ants before he was ready to leave this good hunting place and take a nap in the sunshine.

A few mornings later Cornu found a new ant path and began to catch another breakfast. But just after he took his first ant, a brown beetle crawled into sight. Cornu turned his head to watch, twitching his stubby tail. Then he raised himself high on his front legs and leaned forward. He put down his head and thrust out his tongue. The sticky tongue pulled the beetle off the ground, but not quite into Cornu's mouth. Cornu jumped back, puffed his body out and seemed to wonder, "What will you do now?" The beetle started to walk away, so Cornu followed it for several feet, scrambling over sand and pebbles. Then he caught it with his jaws (not his tongue!) and managed to swallow the big mouthful. That beetle contained more food than several dozen ants and was worth the extra work of catching it, even though its shell-like skin was hard and its feet scratched him as he gulped.

In May, Cornu met his mate. She was larger than he was, and her back was lighter. The spots behind her head were a chocolate brown, and the spines on her sides were light yellow. She was really just as good-looking as Cornu, even though her complexion was not so dark.

Mr. and Mrs. Cornu played a great many games of tag under the creosote bushes. They also dodged round the long, sharp-tipped leaves of yucca, or "Spanish bayonet." They never seemed to hurt themselves on the hard points of the "bayonets," or to get stuck on cactus spines or torn by mesquite thorns. Yet any person who had tried to catch them would have got some very bad pricks.

Both Mr. and Mrs. Cornu liked to play and hunt for ants late in the morning. Some horned lizards of other kinds, who live in drier, warmer deserts, like the hottest part of the afternoon a great deal better. Cornu and his mate did not know anything about their relatives, but they did feel too lazy, during hot afternoons, to do much more than rest in some safe, shady corner.

One day Cornu's mate did not wait to play with him but ran away by herself. She went to a dry, bare hillside and began to dig a small hole. She scratched the dirt loose with her front feet and pushed it away with her hind ones. When the hole was seven inches deep, she laid six yellowish eggs, each about one-half inch long. Then she packed dirt around them, laid six new eggs, and covered them with dirt. She kept busy in this way until she had four layers—twenty-four eggs all tucked away. After filling up the nest, she went hunting for ants and caught a beetle or two besides.

As she went back down the hill, something swooped over her head. Mother Cornu stopped and puffed out her body, but she did not need to be afraid. The hawk had seen what she was and he knew too much to eat anything as spiny as that. To be sure, Churca, the road runner, might have captured her; but even that lizard-eating bird would not have swallowed such a spiny head as this horned lizard had, though Churca sometimes ate less spiny horned lizards.

It was one day in July that Cornu climbed that same hill. He was wandering toward a sunny slope where there were flies to catch. On the way, he stopped to see what was wriggling in the sand. The ground stirred and heaved while he watched—and out came two dozen soft brown things that looked very much like Cornu himself. Why not, since they had just hatched from eggs that Mother Cornu had laid seven weeks before?

But Father Cornu did not understand that these tiny horned lizards were his own children—each looking as he had looked two years ago. As a matter of fact, they did not even interest him, now that he saw that they were nothing he cared to eat and nothing that would hurt him. He merely turned away from them and went on up the hill to a place where some flies were sunning themselves on little gray and white stones. Flies, now, were much more important to him than his family—for he was hungry and these insects would make a very good luncheon.

The next twelve weeks were rather quiet ones for Cornu. Then, one day in October, he had a really exciting adventure. As he walked down a trail he met a stray, hungry, ranch dog. The dog pushed Cornu with his paw, but he seemed afraid to bite. He would not like to get those horny spines into his mouth.

Cornu puffed out his body, lowered his head, and ran toward the timid dog. The dog backed away but stuck out his paw and barked *"wow!"* very sharply. He felt a bit braver after he had barked, so he put his nose rather close to Cornu and sniffed. That sniff was too much for the lizard. His neck grew stiff, his eyes swelled and bulged, and he made a hissing sound. From a corner of each eyelid went jets of blood that hit the dog in the face. By that time the dog had had enough of horned "toads," and dashed off down the trail as scared as if he had met an enormous foe—instead of a little puffed-up lizard. Cornu lay quiet for two or three minutes and then went to hide under a prickly-pear cactus. There he rested an hour or so before going off to catch bees or ants for luncheon.

### SHORTHORN

Shorthorn was a relative of Cornu, for she was a horned lizard, too, though of a different kind.

Shorthorn lived in a valley far from the home of Cornu and his mate. The valley is between high mountains with pine trees growing on their slopes. The climate in this valley is so mild that Shorthorn could live in the open almost until Christmas. She could come out of her hole earlier in the spring than Cornu—while he still was stiff and chilly. That gave her more time to hunt and eat, or to sleep under the prickly chollas, in whose branches cactus wrens like to nest.

Shorthorn was bigger and darker than Cornu, and she had shorter horns on her head. Her back had black blotches and big brick-red spots, and the sides of her face were dark pink. She had only one row of spines on each side, where Cornu had two.

She was different from Cornu in another way, too. As you will remember, when Mother Cornu was ready to lay her eggs, she put them in a hole and pushed dry dirt over them. Shorthorn did not lay her eggs at all, but kept them inside her body while she slept, caught ants, and snapped at grasshoppers. Then, one day in the first week of August, thirty baby Shorthorns were born—or really *hatched* inside their mother.

## JIMMIE, THE WHITE SPARROW[1]

*Padraic Colum*

The Luxembourg Gardens are the center of Paris, and the Medici Fountain is at the very center of the Luxembourg Gardens. All of us know this. And in the center of the Medici Fountain, just above where the statue of the River God is stooping over

[1] From Padraic Colum, *The White Sparrow.*

the two figures that are just above the water, there is a sparrow's nest.

It is in a very important place, and the owner of it thought of himself as a very important member of the sparrow community. And all the little sparrows that grew up in that nest were proud of their father and proud of their home.

"Look," they would hear their father say, "the pigeons are coming down to drink our water."

As the little sparrows looked out of their nest (it was a very big, loose nest made of all sorts of materials that had been collected in all sorts of places) they saw big, awkward birds—pigeons, they knew—coming down and sipping the water just below their nest, and they thought what a grand person their father was to allow the big, awkward pigeons to come down and drink there.

Many families had been reared in the big, loose nest that was just above the fountain, and all who came out of it were the finest kind of sparrows—healthy, busy, sure of themselves, no way different from other sparrows except in being a little bit more healthy, busy, and sure of themselves than were the sparrows they mixed with.

But misfortune is bound to come even into the best situated of nests, and one year, out of five eggs that the mother sparrow laid, only one bird came. When the down on the little bird changed into feathers, the feathers were white—not brown with black marks on them, but white. This little sparrow's breast was white, and his wings down to their edges were white, and his back and tail down to its tip were white; in fact there were only little bits of real sparrow color going round the edge of his tail and wings—trimmings, one might say, trimmings on feathers white as the froth on the water below the nest.

Of course this was a terrible thing to have happened in a family of such well-known sparrows. But the father and mother made the best of it. Anyway, Jimmie could fly and keep himself warm, and this, they said, was what feathers were for. His father and mother told the elder sparrows to keep their youngsters polite when Jimmie came among them—they were not to make remarks about his peculiar color.

His mother first and his father afterwards flew down from the nest, showing him the way, and then called to him from where they stayed. He shook his wings, but he did not like leaving the nest. His father and his mother were telling him different things to do, and the pigeons were flying down and dipping their beaks in the water, and his father and his mother seemed quite little birds when he saw them so far below! It was a very strange world, Jimmie thought, so wide and big and so full of things he had never thought of. But Jimmie flew down at last. He was on the ground, shaking his wings, and his father and mother were putting bits into his beak.

"You'd better have a good breakfast today. I'll come back with something else!"

They were gone, and there he was, shaking his wings and calling to his father and mother.

But when he had been fed for the second time, his father came up and said, "No more of this. He has to come along now."

So Jimmie with his father and mother fluttered over to the grass where a crowd of young sparrows were hopping about.

"This is called a lawn," said his father to him, "and I want you to understand that it is a very exceptional lawn. As lawns go there is no better in the world. Only sparrows belonging to this particular place have a right to be on it. These are leaves that are being blown across the grass. You needn't pay any attention to them. Just do as you see the other youngsters do, and don't mind if they make remarks about your appearance. They always make remarks about the appearance of newcomers.

"They are picking at the roots of the grass. If you get something there—a seed or anything of the kind—eat it without calling to me or your mother. But you won't get anything—very few of the others do. It's just an exercise in picking things up —just as good if you pick up nothing at all; it's part of being educated, you see! Run along, now!"

Jimmie went among the other young sparrows. They gathered round him, and had a lot of talk about his looks; but he didn't mind that so much, for he had been prepared for it. Of course he didn't see how extraordinary he was—a white little bird hopping among all the brown little ones. After shaking his wings and giving a lonesome squeak or two he went hopping about like the others. He picked at the ends of grass whether there was anything there or not, just as the others did. And he began to enjoy doing it. The grass was lovely with the sun shining on it, and the leaves blowing across it, and the other youngsters hopping here and there, this one and that one getting a real something sometimes.

A big bird came upon the lawn. He wasn't as big as a pigeon, but he was big sized. A blackbird, Jimmie heard him called. He ran at a crowd of sparrow youngsters and drove them away. The youngsters didn't mind much; they fluttered to a distance, and then went on doing what they had been doing before. Jimmie saw the blackbird pull something out of the ground and eat it all up. It was no wonder, Jimmie thought, that he was so big and so rushing, eating things like that. And then the blackbird made a rush toward him.

But he stopped as if surprised and looked Jimmie all over. "Are you a what-do-you-call-'em that are in cages—a canary?" he asked.

Jimmie fluttered his wings and showed him the nest he had come from.

"Oh, a 'spadger,' are you?" said the blackbird. "How did you get like that?"

But he didn't wait for Jimmie to tell him anything, but rushed toward where the youngsters were flocking, and made them hop and flutter away. Jimmie wondered why the fathers didn't come down and do something to that blackbird. Then he felt very downhearted. The blackbird had called him a "spadger," naming the sparrows in that way, which showed that he didn't think much of them. And he had looked him over as if he thought Jimmie was a queer sort of bird. What did he mean by pretending to think that he was a canary? Jimmy looked toward where the other youngsters had flocked, and saw them all busy, all nice looking with their brown feathers with black markings on them, and knew there could be nothing wrong about being a sparrow.

And then he saw his own breast and saw it was different—white. He fluttered his wings and, looking at them, saw that they were white except for their very ends. He was queer—he knew that now. He wished he hadn't come upon the lawn where everybody looked at him. He wished he could go back to his nest and stay there. He crouched upon the grass and made a cry like a very young bird. No one came to him, and he felt so downhearted that he wouldn't have cared if the sky fell down on him.

The other youngsters gathered all around him, all so brown and so lively, and all chirruping so cheerfully. "Come on, white chap," they called, "get a move on. Don't stick there like a lost canary."

Jimmie went hopping and fluttering with them. He could never be as light hearted as they were, he knew, but he would try to keep busy like them. So he hopped with them, and chirruped with them, and did everything they did. And before they had crossed the lawn he was just as lively as the others. Sparrows are like that.

His father and mother came to where the youngsters were, and when they started away Jimmie fluttered with them. He wanted to get back to his nest, but he knew that if he tried to fly so high, he would fall into the water. So, with his father and mother he went and perched on a branch a little above the ground and rested there. He did no more running about on the lawn. He was fed; darkness came, and he went to sleep outside the nest, and was wakened up by a lot of different birds singing all around him. He was very numb.

It was not like wakening up in the big, loose nest. But he hopped about a bit and so warmed himself up.

The advantage of living in a city is that such little notice is taken of one. Jimmie had this advantage. After they had once taken stock of him in the Gardens the sparrows, young and old, made no more fuss about his appearance. He went everywhere with the flock of youngsters and was treated exactly like the others—he was a sparrow, no more and no less. And so he was to be seen in the noisy crowd around a bench from which crumbs of bread were being cast, or fluttering across the lawn and picking at the grass roots, or flying up to the branches of the trees, or perching on the head or the outstretched arm of a statue, or picking grains of sand from the gravel walks.

A very busy and stirring life it was indeed—every minute there was something doing! Jimmie got to know, by sight at least, the other birds that shared the Gardens with the sparrows. There was the blackbird that ran upon the lawn in a really angry way and dug up worms still more angrily, and the big pigeons whom the sparrows considered very lazy fellows—loafers—and the redbreasts who, for all their difference in size and color, were relations of the blackbirds. Each of the redbreasts had a little strip of ground for himself which he would let nobody else come upon. Jimmie was told he had better keep away from the ground a redbreast had.

Once, after a rather tiring day, Jimmie was resting with his head under his wing below some bushes. The dusk was coming on and just as he was about to decide that after another tour round the Gardens with his companions he would get ready to go to sleep, he heard something quite new and strange to him. His companions, clustered around a pool that the rain had made, were keeping up the usual din. But this was not what awakened Jimmie's attention. What he heard over the noise that his companions were making was a very sweet sound repeated over and over again. It was a song—Jimmie knew this at once though it was the first time he had heard a bird's song. He wakened up at once and listened. The song came from where a redbreast had his park—under the bushes, beyond a statue.

Jimmie was charmed. He wondered why the others didn't stop their chatter and listen to such lovely sounds. It was a redbreast that was singing. Jimmie could see him, he was perched on a low branch. He sang the same song several times over, a song about the suns that were gone, and the skies that used to be so blue, and the trees that had such beautiful leaves. It was a lovely song, and Jimmie was delighted to know that there was such a singer in the gardens, and that he had a chance of listening to him.

The redbreast stopped singing, and after a while Jimmie hopped over to where he was perched. As he came near, the redbreast left his perch and came to meet him, looking quite furious. "Don't you know," he said threateningly, "that you've come upon my ground?"

"I know," Jimmie answered.

"Well, keep off!" said the redbreast.

"That was a lovely song of yours," said Jimmie.

"What are you?" asked the redbreast. "I haven't seen your like around here before."

"I'm a sparrow," said Jimmie.

The redbreast looked at him and reflected for a moment. Jimmie could see he was a bird given to reflection. "A white sparrow," he said. "Remarkable! I had a grandmother who was a white robin."

"Did you like her?" Jimmie asked.

"Not very well," the redbreast said. "What are you waiting about here for?"

"Won't you sing again?" said Jimmie.

"No," said the redbreast. "I'm through." He went behind the bushes.

Jimmie now went where the sparrow crowd was.

"Oh, here you are!" they said. "Give an account of yourself!"

"I was listening to something," said Jimmie in what he thought was a very tuneful voice.

The others had already forgotten they had asked him anything, and were going on in the usual way, everyone talking and no one listening to anything that was being said, and everyone saying the most ordinary things. What an uproar! It made Jimmie dizzy to listen to it. What was the matter with the sparrows, anyway, that they had to behave in that noisy way? The other birds in the Gardens made no such disturbance.

Then the larger part of the flock flew away and there was quietness among the three or four that remained, among whom was Jimmie's father.

"What about the songs that we can hear?" said Jimmie to his father.

"Songs!" said his father.

"Like that the redbreast sings."

"Well, what of it?" said his father, hopping toward a crumb that was thrown.

"I was wondering," said Jimmie when his father came back, "what the sparrows think of the song I heard."

"The redbreast wastes his time, of course," said Jimmie's father, "but that has nothing to do with us."

"Wastes his time?"

"He spent five minutes singing, didn't he? And he sings again and again. And then think of the time lost getting ready to sing. Just fancy the amount of time the youngsters waste listening to their father singing, and the amount of time the fathers waste teaching the youngsters. We sparrows have cut all that out. We say what we want to say, and that ends it. You don't hear the sparrows sitting on a branch one by one and singing!"

"I should have thought that it was very nice to sing," said Jimmie.

"Well, sparrows gave it up long ago," said his father, "and sparrows have the keenest minds of all the birds. We keep up with the times. We are progressive, you know."

"Progressive—what is that?" asked Jimmie.

"Being like us. Do any of the singers manage to live in cities and keep up big populations? No, indeed. Some of our relations sing. You'll hear the hedge sparrow sometime if you are interested in that kind of thing. The hedge sparrow can do better than the redbreast, I've heard. But what's the good? The hedge sparrows live in the country. And they have no grip on life—no real grip, I'm sorry to say."

All the time they were talking, the din that went with the sparrows' scramble was going on. No other birds were to be heard. No sound came to Jimmie except the chatter and clatter that his companions made. What did the birds that sang think of the birds that made such uproar? Jimmie wondered. Birds that were always telling the world that they were there and that they wanted something. The other birds must think very little of the sparrows—they must look down on them.

As Jimmie thought sadly about this he noticed a small sparrow looking at him. He had seen her before. She was a very little sparrow, and Jemima was her name. She was trying now to say something to him. Then Jimmie remembered what he had heard about her. There had been a very long session in a tree the other day, and everyone had talked and shouted, and this little thing, trying to say something, had lost her voice. She couldn't say anything now. That was the reason that she was shaking her wings and opening her mouth at him.

Jimmie thought that it was nice that she was different from the others. He let her come with him when he flew off. He let her keep beside him the next day. The day after, they left the flock and made tours of the Gardens together, Jimmie and Jemima. And together they listened to the redbreast's song in the evening.

One day Jimmie went alone far out into the country, where he stayed for a time and had some very discouraging, yet very interesting experiences. Being a white sparrow did not make life easier, and he was much wiser when at last he made his way back to the city.

He came back again to the Gardens. Sparrows were flying about, not in the flocks that he expected to see, but in pairs. They were talking to one another, flying up on walls with straws in their beaks, and flying down again and hurrying to some other place. All were so busy that they scarcely paid any attention to him, and they made no remarks whatever about his appearance.

He came to the Fountain. He saw the big pigeons flying down and drinking out of the water, and he saw the big loose nest above, and thought that it was a grand thing, after all, to be a sparrow and to be in possession of that place with statue and water and all. There were birds in the nest above pulling straws about and putting feathers in, and they were his father and mother. Jimmie sat on a stone below, and cheeped, and shook out his wings.

His mother saw him. "Jimmie, Jimmie!" she cried, and rushed down to him.

His father flew down too. "Why, it's Jimmie back again," he said. "What have you been doing, young fellow?"

Jimmie got ready to tell the story of his trip to the country but, just as he began, his father's eye lighted on a straw and he picked it up.

"We're doing some renovating in the nest," said his mother, "so your father is very much occupied."

His father flew up with the straw, and when he came back he said to Jimmie, "You'll be looking for a place of your own one of these days. I'd like to show you around, but I can't leave off for a few days. You must be delighted to be among us all again."

His mother was above at the time. She hopped into the nest and stayed there, and Jimmie felt that he couldn't really talk to them now. So away he flew. He flew around the Gardens, meeting sparrows whom he knew; but they had very little to say to him, and he said hardly anything to them, for he could see that they were all taken up with their own affairs.

It was delightful being in the Gardens, Jimmie thought; there was blue in the sky, and the trees were beginning to look as if they wouldn't always be bare. Still, it was lonely for him, and he would have been glad if any of the sparrows he knew, had shown some interest in his return—if only to make remarks about his odd appearance. As he flew around he was really looking for someone who would recognize him and welcome him back.

And then, on the outstretched hand of a statue, he saw a little sparrow. She looked as if she were lonely too. He flew up on a branch so as to have a real look at her. It was Jemima! He flew to her, and as soon as she saw him her wings shook in great excitement.

"Jimmie," she cried, but her voice was very low. "Jimmie, Jimmie!"

And Jemima listened to the story of Jimmie's trip to the country, and she had him tell it to her over and over again. Afterwards she begged him to take her to the country too. Jimmie did, but she was very nervous at the strange birds and animals they saw, so they decided to return to the city.

On their way back they came to a garden which Jemima declared was every bit as nice as the Luxembourg Gardens they had been brought up in. It was the Trocadéro Garden. The pair stayed there, their circuit being between the Museum and the Eiffel Tower.

A day or two after they arrived Jimmie began to take an interest in the great statuesque elephant that stands before the Museum. His interest was not in the whole of the elephant's body, but in the uplifted trunk and the opening below it—Jimmie's interest, in fact, was fixed on the elephant's mouth. No sooner did he notice it than he flew up on the trunk to look down into it, and no sooner had he looked down into it than he seized some straws and carried them in. He asked Jemima what she thought when she looked at that opening, and she said she thought of a nest. So they carried into the elephant's mouth all the things that go to make a sparrow's nest.

All the sparrows between the Eiffel Tower and the Trocadéro Museum were astonished that they had never thought of using such a wonderful site for a nest. An elephant with a sparrow's nest under his trunk—nothing could be more noteworthy! And there Jimmie and Jemima reared their brood of five. All of them had brown feathers with black marks on them, and all had the full use of their voices. The young ones were just like their grandfathers and grandmothers.

When Jimmie and Jemima would sit quietly together to listen to the song of the redbreast, the young ones would say, "What odd parents we have, to be sure! There's something about them that makes them different from other fellows' parents. They're clever—that's what it is. If they weren't, they wouldn't have been able to get that place for a nest. Everyone says we have come out of the most remarkable nest in the wide world."

## BEASTS OF THE TAR PITS[1]

*W. W. Robinson*

For countless millions of years great beasts ruled the world. That was before the time of man. Today the remains of these beasts are found in many lands.

In southern California, in the heart of present-day Los Angeles, the earth has kept a complete record of prehistoric animal life as it existed there during the last five hundred thousand years. It is in a place called Rancho La Brea, which lies in an oval valley flanked on the north by blue mountains, on the south by flat-topped hills, and opening to the west on the Pacific Ocean. Until fifty years ago rich grasses covered the scene. It was a region of springs, flowing streams, and gentle ravines. Here pools of tar, disguised with a thin layer of shining water, for unnumbered years lured huge creatures to their death. Their bones have been preserved to this day.

These beasts came from long distances to drink. They saw but did not heed the bubbles of gas that rose out of the water and the rainbow-colored streaks that meant oil. Wading or plunging into the cool waters, they were caught in the tar as if in quicksand. The roars and bellowings of these floundering creatures filled the air. Other beasts, attracted by the uproar, came not to aid the victims but to feast upon them. Deadly battles without number took place. The attackers were as likely to sink to their doom as the victims they had attacked.

Before the time of man, these great beasts ruled the world. Headed by the Imperial Mammoth, they have come forth from their asphalt graveyard at the summons of the scientist. Their bodies were not preserved, but their bones were. From them whole skeletons have been reconstructed. Today they stand in galleries of museums, and tell the story of that ancient time.

In the procession are not only the great creatures, but also such smaller ones as coyotes, turkey vultures, striped and spotted skunks, water beetles, pumas, the grasshopper mouse, kangaroo rats, ground fowl, black-tailed jack rabbits, peccaries, whooping cranes, tiny antelopes, storks, the great blue heron, toads, band-tailed pigeons, pigmy owls, the cedar waxwing, mudturtles, golden eagles, and a host of others. The small creatures for the most part are not extinct; their size and their ability to adapt themselves to changing surroundings worked in their favor. The huge and ferocious ones have for the most part vanished from the world.

Before man lived in America, Imperial Mammoths roamed over the southern part of the United States. They lived mostly west of the Mississippi River. Sometimes they traveled far down into Mexico.

These beasts looked like elephants but were much larger. Often they were thirteen feet high. From their upper jaws grew huge,

[1] From W. W. Robinson, *Beasts of the Tar Pits.*

curving tusks. To support their great bodies Imperial Mammoths had legs as strong as stone pillars. In their time they were the largest of land beasts and usually could defend themselves against even the giant prehistoric lions.

They rested in the hills during the day. Then when it was cool in the evening they came forth to the open country, to the rivers and water holes. They stood in water by the hour and covered their legs with wet mud so that they might have freedom from insects.

Young branches of trees with fresh green leaves were the Imperial Mammoth's chief food and enjoyment. And with their long tusks they could dig up roots which to them were delicious. They were not meat eaters.

These huge animals sought one another's company and lived in herds. The biggest and strongest mammoth in the herd was the leader; he it was who gave warning to the others if he thought danger threatened. But the Imperial Mammoth was a peaceful animal except when forced to defend himself.

Not so the giant cat, named Saber-tooth, who once roamed not only over North and South America, but over Asia and Europe as well. It was as big as an African lion, but more savage than any lion. Also, it had two great dagger teeth in its upper jaw. These teeth, which were like sabers or swords, gave the name of Saber-tooth. This beast has another name—a long Greek one —"Smilodon," but not because it ever smiled. Often it is called, also, though incorrectly, "Saber-toothed Tiger." As a matter of fact, it was not a tiger, more nearly it was an enormous wildcat.

The Saber-tooth, when hungry, used to slip down from the mountains to the grassy plains where the water holes were. He had learned that horses, camels, bears, elephants, ground sloths, and all sorts of large creatures came there to drink.

The Saber-tooth slunk through the high grass that grew rankly over La Brea. The long green blades were cool against his flanks. He hid behind bushes or in clumps of trees. He waited his chance. He feared no animal—not even the Imperial Mammoth. When he was stalking a victim, his short tail would lash threateningly, his eyes would narrow, then he would spring.

Saber-toothed cats were the enemies of all other great beasts, but they were not so wise as they were strong and cruel. They, like their victims, grew careless of the tar, were trapped, sank down, and died.

Nowadays there are no saber-toothed cats. When the other big animals they lived upon disappeared from the earth, these great cats could not adjust themselves to living on small game, wild vegetables, or other foods. The sabers, too, were then only a handicap. Thus, like their favorite victims, the ferocious saber-toothed cats became extinct.

One of the strangest beasts of these ancient days was the Giant Ground Sloth. It was a huge, clumsy creature with a heavy body and short, powerful legs. Large claws grew out of its hands and feet. With them it could dig holes in the ground. With them also, it could rip up a great lion or a saber-toothed cat.

The Giant Ground Sloth fed on the leaves and young buds of trees. It liked wild vegetables. In fact, it was a vegetarian and not a meat eater. With claws turned under, sloths lumbered over the rolling plains.

In addition to tearing with its claws, the Giant Ground Sloth was powerful enough to crush slowly any beast it embraced. Also, it had another means of self-protection. In the thick layers of its hide grew many tiny bones, like pebbles. These formed an armor. A distant and smaller cousin of the sloth, the armadillo—living in South America today—has also a protective armor.

Fifty million years or so ago, horses, like the first of the camel family, were tiny animals no bigger than foxes. They had four, possibly five, toes, short necks, small heads, and teeth like those of monkeys or pigs.

As the ages rolled by, there developed from these fox-like creatures the magnificent horses of today, with their curving necks, proud heads, flying manes, and plunging hoofs. The horse changed partly because the country changed and partly because he had to avoid being killed by lions and other dangerous enemies. As the tropical forests thinned out and gave way to open, grassy country, the horse continually had to meet new conditions and become accustomed to new food. His feet changed to adapt themselves to the hardened plain. The side toes became more slender, with the weight thrown on the middle toe. The legs grew longer, giving him more speed. With long legs came the longer neck, so that he could reach the ground to graze. There was plenty of food—grass—and the horse grew larger and larger. Steadily his side toes became smaller until, as in the horse of today, there was only one toe left, and that middle toe alone became the foot or hoof itself.

The horses whose remains have been found in the tar pits of southern California already had reached the one-toe stage. They much resembled modern horses, except that their heads were like those of zebras, and on their necks grew stiff manes. Their color was that of the brown grasses, with bellies that were white or yellow.

The colts of those olden times raced over the plains, over the rolling hills and valleys, especially when early rains made the country green in springtime. There were no Indians to catch them in those days. They had to keep a sharp lookout, however, for the saber-toothed cat, the great lion, and the dire wolf.

Some of these horses traveled across Alaska to Asia. All those who remanied behind in America died. No one knows just why they became extinct. The remains in the tar pits give no clue.

The horses that went to Asia finally spread, after thousands and thousands of years, into Europe. Then when the Spanish explorers came to America looking for gold, they brought horses with them. From these animals—some of whom the Spaniards left to shift for themselves—came the wild mustangs of the Western plains. Once more horses galloped over the wild regions of America. They were able to come back after man ruled the earth, though most of the huge, floundering beasts of fifty thousand or five hundred thousand years ago have vanished and have yielded only their bones to man.

## PADDLEWINGS GROWS UP[1]

*Wilfrid S. Bronson*

It was hard work for Paddlewings to get out of his egg. The shell of a penguin's egg is very tough, much tougher than a hen's egg. Paddlewings' body had filled up the whole shell as he grew, and there was almost no room for him to make a pecking motion. He was so cramped that he could peck only in one spot right in front of his face. His bill had a good point on it though. He would peck a while and rest, and then peck some more, until finally he pipped out a little piece of shell and there was a small hole. His eyes were half open and he had never seen anything at all before, so the light that came through the hole seemed as bright as a star to him.

Well, the air also came in through the hole and Paddlewings took a bigger breath than he ever had taken before. This gave him strength and he was excited by it. He pecked much harder on both sides of the hole and tried to straighten out his legs.

"Peck, crack! Peck! crack! Let me out of this shell, for pity's sake!" That was the feeling he had, and suddenly as he gave a push with his legs, the end of the shell broke all to bits and his head came out like a jack-in-the-box.

Now his mother and father were excited. They opened their big mouths and cried, "Oowah! Hoowah!" They stood on the edge of the nest, bending over and looking with joy at Paddlewings. They were like two nearsighted people watching a boy crawl out of a barrel.

Paddlewings was taking quick breaths

[1] From Wilfrid S. Bronson, *Paddlewings: The Penguin of Galápagos.*

and his little heart was beating like everything, partly from excitement and partly because this was the first time he had ever had any exercise. He raised one wing and then the other, sticking them out over the broken edges of the shell. Then with one good kick from his legs he came sprawling out into the nest, too weak to do anything but lie under his mother till his down had dried. Newly hatched birds are very damp at first. Besides, he had to get used to the light a little at a time, even though the cave was dim compared to the outside. His mother sat over him while his father went to see what he could catch to bring him for breakfast.

His father did not go and catch one good shrimp or fish and bring it in his bill to feed the baby bird. Instead, he caught a shrimp under water and swallowed it! This might have looked as though he had forgotten that he came out to get something for the young one and was eating all the food himself. Next, he swallowed several sardines. Then he started back toward the cave with his stomach nearly full. On the way he snatched up two more shrimps, and when he swam through the cave door and walked up to the nest, he looked like someone who has got fat while away on a vacation.

Now to get the breakfast out of his stomach and into the stomach of Paddlewings. Some birds, like the robins, carry home food in their bills which they put into the open mouths of their babies. Most sea birds take the food home in their stomachs. They open their bills and the young ones put their own bills way inside.

Paddlewings' father came and stood by the nest. When the mother uncovered Paddlewings, he tried to raise himself on his feeble new legs. His wings quivered, and he made a small squealing sound as his father bent over him. Paddlewings did not need to be told what to do. Still squealing and quivering, he put his whole head clear inside the open bill of his father who humped and shook himself a little. Up came some of the shrimps and fishes, and down they went through Paddlewings' bill into his hungry insides.

The father had brought in much more than was needed, especially as Paddlewings was the only baby they had to feed. Before long the mother took her turn at going for food, and so they kept feeding him all through every day, while he grew very fast.

In about three weeks Paddlewings was a foot high and looked almost as big as his parents. He did not look much like them at that, for his fluffy gray down stuck out all over him and gave him quite a different shape. Their eyes were reddish brown while his were greener, their bills were yellow and black while his was just plain gray and still had the point he used for pipping out his shell.

When he was not being fed he was very likely to be asleep, with only his head under his mother or father, for he was too big now to hide any more of himself. But he was beginning to feel restless and rather tired of just sitting in the nest waiting for them to bring in food. It was about time for him to try to walk, but he did not crawl first. He learned to stand up in the nest, and one day he tried to walk out of it. At first he tottered and fell forward every few steps, but he soon learned better and wandered all about in the cave. By the time he was four weeks old he was very steady on his feet, and the exercise gave him a still better appetite. If he felt extra hungry, he would run to meet his father and mother as they came in, squealing and holding his bill forward as if to say,

"Fill me full for I feel hollow!
Feed me all that I can swallow!"

One day he ran to meet his mother and put his bill into hers, expecting her to hump herself and shake up a fish for him to swallow. She humped herself all right, but she shook up some pebbles and Paddlewings swallowed them before he knew it. I don't think he minded that, but his hunger wasn't satisfied. It is good for penguins to eat a few pebbles once in a while just as it is good for barnyard hens to eat grit.

The little stones help their digestion by grinding the things they swallow whole. After all, birds have no teeth. They never have a toothache and swallowing stones saves them from having a stomach ache.

Paddlewings would soon be five weeks old and he had not been out of the cave yet. This seemed to be on the old birds' minds for they both went out of the cave one day and stayed out a long time, or so it seemed to Paddlewings. He felt too lonesome to sleep and he walked up and down in the cave, calling and squalling and watching the door. This made him feel worse and worse. The walking made him feel hungry, and looking at the door gave him a feeling more and more that his parents were out there and he must go out too. Not in the water though! He did not dare to try to swim all alone, the first swim of his life.

The cave door was rough and jagged, and there was a ridge of rock along one side which started in the cave and ended outside. It made a very rough path, but he had seen the old birds walk along it sometimes when they were just going out to sit in the sun. As he walked back and forth in the cave, he kept getting nearer to the door. When he looked down into the water swirling in the entrance, he felt as nervous as could be, but he was more nervous from not seeing either of his parents. They were the only friends he had; they were everything in his whole life, and now where were they?

As he squealed unhappily to himself and stared at the moving water, he edged over to one side of the entrance, trying to get as near the outside as he could and still stay as far as possible from that water. This put his feet on the beginning of the rocky ridge. Slowly he worked his way along it, half sideways, partly facing out of the cave and partly facing the dangerous water. With every trembling step he took, the light grew brighter until he was much surprised by his first sight of the sky. As soon as he saw that, he all but forgot to watch the water and cocked his head on one side the better to watch a passing big white cloud. He was so interested that he nearly forgot his lonesomeness and empty stomach. The sky and cloud were too bright to watch for long at first. He had always lived in the dimly lighted cave. So he closed his eyes and tried to rest a minute. So much to get used to!

Resting was no use. His ears caught a scratchy sound. Could it be his mother's feet coming along the ridge? But no, when he opened his eyes he saw climbing up the rocks toward him a great big scarlet crab. It was wiggling its short feelers and moving its eyes up and down. Bubbles came breaking out of its mouth, and it kept putting its claws out and back as though unable to decide whether or not to come any closer to Paddlewings, who stood looking at it in wonder. Several more crabs came up from the water until there was a crowd of them. Paddlewings was not exactly frightened; they somehow reminded him of the shrimps he had been fed, and this made him remember his hungriness again.

The crabs ran backwards from him as he moved carefully on, till he came to a place in his path which went up steeply. By now he was well out of the cave entrance, out under the immense sky. The clouds and blue were so much farther above him than the walls and roof of the cave had been that he felt dizzy. He could see a little of the sea between the rocks, but still no sign of his parents.

Here was a big bump in his way. The dizzy feeling left him as he stretched out his neck, held up his paddles and tried to scramble up over it. Halfway up he stubbed his toe and stumbled, thumping his breast on the lumpy rocks, but he kept right on making a mad scramble upward. The harder he tried the more frightened he felt, when suddenly he reached the top of the bump and there on the other side were his mother and father not ten steps away. They were sitting in the sun with their stomachs full of fishes, and as Paddlewings dashed to them they both made ready to feed him. He was well rewarded for all his worry in getting out of the cave.

After that the three birds went in and out of the cave together every day. Sometimes Paddlewings saw other baby penguins outside in the sun with their parents. Most of the old birds had two young ones to feed which kept them busier than Paddlewings' parents. That is why he was bigger than the rest; he never had to wait long for his dinner.

But Paddlewings and all the others were waiting for something else besides dinner. They were waiting for feathers, and before many days their down began to shed. It came off in patches, making them look most messy and miserable. You may have seen young chickens when they are losing their down and starting to grow feathers. They look like chicken scarecrows. So did Paddlewings. I don't think he felt embarrassed about it, but he did not feel quite as fine as he had been feeling.

Everywhere the down came off, there were little points of pinfeathers starting to come through his skin and all this made him peevish, like a baby who is cutting its first teeth. Besides, the sun shone on his naked places and he had to hide in the cave a lot to keep from getting sunburn blisters.

A little more down came off every day, first along both sides of his body and his legs, then from his head about the bill and down at his tail. Next, his neck and back and breast were bare, and last of all the back of his head and neck and shoulders. When he was all fitted out at last with new shiny feathers, he felt fine. His new coat was not black and white like his parents' but light gray on his breast, and dark gray everywhere else. It would take him a year to grow up, and these were the feathers he had to wear until then. They were very short and close to his body; in a way they were more like a fish's scales than a bird's feathers. For a bird who was going to spend much time chasing fish under water, this was just right.

Our hair, animals' fur, birds' feathers, and the scales of reptiles and fish are all different forms of the same thing. Each creature has a covering which suits his life best. If a hen falls into a tub of water or stays out in the rain, she gets wet to the skin. It is not natural for her to go swimming or take shower baths and her feathers are not able to keep the water from soaking through. A duck's feathers are oily and they keep out the water very well, and a penguin's feathers are oily and even better than a duck's for keeping dry while swimming.

The way the old birds made Paddlewings come out of the cave was to go out themselves and wait till he was so hungry and lonesome that he could not stay in any longer. They taught him to swim in the same way. First they stopped feeding him again. He became so hungry that instead of waiting for them to bring food to him he ran squealing after them, begging. But they wouldn't give him one little bit. When they thought he was hungry enough to follow them, they started off for a walk. Over the rough lava rocks they went till they came to a sandy beach. Big rocks stuck up out of the sand here and there, and behind some of them were pools of water which the ocean had left when the tide went down. Paddlewings kept right up with his father and mother till they came to one of these pools. When they waded into the water he stepped in behind them, but as soon as he felt the wet on his legs he turned right around and ran out, very much surprised, while his parents swam a yard or so.

Paddlewings wanted to follow them so badly, but he was afraid and stood squealing with toes in the water, leaning his head forward and flipping his small flat wings. The mother swam in close to him and turned to swim away again. Just as she turned, poor hungry Paddlewings stretched out to her as far as he could reach, lost his balance, and fell on his face in the water. He lifted his head, very much afraid, but he was not sinking at all! He moved his wings in his excitement and found that they helped him along. In a few moments he was following the old birds all over the pool. Once he found he was in no danger he began to like the clear quiet pool, and he kept putting his face under the water to look at the bottom, full of pebbles, bright shells, and little seaweeds.

When he did this he used his extra set of eyelids. That sounds queer. He had eyelids that worked the way ours do, and another over each eye besides. Most birds have an extra eyelid, but to a sea bird like Paddlewings they are especially useful. His were very thin, and clear as glass. Instead of being above and below his eyes as ordinary eyelids are, they folded out of sight in the corners of his eyes nearest his bill. They moved across his eyes from front to back instead of up and down; and because they were clear as glass, he could still see. He used them to keep the water out of his eyes when his head was below the surface, as an aviator uses goggles to keep the wind out of his eyes. They worked like a sliding window which can be closed when a shower of rain comes.

While Paddlewings was holding his head under water, he spied small fishes swimming near the bottom. It was the first time he had seen a live fish. To see that fine food darting about down there while he was floating around on top of the water, made him feel very hungry. He expected one of his parents to swim down and bring a fish up to him, but they simply floated near by.

Suddenly he took a good breath, ducked his head deep, worked his wings as hard as he could, and swam down to the fishes. But when he tried to catch one, they all turned and swam swiftly to one side, while he sped straight ahead, missing his mark and his meal. He stopped flipping his wings and bobbed to the surface to get some air. Then he began to squeal miserably. Presently his mother ducked her head and went down after the fishes. Paddlewings held his face under the water to watch. He saw her stick out her foot and turn when the fishes turned and then catch one easily. Of course he expected her to feed him when she came up, but no such thing.

There was no use begging, he would have to try again and do what his mother did. He swam down and when the fishes flitted to the right he put out his right foot and kept his paddles going. This turned him in the same way you turn your sled while coasting, by dragging one foot on the snow. He made a grab and got a fish's tail in his bill. That was a mistake, but he was not quick enough to get it by the belly. Each time he let go a bit to grab it further forward, the fish wriggled forward too. When Paddlewings, nearly out of breath, finally did get a firmer hold and tried to swallow the fish, tail first, it stuck in his throat. He had to let it go and come up for air.

Meanwhile his father went down. Paddlewings, watching him, saw him catch a fish in its middle, give it a quick twist, and swallow it head first. So that was the way! Down he went and as the fishes went to the left, he put out his left foot, turned and caught a good one by the belly, pinched hard, twisted it about, and swallowed it! A fish has to be swallowed head first, because the sharp edges of the gill-covers and all the scales point backward. The scales catch and may hurt the penguin's throat if the fish is swallowed tail first. Perhaps that is the reason why so many fishes in the tropic seas have bright yellow tails, to attract the notice of enemies about to eat them and make them try to swallow the wrong end first!

That was all the old penguins needed to teach Paddlewings. If he could swim and catch his own dinner, he would be all right. The other fancy things penguins do in the water, they let him find out for himself. And Paddlewings was quick to find them out, for now he was growing up.

## WHAT WE FOUND IN A FOX DEN[1]

*Ernest Harold Baynes*

We wanted some fox cubs to study, and we wanted them that very spring. We were living not far from Boston, on the edge of the Reservation, and close to Spot Pond.

[1] From Ernest Harold Baynes, *The Sprite: The Story of a Red Fox.*

There were plenty of foxes in the Reservation, and at first we expected to get some young ones near at hand. In this we were disappointed. To be sure we found several dens, but they were not to be disturbed by any ordinary digging. The foxes, in their wisdom, had taken advantage of the natural condition of the country and had made their homes in certain rocky ravines. Here, in deep-mouthed fissures, their young were safe from all but the old fox hunter whose business it was to lie in wait on warm May mornings and shoot these juvenile poachers when they came out to romp on the grass before the den.

We had almost given up hope when we received a letter from a friend in Topsfield, telling us that he had found a promising fox burrow and inviting us to come and help him to dig it out. Of course we were delighted at the prospect, and next morning, the eleventh of April, we arose before daylight and caught a very early train for Topsfield. Our friend met us at the station and in a light trap we were soon rattling away over the country roads, with a very wise-looking foxhound, Diana, sitting in front of our knees.

Oh, what a morning it was, with blue sky and white clouds and just a touch of frost in the bracing air! Bluebirds were purling in the smoke-gray orchards, and red-winged blackbirds called from the alders which lined the swamps. By the side of the road the maples and elms were budding and the grass was tinged with green. The pussy willows were in full bloom, and sent us occasional fragrant whiffs of spring.

After trotting along for perhaps two miles, we turned into a pine forest, through which we drove as far as we could. Presently we reached a point where the closeness of the trees made it impossible to drive any farther, so we unhitched and blanketed the horse, took from the trap sundry shovels, an axe, a pick, and a crowbar, and forced our way through a thicket of scrub oaks, until we came to a thinly wooded bit of country near the shore of a lake.

Here we came upon the foxhound, who had run on ahead of us. All we could see of her was her tail; the rest of her body was out of sight in a burrow, which started near the foot of a tree, and descended into the ground at a gentle slope. This was the fox den we had come to dig out. There was nothing remarkable about the entrance; I have seen a bigger one at the home of a woodchuck. But the amount of sand which had been thrown out in digging the burrow was good proof that the tunnel was a long one. Over this pile of sand, and down into the burrow, ran several lines of fox tracks, most of the footprints being those of a small fox, probably the vixen. There were no bones or feathers about, for of course the young ones could not yet be old enough to eat solid food.

On examining the burrow a little closer we found numerous yellowish hairs, and there were other evidences that the den was occupied. So we cut a straight stick about ten feet long, and thrust it into the hole to get the general direction. It ran about northwest, as far as we could reach. Ten feet from the entrance, we started to dig a pit. For a few inches we dug through loam and leaf-mold, and then we struck sand, which of course made the work very easy. At a depth of two feet we came to the burrow, which at this point was running toward the surface. Here we found another tunnel, branching toward the south, and it was a question which of the two we should follow.

The answer was given by Diana, who evinced such a lively interest in the main burrow, to the neglect of the branch, that we decided to take her advice. So we thrust in a stick again, and were soon digging our second pit. This time we had to go a little deeper before we reached the burrow. Pit after pit we dug, each time having to go a little deeper than before, until at a depth of over six feet, and about forty-five feet from the entrance, we heard a sound which led us to believe that our reward was near. It was a soft singing or whining, and came from a point not far beyond where I was digging.

After throwing out a few more shovelfuls of earth, I stooped and thrust my arm into the burrow. The tunnel took a sharp bend at this point, and turning the corner with my hand, my fingers clutched a warm little ball of fur. I drew it out and handed it up to Mrs. Baynes, who laid it in her lap. Reaching in again, I took out two other balls of fur, and not finding any more, I climbed out to take a good look at our prizes. We set them on the ground, and there they lay on the dry leaves, among the hepatica blossoms, three woolly little fox cubs, two of them still blind, the third taking his first look at the world through a pair of the most innocent blue eyes I had ever seen. It did not seem possible that from such soft, trembling, helpless mites as these could come the sly, resourceful, and destructive poultry thieves of the future. The color of their fur was dark gray on the bodies, legs, and tails, tawny on the faces, while the tips of the tails were white. Nearly every foot had some white on it, if only on one toe. The feet were the feet of puppies, but the texture of the fur was more like that of kittens. The noses only were decidedly foxy.

Our friend now got into the pit and dug out to the end of the burrow, which did not extend more than a foot around the turn. He found no more cubs, however. The spot from which I had taken the three youngsters was entirely fresh and sweet and there was no evidence to show that they had been born there. As they were too young to move about much, our conclusion was that probably they had been carried by one of the parents. It seemed likely that they had been born in one of the branch burrows, and perhaps the mother, hearing us digging near by, had picked up her children one at a time, and carried them to the farthest corner of the whole den. Very likely there were some more cubs, which she did not have time to carry off, and these, contrary to her calculations, were the ones we did not find.

I now went to the branch burrow, which ran toward the south, and putting my ear to the mouth of it, I could hear a distant whining which told me that the cubs we had found were only a part of the litter. We were very glad to know that, for it is sad to cause heartaches even in the interest of science, and now we knew that the mother fox would have a part of her family, at any rate, to console her for the loss of the babies we had stolen. The latter we took home to study. After a good meal of warm cow's milk, administered with a dropper, two of them curled up in a box of dry leaves, and soon they were as sound asleep as they would have been in their own sandy burrow.

The third was more lively and though quite blind seemed bent on adventure. I let him crawl about a bit, but he soon grew tired, and I picked him up. Even at this age he was different from his brothers. As we studied his face and compared it with theirs, there seemed to be something finer, more appealing about him. As we gazed at the mysterious little countenance we could not wonder that foxes and folklore always have been closely interwoven. Because there was something fairylike about him, at least in our imagination, we named him "the Sprite." And after I had squeezed a few more drops of warm milk between his sleepy lips, he curled up in my hand, his little limbs relaxed, and with his white-tipped—shall we call it his brush—hanging limp beside them, he passed into the land of dreams.

## WITH HELMET AND HOSE[1]

*William Beebe*

I am twenty feet under water with a huge copper helmet on my head, tilting with my trident against an olive-green grouper over a yard long, who is much too fearless and inquisitive for my liking. Not until I have pricked him sharply with the grains does he leave off nosing my legs with his mean jaws and efficient teeth. It

[1] From William Beebe, *Exploring with Beebe.*

suddenly occurs to me how knightlike I am as far as the metal cask goes, and then in spite of the strange world all about, my mind goes back to the long-ago Christmases when a new-published Henty book was an invariable and almost the best gift. I instantly know that if ever I succeed in shackling these divings to mere, awkward words it must be called "With Helmet and Hose," and if any modern boy, grown-up or gentle reader does not know why, explanations will do no good.

I wish I could credit my present passionate enthusiasm for diving beneath strange tropical waters to a life-long suppressed desire, but unfortunately this is not so. My only excuse is that I suffer intermittently from what my artist once offered as a definition of a monkey, a desire to be somewhere else than I am.

Considering carefully this whirling ball of mud upon which I found myself, I read in books and saw pictures of jungles and deserts, and my desire to see them was just a little stronger than the many obstacles between; I had breathed the air and watched birds fly for an unconscionable number of years before I began my first wobbly taxiing across a flying field. Since then I have left the earth under pleasant and unpleasant conditions over three hundred times, and, except twice, returned safely.

Without shame I confess that I have lain awake nights and spent innumerable hours of my life in gazing at the moon and planets—nay, even at the Small Magellanic Cloud with desire and longing, for if one wishes to visit inter-stellar space, one might as well hold the thought of a passage on Tomlinson's route as on a mensurable moon trip. Up to the present, twenty-two thousand feet is as far as I have been able to rise above solid ground.

Another realm which has always seemed as remote as the moon is the depth of the ocean. My reading and wishing never took any concrete, definite direction until the trip I made to the Galápagos on the *Noma*. Then I first realized the glories and desirability of the submarine world. This at once encouraged and then disheartened me—the encouragement coming from the ease of diving from a boat or a pier and watching for a brief moment the fish and sea-things, simultaneously with the realization of the futility of such a brief, blurred glimpse.

I inspected a number of diver's outfits one day and found nothing tempting in the enormously cumbersome suits. Then, just before I sailed on the *Arcturus,* I bought my helmet. The paraphernalia accompanying it were so simple that I doubted its efficiency, but at least it was an effort in the right direction of investigation of a new world.

During the first part of the *Arcturus* adventure the sea was too rough to think of using it, even a few feet below the gangway, but when we moored close under the cliffs of Darwin Bay at Tower Island—our old Galápagos anchorage—I brought up the box from the hold and unlimbered the diving apparatus. The helmet was a big, conical affair of copper, made to rest on the shoulders, with a hose connection on the right side and two oblique windows in front. Around the bottom extended a flange on which four flattened pieces of lead were hung, each weighing ten pounds. This made a total weight of sixty pounds for the entire thing. The hose, which was of the ordinary common or garden variety, was attached at one end to the helmet and at the other to a double-action automobile pump, which screwed to a board, and was operated by a long iron lever, pushed back and forth. Almost at once we elaborated a method of operation which was so simple and satisfactory, even to the slightest details, that no change was necessary after weeks and months of use.

Our regular mode of diving is as follows: We start out from the *Arcturus* in a flat-bottomed boat which has a square, eighteen-inch glass set in the bottom amidships. To the stern is fastened a long, metal Jacob's-ladder, rolled up when not in use. We are towed or we row to the shore, preferably to the base of cliffs or steep rocks, as that affords considerable depth close inshore and rocky places are beloved by hosts of fish. We anchor as close to the cliffs as is safe, and roll out the ladder, so that it sways in midwater or rests upon the bottom. The pump is in the bow, the handle fixed, and the leather washer carefully screwed in. The hose is cleared of kinks, and is looped, partly overboard. A hand line is tied to the top of the helmet, and the inside of the glass windows is coated with a film of glycerine to prevent the breath of the diver from condensing and so clouding it. The four lead weights are slipped over the flange on the helmet base and all is ready for the diver. A hand water-glass is near for constant lookout for danger, and one or two long-handled harpoons.

In bathing suit I climb down the ladder over the stern, and dip to my neck, being careful not to wet my head. Then John lifts the helmet; I give a last, quick look around, draw a deep breath, duck into it, and as it settles firmly on my shoulders, I climb slowly down. The sensation just above water is of unbearable weight, but the instant I immerse this goes and the weight of the helmet with all the lead is only a gentle pressure, sufficient to give perfect stability. Meanwhile Ruth Rose has started the pump.

From a blurred view of the water surface and the boat's stern, I sink instantly to clear vision under water. I descend three rungs and reach up for the short harpoon or grains which is put into my hand. At the fourth or fifth rung the air presses perceptibly on my ears and I relieve it by swallowing. I descend slowly, swallowing now and then, and when the last rung has been reached, I lower myself easily by one arm, and lightly rest on the bottom. If serious danger threatens or the pumping should go wrong for any reason, I have only to lift up the helmet, duck out from under it and swim to the surface. The level of the water keeps constantly at the level of my neck or throat, and if I lean far forward it gradually rises to my mouth. But there is no splashing, no sense of oppression.

During a descent on a later day as I was reveling in the delight of colors under water, a small object appeared in mid-water close to my little glass window, and was instantly obscured by half a dozen little fish which darted about it, some actually flicking my helmet with their tails. Just as I saw that the suspended object was a baited hook, a baby scarlet snapper snatched at it, darted downward, and was at once drawn up into the boat. As I looked after it an idea came to me and I followed the snapper upward by way of the ladder. When the helmet was lifted off and I could speak, I expressed my wants, and descended again. Soon there fell slowly at my feet a small stone to which was tied a juicy and scarcely dead crab. I picked this up, waved it back and forth so as to scatter the impelling incense of its body, and as if by magic, from behind me, from crevices upon which I was seated, seemingly materializing from the clear water, came fish and fish and fish.

I waved my magic crab. I may have murmured Plop! Glub! and Bloob! which is what the bubbles say when I first immerse—and the hosts came. Within three minutes from the time when the crab first fell into my hand, I had five hundred fish swirling around my crab and hand and head. Similes failed. I thought of the hosts of yellow butterflies I have seen fluttering at arm's length of Boom-Boom Point; I thought of the maze of wings of the pigeons of St. Mark's, but no memory of the upper world was in place here—this was a wholly new thing.

Often there was a central nucleus a foot or more in diameter, of solid fish, so that the bait and my arm to the elbow were quite invisible. Twenty or twenty-five species were represented, and, like birds, they were graded with exquisite exactness as to correlation of fear and size. The great majority were small, from two to four inches in length, and these were wholly without fear, nibbling my hand—passing between my fingers but always just avoiding capture, no matter how quickly I shut my fist. Six- and eight-inch fish also came near, but were more ready to dart off at any sudden movement of mine.

On the outskirts hung a fringe of still larger fish, hungry, and rushing in now and then for a snap at the delicious morsel which they saw their lesser fellows enjoying, but always with less abandon to the temptation of the moment. The tameness of the little chaps, however, was so astounding that the relatively greater wariness of the larger fish scarcely deserved the name of suspicion, not to say fear. Another unexpected thing was the rapidity with which these fish lost even this slight suspicion and learned to connect my appearance with food.

If I dived in the same spot several times a day and several days in succession, fish would approach in numbers and investigate my hands and trident with much greater eagerness and, I presume, with expectancy, than they ever displayed on the occasion of the first dive, before I had repeatedly tempted them with freshly killed crabs. I could even recognize certain individuals, characterized by some peculiarity of color or form.

## JANGWA BEGINS TO HUNT[1]

*Walter J. Wilwerding*

Some lions spend their entire lives in the forest-clad hills, but Kuu was a lion of the more open veld country. He had spent his days in hunting the beasts of the veld-land and in the bush country that separated the veld from the forest-covered mountains. He had no special liking for the deep forests, nor for the stalking of game in this dark, moss-draped jungle. There were no monkeys to screech warnings when he hunted on the veld, no multitudes of birds in the branches of thickly growing trees to watch his every movement. Elephants did not make life hazardous on the lower veld, nor did he have to fight his prey every time he went hunting there, as was the case with the fierce buffaloes. True, there were men on the veld, but these could be avoided. Farther and farther down the mountainside he led Jangwa each day until one night they again made their beds in the bush country that bordered on the veld.

Jangwa still had a spotted coat, for young lions have these tawny-colored spots until they are well grown. Even then the spots show on the lighter parts of their bodies and some lions never lose these entirely. Jangwa was getting bigger and stronger as the days went on, for Kuu provided well, but it was now nearing the time when Jangwa must take an actual part in the hunting. This may have been the reason why Kuu took him down into the veld country. Here large herds of antelopes grazed and there were zebras and countless other creatures which the young Jangwa could be taught how to hunt.

Their first night in the bush brought easy hunting. The impallas—those graceful, tan-colored antelopes with lyre-shaped horns, that can make such long leaps over the tops of bushes—love the bush country. A large herd of these came through the bushes, grazing and browsing on the way to water. With so much game about, Kuu had little difficulty in obtaining their supper.

The two fed until they had their fill and then went to water in the early morning hours while it was still dark. This enabled them to drink without the danger of meeting the Masai and they could be back in the bush country before the sun was up.

The remains of their meal fed others, for the hyenas and jackals devoured all they could and the rising sun brought vultures that picked up what was left. This did not trouble Kuu, for he knew that, in this land of plenty, he would have no difficulty in procuring more meat when the time came for another meal.

The Masai were aware that a lion was hunting near by, for Kuu roared mightily in the early hours of the night and kept it

[1] From Walter J. Wilwerding, *Jangwa: The Story of a Jungle Prince.*

up until he had made a successful stalk. Then he again roared in a satisfied manner when the two returned to their beds in the early morning. But the Masai did not know that it was Kuu, the mate of the lioness whom they had speared, for other lions came to this place, where the hunting was so good. Sometimes other lions roared back in answer to Kuu and on many nights the answering roars seemed as echoes that came from many directions.

Jangwa was now learning to grunt a bit, but his grunting was much like the attempted crowing of a young rooster. It had neither the volume nor did it resemble a roar. Yet he was growing into a swaggering young fellow and his first attempts at roaring satisfied him, even as his first attempts at whistling satisfy a small boy.

Kuu now took Jangwa on long hunts across the grass veld. They would leave the bush country in the early evening, cross an open stretch of veld, and then circle around some low, cone-shaped hills. Here grew scattered yellow-barked and gall-acacia trees, and the place resembled a rather open park. Between the cone-shaped hills there were rocky ravines, bush-choked and shaded in spots by clumps of tall euphorbia trees. The euphorbia trees looked like giant cactus plants, having rather slender stems, with clumps of blue-green cactuslike leaves. These ravines afforded cover for the lions when they wanted to lie here during the heat of the day, instead of returning to the bush country. In them, they could also hide in ambush for game. The long-faced, brown kongoni antelopes, whose horns had an odd twist forward and then backward, often grazed about the cone-shaped hills, as did the goatlike gazelles. Zebras and giraffes also made their homes here. The zebras kept much to the valleys, but the giraffes often walked about on the tops of the hills. For miles beyond these small hills there were vast stretches of veld, in a wide, flat valley, bordered with extinct volcano cones and craters. Herds of game were everywhere.

Jangwa learned that if one wanted to be really successful on the hunt one must wait for dark, for in the daytime the game had sentinels to watch while it grazed. The kongonis were especially good as sentinels; the lions never could get close to them in the daytime. These sentinels stood on high places, usually an old, grass-grown ant hill. They had very keen eyes and could detect any movement in the grass for long distances. As soon as the lions started stalking them, the sentinels would snort and every head would come up from the grass at once. Then every kongoni would stand and watch the lions and, at the first stealthy movement, the whole crowd would gallop away.

At night it was necessary only to keep the wind in their faces. This brought the scent of the game to the lions, without giving their scent to the game. Now Jangwa always stalked beside Kuu and only stayed behind during the time when Kuu made the final rush to capture the game. To Kuu this was easy and so it may have appeared easy to Jangwa. But he still made no special effort to catch game, though he did practice stalking hour after hour. Even in the daytime he would sneak through the grass to see how close he could get to the game. Then one day he managed, by a bit of luck, to catch one of the small, goatlike steinbucks. These little antelope go about singly or in pairs, instead of in herds, and, as this one was alone, it was easier to stalk than when many eyes, ears and noses warn the animals in a herd of danger. Jangwa was exceedingly proud of his feat. Kuu looked at him with approval, but did not seem unduly stirred by the fact that Jangwa had succeeded in catching game. Perhaps he thought it was about time that Jangwa showed how well he had learned his lessons.

Kuu helped Jangwa eat the meat, though it was hardly enough for Jangwa alone. This whetted Kuu's appetite for more and he set out on the hunt. Jangwa followed closely, determined always to remain within sight and hearing of Kuu. Soon the two came upon a herd of zebras. It was just past sundown and not yet dark, for there is a period of a bit less than half an hour between sundown and darkness in East Africa. The zebras knew it would soon be dark. They were nervous and on the alert. Darkness meant the meat-eaters would soon be about and those who would save their lives must be ever on the watch. Each animal is its own policeman in the wild. Each must guard its own life. When sentinels happen to scent or see danger, they snort and warn the herd, but after that it is everyone for itself.

These zebras were strung out in a long line on their way to water. All day they had grazed on the hot, open veld. They were thirsty, but were afraid to go to drink until the Masai had driven their cattle away from the water and taken them to their villages for the night. No wild beast will approach water in the daytime when natives are watering their cattle, and natives are everlastingly at the water holes with one herd after another.

The zebra is a quarrelsome beast and this herd came along squealing, biting, and kicking at one another. Now and then they would neigh in their peculiar, barking manner, "Qua-ha, quah-ha, qua-ha!"

Kuu crouched low in the grass and waited for them to come on while Jangwa, tense and quivering, hid close by. Then, when the herd was just a bound or two away, Kuu made a rush at the zebras and was soon within paw stroke of one. As he crouched over his prey, he saw another zebra lash out with both hind legs and send Jangwa rolling. It turned to kick once more, while others also came galloping up to squeal and kick at their enemy. Kuu charged at them, coughing a volley of furious grunts as he came, and the striped troop scattered before his rush.

Jangwa lay dazed upon the ground. All the pride of his success in catching the steinbuck had deserted him now. That little bit of luck had made him too confident of his abilities as a hunter. The moment Kuu had charged at the zebras, he had also rushed forward. He had even succeeded in landing on one's hindquarters, digging claws into its striped haunches and hanging there at its tail, like a huge, tawny burr. It bucked at once, lashing out with its hoofs at the same time, and Jangwa found himself sailing through the air.

Had not Kuu come to the rescue, other zebras, coming up at the rear of the herd, would soon have kicked Jangwa into oblivion, as he lay rolling on the ground. These animals looked easy to catch, but the trick had to be done just right, or one would get a pair of hoofs in the stomach.

After a bit, Jangwa felt able to come over to where Kuu was feeding, but he did not feel very hungry now and fed but sparingly. A kick in the stomach does not help one's appetite. Kuu had jumped at the withers of the zebra he had brought down, for he knew about the zebra's hind legs and hoofs. Long ago, when he had been a young lion, he had been kicked several times. Perhaps he thought this a good lesson for Jangwa. Experience always seems to be a very good teacher.

Some days later, in the early evening, they came upon a small herd of giraffes and Kuu waited for them to get close. This time he lay crouched very low in a thick bunch of grass and bushes, for these tall fellows could see everything round about. Their large, keen eyes were forever searching the land for miles around and any strange sight would cause them to stop feeding and stare. Then, if things looked suspicious, they would go away with that funny, swaying gallop of theirs, necks rocking back and forth, like tottering telegraph poles.

Kuu rarely hunted giraffes. When he did, he hunted them after dark, for then they could not see him hiding in the shadows. But the lions had had poor hunting the night before. The game was getting wild and jumpy because of their persistent hunting in this place and all had moved off into the lower veld, far to the west. Until they got over their nervousness and returned, the two lions would either have to follow them or make out the best they could with what remained.

As Kuu had not hunted giraffes since returning from the forest, they had not yet deserted this place. There were, of course, many smaller bucks about, which always remained in the same vicinity, but small bucks did not satisfy the hunger of these two. Also because of their small size, they were nervous and alert and hard to catch.

Kuu waited until one huge giraffe came close. He would have preferred to attack a smaller one, for old giraffe bulls are very tough of hide and, being tall and heavy, are not easy to bring down. As it approached within springing distance, he rushed out at it with a volley of coughing grunts. This was his hunting cry and was designed to make the game panicky, so it would turn to run away. In that instant when the game stopped in alarm and wheeled to run, Kuu could easily spring close to it. Then, when its back was turned, he could bound upon its withers without trouble.

But this old giraffe bull had come to his age and eighteen feet of height because he was wise in the ways of the lion. Instead of turning to bolt away, he lifted his huge front hoofs and kicked downward at Kuu. Kuu jumped to one side to avoid those hoofs, and now it became a game where the lion charged in and the giraffe wheeled about to face Kuu and kick at him. Jangwa seemed to think it was a jolly game and he came rushing up to join in. This really would have helped Kuu, had Jangwa used some system in his manner of attack. With Jangwa on one side and Kuu on the other, the giraffe would have become bewildered and Kuu could easily have bounded on its withers while its attentions were turned to Jangwa. But this beast was big and so Jangwa stayed by the side of Kuu, where he felt safer. Once more the giraffe kicked at Kuu, who was a bit confused because Jangwa got in his way. Kuu jumped to one side and barely escaped that kick, while Jangwa got the benefit of a glancing blow. He rolled over and over for a moment, but was quickly on his feet again, looking wildly about. This was no fun. Here was another of those things that kicked. He left the field to Kuu and slunk off into some bushes.

Soon the enraged Kuu became reckless and rushed in a bit too close. Then he also received a resounding blow from one of those large, split hoofs. That finished the attack for him too and he joined Jangwa in the bushes, while the giraffe went his insulted and dignified way.

The lion does not always come off victorious. If zebras could talk, those with unevenly matched stripes on their hindquarters, that were torn by a lion's claws and did not match evenly when healing, could have told Jangwa how lions sometimes came off second best. But, as zebras do not talk and also do not associate with lions, Jangwa had to learn these things by experience.

Later that night, when the two had recovered from the effects of the giraffe's kicks, they once more set out on the hunt. They followed the scent of a herd of the large Grant's gazelles. These gazelles are twice the size of the little, goatlike Thomson's gazelles and have long, beautiful horns. Their trail led the lions up a grassy hillside. Here they found that a leopard had lain in wait and captured one of the gazelles. The scents of both leopard and gazelle were strong where the leopard had dragged his meat along the ground. The leopard was apparently a large one, but the gazelle was as heavy as the leopard and the work of dragging it was not easy. The two lions followed the trail with the hope of making things easier for the leopard. They would eat the gazelle for the leopard, so he would not have to drag it.

They loped easily along the trail, for the scent was not difficult to follow. Coming to a wooded ravine, they found that the scent led up a tree. The leopard was there all right and so was the gazelle, but both were out of reach. The leopard had taken no chances with having his meat stolen. He had grasped the gazelle firmly in his teeth and, digging his claws into the bark of the tree trunk, had clawed his way up by the strength of his supple muscles. The gazelle was lodged securely in a crotch and near it the leopard lay flattened on a horizontal limb.

Kuu grunted a hoarse growl at him, as if trying to scare him into dropping his prey, but he only lay flat-eared and snarled down at them. Old lions do not climb trees. They are too heavy for this. The leopard knew this, even as he knew that hyenas cannot climb trees, and so he had taken his food up a tree.

But the tree leaned a bit, and the branch on which the leopard lay was not very high. Jangwa could climb and, as he was bolstered by his father's presence, he at once started to scramble up the trunk. A moment later he wished he had not been quite so forward. He had no sooner come close to the leopard, than he was cuffed viciously across the nose, left and right. He snarled at the leopard and tried to strike back, but this climbing was a bit awkward for him and he could not fight and hold fast to the tree trunk at the same time. Jangwa had expected this leopard to desert his food as soon as he came close, as that other one had done back in the forest. This was, however, an old male. He was evil-tempered and strong. Once more he struck viciously at Jangwa, and then Jangwa scrambled hastily to the ground. His face was scratched and bleeding and he was considerably cowed.

For a while, the two lions stayed underneath the tree, while Kuu prowled, growling, below. Then, as their vigil seemed useless, they again went about their own affairs.

Jangwa lagged behind, while Kuu led the way. The cub was losing some of his overconfidence. A short time before he had been kicked by a zebra. This night he had been kicked by a giraffe and scratched by a leopard. When they came upon a herd of eland, that had wandered this way from another district, Jangwa looked once at these large, cattlelike antelopes and promptly crawled into the nearest bush. If smaller beasts could hurt one, these huge antelopes, with such long, heavy, twisted horns, would surely kill one. He was taking no more chances until the game was down.

Kuu knew these eland better. They are docile enough, even when wounded and make no attempt to fight back. Hunting eland was easy for Kuu and, at his roar of triumph over his success, Jangwa came furtively from cover to join him at the meal.

This night the hyenas came in great numbers and were very bold. Some of these had young in the den and could not follow the game that had gone away. They had to stay here and pick up what they could. Their hunger made them bolder than usual and they crowded close to the meat. Kuu was continually charging about to drive them off. It was truly a contest to see who would devour this eland.

The eland was as large as a Jersey cow and while Kuu and Jangwa fed on one end, the hyenas would essay to slice off chunks of meat at the other end. They were forever flitting in and out, gibbering, chattering, and calling in their doleful manner. It seemed that they were trying to attract all the hyenas for miles around to this banquet, so that the crowd of them might hope to overwhelm the lions. But no more hyenas answered their calls and it became just a run-in-and-grab contest.

Kuu was furious. His charging about at them gave him little time to eat. Then, when the night was well along and he knew that it would be necessary to desert this meat to go to water and lie up for the day, he suddenly became enraged and charged wildly among the hyenas, punishing several of them severely for their thievery. This caused them to draw off and gave the lions a chance to finish their meal unmolested. But no sooner had Kuu and Jangwa left for the river than the hyenas fell upon what was left and reduced it to a mere skeleton.

The river was a long way off, but the lions went along with an easy, swinging pace that soon covered the distance. As they approached the water, Kuu stopped for a moment, sniffing and growling throatily. Jangwa, noting the warning growl, looked about to see what could have disturbed

Kuu. Then Kuu swung off to one side, to go to water lower down, but something came puffing and snorting at them out of the darkness and two forms loomed up eerily in the faint light just before the dawn. One was huge and bulky and came on with a loud, "Push-push!" The other was smaller and kept close to the side of the larger one. Kuu quickly led Jangwa aside to let these beasts pass, but the larger one charged back and forth, puffing and wheezing. It seemed to be searching for the lions' scent so that it could run them down. At last it went puffing off with the smaller one and they heard the heavy thumps of galloping feet recede into the distance.

Jangwa was again all atremble with excitement. Perhaps he wondered what manner of beasts these could be. He remembered their scent and would watch out for them in the future. This was his way of learning new things, for Kuu had no language to tell him that these were rhinoceroses and that the old one, accompanying her young, had suspected the lions of trying to kill the young one. She would have tossed them with that long horn on her nose, if she had managed to run into them. Being trampled by a rhinoceros is bad enough, but being tossed with that sharp front horn is an evil to be avoided.

This had been an exciting night for Jangwa. It had even been so for Kuu. Both were glad to quench their thirst at the cool river and hunt their beds in a thicket.

## THE STORY OF A STONE[1]

*David Starr Jordan*

Once upon a time, a great many years ago, so many years ago that one grows very tired in trying to think how long ago it was; in those old days when the great Northwest consisted of a few ragged and treeless hills, full of copper and quartz, bordered by a dreary waste of sand-flats, over which the Gulf of Mexico rolled its warm and turbid waters as far north as Escanaba and Eau Claire; in the days when Marquette Harbor opened out towards Baffin's Bay, and the Northern Ocean washed the crest of Mount Washington and wrote its name upon the Pictured Rocks; when the tide of the Pacific, hemmed in by no snow-capped Sierras, came rushing through the Golden Gate between the Ozarks and the north peninsula of Michigan, and swept over Plymouth Rock, and surged up against Bunker Hill; in the days when it would have been fun to study geography, for there were no capitals, nor any products, and all the towns were seaports; —in fact, an immensely long time ago there lived somewhere in the northeastern part of the State of Wisconsin, not far from the city of Oconto, a little jellyfish.

It was a curious little fellow, about the shape of half an apple, and the size of a pin's head; and it floated around in the water, and ate little things, and opened and shut its umbrella pretty much as the jellyfishes do now on a sunny day off Nahant Beach when the tide is coming in. It had a great many little feelers that hung down all around like so many little snakes; so it was named Medusa, after a queer woman who lived a long while ago, when all sorts of stories were true. She wore snakes instead of hair, and used to turn people into stone images if they dared to make faces at her. So this little Medusa floated around, and opened and shut her umbrella for a good while—a month or two, perhaps, we don't know how long. Then one morning, down among the seaweeds, she laid a whole lot of tiny eggs, transparent as crabapple jelly, and smaller than the dewdrop on the end of a pine leaf. That was the last thing she did; so she died, and our story henceforth concerns only one of those little eggs.

One day the sun shone down into the water—the same sun that shines over the Oconto sawmills now—and touched these eggs with life; and a little fellow whom we will call Favosites, because that was his name, woke up inside of the egg, and came out into the world. He was only a little

[1] From David Starr Jordan, *Science Sketches.*

piece of floating jelly, shaped like a cartridge pointed at both ends, or like a grain of barley, although very much smaller. He had a great number of little paddles on his sides. These kept flapping all the time, so that he was constantly in motion. And at night all these little paddles shone with a rich green light, to show him the way through the water. It would have done you good to see them some night when all the little fellows had their lamps burning at once, and every wave as it rose and fell was all aglow with Nature's fireworks, which do not burn the fingers, and leave no smell of sulphur.

So the little Favosites kept scudding along in the water, dodging from one side to the other to avoid the ugly creatures that tried to eat him. There were crabs and clams of a fashion neither you nor I shall ever see alive. There were huge animals with great eyes, savage jaws like the beak of a snapping turtle and surrounded by long feelers. They sat in the end of a long round shell, shaped like a length of stovepipe, and glowered like an owl in a hollow log; and there were smaller ones that looked like lobsters in a dinner horn. But none of these caught the little fellow, else I should not have had this story to tell.

At last, having paddled about long enough, Favosites thought of settling in life. So he looked about till he found a flat bit of shell that just suited him. Then he sat down upon it and grew fast, like old Holger Danske in the Danish myth, or Frederic Barbarossa in the German one. He did not go to sleep, however, but proceeded to make himself a home. He had no head, but between his shoulders he had an opening which would serve him for mouth and stomach. Then he put a whole row of feelers out, and commenced catching little worms and floating eggs and bits of jelly and bits of lime—everything he could get—and cramming them into his mouth. He had a great many curious ways, but the funniest of them all was what he did with the bits of lime. He kept taking them in, and tried to wall himself up inside with them, as a person would "stone a well," or as though a man should swallow pebbles, and stow them away in his feet and all around under the skin, till he had filled himself all full with them, as the man filled Jim Smiley's frog.

Little Favosites became lonesome all alone in the bottom of that old ocean among so many outlandish neighbors. So one night when he was fast asleep, and dreaming as only a coral animal can dream, there sprouted out from his side, somewhere near where his sixth rib might have been if he had had any ribs, another little Favosites; and this one very soon began to eat worms and to wall himself up as if for dear life. Then from these two another and another little bud came out, and other little Favosites were formed. They all kept growing up higher and cramming themselves fuller and fuller of stone, till at last there were so many and they were so crowded together that there was not room for them to grow round, and so they had to become six-sided like the cells of a honeycomb. Once in a while some one in the company would feel jealous because the others got more of the worms, or would feel uneasy at sitting still so long and swallowing lime. Such a one would secede from the little union without even saying "good-by," and would put on the airs of the grandmother Medusa, and would sail around in the water, opening and shutting its umbrella, at last laying more eggs, which for all we know may have hatched out into more Favosites.

So the old Favosites died, or ran away, or were walled up by the younger ones, and new ones filled their places, and the colony thrived for a long while, until it had accumulated a large stock of lime.

But one day there came a freshet in the Menomonee River, or in some other river, and piles of dirt and sand and mud were brought down, and all the little Favosites' mouths were filled with it. This they did not like, and so they died; but we know that the rock house they were building was not spoiled, for we have it here. But it was tumbled about a good deal in the dirt, and the rolling pebbles knocked the corners off, and the mud worked into the cracks, and its beautiful color was destroyed. There it lay in the mud for ages, till the earth gave a great long heave that raised Wisconsin out of the ocean, and the mud around our little Favosites packed and dried into hard rock and closed it in. So it became part of the dry land, and lay embedded in the rocks for centuries, while the old-fashioned ferns grew above it, and whispered to it strange stories of what was going on above ground in the land where things were living.

Then the time of the first fishes came, and the other animals looked in wonder at them, as the Indians looked on Columbus. Some of them were like the little garpike of our river here, only much larger—big as a stovepipe, and with a crust as hard as a turtle's. Then there were sharks, of strange forms, and some of them had teeth like bowie knives, with tempers to match. And the time of the old fishes came and went, and many more times came and went, but still Favosites lay in the ground at Oconto.

Then came the long, hot, wet summer, when the mists hung over the earth so thick that you might have had to cut your way through them with a knife; and great ferns and rushes, big as an oak and tall as a steeple, grew in the swamps of Indiana and Illinois. Their green plumes were so long and so densely interwoven that the Man of the Moon might have fancied that the earth was feathering out. Then all about, huge reptiles, with jaws like the gates of doom and teeth like cross-cut saws, and little reptiles with wings like bats, crawled, and swam, and flew.

But the ferns died, and the reptiles died, and the rush trees fell in the swamps, and the Illinois and the Sangamon and the Wabash and all the other rivers covered them up. They stewed away under layers of clay and sand, till at last they turned into coal and wept bitter tears of petroleum. But all this while Favosites lay in the rocks in Wisconsin.

Then the mists cleared away, and the sun shone, and the grass began to grow, and strange animals came from somewhere or nowhere to feed upon it. There were queer little striped horses, with three or four hoofs on each foot, and no bigger than a Newfoundland dog, but as smart as ever you saw. There were great hairy elephants with teeth like sticks of wood. There were hogs with noses so long that they could sit on their hind legs and root. And there were many still stranger creatures which no man ever saw alive. But still Favosites lay in the ground and waited.

And the long, long summer passed by, and the autumn and the Indian summer. At last the winter came, and it snowed and snowed, and it was so cold that the snow did not go off till the Fourth of July. Then it snowed and snowed till the snow did not go off at all. And then it became so cold that it snowed all the time, till the snow covered the animals, and then the trees, and then the mountains. Then it would thaw a little, and streams of water would run over the snow. Then it would freeze again, and the snow would pack into solid ice. So it went on snowing and thawing and freezing, till nothing but snowbanks could be seen in Wisconsin, and most of Indiana was fit only for a skating rink. And the plants and animals which could get away, all went south to live, and the others died and were frozen into the snow.

So it went on for a great many years. I dare not tell you how long, for you might not believe me. Then the spring came, the south wind blew, and the snow began to thaw. Then the ice came sliding down from the mountains and hills, and from the north toward the south. It went on, tearing up rocks, little and big, from the size of a chip to the size of a house, crushing forests as you would crush an eggshell, and wiping out rivers as you would wipe out a chalk mark. So it came pushing, grinding, thundering along—not very fast, you understand, but with tremendous force, like a plow drawn by a million oxen, for a thousand feet of ice is very heavy. And the ice plow scraped over Oconto, and little Favosites was torn from the place where he had lain so long; but by good fortune he happened to fall into a crevice of the ice where he was not much crowded, else he would have been ground to powder and I should not have had this story to tell. And the ice melted as it slid along, and it made great torrents of water, which, as they swept onward, covered the land with clay and pebbles. At last the ice came to a great swamp overgrown with tamarack and balsam. It melted here; and all the rocks and stones and dirt it had carried—little Favosites and all—were dumped into one great heap.

It was a very long time after, and man had been created, and America had been discovered, and the War of the Revolution and the War of the Rebellion had all been fought to the end, and a great many things had happened, when one day a farmer living near Grand Chûte, in Outagamie County, Wisconsin, was plowing up his clover field to sow to winter wheat. He picked up in the furrow a curious little bit of "petrified honeycomb," a good deal worn and dirty, but still showing plainly the honey cells and the beebread. Then he put it into his pocket and carried it home, and gave it to his boy Charley to take to the teacher and hear what he had to say about it. And this is what he said.

## THE CAPTURE OF THE GIANT ARMADILLO[1]

*Raymond L. Ditmars*

A week and more had passed since Professor Smith's escapade had turned the camp in the Cuban jungle upside down. Platt plied him with questions. There seemed to be little doubt about it. The professor had literally stuck his foot into it—the burrow of the giant armadillo they were after. They had returned to the place and had followed out their carefully laid plans of discovering and capturing the rare animal. The building of the observation platform had been a revelation of the ingenuity and skill of the natives, Daguardo and Pascal, and Platt was ready for the first night of observation of the animal's habits.

Platt and Daguardo were on their platform. It was close to dusk. The light impressed Platt as "dropping out," like the dimming of lights in a theater. He figured that this was caused by the decrease in glow as the rays of the setting sun were successively shut off by ridges of the hills. On the way to the tree he made a final survey of their surroundings. Opposite the knoll and at a distance which he estimated at three hundred feet, the forest opened at the edge of a steep slope. At the bottom was a mass of vegetation so dense that irregularities in the foliage looked like black caverns. This growth continued up the slope, the solid green variegated by a few slender trunks of reddish trees, quite vertical, but undulating in outline as if they had writhed through the mass.

"Think he goes in there—to hunt," suggested Platt. He had found that the young man could understand slow-spoken sentences, in English.

Daguardo looked at the jungly mass.

"He show—if come out," was the reply.

Once in the tree Platt was tingling with excitement. He reached for the little tin containing his cigarettes. Daguardo held up a hand in the familiar gesture of restraint that had been noted among the guides.

"No smoke cigarro. Smell go all over. Scare him."

Platt felt himself flushing. He should have known better, he thought. Daguardo was stretching himself prone on the platform, facing the burrows. He adjusted the headband of his lamp; put a hand in front of it and snapped on the switch of the aluminum battery-casing at his belt. The margins of his fingers shone red as the

[1] From Raymond L. Ditmars, *The Forest of Adventure.*

light penetrated them. He suggested that Platt seek a comfortable position, as his standing posture made the bamboo cross-pieces turn slightly and creak.

Platt occasionally looked at his watch. The heat and dampness intensified the glow of illuminated hands and numerals. The figures shone in satiny green. It was ten minutes after nine and nothing had happened that was apparent to Platt's ears, although Daguardo had twice hissed, long and softly, warnings for utter cessation of movement.

Daguardo was hissing again.

Yes, there was a sound—now! It was repeated, much louder—a rattling, among leaves. Then Platt heard the unmistakable impact of one fragment of rock hitting another.

While realizing he was gazing into what to him was blank darkness, he built up a picture of what was happening. A powerful foot was shooting earth from a burrow. Fragments struck among some leaves. A rock was ejected from the tunnel. It rolled down the slope and hit another, from previous digging.

"He comes out!" whispered Daguardo.

To Platt's ears, the sounds had ceased, but a hiss from his companion, barely louder than a breath, warned him that the critical moment was at hand.

Daguardo's light flashed, for possibly two seconds. Platt distinguished nothing more than a gray-brown form moving slowly from the knoll. Daguardo's hearing had been up to expectation. The circle of light had accurately hit the target.

A minute went by. The creature came nearer—for there were sounds comparable to the snuffling of a pig rooting in soft soil.

Peering in the direction of the sound, Platt snapped on his light.

While his mind had conjured up visions of what he was to see, he was so impressed that he caught his breath.

What he saw was an armored creature close to six feet long. The leathery cuirass covering its back was of small plates, set in rings. Its head, two-foot tail, and legs were similarly plated. It was an animated tank, on short legs, but its forefeet riveted attention. They were provided with several claws, but a single one on each foot was of excessive length.

"Five inches long," muttered Platt. "Like the end of a knife plough."

How long the animal posed in the spotlight is problematical. Platt afterward figured they had gaped at it for a full minute, forgetting about the hazard of driving it away. But it stood motionless. Then, seeming to realize that it was losing time in starting on its nightly prowl, it turned to a fallen tree trunk beside it and hooked one of the massive claws into a crack. There was a crackle of wood as it tore a section away. They saw it thrust an elongated tongue into crevices. That it had formerly investigated this log was evident from other strips lying nearby.

*"Hiss-s-s-s-s,"* came the caution from Daguardo.

Platt snapped off the light. There was a further sound of snuffling and rooting, of feet scuffling through vegetation on the other side of their tree, indicating a leisurely trot.

"All right cigarro. Me one, too," came from Daguardo.

Platt passed the tin, nudging his companion with it in the darkness.

"He was not afraid of the light."

"No mind light—s'prised—no afraid."

By mutual arrangement, they alternately dozed and kept watch. There was a clammy chill with the dawn. Sheets of mist filled the hollows. Platt turned up the collar of his jacket and looped a handkerchief about it to keep it tight. Chills ran through him, causing his jaw to quiver. But the balance of their watching was of no avail. With the increasing glow in the easterly sky they decided to give it up. The prize had vacated the neighborhood or returned by a different route. Platt was already depressed with anxiety and the restlessness of waiting to see what another night would bring forth.

The second night of observation had showed that the armadillo's habits were well established, and the next day was given to preparation for his capture.

An oblong pit was dug between the stones at the bottom of the wash and the rotting log. It was eight feet long and six feet wide, with indentation for the cage. It was to be five feet deep, and finished well before dark. All of the excavated earth had to be carried well to one side, to remove all traces of disturbance.

In their hurry to complete the task they reeked with perspiration, which worked in salty drops into their eyes and dripped from their chins.

While some were digging, others were gathering loose earth with their hands and throwing it into a section of the rainproof canvas used for carrying it aside. Fortunately, the spot was free of rock, but many roots were encountered. These were cut cleanly with the belt hatchets. Pascal sharpened two saplings and they used them to strike deeply and loosen the soil. They made surprisingly good progress and by mid-afternoon the excavation was completed, trampled firmly at the bottom and the indispensable Daguardo was in the swamp collecting long thin stems of bamboo to cover the pit.

When the cane, which was as thin as a fishing pole, arrived, it was laid crosswise over the trap. The sticks to cover two-thirds of the central area were slightly hacked in the middle by the cutting knives, so that they would suddenly give away under a weight. Several trips were made to the back of the knoll to obtain vines to form a mat over the sticks.

At Platt's insistence there was little talking. The waiting relays sat well off on a rise watching operations. Platt came back to them.

"Clamps of the cage screwed tight, Hoskins?"

"Been twice over every one of them with the wrench. Do you expect that beast to walk into the thing?"

Platt outlined his tactics. The cage was to be bound all around with vines, to make it look like a leafy cavern. It would be placed in the pit. If the animal went into it the length of its body, it would touch a wire releasing the drop-door. The door would be blocked at the bottom so it would not fall all the way to the floor and injure the animal's plated tail, which, on account of the odd structure of the beast, was of a dragging type, sprouting from beneath the sheet of leathery armor covering the back.

If the beast fell into the pit, the watchers were to allow a couple of minutes while they listened for the fall of the cage door. If this failed to occur, the covering of the pit would be stripped away and they would try to drive the armadillo into the cage with poles. Various things might happen, of course. The creature might start to dig through the walls of the pit—and it was capable of this prodigious effort. It might also climb the cage and thus seek to escape from the pit, but the cane directly over the cage would be woven together and spiked to the ground so as to offer considerable resistance. At any rate, this type of beast could not leap, nor was there much probability of it climbing the sides of the pit. Upon no consideration, if it broke past them, was anyone to get within reach of its enormous claws. Whether or not it would deliberately attack was problematical. The Indian legends carried ugly stories about it.

The cage was brought over from the camp, swathed in vines and placed in the pit, the balance of thin sticks laid across, and the matting to hide the pitfall skillfully arranged. Daguardo gathered dead leaves and sprinkled them over the covering. He followed this by breaking away some light fragments of the rotting log and dropping these near the center. All was ready—and so was supper.

The giant armadillo that night ambled down the wash, but turned from his usual path to go around their trap. Then they made preparations to lead the armadillo into the pit on the fourth night by baiting the trap.

A batch of big grasshoppers had been collected, and once they started intensive hunting for these insects, they found gigantic members of the clan. In a literal sense these creatures could not be called grasshoppers, as they were stirred out of low bushes. Some were as long as a man's finger, but much stouter. They were armed with a row of spikes on the shin portion of their hind legs and could administer a kick which drove the spikes into the collector's fingers, like needle points.

Professor Smith entered into the hunt with great enthusiasm and declared that here was a phase of collecting he had hitherto neglected. He delayed operations by rushing from one hunter to another in deciding whether specimens should go into the can Daguardo was carrying, or the entomologist's cyanide jar. When Frank came panting back with an enormous grasshopper, which both jumped and flew—an astonishing insect close to eight inches long—the professor praised the boy warmly, and appropriated the specimen. They obtained an ample supply, however, and the insects were killed, ground up, mixed with shreds of fish and the whole rendered into a "mash" with a diluted portion of evaporated milk from one of three remaining cans.

This was the mixture which Platt and Daguardo had taken along to the knoll. A sprinkle of it was to be placed in the upper part of the water wash, along which the armadillo emerged from its burrow. There was to be another sprinkling near the end of the wash. The major portion of the bait was to be scattered over the covering of the pit.

Darkness settled. The luminous larvae writhed in and out of the stump. The beam was shining from the tree. It was directed more obliquely than the preceding night. It remained motionless, for perhaps a minute. Then it moved slowly. Its motion thrilled them, as it plainly told what was happening. The animal had stopped to investigate the first traces of bait in the wash. It was moving forward. The light was motionless again. It was investigating—possibly eating—the second spreading of the bait. Again, the light moved slowly and stopped—over the pitfall. Then it went out. Somebody heaved a tremulous sigh.

Two minutes to wait for the cage door to drop!

Hoskins broke the silence.

"I'll be hanged if they aren't coming back again!"

Sure enough. Two bobbing lights were striking in their direction.

Price hailed the returning pair.

"What happened?"

Platt spoke in a monotone of disappointment.

"Took the bait we laid in the gully—lapped up both batches. When he came to the pit he stopped and sniffed and made quite a fuss, stuck out a tongue as long as his head. He has a tongue similar to those long-nosed anteaters, but thicker and shorter. He was keen for that bait, but he walked around the pit in a precise, oblong inspection, went over to the log, ripped the side out of it—and went his way."

"Figure you're licked, Platt?"

"Not by a long shot!" flashed Platt, his enthusiasm returning. "We're getting acquainted with the beast. I have another idea."

"If it doesn't work tomorrow night, we shall have to go for fresh supplies. Sorry this will delay you close to a week, but we'll come back prepared to stick it out."

Platt outlined the new plan. He had decided they were not dealing with a particularly wary animal. It acted as if it were more interested in than afraid of their lights. Nor was it disturbed by the pit, other than by deciding to keep on familiar-looking ground. The new plan was to drive a fifteen-foot row of poles extending from the end of the pit to beyond the log. In this instance, the watchers would be extended in a semicircle, not more than a hundred feet from the log. Daguardo would be in the tree. Bait would be placed in the wash and more of it at the approach to the log. When the observer's light showed the animal to be busy with the last batch of bait, he would signal by a sweep of the light, they would rush in, block the armadillo's retreat up the wash, flank him at the log, and endeavor to drive him into the pit along the row of poles.

The plan sounded encouraging, but before the camp retired, Amaro was instructed to start for the river in the morning for fish. Pascal's hunting the preceding day had produced nothing but some small waterfowl and two parrots—with eighteen persons to consider.

"Amaro's smoked fish may taste like leather," declared Price, "but his men like it and it will help us out for the time being. Lucky we have these ingenious Indians."

Arrangements for the fifth night's contact with the armadillo occupied the greater part of the day. There were the young trees to be cut and trimmed, firmly embedded, then lashed together to withstand the onslaught of a powerful animal. Daguardo solved the problem of embedding the poles by hacking down a young tree with very hard wood. When it fell and Hoskins lifted the end of it, a look of astonishment spread over his face. It felt as heavy as if it were metal. The axe slipped and bounded from its branches as it was trimmed and there was difficulty in sharpening one end to a point. It was of a kind the Indians called "ironwood," and Daguardo's idea was to make holes for the poles by driving it into the ground. On account of the weight of the tree, it would be like using an iron crowbar.

The poles were set up and lashed at several levels with grass strands. Morlan looked up at Daguardo's handiwork in the tree, then at the row of poles, which looked like the wall of a stockade.

"It doesn't take that boy long to make a showing out of nothing," he remarked.

"That is a thing these tropical people get very little credit for—in northerly countries," said Price. "The greater number of the workers are resourceful, industrious, and quite uniformly cheerful. You notice it with our boys—a mixed lot?"

"I certainly have, at times when everybody was dog-tired and we were still running into obstacles. The way some cut through thick places, while others doubled the loads; and later swung into the work of making camp."

With the "shute" completed they moved back to camp, which had become a very orderly-looking clearing. There was a bamboo working bench for Professor Smith, a similar arrangement for writing and sorting notes, while Hoskins' instruments hung under a thatched screen.

Platt produced for the first time a net he had stowed in the end of his duffel bag. It made a smaller bundle than one of the hammocks and its mesh was but slightly coarser. As he spread it out, it was seen to have a circular opening of a yard, and to form a bag of about the same depth. There was joking about such a light net restraining the formidable animal they were after, but Platt argued otherwise. He conceded that if there was a chance of utilizing the net, it would be badly torn in the first encounter; but his reason for selecting such light material was because it could be dexterously manipulated. He was convinced that light as it appeared, it would entangle a strong animal for a minute, or slightly more—and men moving quickly could do a lot in a minute. The zoologist was preparing the net in the faint hope that if the armadillo charged through their lines, a "rear tackle," carrying the net, could throw it over the animal, when it could be forced into the cage.

Platt had a feeling that tonight's contact with the giant armadillo, if unsuccessful, would be the last; that the scare it received would drive it away. He had lain awake thinking it over; and had considered trying to dig the animal out during the day. But he had given up the idea, owing to the stony nature of the knoll, traversing roots, and the probability of deep connecting tunnels. Also, there was no doubt that such an animal in evading capture, could dig faster than men. "No," reasoned Platt, "the barrier idea and driving him into the pit seems the only way;

and trying to get him tangled in the net if he makes a break."

"Come on, boys," sang out Platt to the three junior members, "we must find two long, springy branches, same diameter end to end, to splice together as our ring. That thicket over there looks pretty good."

"Platt," cautioned Morlan, "don't go far in there. Remember the bushmaster. It's near here. Between the bats and that snake —and your long-clawed friend sleeping in that hole—I feel extra cautious about this place."

"We'll be careful," was the assurance. "That snake has gone. Since Pascal found the logs the professor dug into I've been over there a dozen times. I think that snake came from the ledges on the slope and was among those bushes waiting for some animal to go by."

"He may be trying the same tactics somewhere around here."

"We'll watch out."

They returned with springy branches, spliced them into a ring, and bound the net to the ring with stout twine.

Daguardo's eyes were glowing with excitement. His Indian blood speeded at the thought of nets and snares, although he was awed at trying to capture a giant armadillo. He went over to the neat layout of straps.

"I take straps, Doctor. All right?"

"Yes," said Platt. "What's the idea?"

"I have idea. Me carry straps."

"All right, Daguardo. You take the straps."

Daguardo took two of the shoulder straps used in transporting the cage panels, and wound them through his belt.

Price and Hoskins jotted notes and figures, and Professor Smith prepared paper triangles for specimens and inspected the condition of previously stored treasures. Amaro and his men returned. They had three big fish and a good string of the "pan" variety. A fire soon sent a column of smoke to the tree tops. Pascal and one of the helpers appeared. Four parrots and a brace of small waterfowl formed the bag of the shooting trip.

"All told, I think we have about twelve shotgun shells remaining," said Price. "Owing to salvos for our exploring entomologist, and shooting fish, even the ammunition is scratching bottom."

Smith, hearing his title, glanced up with a benign smile, good nature beaming through his thick glasses.

"Yes, yes," he replied, "and may I remind the leader that there are no more batteries for the headlamps. I felt restrained from using my light-box last night."

"The deuce!" exclaimed Price, diving for the packets.

The professor was right. Only two of the little cells were found after rummaging—and five were needed to reload each of the battery boxes!

Supper was eaten in a spirit of tense excitement. All felt that the evening would be a climax to planning and waiting.

"All set?" whispered Platt. "Everybody quiet. Remember, we're close to the tunnel. Don't break any twigs. Watch Daguardo's light. When he ducks forward—dash in. Use your poles. Drive the armadillo into the pit. Pascal, stand to the rear with the net. If he breaks through, throw the ring over him."

The moon was rising, as was evident from the purplish glow in openings of the forest canopy. Where they were, utter darkness had descended. In a small patch above was a single star. Morlan watched it. It seemed to be floating in luminous space. He pondered over this effect, which he had seen nowhere but in these tropics. He looked straight ahead, moved his hand in front of his face. No, he could see nothing. Then he glanced upward, raised his hand and saw its outline against the glowing sky—

They jumped as at an explosion! Daguardo's light had stabbed downward from the tree. A rub of clothing, the creak of boots, showed a simultaneous start along the line of watchers. It was the critical moment. When that beam moved again they would snap on their lights and rush forward!

A minute—possibly another minute—and the shaft swept forward like a pointing finger.

"Your lights!" shouted Platt. "Close in!"

Fingers had been in readiness to press the switches at their belts, but all remembered that one light shot out ahead, possibly a second in advance of the others. It was followed by a semicircle of rays which looked milky in the misty air. The wavering beams advanced, throwing every leaf and declivity of the ground into brilliant relief. One end of the line reached the pole barrier. The other end swung inward, flanking the opposite boundary of the pit.

In that concentration of light all saw for the first time—with the exception of Platt—an apparition like an animated barrel sheathed with scaly plates. From one end protruded a pig-like head, and from the other there trailed a plated tail. The thing looked antediluvian, but not dangerous, as its short legs only slightly raised the body from the ground. This impression came in a flash as they closed in around the beast. There was a uniform thought that it was practically captured. This monstrosity could be pushed or rolled into the pit with their poles—and already the ends of a couple of poles were being shoved against it.

But as the poles touched the animal, the picture changed—instantly. It reared and thrust out a front foot bearing a claw like the blade of a heavy hunting knife. It made a sweep at the pole Anderson had pushed at it, and the bark showed a rip a foot long. It followed this gesture with a series of grunts. Other poles were pushing at it, but it made a swing, thrust them aside, and charged through the attacking line.

Although it barely hesitated in passing Morlan, he heard a sound like a combination of bark and grunt and felt a tug at his boot. As he instinctively ducked his head, his lamp showed him a gash through the leather. Through the hubbub came the voice of Platt.

"Get him, Pascal! Hoskins, help me with the cage."

There was a splintering of bamboo as Platt jumped into the pit.

Lights were turned on Pascal, who was on the outskirts of the broken lines. The animal was not going fast, but at an ambling gait. Pascal ran to head it off, his net held forward. A figure rushed parallel to the animal, getting well ahead of it, and they saw it was the professor making a vain effort to turn the beast's course. Pascal aimed his net for a throw and as he did so he caught it on the spike of a branch. Realizing the tragedy of a second's delay, he shook the ring furiously from side to side, but the branch bent and swayed with the movements, and the net failed to come free. Light beams were divided between him and the armadillo. The few seconds that had passed had been most disturbing, and the beast was thinking fast.

It saw but one obstacle in its way—Pascal, and decided to leave a stern reprimand in its wake. It charged straight at him, with its sharp grunts, and the startled man jumped nimbly over its back, landing in its wake and freeing his net from the branch in the effort.

If they reckoned that the animal could do no better than amble, they now changed their minds. Clear of the group the beast speeded up, and selected its best course of escape. Lamps shone on its retreating form as the party thrashed and stumbled in pursuit through bushes and obstructions, but it increased its lead.

Ahead of them, the beam of a single light picked it up.

"That's Smith," panted Price. "I hope to heaven he doesn't get in the way of that brute. What is he doing? He's heading it off—he's in front of it—his light is out!"

From the very surface of the ground there came a dazzling burst of golden light. In their excited imagination it looked as if the forest floor had taken fire. Against this radiance they could see the form of the armadillo posed motionless, a great claw reared to strike.

Pascal instantly solved the puzzle, and with raised net rushed for a light.

"Wait a second, everybody," barked Price, also grasping the situation. "Hold still."

The action was in black, like a shadowgraph against the flood of light. They saw the approach of Pascal's net, then his arms. The beast turned slightly. Its striking claw was elevated higher; then the net descended. They were rushing forward. There was a frenzied cry from Pascal. A figure darted through them like a cat. It was Daguardo. Gasping voices were shouting from the rear. "We're coming with the cage."

When the tossing beams had centered around the scene of action it looked as if success was once more slipping away, in spite of frantic efforts. The armadillo was in the net—or what remained of it, but one of its claws had gouged through and a free forelimb was furrowing the ground. The pig-like head was rooting for an opening and, once located, the formidable creature would be free again.

Professor Smith was flat on his stomach holding a lamp emitting the yellow radiance. But now most startling of all was the writhing form of Daguardo.

He was prone, behind the animal, cutting holes in the net and attaching the loop of a strap over a hind foot. With one attached, he sprang like a weasel for the other hind foot.

At this contact with its foot the armadillo turned and struck, but the boy rolled out of harm's way and was at the foot again. He noosed the other foot. The animal tore through another part of the net and its head appeared.

"Cage for him. Cage for him," shrieked Daguardo.

"They're coming," groaned Price, but with a feeling that the passing of a few more seconds would result in bitter disappointment. "Platt, *Platt!*"

"Hold him," yelled Platt. Two lights wavered through brush.

It was easier said than done. The entangling restraint of the net was torn away. Daguardo hung to his straps and was almost pulled off his feet. Morlan seized one of the straps—and it slipped off the animal's foot! But Daguardo was still hanging to the remaining strap, and they heard the metal jangle of the cage as it was set down.

Platt sized up the situation. That strap was their only hope. He raised the door of the cage, picked up the loose end of the strap behind Daguardo, passed it into the cage and through the mesh at the rear.

"Couple of you get hold of this!"

Eager hands grasped the strap and pulled. Daguardo let go and twisted out of the way. Additional hands seized the strap. It stretched and squeaked. There were showers of soil and leaves from the digging claws, grunts, and explosive snorts—but the armadillo was hauled into the cage, and the door dropped down.

As the cage rocked and jumped from the beast's struggles, the voice of Professor Smith came as clearly as in the lecture hall.

"Application of the diffuse reflector and amber screen. Thought it might hold him. Strong radial rays, gentlemen, absolutely blinding—"

In their hearts they were blessing Professor Smith, but their immediate anxiety concerned the strength of the cage. Would it hold their prize?

Two poles were lashed to the top of the cage and it was carried back to camp. Khan was barking furiously. The shouts and cries had sorely worried the restrained dog.

"All right to turn Khan loose?" asked Morlan.

"Yes, but keep him away from the cage," cautioned Platt.

"Might as well get him acquainted with our new member now, as any time. I'll handle him."

Morlan freed the dog and stood close to the armadillo's cage. Khan approached the cage with a growl, but was reprimanded. He inspected it from all sides, getting his nose within a foot of it. The armadillo greeted this familiarity with nothing more than the raising of a striking claw and sniffing like the exhaust of a small engine.

"He may take to this reasonably enough," said Price. "Seems to be pretty sensible."

The remark was premature. Platt started to shift the cage, to level its base. The animal reared, struck at him, then attacked the mesh with a vigor that made the cage dance.

"I'll take that back," commented Price.

"I think he's going to quiet down soon, at that," declared Platt. "After he finds these whirlwind tactics are not getting him anywhere."

Back at the camp they held a celebration in honor of Professor Smith's exploit and Daguardo's ingenuity. Anderson advised the *Oraloo* by radio of their success; and warned them to prepare a strong and roomy cage. He could barely pick up return signals as the batteries of the now battered set were losing life, and besides, there was constant, "frying" static. "Are there other species in the genus to which your example belongs?" Professor Smith asked Platt.

"No. The giant armadillo stands alone, forming a genus of a single species. There were probably prehistoric, related forms. Its name is *Priodon giganteus,* the generic name from the Greek, meaning saw-toothed and referring to ridges like rows of minute teeth, on the tongue. The animal has molars, but no front teeth.

"Small loss, when gifted with a brace of bayonets!" said Hoskins.

"We have heard its scientific name, Platt, but how are we to address him as a member of our group?" asked Price.

"I'd suggest that we become fairly familiar, and call him by his first name," laughed Platt. "Simply, Mr. Priodon."

There was a commotion from the cage, which bulged, and rocked.

"I question the dignity of 'Mister,' as yet," commented Price.

## *The World and Its Creatures: Suggested Grades*

*Grade One*
Blue Barns

*Grade Two*
Plouf, the Little Wild Duck

*Grade Three*
The Gentleman in Brown
Hide and Go Seek
Skunks

*Grade Four*
Rocky Billy Goes Visiting
Keeping Still in the Woods
The Horny Ones
Jimmie, the White Sparrow

*Grade Five*
Beasts of the Tar Pits
Paddlewings Grows Up

*Grade Six*

What We Found in a Fox Den
Jangwa Begins To Hunt

*Grade Seven*

With Helmet and Hose
The Story of a Stone

*Grade Eight*

The Capture of the Giant Armadillo

## *Books about the World and Its Creatures*

### Grades One and Two

Brooks, Anne, *The Black Pup,* illus. by Margaret Van Doren. Viking.

Fox, Frances Margaret, *Little Toad,* illus. by Sjerman C. Hoeblich. Appleton-Century.

Gall, Alice, and Fleming Crew, *Wagtail,* illus. by Kurt Wiese. Oxford.

Lathrop, Dorothy P., *Who Goes There?* illus. by the author. Macmillan.

Lida, *Plouf, the Little Wild Duck* (trans. by Georges Duplaix), illus. by Rojan. Harper.

Patch, Edith M., *Holiday Pond,* illus. by photographs. Macmillan

Sewell, Helen, *Blue Barns,* illus. by the author. Macmillan.

Smalley, Janet, *Do You Know?* illus. by the author. Morrow.

Webb, Clifford, *Animals from Everywhere,* illus. by the author. Warne.

Wiese, Kurt, *Buddy, the Bear,* illus. by the author. Coward-McCann.

———, *Karoo, the Kangaroo,* illus. by the author. Coward-McCann.

### Grades Three and Four

Atkinson, Agnes Akin, *Skinny, the Gray Fox,* illus. by photographs. Viking.

Baynes, Ernest Harold, *Jimmy: The Story of a Black Bear Cub,* illus. by photographs. Macmillan.

Bianco, Margery, *All about Pets,* illus. by Grace Gilkison. Macmillan.

———, *More about Animals,* illus. by Helen Torrey. Macmillan.

Chaffee, Allen, *Tawny Goes Hunting,* illus. by Paul Bransom. Random House.

Colum, Padraic, *The White Sparrow,* illus. by Lynd Ward. Macmillan.

Grey Owl, *Sajo and the Beaver People,* illus. by the author. Scribner.

Hader, Berta, and Elmer Hader, *Spunky: The Story of a Shetland Pony,* illus. by the authors. Macmillan.

Holling, Holling Clancy, *Rocky Billy: The Story of a Rocky Mountain Goat,* illus. by the author. Macmillan.

Kipling, Rudyard, *The Jungle Book,* illus. by Kurt Wiese. Doubleday, Doran.

Lathrop, Dorothy P., *Hide and Go Seek,* illus. by the author. Macmillan.

Lida, *Spiky, the Hedgehog* (trans. by Lily Duplaix), illus. by Rojan. Harper.

Linderman, Frank B., *Stumpy,* illus. by H. M. Stoops. John Day.

McKenny, Margaret, *A Book of Wild Flowers,* illus. by Edith F. Johnston. Macmillan.

Mukerji, Dhan Gopal, *Fierce-Face: The Story of a Tiger,* illus. by Dorothy P. Lathrop. Dutton.

Patch, Edith M., and Carroll L. Fenton, *Desert Neighbors,* illus. by Carroll L. Fenton. Macmillan.

———, *Holiday Shore,* illus. by Carroll L. Fenton. Macmillan.

Roberts, Charles G. D., *Children of the Wild,* illus. by Paul Bransom. Macmillan.

Seton, Ernest Thompson, *The Biography of a Grizzly,* illus. by the author. Appleton-Century.

Tee-Van, Helen Damrosch, *Red Howling Monkey: The Tale of a South American Indian Boy,* illus. by the author. Macmillan.

Wells, Rhea, *Ali, the Camel,* illus. by the author. Doubleday, Doran.

———, *Zeke, the Raccoon,* illus. by the author. Viking

## *Grades Five and Six*

Baynes, Ernest Harold, *The Sprite: The Story of a Red Fox,* illus. by photographs. Macmillan.

Boulton, Rudyard, *Traveling with the Birds,* illus. by Walter Alois Webber. Donahue.

Bronson, Wilfrid S., *Fingerfins: The Tale of a Sargasso Fish,* illus. by the author. Macmillan.

———, *Paddlewings: The Penguin of Galápagos,* illus. by the author. Macmillan.

———, *The Wonder World of Ants,* illus. by the author. Harcourt, Brace.

Burgess, Thorton W., *The Burgess Bird Book for Children,* illus. by Louis Agassiz Fuertes. Little, Brown.

———, *The Burgess Flower Book for Children.* Little, Brown.

Cormack, Maribelle, and William P. Alexander, *The Museum Comes to Life,* illus. by Henry F. Meloy. American Book.

Gorse, Golden, *Moorland Mousie,* illus. by Lionel Edwards. Scribner.

Huey, Edward G., *A Child's Story of the Animal World,* illus. by H. R. Daugherty and Olive Earle. Reynal and Hitchcock.

Jordan, David Starr, *The Story of Matka,* illus. by Chloe Lesley Starks. World Book.

Long, William J., *Wilderness Ways,* illus. by Charles Copeland. Ginn.

McFee, Inez, *The Tree Book,* illus. by photographs. Stokes.

Miller, Olive Thorne, *Children's Book of Birds,* illus. by Louis Agassiz Fuertes. Houghton Mifflin.

Mukerji, Dhan Gopal, *Gay-Neck: The Story of a Pigeon,* illus. by Boris Artzybasheff. Dutton.

Patch, Ethel M., and Carroll L. Fenton, *Mountain Neighbors,* illus. by Carroll L. Fenton. Macmillan.

Reed, William Maxwell, *Earth for Sam,* illus. by Karl Moseley. Harcourt, Brace.

———, *Stars for Sam,* illus. with photographs. Harcourt, Brace.

Robinson, W. W., *Beasts of the Tar Pits,* illus. by Irene B. Robinson. Macmillan.

Seton, Ernest Thompson, *Wild Animals I Have Known,* illus. by the author. Scribner.

Sewell, Anna, *Black Beauty,* illus. by Maude Scrivener. Macrae, Smith.

Wilwerding, Walter J., *Jangwa: The Story of a Jungle Prince,* illus. by the author. Macmillan.

———, *Punda, the Tiger-Horse,* illus. by the author. Macmillan.

## Grades Seven and Eight

Beebe, William, *Exploring with Beebe,* illus. by photographs. Putnam.

Burroughs, John, *Bird Stories from Burroughs,* illus. by Louis Agassiz Fuertes. Houghton Mifflin.

Ditmars, Raymond L., *The Book of Insect Oddities,* illus. by Helene Carter. Lippincott.

———, *The Forest of Adventure.* Macmillan.

Du Chaillu, Paul, *In African Forest and Jungle,* illus. by Erick Berry. Scribner.

Hornaday, William T., *The Minds and Manners of Wild Animals.* Scribner.

Hylander, Clarence J., *American Scientists.* Macmillan.

James, Will, *Smoky, the Cowhorse,* illus. by the author. Scribner.

Jordan, David Starr, *Science Sketches.* McClurg.

Kenly, Julie Classon, *Green Magic,* illus. by Edna M. Reindel. Appleton-Century.

Medary, Marjorie, *Topgallant,* illus. by Lynd Ward. Random House.

Mills, Enos A., *The Story of a Thousand-Year Pine.* Houghton Mifflin.

Mukerji, Dhan Gopal, *Kari the Elephant,* illus. by J. E. Allen. Dutton.

Olcott, William T., *A Field Book of the Skies,* illus. by photographs. Putnam.

Pope, Clifford, *Snakes Alive,* illus. by photographs. Viking.

Putnam, David Binney, *David Goes Voyaging.* Putnam.

Roberts, Charles G. D., *Kings in Exile,* illus. by Paul Bransom. Macmillan.

Salten, Felix, *Bambi: A Life in the Woods,* illus. by Kurt Wiese. Simon and Shuster.

Sharp, Dallas Lore, *Year Out-of-Doors,* illus. by Robert Bruce Horsfall. Houghton Mifflin.

# Stories about Boys and Girls

## LUCKY LITTLE LENA [1]

*Marjorie Flack*

Once upon a time there was a little dog named Lena.

Lena belonged to a little boy named Ted and his sister whose name was Nell.

Lena and Ted and Nell lived in the city in a city house.

Whenever Ted and Nell put on their coats and their hats to go outdoors, Lena would bring her little coat and beg to go with them.

When Ted and Nell went out to play in the park, Lena went too. But–

When Ted and Nell went other places, Lena had to stay at home.

When Ted and Nell rode in a taxicab, Lena stayed at home.

And Ted said, "Poor little Lena, I wish she could ride in a taxicab too!"

When Ted and Nell rode up in the air in an airplane, Lena stayed at home. And Nell said,

"Poor little Lena, I wish she could ride up in the air in an airplane too!"

When Ted and Nell went riding on the train, Lena stayed at home. And Ted said,

"Poor little Lena, I wish she could ride on the train too!"

When Ted and Nell went riding on the bus, Lena stayed at home. And Nell said,

"Poor little Lena, I wish she could ride on the bus too!"

When Ted and Nell went sailing on a big steamship, Lena stayed at home. Ted said,

"Poor little Lena, I wish she could sail on a big steamship too!"

But always when Ted and Nell put on their hats and their coats to go out in the park, they would put on Lena's little coat and take her down in the elevator and out in the street and into the park.

And Lena was very happy, because all the time that was where she wanted to go.

Lena did not want to go riding in a taxicab, because she did not like taxicabs.

Lena did not want to ride up in the air in an airplane, because she did not know about airplanes.

Lena did not want to ride on a train, because she did not know about trains.

Lena did not want to go riding in a bus, because she did not like buses.

Lena did not want to go sailing on a big

[1] From Marjorie Flack, *Lucky Little Lena.*

steamship, because she did not know about steamships.

So little Lena was very happy to run on her four little legs in the park.

Lucky little Lena!

## BILLY AND BLAZE [1]

*C. W. Anderson*

Billy was a little boy who loved horses more than anything else in the world. Whenever he had a chance to ride some farmer's horse he used to pretend that it was a prancing pony.

One birthday morning his father said to him, "Out on the lawn you will find your birthday present."

And there stood a beautiful bay pony with four white feet and a white nose. Billy had never been so happy.

No boy was ever more proud and happy than Billy when he went out for his first ride. Right from the very start Billy and his new pony seemed to like and understand each other.

After thinking for a long time about many names, Billy decided to call the pony Blaze because he had a white blaze down his face.

Before going to bed that first night he took a flashlight and went down to the stable to see if Blaze was all right. Already Blaze seemed to feel at home and was glad to see him.

As soon as it was daylight Billy was up cleaning and brushing Blaze so they could take a long ride after breakfast.

It was not long before Blaze would come galloping whenever Billy called, for he knew there would be a carrot or a piece of sugar for him as well as much petting. And he, too, enjoyed the rides through the woods where there was so much to see.

One day when they were riding along a path through the woods they came to a tree fallen across the path and Blaze jumped quickly over it. Billy was so surprised he almost fell off. But it was very exciting and he decided to try it again. So when they came to the next small fence he leaned forward and gripped with his knees and over they sailed. It felt like flying.

One day in the woods they heard a dog howling as if in pain. They rode to the spot and there they found a dog caught in a trap that had been set for some wild animals. Although the dog was badly hurt he seemed to know that Billy was trying to help him. He stood very still while Billy opened the trap and set him free. And then he limped along home with Billy and Blaze.

When they got home Billy bandaged the dog's foot and gave him something to eat. He was very hungry.

The dog seemed to have no home. No one could find out where he came from, so Billy's father let him keep him. He named the dog Rex and wherever Billy went there you were sure to find Rex, too.

Rex and Blaze were great friends. He went down to the stable to see Blaze very often and usually slept there with him.

One day when Billy and Blaze were out riding they saw a sign on a tree telling about a Horse Show and a silver cup that was to be given to the best pony. "Let's try for it," said Billy to Blaze.

When Billy got to the show with Blaze and Rex and saw how many fine ponies were there, he began to be afraid that he might not win the cup after all. But one pony after another knocked down the rail when he jumped, and Billy began to think that Blaze might win after all. He knew that he and Blaze had often jumped over fences almost as high as these.

At last Billy's turn came. Blaze jumped perfectly and Rex jumped beside him. Everybody clapped and cheered. Rex was not supposed to jump, but everybody liked to see a dog jump so well.

"You have a fine pony," said the judge as he gave Billy a silver cup almost too big for him to hold. A man came out and took a picture of all three of them. Then the judge pinned a blue ribbon on Blaze's

[1] From C. W. Anderson, *Billy and Blaze*.

bridle, with "First Prize" printed in gold letters on it.

The grass and trees looked very green and the birds sang very gaily as they rode home. Blaze seemed to know he had done well for he carried his head very high and pranced all the way.

Billy was as happy as any boy could be. For Blaze's supper that evening he took him many carrots and lumps of sugar, and Rex had the finest bone in the house.

Billy set the silver cup up in his room. Every time he looked at it, he was very, very proud of Blaze.

## GRANDMOTHER'S BUTTONS[1]

*George* and *Doris Hauman*

It was raining. It was raining dreadfully hard. Grandmother said it was raining cats and dogs. But of course Peter knew that that wasn't really true.

Grandmother's hair was white. She had crinkly eyes and a twinkly smile. She lived in a little old-fashioned house. There was a big barn, much bigger than the house. That was where you hunted eggs and rolled in the hay. There was a sweet, green meadow in back of the barn. That was where you ran, and ran, and ran. There was a clear little brook at the edge of the meadow. That was where you waded and caught tiny fish. Oh, it was a lovely place to play in the sunshine. But today—well, it was raining too hard to go outdoors at all.

Peter's nose was pressed close to the window. The corners of his mouth turned down. For the forty-'leventh time he said, "What time is it now? When will Daddy and Mother come?"

Yes, Peter was fidgety. He stood on his heels. He stood on his toes. He wiggled and he squirmed. Then he asked, "What can I do now, Grandmother? I've made a town with my blocks. I've played with my train. I've had a battle with my soldiers. I've pushed all my trucks and, anyway, I want someone to play with. I wish it would really truly rain me a dog. Then I guess I'd be happy. What *can* I do, Grandmother?"

Grandmother sighed. But soon her eyes twinkled again and she said, "I know. It's something that I used to do when I was a little girl."

She went to her big mending drawer and took out a shiny round tin box. And what do you think was in it? It was just full of buttons—all sizes and colors.

"Now, I will get you a thread and a needle," she said. "Then I want you to string just as many buttons as you can."

"Oh, that's girls' play! Why, that's sewing, just like Jane does for her dolls." And Peter's nose went plop against the window again.

But Grandmother looked into the button box. "Oh, my! Oh, my!" she said. "Here is a button that was on your Daddy's soldier coat. See, Peter, it still shines when I rub it. It's just like a magic button. I'm going to tie it on the end of the string. Then the rest of the buttons won't slip off."

"Let me see it first, please," said Peter. "Daddy tells me stories about the time he went across the ocean with the soldiers. I like to hear stories. Do you know any, Grandmother?"

"I can't tell you soldier stories, Peter," said Grandmother, reaching again into the button box, "but here are some buttons that were on a dress I had when I was a little girl. I can tell you a story about them. There were twelve of them all alike. Now, you find them all, and, while you are stringing them, I'll tell you the story."

So Grandmother began.

"This story happened a long time ago when I was a little girl. I was just about as big as Jane. One day I was invited to go to the city with my two aunts. Aunt Prissie was tall and thin and kept peppermint sticks in her pocket. Aunt Polly was short and fat and kept sugarplums in her pocket. Aunt Prissie and Aunt Polly always made me think of a peppermint stick and a sugar-

[1] From George and Doris Hauman, *Buttons.*

plum, too. And I loved them both very much.

"We were to go to the city by train. I was very much excited, for I had never been on a train before.

"My mother had just made me a new dress. The buttons you are stringing went all the way down the back of the waist. There was a blue ribbon bow fastened to the collar in front. My, how grand I felt when I tried it on! Of course I wanted to wear this dress to the city.

"So the day of the train ride came. How happy I was! My aunts told me to meet them at the station at two o'clock. I stood in front of the old grandfather's clock most of the morning, watching the hands creep slowly around. You see, I did not want to be a minute late.

"Now, that day my mother had to visit a sick lady. Before she went she laid the new dress carefully on my bed. Then she told me not to put it on until half-past one. I must not get it soiled. She scrubbed my face till it shone like a rosy apple. She brushed and braided my hair in two stiff little pigtails. She kissed me good-by and hurried away.

"At last the grandfather's clock told me it was half-past one. Away I ran to my room, to put on my new dress. But—oh, my! We had forgotten that the buttons went up and down the back and that my fat little arms could never reach them.

"I tried and I tried, but the minutes were ticking away. Tears filled my eyes and ran down my cheeks. One went, *splash,* on the beautiful blue bow under my chin and made a horrid dark spot. Oh, why did mother have to go away that morning?

"But I just couldn't miss that train ride. What do you think I did? I just turned my dress around. Then I buttoned every one of those twelve buttons right down the front and let the blue bow flap out in back.

"Then, how I ran! I didn't care if there were tears still shining in my eyes. I didn't even care if there was a horrid, dark spot on my beautiful blue bow. I couldn't see it in back, anyway.

"I got to the station just as the funny little train puffed in. How my aunts laughed to see me. They often called me the 'back-side-to girl'—but I had my train ride and I was happy."

## PITA'S PAINTED PIG [1]

*Elizabeth Morrow*

He was painted yellow, with pink roses on his back and a tiny rosebud on his tail. He looked fat, but he was fed nothing at all. In his side was a small slit where you were supposed to put pennies, but his little mistress never had a centavo to drop into the hole; so his savings-bank stomach remained permanently empty.

His mistress was a little Indian girl who lived in Mexico between the smoking mountains and the cactus with red flowers. Her full name was Guadalupe Faustina Jovita Chimalpopoca, but everybody called her Pita, which is much shorter, prettier, and just as good. She was only ten years old but she wore a long blue scarf and a long skirt like her mother and also big gold earrings and a gold necklace. Her hair was parted in the middle, and the two braids at the back were tied together with a brown shoestring.

Pita's brother was eight years old. His name was Felipe Camerino Victoriano Tlaxochimaco. If you say that correctly, it makes your whole tongue and all your teeth work. Like Pita he had another name not so long and wide. Most people called him Pedro. He wore brown sandals, no stockings, a red shirt, and long, white trousers. His coat was a blue and white blanket with a hole in the middle where he stuck his head. His hat was big as an umbrella, so he always had to put it on after the blanket; it would never have squeezed through the hole. It was made of bright yellow straw, and the brim had pictures on it worked in green and white wool.

[1] From Elizabeth Morrow, *The Painted Pig.*

Pedro always liked his sister's playthings better than his own. He had a toy general, made of glass, riding on a rooster. It was the third general his mother had given him, but glass generals are brittle and go to pieces easily. After the soldier was broken, Pedro never cared for the little rooster left crowing without him. He had a yellow jumping jack besides and two dogs, but they looked like reindeer and their heads were a little twisted. Pedro used to beg Pita to let him play with her painted pig.

"But you will break him," she said.

"Oh, no! I promise to be very careful."

"But you broke your general," his sister reminded him.

"Yes, but he wasn't strong."

"My pig isn't strong."

"Yes, he is," cried Pedro. "A pig is always strong. And I like the rosebud on his tail. My dogs have such plain tails!"

"I'm afraid you will rub the roses off with your dirty fingers," Pita objected.

"My fingers aren't dirty."

"Why don't you play with your wiggly man?"

"I don't want my wiggly man. I want your pig."

Then after Pedro had begged and begged like this, Pita would run away from him and pretend not to see him or hear him wail. She would tease him by singing:

"I ride on my pig,
I gallop and jig,
I jounce and I bounce,
I prance and I dance,
I leap and I creep,
I jump and I stump!"

One day when they were tired of quarrelling, Pita thought of going to Pancho, the toy-maker, and asking him to make Pedro a pig of his very own.

It was a long time before Pancho made a pig for Pedro. But at last he did, and Pedro thought it a much more beautiful pig than Pita's. Pedro's pig was painted yellow, with blue circles on his back and a large blue dot behind each ear. When the children saw him, they danced for joy.

## LETTERS TO CHANNY[1]

*Heluiz Chandler Washburne*

Bound for Hawaii

Channy Dear:

Here we are on a great big Japanese boat three days out in the Pacific Ocean. We haven't seen a thing all this time but water and sky.

Leaving the pier at San Francisco was very exciting. Lots of friends came to see us off. Japanese boys from the boat, in white coats and caps, ran up and down the gangplank carrying the baggage. Everybody was saying good-by to his friends. Then all of a sudden we heard the "Gong! gong! gong! gong!" that told all the people who hadn't tickets that they must hurry and get off the boat. It was sailing time. The orchestra out on deck started to play the good-by music, and then what do you think happened? All the people on the boat began throwing rolls of serpentine to their friends down on the dock below. The whole side of the boat was covered with the pretty colored paper streamers, waving in the breeze. The next thing we knew, our boat was sliding away from the pier and we were off!

The whole first day out, hundreds of gulls followed us, flying very close, and dipping down into the water to get the food that was thrown out from the boat. But they have left us now. Perhaps they went back to follow another ship.

If you were here with us, little son, you would have some Japanese boys and girls to play with. They have been running all over the boat. I can't tell them apart, for they all have yellow skins, bright black eyes, and the blackest of straight black hair. But they can do something most American boys and girls can't do. They speak two languages. If I say "Hello" to them, they

[1] From Heluiz Chandler Washburne, *Letters to Channy*.

smile and say "Hello" back to me. But if I say *"Ohio"* (the Japanese word for "Hello"), they think it is a great joke and start to say a whole lot of Japanese to me, which of course I can't understand.

The Captain and all his officers are Japanese; so are all the servants. Most of the passengers are Japanese, too; so at every meal there is a special dish of Japanese food. You know the Japanese and Chinese people don't use knives and forks the way we do. They use two long, thin, round sticks like pencils, only longer, called "chopsticks." They hold them both in one hand. You would have laughed to see Papa trying to eat his Japanese breakfast this morning with chopsticks. And this is what he had: a bowl of thick pea soup with pieces of celery in it, a bowl of rice, some smoked fish, a little saucer of different kinds of salty pickles, and a pot of tea.

The waiters don't understand English very well, so there are numbers on the menu card in front of the different words that tell you what kind of food you can order. If you want orange juice, you say "four," or if you want ice cream, perhaps, you say "twenty-seven." You see?

The other day we went exploring around the boat and you would never guess what we found. A real little Japanese house! There was a sign asking us please to take off our shoes before we went in, just as the Japanese people do. So we did, and left them lying on the stone doorstep. The floor was covered with the softest mats, made of very finely woven straw. It is called matting. The rooms were not divided by thick walls like rooms in our houses, but by sliding screens of paper or thin silk painted with pretty pictures. When you want little rooms, you just slide the screens across, and when you want a big room, you push them all open.

The Japanese people don't like to sit on chairs—they sit on the floor on big square cushions covered with pretty silk. And they have cute little stools—to rest their arms on. Perhaps there will be a very low table for their teacups. After we had taken down one of the big cushions from the pile in the corner to sit on and had looked in all the cunning cupboards and slid all the screens open and shut, we came out and put on our shoes again. I think I should like to live in a Japanese house. But how would you like to have to stop to take off your shoes every time you wanted to go inside?

Another nice thing that we have found on the boat is a swimming pool with a gymnasium close beside it. There are more funny things in that gym than you can imagine. There is one queer thing called a "camel." You get on a sort of saddle, press the button, and it starts to go, jiggling you around just as if you were riding a real camel. Then there is a horse (not a real one of course). I got on it and started it going. It trotted so hard and jiggled me so fast I couldn't get hold of the button to turn it off. It was worse than a bucking broncho pony and nearly shook my teeth out before Beatrice stopped it for me. I couldn't help laughing. You would have laughed, too.

A whole boatful of love for my little son, from his

MOTHER

Bound for Japan

My Dearest Little Boy:

When we got off our boat at Honolulu Christmas morning, our friends came down to meet us, and hung beautiful wreaths of fresh flowers around our necks. This is the Hawaiian way of greeting people, and these wreaths are called *leis*. I had a carnation lei (you pronounce it "lay-e") that smelled all cinnamony and good, a pretty purple one, and one that looked like a string of large bright yellow wooden beads. Papa, Florence, Margaret, Beatrice, and Margie all had a lot of pretty leis, too, around their necks. We certainly felt dressed up.

Out on the street corners we saw big, fat Hawaiian women in bright figured dresses, making these leis and selling them. The nicest ones are made of fresh flowers, but they also make them of paper and silk,

We had a great big Christmas dinner with our friends—a huge turkey and all the trimmings. I thought of you, because there was a little boy there named Brody, who was just about your age. You would have had lots of fun with him, going down the big slide on the porch. I wondered if you had finished your dinner when we ate ours, because our time is different from yours. You see when the sun comes up in the east, it gets to you before it does to us farther west. So it is dinner time for you long before it is dinner time for us way out here.

After dinner we went down to the beach to go swimming. It was warm and sunny, and I could hardly believe it was Christmas. I guess you played out in the snow, didn't you? Perhaps you went tobogganing.

Christmas night we took a big boat over to Kauai, one of the other islands. It is called the Garden Island of the Pacific because it is so beautiful.

We slept in a little cottage there. Out in the front yard of the little cottage there were three or four big coconut-palm trees. Some of the coconuts had fallen right beside our doorstep.

Did you get the big coconut we sent you? You will have to chop off that outside husk and then break the shell. The Hawaiians like the coconuts when they are green, because then the inside is soft like custard and they can eat it with a spoon.

The first morning we were in Kauai a big car drove up to our door. A Japanese chauffeur was sitting in front. When we came out, the lady who owned the car said to him, "Take them for some nice rides, Itchi-Masu." So Itchi was our chauffeur for the two days we were on the island. And he took us to see many interesting things.

I wish you had been with us, Channy. As we drove through the little town and came to the street crossing, there in the middle stood the traffic cop with a huge canvas umbrella over his head and a canvas fence around him. There was a big STOP and GO sign fastened to the top of his umbrella. When he saw our car coming, he quickly turned the sign to GO and we went right through without stopping. They don't do that in Chicago.

We drove for a long time between the fields of sugar cane. Sugar cane looks like very tall corn with big silky tassels on top. We thought it would be fun to have some to chew, so we asked Itchi-Masu to get us some. He was very polite and got out of the car and dove out of sight among the cane stalks. In a minute he appeared again with a big brown stick dripping with syrup. Papa cut it up and peeled it and gave us each a chunk. It was filled with juice and we made terrible noises as we sucked and chewed. But, oh, it was sweet and good!

We wondered why some of the sugar-cane fields we saw looked all burned, with just the brown stalks sticking up out of the red ground. And then we found that some of the sugar growers set fire to the fields just before the cane is ready to be cut. This burns off all the leaves and makes the stalks much easier to cut. Before they found out about burning the cane, the men who worked in the fields used to get badly hurt on the long, sharp-pointed leaves.

Down in the low parts of the island we saw lots of rice fields—rice paddies, they are called—and we saw Chinamen plowing them with big, horned water buffaloes. Rice needs lots of water to grow well, so the farmers make low walls of dirt about eighteen inches high all around the little plots of ground where the rice is planted. Then every so often they flood these paddies with water and the walls hold it in.

The birds make the poor farmers a great deal of trouble by eating the rice just as soon as it is ripe. But the farmers have thought of a way of scaring them off. They build a high platform in the center of the field with a roof over it to keep off the hot sun. Then they stretch long ropes from this platform to all parts of the field. On these ropes they hang tin cans and all sorts of things that make a noise. A man stands up on the platform, and, when he sees the birds gathering over in some part of the field, he pulls the string to that part, jangling the tin cans and frightening all the birds away. Isn't that a smart idea?

We saw a water buffalo working in a field close by the road the other day. Margaret wanted to look at him, so Itchi-Masu stopped the car while she and Papa got out and climbed over the fence. Margaret edged up to the buffalo very carefully and was just about to pat him when he swung his big horns around and stood there shaking his head from side to side.

The Chinaman who owned the buffalo kept jabbering something to us, but we didn't know whether he was warning us to go away or telling us that the buffalo wouldn't hurt us. Papa wanted to get a movie of Margaret patting the buffalo, so he told her not to be frightened. Step by step Margaret sneaked up to him, and this time she got close enough to give him a pat on the end of his wet nose. When they got back into the car again, Itchi-Masu told us that the Chinaman was only trying to tell us not to be afraid, that the buffalo was very gentle.

The tops of the hills are covered with acres and acres of pineapples. We had never seen them growing before, so we stopped by the side of a big field of them and were allowed to pick a couple to take back to the hotel with us. They grow close to the ground in the center of a big bunch of long, sharp-pointed leaves like the ones on the top of the pineapple, only bigger.

Later on we passed a pineapple cannery where tons and tons of pineapples are brought in from the fields every day and are made into sliced pineapple, crushed pineapple, and pineapple jam. We went all through the factory and saw the big machines that slipped the pineapples from their skins and cored them faster than we could count. Then the golden pineapples—all sliced and dripping with juice—passed on a long belt between rows of pretty little Japanese and Hawaiian girls who picked out the best slices and put them into tin cans. The rest slid into a big bucket at the end, to be ground up for jam. We stood there and pulled off some of the slices as they came by, and ate them. They were much sweeter and more tender than pineapples at home, because they were not picked until ripe.

When we left Kauai on the boat to go back to Honolulu, lots and lots of people came down to say good-by to us. Many of them brought us pretty leis, and before Papa could get on the boat, he had silk leis, paper leis, and flower leis around his neck so high that he could hardly see over the top of them all. Then they sang the Hawaiian good-by song, "Aloha," until our boat was far, far out in the water.

I've been telling you all about what *we* have been doing. Now I want to hear all about *you*. Where's that nice big fat letter? I didn't get it in Hawaii. Maybe it missed the boat and I'll get it in Japan. I'll mail this letter from Japan. You'd better save the stamp for your collection.

This old Pacific Ocean is terribly big. We have been on the ship for ten days since we left Hawaii, and it will be two or three more before we get to Japan.

But I love my little son more than all the big oceans put together.

MOTHER

## MR. MURDLE'S LARGE HEART[1]

*Margery Bianco*

In nearly every town you will find one store which keeps all those foolish little things that the other stores forget, or are so apt to be out of. Mr. Murdle's is just such a store. Many many years ago, when Mr. Murdle was a round-faced little boy, he must have said to his mother: "When I grow up I'm going to keep a store!"

He had no idea at all of what he wanted to sell in his store; it was just going to be a store. And so it turned out. He started by buying a little bit here and a little bit there, just as he fancied, and all sorts of funny cardboard boxes began to pile up on

[1] From Margery Bianco, *A Street of Little Shops.*

his shelves. He thought of ginger ale and slate pencils and newspapers and paper clips, and of course candy; of little celluloid dolls and hairpins and pencil sharpeners, and ash trays with scalloped gilt edges and pictures on them, and lots and lots of cigars. Mr. Murdle himself doesn't really know all that he has in his store, and certainly no one else does. But if ever it happens that you want to buy something that you cannot find in any of the other stores along the street, sooner or later someone will scratch his head and say:

"Well, you *might* try Mr. Murdle, across the way!"

So across the way you go, and sure enough, after Mr. Murdle has stood for a moment thinking, he will rummage about among his cardboard boxes and pull one of them out, and nine times out of ten there it is, the very thing you were looking for!

All this is wonderful enough, but it isn't the most remarkable thing about Mr. Murdle, by any means.

The most remarkable thing about Mr. Murdle is his Large Heart.

Everyone who knows Mr. Murdle will tell you what a Large Heart he has. And it is really true. I have seen it myself, hanging up at the back of Mr. Murdle's store. It is pink and purple, with yellow around the edges, and in the middle, which is white, there are rows of little elastic loops, which once upon a time held tiny bottles of pink and purple and yellow lozenges. Fairy lozenges, they must have been, but that is so long ago that no one knows what they really were like. But the Heart is still there.

It is a fine thing for anyone to have such a Large Heart. But there are disadvantages also, especially for anyone like Mr. Murdle, who is in business, and who really ought to be thinking of money every minute, as the other storekeepers do. It makes it very nice of course for Mr. Murdle's customers, but it must be difficult for Mr. Murdle. That Large Heart of his is always getting in the way.

When a little girl comes into his store, for instance, and wants an ice-cream cone and has only three cents, or when some little boy wants candy and Mr. Murdle knows perfectly well that he should only give him five chocolates for a nickel, then that Large Heart begins to whisper to him, and before Mr. Murdle knows it he has handed out the cone with an extra lump of strawberry ice cream on, or he has slipped seven chocolates into the bag instead of five. And if you want some particular sized envelopes, or some special kind of paper clip such as you bought three years ago and have never been able to find since, and Mr. Murdle has hunted through and through his cardboard boxes and finally found it, then as likely as not he will say: "Oh, I've had that in stock so long I wouldn't know what to charge you for it. We'll make it up next time!" And next time, of course, never comes.

Then there are the cats.

It began with one cat. She was a tortoiseshell cat, and she found that the pleasantest place to spend the morning was curled up in the sun, on top of Mr. Murdle's stack of daily papers, just inside the store. She spent every morning there, and usually the afternoon as well. Mr. Murdle used to give her the melted ice cream that was left over at night.

Presently she married and had a family, and they all came to live in Mr. Murdle's store. Several of her cousins came, too. Now there were eleven cats, and not nearly enough melted ice cream to go round. So Mr. Murdle—having such a Large Heart—took to melting the ice cream on purpose. He found that the cats liked vanilla best, so he always ordered more of the vanilla than of any other kind, and with it he gave them crumbled-up wafers and peppermint creams.

Early every morning when Mr. Murdle came to open the store, there were the cats waiting for him, and the very first thing he did was to look in the ice-cream can and see if there was anything left over from the day before. Usually there wasn't, and then Mr. Murdle would take eight pennies from the till behind the counter and go over to the grocery to buy milk for the cats' breakfast.

Everyone liked Mr. Murdle, including the cats, and Mr. Murdle himself was one of the happiest people in the world, and all on account of his Large Heart.

But there was one person who did not at all approve of Mr. Murdle's Large Heart. This was Mr. Murdle's aunt. It may seem funny for anyone like Mr. Murdle, who is at least forty and quite bald on the top of his head, to have an aunt; but he had, and one fine day she came to keep house for him. She was a busy, active sort of woman, and not content with managing Mr. Murdle's house for him, she soon began to think of managing his store as well.

She didn't approve of the cats and she didn't approve of the little boys and girls. In fact, she didn't approve of anything at all that Mr. Murdle liked and least of all of the way he did business. She decided that all that sort of thing must be changed.

At first she didn't have much success. Mr. Murdle had been going along very comfortably in his own way for so long that it wasn't easy, even for a determined person like Mr. Murdle's aunt, to change him. But she did her best, and as luck would have it, while she was rummaging about and tidying the store out one day, she came upon Mr. Murdle's Large Heart. She didn't at all know what it was, but she certainly didn't like the look of it. She leaned on her broom and stared.

"Now that's a foolish sort of thing," she said. "Cluttering the store up and taking space where it isn't wanted. I'm just going to throw it out!"

And she did.

From that moment, a very dreadful change came over Mr. Murdle.

The aunt thought it was all due to her lecturing and her good advice. But it wasn't at all. It was just because Mr. Murdle had lost his Large Heart.

In two days you wouldn't have known Mr. Murdle's store.

Everything was tidy, and Mr. Murdle himself just as businesslike as he could be. He knew the price of everything. When little boys came in and asked for a nickel's worth of candy, believe me they *got* a nickel's worth of candy, and not one speck more, and if the little girls hadn't enough money for their ice-cream cones they might just turn right around and walk out again. It was terrible, and as for the cats, they all left in a body and went to live with the fat lady at the delicatessen store across the way. Mr. Murdle said he couldn't afford to feed a lot of lazy cats that did nothing but sleep all day, and that moreover they mussed up his newspapers.

Can you *imagine* that!

All the little boys and girls were very upset. But luckily there was one little boy who had more sense than the rest.

He was loitering in the store one day. Mr. Murdle's aunt happened to be away shopping, or you may be very sure she would have chased him out. But there he was staring about him, and trying to make out just why it was that everything should look so different. And all at once he realized that something was missing.

It was Mr. Murdle's Large Heart.

It wasn't there in its usual place above the counter, and it wasn't anywhere in the store, though he searched high and low. Being a clever little boy he soon put two and two together.

"I bet you," he said, "that mean old woman has thrown it out!"

He went straightway into the yard behind the store, where Mr. Murdle kept all his old boxes and empty crates, and began to hunt. And sure enough, after a little while there he found it, thrown out with a pile of rubbish and broken pasteboard boxes, waiting to be burned.

It was torn at one side and a bit crumpled, but he smoothed it out and carried it back to its old place on the wall behind the counter, and to make sure this time, he fetched a hammer and nails and he *nailed* it, all around the edge.

Not even Mr. Murdle's aunt could have torn it down again!

What's more, she never got a chance.

For as soon as Mr. Murdle set foot in the store, now that his Large Heart was back in its right place again, he became just the same Mr. Murdle that he had been before.

The very first thing that he did was to send his aunt packing.

Then he telephoned for fresh ice cream —every kind he could think of—and he opened all the candy boxes and told the little boys and girls, who by this time had heard the news and had all come trooping round, that they might help themselves, and if they didn't have any money they could pay him next year.

And he dragged his old armchair out, and lit a big cigar and settled down by the doorway, as happy as could be.

When the cats saw that, they all came trooping back again too.

So today things are just as they used to be, and there is very little danger they will ever change again. Not so long as Mr. Murdle's Large Heart stays there, right in its place, and that, you may be very sure, will be for a long time to come.

As for Mr. Murdle's aunt, she gave him up as a bad job and went home, broom and all.

And if you don't believe me, all you need do is to walk into Mr. Murdle's store some fine morning, past the curled-up cats and the newspapers, and ask for a nickel's worth of candy.

You will see how much you get!

## THE BLUE TEAPOT [1]

*Alice Dalgliesh*

There was once a nice old lady whose name was Miss Letitia Brown. She was so kind and friendly that no one ever thought of calling her Miss Brown or even Miss Letitia. Everyone called her Miss Letty.

Miss Letty lived all by herself in a cottage at the top of a hill, overlooking the sea. It was a white cottage with a green door, a roof of weathered gray shingles, and a cheerful brick chimney from which there rose a curl of white smoke. All around the house were flowers and dark green fir trees.

Sometimes people asked Miss Letty if she did not feel lonely living all by herself in the little cottage.

"Lonely?" said Miss Letty. "Why should I be? I have Thomas, my big black cat, I have my flowers, and I can watch the fishing boats as they go and come. Why should I be lonely?"

Miss Letty's father had been a sea captain, and so Miss Letty loved the sea. Winter and summer she liked to sit at her window and look out across the blue waters of the Bay of Fundy. She could see the wharf and the beach. There at low tide the fishing boats lay stranded, looking awkward and ridiculous, while at high tide they floated proudly on the water.

Next to the sea, Miss Letty loved her garden. It was quite the loveliest garden in the village of Sandy Cove. It was really the loveliest garden in Nova Scotia. On the sloping ground at the back of Miss Letty's house grew every flower you can possibly imagine. There was a border of lavender and white alyssum. Miss Letty planted that because it smelled so sweet on summer evenings. There was mignonette, there was snapdragon, white, yellow, and pink, and there was tall blue larkspur. Cosmos and dahlias grew against the fence.

Almost every time anyone passed by Miss Letty's house, she was in the garden, planting, weeding, watering. Or she would be coming down the path, with her arms full of flowers, and with Thomas, very dignified, waving his tail as he walked before her.

The only time that Miss Letty could not be seen in the garden was in the winter, when the snow lay thick on the ground and the wind sighed and moaned through the fir trees. Then Miss Letty sat snugly indoors by the fire and Thomas sat on the hearth rug, purring cozily and contentedly as the flames danced and the logs crackled.

[1] From Alice Dalgliesh, *The Blue Teapot.*

Now for a long time Miss Letty was very happy. Then, one bright spring day when the fir-trees were wearing their new green tips and the roads were bordered with violets and columbine, Miss Letty went down the hill to the village. She carried a basket on her arm, for she was going to the village store to buy tea and sugar and bacon.

Before she went into the store Miss Letty stopped to look in the window. Usually the window was not very interesting, for it held only the kettle that had been there for three years, some mixing bowls, and a few dusty plates. Today it was different. The storekeeper must have felt it was spring, for the window was clean and the wares in it were neatly arranged. The kettle was still there, it is true, and so were the plates and the mixing bowls, but in the middle of the window was *a blue teapot.* It was as blue as larkspur, as blue as the water of the Bay of Fundy, as blue as Miss Letty's Sunday dress. There were also four blue cups and saucers, four blue plates, and a blue sugar bowl and cream pitcher.

"I must have that teapot," said Miss Letty, walking into the store very quickly so that she would not have time to change her mind. In a very short time she came out with the blue teapot, the plates, the cups and saucers, and the pitcher and sugar bowl, all neatly packed in her basket. There was no sugar in the basket, nor was there any bacon. Miss Letty had forgotten those, though she had remembered the tea.

At supper time Miss Letty put a white cloth on her little square table and set it very neatly with one blue plate, one blue cup, the cream pitcher and the empty sugar bowl. She made herself a cup of tea, cooked herself a piece of finnan haddie, and sat down to enjoy her supper. Somehow she did not enjoy it at all.

"There should be more blue cups and plates on this table," said Miss Letty. "Thomas, I believe that, after all, we are lonely."

Thomas tucked his paws under him and purred cozily.

"Yes, Thomas," said Miss Letty, "we are lonely. Tomorrow we are going to find someone to live with us."

Thomas yawned, a wide pink yawn. He was tired of waiting for his share of finnan haddie.

The next morning, before Miss Letty had time to change her mind, she set out for the Orphans' Home, which was not very far from the village.

"I think I shall get a good, strong, plain girl of about fourteen," said Miss Letty to herself. "Then she can help me with the work and she will be most useful in the garden."

But, as Miss Letty went in the gate of the Orphans' Home, she saw two little girls standing under an apple tree. They were about seven years old, they had pink cheeks and blue eyes, and—best of all—they had braids of long yellow hair.

It was quite too much for Miss Letty.

"Oh!" she said. "O-oh! Are you by any chance orphans and do you want to be adopted?"

"We would love to be adopted," said the two little girls, together "No one has taken us because everyone seems to want one little girl with curls. We haven't curls and we are twins."

"I have always liked twins," said Miss Letty. "What are your names, my dears?"

"Dorothea," answered one twin.

"Dorinda," answered the other.

"Well," said Miss Letty, firmly, "I don't believe in fancy names, and I shall call you Sara and Abigail."

"We like those names as well as our own," said the twins, politely.

The long and the short of it was that when Miss Letty left the Orphans' Home she had promised to adopt the two little girls, but she asked for a week to get the house ready for them. As for the strong, plain, fourteen-year-old girl to help with the work, Miss Letty had forgotten all about her. She had a most remarkable way of forgetting things that did not seem particularly important.

"Twins!" said Miss Letty as she walked

home feeling quite dazed but very happy. "Twins—seven years old—yellow hair—blue eyes—Sara—Abigail—what will Thomas think!"

The week that followed was the busiest one of Miss Letty's life. From morning till night she washed and scrubbed and ironed and arranged things. She spent a great deal of time getting a room ready for the two little girls. From the old chest in the closet under the stairs she unearthed the most surprising and interesting things. After a good deal of thought she selected two patchwork quilts made by her mother, and a braided rug made by her grandmother. Fortunately there were already two beds in the room; indeed, as Miss Letty thought, the room seemed to have been planned for two little girls and to have stood waiting for them all these years.

"Thomas," said Miss Letty as she ironed the white frilly curtains, "Thomas, isn't it strange that all these years we did not know that we were lonely?" Thomas arched his back and rubbed against her legs.

At last the great day came and Miss Letty brought Abigail and Sara to their new home. It was a lovely, sunshiny afternoon as they walked up the fir-bordered road and turned in at Miss Letty's gate. The daffodils along the garden path danced in the breeze, a home-like curl of white smoke came from the chimney, and Thomas sat on the doorstep to welcome them.

"Oh, Miss Letty," said Abigail, "what a lovely place to live!"

"Oh, Miss Letty," said Sara, "is this dear little house really ours?"

Inside the house there were a great many *ah's!* and *oh's!* The blue tea set did not make Miss Letty feel at all lonely that night, for she could use three cups and three plates; in fact she used four because she even set a place for Thomas.

At eight o'clock, quite worn out with excitement, the little girls went to bed. Miss Letty went in quietly when she thought they were asleep. There was Abigail fast asleep under the blue and white patchwork quilt, and there was Sara fast asleep under the lavender and white patchwork quilt.

"I am not going to keep puzzling over which of these twins is which," said Miss Letty. "Most of the time I shall dress Abigail in blue or pink, and Sara in lavender or yellow. On Sundays they can dress alike. I think I shall be able to tell them apart, anyway, for Abigail's eyes are just a trifle bluer than Sara's, and Sara's hair is a trifle yellower than Abigail's."

Miss Letty and the twins had such good times together. They were polite and amiable little girls. When the minister came to call they put on their best dresses, they curtsied when he spoke to them, and Abigail handed him a cup of tea, while Sara brought in a little tray with cream and sugar. Miss Letty was very proud of them.

On summer evenings Miss Letty and the twins often had tea in the garden. They took out the small square table, the white tablecloth with the blue border, and, of course, the blue tea set. Miss Letty poured tea from the blue teapot, and Abigail and Sara took bites of Miss Letty's crisp, brown, crunchy cookies and thought what very lucky little girls they were. Thomas was not forgotten; he had a large saucer of milk under the tiger lilies.

One of the things that Sara and Abigail liked best of all was to stand at the edge of the bluff overlooking the sea, to stand just as close to the edge as was perfectly safe, and watch the fishing boats come in. The sea was clear and blue, the beach was a long sandy crescent, and the gulls wheeled and screamed above the water.

Thomas often sat at the edge of the bluff with the children. He had been born on a sailing vessel, which, Miss Letty said, was probably the reason why he was so fond of the sea. The twins thought that his interest might have something to do with the smell of fish that so often came to them when the wind blew from the fish houses near the wharf, but they were too polite to mention this to Miss Letty.

Another pleasant thing about the twins was that they were extremely helpful about the house. Abigail was especially interested in cooking, and whenever Miss Letty went into the kitchen Abigail was at her heels. Miss Letty would tie on her big white apron and Abigail would tie on hers. Miss Letty would get down the big blue mixing bowl and Abigail was always ready to beat the eggs and sift the flour. Soon she could make cookies that were almost as good as Miss Letty's.

On a rainy day Miss Letty would find Abigail sitting by the kitchen window turning the pages of the big cook book and murmuring dreamily to herself, "Molasses cookies—Aunt Deborah's spice cake—apple Betty—blueberry muffins—Scotch fancies—brambles—"

"She is a child after my own heart," said Miss Letty.

Now it is not to be supposed that while Abigail was busy, Sara was idle. Sara was especially interested in gardening, and whenever Miss Letty went out to the garden Sara was at her heels. Together they raked and dug and sowed and weeded. Soon Sara knew almost as much about gardening as Miss Letty.

On rainy days Miss Letty often found Sara in a chair by the living-room window looking out at the garden or turning the pages of a seed catalogue and murmuring dreamily, "Nasturtiums—clove pinks—marigolds and lobelia—asters and Shasta daisies—snapdragon and tiger lilies—"

"She is a child after my own heart," said Miss Letty.

If Abigail and Sara had been content with the cook book and the seed catalogue all would have gone well in the little house among the fir trees. Unfortunately they were also very much charmed by a catalogue from Runciman's, a large fat catalogue which told about all the beautiful things that might be ordered from Runciman's for just a little—oh, so little—money.

As the winter evenings went on the twins spent more and more time lying flat on the rug in front of the fire, with the Runciman catalogue spread out before them.

"Oh, look, Miss Letty—such a pretty blue coat with a squirrel collar! And the pockets are just the kind we both like best of all!"

"And, Miss Letty, see this—"

"We need new linoleum for the kitchen floor—"

"New frilly curtains for our rooms—"

"Warm pink and blue slippers!"

"A red leather collar for Thomas!"

So it went, on and on and on. At last even Miss Letty grew interested in the gay pictures in Runciman's catalogue, and when she found Thomas asleep with both his paws resting on the book she knew it was hopeless. Then the first order was sent. It was for a red leather collar for Thomas. This first package was most exciting, and soon more orders went to Runciman's.

More and more packages arrived. At least twice a week Abigail and Sara went down the road to the post office by the cove, and came away laden with big and little packages of every size and shape.

The village children watched with wide eyes, wondering whatever could be in the packages. Abigail and Sara could scarcely wait until they reached the cottage to open them. How long the road seemed!

Winter was coming near. The packages from Runciman's began to contain coats and sweaters and galoshes as well as many things that were much more interesting. The days grew shorter and colder.

One morning when the twins awoke, the ground was covered with snow. All day long it snowed, so hard and fast that there was nothing but whiteness to be seen. The wind howled and moaned, then it gave loud, fierce shrieks. The windows rattled and the little house on the hill trembled.

"This is one of the worst storms I have known," said Miss Letty. "Strange things must be happening down at the wharf."

"Do you suppose the house will blow away?" asked Abigail.

"No indeed," said Miss Letty, "it has weathered many a storm."

At bedtime the blizzard was still raging.

Abigail and Sara shivered as they crept into bed and drew the bedclothes closely around them. For a time they lay and trembled as they listened to the wind in the firs, but it was not very long before they fell asleep.

In the morning everything was calm and quiet. The sky was clear and blue and the sun was shining. The fir trees bent their branches to the ground, and, as Miss Letty said, one could almost hear them complaining about the weight of the snow. The snow lay in great drifts and the lilac hedge in front of the house had completely disappeared. The twins and Miss Letty put on rubber boots and went out into the white world to dig a path to the gate. The snow was hard and crusty and Abigail walked right over the top of the lilac hedge!

Down to the beach they went and found it was a sad-looking place. It was strewn with driftwood and seaweed, and with wreckage of two fishing boats. In the middle of the wharf was a gaping hole, for the fury of the storm had torn loose the heavy piles and boards, and washed them up on the beach. It was so cold that Abigail and Sara were glad to get back to their own warm fireside with Thomas purring on the hearth rug.

In a few days the snow began to melt. Then little rivulets of icy water crept under the shingles of the roof, and in many places inside the house there was a steady drip-drip-drip. Then Miss Letty realized that the roof needed to be reshingled, that there were many necessary things to be bought, and that there was no money in the bank! Miss Letty was not practical.

"It's all the fault of the Runciman catalogue!" said Miss Letty.

"It's all our fault for wanting so many things," said Abigail. "Let's think what can be done." Miss Letty, Abigail, and Sara sat in front of the fire and thought deeply. There was silence for a long time and the only sounds were the steady tick-tick of the big clock on the wall and the contented purr of Thomas.

"I know!" said Abigail suddenly. "Patchwork quilts! People love to buy them and you make such nice ones, Miss Letty. Patchwork quilts for Miss Letty, cookies for me, and—Sara—what will you do? You don't cook, but can't you think of something?"

"I'll go down to the farm and ask if they want a good, strong, helpful girl," said Sara. "But that will be in the spring."

So the patchwork quilts were started and in the winter evenings Miss Letty sat by the fire, sewing squares together, while the twins sat on little stools and joined patches. Abigail and Sara liked the names of the quilt patterns as much as they liked the names in the cook book and the seed catalogue. It was fun to help Miss Letty choose the next pattern to be used: Wedding Ring, Cherokee Rose, Round-about, Wind-Blown Square, Broken Dishes, Give-and-Get. The quilts grew under Miss Letty's skillful fingers and each one seemed more attractive than the one before it.

Abigail and Sara liked the quilting parties, when the big quilting frame filled the little living room, and the neighbors came in and sat quilting, two to a side, tongues going as fast as needles. The twins sat and listened to all the stories that were told, stories of wrecks on the coast, of a mysterious man left stranded on the beach by a passing ship, of Collie the hermit who continued to sit by his fire quite calmly when his roof blew off in the storm. Abigail and Sara wished the neighbors would tell stories all the time instead of talking, as they quite often did, about Mrs. Smith's baby's croup, Aunt Mary's new stove, and Mrs. Hoskin's rheumatism.

When summer came, and with it summer visitors, the quilts were ready! Wedding Ring, Cherokee Rose, Round-about, Broken Dishes—all of them. There were hooked rugs, too. All Miss Letty's hooked rugs had pictures of ships on them, because her father had been a sea captain. There was just one rug that could not be sold, because Thomas had taken it for his own. There he would lie, right in the middle of blue sea and sails, refusing to sleep in any other place. "That is because he was born on the sea," said Miss Letty, indulgently.

Abigail and Sara were busy all summer. Abigail spent mornings in the kitchen and I cannot tell you how many of her crisp brown cookies were eaten by summer visitors. Abigail was glad that the sea air gave them such good appetites.

Sara was most useful on the farm. The farmer just down the road had laughed when Sara asked him if he wanted a good, strong, useful girl, but he soon stopped laughing and said that she was "worth her weight in gold." Sara brought the ducks up from the pond, fed the chickens, and took care of the garden. The farmer's wife said she wondered how she had ever managed without her.

As for the Runciman catalogue, Sara and Abigail had hidden that among the quilts in the chest under the stairs. "It can stay there until we truly need it," they said.

So, with quilts and rugs, cookies and ducks, soon there was a nice sum of money in the bank.

The green, sunny fields looked very peaceful as Miss Letty and the twins walked to church on Sunday mornings. Miss Letty, Abigail and Sara felt peaceful, too, for the roof was newly shingled, the doors and windows freshly painted, and everything was snug and comfortable in the little cottage among the fir trees.

## JANCSI AND KATE[1]

*Kate Seredy*

Jancsi was up bright and early that morning and at work milking the cows. He was so excited he couldn't stay in bed. For today Cousin Kate was coming. She was the only cousin he had, and she was a city girl. A real city girl from Budapest. Ever since the letter came from his uncle, Jancsi had been the proudest boy on the big Hungarian plain. He was the only boy in the neighborhood who had a cousin in the city. And she was coming today, to stay for a long time. Father had told Jancsi what was in the letter. It said that Kate had had the measles last winter. Jancsi had never had the measles—he thought it must be something wonderful to have. And she was delicate, the letter said, too, so she was coming to the country. A *delicate* city cousin, who had had the *measles*—that was something.

If it were only Sunday, they would go to church and he could tell everybody about her. Sunday was the only time when Jancsi saw anyone outside his own family. Father had a ranch, with thousands of sheep, horses, cows, and pigs. He had chickens and ducks and geese; he even had donkeys, but he didn't have enough children to suit Jancsi. It got *so* lonesome for poor Jancsi, he would have given ten horses for a brother. He had it all figured out—he would give a donkey for even a sister. Not horses, just a donkey.

The ranch was miles and miles from the village. It was too far to walk, and they were too busy to drive on weekdays. So, although Jancsi was ten years old and quite a man if you asked his opinion, he had never been to school, and he did not know how to read or write. The ranch was the only reality to him—the world outside was just a fairy story. Mother knew lots of fairy stories about dragons and golden-haired princesses who lived in glittering castles. Jancsi thought that houses in Budapest were made of gold and had diamond windows. All the city people rode around on pure white horses and wore silk gowns. Cousin Kate would have golden curls, rosy cheeks, big blue eyes; she would wear a white silk flowing gown, and her voice would be like honey. Now—Jancsi is off in dreamland—some day a dragon will capture her, and it will be up to Jancsi to go to the rescue. He is clad in green velvet, red boots, riding a coal-black steed. Here comes the dragon! Jancsi pulls out his golden sword, and one-two-three heads are at his feet! All good dragons have twelve perfectly hideous heads. Four—slash, five—swish goes his sword—

[1] From Kate Seredy, *The Good Master.*

"Mo-o-o-o!" bellowed something close to him. And crash-bang went Jancsi together with the milking-stool. He sat and blinked. Máli, the mottled cow, looked at him with reproachful eyes. Reality closed around the hero—oh, yes, here he was in the barn, milking the cow.

"Jancsi! Ja-an-ncsi-i! Hurry up with the milk or you'll be late for the train!" It was his mother's voice calling from the house. He scrambled to his feet, scowled at Máli, and picking up the full pails made his way back to the kitchen. Mother took the milk from him. "I'll strain it today, Jancsi. You eat your breakfast and get dressed. And get a good scrub—why, you're all full of mud!"

Jancsi kept his back out of Mother's sight —the seat of his white pants would need explaining. He gulped down his bread and milk. Then, backing out of the kitchen, he ran to the well. He filled a wooden bucket with the icy water and, stripping off his clothes, stepped into it. With great splutters and groans he scrubbed himself, using sand on the most disgraceful spots. Then he took a bit of salt from a mug and scrubbed his teeth with his fingers. Squirting out the salty water, he set a new long-distance record; he even paused long enough to gaze at it admiringly and mark the spot with a stone. "Can spit almost as far as Father," he muttered with pride.

He ran back to the house. His very best Sunday clothes were all laid out on the bench, near the big white stove—his embroidered shirt, the wide pleated pants, his shiny black boots, his round hat with the bunch of flowers. He put them on. Mother wasn't in the kitchen. He went to the bedroom. No Mother in the bedroom. But on the windowsill, glittering in the sunshine, was a green bottle. He gazed at it for a while, torn between desire and discipline. It was too much for him. Tiptoeing to the window, he took the bottle and the little red comb next to it. It was perfumed hair oil—and only *men* used perfumed hair oil! He put a little on his hair. Then a little more, and still more, until his hair looked as if it were made of black enamel. Then with a sigh of satisfaction he put on his hat and strutted out. He heard the wagon —time to go!

When he saw the wagon drive up to the door, he gave a whoop of joy. Father had harnessed his four black horses with the very best brass-studded harness. Each horse had a big bunch of geraniums fastened to the headband, and long streamers of gayly colored ribbons floated in the breeze. He jumped up next to Father, and off they went down the long poplar-lined lane leading to the main road.

It was early April, and fields and pastures were a fresh pale green. The poplars stood like solemn sentinels, whispering to the wind. Father was a man of few words; men never spoke, he believed, unless they had something important to say. Gossip was only for the womenfolks. Jancsi was quiet, too, busy with his own thoughts. He was going to the town for the first time in his life—he would see a train. Trains were a mystery to him. One of the shepherds had told him trains were fire-eating dragons; they roared, and snorted black smoke. "They pull little houses; people go from one place to another in the little houses. And trains kill everybody who gets in their way." Jancsi wondered if he could hitch their own house to one of these dragons. Then he could go and see the world. But he would take his dog Peti, he'd take his favorite horse, he'd take Máli, the cow. . . . No, he scowled and rubbed his side, remembering this morning. No, he wouldn't take Máli.

Deeply absorbed in deciding whom he would take with him, he hardly noticed how fast they were traveling. Soon they left the open country and entered the long village street. The village was always interesting to him, so he began to look around. Father turned to him. "I'll stop at the store to buy some tobacco. You hold the reins, Jancsi." Jancsi slid over to Father's seat and grabbed the reins. He sat there, head up, shoulders erect, looking straight ahead. Just then a village boy walked by. He stopped and looked at Jancsi with open admiration.

"Hey! You driving *alone?*"

Jancsi gulped and replied evasively: "Going to fetch my cousin from the train. She comes from Budapest." Then, unable to keep from gossiping like womenfolks, he blurted out his news: "She had the measles and is delicate and her name is Kate! She'll live with us!"

Father came down the store steps, stuffing his pipe. Jancsi prayed for a miracle. If the boy would only go away or if Father would only let him drive . . .!

The miracle came. Father walked around the wagon and, getting up next to Jancsi, said: "Let's see how you handle wagon and four!"

So they left the boy staring after them open-mouthed. Jancsi drove through the village like a king in a golden coach. The clouds of white dust around the horses' hoofs were like stardust to him. The glittering hoofs were made of diamonds. Everything looked new and beautiful to him today. The endless rows of snow-white houses with their gayly painted doors and shutters were like pearls in a row. The geraniums in the windows were a brighter red than ever. The church seemed taller, the grass greener. He flipped his whip impatiently at the barking dogs and almost rode over a flock of honking geese slowly plodding across the street. Then they were in the open country again. It was almost noon; the spring sun beat down on the shimmering fields. They passed a long fence. Horses were grazing in the fields.

"Good horseflesh," remarked Father. "See how sleek they look now, but it's a man's job to stay on one of those beasts."

"I can get on one and stay on it, Father. Those aren't worse than your own horses."

"Think you can, Son?"

"I *know* I can!" asserted Jancsi hastily, forgetting that this would call for explanations. He was not yet allowed to ride unbroken horses.

"You *know* you can?" said Father, reaching for his pocket knife. Jancsi watched him in shocked silence. He knew he was in for it, but somehow he didn't mind. After the pocket knife came a little round stick of wood with many cross-marks cut into it. It was the score pad. One notch was cut in for each sin Jancsi committed, and after a while it was crossed out. But the "after a while" usually included moments Jancsi didn't like to remember. Holding knife and stick in his hands, Father looked at Jancsi. Jancsi looked far, far ahead. Suddenly Father laughed and, putting away the "score," slapped Jancsi on the back.

"You're no worse than I was at your age, Son. You'll make a good rancher."

Jancsi heaved a sigh of relief. This was a man's world, and he was accepted!

After a time Father pointed ahead. "See those houses and chimneys? That's the town and the station." Jancsi was all eyes and ears now. Soon the wagon was rattling on the cobbled street. They passed lots of buildings, and there were a great many people walking around. Father told him where to stop and, after the horses were hitched to a post, said: "Well done, boy!" This made Jancsi feel still better. Praises from Father were few and far between, but they were all the more satisfying.

Walking through the station building, they came to the platform. "Those long shiny snakes are rails, Son; the train travels on them. It'll be here soon now."

Jancsi heard a great rumbling, snorting, and pounding in the distance. He felt the platform shake under his feet. Casting a frightened look at his father, he saw that Father wasn't afraid, so it must be all right. Then he saw a black monster rushing around the curve. It must be the dragon. It had an immense eye glittering in the sunshine. Vicious-looking black teeth, close to the ground. And black smoke poured out of its head. Then it gave a shrill scream, blew white smoke out of its ears, and came to a groaning halt. Men jumped down, opened the doors of the funny little black houses. Jancsi waited with eyes round and shiny like big black cherries. He expected to see people in silks and velvets, glorious people. But not one of them had good clothes on; they were just everyday people dressed in drab grays and browns. And Cousin Kate was just any kind of little girl, with plain black hair, a smudgy face, and skinny legs.

Before the day was over, Jancsi and Father were to learn that Kate was a special kind of little girl—a naughty one, who was always getting into trouble.

That night dozing off to a contented sleep, Jancsi's last thought was: "I'm glad she isn't a golden-haired princess—she's almost as good as a real boy!"

## CALYPSO[1]

*Elizabeth Coatsworth*

Although Alice was very fond of animals, she had none of her own. Her father thought that dogs barked a good deal and kept things in an uproar. Her mother didn't want a cat to catch the birds and scare away the chipmunks, so Alice, as I said, had no animals of her own.

Alice was a quiet child with a bang of dark hair and two small braids tied with red ribbon, who went about with her thoughts often in a dream; and often her dreams were of the sea, for twice every day the great salt tides of the ocean poured up the river on which the town of Damariscotta, Maine, was built and spread inland like a flood of green glass, and twice every day the tides raced down the river to the sea once more. Alice was accustomed to the smell of salt water mixed with the scent of her mother's garden, and nearly every day of her life she saw sea gulls perched on the roofs of the brick stores that lined the main street of the town.

The house, too, reminded her of the sea, for there were two shells at the door with pink mouths and the wallpaper in the dining room had been captured from an English vessel sailing to the West Indies during the War of 1812.

Beyond the old orchard was a little cove, which was almost dry at low tide, and the water coming in over the sunwarmed mud flats was good for swimming. Alice had absent-mindedly learned to swim very well, and she could row a small dory and scarcely know she was doing it. She had noticed which way the wind was blowing and how the tides were running before she could read the alphabet. Everyone she knew looked at the weathervane before he looked at the morning paper. They were part of life, like the sun and rain. Where Alice lived the land and sea were neighbors.

One summer evening Alice's father and mother were away. She had her supper early, a chop and string beans, milk and brown bread and jam from the wild strawberries she herself had picked in the hayfields. The dishes she used had come from England and were part of Great-grandmother Prescott's dowry; the silver spoon with the dent in it had been buried long before under a log-house doorstep when the Indians were about to attack the settlement.

After supper Alice wandered into the garden. The setting sun shone across the flowers full into the face of a moon rising very round and large over the pines of Tuesday Point. The sun and moon seemed staring quietly at each other across Alice. She felt rather lonely with her family away and wandered down to the cove without thinking about it. She saw that the tide was still running toward the sea, but would soon be turning again.

Alice was an obedient child, but she was absent-minded. As she got into the dory and rattled the oars into the oarlocks she was thinking about a poem.

> "The moon on one hand
> And the sun on the other,
> The moon is my sister,
> The sun is my brother,"

was the way she remembered it. She was not thinking about rowing at all, nor about her father's rule that she must never go out on the river alone, and must be home

[1] From Elizabeth Coatsworth, *Alice-All-by-Herself*.

before dark. Alice was dreaming as she rowed out and caught the current; it needed only a little steering on her part to be carried along swiftly, by the shore edged with a white rim of boulders, with pines sometimes overhanging the water and sometimes fields of stubble.

Alice faced the town and the setting sun. As she half drifted and half rowed, the buildings grew smaller and the sun sank from sight among a great swirl of clouds like wings, very rosy. But for all their rosiness Alice felt over her shoulder the white light of the moon streaming past her, and gradually the cloud wings turned ashy and stars appeared between the feathers; but the cool white light of the moon grew brighter and brighter and danced on the water and lighted the leaves to a dull soft green and shone dim red on Alice's dress.

A bend in the river hid the town; far off she could see the wink of automobile lights like glaring beads strung along a road no wider than a thread. The lisp of the water against the sides of her boat, the kind, quiet help of the tide that seemed to have set its shoulder to the dory stern and be pushing it along, kept Alice in her daydream.

A great heron rose from a boulder and flew almost overhead, its wings flapping very slowly, its legs trailing gracefully behind it. Alice was used to herons, but its rising up so near her brought her back to herself.

"I've gone far enough," she thought hastily. "I'd better get back before Olga misses me. Father wouldn't like this a bit," and she tried to turn the dory into the oncoming tide.

But though a man might have succeeded, making use of the slow currents by the shore, Alice didn't have the strength. The water kept its great shoulder to the dory like a genie which had been released from his bottle and knew that no one remembered the spell to make him go back.

"It will turn soon," thought Alice, giving up the struggle. "Mercy! I'm almost at Seal Rocks."

But now Alice no longer moved in a dream of moonlight. She kept thinking how upset her father and mother would be if they came home before she did. In her anxious state she noticed everything; the little cool breeze that had sprung up; the chirping of the crickets from the stubble; the leaping of the fish in their widening silver circles. A round velvet head appeared and dark eyes looked at her; then another. She was abreast Seal Rocks, and the seals, too, were awake. She could see them crawling clumsily along the beach or playing in the moonlit water; they seemed to take her boat for a large seal and sported about it, swimming close without any fear.

Alice knew that the fishermen sometimes fed the seals and that some of them were very tame. She could find only a little bait in a pail, but she threw that to them and they ate it greedily.

At last the tide turned, and Alice, too, turned the dory and started home. Now she faced into the moon which was much higher in the sky than it had been when she started, and smaller and brighter. It was not so magical; it was more like a bright lamp held in unseen hands. Anyway, it was lighting home a disobedient little girl and Alice was grateful to it.

Up the river went the tide from the great plains of the sea, carrying with it Alice and the dory. And behind the dory came the seals, at first all of them, and finally only two or three. Alice sang to them:

"Row, row, row your boat  
Gently down the stream,  
Merrily, merrily, merrily, merrily,  
Life is but a dream,"

and "Jolly boating weather," keeping time with her oars.

At last, over her shoulder, she could see the lights of the town and the little bristling lights of the cars, and then she heard the bell of the red church booming, ding-dong, ding-dong, very, very slowly—seven o'clock, eight o'clock, nine o'clock, surely it would stop now, but no, ten o'clock. Her mother and father would be wild.

She rowed hard now, adding her strength to the strength of the sea. When she thought about the seals again, they were all gone but one. It was cold, and a mist was beginning to rise. Alice was wide awake. When she reached the cove, she saw that the house was full of lights—her family were home and looking for her. Across the still air she heard a telephone bell jangle and then the door opened on a flood of light and a figure hurried out toward the car.

"Father!" she called. "Father! I'm down here tying up the boat!"

Her father turned and ran toward her through the apple trees.

He was shaking her by the shoulders. "Alice! Alice! What do you mean? On the river at this time of night all by yourself?"

"But I wasn't all by myself," said Alice, saying anything that came into her head. "There was the seal."

Her father's eye followed Alice's small pointing finger. Sure enough, there was a round velvet head and two eyes shining in the moonlight. The seal opened its mouth and barked throatily, rolled slowly out of sight, stuck up his head in a new place, and barked again.

"Quick, run up and see if Olga hasn't some fish in the ice box," said Alice's father, forgetting to scold just then.

And that is how Calypso happened to come to the cove and stay there and move, flip-flop, up through the orchard to the kitchen door when she was hungry, and swim all about Alice when she swam on warm days.

And though, of course, her father and mother spoke seriously to Alice about forgetting what people told her not to do, they were so charmed with Calypso and her friendly coaxing ways that they couldn't scold very much.

And, really, Alice was much better after that night and the coming of a gift from the sea and the moon. She was so busy playing with Calypso and with all the children who came to see Calypso that she forgot some of her old daydreaming ways; her smooth dark head with its brown bangs and small red-ribboned braids moved about as busily as anyone's, and she remembered what people told her to do and not to do.

As for Calypso, she grew fatter and fatter, for she had only to bark and someone was sure to throw her a mackerel or a slice of fish. It was hard to believe that one young seal could ever eat all that Calypso managed to eat.

But everyone was well pleased: Alice and her father and mother, who had a playmate from the sea; Calypso, who was fat and merry with so much food; and the man with the fishcart who stopped morning and afternoon at the kitchen door, and smiled with satisfaction as he made out his bill at the end of the month.

## STORIES OF OTHER DAYS IN OLD BERGEN [1]

*Ragnhild Chevalier*

### A NORWEGIAN KITCHEN

It was a cold, wintry afternoon about three weeks before Christmas. All day it had been snowing. The wind howled around Bakkehuset, the Hill House, high above Bergen, and drove the snow in great drifts against the house and doorways. It was already banked so high against the double windows that the light filtered through dimly, and we could not even see the sheaves of wheat that Olaf had put for the birds at all the windows.

Mother and Father had both gone to Kristiania for a few days, and we children were gathered in the large, cozy kitchen, hoping that Nilla, the cook, might take pity on us and give us a few of the cookies that she was baking in great panfuls. Already there were rows upon rows of crocks filled with delicious Christmas cookies, doughnuts, apple-rings, and honey cakes. We eyed them hungrily. Nilla, with her sleeves rolled high and her husky arms

[1] From Ragnhild Chevalier, *Wandering Monday*.

covered to the elbows with flour, seemed to us a true goddess of bounty.

Gyda, Olaf, and I sat by the square white porcelain stove, roasting chestnuts. Near the windows, trying to make use of the pale glimmer of the afternoon light, our two nurses, Margit and Inger, sat silently darning endless piles of woolen stockings. The flickering firelight cast fantastic shadows in the far-away corners of the darkly paneled kitchen, and was brightly reflected in the copper kettles and brass candlesticks that stood on high shelves around the walls.

We all watched Nilla eagerly as she bustled back and forth between the two tables and the stove; the warm fragrance of rich spices, which flowed out every time she opened the heavy oven door, made our mouths water. While we were watching and eating our chestnuts, we were telling one another all the stories that we knew about the *huldrer*—strange people with long cows' tails—and the giant *trold,* and especially about Nissen, that mischievous little dwarf who is blamed for so many things that happen in every Norwegian home. If anything disappears in the kitchen, it is surely Nissen who has taken it. If the fire won't burn in the morning, it is because Nissen has hidden himself in the chimney. If the horses are unmanageable on market day, it is because they have seen Nissen and are nervous. And the only way to make friends with Nissen is to put a large bowl of porridge in the woodshed every evening, especially at Christmastime.

As we were discussing these things, Olaf suddenly turned to Nilla and asked, "Nilla, have you ever seen Nissen?"

"Yes," answered Nilla, "but just once."

"Oh, please tell us about him!" we all three shouted in chorus.

"Well," replied Nilla, "it was when I was at home on the summer farm, in the summertime, far up in Hardangerfjord. Hans, the farm boy, asked me one evening to feed the horses, since he was not feeling very well; and I agreed, as he had many times helped me with the churning of the butter. Well, about dusk, I entered the stable; and I was just going toward Blakka's stall—when I saw him!"

"Pooh!" said Olaf. "I bet it was just a cat that you saw!"

"A cat!" cried Nilla. "I should say not! He had two large eyes like living coals, and his teeth gleamed in the darkness. I saw the red cap on his head, too, for the moon was shining on him through the window."

"Well, what did you *do?*" asked Gyda, who was younger than Olaf and I, and who had sat open-mouthed listening to Nilla's account.

"Oh, I ran out of the stable as fast as I could," said Nilla. "And the horses must have been well taken care of, for the next morning when Hans went to the stable they neighed contentedly, and did not seem to be very hungry. They say that Nissen can take better care of horses than any farm boy. But I would just as soon not see Nissen around here!"

While she was talking, Olaf had slipped out of the kitchen unnoticed. It was now dusk. Margit and Inger could no longer see by the window, so they had set aside the baskets of stockings and were busily getting ready the rice porridge and warm milk for our supper. Nilla lighted the two large oil lamps and the candles, and began stacking the newly baked cakes in two enormous jars. By this time, Gyda and I were so hungry that even the porridge seemed tempting.

The fire which had crackled so gayly all afternoon was beginning to die down. Nilla, observing this, left the cakes, and wrapped herself from top to toe in a dark, heavy shawl, so that just the tip of her nose and her eyes were visible; taking the big wood basket and a lantern, she started toward the door to go to the woodshed. As she opened the door, great flurries of snow blew in her face and into the kitchen. It seemed very dark outside, and I was glad that I could stay in the warm, bright kitchen. The woodshed was quite a distance from the house, and poor Nilla grumbled and mumbled to herself as she went out. The massive kitchen door, caught by the wind, closed with such a bang that all the copper and brass kettles rattled, and the sound reëchoed throughout the whole house. Inger, who was very superstitious, said to Margit that she would be glad when my father and mother returned from Kristiania.

All of a sudden we heard a muffled scream outside, and a moment later, Nilla, her face pale, her scarf half dragging in the snow, and her hair and skirts blowing wildly in the wind, appeared at the open door. She had neither wood basket nor lantern, and I shall never forget her expression as she stood there, completely dazed. Margit quickly closed the door and drew the half-frozen Nilla to a seat near the fire.

"What in the world is the matter, Nilla?" Gyda and I asked in one breath.

"Oh," panted poor Nilla. "I've seen him again!"

"Him!" I cried. "Whom might you mean, Nilla?"

"God be with us! Nissen, of course!"

Nissen! We were all astounded.

"But, Nilla, there is no Nissen here at Bakkehuset," said Gyda, very much frightened. "I heard father tell Olaf that, not long ago."

"Well, I certainly saw him with my own eyes!" answered Nilla. "I noticed him as soon as I had pushed open the door. It was pitch black in the woodshed; but I saw *him* sitting cross-legged on top of the woodpile, and his teeth and eyes just glowed! When I saw him sitting there, grinning at me, I couldn't move at first. Then, I guess, I screamed and dropped the wood basket and the lantern, and ran back here as fast as the wind and the snow and my old legs would let me!

"By the way, where is Olaf?" added Nilla, looking around. "He will have to go to the woodshed. I, for one, am not going out there again to-night!"

Just then Olaf entered the kitchen, looking quite unconcerned.

"Why are you all so excited?" asked Olaf.

"Excited!" said I. "There's a very good reason, I should think. Nilla has just seen Nissen out in the woodshed!"

"Ho! ho! ho! ha! ha! ha! That's a good joke!" laughed Olaf. "What will Nilla tell us next?" And he kept on laughing so hard that the tears rolled down his cheeks.

"Well, I really don't see why you are laughing," said Nilla, very much offended. "I tell you I saw Nissen sitting on top of the woodpile, as sure as I'm an old woman!"

"I tell you what I'll do, Nilla," interrupted Olaf, as soon as he could stop laughing. "If you will give me a handful of cookies every afternoon when I return from school, I'll fetch the wood for you every day!"

"All right," said Nilla, "I will. But you must start this evening, for the fire is almost out, and there is still a panful of cakes to bake."

Olaf left the kitchen to fetch his coat and cap, and I followed him to the hall.

"Tell me, Olaf," I said, when we were alone. "How is it that you have become so brave all of a sudden?"

"Do you want to know a secret, Sigrid? Come over here, and I'll whisper it in your ear, if you promise not to tell anyone! Nissen out in the woodshed was *your own brother Olaf!*"

"You, Olaf!" I could scarcely believe my ears.

"And now," added Olaf, "I shall have plenty of cookies every day!"

When I came back to the kitchen, Nilla was hunting high and low for something.

"What are you looking for, Nilla?" I asked, very much mystified by her actions.

"Oh, nothing!" mumbled Nilla, shaking her head.

But she still looked all around, behind the stove, in the cupboard; she even moved the wood chest. I was getting more and more curious. Finally Nilla said:

"Well, Sigrid, I am scared to death to meet Nissen out in the woodshed again. I am trying to find a piece of steel. If I have a little piece of steel sewed in my pocket, I am sure that Nissen will not come around here any more!"

AN OLD-FASHIONED CHRISTMAS

The streets of Bergen were wet and slippery with sleet. Christmas Eve, and almost no snow! Gyda and I, trudging down Strand Street, doing the last minute shopping for Mother, felt very sad. Everything had gone wrong since Father had announced a week ago that we couldn't have a tree this year. No tree! How could we have Christmas without a tree! Father had had very heavy losses during the past year, and a tree in our family was a great expense, even in Norway where fir trees are plentiful. Our drawing room, which was so large that it could be used as a ballroom and reception room, needed an enormous tree to fill it. Father had always prided himself on having the largest and finest tree that could be obtained in Bergen. How beautiful our Christmas tree had always been: a gigantic tree, fully two stories high, with dozens and dozens of golden apples and hundreds of white candles! Every year we children and the servants had spent evening after evening covering a barrelful of apples, as well as dozens of blown-out eggs, with gold-leaf. How gayly these golden eggs and apples had glittered in the candlelight every Christmas Eve, as we had danced hand-in-hand around the tree, to the tunes of the sweet carols which Mother always played for us!

Gyda and I glanced at each other, as if moved by the same thought, and in spite of ourselves, tears came to our eyes.

Our bundles were heavy and we were thoroughly wet and frozen. The wind howled around the street corners and blew the sleet in our faces, so that it was hard to see. The streets and sidewalks, which had been covered with ice the night before, were so slippery that when the wind caught up our heavy woolen skirts, it was quite difficult to keep our balance.

As we turned from the brightly lighted streets toward the hill which we had to climb to reach our house, a sudden gust of wind almost blinded us. Gyda, who was trying to recover a package that was slipping, suddenly tripped and fell sprawling in the street, her packages scattered in all directions. Poor Gyda just lay there and cried and cried as if her heart would break.

"Cheer up, Gyda," I said, though I confess my voice was not very hearty. "At least there are the gifts and the cozy tea which we shall have in front of the fire, and later, the Christmas supper. So let's hurry, and get home!"

As we were picking up the bundles, the sound of sleigh bells, which we had heard in the distance, grew near and nearer, and finally stopped quite close to us. What was our surprise to see that it was Grandmother Falch, with her coachman, Hans! Gyda, whose teeth were chattering from the cold, was bundled in the fur rug next to Grandmother, and I cheerfully took the seat beside Hans. Although my feet and hands were aching from the cold, I was thankful that we did not have to trudge home up the long hill.

Candles shone from all the windows of the homes that we passed; as we drew near Bakkehuset, the house seemed to be ablaze with candlelight. My throat felt tight, and I had to swallow hard to keep the tears back. I realized that poor Mother was trying to make us forget that there would be no tree.

As the sleigh drew up before the house, the door flew open; and there stood Mother smiling bravely, her large gray eyes expressing a world of love and kindness, and behind her, my two sisters, Henny and Beate, all anxiously waiting for our return.

"Hurry, children, and change your clothes," said Mother, as she kissed my Grandmother Falch. "Father will soon be home, and tea is all ready."

Gyda was so stiff from the cold that she had to be carried upstairs, and Margit had to rub her numb hands and feet with snow and ice.

Mother had the priceless gift of putting everyone around her at ease, and ordinarily she could make us radiantly happy. But tea, in spite of all that Mother could do to cheer us up, was not very gay. Father looked sad, as if he would rather have gone to any expense, after all, to see us happy. The water in the charcoal-filled samovar bubbled merrily, the fire of huge Yule logs burned brightly and cast amusing reflections on the intricately carved birch panels above the mantel. The flowers on the deep window sills in front of the double windows looked like the very spirit of Christmas. The floor of the library, strewn with bearskins, had been scoured and polished till it shone in the candle- and firelight. It seemed just made for dancing, and therefore reminded us all the more that there would be no tree to dance around this Christmas Eve.

Grandmother, a gentle little old lady in her lace cap, did the honors of pouring the tea, and kept urging us to eat more cakes, and more of the delicious little open-faced sandwiches for which Nilla, our cook, was famous. Every once in a while, when she thought no one was observing her, I caught the merriest twinkle in her eye. I could not for the life of me understand how she could feel merry or glad under the circumstances.

Finally, when we really couldn't eat any more—even the large marzipan pig with its bright red ribbon couldn't tempt us—Mother said:

"Come, Father; come, children! Call the servants, and we will at least sing some of the Christmas songs."

Olaf ran out to the kitchen, and mother walked toward the drawing-room door, for the big piano stood in the large room.

She opened the heavy double doors, and there—wonder of wonders!—stood the tallest, the most beautiful tree that I have ever seen. Such a shining and twinkling and sparkling and glittering tree! It was covered with snowballs, golden apples, and myriads of white candles. Gathered along one side of the room stood all the servants in their holiday peasant suits and dresses: Margit and Nilla in dresses with gayly beaded bodices and full-sleeved blouses, with snowy embroidered kerchiefs and aprons; Inger in her green-embroidered dress and little round cap; all the other servants in the suits and dresses of their native villages and valleys, all smiling and curtseying and saying:

"Merry Christmas! Merry Christmas!"

Father's face was a study. A man might well have counted a score while he stood looking at the tree, too dazed to speak. His eyes were smiling, and bright because there was a shining tear in each of them; and his mouth twitched at the corners, always a sign that he was much moved.

But the happiest face of all, was my Grandmother Falch's; and I knew then that, somehow, she must have supplied the tree.

Mother went to the piano, and, hand-in-hand, we danced around the tree, singing all the old favorites: "Silent Night, Holy Night," "It Was on Christmas Night," "A Child Was Born at Bethlehem." We sang and laughed and danced far into the evening.

When the chimes above the drawing-room mantel struck midnight, we all followed Nilla out to the woodshed with an enormous bowl of porridge, for Nissen. We wanted to be sure that our fires would burn, our kitchen things would stay put, our horses would pull the sleighs.

The wet, icy sleet had turned into soft white snow; the ground was freezing hard.

"Hurrah!" cried Olaf. "Look at the snow! Now there will be skiing and skating for us during the holidays. Hurrah!" He laughed a merry laugh and threw his new red cap high in the air.

## SWISS FAMILY ROBINSON [1]

*Johann David Wyss*

### SHIPWRECK

Our voyage had been a long but prosperous one, and it seemed that soon my family and I would reach the island in the South

[1] From Johann David Wyss, *Swiss Family Robinson*, edited by C. E. Mitton. For discussion of the background of this story, see page 839.

Pacific Ocean where I had planned to establish Christianity among the savage tribes. When our goal seemed at last about to be realized, we were overtaken by a fearful hurricane.

Already the storm had continued six days; on the seventh its fury seemed still increasing; and the morning dawned upon us without a prospect of hope, for no one on board even knew where we were. My four boys clung to me in their fright, while my wife wiped the tears from her cheeks.

At this moment a cry of "Land, land!" was heard through the roaring of the waves, and instantly the vessel struck against a rock so violently as to drive every one from his place; a tremendous cracking succeeded, as if the ship was going to pieces.

I hurried on deck, and saw a terrible sight. The crew had crowded into the boats till there was no room for us, and even as I appeared they cut the ropes to move off. I cried to them frantically not to leave us, but in vain, for the roaring of the sea prevented my being heard.

As all hope from this direction was over, I examined the ship to see if she would hold together for a little while, and was reassured. She was wedged stern first between two rocks, and it did not seem likely that the waves would drive her off at present. Therefore, when I returned to the cabin, which happened, fortunately, to be in the high part, and out of reach of the water, I was able to speak cheerfully of our position.

Comforted by this, my wife prepared something to eat, and the four boys at least ate heartily, and then the three youngest went to bed, and, tired out, soon were sleeping soundly. Fritz, the eldest, sat up with us.

"I have been thinking," he said, "that if we had some bladders or cork-jackets for mother and the others, you and I, father, could perhaps swim to land."

I thought there was some sense in what he said, so, in case the ship should break up in the night, he and I looked about for some small empty barrels; these we tied two and two together, and fastened them under the arms of each child.

Fritz then lay down, and was soon asleep; but his mother and I kept watch throughout this awful night. In the morning the sky was brighter, and the wind had fallen.

The boys sprang up in capital spirits, and Fritz advised that we should swim to land while the sea was calm. Ernest, the second boy, protested, not being able to swim himself, and suggested a raft.

I sent them all to look about the ship, and bring what things they could find that were likely to be useful, while I and my wife discussed the situation.

Presently they all rejoined me, bringing various treasures. Fritz had two guns, some powder and shot and bullets; Ernest produced a lot of carpenter's tools; while Jack, the third boy, came up laughing on the back of a huge dog, named Turk, and followed by another called Flora. The poor creatures had almost knocked him down in their eagerness when he had released them; and though at first I thought more of the food they would eat than of their usefulness, I agreed they might certainly assist us in hunting should we ever get on shore

Little Francis had found some fishing-hooks, at which his brothers mocked, until I reminded them it was likely we might have to depend for our food on fishing for some time to come.

My wife had found on board a cow and an ass, two goats, six sheep and a sow, which she had fed. All this was good so far as it went.

But now once more occurred to us the difficulty of crossing the broad strip of water that separated us from some kind of land, which we could just see far off. Jack, who was generally ready with an idea, cried out that he had often careered about on a pond at home in a tub, and that, as there seemed plenty of large barrels here, we might each have one and try.

This was not quite so simple as it sounded, but after some thinking I set to work, and, with the help of the boys, sawed four of the great barrels in half. This was tiring work, and took a long time, and there was much else to do before we could venture to trust ourselves on the water in them.

To make them more secure, we found a long pliant plank, and placed the eight tubs upon it, leaving a piece at each end reaching beyond the tubs. This being bent upward, like the keel of a vessel, made the whole contrivance more like a boat. We next nailed all the tubs to the plank, and afterwards put two other planks, of the same length as the first, on each side of the tubs. When all this was finished, we found we had produced a kind of narrow boat, divided into eight compartments. But then the difficulty was to move this great boat at all, for its weight was enormous. However, by putting rollers under it and using all our strength, we launched it into the sea. I had taken the precaution to attach a rope to it first, so it rode tethered; but, alas! in the first moment, we saw that it leaned far over to one side in a most alarming fashion. It soon occurred to me that this was only because it was so buoyant it danced up too far above the water, and after throwing some heavy things into the tubs, we saw it sink a little, and then float quite level.

However, all this had taken the whole day, and we had worked so hard that we had only eaten a bit of bread and taken a drink of milk occasionally, so now we sat down to a regular supper, and then went to bed, in high expectation of getting to the land next morning.

### LANDING ON THE DESERT ISLAND

By break of day we were all awake and alert, and I began to give orders to my little crew. First we gave each animal on board a hearty meal, and then put food and water enough for several days near them, as we hoped to come back and fetch them shortly. Our first cargo consisted of a barrel of gunpowder, three guns, and three rifles with ammunition, two pairs of pocket pistols, a chest containing cakes of portable soup, another full of hard biscuits, an iron pot, a fishing rod, a chest of nails and another of carpenter's tools, and, lastly, some sailcloth to make a tent.

When all was ready we each stepped bravely into a tub. At the moment of our departure the cocks and hens, of which there were numbers on board, began to cluck as if to protest against being left behind. So we put some of them into one of the tubs and covered it with planks, and left the rest of the fowls to themselves in the hope that they would follow us, the geese and the ducks by water, and the pigeons in the air.

We were waiting for my wife, who joined us loaded with a large bag, which she threw into the tub that already contained little Francis. I imagined that she intended it for him to sit upon, so asked no questions.

In the first tub, at the boat's head, was my wife.

In the second was little Francis, a boy six years old, remarkable for his sweet disposition.

In the third, Fritz, the eldest, nearly sixteen, a handsome lad, full of intelligence and vivacity.

In the fourth was the barrel of gunpowder, with the cocks and hens and the sailcloth.

In the fifth, the provisions of every kind.

In the sixth, Jack, my third son, a lighthearted, bold, careless boy, about thirteen years old.

In the seventh, Ernest, the second in age, a boy of fourteen, of a studious disposition, well read and thoughtful, but inclined to be both lazy and greedy.

In the eighth was I myself, holding a pole by which I steered while I, as well as the others, was provided with an oar to propel the boat. The boys devoured with their eyes the blue land they saw at a distance. We rowed with all our strength to reach it, but at first the boat only turned round and round; at length I managed to steer so that it went in a straight line. As we started, the two dogs, after whining and running up and down the deck for a while, plunged into the sea and swam after us.

They were too large for us to think of taking them in; but they did not try to climb up the sides of the boat, only rested their paws on the edges of the planks when they were tired.

Thus we proceeded slowly; but the nearer we approached the land, the more gloomy and unpromising it appeared. The coast was nothing but barren rocks. However, the sea was calm, and we could see casks, bales, chests, and other vestiges of the shipwreck, floating round us. We managed to get hold of two of these, and towed them after us in the water. As we drew nearer to the land, Fritz, who had keen eyes, saw some trees, and exclaimed that they were palm trees. Ernest expressed his joy that he should now get some fine coconuts. Jack drew a small telescope from his pocket and handed it to me, so that by its aid I got a good idea of the shore, and saw a little opening between the rocks, near the mouth of a creek, towards which all our geese and ducks were heading. I steered for it too, and found it was the entrance to a little bay; the water was neither too deep nor too shallow to receive our boat. So we entered it and ran ashore.

The moment our unwieldy boat grated on the shore the elder boys leaped out, and even little Francis, who had been wedged in his tub like a potted herring, sprang forward. The dogs, who had arrived first, greeted us with every demonstration of joy; the geese kept up a loud cackling, and the ducks contributed a deep quacking; the cocks and hens clucked; and the boys chattered all together. To this was added the disagreeable scream of some penguins and flamingoes, which flew over our heads or sat on the points of the rocks at the entrance of the bay.

The first thing we did on finding ourselves safe on dry land was to fall on our knees and utter a short thanksgiving to God our Father.

We next unloaded the boat, and then looked about for a convenient place to set up a tent under the shade of the rocks. Having agreed upon a place, we set to work, and drove one of our poles firmly into a fissure of the rock; this rested upon another pole, which was driven perpendicularly into the ground. Over the ridge we threw some sailcloth, and fastened it down on each side to the ground with stakes. The next thing to be done was to collect grass and moss, to be spread and dried in the sun, to serve us for beds. While the boys were doing this, I made near the tent a kind of little kitchen.

A few flat stones served for a hearth, and with some little twigs a brisk, cheering fire was soon alight. We put some of the soup-cakes, with water, into our iron pot over the flame. When Francis saw the soup-cakes he mistook them for glue, and asked with such an appearance of earnestness what we were going to stick together that his mother smiled as she explained that these cakes were made of the juices of meat, pressed out and consolidated to make them easy to pack.

In the meanwhile Fritz, taking one of the guns, had wandered along the side of the river; Ernest had gone to the seashore; and Jack took the direction of a chain of rocks which jutted out into the sea.

The sun began to sink into the west. The fowls gathered round, pecking here and there at the morsels of biscuit which had fallen on the ground. Then my wife produced the bag she had so mysteriously huddled into the tub, and drawing from it handfuls of grain, scattered them upon the ground for the ducks and hens. Seeing this, I suggested that we should not use anything so valuable so lavishly, but keep it as seed for a future harvest, in which she agreed. Then the pigeons sought a roosting-place among the rocks; the hens ranged themselves in a line along the ridge of the tent; and the geese and ducks betook themselves in a body, cackling and quacking as they proceeded, to a marshy bit of ground near the sea, where some thick bushes afforded them shelter.

A little later we began to follow their example by preparing for bed. First, we loaded our guns and pistols, and laid them carefully in the tent; next, we held evening prayer, and with the last ray of the sun we entered our tent, and, after drawing the sailcloth over the hooks, to close the entrance, we laid ourselves down on the grass and moss we had previously collected.

The boys noticed with surprise that darkness came down all at once without any twilight. This fact made me suspect we were not far from the equator, where day and night succeed each other very suddenly. Though the day had been hot, the night was quite cold; but we were all so tired that in spite of this we soon fell asleep, and found our first night on the desert island very tolerably comfortable.

### WE MOVE TO THE FOREST

On the days that followed, we searched diligently along the shore for the crew of the ship, but not a trace did we find. We were able to make a voyage to the wrecked ship and take off supplies that added much to our comfort in establishing ourselves for a long stay upon our island. After much planning and perseverance we were able to take off from the ship the cow, ass, sheep, goats, and sow.

We discovered many edible fruits and plants upon the island—these with fish and game furnished all we desired in the way of food. We did not feel secure living so near the shore and made several trips of exploration to locate a better site. We found it in a grove of fine trees and determined to move there and make a dwelling upon a high tree if such were possible.

The night before we started we gave thanks in prayer as was our custom. Then wrapped in soft woolen coverlets brought from the wreck we sought repose in sleep.

As soon as we were up and had breakfasted the next morning, I directed my sons to gather together our whole flock of animals, and to leave the ass and the cow to me, that I might load them with the sacks. I had filled these, putting in them all the things we should stand most in need of for the two or three days—working implements, kitchen utensils, the captain's service of plate, and a small provision of butter. I afterwards added our hammocks, and we were about to start when my wife said:

"We must not leave our fowls behind, for fear that the jackals should eat them. We must find a place for them among the luggage, and also one for little Francis, who cannot walk so far. Then there is my enchanted bag," she added, smiling, "which must not be left behind; for who can tell what may yet pop out of it?"

I therefore placed the child on the ass's back, fixing the enchanted bag in such a way as to support him.

In the meanwhile the other boys had been running after the cocks and hens and pigeons, but had not succeeded in catching one of them. Their mother laughed at them, and, stepping into the tent, brought out two handfuls of corn, which she scattered. The fowls came at once to pick them up. She then walked slowly before them, dropping the grain all the way, till they had followed her into the tent. When she saw them all inside, busily employed in picking up the grain, she shut the entrance, and caught one after the other without difficulty. The fowls were tied by the feet and wings, put into a basket covered with a net, and placed in triumph on the top of our luggage.

We had packed and put in the tent everything we meant to leave, and for greater security fastened down the ends of the sailcloth at the entrance by driving stakes through them into the ground. Then at last we set out, each of us, great and small, carrying a gun upon his shoulder and a game bag at his back. My wife led the way with her eldest son, the cow and the ass followed immediately behind them; the goat, conducted by Jack, came next, with a little monkey seated on his back, making grimaces; after this came Ernest, driving the sheep; while I brought up the rear, and the dogs ran up and down. Our march was slow, and there was something solemn and patriarchal about it; I fancied we were like our forefathers journeying in the desert, accompanied by their families and their possessions.

When we had advanced halfway across the bridge the sow thought she would come too. At the moment of our departure she had shown herself so restive that we had been compelled to leave her behind; but, seeing that we had all left the place, she set out to overtake us.

In order that our animals should not stray among the thick grass on the other side of the river I directed our march toward the seashore. But scarcely were we on the sands when our two dogs, which had strayed behind among the grass, set up a howl, as if they had been attacked by some formidable animal. Fritz in an instant raised his gun ready to fire; Ernest drew back to his mother's side; Jack ran bravely after Fritz with his gun upon his shoulder; while I followed. In spite of my exhortations to proceed with caution, the boys made but three jumps to the place from whence the noise proceeded, and Jack cried out:

"Come quickly, father; here is an enormous porcupine."

I soon reached the spot. The dogs were running to and fro with bleeding noses, and when they went too near the animal he made a noise, and darted his quills so suddenly at them that a number stuck into their coats, and made them howl violently.

While we were looking on, Jack took one of the pistols which he carried in his belt, and fired it at the head of the porcupine, so that he fell dead. This success raised Jack to the height of joy and vanity, while Fritz was so jealous he almost shed tears.

"Is it right, Jack," he said, "that such a little boy as you should fire like that?"

Jack only laughed.

"Pop—dead as a herring!" cried he gleefully. "Don't you wish you had done it?"

"Come, come, boys," said I, "no envious speeches and no reproaches; luck for one today, for another tomorrow; but all for the common good."

We now all examined the porcupine, which was an extraordinary animal. The boys tried to take hold of it, but the quills pricked their hands, and made them grimace. After some difficulty, however, we wrapped it up in a piece of sailcloth and slung it on to the back of the donkey behind Francis, for I knew that porcupine's flesh was good to eat, and so I did not like to waste so much valuable meat. A rather ludicrous incident occurred, however, when the donkey felt the prick of the spines through the wrappings; he flung up his heels, and would have dashed off had not Fritz caught him. We thereupon readjusted the bundle so that it should not hurt him, and reassured Francis, who was a little frightened at the unexpected friskiness of his steed. After this incident we at length formed our procession again, and marched on to the giant trees. These were indeed astonishing to me, who had not seen them before, and I gratified my wife by my loudly expressed admiration of her cleverness in judging how delightful a residence they would make.

We first released our animals from their burdens and tied their forelegs loosely together with a cord, that they might not go far away. We then let out the cocks and hens from their basket, and settled down to discuss how we could best pass the night.

Meantime Fritz, who was longing to distinguish himself as Jack had done, had slipped way, and we now heard a shot, and a few minutes later saw him running towards us, holding a dead animal of uncommon beauty by the paws.

"Father, father, look, here is a tiger-cat," said he, proudly raising it in the air to show it to the best advantage.

I congratulated him on having rid the world of a beast that would have made short work of our fowls.

"I saw it creeping along a branch," he said, "and fired at it; it fell to the ground furious and snarling, then I finished it off with another shot."

"You were lucky to get off so easily," I said. "I recognize the creature very well—it is a kind of wild cat called the margay, and though it is so small, it is very savage, and might easily have wounded you dangerously."

"Its eyes glared fiercely," he remarked. "Look at its lovely skin, all black and gold! May I make a belt of it?"

I agreed readily, and after this I had no peace until I had shown him how to flay the animal in the best way, which I did by hanging up the porcupine to the bough of a tree and skinning it, while Fritz watched me intently, and afterwards applied the same method to his wild cat. I then cut off part of the flesh of the porcupine to be roasted and set aside the remainder to be smoked or salted for future use.

Presently little Francis came running up to us, with his mouth crammed full of something, and called out: "Mamma, I have found a nice fruit to eat, and I have brought you some of it!"

"You greedy boy!" replied his mother, quite alarmed. "What have you got there? Do not put into your mouth everything you find or you will be poisoned." She made him open his mouth, and with some difficulty drew out the remains of a fig.

"A fig!" I exclaimed. "Where did you get it?"

"I got it among the grass, papa; and there are a great many more. I thought it must be good to eat, for the fowls and the pigeons, and even the pig, ate up all they could find."

"We are, then, in a grove of fig trees," I said. "Not the dwarf figs we see in Europe, but a kind called yellow mangoes, which I know do send down their branches to take root in just this peculiar way."

I took this opportunity to tell the boys never to eat anything they found till they had seen it eaten by birds and monkeys. At the word monkeys they turned to look at our little monkey, who was sitting on the root of a tree, examining with the oddest grimaces the half-skinned tiger-cat which lay near him. Francis offered him a fig, which he first turned round and round, then smelt, and finally ate with pleasure.

"Brave Mr. Monkey!" exclaimed the boys, clapping their hands.

My wife had made a fire by this time, and put on the pot to prepare our dinner. The tiger-cat was given to the dogs, who tore it to pieces. While our dinner was being made ready, I employed my time in making packing needles with some of the quills of the porcupine, which I had pulled out. I heated a large nail red-hot; then pierced the thick end of the quills with it, and soon had presented my wife with a large packet of long, stout needles, which she was delighted with, as she meant to make some better harness for our animals. I recommended her to be careful in the use of her packthread, for I saw we should want it to make a ladder for ascending the tree when we began to live there.

For this purpose I had chosen the highest fig tree; and while we were waiting for dinner I made the boys try how high they could throw a stick or stone into it. I also tried myself; but the lowest branches were so far from the ground that none of us could touch them. I saw, therefore, that we must think of some idea for fastening the end of the ladder to them. Then Fritz asked me how he could clean his new margay skin, and I showed him how to spread it out in the bed of the stream, under running water, fixed down by large stones. After this we returned, and dined heartily on some slices of ham and bread and cheese, under the shade of our beautiful trees.

While we ate I was considering the difficulty of getting up the tree, and at last I saw that we should be obliged to pass the night on the ground. So we began to sling our hammocks to some of the arched roots of the trees, spreading over them a piece of sailcloth large enough to cover them, to keep off the dew and the insects. I then went with the two eldest boys to the sea shore, to choose some pieces of wood to make steps for the ladder. Ernest discovered in a sort of bog some bamboo canes, which were just the thing. I cut them with my hatchet in pieces of four or five feet long, and the boys bound them together to carry back. At the same time I chose some of the straightest and most slender of the stalks, with which to make arrows, in case we might want them.

Seeing that the bamboos grew more thickly a little way off, I went towards them, when suddenly Flora, who had come with us, made several jumps, and threw herself furiously into the middle of the bushes; at the same moment a flock of flamingoes sprang out, and mounted into the air. Fritz fired, and two of the birds fell. One of them was quite dead; the other was only slightly wounded in the wing, and ran so fast towards the water that we were afraid he would escape us. Fritz plunged after him, up to his knees in the water; and Flora, coming to his help, caught hold of the flamingo and held him by the wing, though the bird struggled and flapped violently. When he had been dragged out we found some difficulty in securing him, though I tied his feet with my handkerchief, and held him under my left arm.

The boys were delighted to have captured such a fine bird alive, and spoke of being able to tame him.

"He is a bird to be easily tamed," I said, "for he is of a tractable though timid disposition."

"We will catch some little fish for him," said Ernest, who knew something of the habits of these birds. Then he examined the prize more attentively. "What long legs he has!" he added. "Are all flamingoes like this—of such a beautiful red color, with wings tinted with purple? I think I have seen the flamingo in my Natural History, and the colors were not like these."

"I believe that the plumage is differently colored according to the age of the birds," I told him. "When very young they are gray; then they turn white; and it is only when they are full grown that they are adorned with this beautiful tinted plumage."

Talking like this, we returned to our camp laden with bundles of canes of various sizes, and with the dead and living birds. We were greeted with the delight that a new discovery never failed to bring; only my wife, with her usual anxiety about ways and means, asked where we should get food enough for all the animals we brought home.

I told her I expected this acquisition would soon be able to feed himself; and I proceeded to examine his wound. I found that only one wing was injured by the shot, but that the other had also been slightly hurt by the dog laying hold of him. I rubbed some ointment on both, and this seemed to relieve him. I next tied him by one of his legs with a long string to a stake I had driven into the ground quite near to the river, that he might go in and wash himself when he liked.

Now I had begun to think seriously of the difficulty of getting a rope ladder to reach even the lowest of the branches, for the nearest to the ground were at a height of forty feet, and it would be necessary to carry a rope over these before we could fix it. I had an idea, however, and, sitting down on the grass, I began to make some arrows with the slenderest pieces of the bamboo that I had so carefully chosen. As the arrows were hollow, I filled them with the moist sand to give them a little weight; and, lastly, I tipped them with a bit of feather from the flamingo, to make them fly straight.

The boys watched me with interest, and soon saw what I was doing. Laying the arrows aside for a moment, I chose a flexible rod for a bow, and making a niche at each end, soon fixed a piece of string to draw it into a curve. Then I asked my wife if she had such a thing as a ball of string, which would unravel as I required it. She produced this with a laugh from what she called her enchanted bag. I tied the end of the ball of string to an arrow, and fixing it to the bow, I shot it off so as to make the arrow pass over one of the largest branches of the tree, and fall again to the ground; thus I had overcome the first difficulty. It was now easy to tie a piece of rope to the end of the string, and draw it upwards, till the knot reached the same branch. Then I knew that, when the ladder was finished, we should at any rate be able to pull it up to the bough.

So I turned my attention to the ladder itself, a much more difficult job. The first thing was to cut a length of about one hundred feet from our stock of ropes; this I divided into two equal pieces, which I laid on the ground at the distance of a foot from each other. I told Fritz to cut the canes we had brought in pieces each two feet in length. As he did this, Ernest handed them to me one after another; and I inserted them into my ropes at the distance of twelve inches apart, fixing them with knots in the rope. Jack, at the same time, by my order, drove into each a long nail at both ends to prevent their slipping out again. Thus, in a very short time, we had made a ladder of forty steps, firm and compact, which we all regarded with joyful surprise. I now tied it with strong knots to the end of the rope which hung from the tree, and pulled it up till it reached the branch, and rested so well upon it, that the exclamations of the boys resounded from all sides. Everyone wished to be the first to ascend, but I decided that it should be Jack, he being the nimblest and the lightest among them. Accordingly, I and his brothers held the ends of the rope, and of the ladder, as well as we could, while he ran easily up, and reached the branch without an accident; but, when he got there, I saw that he had not strength enough to tie the ladder firmly to the tree. So I sent Fritz up after him, not without some little anxiety, as he was much heavier than his brother. But it was not long before we saw him side by side with Jack, forty feet above our heads.

Fritz set to work to fasten the ladder by passing the rope round and round the branch, and this he did with so much sense, that I felt I might ascend myself in safety. But first I tied a large pulley to the end of the rope, and took it up with me. When I was at the top, I fastened the pulley to a branch, so that I might be able the next day to draw up the planks and timbers for building the platform of our hut. All this took so long that it was finished by the light of the moon.

For the last few minutes I had been alone on the branch, and concluded that Jack and Fritz had descended, when I suddenly heard their voices singing an evening hymn which seemed to come from the clouds. I soon gathered that instead of going down, they had gone up, and had climbed upwards from branch to branch, till they had reached the very top. I called out to them to take great care in coming down, for it was almost night, and the light of the moon scarcely penetrated the thick foliage. They soon appeared without any accident, and then I told them to gather together all our animals, and to get what dry wood we should want for making fires, which we must keep up through the night as a precaution against the attacks of wild beasts.

My wife now showed me the work she had been busy with throughout the day; some harness for the cow and the ass. Then we had our supper, while all the animals stood round us. My wife threw some grain to the fowls, and afterwards the pigeons flew up to the top of the giant tree, while the cocks and hens perched, cackling all the time, upon the rounds of the ladder. The cow and donkey we tied to the arched roots of the tree, quite near to our hammocks. Our beautiful flamingo was not forgotten. Fritz fed him with some crumbs of biscuit soaked in milk, and afterwards, putting his head under his right wing, and tucking up one leg, he went quietly to sleep, too ignorant of the ways of human beings to have any dread of them.

Before retiring I made up the brushwood the boys had gathered into heaps, and set fire to several of them, and then threw myself contentedly upon my hammock. The lads were already in theirs, but we soon heard them grumbling at being obliged to lie so close to each other. I called out mockingly, that they were much better off than many sailors, and that unless beds dropped from the clouds, they must put up with it; whereupon they ceased, and being really tired by their long day in the open air, they were soon asleep.

These were some of the adventures of the

early days upon our island, days that lengthened into years—years in which God blessed our endeavors. Our story proves how many are the gifts of the Creator as seen in nature if we search for them, and that all these benefits can be made useful and profitable to ourselves by intelligence and industry. Under God's guidance, the Swiss family Robinson spent the years upon our island happily and comfortably.

## THE QUEEN OF THE PIRATE ISLE[1]

*Bret Harte*

I first knew her as the Queen of the Pirate Isle. It was a long while ago, but to the best of my recollection she had no reasonable right to that title. She was only nine years old, inclined to plumpness and good humor, disliked violence, and had never been to sea. Need it be added that she did *not* live on an island and that her name was Polly?

Perhaps I ought to explain that she had already known other experiences of a purely imaginative character. Part of her existence had been passed as a Beggar Child—solely indicated by a shawl tightly folded round her shoulders and chills; as a Schoolmistress, unnecessarily severe; as a Preacher, singularly personal in his remarks; and once, after reading one of Cooper's novels, as an Indian Maiden. This was, I believe, the only instance when she had borrowed from another's fiction. Most of the characters that she assumed for days and sometimes weeks at a time were purely original; some so much so as to be vague to others. I remember that her impersonation of a certain Mrs. Smith, whose individuality was supposed to be sufficiently represented by a sunbonnet worn wrong side before and a weekly addition to her family, was never perfectly appreciated by her own circle although she lived the character for a month. Another creation known as the Proud Lady—a being whose haughtiness was so pronounced as to give her features an expression of extreme nausea —caused her mother so much alarm that it had to be abandoned. This was easily effected. The Proud Lady was understood to have died. Indeed, most of Polly's impersonations were got rid of in this way, although it by no means prevented their reappearance. "I thought Mrs. Smith was dead," remonstrated her mother at the reappearance of that lady with a new infant. "She was buried alive and kem to!" said Polly with a melancholy air.

The origin of the title of the Queen of the Pirate Isle may be briefly stated as follows:

An hour after luncheon one day, Polly, Hickory Hunt, her cousin, and Wan Lee, a Chinese page, were crossing the nursery floor in a Chinese junk. The sea was calm and the sky cloudless. Any change in the weather was as unexpected as it is in books. Suddenly a West Indian Hurricane, purely local in character and unfelt anywhere else, struck Master Hickory and threw him overboard, but wildly swimming for his life and carrying Polly on his back, he eventually reached a Desert Island in the closet. Here the rescued party put up a tent made of a tablecloth providentially snatched from the raging billows and from two o'clock until four, passed six weeks on the island, supported only by a piece of candle, a box of matches, and two peppermint lozenges. At this time it became necessary to account for Polly's existence among them; Hickory and Wan Lee instantly became *Pirates,* and at once elected Polly as their Queen. The royal duties, which seemed to be purely maternal, consisted in putting the Pirates to bed after a day of bloodshed, and in feeding them with licorice water through a quill in a small bottle. Limited as her functions were, Polly performed them with gravity and sincerity. Even when her companions sometimes hesitated from actual hunger or fatigue and forgot their guilty part, she never faltered. It was her real existence; her other life of being washed,

[1] From Bret Harte, *The Queen of the Pirate Isle.*

dressed, and put to bed at certain hours was the *illusion*.

Doubt and skepticism came at last—and came from Wan Lee! Wan Lee of all creatures! Wan Lee, whose silent, stolid, mechanical performance of a pirate's duties had been their delight and fascination!

It was just after the exciting capture of a merchantman with the indiscriminate slaughter of all on board—a spectacle on which the round blue eyes of the plump Polly gazed with royal and maternal tolerance. They were burying the booty, two tablespoons and a thimble, in the corner of the closet, when Wan Lee stolidly rose.

"Melican boy pleenty foolee! Melican boy no pilate!" said the little Chinaman, substituting "l's" for "r's" after his usual fashion.

"Wotcher say?" said Hickory, reddening with sudden confusion.

"Melican boy's papa heap lickee him—s'pose him leal pilate," continued Wan Lee doggedly. "Melican boy pilate *inside* housee. Chinee boy pilate *outside* housee."

Staggered by this humiliating statement, Hickory recovered himself in character. "Ah! Ho!" he shrieked, dancing wildly on one leg, "Mutiny and Splordinashun! 'Way with him to the yardarm."

"Yaldalm—heap foolee! Alee same clotheshorse for washee washee."

It was here necessary for the Pirate Queen to assert her authority, which was somewhat confusingly maternal.

"Go to bed instantly without your supper," she said seriously. "Really, I never saw such bad pirates. Say your prayers, and see that you're up early to church tomorrow."

It should be explained that in deference to Polly's proficiency as a preacher, and probably as a relief to their uneasy consciences, Divine Service had always been held on the Island. But Wan Lee continued:—

"Me no pilate *inside* housee; me pilate *outside* housee. S'pose you lun away longside Chinee boy—Chinee boy make you pilate."

Hickory softly scratched his leg, while a broad, bashful smile almost closed his small eyes. "Wot?" he asked.

"Mebbe you too flightened to lun away. Melican boy's papa heap lickee."

This last infamous suggestion fired the corsair's blood. "Dy'ar think we daresen't?" said Hickory desperately, but with an uneasy glance at Polly. "I'll show yer tomorrow."

The entrance of Polly's mother at this moment put an end to Polly's authority and dispersed the pirate band, but left Wan Lee's proposal and Hickory's rash acceptance ringing in the ears of the Pirate Queen. That evening she was unusually silent. She would have taken Bridget, her nurse, into her confidence, but this would have involved a long explanation. She, however, made preparation for the proposed flight by settling in her mind which of her two dolls she would take. A wooden creature with easy-going knees and movable hair seemed to be more fit for hard service and any scalping that might turn up hereafter. She timidly asked a question of Bridget. "Did ye ever hear the loikes uv that, ma'am?" said the Irish nurse with affectionate pride. "Shure the darlint's head is filled noight and day with ancient history. She's after asking me now if Queens ever run away!" To Polly's confusion her father, equally proud of her interest and his own knowledge, at once interfered with a long account of the abdication of various queens in history until Polly's head ached again. Well meant as it was, it only settled in her mind that she must keep the awful secret to herself and that no one could understand her.

The eventful day dawned without any unusual sign of importance. It was one of the cloudless summer days of the Californian foothills, bright, dry, and, as the morning advanced, hot in the white sunshine. The actual, prosaic house in which the Pirates lived was a mile from a gold mining settlement on a beautiful ridge of pine woods sloping gently towards a valley on the one side, and on the other falling abruptly into a dark, deep gulf of pine-trees, rocks, and red soil. Beautiful as the slope was, looking over to the distant snow peaks which seemed to be in another world than theirs, the children found a greater attraction in the fascinating depths of the mysterious gulf, or canyon, as it was called. To creep to the edge of the cliff, to sit upon the brown branches of some fallen pine, and, putting aside the dried tassels, to look down upon the backs of wheeling hawks that seemed to hang in mid-air was a never-failing delight. Here Polly would try to trace the winding red ribbon of road that was continually losing itself among the dense pines of the opposite mountains; here she would listen to the far-off strokes of a woodman's axe, or the rattle of some heavy wagon, miles away, crossing the pebbles of a dried-up watercourse. Here, too, the prevailing colors of the mountains, red and white and green, most showed themselves. There were no frowning rocks, but everywhere along the ridge pure white quartz bared itself through the red earth like smiling teeth; the very pebbles they played with were streaked with shining mica like bits of looking glass. The distance was always green and summerlike, but the color they most loved, and which was most familiar to them, was the dark red of the ground beneath their feet. It showed itself in the roadside bushes; its red dust pervaded the leaves of the overhanging laurel; it colored their shoes and clothes; I am afraid it was often seen in patches on their faces and hands.

It was on this ridge that the three children gathered at ten o'clock that morning. An earlier flight had been impossible on account of Wan Lee being obliged to perform his regular duty of blacking the shoes of Polly and Hickory—a menial act which the children did not think inconsistent with the loftiest piratical ambition. On the ridge they met one "Patsey," the son of a neighbor. As there were afterwards some doubts expressed whether he joined the Pirates of his own free will, or was captured by them, I endeavor to give the colloquy exactly as it occurred:

Patsey: "Hallo, fellers."

The Pirates: "Hello!"

Patsey: "Goin' to hunt bars? Dad seed a lot o' tracks at sunup."

The Pirates (hesitating): "No—o—"

Patsey: "I am; know where I kin get a six-shooter?"

The Pirates (almost ready to abandon piracy for bear-hunting, but preserving their dignity): "Can't! We've runn'd away to be real pirates."

Patsey: "Not for good!"

The Queen (interposing with sad dignity and real tears in her round blue eyes): "Yes!" (slowly and shaking her head) "Can't go back again. Never! Never! Never! The—the—eye is cast!"

Patsey (bursting with excitement): "No-o! Sho'o! Wanter know."

The Pirates: "The Perleese is on our track!"

Patsey: "Lemme go with yer!"

Hickory: "Wot'll yer giv?"

Patsey: "Pistol and er bananer."

Hickory (with judicious prudence): "Let's see 'em."

Patsey was off like a shot. In a few minutes he returned with an old-fashioned revolver and a large banana. He was at once enrolled, and the banana eaten.

As yet they had resolved on no definite plan. Hickory, looking down at Patsey's bare feet, instantly took off his own shoes. This bold act sent a thrill through his companions. Wan Lee took off his cloth leggings, Polly removed her shoes and stockings, but, with royal foresight, tied them up in her handkerchief. The last link between them and civilization was broken.

"Let's go to the Slumgullion."

"Slumgullion" was the name given by the miners to a certain soft, half-liquid mud, formed of the water and finely powdered earth that was carried off by the sluice-boxes during gold-washing, and eventually collected in a broad pool or lagoon before the outlet. There was a pool of this kind a quarter of a mile away, where there were "diggings" worked by Patsey's father, and thither they proceeded along the ridge in single file. When it was reached they solemnly began to wade in its thick, paint-like shallows. Possibly it was pleasant to the touch; possibly there was fascination in the fact that their parents had forbidden them to go near it, but probably the principal object of this performance was to produce a thick coating of mud on the feet and ankles, which, when dried in the sun, was supposed to harden the skin and render their shoes superfluous. It was also felt to be the first real step towards independence; they looked down at their red feet and recognized the impossibility of their ever again crossing (unwashed) the family threshold.

Then they again hesitated. They gazed at each other. There was a stolid look of resigned and superior tolerance in Wan Lee's eyes.

Polly's glance wandered down the side of the slope to the distant little tunnels or openings made by the miners who were at work in the bowels of the mountain. "I'd like to go into one of them funny holes," she said to herself, half aloud.

Wan Lee suddenly began to blink his eyes with unwonted excitement. "Catchee tunnel—heap gold," he said quickly. "When manee come outside to catchee dinner—Pilates go inside catchee tunnel! Pilates catchee gold alle samee Melican man!"

"And take perseshium," said Hickory.

"And hoist the Pirate flag," said Patsey.

"And build a fire, and cook, and have a family," said Polly.

The idea was fascinating to the point of being irresistible. They seized each other's hands and swung them backwards and forwards, occasionally lifting their legs in a solemn rhythmic movement.

"It's orful far off!" said Patsey with a sudden look of dark importance. "Pap says it's three miles on the road. Take all day ter get there."

The bright faces were overcast.

"Less go down er slide!" said Hickory boldly.

They approached the edge of the cliff. The "slide" was simply a sharp incline zigzagging down the side of the mountain used for sliding goods and provisions from the summit to the tunnel-men at the different openings below. The traffic had gradually worn a shallow gully half filled with earth and gravel into the face of the mountain. It checked the momentum of the goods in their downward passage, but afforded no foothold for a pedestrian. No one had ever been known to descend a slide. That feat was evidently reserved for the Pirate Band. They approached the edge of the slide, hand in hand, hesitated, and the next moment disappeared.

Five minutes later the tunnel-men of the Excelsior mine, a mile below, taking their luncheon on the rude platform of debris before their tunnel, were suddenly driven to shelter in the tunnel from an apparent rain of stones, rocks, and pebbles from the cliffs above. Looking up, they were startled at seeing four round objects revolving and bounding in the dust of the slide, which eventually resolved themselves into three boys and a girl. For a moment the men held their breath in helpless terror. Twice one of the children had struck the outer edge of the bank and displaced stones that shot a thousand feet down into the dizzy depths of the valley; and now one of them, the girl, had actually rolled out of the slide and was hanging over the chasm supported only by a clump of chaparral to which she clung! "Hang on by your eyelids, sis! But don't stir, for Heaven's sake!" shouted one of the men, as two others started on a hopeless ascent of the cliff above them.

But a light childish laugh from the clinging little figure seemed to mock them! Then two small heads appeared at the edge of the slide; then a diminutive figure, whose feet were apparently held by some invisible companion, was shoved over the brink and stretched its arms towards the girl. But in vain, the distance was too great. Another laugh of intense enjoyment followed the failure, and a new insecurity was added to the situation by the unsteady hands and shoulders of the relieving party, who were apparently shaking with laughter. Then the extended figure was seen to detach what looked like a small black rope from its shoulders and throw it to the girl. There was another little giggle. The faces of the men below paled in terror. Then Polly—for it was she—hanging to the long pigtail of Wan Lee, was drawn with fits of laughter back in safety to the slide. Their treble of appreciation was answered by a ringing cheer from below.

Meantime the children had reached the goal and stood before the opening of one of the tunnels. Then these four heroes who had looked with cheerful levity on the deadly peril of their descent became suddenly frightened at the mysterious darkness of the cavern and turned pale at its threshold.

"Mebbee a wicked Joss backside holee, he catchee Pilates," said Wan Lee gravely.

Hickory began to whimper, Patsey drew back, Polly alone stood her ground, albeit with a trembling lip.

"Let's say our prayers and frighten it away," she said stoutly.

"No! no!" said Wan Lee, with a sudden alarm. "No frighten Spillits! You waitee! Chinee boy he talkee Spillit not to frighten you."

Tucking his hands under his blue blouse, Wan Lee suddenly produced from some mysterious recess of his clothing a quantity of red paper slips which he scattered at the entrance of the cavern. Then drawing from the same inexhaustible receptacle certain squibs or fireworks, he let them off and threw them into the opening. There they went off with a slight fizz and splutter, a momentary glittering of small points in the darkness, and a strong smell of gunpowder. Polly gazed at the spectacle with awe and fascination. Hickory and Patsey breathed hard with satisfaction; it was beyond their wildest dreams of mystery and romance. Even Wan Lee appeared transfigured into a superior being by his own spells. But an unaccountable disturbance of some kind in the dim interior of the tunnel quickly drew the blood from their blanched cheeks again. It was a sound like coughing, followed by something like an oath.

"He's made the Evil Spirit orful sick," said Hickory in a loud whisper.

A slight laugh came from the tunnel.

"See!" said Wan Lee. "Evil Spillet he likee Chinee; try talkee him."

The Pirates looked at Wan Lee, not without a certain envy. A fearful desire to continue their experiments was taking possession of them; but Polly immediately began to extemporize a house for the party at the mouth of the tunnel and, with parental foresight, gathered the fragments of the squibs to build a fire for supper. That frugal meal, consisting of half a biscuit divided into four small portions, each served on a chip of wood and having a deliciously mysterious flavor of gunpowder and smoke, was soon over. It was necessary after this that the Pirates should at once seek repose after a day of adventure, which they did for the space of forty seconds in singularly impossible attitudes and far too aggressive snoring. Indeed, Master Hickory's almost upright pose, with tightly folded arms and darkly frowning brows, was felt to be dramatic, but impossible for a longer period. The brief interval enabled Polly to collect herself and to look around her in her usual motherly fashion. Suddenly she started and uttered a cry. In the excitement of the descent she had quite overlooked her doll, and was now regarding it with round-eyed horror.

"Lady Mary's hair's gone!" she cried, convulsively grasping the Pirate Hickory's legs.

Hickory at once recognized the battered doll under the aristocratic title which Polly had long ago bestowed upon it. He stared at the bald and battered head.

"Ha! ha!" he said hoarsely; "skelped by Injins!"

For an instant the delicious suggestion soothed the imaginative Polly. But it was quickly dispelled by Wan Lee.

"Lady Maley's pigtail hangee top side hillee. Catchee on big quartz stone allee same Polly; me go fetchee."

"No!" quickly shrieked the others. The prospect of being left in the proximity of Wan Lee's evil spirit, without Wan Lee's exorcising power, was anything but reassuring. "No, don't go!" Even Polly (dropping a maternal tear on the bald head of Lady Mary) protested against this breaking up of the little circle. "Go to bed!" she said authoritatively, "and sleep till morning."

Thus admonished, the Pirates again retired. This time effectively; for, worn by actual fatigue or soothed by the delicious coolness of the cave, they gradually, one by one, succumbed to real slumber. Polly, withheld from joining them by official and maternal responsibility, sat and blinked at them affectionately.

Gradually she, too, felt herself yielding to the fascination and mystery of the place and the solitude around her. Beyond the pleasant shadows where she sat, she saw the great world of mountain and valley through a dreamy haze. Long waves of spicy heat rolling up the mountain from the valley brought her the smell of pine trees and bay and made the landscape swim before her eyes. She could hear the far-off cry of teamsters on some unseen road; she could see the far-off cloud of dust following the mountain stagecoach, whose rattling wheels she could not hear. She felt very lonely, but was not quite afraid; she could have easily awakened her sleeping companions if she wished.

No; she was a lone widow with nine children, six of whom were already in the lone churchyard on the hill, and the others lying ill with measles and scarlet fever beside her. She had just walked many weary miles that day, and had often begged from door to door for a slice of bread for the starving little ones. It was of no use now—they would die! This was a favorite imaginative situation of Polly's, but only indulged when her companions were asleep. She glanced timidly around. Satisfied that no one could observe her, she softly visited the bedside of each of her companions, and administered from a purely fictitious bottle spoonfuls of invisible medicine. But in vain; they succumbed to the fell disease—they always died at this juncture—and Polly was left alone. She thought with melancholy satisfaction of the nine litle tombstones in the graveyard, each with an inscription, and looked forward with gentle anticipation to the long summer days when, with Lady Mary in her lap, she would sit on those graves clad in the deepest mourning. The fact that the unhappy victims at times moved, as it were, uneasily in their graves, or snored, did not affect Polly, nor withhold the tears that gathered in her round eyes.

Presently, the lids of the round eyes began to droop, the landscape beyond began to be more confused, and sometimes to disappear entirely. Then a sound of rippling water from the little stream that flowed from the mouth of the tunnel soothed her and seemed to carry her away with it, and soon she too was asleep.

The next thing that she remembered was that she was apparently being carried along on some gliding object to the sound of rippling water. She was not alone, for her three companions were lying beside her, rather tightly packed and squeezed in the same mysterious vehicle. Even in the profound darkness that surrounded her, Polly could feel and hear that they were accompanied, and once or twice a faint streak of light from the side of the tunnel showed her gigantic shadows walking slowly on either side of the gliding car. She felt the hands of her associates seeking hers and knew they were awake; she gave each a reassuring pressure. Presently the car glided into an open space of bright light and stopped. The transition from the darkness of the tunnel at first dazzled their eyes. It was like a dream.

They were in a circular cavern from which three other tunnels, like the one they had passed through, diverged. The walls, lit up by fifty or sixty candles stuck at irregular intervals in crevices of the rock, were of glittering quartz and mica. But more remarkable than all were the inmates of the cavern, who were ranged round the walls—

men who, like their attendants, seemed to be of extra stature; who had blackened faces, wore red bandana handkerchiefs round their heads and their waists, and carried enormous knives and pistols stuck in their belts. On a raised platform made of a packing box on which was rudely painted a skull and crossbones, sat the chief or leader of the band covered with a buffalo robe; on either side of him were two small barrels marked "Grog" and "Gunpowder." The children stared and clung closer to Polly. Yet, in spite of these desperate and warlike accessories, the strangers bore a singular resemblance to "Christy Minstrels" in their blackened faces and attitudes that somehow made them seem less awful. In particular, Polly was impressed with the fact that even the most ferocious had a certain kindliness of eye, and they showed their teeth almost idiotically.

"Welcome!" said the leader. "Welcome to the Pirates' Cave! The Red Rover of the North Fork of the Stanislaus River salutes the Queen of the Pirate Isle!" He rose up and made an extraordinary bow. It was repeated by the others with more or less exaggeration, to the point of one losing his balance!

"Oh, thank you very much," said Polly timidly, but drawing her little flock closer to her with a small protecting arm. "But could you—would you—please—tell—us—what time it is?"

"We are approaching the middle of Next Week," said the leader gravely, "but what of that? Time is made for slaves! The Red Rover seeks it not! Why should the Queen?"

"I think we must be going," hesitated Polly, yet by no means displeased with the recognition of her rank.

"Not until we have paid homage to Your Majesty," returned the leader. "What ho! there! Let Brother Step-and-Fetch-It pass the Queen around that we may do her honor." Observing that Polly shrank slightly back, he added: "Fear nothing; the man who hurts a hair of Her Majesty's head dies by this hand. Ah! ha!"

The others said "Ah! ha!" and danced alternately on one leg, then on the other, but always with the same dark resemblance to Christy Minstrels. Brother Step-and-Fetch-It, whose very long beard had a confusing suggestion of being a part of the leader's buffalo robe, lifted her gently in his arms and carried her to the Red Rovers in turn. Each one bestowed a kiss upon her cheek or forehead, and would have taken her in his arms, or on his knees, but they were sternly restrained by their leader. When the solemn rite was concluded, Step-and-Fetch-It paid his own courtesy with an extra squeeze and deposited her again in the truck, a little frightened, a little astonished, but with considerable accession to her dignity. Hickory and Patsey looked on with stupefied amazement. Wan Lee alone remained stolid and unimpressed, regarding the scene with calm and triangular eyes.

"Will Your Majesty see the Red Rovers dance?"

"No, if you please," said Polly, with gentle seriousness.

"Will Your Majesty fire this barrel of gunpowder, or tap this beaker of grog?"

"No, I thank you."

"Is there no command Your Majesty would lay upon us?"

"No, please," said Polly, in a failing voice.

"Is there anything Your Majesty has lost? Think again! Will Your Majesty deign to cast your royal eyes on this?"

He drew from under his buffalo robe what seemed like a long tress of blond hair, and held it aloft. Polly instantly recognized the missing scalp of her hapless doll.

"If you please, sir, it's Lady Mary's. She's lost it."

"And lost it, Your Majesty, only to find something more precious. Would Your Majesty hear the story?"

A little alarmed, a little curious, a little self-anxious, and a little induced by the nudges and pinches of her companions, the Queen blushingly signified her royal assent.

"Enough. Bring refreshments. Will Your

Majesty prefer wintergreen or peppermint drops? Red or white? Or perhaps Your Majesty will let me recommend these bull's-eyes," said the leader, as a collection of sweets in a hat were suddenly produced from the barrel labeled "Gunpowder" and handed to the children.

"Listen," he continued, in a silence broken only by the gentle sucking of bull's-eyes. "Many years ago the old Red Rovers of these parts locked up all their treasures in a secret cavern in this mountain. They used spells and magic to keep it from being entered or found by anybody, for there was a certain mark upon it made by a peculiar rock that stuck out of it, which signified what there was below. Long afterwards, other Red Rovers who had heard of it came here and spent days and days trying to discover it, digging holes and blasting tunnels like this, but of no use! Sometimes they thought they had discovered the magic marks in the peculiar rock that stuck out of it, but when they dug there, they found no treasure. And why? Because there was a magic spell upon it. And what was that magic spell? Why, this! It could only be discovered by a person who could not possibly know that he or she had discovered it; who never could or would be able to enjoy it; who could never see it, never feel it, never, in fact, know anything at all about it! It wasn't a dead man, it wasn't an animal, it wasn't a baby!"

"Why," said Polly, jumping up and clapping her hands, "it was a dolly."

"Your Majesty's head is level! Your Majesty has guessed it!" said the leader, gravely. "It was Your Majesty's own dolly, Lady Mary, who broke the spell! When Your Majesty came down the slide, the doll fell from your gracious hand when your foot slipped. Your Majesty recovered Lady Mary, but did not observe that her hair had caught on a peculiar rock, called the 'Outcrop,' and remained behind! When, later on, while sitting with your attendants at the mouth of the tunnel, Your Majesty discovered that Lady Mary's hair was gone, I overheard Your Majesty, and dispatched the trusty Step-and-Fetch-It to seek it on the mountainside. He did so, and found it clinging to the rock, and beneath it—the entrance to the Secret Cave!"

Patsey and Hickory, who had failed to understand a word of this explanation, gave themselves up to the enjoyment of the sweets. Polly, who had closely followed the story, albeit with the embellishments of her own imagination, made her eyes rounder than ever. A bland smile broke on Wan Lee's face, as, to the children's amazement, he quietly disengaged himself from the group and stepped before the leader.

"Melican man plenty foolee Melican chilern. No foolee China boy! China boy knowee you. *You* no Led Lofer. *You* no Pilate—you allee same tunnel-man—you Bob Johnson! You dressee up allee same as Led Lofer—but you Bob Johnson—allee same. My fader washee washee for you. You no payee him. You owee him folty dolla! Me blingee you billee. You no payee billee! You say, 'Chalkee up, John.' You say, 'Bimeby, John.' But me no catchee folty dolla!"

A roar of laughter followed, in which even the leader forgot himself enough to join. But the next moment springing to his feet he shouted, "Ho! ho! A traitor! Away with him to the deepest dungeon beneath the castle moat!"

Hickory and Patsey began to whimper, but Polly, albeit with a tremulous lip, stepped to the side of her little friend. "Don't you dare touch him," she said with a shake of unexpected determination of her curly head. "If you do, I'll tell my father, and he will slay you! All of you—there!"

"Your father! Then you are *not* the Queen!"

It was a sore struggle to Polly to abdicate her royal position; it was harder to do it with dignity. To evade the direct question she was obliged to abandon her defiant attitude. "If you please, sir," she said hurriedly, with an increasing color and no stops, "we're not always Pirates, you know, and Wan Lee is only our boy that brushes our shoes in the morning, and runs errands, and he doesn't mean anything bad, sir, and we'd like to take him back home with us."

"Enough," said the leader, changing his entire manner. "You shall go back together, and woe betide the miscreant who would prevent it! What say you, brothers? What shall be his fate who dares to separate our noble Queen from her faithful Chinese henchman?"

"He shall die!" roared the others, with beaming cheerfulness.

"And what say you—shall we see them home?"

"We will!" roared the others.

Before the children could fairly comprehend what had passed, they were again lifted into the truck and began to glide back into the tunnel they had left. But not again in darkness and silence; the entire group of Red Rovers accompanied them, illuminating the dark passage with the candles they had snatched from the walls. In a few moments they were at the entrance again. The great world lay beyond them once more with rocks and valleys in the light of the setting sun. Their past seemed like a dream.

But were they really awake now? They could not tell. They accepted everything. It was without surprise, therefore, that they felt themselves lifted on the shoulders of the men who were making quite a procession along the steep trail towards the settlement again. Polly noticed that at the mouth of the other tunnels they were greeted by men as if they were carrying tidings of great joy; that they stopped to rejoice together, and that in some mysterious manner their conductors had got their faces washed, and had become more like beings of the outer world. When they neared the settlement the excitement seemed to have become greater; people rushed out to shake hands with the men who were carrying them, and overpowered even the children with questions they could not understand. Only one sentence Polly could clearly remember as being the burden of all congratulations. "Struck the old lode at last!" With a faint consciousness that she knew something about it, she tried to assume a dignified attitude on the leader's shoulders, even while she was beginning to be heavy with sleep.

And then she remembered a crowd near her father's house, out of which her father came smiling pleasantly on her, but not interfering with her triumphal progress until the leader finally deposited her in her mother's lap in their own sitting room. And then she remembered being cross and declining to answer any questions, and shortly afterwards found herself comfortably in bed. Then she heard her mother say to her father:

"It really seems too ridiculous for anything, John; the idea of those grown men dressing themselves up to play with children."

"Ridiculous or not," said her father, "these grown men of the Excelsior mine have just struck the famous old lode of Red Mountain, which is as good as a fortune to everybody on the Ridge, and they are as wild as boys! And they say it never would have been found if Polly hadn't tumbled over the slide directly on top of the outcrop, and left the absurd wig of that wretched doll of hers to mark its site."

"And that," murmured Polly sleepily to her doll as she drew it closer to her breast, "is all that they know about it."

## LITTLE GOODY TWO-SHOES [1]

All the world must allow that Two-Shoes was not her real name. No; her father's name was Meanwell, and he was for many years a considerable farmer in the parish where Margery was born; but by the misfortunes which he met with in business, and the wicked persecutions of Sir

[1] From *The Renowned History of Little Goody Two-Shoes,* ascribed to Oliver Goldsmith.

Timothy Gripe, and an overgrown farmer called Graspall, he was effectually ruined. These men turned the farmer, his wife, Little Margery, and her brother out of doors, without any of the necessaries of life to support them.

Care and discontent shortened the days of Little Margery's father. He was seized with a violent fever, and died miserably. Margery's poor mother survived the loss of her husband but a few days, and died of a broken heart, leaving Margery and her little brother to the wide world. It would have excited your pity and done your heart good to have seen how fond these two little ones were of each other, and how, hand in hand, they trotted about.

They were both very ragged, and Tommy had no shoes, and Margery had but one. They had nothing, poor things, to support them but what they picked from the hedges or got from the poor people, and they lay every night in a barn. Their relatives took no notice of them; no, they were rich, and ashamed to own such a poor little ragged girl as Margery and such a dirty little curly-pated boy as Tommy. But such wicked folks, who love nothing but money and are proud and despise the poor, never come to any good end, as we shall see by and by.

Mr. Smith was a very worthy clergyman who lived in the parish where Little Margery and Tommy were born; and having a relative come to see him, he sent for these children. The gentleman ordered Little Margery a new pair of shoes, gave Mr. Smith some money to buy her clothes, and said he would take Tommy and make him a little sailor.

The parting between these two little children was very affecting. Tommy cried, and Margery cried, and they kissed each other a hundred times. At last Tommy wiped off her tears with the end of his jacket, and bade her cry no more, for he would come to her again when he returned from sea.

As soon as Little Margery got up the next morning, which was very early, she ran all round the village, crying for her brother; and after some time returned greatly distressed. However, at this instant, the shoemaker came in with the new shoes, for which she had been measured by the gentleman's order.

Nothing could have supported Little Margery under the affliction she was in for the loss of her brother but the pleasure she took in her two shoes. She ran out to Mrs. Smith as soon as they were put on, and, stroking down her ragged apron, cried out, "Two shoes, mamma, see, two shoes!"

And she so behaved to all the people she met, and by that means obtained the name of Goody Two-Shoes, though her playmates called her Old Goody Two-Shoes.

Little Margery was very happy in being with Mr. and Mrs. Smith, who were very charitable and good to her, and had agreed to bring her up with their family. But at last they were obliged to send her away, for the people who had ruined her father commanded them to do this, and could at any time have ruined them.

Little Margery saw how good and how wise Mr. Smith was, and concluded that this was owing to his great learning; therefore she wanted, of all things, to learn to read. For this purpose she used to meet the little boys and girls as they came from school, borrow their books, and sit down and read till they returned. By this means she soon got more learning than any of her playmates, and laid the following scheme for instructing those who were more ignorant than herself. She found that only the following letters were required to spell all the words in the world; but as some of these letters are large and some small, she with her knife cut out of several pieces of wood ten sets of each of these:

a b c d e f g h i j k l m n o p q r s t u
v w x y z

And six sets of these:

A B C D E F G H I J K L M N O P
Q R S T U V W X Y Z

And having got an old spelling book, she made her companions set up all the words they wanted to spell, and after that she taught them to compose sentences. You know what a sentence is, my dear. *I will be good* is a sentence; and is made up, as you see, of several words.

Every morning she used to go round to teach the children, with these rattle-traps in a basket. I once went her rounds with her. It was about seven o'clock in the morning when we set out on this important business, and the first house we came to was Farmer Wilson's. Here Margery stopped, and ran up to the door, tap, tap, tap.

"Who's there?"

"Only little Goody Two-Shoes," answered Margery, "come to teach Billy."

"Oh! little Goody," said Mrs. Wilson, with pleasure in her face, "I am glad to see you. Billy wants you sadly, for he has learned all his lesson."

Then out came the little boy. "How do, Doody Two-Shoes," said he, not able to speak plain. Yet this little boy had learned all his letters; for she threw down this alphabet mixed together thus:

b d f h k m o q s u w y z a c e g i l n p r t v x j

and he picked them up, called them by their right names, and put them all in order thus:

a b c d e f g h i j k l m n o p q r s t u v w x y z.

The next place we came to was Farmer Simpson's. "Bow, bow, bow," said the dog at the door.

"Sirrah," said his mistress, "why do you bark at Little Two-Shoes? Come in, Madge; here, Sally wants you sadly; she has learned all her lesson."

Then out came the little one.

"So, Madge!" says she.

"So, Sally!" answered the other. "Have you learned your lesson?"

"Yes, that's what I have," replied the little one in the country manner; and immediately taking the letters she set up these syllables:

ba be bi bo bu, ca ce ci co cu,
da de di do du, fa fe fi fo fu,

and gave them their exact sounds as she composed them.

After this, Little Two-Shoes taught her to spell words of one syllable, and she soon set up pear, plum, top, ball, pin, puss, dog, hog, fawn, buck, doe, lamb, sheep, ram, cow, bull, cock, hen, and many more.

The next place we came to was Gaffer Cook's cottage. Here a number of poor children were met to learn. They all came round Little Margery at once; and, having pulled out her letters, she asked the little boy next her what he had for dinner. He answered, "Bread." "Well, then," said she, "set the first letter."

He put up the letter *B,* to which the next added *r,* and the next *e,* the next *a,* the next *d* and it stood thus, *"Bread."*

"And what had you, Polly Comb, for your dinner?" "Apple-pie," answered the little girl: upon which the next in turn set up a great *A,* the two next a *p* each, and so on until the two words *Apple* and *pie* were united and stood thus, *"Apple-pie."*

The next had Potatoes, the next Beef and Turnips, which were spelt, with many others, until the game of spelling was finished. She then set them another task, and we went on.

The next place we came to was Farmer Thompson's, where there were a great many little ones waiting for her.

"So, little Mrs. Goody Two-Shoes," said one of them. "Where have you been so long?"

"I have been teaching," said she, "longer than I intended, and am afraid I am come too soon for you now."

"No, but indeed you are not," replied the other, "for I have got my lesson, and so has Sally Dawson, and so has Harry Wilson, and so have we all"; and they capered about as if they were overjoyed to see her.

"Why, then," said she, "you are all very good, and God Almighty will love you; so let us begin our lesson."

They all huddled round her, and though at the other place they were employed about words and syllables, here we had people of much greater understanding, who dealt only in sentences.

Little Margery then set them to compose the following:

LESSON FOR THE CONDUCT OF LIFE

He that will thrive
Must rise by five.

He that hath thriv'n
May lie till seven.

Truth may be blamed,
But cannot be shamed.

Tell me with whom you go,
And I'll tell what you do.

A friend in your need
Is a friend indeed.

They ne'er can be wise
Who good counsel despise.

As we were returning home, we saw a gentleman, who was very ill, sitting under a shady tree at the corner of his rookery. Though ill, he began to joke with Little Margery, and said laughing, "So, Goody Two-Shoes! They tell me you are a cunning little baggage; pray, can you tell me what I shall do to get well?"

"Yes," said she, "go to bed when your rooks do and get up with them in the morning; earn, as they do, every day what you eat, and eat and drink no more than you earn, and you will get health and keep it."

The gentleman, laughing, gave Margery sixpence, and told her she was a sensible hussy.

Mrs. Williams, who kept a college for instructing little gentlemen and ladies in the science of A, B, C, was at this time very old and infirm, and wanted to decline that important trust. This being told to Sir William Dove, who lived in the parish, he sent for Mrs. Williams, and desired she would examine Little Two-Shoes and see whether she was qualified for the office.

This was done, and Mrs. Williams made the following report in her favor; namely, that Little Margery was the best scholar, and had the best head and the best heart of any one she had examined. All the country had a great opinion of Mrs. Williams, and her words gave them also a great opinion of Mrs. Margery, for so we must now call her.

No sooner was Mrs. Margery settled in this office than she laid every possible scheme to promote the welfare and happiness of all her neighbors, and especially of the little ones, in whom she took great delight; and all those whose parents could not afford to pay for their education, she taught for nothing but the pleasure she had in their company; for you are to observe that they were very good, or were soon made so by her good management.

The school where she taught was that which was before kept by Mrs. Williams. The room was large, and as she knew that nature intended children should be always in action, she placed her different letters, or alphabets, all round the school, so that every one was obliged to get up to fetch a letter or spell a word when it came to his turn; which not only kept them in health but fixed the letters and points firmly in their minds.

She had the following assistants to help her, and I will tell you how she came by them. One day as she was going through the next village she met with some wicked boys who had got a young raven, which they were going to throw at; she wanted to get the poor creature out of their cruel hands, and therefore gave them a penny for him, and brought him home. She called his name Ralph, and a fine bird he was.

Some days after she had met with the raven, as she was walking in the fields she saw some naughty boys who had taken a pigeon and tied a string to its leg, in order to let it fly and draw it back again when they pleased; and by this means they tortured the poor animal with the hopes of liberty and repeated disappointment. This pigeon she also bought. He was a very pretty fellow, and she called him Tom.

Some time after this a poor lamb had lost its dam, and the farmer being about to kill it, she bought it of him and brought it home with her to play with the children and teach them when to go to bed; for it was a rule with the wise men of that age (and a very good one, let me tell you) to: *Rise with the lark and lie down with the lamb.*

This lamb she called Will, and a pretty fellow he was.

Soon after this a present was made to Mrs. Margery of a little dog, Jumper, and a pretty dog he was. Jumper, Jumper, Jumper! He was always in good humor and playing and jumping about, and therefore he was called Jumper. The place assigned for Jumper was that of keeping the door, so that he may be called the porter of the college, for he would let nobody go out or any one come in without the leave of his mistress.

But one day a dreadful accident happened in the school. It was on a Thursday morning, I very well remember, when the children having learned their lessons soon, she had given them leave to play, and they were all running about the school and diverting themselves with the birds and the lamb. At this time the dog, all of a sudden, laid hold of his mistress's apron and endeavored to pull her out of the school. She was at first surprised; however, she followed him to see what he intended.

No sooner had he led her into the garden than he ran back and pulled out one of the children in the same manner; upon which she ordered them all to leave the school immediately; and they had not been out five minutes before the top of the house fell in. What a miraculous deliverance was here! How gracious! How good was God Almighty, to save all these children from destruction, and to make use of such an instrument as a little sagacious animal to accomplish His divine will! I should have observed that as soon as they were all in the garden, the dog came leaping round them to express his joy, and when the house had fallen, laid himself down quietly by his mistress.

Some of the neighbors, who saw the school fall and who were in great pain for Margery and the little ones, soon spread the news through the village, and all the parents, terrified for their children, came crowding in abundance; they had, however, the satisfaction to find them all safe, and upon their knees, with their mistress, giving God thanks for their happy deliverance.

You are not to wonder, my dear reader, that this little dog should have more sense than you, or your father, or your grandfather.

Though God Almighty has made man the lord of creation, and endowed him with reason, yet in many respects He has been altogether as bountiful to other creatures of His forming. Some of the senses of other animals are more acute than ours, as we find by daily experience.

The downfall of the school was a great misfortune to Mrs. Margery; for she not only lost all her books, but was destitute of a place to teach in. Sir William Dove, being informed of this, ordered the house to be built at his own expense, and till that could be done, Farmer Grove was so kind as to let her have his large hall to teach in.

While at Mr. Grove's, which was in the heart of the village, she not only taught the children in the daytime, but the farmer's servants, and all the neighbors, to read and write in the evening. This gave not only Mr. Grove but all the neighbors a high opinion of her good sense and prudent behavior; and she was so much esteemed that most of the differences in the parish were left to her decision.

One gentleman in particular, I mean Sir Charles Jones, had conceived such a high opinion of her that he offered her a considerable sum to take care of his family and the education of his daughter, which, however, she refused. But this gentleman, sending for her afterwards when he had a dangerous fit of illness, she went and behaved so prudently in the family and so tenderly to him and his daughter that he would not permit her to leave his house, but soon after made her proposals of marriage. She was truly sensible of the honor he intended her, but, though poor, she would not consent to be made a lady until he had effectually provided for his daughter.

All things being settled and the day fixed, the neighbors came in crowds to see the wedding; for they were all glad that one who had been such a good little girl, and was become such a virtuous and good woman, was going to be made a lady. But just as the clergyman had opened his book, a gentleman richly dressed, ran into the church, and cried, "Stop! stop!"

This greatly alarmed the congregation, particularly the intended bride and bridegroom, whom he first accosted and desired to speak with them apart. After they had been talking some little time, the people were greatly surprised to see Sir Charles stand motionless and his bride cry and faint away in the stranger's arms. This seeming grief, however, was only a prelude to a flood of joy which immediately succeeded; for you must know, gentle reader, that this gentleman, so richly dressed and bedizened with lace, was that identical little boy whom you before saw in the sailor's habit; in short, it was Tom Two-Shoes, Mrs. Margery's brother, who had just come from beyond the sea, where he had made a large fortune. Hearing, as soon as he landed, of his sister's intended wedding, he had ridden in haste to see that a proper settlement was made on her; which he thought she was now entitled to, as he himself was both able and willing to give her an ample fortune. They soon returned to their places and were married in tears, but they were tears of joy.

## THE BEARS OF BLUE RIVER [1]

*Charles Major*

Away back in the "eighteen-twenties" when Indiana was a baby state, and great forests of tall trees and tangled underbrush darkened what are now her bright plains and sunny hills, there stood upon the bank of Big Blue River, a cozy log cabin of two rooms—one front and one back.

Immediately at the water's edge was a steep slope of ten or twelve feet. Back of the house, mile upon mile, stretched the deep dark forest, inhabited by deer and bears, wolves and wildcats, squirrels and birds, without number.

In the river the fish were so numerous that they seemed to beg the boys to catch them, and to take them out of their crowded quarters.

South of the house stood a log barn, with room in it for three horses and two cows; and enclosing this barn, together with a piece of ground, was a palisade fence, eight or ten feet high, made by driving poles into the ground close together. In this enclosure the farmer kept his stock, consisting of a few sheep and cattle, and here also the chickens, geese, and ducks were driven at nightfall to save them from "varmints," as all prowling animals were called by the settlers.

The man who had built this log hut, and who lived in it and owned the adjoining land at the time of which I write, bore the name of Brent, and his son Balser was the hero of the bear story which I am about to tell you.

Mr. Brent and his young wife had moved to the Blue River settlement from North Carolina, when young Balser was a little boy five or six years of age.

At the time when my story opens Little Balser, as he was called to distinguish him from his father, was about thirteen years of age, and was the happy possessor of a younger brother, Jim, aged nine, and a little sister one year old, of whom he was very proud indeed.

[1] From Charles Major, *The Bears of Blue River.*

On the south side of the front room of the log house was a large fireplace. The chimney was built of sticks, thickly covered with clay. The fireplace was almost as large as a small room in one of our modern houses, and was broad and deep enough to take in backlogs which were so large and heavy that they could not be lifted, but were drawn in at the door and rolled over the floor to the fireplace.

The settlers had no stoves, but did their cooking in round pots called Dutch ovens. They roasted their meats on a spit or steel bar like the ramrod of a gun. The spit was kept turning before the fire, presenting first one side of the meat and then the other, until it was thoroughly cooked. Turning the spit was the children's work.

The daily food of the family all came from the farm, the forest, or the creek. Their sugar was obtained from the sap of the sugar-trees; their meat was supplied in the greatest abundance by a few hogs, and by the inexhaustible game of which the forests were full. In the woods were found deer just for the shooting; and squirrels, rabbits, wild turkeys, pheasants, and quails, so numerous that a few hours' hunting would supply the table for days. The fish in the river, as I told you, fairly longed to be caught.

One day Mrs. Brent took down the dinner horn and blew upon it two strong blasts. This was a signal that Little Balser, who was helping his father down in the clearing, should come to the house. Balser was glad enough to drop his hoe and to run home. When he reached the house his mother said:

"Balser, go up to the drift in the river and catch a mess of fish for dinner. Your father is tired of deer meat three times a day, and I know he would like a nice dish of fried redeyes at noon."

"All right, mother," said Balser. And he immediately took down his fishing pole and line, and got the spade to dig bait. When he had collected a small gourdful of angleworms, his mother called to him:

"You had better take a gun. You may meet a bear; your father loaded the gun this morning, and you must be careful in handling it."

Balser took the gun, which was a heavy rifle considerably longer than himself, and started up the river toward the drift, about a quarter of a mile away.

There had been rain during the night and the ground near the drift was soft.

Here, Little Balser noticed fresh bear tracks, and his breath began to come quickly. You may be sure he peered closely into every dark thicket, and looked behind all the large trees and logs, and had his eyes wide open lest perchance, "Mr. Bear" should step out and surprise him with an affectionate hug, and thereby put an end to Little Balser forever.

So he walked on cautiously, and, if the truth must be told, somewhat fearfully, until he reached the drift.

Balser was only a boy, yet the stern necessities of a settler's life had compelled his father to teach him the use of a gun; and although Balser had never killed a bear, he had shot several deer, and upon one occasion had killed a wildcat, "almost as big as a cow," he said.

I have no doubt the wildcat seemed "almost as big as a cow" to Balser when he killed it, for it must have frightened him, as wildcats were sometimes dangerous animals for children to encounter. Although Balser had never met a bear face to face and alone, yet he felt, and many a time had said, that there wasn't a bear in the world big enough to frighten him, if he but had his gun.

He had often imagined and minutely detailed to his parents and little brother just what he would do if he should meet a bear. He would wait calmly until his bearship should come within a few yards of him, and then he would slowly lift his gun. Bang! and Mr. Bear would be dead with a bullet in his heart.

But when he saw the fresh bear tracks, and began to realize that he would probably have an opportunity to put his theories about bear killing into practice, he began to wonder if, after all, he would become frightened and miss his aim. Then he thought of how the bear, in that case, would be calm and deliberate, and would put his theories into practice by walking very politely up to him, and making a very satisfactory dinner of a certain boy whom he could name. But as he walked on and no bear appeared, his courage grew stronger as the prospect of meeting the enemy grew less, and he again began saying to himself that no bear could frighten him, because he had his gun and he could and would kill it.

So Balser reached the drift; and having looked carefully about him, leaned his gun against a tree, unwound his fishing line from the pole, and walked out to the end of a log which extended into the river some twenty or thirty feet.

Here he threw in his line, and soon was so busily engaged drawing out sunfish and redeyes, and now and then a bass which was hungry enough to bite at a worm, that all thought of the bear went out of his mind.

After he had caught enough fish for a sumptuous dinner he thought of going home, and as he turned toward the shore, imagine, if you can, his consternation when he saw upon the bank, quietly watching him, a huge black bear.

If the wildcat had seemed as large as a cow to Balser, of what size do you suppose that bear appeared? A cow? An elephant, surely, was small compared with the huge black fellow standing upon the bank. It is true Balser had never seen an elephant, but his father had, and so had his friend Tom Fox, who lived down the river; and they all agreed that an elephant was "purty nigh as big as all outdoors."

The bear had a peculiar, determined expression about him that seemed to say:

"That boy can't get away; he's out on the log where the water is deep, and if he jumps into the river I can easily jump in after him and catch him before he can swim a dozen strokes. He'll have to come off the log in a short time, and then I'll proceed to devour him."

About the same train of thought had also been rapidly passing through Balser's mind. His gun was on the bank where he had left it, and in order to reach it he would have to pass the bear. He dared not jump into the water, for any attempt to escape on his part would bring the bear upon him instantly. He was very much frightened, but, after all, he was a cool-headed fellow for his age. So he concluded not to press matters, as the bear did not seem inclined to do so; so long as the bear remained watching him on the bank, he would stay on the log where he was, and allow the enemy to eye him to his heart's content.

There they stood, the boy and the bear, each eyeing the other as though they were the best of friends, and would like to eat each other, which, in fact, was literally true.

Time sped very slowly for one of them, you may be sure; and it seemed to Balser that he had been standing almost an age in the middle of Blue River on that wretched shaking log, when he heard his mother's dinner horn, reminding him that it was time to go home.

Balser quite agreed with his mother and gladly would have gone, as I need not tell you; but there stood the bear, patient, determined, and fierce; and Little Balser soon was convinced in his mind that his time had come to die.

He hoped that when his father should go home to dinner and find him still absent, he would come up the river in search of him, and frighten away the bear. Hardly had this hope sprung up in his mind, when it seemed that the same thought had also occurred to the bear, for he began to move down toward the shore end of the log upon which Balser was standing.

Slowly came the bear until he reached the end of the log, which for a moment he examined suspiciously, and then, to Balser's great alarm, cautiously stepped out upon it and began to walk toward him.

Balser thought of the folks at home, and, above all, of his baby sister; and when he felt that he would never see them again, and that they would in all probability never know of his fate, he began to grow heavy-hearted and was almost paralyzed with fear.

On came the bear, putting one great paw in front of the other, and watching Balser intently with his little black eyes. His tongue hung out, and his great red mouth was open to its widest, showing the sharp, long, glittering teeth that would soon be feasting on a first-class boy dinner.

When the bear got within a few feet of Balser—so close he could almost feel the animal's hot breath as it slowly approached—the boy grew desperate with fear, and struck at the bear with the only weapon he had—his string of fish.

Now, bears love fish and blackberries above all other food, so when Balser's string of fish struck the bear in the mouth, he grabbed at them, and in doing so lost his foothold on the slippery log and fell into the water with a great splash and plunge.

This was Balser's chance for life, so he flung the fish to the bear, and ran for the bank with a speed worthy of the cause.

When he reached the bank his self-confidence returned, and he remembered all the things he had said he would do if he should meet a bear.

The bear had caught the fish, and again had climbed upon the log, where he was deliberately devouring them.

This was Little Balser's chance for death—to the bear. Quickly snatching up the gun, he rested it in the fork of a small tree nearby, took deliberate aim at the bear, which was not five yards away, and shot him through the heart. The bear dropped into the water dead, and floated downstream a little way, where he lodged at a ripple a short distance below.

Balser, after he had killed the bear, became more frightened than he had been at any time during the adventure and ran home. That afternoon his father went to the scene of battle and took the bear out of the water. It was very fat and large, and weighed, so Mr. Brent said, over six hundred pounds.

Balser was firmly of the opinion that he himself was also very fat and large, and weighed at least as much as the bear. He was certainly entitled to feel "big," for he had got himself out of an ugly scrape in a cool-headed manner, and had achieved a victory of which a man might have been proud.

The news of Balser's adventure soon spread among the neighbors and he became quite a hero; for the bear he had killed was one of the largest that had ever been seen in that neighborhood, and, besides the gallons of rich bear oil it yielded, there were three or four hundred pounds of bear meat; and no other food is more strengthening for winter diet.

There was also the soft, furry skin, which Balser's mother tanned, and with it made a coverlid for Balser's bed, under which he and his little brother lay many a cold night, cozy and "snug as a bug in a rug."

## HANS BRINKER AND HIS SISTER [1]

*Mary Mapes Dodge*

At noon our young friends poured forth from the schoolhouse intent upon having an hour's practicing upon the canal.

They had skated but a few moments when Carl Schummel said mockingly to Hilda:

"There's a pretty pair just coming upon the ice! The little ragpickers! Their skates must have been a present from the king direct."

"They are patient creatures," said Hilda, gently. "It must have been hard to learn to skate upon such queer affairs. They are very poor peasants, you see. The boy has probably made the skates himself."

Carl was somewhat abashed.

"Patient they may be, but, as for skating, they start off pretty well only to finish with

[1] From Mary Mapes Dodge, *Hans Brinker; or, The Silver Skates.*

a jerk. They could move well to your new *staccato* piece I think."

Hilda laughed pleasantly and left him. After joining a small detachment of the racers, and sailing past every one of them, she halted beside Gretel who, with eager eyes, had been watching the sport.

"What is your name, little girl?"

"Gretel, my lady," answered the child, somewhat awed by Hilda's rank, though they were nearly of the same age, "and my brother is called Hans."

"Hans is a stout fellow," said Hilda, cheerily, "and seems to have a warm stove somewhere within him, but you look cold. You should wear more clothing, little one."

Gretel, who had nothing else to wear, tried to laugh as she answered:

"I am not so very little. I am past twelve years old."

"Oh, I beg your pardon. You see I am nearly fourteen, and so large for my age that other girls seem small to me, but that is nothing. Perhaps you will shoot up far above me yet; not unless you dress more warmly though, for shivering girls never grow."

Hans flushed as he saw tears rising in Gretel's eyes.

"My sister has not complained of the cold; but this is bitter weather they say—" and he looked sadly upon Gretel.

"It is nothing," said Gretel, "I am often warm—too warm when I am skating. You are good, jufvrouw, to think of it."

"No, no," answered Hilda, quite angry at herself. "I am careless, cruel; but I meant no harm. I wanted to ask you—I mean—if—" and here Hilda, coming to the point of her errand, faltered before the poorly clad but noble-looking children she wished to serve.

"What is it, young lady?" exclaimed Hans eagerly. "If there is any service I can do? any—"

"Oh! no, no," laughed Hilda, shaking off her embarrassment, "I only wished to speak to you about the grand race. Why do you not join it? You both can skate well, and the ranks are free. Anyone may enter for the prize."

Gretel looked wistfully at Hans, who tugging at his cap, answered respectfully:

"Ah, jufvrouw, even if we could enter, we could skate only a few strokes with the rest. Our skates are hard wood, you see," holding up the sole of his foot, "but they soon become damp, and then they stick and trip us."

Gretel's eyes twinkled with fun as she thought of Hans' mishap in the morning, but she blushed as she faltered out timidly:

"Oh no, we can't join; but may we be there, my lady, on the great day to look on?"

"Certainly," answered Hilda, looking kindly into the two earnest faces, and wishing from her heart that she had not spent so much of her monthly allowance for lace and finery. She had but eight kwartjes left, and they would buy but one pair of skates, at the furthest.

Looking down with a sigh at the two pair of feet so very different in size, she asked:

"Which of you is the better skater?"

"Gretel," replied Hans, promptly.

"Hans," answered Gretel, in the same breath. Hilda smiled.

"I cannot buy you each a pair of skates, or even one good pair; but here are eight kwartjes. Decide between you which stands the best chance of winning the race, and buy the skates accordingly. I wish I had enough to buy better ones—good-by!" and, with a nod and a smile, Hilda, after handing the money to the electrified Hans, glided swiftly away to rejoin her companions.

"Jufvrouw! Jufvrouw van Gleck!" called Hans in a loud tone, stumbling after her as well as he could, for one of his skate strings was untied.

Hilda turned, and with one hand raised to shield her eyes from the sun, seemed to him to be floating through the air, nearer and nearer.

"We cannot take this money," panted Hans, "though we know your goodness in giving it."

"Why not indeed?" asked Hilda flushing.

"Because," replied Hans, bowing like a clown, but looking with the eye of a prince at the queenly girl, "we have not earned it."

Hilda was quick-witted. She had noticed a pretty wooden chain upon Gretel's neck.

"Carve me a chain, Hans, like the one your sister wears."

"That I will, lady, with all my heart; we have white-wood in the house, fine as ivory; you shall have one tomorrow," and Hans hastily tried to return the money.

"No, no," said Hilda, decidedly. "That sum will be but a poor price for the chain," and off she darted, outstripping the fleetest among the skaters.

Hans sent a long, bewildered gaze after her; it was useless, he felt, to make any further resistance.

"It is right," he muttered, half to himself, half to his faithful shadow, Gretel. "I must work hard every minute, and sit up half the night if the mother will let me burn a candle; but the chain shall be finished. We may keep the money, Gretel."

"What a good little lady!" cried Gretel, clapping her hands with delight. "Oh! Hans, was it for nothing the stork settled on our roof last summer? Do you remember how the mother said it would bring us luck, and how she cried when Janzoon Kolp shot him? And she said it would bring him trouble. But the luck has come to us at last! Now, Hans, if mother sends us to town tomorrow you can buy the skates in the market place."

Hans shook his head. "The young lady would have given us the money to buy skates; but if I earn it, Gretel, it shall be spent for wool. You must have a warm jacket."

"Oh!" cried Gretel, in real dismay, "not buy the skates! Why I am not often cold! Mother says the blood runs up and down in poor children's veins humming 'I must keep 'em warm! I must keep 'em warm.' "

"Oh, Hans," she continued with something like a sob, "don't say you won't buy the skates; it makes me feel just like crying—besides, I want to be cold—I mean I'm real, awful warm—so now!"

Hans looked up hurriedly. He had a true Dutch horror of tears, or emotion of any kind, and, most of all, he dreaded to see his sister's blue eyes overflowing.

"Now mind," cried Gretel, seeing her advantage, "I'll feel awful if you give up the skates. I don't want them. I'm not such a stingy as that; but I want you to have them, and then when I get bigger they'll do for me—oh-h—count the pieces, Hans. Did ever you see so many!"

Hans turned the money thoughtfully in his palm. Never in all his life had he longed so intensely for a pair of skates, for he had known of the race and had, boylike, fairly ached for a chance to test his powers with the other children. He felt confident that with a good pair of steel runners, he could readily distance most of the boys on the canal. Then, too, Gretel's argument was so plausible. On the other hand, he knew that she, with her strong but lithe little frame, needed but a week's practice on good runners, to make her a better skater than Rychie Korbes or even Katrinka Flack. As soon as this last thought flashed upon him his resolve was made. If Gretel would not have the jacket, she should have the skates.

"No, Gretel," he answered at last, "I can wait. Some day I may have money enough saved to buy a fine pair. You shall have these."

Gretel's eyes sparkled; but in another instant she insisted, rather faintly:

"The young lady gave the money to you, Hans. I'd be real bad to take it."

Hans shook his head, resolutely, as he trudged on, causing his sister to half skip and half walk in her effort to keep beside him; by this time they had taken off their wooden "rockers," and were hastening home to tell their mother the good news.

"Oh! I know!" cried Gretel, in a sprightly tone. "You can do this. You can get a pair a little too small for you, and too big for me, and we can take turns and use them. Won't that be fine?" and Gretel clapped her hands again.

Poor Hans! This was a strong temptation, but he pushed it away from him, brave-hearted fellow that he was.

"Nonsense, Gretel. You could never get on with a big pair. You stumbled about with these, like a blind chicken, before I curved off the ends. No, you must have a pair to fit exactly, and you must practice every chance you can get, until the 20th comes. My little Gretel shall win the silver skates."

Gretel could not help laughing with delight at the very idea.

"Hans! Gretel!" called out a familiar voice.

"Coming, mother!" and they hastened toward the cottage, Hans still shaking the pieces of silver in his hand.

On the following day, there was not a prouder nor a happier boy in all Holland than Hans Brinker as he watched his sister, with many a dexterous sweep, flying in and out among the skaters who at sundown thronged the canal. A warm jacket had been given her by the kind-hearted Hilda, and the burst-out shoes had been cobbled into decency by Dame Brinker. As the little creature darted backward and forward, flushed with enjoyment, and quite unconscious of the many wondering glances bent upon her, suddenly earth turned into Fairyland, while "Hans, dear, good Hans!" echoed itself over and over again in her grateful heart.

"By den donder!" exclaimed Peter van Holp to Carl Schummel, "but that little one in the red jacket and patched petticoat skates well. Gunst! she has toes on her heels, and eyes in the back of her head! See her! It will be a joke if she gets in the race and beats Katrinka Flack, after all."

"Hush! not so loud!" returned Carl, rather sneeringly. "That little lady in rags is the special pet of Hilda van Gleck. Those shining skates are her gift, if I make no mistake."

"So! so!" exclaimed Peter, with a radiant smile, for Hilda was his best friend. "She has been at her good work there, too!" And Mynheer van Holp, after cutting a double 8 on the ice, to say nothing of a huge P, then a jump, and an H, glided onward until he found himself beside Hilda.

Hand in hand, they skated together, laughingly at first, then staidly talking in a low tone.

Strange to say, Peter van Holp soon arrived at a sudden conviction that his little sister needed a wooden chain just like Hilda's.

Two days afterward, on St. Nicholas' Eve, Hans, having burned three candle ends, and cut his thumb into the bargain, stood in the market place at Amsterdam, buying another pair of skates.

## DAVID AND GOLIATH

THE BIBLE: I SAMUEL 17

Now the Philistines gathered together their armies to battle. And Saul and the men of Israel were gathered together, and pitched by the valley of Elah, and set the battle in array against the Philistines.

And the Philistines stood on a mountain on the one side, and Israel stood on a mountain on the other side; and there was a valley betwen them.

And there went out a champion out of the camp of the Philistines, named Goliath, of Gath, whose height was six cubits and a span.

And he had a helmet of brass upon his head, and he was armed with a coat of mail; and the weight of the coat was five thousand shekels of brass.

And he had greaves of brass upon his legs, and a target of brass between his shoulders.

And the staff of his spear was like a weaver's beam; and his spear's head weighed six hundred shekels of iron; and one bearing a shield went before him.

And he stood and cried unto the armies of Israel, and said unto them, "Why are ye come out to set your battle in array? Am not I a Philistine, and ye servants to Saul?

Choose you a man for you, and let him come down to me.

"If he be able to fight with me, and to kill me, then will we be your servants; but if I prevail against him, and kill him, then shall ye be our servants, and serve us."

And the Philistine said, "I defy the armies of Israel this day; give me a man, that we may fight together."

When Saul and all Israel heard those words of the Philistine, they were dismayed and greatly afraid.

Now the three eldest sons of Jesse went and followed Saul to the battle.

And Jesse said unto David, his son, "Take now for thy brethren an ephah of this parched corn, and these ten loaves, and run to the camp to thy brethren.

"And carry these ten cheeses unto the captain of their thousand, and look how thy brethren fare, and take their pledge."

And David rose up early in the morning, and left the sheep with a keeper, and took, and went, as Jesse had commanded him; and he came to the trench, as the host was going forth to the fight and shouted for the battle.

For Israel and the Philistines had put the battle in array, army against army.

And David left his bundle in the hand of the keeper of the baggage, and ran into the army, and came and saluted his brethren.

And as he talked with them, behold, there came up the champion, the Philistine of Gath, Goliath by name, out of the armies of the Philistines, and spake according to the same words; and David heard them.

And all the men of Israel, when they saw the man, fled from him, and were sore afraid.

And the men of Israel said, "Have ye seen this man that is come up? Surely to defy Israel is he come up; and it shall be, that the man who killeth him, the king will enrich him with great riches, and will give him his daughter, and make his father's house free in Israel."

And David spake to the men that stood by him, saying, "What shall be done to the man that killeth this Philistine, and taketh away the reproach from Israel? For who is this Philistine, that he should defy the armies of the living God?"

And the people answered him after this manner, saying, "So shall it be done to the man that killeth him."

And Eliab, his eldest brother, heard when he spake unto the man; and Eliab's anger was kindled against David, and he said, "Why camest thou down hither? And with whom hast thou left those few sheep in the wilderness? I know thy pride, and the naughtiness of thine heart; for thou art come down that thou mightest see the battle."

And David said, "What have I now done? Is there not a cause?"

And he turned from him toward another, and spake after the same manner; and the people answered him again after the former manner.

And when the words were heard which David spake, they rehearsed them before Saul; and he sent for him.

And David said to Saul, "Let no man's heart fail because of him; thy servant will go and fight with this Philistine."

And Saul said to David, "Thou art not able to go against this Philistine to fight with him; for thou art but a youth, and he a man of war from his youth."

And David said unto Saul, "Thy servant kept his father's sheep, and there came a lion, and a bear, and took a lamb out of the flock;

"And I went out after him, and smote him, and delivered it out of his mouth; and when he arose against me, I caught him by his beard, and smote him, and slew him.

"Thy servant slew both the lion and the bear; and this Philistine shall be as one of them, seeing he hath defied the armies of the living God."

David said moreover, "The Lord that delivered me out of the paw of the lion, and out of the paw of the bear, he will deliver me out of the hand of this Philistine."

And Saul said unto David, "Go, and the Lord be with thee."

And Saul armed David with his armor, and he put a helmet of brass upon his head; also he armed him with a coat of mail. And David girded his sword upon his armor, and he assayed to go; for he had not proved it.

And David said unto Saul, "I cannot go with these; for I have not proven them." And David put them off him.

And he took his staff in his hand, and chose him five smooth stones out of the brook, and put them in a shepherd's bag which he had, even in a scrip; and his sling was in his hand; and he drew near to the Philistine.

And the Philistine came on and drew near unto David; and the man that bare the shield went before him.

And when the Philistine looked about, and saw David, he disdained him; for he was but a youth, and ruddy, and of a fair countenance.

And the Philistine said unto David, "Am I a dog, that thou comest to me with staves?" And the Philistine cursed David by his gods.

And the Philistine said to David, "Come to me, and I will give thy flesh unto the fowls of the air, and to the beasts of the field."

Then said David to the Philistine,

"Thou comest to me with a sword, and with a spear, and with a shield.
But I come to thee in the name of the Lord of hosts,
The God of the armies of Israel, whom thou hast defied.

"This day will the Lord deliver thee into mine hand;
And I will smite thee, and take thine head from thee;
And I will give the carcasses of the hosts of the Philistines this day
Unto the fowls of the air, and to the wild beasts of the earth;
That all the earth may know that there is a God in Israel.

"And all this assembly shall know
That the Lord saveth not with sword and spear;
For the battle is the Lord's,
And he will give you into our hands."

And it came to pass, when the Philistine arose, and came and drew nigh to meet David, that David hasted, and ran toward the army to meet the Philistine.

And David put his hand in his bag, and took thence a stone, and slung it, and smote the Philistine in his forehead, that the stone sunk into his forehead; and he fell upon his face to the earth.

So David prevailed over the Philistine with a sling and with a stone, and smote the Philistine, and slew him; but there was no sword in the hand of David.

Therefore David ran, and stood upon the Philistine, and took *his* sword, and drew it out of the sheath thereof, and slew him, and cut off his head therewith. And when the Philistines saw their champion was dead, they fled.

And the men of Israel and of Judah arose, and shouted, and pursued the Philistines to the gates of Ekron.

And the children of Israel returned from chasing after the Philistines, and they spoiled their tents.

And when Saul saw David go forth against the Philistine, he said unto Abner, the captain of the host, "Abner, whose son is this youth?"

And Abner said, "As thy soul liveth, O king, I cannot tell."

And the king said, "Inquire thou whose son the stripling is."

And as David returned from the slaughter of the Philistine, Abner took him, and brought him before Saul with the head of the Philistine in his hand.

And Saul said to him, "Whose son art thou, thou young man?"

And David answered, "I am the son of thy servant Jesse, the Bethlehemite."

## THE FAR-DISTANT OXUS[1]

*Katherine Hull* and *Pamela Whitlock*

"The ponies!" shouted Bridget, pulling back the stable door and gazing with adoring eyes at the long line of flickering tails.

"May we choose our own?" asked Frances, the youngest of the family, who was striding along amicably with Mr. Fradd, the farmer.

"Certainly," he assured her. "I arranged with your mother that you should ride whenever you like, so choose the ponies that you want, because I hire out the others."

Anthony, the only boy, younger than Bridget and older than Frances, who had been helping Mrs. Fradd to carry their suitcases up the rickety farm staircase to their rooms, now ran across the yard to the stable.

"How many ponies have you got, Mr. Fradd?" he asked.

"Ten here in the stable, but out on the moor I have a herd wandering about somewhere."

"A whole herd?"

"How marvelous!"

Bridget was already in the first stall, patting the pony and fondling his matted mane. All the way down in the train she had been thinking of this moment. She had imagined a hundred times the fresh smell of clean straw and the warm feel of a pony's neck under her hand. Now she was actually here, her imaginings were happening at this very moment, Frances ran down the stable, patting each pony and trying to choose the one she would like for the holidays. In the last stall a tiny shaggy Dartmoor butted her with his head, whinnying sorrowfully when she started to go away.

"You silly old thing," she said, "I'd like to have you, but you're much too small."

She handed him a lump of sugar and called Mr. Fradd. The farmer hobbled up. He was a small, rather bent man, with a face that shone when it caught the light. His short bowlegs reminded the children of Jeremy Fisher.

"What is this pony's name?" she asked. "I think he's awfully sweet."

"That little one? He's Toby. Nearly every one who sees him thinks the same, but take him out with the hounds, and the devil himself wouldn't stop that bag of fireworks."

"Does he bolt?"

"The moment he hears hound music, right away over the hills, on and on till he drops exhausted. Then the rider has to walk home with him, thirty miles or so."

"Little beast," said Frances, and moved on to the next stall, where Anthony was examining a dark-brown Exmoor with a trailing tail and a shaggy mane that fell on both sides of his neck.

"That's Timothy," said Mr. Fradd, "and a fine little pony, too; one of the neatest jumpers I've seen."

Anthony looked up eagerly. He had been privately making friends with Timothy, and, now that Mr. Fradd praised the pony, he was determined to choose him as his own.

"May we try them in the meadow?" he asked; "the one up behind the stables?"

"Why, certainly. The bridles are here and the saddles down in the harness room."

Anthony assured the farmer that he could ride bareback, and started to bridle Timothy. His was an ordinary snaffle bridle and the well-kept leather was soft and pliable.

"Always put your bridle away clean," instructed the farmer, "then it will be clean when you next need it."

Bridget was torn between the first pony she had seen, Tinker, and another, Talisman, a slightly larger dark chestnut. Mr. Fradd decided her choice by informing her that Talisman had once led the herd on the Porlock hills, and could gallop like "the wind on Dunkery Beacon." As Bridget had a passion for speed, she did not hesi-

[1] From Katherine Hull and Pamela Whitlock, *The Far-Distant Oxus*. The authors were fifteen and sixteen years old when they wrote this book.

tate. Talisman's bridle was fitted with what Mr. Fradd called "an Exmoor bit." Actually it was a double bit, snaffle, and curb.

"You'll find him fresh at first," he warned her, "but he's well mannered and very willing."

"I love fresh ponies," Bridget assured him, now ecstatically happy with the bridle in her hands and her arm over Talisman's chestnut neck.

Frances took a long time to choose, while the others waited, making helpful suggestions.

"That black one looks a beautiful mover," said Bridget.

"Try the grey, or is too big?" suggested Anthony.

"That little dun there, that's Treacle; he once won a pony race over Dunster way," put in the farmer; "good little goer he is, to be sure."

That seemed to clinch the matter for the moment anyway, because Frances began to bridle Treacle, though all the time she assured the black and grey by promising to try them afterwards.

The three led their ponies to the meadow, where Mr. Fradd held open the gate.

"You haven't got long," he warned as they passed through; "supper at seven-fifteen, and my wife has no patience with folk who are late for meals."

They promised to hurry and, urging their ponies into a canter, for trotting bareback is no joke, raced up the field.

Bridget dug her knees into Talisman's well-groomed flanks. She could see his muscles moving in his shoulders so that the light slid up and down on them, and was filled with the joy of being able to ride this animal, whose strength must equal at least ten times hers.

At the top of the meadow they paused. Frances, who had almost lost her balance in the last mad rush, hoisted herself into the middle of Treacle's back, and sat up panting. Anthony leant forward to pat Timothy's neck. "Wonderful pony," he whispered.

Behind them the whitewashed farmhouse and outbuildings lay huddled in a wide hollow, with a lane leading away to join the high road beyond the hills. In front another led down to the stream where the ponies and other animals were watered. In this valley a tiny brook wandered on, and round it clustered wide fans of stunted oaks and hawthorns. From their high position they could look across the valley to a ridge of moor, and beyond that to another and another, stretching like a great purple eiderdown strewed with grey books.

The late August sun that had blazed over the rugged moors all day, now slid slowly behind the highest peak of the range which towered out of the heathered desert to the rear of Cloud Farm. Bridget turned Talisman downhill.

"Come on," she said, "we shall be late for supper."

Bridget, Frances, and Anthony sat round the long deal table in the farm kitchen with Mr. and Mrs. Fradd. The meal of poached eggs and stewed plums was nearly over, and now Mr. Fradd was helping them to large hunks of cheese.

This farm kitchen was almost exactly similar to many others in cottages all over Exmoor. It was a low room with white, clean-looking walls, and a wide, open fireplace containing the cooking range. On the mantelpiece and lofty dresser that dominated one corner of the room was arranged a varied collection of old pewter pots and Devon crockery.

"Are there many children who live round here?" Bridget asked suddenly, having finished a large mouthful of biscuit and cheese. Mr. Fradd scratched his head.

"I wouldn't say that there are many," he said, "but there's some."

"The Clevertons in the large house on the opposite side of the valley," put in his wife.

"Yes, and a few others in the town you arrived at. Also there's a boy with a black pony that I've seen round here once or twice, but I couldn't say where he lives."

The farmer looked out of the window

and, seeing that it was dusk on the hills, pushed back his chair, making a scraping sound on the old tiles.

"I must go and shut up the chickens," he said. "These long evenings they won't go into their houses till the light goes."

"May we come and help you?" asked Frances.

"There is nothing to do save shutting the doors of the fowl-houses and rounding up a few odd ducks that may not have gone in, but you may come if you like."

Mr. Fradd led the children across the yard. It was much lighter outside than in the farm kitchen, and the air was warm. Rusty, the sheepdog, bounded up to his master and barked with delight. He had been lying outside the kitchen door on a stone slab, basking in the last rays of sunshine, waiting for the farmer to set out on his nightly round.

"Where does he sleep?" Frances asked.

"Always out here. He has done it for four years now."

"Whatever the weather?" asked Anthony.

"Not snow nor sleet will move him from outside the kitchen door, though to be sure the barn is always left open for him."

"Faithful dog!" Bridget said.

They wandered down the lane to the valley and turned off into a meadow full of chicken-houses. There were no birds about, for they had all retired with the setting sun. As they shut each door the inhabitants fluttered and squawked with fright, in spite of the fact that this same process had been gone through every day of their lives.

"That's where chickens are so silly," Mr. Fradd explained; "no fox would rob a hen-house if it wasn't for the welcoming flutter that the fowls give him. If they'd all kept quiet, he'd slink away afraid."

Anthony looked inside the next house before he bolted the door. The hens were huddled together in groups on their perches, their heads raised in alarm. A few fluttered on to the ground and tried to escape through his feet, but he slammed the door in their faces. Looking through the window, he saw them peck once or twice moodily at the floor and then flutter lazily back to the perches.

Frances found an egg in one of the houses, laid after they had been collected at tea time. She had been looking hopefully in all the nesting boxes, but up to now they had contained nothing but a few handfuls of hay and a sprinkling of rotten feathers. Now she had discovered this warm, smooth, brown egg. It was like finding a pearl in an oyster.

"I shall have it for breakfast," she announced as they stumbled back up the lane.

"Not if you put it in your pocket," warned Mr. Fradd, who had seen what she was trying to do.

Frances laughed.

The ducks were routed out of one corner of the yard, where they had chosen to sleep among the muddy straw, and with many pitiful quacks shooed to their house.

"May we say good night to the ponies?" said Bridget.

"Why, yes," answered Mr. Fradd, slightly puzzled by this strange request. "But don't be long; the missus will be waiting for you."

The three children disappeared into the stable. It was dark, but Mr. Fradd lit a lantern and hung it in the doorway, so that they could see to move about. Then he leant against the wall to watch and wait for them.

The flickering rays of the lantern flashed on Bridget's long legs and arms as she climbed into the stall. Her straight black hair fell forward like a curtain on each side of her head, but when she shook it back her face showed surprisingly white.

"She'll soon get tanned up here," thought the old man to himself as he felt for his pipe.

"Good night, pony," said Frances to Treacle; "sleep well and be fresh tomorrow."

Then she stumped down the stable to Mr. Fradd, her thick brogues clattering on the stone floor. He was struck by the likeness between the two sisters. Frances was a smaller reproduction of Bridget save for the brown in her hair and the color in her cheeks.

Anthony gave Timothy a lump of sugar and joined the others at the door.

"We must hurry in," said Bridget. "Good night, Mr. Fradd, and thank you very much."

"Good night, miss," said the farmer, and he wandered off, followed by the faithful Rusty, to continue his round of the farm.

Mrs. Fradd was waiting for them in the kitchen.

"No baths to-night," she said; "you must go straight to bed."

She led the way up a winding little staircase to a dark landing, where a case of stuffed fish and a grandfather clock loomed out of the shadows. Bridget had a room of her own, which led straight into that shared by her brother and sister.

"Candles out in thirty minutes," said Mrs. Fradd as she closed the door.

Anthony and Frances jumped on to their beds and bounced about.

"Quite soft," said Anthony, endeavoring to perch on the rail at the end as a hen would have done.

"Funny sort of person, isn't she?" said Bridget, collecting a few of her belongings that had been packed in Frances' case.

"Who? Mrs. Fradd?" she asked.

"Yes."

"She is a bit queer, but quite nice."

They lit the candles and Bridget went into her own room to get undressed. Frances and Anthony put the lights on the tables by their beds and surveyed the room. It was fairly large and looked even bigger because of the absence of much furniture. The walls were covered with pink rosebuds trailing round and up silver trellises, so that it produced the effect of a gigantic birthday card. The two brass bedsteads stood on each side of the door into Bridget's room. Bare boards spread over the floor, except for three rush mats that slid about, rather as if they were floating islands, every time they were stepped on.

Anthony and Frances put on their pajamas and leaned out of the window. It was very warm. A mist had crawled up from the valley like the attack of a crumpled army, so that they could see nothing beyond the farmyard.

Presently Bridget burst in to demand her sponge-bag, and sat on the end of a bed twiddling the brass knobs and watching her brother and sister.

"Do you like this place?" she asked at last.

"Rather," they both assented.

"Moors and ponies and streams! It'll be marvelous," said Anthony.

But Bridget was not thinking of that. She was the eldest of the family, and, always being the best at everything, she was inclined to be left out by Anthony and Frances in their plans. She did not mind, as she usually had plenty of her own, but the careless mention of a boy on a black pony had roused her curiosity and imagination.

"That boy Mr. Fradd was talking about," she said. "I hope we meet him."

"Yes," said Anthony.

"We shall have fun here, all right," Frances declared conclusively.

"Fun!" Bridget stood on the bed in her excitement. "We shall have that all right; but this isn't a place for fun only. It's a place for travel, discovery, adventure. How do we know that there are not hundreds of hidden valleys, dozens of unscalable peaks, heaps of unrideable rides; all waiting to be found, climbed, and accomplished by us? Oh, we are going to have fun here all right—but more as well, much more." After which spirited speech she added a hasty good night and, seizing her sponge-bag, barged back into her room. Anthony and Frances looked at each other.

"It's all true what she said," he declared.

"Umn. We must do it all too."

"Yes."

"Let's go to bed so that we wake up early."

"Right—after you with that basin. Hurry up."

After ten minutes the splashings in the

tin wash-basin ceased and the two curled up in their big old bedsteads. The candle-stump that Mrs. Fradd had given them was almost burnt out, so Frances suggested that they should lie awake and watch it till it died out. Anthony agreed, but the length of candle was deceiving, and outlasted them. Long after they had both slid deeper into their beds and fallen fast asleep, the little flame flickered perilously, making the shadows leap about. They jumped from the rickety washstand to the rosebuds in the wallpaper, from the brass knobs of the bedsteads to the lock of Anthony's suitcase.

Beyond the window the mist lay over the valley. A breeze slid in and out once or twice, rustling the curtains. The candle flickered, spluttered, darted up for a last effort—then sank back silently into the pool of melted wax.

And so began the summer on Exmoor, a summer full of fun and adventure. They were afterward to know the boy on the black pony and with him camp outdoors, explore by day and by night, catch wild ponies, and light beacon fires on the hill-tops. There were also days to be spent on a raft on the river—that river in reality only a few miles away but which they came to call "the far-distant Oxus."

## LITTLE WOMEN PLAN CHRISTMAS [1]

*Louisa M. Alcott*

"Christmas won't be Christmas without any presents," grumbled Jo, lying on the rug.

"It's so dreadful to be poor," sighed Meg, looking down at her old dress.

"I don't think it's fair for some girls to have plenty of pretty things, and other girls nothing at all," added little Amy, with an injured sniff.

"We've got father and mother and each other," said Beth contentedly, from her corner.

The four young faces on which the firelight shone brightened at the cheerful words, but darkened again as Jo said sadly:

"We haven't got father, and shall not have him for a long time." She didn't say "perhaps never," but each silently added it, thinking of father far away, where the fighting was.

Nobody spoke for a minute; then Meg said in an altered tone,—

"You know the reason mother proposed not having any presents this Christmas was because it is going to be a hard winter for every one; and she thinks we ought not to spend money for pleasure, when our men are suffering so in the army. We can't do much, but we can make our little sacrifices, and ought to do it gladly. But I am afraid I don't"; and Meg shook her head, as she thought regretfully of all the pretty things she wanted.

"But I don't think the little we should spend would do any good. We've each got a dollar, and the army wouldn't be much helped by our giving that. I agree not to expect anything from mother or you, but I do want to buy *Undine and Sintram* for myself; I've wanted it so long," said Jo, who was a bookworm.

"I planned to spend mine in new music," said Beth, with a little sigh, which no one heard but the hearth-brush and kettle-holder.

"I shall get a nice box of drawing-pencils; I really need them," said Amy decidedly.

"Mother didn't say anything about our money, and she won't wish us to give up everything. Let's each buy what we want, and have a little fun; I'm sure we work hard enough to earn it," cried Jo, examining the heels of her shoes in a gentlemanly manner.

"Don't you wish we had the money papa lost when we were little, Jo? Dear me! how happy and good we'd be, if we had no worries!" said Meg, who could remember better times.

"You said, the other day, you thought

[1] From Louisa M. Alcott, *Little Women.*

we were a deal happier than the King children, for they were fighting and fretting all the time, in spite of their money."

"So I did, Beth. Well, I think we are; for, though we do have to work, we make fun for ourselves, and are a pretty jolly set, as Jo would say."

"Jo does use such slang words!" observed Amy, with a reproving look at the long figure stretched on the rug. Jo immediately sat up, put her hands in her pockets, and began to whistle.

"Don't, Jo; it's so boyish!"

"That's why I do it."

"I detest rude, unladylike girls!"

"I hate affected, niminy-piminy chits!"

"'Birds in their little nests agree,'" sang Beth, the peacemaker, with such a funny face that both sharp voices softened to a laugh.

"Really, girls, you are both to be blamed," said Meg, beginning to lecture in her elder-sisterly fashion. "You are old enough to leave off boyish tricks, and to behave better, Josephine. It didn't matter so much when you were a little girl; but now you are so tall, and turn up your hair, you should remember that you are a young lady."

"I'm not! And if turning up my hair makes me one, I'll wear it in two tails till I'm twenty," cried Jo, pulling off her net, and shaking down a chestnut mane. "I hate to think I've got to grow up, and be Miss March, and wear long gowns, and look as prim as a China aster! It's bad enough to be a girl, anyway, when I like boys' games and work and manners! I can't get over my disappointment in not being a boy; and it's worse than ever now, for I'm dying to go and fight with papa, and I can only stay at home and knit, like a poky old woman!" And Jo shook the blue army-sock till the needles rattled like castanets, and her ball bounded across the room.

"Poor Jo! It's too bad, but it can't be helped; so you must try to be contented with making your name boyish, and playing brother to us girls," said Beth, stroking the rough head at her knee with a hand that all the dishwashing and dusting in the world could not make ungentle in its touch.

"As for you, Amy," continued Meg, "you are altogether too particular and prim. Your airs are funny now; but you'll grow up an affected little goose, if you don't take care. I like your nice manners and refined ways of speaking, when you don't try to be elegant; but your absurd words are as bad as Jo's slang."

"If Jo is a tomboy and Amy a goose, what am I, please?" asked Beth, ready to share the lecture.

"You're a dear, and nothing else," answered Meg warmly; and no one contradicted her, for the "Mouse" was the pet of the family.

As young readers like to know "how people look," we will take this moment to give them a little sketch of the four sisters, who sat knitting away in the twilight, while the December snow fell quietly without, and the fire crackled cheerfully within. It was a comfortable old room, though the carpet was faded and the furniture very plain; for a good picture or two hung on the walls, books filled the recesses, chrysanthemums and Christmas roses bloomed in the windows, and a pleasant atmosphere of home peace pervaded it.

Margaret, the eldest of the four, was sixteen, and very pretty, being plump and fair, with large eyes, plenty of soft, brown hair, a sweet mouth, and white hands, of which she was rather vain. Fifteen-year-old Jo was very tall, thin, and brown, and reminded one of a colt; for she never seemed to know what to do with her long limbs, which were very much in her way. She had a decided mouth, a comical nose, and sharp, gray eyes, which appeared to see everything, and were by turns fierce, funny, or thoughtful. Her long, thick hair was her one beauty; but it was usually bundled into a net, to be out of her way. Round shoulders had Jo, big hands and feet, a fly-away look to her clothes, and the uncomfortable appearance of a girl who was rapidly shooting up into a woman, and didn't like it. Elizabeth—or Beth, as every one called her—was a rosy, smooth-haired, bright-eyed girl of thirteen, with a shy manner, a timid voice, and a peaceful expression, which was seldom disturbed. Her father called her "Little Tranquillity," and the name suited her excellently; for she seemed to live in a happy world of her own, only venturing out to meet the few whom she trusted and loved. Amy, though the youngest, was a most important person—in her own opinion at least. A regular snow-maiden, with blue eyes and yellow hair curling on her shoulders, pale and slender, and always carrying herself like a young lady mindful of her manners.

The clock struck six; and, having swept up the hearth, Beth put a pair of slippers down to warm. Somehow the sight of the old shoes had a good effect upon the girls; for mother was coming, and every one brightened to welcome her. Meg stopped lecturing, and lighted the lamp, Amy got out of the easy-chair without being asked, and Jo forgot how tired she was as she sat up to hold the slippers nearer to the blaze.

"They are quite worn out; Marmee must have a new pair."

"I thought I'd get her some with my dollar," said Beth.

"No, I shall!" cried Amy.

"I'm the oldest," began Meg, but Jo cut in with a decided—

"I'm the man in the family now papa is away, and *I* shall provide the slippers, for he told me to take special care of mother while he was gone."

"I'll tell you what we'll do," said Beth; "let's each get her something for Chistmas, and not get anything for ourselves."

"That's like you, dear! What will we get?" exclaimed Jo.

Every one thought soberly for a minute; then Meg announced, as if the idea was suggested by the sight of her own pretty hands, "I shall give her a nice pair of gloves."

"Army shoes, best to be had," cried Jo.

"Some handkerchiefs, all hemmed," said Beth.

"I'll get a bottle of cologne," said Amy.

"How will we give the things?" asked Meg.

"Put them on the table and bring her in and see her open the bundles," answered Jo. "Don't you remember how we used to do on our birthdays?"

## CHRISTMAS WITH THE CRATCHITS[1]

*Charles Dickens*

Then up rose Mrs. Cratchit, Cratchit's wife, dressed out but poorly in a twice-turned gown but brave in ribbons, which are cheap and make a goodly show for sixpence; and she laid the cloth, assisted by Belinda Cratchit, second of her daughters, also brave in ribbons; while Master Peter Cratchit plunged a fork into the saucepan of potatoes, and getting the corners of his monstrous shirt collar (Bob's private property, conferred upon his son and heir in honor of the day) into his mouth, rejoiced to find himself so gallantly attired and yearned to show his linen in the fashionable parks. And now two smaller Cratchits, boy and girl, came tearing in, screaming that outside the baker's they had smelled the goose, and known it for their own; and basking in luxurious thoughts of sage and onion, these young Cratchits danced about the table and exalted Master Peter Cratchit to the skies, while he (not proud, although his collar nearly choked him) blew the fire until the slow potatoes, bubbling up, knocked loudly at the saucepan lid to be let out and peeled.

"What has ever got your precious father then?" said Mrs. Cratchit. "And your brother, Tiny Tim! And Martha warn't as late last Christmas Day by half an hour!"

"Here's Martha, mother!" said a girl, appearing as she spoke.

"Here's Martha, mother!" cried the two

[1] From Charles Dickens, *A Christmas Carol.*

young Cratchits. "Hurrah! There's *such* a goose, Martha!"

"Why, bless your heart alive, my dear, how late you are!" said Mrs. Cratchit, kissing her a dozen times and taking off her shawl and bonnet for her with officious zeal.

"We'd a deal of work to finish up last night," replied the girl, "and had to clear away this morning, mother!"

"Well! Never mind so long as you are come," said Mrs. Cratchit. "Sit ye down before the fire, my dear, and have a warm, Lord bless ye!"

"No, no! There's father coming," cried the two young Cratchits, who were everywhere at once. "Hide, Martha, hide!"

So Martha hid herself, and in came little Bob, the father, with at least three feet of comforter exclusive of the fringe, hanging down before him; and his threadbare clothes darned up and brushed to look seasonable; and Tiny Tim upon his shoulder. Alas for Tiny Tim, he bore a little crutch, and had his limbs supported by an iron frame!

"Why, where's our Martha?" cried Bob Cratchit, looking round.

"Not coming," said Mrs. Cratchit.

"Not coming!" said Bob, with a sudden declension in his high spirits; for he had been Tim's blood horse all the way from church and had come home rampant. "Not coming upon Christmas Day!"

Martha didn't like to see him disappointed, if it were only in joke; so she came out prematurely from behind the closet door and ran into his arms, while the two young Cratchits hustled Tiny Tim and bore him off into the wash house that he might hear the pudding singing in the copper.

"And how did little Tim behave?" asked Mrs. Cratchit, when she had rallied Bob on his credulity and Bob had hugged his daughter to his heart's content.

"As good as gold," said Bob, "and better. Somehow he gets thoughtful, sitting by himself so much, and thinks the strangest things you ever heard. He told me, coming home, that he hoped the people saw him in the church, because he was a cripple and it might be pleasant to them to remember upon Christmas Day who made lame beggars walk and blind men see."

Bob's voice was tremulous when he told them this, and trembled more when he said that Tiny Tim was growing strong and hearty.

His active little crutch was heard upon the floor, and back came Tiny Tim before another word was spoken, escorted by his brother and sister to his stool before the fire; and while Bob, turning up his cuffs—as if, poor fellow, they were capable of being made more shabby—compounded some hot mixture in a jug and stirred it round and round and put it on the hob to simmer, Master Peter and the two ubiquitous young Cratchits went to fetch the goose, with which they soon returned in high procession.

Such a bustle ensued that you might have thought a goose the rarest of all birds, a feathered phenomenon, to which a black swan was a matter of course—and in truth it was something very like it in that house. Mrs. Cratchit made the gravy (ready beforehand in a little saucepan) hissing hot; Master Peter mashed the potatoes with incredible vigor; Miss Belinda sweetened up the apple sauce; Martha dusted the hot plates; Bob took Tiny Tim beside him in a tiny corner at the table; the two young Cratchits set chairs for everybody, not forgetting themselves, and mounting guard upon their posts, crammed spoons into their mouths lest they should shriek for goose before their turn came to be helped. At last the dishes were set on and grace was said. It was succeeded by a breathless pause as Mrs. Cratchit, looking slowly all along the carving knife, prepared to plunge it in the breast; but when she did and when the long expected gush of stuffing issued forth, one murmur of delight arose all around the board, and even Tiny Tim, excited by the two young Cratchits, beat on the table with the handle of his knife and feebly cried Hurrah!

There never was such a goose. Bob said he didn't believe there ever was such a goose cooked. Its tenderness and flavor, size and cheapness, were the themes of universal admiration. Eked out by the apple sauce and mashed potatoes, it was a sufficient dinner for the whole family; indeed, as Mrs. Cratchit said with great delight (surveying one small atom of a bone upon the dish) they hadn't ate it all at last! Yet everyone had had enough, and the youngest Cratchits in particular were steeped in sage and onion to the eyebrows! But now, the plates being changed by Miss Belinda, Mrs. Cratchit left the room alone—too nervous to bear witness—to take the pudding up and bring it in.

Suppose it should not be done enough! Suppose it should break in turning out! Suppose somebody should have got over the wall of the back yard and stolen it while they were merry with the goose—a supposition at which the two young Cratchits became livid! All sorts of horrors were supposed.

Hallo! A great deal of steam! The pudding was out of the copper. A smell like a washing day! That was the cloth. A smell like an eating house and a pastry cook's next door to each other, with a laundress's next door to that! That was the pudding! In half a minute Mrs. Cratchit entered—flushed but smiling proudly—with the pudding, like a speckled cannon ball, so hard and firm, blazing in half of half-a-quartern of ignited brandy, and bedight with Christmas holly stuck into the top.

Oh, a wonderful pudding! Bob Cratchit said, and calmly too, that he regarded it as the greatest success achieved by Mrs. Cratchit since their marriage. Mrs. Cratchit said that now the weight was off her mind she would confess she had had her doubts about the quantity of flour. Everybody had something to say about it, but nobody said or thought it was at all a small pudding for a large family. It would have been flat heresy to do so. Any Cratchit would have blushed to hint at such a thing.

At last the dinner was all done, the cloth was cleared, the hearth swept, and the fire made up. The compound in the jug being tasted and considered perfect, apples and oranges were put upon the table and a shovelful of chestnuts on the fire. Then all the Cratchit family drew around the hearth in what Bob Cratchit called a circle, meaning half a one; and at Bob Cratchit's elbow stood the family display of glass—two tumblers and a custard cup without a handle.

These held the hot stuff from the jug, however, as well as golden goblets would have done; and Bob served it out with beaming looks, while the chestnuts on the fire sputtered and cracked noisily. Then Bob proposed:

"A Merry Christmas to us all, my dears. God bless us!"

Which all the family reëchoed.

"God bless us every one!" said Tiny Tim, the last of all.

## "MARK TWAIN" [1]

*Cornelia Meigs*

The morning was still early, yet the sun was already hot on the sand bar, shining up into Sam's eyes in a white glare. He pulled down his battered straw hat and stood for a minute listening to the ripples of the big river as they went hissing along the edge of the sand. Behind him the town of Hannibal was waking up to a blazing hot summer day. Thin columns of smoke were rising from the houses crowded below the bluff, and above Cardiff Hill the sky was scorching blue.

Sam had gone to sleep last night with a strange, rather terrible idea in his head, and even this morning it would not be put out of his mind. It was filling his thoughts now, even though he was walking so care-

[1] From Cornelia Meigs, *Young Americans: How History Looked to Them While It Was in the Making.* Used by permission of Ginn and Company, publishers. In this story only the conversations are imaginary; the people and the facts are all real.

fully beside the water on an entirely different errand. He was looking for a simple thing which all boys learned how to find if they lived beside the Mississippi River about ninety years ago. Most of the time Sam Clemens had no idea where his hat was; he only wore it this morning because he needed it for a different use than that of keeping the sun away from his mop of reddish-yellow hair.

Now he saw what he had been seeking—a line of small, scrambling footprints leading up from the water. He followed them until they turned toward the shore again, and there he threw down his hat and began digging with his hands in the warm sand. He felt something. A grin of delight crossed his face, and he brought up the first of his prize, pink, leathery, oval things—turtle eggs! He knew, better than anyone else, how to find the tracks of the turtle where she came out to lay her eggs to be hatched by the heat of the sun. Back on the main shore the other boys were waiting under the buttonwood trees. They had built a little fire; for Sam Clemens had promised them turtle eggs for breakfast.

He filled his hat and walked slowly back with his mind full once more of that thought which had been troubling him ever since he awoke. Should he tell the other boys? Should he startle them with the news of what he meant to do? No, not quite yet, because he was not exactly certain that he was going to do it.

His three friends were waiting—John Briggs, Will Bowen, and Tom Blankenship. They were his own size, they wore torn trousers and hickory shirts just as he did, and they were barelegged and freckled like himself. Tom Blankenship was a perfect marvel of raggedness, but what did any of them care? They none of them had anything like Sam's mop of sandy hair, or his eager, watchful eyes, or that slow speech with which he greeted them: "Well, I told you I was goin' to bring turtle eggs. Got some good coals to roast 'em?"

They had a wonderful breakfast there under the trees, listening to the wide river slip by. John Briggs was telling about how there had been a fight last night down at the steamboat landing, and how the *Mary Evans* had backed off in the morning, leaving a big Negro with a broken head on the bank. "Someone'll take him in," Will Bowen said, "and let him lie on the hay in the barn until he gets well."

Tom Blankenship listened, digging his toe, the one with the rag on it, into the soft dirt under the tree.

"My pop got left like that, down on the Louisiana levee," he remarked carelessly. "He didn't come home for a month, and we wondered a lot where he'd got to."

Sam was scarcely paying attention. He was watching the bowing willows on the bank opposite, more than half a mile away, and staring at the current. A long raft was coming into view around the bend above them. Pushed by a dingy, gray steamboat, it moved slowly downstream. It would be in sight for two hours or more before it slid beyond the next turn in the smooth, clean road of the river. It was nearly in front of them when he burst out suddenly with the thought which had been troubling him ever since he had opened his eyes that morning.

"I've got to get out of here. I've got to get away from a place like this, where nothing ever happens. I'm goin' to run away."

What did he want? He did not know himself. Knights in armor, perhaps, castles to be captured, buried treasure to be discovered? Hannibal, with its little rude houses, its dusty streets where the pigs ran free and ragged men like Tom Blankenship's father walked slowly past on no special business, was not the place to satisfy those strange desires which were always rising up within him. He sat looking out at the river while Will Bowen spoke sternly.

"You've been reading those books again, Sam. There never was any good in readin' so many books. Anyway, come on, now; you promised you'd go with us to the cave."

They left the rest of their breakfast and set out. The hot miles of the road were deep in dust where the road looped along the hill above the river. The little valley, when they reached it presently, looked green and shady and deliciously cool. They threw themselves down on the deep grass under the shade of the pecan trees. The mouth of the cave showed black and gaping on the slope above them.

They talked for a while, resting their weary legs, and going over the tales of adventure that hung about the cave. Indians had hidden in it; white men had taken shelter from their enemies and lain in the doorway with rifles leveled, daring anyone to come up the hill and chase them out. Sam himself had been lost once in the winding passages, and had felt that terrible instant of panic when he knew that he had missed the way. He had been wise enough simply to sit down and wait until he was found, even though his candle burned down until it was too small to hold and he was within a minute of being left in the blind dark. No one knows what real darkness is who has not seen it inside the deep hollows of a hillside cave. One of the boys asked Sam to tell about it again, but he put the idea aside. "Oh, that wasn't anything. Anybody might get lost in a cave."

They filed in at last. They had brought a few candle ends, and Sam, the most daring, even had a handful of matches. There was every danger that they might go too far and all the candles burn out, but they did not think for a minute about that.

It was a clean, dry cave, with its low passages hung thick with stalactites (the iciclelike sticks of white limestone which hang from the roofs of caves) and with great blocks of stone here and there which had fallen from the roof. The fresh air was like late autumn, not only cool but cold. They grew tired at last of wandering and shouting to make echoes, and they came out of the dark passage into the blazing sun and the smothering heat again. The other boys were grinning over the games inside, but Sam's face was dark and thoughtful. Tom Blankenship looked at him anxiously, but did not say a word. No one ever knew what would come out of those queer moods of Sam Clemens's. Not even Sam himself could tell what he was going to do. But never before had the spirit of restlessness and discontent clutched him so firmly; never before had such wild thoughts and plans swung back and forth within him. They walked home saying little, the boys trailing after Sam.

Even his own family remarked on his silence as he sat at the supper table.

"What's got into you?" his sister Pamela asked, as she passed him his plate. She looked really worried, for Sam was hardly ever so quiet. His mother said quickly: "Oh, don't start anything, Pamela. Just be thankful when the boy isn't in some kind of mischief."

Sam glanced at her thoughtfully, and even she began to look uneasy. "It's been pretty hot," he said at last. "I think I'll go to the top of the hill and see if there's a breeze." He was up and out of the door before anyone could say another word.

He climbed to the top of the great hill which stood so boldly above the little town. It was beginning to grow dark as he threw himself down on grass that was dry and stiff and springy. He stretched himself at full length and looked down at the world below him. There are few places on earth where you can see such a view as is spread at the foot of Cardiff Hill. The clear, wide Mississippi turns in a great bend and, as far as the eye can see, flows away past low "bottom lands" which are dotted with clumps of willows and with cleared green meadows, with little winding streams and arms of the river twisting in and out among the trees. In the smooth water the islands look as though they were afloat, mere clusters of green, with white sand bars and a ripple of current at the head of each.

Almost below where Sam had thrown himself down, a steamboat lay with her nose against the bank, big and white, with her lights being lit as twilight fell. He knew from the bustle on board her, from the rows of lamps which beaded her sides, and from the slow drift of smoke from her great smokestacks that she was making ready to back out into the river and go downstream. Where would she go? What would she see? And here the desire which had been gnawing at his restless heart all day grew suddenly big and powerful, and he knew, not what he wanted to do but what he was going to do. There was his mother at home, and Pamela and his two brothers. He did not let himself think about them. Sam knew without being told—although he often was told—that he was a mischievous, troublesome son, a boy who brought no peace or comfort to the house. He did not mean to be that. He wanted so to help them, not just by filling the woodbox, perhaps, or whitewashing the fence, but in some bigger, more splendid way. If he could once get out into the great world, of course he would do great things; he was sure of it. Then they would all be proud of him, and people would say: "Do you remember Sam Clemens? Why, he used to live right here in Hannibal. We all knew him; he wasn't a bit proud."

Sam grinned. Even at that minute he could see the joke of it. He had more respect at that instant for Tom Blankenship, in his ragged, secondhand clothes and his scrap of a shirt, than he had for himself. Tom had certainly had adventures with his wandering, good-for-nothing father, while he, Sam—

The steamboat bell rang, very clear in the still evening air. The smoke began rolling out dark and thick above the stacks. Without one more thought, without drawing breath, Sam flung himself over the edge of the hill and ran, slid, and scrambled to the bottom. The whole company of deck helpers, with the mate who had charge of them, was on shore struggling with some last difficult pieces of freight. No one saw a small barelegged boy slip over the gangplank and lose himself in the shadows of the lower deck. He found a pile of grain bags, from which he lifted one sack and climbed into the middle of the heap like a gopher into a hole. There was a tramping of feet, a hail of orders from the mate, commands shouted as one would throw them at a snarling dog or a balky mule. That, so it was supposed, was the way to talk to Negro workers on a Mississippi steamboat. The slow splash of the paddle wheels and the steady beat of the engines began. They were off.

An hour passed, and Sam got very tired of hiding. There were cramps in his legs, and the sharp dust of grain husks in his hair and down his neck. Every time he began to move, heavy feet would come tramping by, and he had to lie still again. At last he heard the voices of two who had stopped beside him. By peeping out he could see that a big Negro, with a smaller man beside him, had stopped under a swinging lantern while the bigger one lighted his pipe.

"You better push right on, Joe," said the little man. "If the boss ketches you here, you'll git what for."

"Let him ketch me! I ain't afraid of all the mates on the whole Mississippi," answered the big one. "Let Tim Carter just try to ketch me. I've got a long knife for him; it's been ready for him this whole trip. Got it right here inside my shirt." Sam could both hear and guess how he put his hand inside his belt and patted the handle of the knife while he whispered to it in his big, soft voice: "There now, gal, you lay quiet. Did you git tired waitin' for Tim Carter? Well, it's not so long now."

There was another sound. Someone else was coming. Sam heard the big Negro mutter something and draw closer into the shadow. The little man gave a high, shrill giggle from pure nervous terror. The voice of the mate, Tim Carter, came gruffly in the dark.

"What are you doin', you Joe? Git out of—" There was a roar from the big Negro, a leap and a struggle, the sound of a heavy blow, and a loud, thin cry from the little man. After a second of silence Tim Carter spoke to his companion, who had come hurrying up behind him—the second mate, whom Sam had seen as he slipped on board. The assistant was a thin, very tall young man, evidently making his first trip. The first mate's voice was quite calm.

"Just let him lie there a bit, and he'll be all right. Shorty's had a good many bumps like that before, and not been the worse."

The younger man spoke unsteadily. "But it wasn't him with the knife, Mr. Carter. It was big Joe."

"Doesn't make a bit of difference," replied Carter. "Every deck man on the boat has a knife in his shirt or a razor in his pocket, and thinks he's going to get the mate with it. Whenever you see something stir in the dark and you don't know what it is, hit out or shoot; don't wait. That's one of the first things a boat's officer has to know. Knock the man overboard, but don't ask him any questions. And always have your pistol handy in your pocket."

They moved on. If their feet had not been so loud on the planks, they might have heard a noise that was very like a boy's teeth chattering. Who would come across him first, Sam was wondering. Who would hear a rustle in the dark among the grain sacks? Would it be Joe with his knife or the mate with his gun? He hardly knew which would be the worse.

A long half-hour went by, and he grew a little quieter. He could peer out between the sacks and see, on the open deck, the dark shapes of men who had thrown themselves down, anywhere, to sleep the short night out. One of them began a deep humming under his breath, and another took it up until the note of music grew to a swinging, mournful song: "Gone are the days when my heart was young and gay—"

Sam moved carefully, inch by inch, leg by leg, until he had crawled from the heap of sacks and was sitting comfortably on the planks, still warm from the sun of the day past, but with the cool night wind blowing over him. The moon had climbed up and made a pavement of silver of the whole river, with shadows so black across the deck that they would hide anyone. It was beautiful to watch the moving water; to look up at the dark pilothouse; and to see the tall smokestacks, with the long roll of smoke drifting away across the bright sky.

The mate's voice called an order, and two of the men nearest Sam got up and took, each of them, a long sounding pole. The boat was coming close to a difficult sand bar, and there was danger of getting stuck on the bottom. The first—it was Joe, as Sam could see in the moonlight—plunged his pole overboard and called the depth of the water, "No bottom!" which meant that the pole did not reach the bottom. The man opposite, whose high voice answered Joe's deep bass, sang out, in his turn, "N-o-o bottom!" The mate repeated the call, so that the captain, up in the pilothouse, could hear. Sam felt himself trembling all over with a strange delight, with the wonder of the shining river, the cooling wind, and the music of those voices calling back and forth. Presently the water became shallower and the cry changed: "Mark twain! M-a-ark twain!"

Sounding, it may be explained, is done with a pole which can measure twelve feet (two fathoms), since every boat and ship uses the fathom as its unit of measure. The pole is painted round with black and white to show the feet, and it is plainly marked at one fathom and at two. From long, long custom, older certainly than steamboats themselves, comes the habit of crying the depth of the river in such a way that it cannot be mistaken. "Two" sometimes sounds like some other number, but the old word "twain" can never be mistaken. "Mark twain" means two fathoms at the mark, twelve feet deep—safe water even for a steamboat.

"Quarter less twain! Half less twain!" came the cry. The water was less and less deep; the boat slowed down, nosing out her way. There was a little soft shudder that ran through the whole of her great length; she had just touched the sand and was slipping down into deeper water. "M-a-ark twain!" came the comforting call; and then finally the pole plunged deep and did not touch, and once more came the cry "No bottom!" They were over the bar.

The sounding came to an end, and quiet fell upon the great, steadily moving boat.

Sam was still too much excited to sleep, but his thought began to move more slowly, to go back a little and to wander. Had he done quite well in running away? Just where was he going? And what would become of him the next day and the next? They were no gentle people, any of those who were going to find him, as they were surely bound to do. He shivered a little in the cool night breeze. His mind went back to home, where they would all be asleep except his mother, perhaps lying awake and thinking about him. She would have believed, so far, that he was spending the night with Will Bowen, as he so often did. Not until tomorrow would she begin to be anxious. Was he really someone that any mother would want to get back again, or was he just a worthless, freckled-faced, sandy-haired boy who was always making trouble? His eyes were growing heavy; for the night air was at last making him sleepy.

He did not dare lie down on the deck, even in the shadows, but crawled back among the freight and got into his old place among the sacks. It was not an easy bed, but he curled himself up as comfortably as he could. He was very tired, and there is no more sleepy lullaby than the deep, big, regular breathing of a moving steamboat.

A sudden sharp pain in his leg, and a voice exclaiming angrily in the darkness—it was these which woke him. Only then did he realize that he had not crawled all the way into the heap of sacks and that his legs remained uncovered. Somebody had stumbled over them in the dark. "What—what's this?" Sam did not recognize the voice. Was it Joe, sleepy and angry, tugging at the knife in his shirt? Was it the mate, always ready for trickery and hidden danger? Was he pulling out his pistol? The sacks were being dragged away, and a hard hand caught him by the collar and jerked him to his feet. Sam fought, tried to cry out, and couldn't. The man who had found him pulled him over within the light of a hanging lantern.

"Why, it's Sam Clemens!"

It was neither the mate nor Joe. It was "the old man" himself, the captain of the boat, going on watch again in the pilot-house after two hours of sleep, and making a tour of inspection first. One does not often find small sandy-haired boys mixed up with the piles of freight. "What are you doing?" he finally asked.

"Running away." Sam tried not to let his voice sound sheepish, but he stood staring, at the planks at his feet, where the splinters showed in the orange light of the lantern.

It was possible that the captain did not know at once what to say. He stood staring at his uninvited passenger for some minutes. "Like to come up into the pilot-house?" he asked at length and, not waiting for an answer, walked away with Sam following.

It was still so dark that Sam stumbled more than once in going up the steps to the top deck to reach the high, glass-sided shelter from which the boat is steered. The great wheel was much taller than Sam, even with part of its rim disappearing below the floor. The assistant pilot gave up his place and went away with only a word or two of where they were, "Just crossing the foot of Catfish Bar." The captain shifted the wheel a little, and Sam climbed up on the high bench behind him. For a while they sat in silence. The sky was growing faintly gray, but the water was still dark.

"So you were running away?" the captain said after a long time, but as though he had really spoken only a minute before. "And did you have any idea where you were going to run to?"

"Why—why, no, sir," Sam stammered, and then brought it all out with a rush. "Hannibal's so little! Nothing ever happens there. I want to—to see things and—do things. I think I could."

The captain nodded. "Yes, I know! that's how most people feel. But time goes by, and everyone has a chance to see plenty; yes, they see enough without having to be in a hurry about it." He broke off suddenly. "How does your ma get on?"

"Why," Sam answered in some surprise,

"she gets on all right." Why wouldn't a capable woman with as much courage as his mother get on as well as anyone else?

"Do you remember," the captain was saying slowly, "do you remember about that widow who lived under the hill, not so far from you—lived there with her daughter, and how a man tried to break in and rob them, and how she had to shoot him?" Sam trembled in the dark. He did remember. He had happened to see the shooting; had seen the man fall. The captain went on without paying much attention to him. "Do you remember that poor woman married to the drunken Corsican, and how, when her husband was after her, trying to beat her, she ran to your ma and your ma stood in the door and ordered the man off and threatened him so that he really went? A woman like that is brave enough to meet anything," he added after a pause; "but with the kind of things she has to face, and with your father having to be away so much of the time, she kind of needs her boys to stand by her. Don't you think so, Sam?"

"Yes," answered Sam, miserably. He had not thought of that.

"You might make a good pilot some day," Captain Howard almost seemed to be thinking aloud. "You notice things and remember them; that is what a man has to do who is to learn the river mile by mile. But we do make a rule, before we take on a man to teach him steamboating, that he has to be taller than the wheel he steers by." There was a very long silence, so long that pink streaks began to show above the dark hills, and the gray in the sky had almost turned to white. The captain asked one more question. "You've got relatives in the town of Louisiana, haven't you—someone who would take you in until the next boat goes north to Hannibal? We'll find a way to send word to your family, and I'll speak to somebody about taking you up, and by and by we'll see about making a pilot of you. Give my good wishes to your ma. She's my idea of a brave woman."

"Yes," said Sam. "I will."

They did not talk any more, but sat together while the pink in the sky turned to red and then to yellow sunlight. The water was growing shallow off Hickory Point, and they were sounding again. Some day Sam, although he knew it so little then, was going to make books, great books, out of all that he was seeing then: the water dappled with silver, the bending willows, and the great, sliding river. Tom Blankenship, renamed Huck Finn, was to come into those books; so were Will Bowen and many of the things that happened in Hannibal—larger things, so Sam was to find, than they seemed to be when he lived among them. He knew nothing of all that; he only knew that all he was seeing and learning at this moment was making him queerly happy, and that through it all there seemed to run strange music in the long ringing call: "Quarter less twain! By the mark! M-a-ark twain!"

## TOM SAWYER AND HIS PIRATE CREW[1]

*Samuel L. Clemens*

Tom's mind was made up now. He was gloomy and desperate. He was a forsaken, friendless boy, he said; Aunt Polly did not love him; nobody loved him. When they found out what they had driven him to, perhaps they would be sorry; he had tried to do right and get along, but they would not let him. Yes, they had forced him to it at last; he would lead a life of crime. There was no choice.

By this time he was far down Meadow Lane, and the bell for school to "take up" tinkled faintly upon his ear. He sobbed, now, to think he should never, never hear that old familiar sound any more.

Just at this point he met his soul's sworn comrade, Joe Harper—hard-eyed, and with evidently a great and dismal purpose in his heart. Plainly here were "two souls with but a single thought." Tom, wiping his eyes with his sleeve, began to blubber out

[1] From Samuel L. Clemens, *The Adventures of Tom Sawyer.*

something about a resolution to escape from hard usage and lack of sympathy at home by roaming abroad into the great world never to return; and ended by hoping that Joe would not forget him.

But it transpired that this was a request which Joe had just been going to make of Tom, and had come to hunt him up for that purpose. His mother had whipped him for drinking some cream which he had never tasted and knew nothing about; it was plain that she was tired of him and wished him to go; if she felt that way, there was nothing for him to do but succumb; he hoped she would be happy, and never regret having driven her poor boy out into the unfeeling world to suffer and die.

As the two boys walked sorrowing along, they made a new compact to stand by each other and be brothers and never separate till death relieved them of their troubles. Then they began to lay their plans. Joe was for being a hermit, and living on crusts in a remote cave, and dying, some time, of cold and want and grief; but after listening to Tom, he conceded that there were some conspicuous advantages about a life of crime, and so he consented to be a pirate.

Three miles below St. Petersburg, at a point where the Mississippi River was a trifle over a mile wide, there was a long, narrow, wooded island, with a shallow bar at the head of it, and this offered well as a rendezvous. It was not inhabited; it lay far over toward the further shore, abreast a dense and almost wholly unpeopled forest. So Jackson's Island was chosen. Who were to be the subjects of their piracies, was a matter that did not occur to them. Then they hunted up Huckleberry Finn, and he joined them promptly, for all careers were one to him; he was indifferent. They presently separated to meet at a lonely spot on the river bank two miles above the village at the favorite hour—which was midnight. There was a small log raft there which they meant to capture. Each would bring hooks and lines, and such provision as he could steal in the most dark and mysterious way—as became outlaws. And before the afternoon was done, they had all managed to enjoy the sweet glory of spreading the fact that pretty soon the town would "hear something." All who got this vague hint were cautioned to "be mum and wait."

About midnight Tom arrived with a boiled ham and a few trifles, and stopped in a dense undergrowth on a small bluff overlooking the meeting place. It was starlight, and very still. The mighty river lay like an ocean at rest. Tom listened a moment, but no sound disturbed the quiet. Then he gave a low, distinct whistle. It was answered from under the bluff. Tom whistled twice more; these signals were answered in the same way. Then a guarded voice said:

"Who goes there?"

"Tom Sawyer, the Black Avenger of the Spanish Main. Name your names."

"Huck Finn the Red-Handed, and Joe Harper, the Terror of the Seas." Tom had furnished these titles, from his favorite literature.

" 'Tis well. Give the countersign."

Two hoarse whispers delivered the same awful word simultaneously to the brooding night:

"Blood!"

Then Tom tumbled his ham over the bluff and let himself down after it, tearing both skin and clothes to some extent in the effort. There was an easy, comfortable path along the shore under the bluff, but it lacked the advantages of difficulty and danger so valued by a pirate.

The Terror of the Seas had brought a side of bacon, and had about worn himself out with getting it there. Finn the Red-Handed had stolen a skillet and a quantity of half-cured leaf tobacco, and had also brought a few corncobs to make pipes with. But none of the pirates smoked or "chewed" but himself. The Black Avenger of the Spanish Main said it would never do to start without some fire. That was a wise thought; matches were hardly known there in that day. They saw a fire smoldering upon a great raft a hundred yards above, and they went stealthily thither and helped themselves to a chunk. They made an imposing adventure of it, saying, "Hist!" every now and then, and suddenly halting with finger on lip; moving with hands on imaginary dagger hilts; and giving orders in dismal whispers that if "the foe" stirred, to "let him have it to the hilt," because "dead men tell no tales." They knew well enough that the raftsmen were all down at the village laying in stores or having a spree, but still that was no excuse for their conducting this thing in an unpiratical way.

They shoved off in their own raft, presently, Tom in command, Huck at the after oar and Joe at the forward. Tom stood amidships, gloomy-browed, and with folded arms, and gave his orders in a low, stern whisper:

"Luff, and bring her to the wind!"

"Aye, aye, sir!"

"Steady, steady-y-y-y!"

"Steady it is, sir!"

"Let her go off a point!"

"Point it is, sir!"

As the boys steadily and monotonously drove the raft toward midstream it was no doubt understood that these orders were given only for "style," and were not intended to mean anything in particular.

"What sail's she carrying?"

"Courses, tops'ls, and flying-jib, sir."

"Send the r'yals up! Lay out aloft, there, half a dozen of ye–foretopmaststuns'l! Lively, now!"

"Aye, aye, sir!"

"Shake out that maintogalans'l! Sheets and braces! *Now,* my hearties!"

"Aye, aye, sir!"

"Hellum-a-lee–hard-a-port! Stand by to meet her when she comes! Port, port! *Now,* men! With a will! Steady-y-y-y!"

"Steady it is, sir!"

The raft drew beyond the middle of the river; the boys pointed her head right, and then lay on their oars. The river was not high, so there was not more than a two- or three-mile current. Hardly a word was said during the next three-quarters of an hour.

Now the raft was passing before the distant town. Two or three glimmering lights showed where it lay, peacefully sleeping, beyond the vague vast sweep of star-gemmed water, unconscious of the tremendous event that was happening. The Black Avenger stood still with folded arms, "looking his last" upon the scene of his former joys and his later sufferings, and wishing "she" could see him now, abroad on the wild sea, facing peril and death with dauntless heart, going to his doom with a grim smile on his lips. It was but a small strain on his imagination to remove Jackson's Island beyond eye-shot of the village, and so he "looked his last" with a broken and satisfied heart. The other pirates were looking their last, too; and they all looked so long that they came near letting the current drift them out of the range of the island. But they discovered the danger in time, and made shift to avert it.

About two o'clock in the morning the raft grounded on the bar two hundred yards above the head of the island, and they waded back and forth until they had landed their freight. Part of the little raft's belongings consisted of an old sail, and this they spread over a nook in the bushes for a tent to shelter their provisions; but they themselves would sleep in the open air in good weather, as became outlaws.

They built a fire against the side of a great log twenty or thirty steps within the somber depths of the forest, and then cooked some bacon in the frying pan for supper, and used up half of the corn "pone" stock they had brought. It seemed glorious sport to be feasting in that wild free way in the virgin forest of an unexplored and uninhabited island, far from the haunts of men, and they said they never would return to civilization. The climbing fire lit up their faces and threw its ruddy glare upon the pillared tree trunks of their forest temple, and upon the varnished foliage and festooning vines.

When the last crisp slice of bacon was gone, and the last allowance of corn pone devoured, the boys stretched themselves out on the grass, filled with contentment. They could have found a cooler place, but they would not deny themselves such a romantic feature as the roasting campfire.

"*Ain't* it gay?" said Joe.

"What would the boys say if they could see us?" said Tom.

"Say? Well, they'd just die to be here—hey, Hucky!"

"I reckon so," said Huckleberry; "anyways, *I*'m suited. I don't want nothing better'n this. I don't ever get enough to eat, gen'ally—and here they can't come and pick at a feller and bullyrag him so."

"It's just the life for me," said Tom. "You don't have to get up, mornings, and you don't have to go to school, and wash, and all that blame foolishness. You see a pirate don't have to do *anything*, Joe, when he's ashore, but a hermit *he* has to be praying considerable, and then he don't have any fun, anyway, all by himself that way."

"Oh, yes, that's so," said Joe, "but I hadn't thought much about it, you know. I'd a good deal rather be a pirate, now that I've tried it."

"You see," said Tom, "people don't go much on hermits, nowadays, like they used to in old times, but a pirate's always respected. And a hermit's got to sleep on the hardest place he can find, and put sackcloth and ashes on his head, and stand out in the rain, and—"

"What does he put sackcloth and ashes on his head for?" inquired Huck.

"I dunno. But they've *got* to do it. Hermits always do. You'd have to do that if you was a hermit."

"Dern'd if I would," said Huck.

"Well, what would you do?"

"I dunno. But I wouldn't do that."

"Why, Huck, you'd *have* to. How'd you get around it?"

"Why, I just wouldn't stand it. I'd run away."

"Run away! Well, you *would* be a nice old slouch of a hermit. You'd be a disgrace."

The Red-Handed made no response, being better employed. He had finished gouging out a cob, and now he fitted a weed stem to it, loaded it with tobacco, and was pressing a coal to the charge and blowing a cloud of fragrant smoke—he was in the full bloom of luxurious contentment. The other pirates envied him this majestic vice, and secretly resolved to acquire it shortly. Presently Huck said:

"What does pirates have to do?"

Tom said:

"Oh, they have just a bully time—take ships and burn them, and get the money and bury it in awful places in their island where there's ghosts and things to watch it, and kill everybody in the ships—make 'em walk a plank."

"And they carry the women to the island," said Joe; "they don't kill the women."

"No," assented Tom, "they don't kill the women—they're too noble. And the women's always beautiful, too."

"And don't they wear the bulliest clothes! Oh, no! All gold and silver and di'monds," said Joe, with enthusiasm.

"Who?" said Huck.

"Why, the pirates."

Huck scanned his own clothing forlornly.

"I reckon I ain't dressed fitten for a pirate," said he, with a regretful pathos in his voice; "but I ain't got none but these."

But the other boys told him the fine clothes would come fast enough, after they should have begun their adventures. They made him understand that his poor rags would do to begin with, though it was customary for wealthy pirates to start with a proper wardrobe.

Gradually their talk died out and drowsiness began to steal upon the eyelids of the little waifs. The pipe dropped from the fingers of the Red-Handed, and he slept the sleep of the conscience-free and the weary. The Terror of the Seas and the Black Avenger of the Spanish Main had more difficulty in getting to sleep. They said their prayers inwardly, and lying down, since there was nobody there with authority to make them kneel and recite aloud; in truth, they had a mind not to say them at all, but they were afraid to proceed to such lengths at that, lest they might call down a sudden and special thunderbolt from Heaven.

Then at once they reached and hovered upon the imminent verge of sleep—but an intruder came, now, that would not "down." It was conscience. They began to feel a vague fear that they had been doing wrong to run away; and next they thought of the stolen meat, and then the real torture came. They tried to argue it away by reminding conscience that they had purloined sweetmeats and apples scores of times; but conscience was not to be appeased by such thin plausibilities; it seemed to them, in the end, that there was no getting around the stubborn fact that taking sweetmeats was only "hooking," while taking bacon and hams and such valuables was plain simple *stealing*—and there was a command against that in the Bible. So they inwardly resolved that so long as they remained in the business, their piracies should not again be sullied with the crime of stealing. Then conscience granted a truce, and these curiously inconsistent pirates fell peacefully to sleep.

. . . . . . . . . . .

When Tom awoke in the morning, he wondered where he was. He sat up and rubbed his eyes and looked around. Then he comprehended. It was the cool gray dawn, and there was a delicious sense of repose and peace in the deep pervading calm and silence of the woods. Not a leaf stirred; not a sound obtruded upon great Nature's meditation. Beaded dewdrops stood upon the leaves and grasses. A white layer of ashes covered the fire, and a thin blue breath of smoke rose straight into the air.

Tom stirred up the other pirates and they all clattered away with a shout, and in a minute or two were stripped and chasing after and tumbling over each other in the shallow limpid water of the white sand bar. They felt no longing for the little village sleeping in the distance beyond the majestic waste of water. A vagrant current or a slight rise in the river had carried off their raft, but this only gratified them, since its going was something like burning the bridge between them and civilization.

They came back to camp wonderfully refreshed, glad-hearted, and ravenous; and they soon had the campfire blazing up again. Huck found a spring of clear cold water close by, and the boys made cups of broad oak or hickory leaves, and felt that water, sweetened with such charm, would be a good enough substitute for coffee. While Joe was slicing bacon for breakfast, Tom and Huck asked him to hold on a minute; they stepped to a promising nook in the river bank and threw in their lines; almost immediately they had their reward. Joe had not had time to get impatient before they were back again with some handsome bass, a couple of sun-perch, and a small catfish—provisions enough for quite a family. They fried the fish with the bacon, and were astonished; for no fish had ever seemed so delicious before. They did not know that the quicker a fresh-water fish is on the fire after he is caught the better he is; and they reflected little upon what a sauce open-air sleeping, open-air exercise, bathing, and a large ingredient of hunger makes, too.

After breakfast they then went off through the woods on an exploring expedition. They tramped gaily along, over decaying logs, through tangled underbrush, among solemn monarchs of the forest, hung from their crowns to the ground with a drooping regalia of grapevines. Now and then they came upon snug nooks carpeted with grass and jeweled with flowers.

They found plenty of things to be delighted with, but nothing to be astonished at. They discovered that the island was about three miles long and a quarter of a mile wide, and that the shore it lay closest to was only separated from it by a narrow channel hardly two hundred yards wide. They took a swim about every hour, so it was close upon the middle of the afternoon when they got back to camp. They were too hungry to stop to fish, but they fared sumptuously upon cold ham, and then threw themselves down in the shade to talk. But the talk soon began to drag, and then died. The stillness, the solemnity that brooded in the woods, and the sense of loneliness, began to tell upon the spirits of the boys. They fell to thinking. A sort of undefined longing crept upon them. This took dim shape, presently—it was budding homesickness. But they were all ashamed of their weakness, and none was brave enough to speak his thought.

For some time, now, the boys had been dully conscious of a peculiar sound in the distance, just as one sometimes is of the ticking of a clock which he takes no distinct note of. But now this mysterious sound became more pronounced, and forced a recognition. The boys started, glanced at each other, and then each assumed a listening attitude. There was a long silence, profound and unbroken; then a deep, sullen boom came floating down out of the distance.

"What is it?" exclaimed Joe, under his breath.

"I wonder," said Tom in a whisper.

" 'Tain't thunder," said Huckleberry, in an awed tone, "becuz thunder—"

"Hark!" said Tom. "Listen—don't talk."

They waited a time that seemed an age, and then the same muffled boom troubled the solemn hush.

"Let's go and see."

They sprang to their feet and hurried to the shore toward the town. They parted the bushes on the bank and peered out over the water. The little stream ferryboat was about a mile below the village, drifting with the current. Her broad deck seemed crowded with people. There were a great many skiffs rowing about or floating with the stream in the neighborhood of the ferryboat, but the boys could not determine what the men in them were doing. Presently a great jet of white smoke burst from the ferryboat's side, and as it expanded and rose in a lazy cloud, that same dull throb of sound was borne to the listeners again.

"I know now!" exclaimed Tom; "somebody's drownded!"

"That's it!" said Huck; "they done that last summer, when Bill Turner got drownded; they shoot a cannon over the water, and that makes him come up to the top. Yes, and they take loaves of bread and put quicksilver in 'em and set 'em afloat, and wherever there's anybody that's drownded, they'll float right there and stop."

"Yes, I've heard about that," said Joe. "I wonder what makes the bread do that."

"Oh, it ain't the bread, so much," said Tom; "I reckon it's mostly what they *say* over it before they start it out."

"But they don't say anything over it," said Huck. "I've seen 'em and they don't."

"Well, that's funny," said Tom. "But maybe they say it to themselves. Of *course* they do. Anybody might know that."

The other boys agreed that there was reason in what Tom said, because an ignorant lump of bread, uninstructed by an incantation, could not be expected to act very intelligently when sent upon an errand of such gravity.

"By jings, I wish I was over there, now," said Joe.

"I do too," said Huck. "I'd give heaps to know who it is."

The boys still listened and watched. Presently a revealing thought flashed through Tom's mind, and he exclaimed:

"Boys, I know who's drownded—it's us!"

They felt like heroes in an instant. Here was a gorgeous triumph; they were missed; they were mourned; hearts were breaking on their account; tears were being shed; accusing memories of unkindnesses to these poor lost lads were rising up, and unavailing regrets and remorse were being indulged; and best of all, the departed were the talk of the whole town, and the envy of all the boys, as far as this dazzling notoriety was concerned. This was fine. It was worth-while to be a pirate, after all.

As twilight drew on, the ferryboat went back to her accustomed business and skiffs disappeared. The pirates returned to camp. They were jubilant with vanity over their new grandeur and the illustrious trouble they were making. They caught fish, cooked supper and ate it, and then fell to guessing at what the village was thinking and saying about them; and the pictures they drew of the public distress on their account were gratifying to look upon—from their point of view.

But when the shadows of night closed them in, they gradually ceased to talk, and sat gazing into the fire, with their minds evidently wandering elsewhere. The excitement was gone, now, and Tom and Joe could not keep back thoughts of certain persons at home who were not enjoying this fine frolic as much as they were. Misgivings came; they grew troubled and unhappy; a sigh or two escaped, unawares. By and by Joe timidly ventured upon a roundabout "feeler" as to how the others might look upon a return to civilization—not right now, but—

Tom withered him with derision! Huck, being uncommitted as yet, joined in with Tom, and the waverer quickly "explained," and was glad to get out of the scrape with as little taint of chicken-hearted homesickness clinging to his garments as he could. Mutiny was effectually laid to rest for the moment.

. . . . . . . . . . . . . .

There was no hilarity in the little town that Saturday. The Harpers and Aunt Polly's family were being put into mourning, with great grief and many tears. An unusual quiet possessed the village and the villagers conducted their concerns with an absent air, and talked little; but they sighed often. The Saturday holiday seemed a burden to the children. They had no heart in their sports, and gradually gave them up.

Quite a group of boys and girls—playmates of Tom's and Joe's—came by the schoolhouse yard, and stood looking over the paling fence and talking in reverent tones of how Tom did so-and-so, the last time they saw him, and how Joe said this and that small trifle (pregnant with awful prophecy, as they could easily see now!)—and each speaker pointed out the exact spot where the lost lads stood at the time, and then added something like "and I was a-standing just so—just as I am now, and as if you was as close as that—and he smiled, just this way—and then something seemed to go all over me, like—awful, you know—and I never thought what it meant, of course, but I can see now!"

Then there was a dispute about who saw the dead boys last in life, and many claimed that dismal distinction, and offered evidences, more or less tampered with by the witness; and when it was ultimately decided who *did* see the departed last, and exchanged the last words with them, the lucky parties took upon themselves a sort of sacred importance, and were gaped at and envied by all the rest. One poor chap, who had no other grandeur to offer, said with tolerably manifest pride in remembrance:

"Well, Tom Sawyer he licked me once."

But that bid for glory was a failure. Most of the boys could say that, and so that cheapened the distinction too much. The group loitered away, still recalling memories of the lost heroes, in awed voices.

When the Sunday-school hour was finished, the next morning, the bell began to toll, instead of ringing in the usual way. It was a very still Sabbath, and the mournful sound seemed in keeping with the musing hush that lay upon nature. The villagers began to gather, loitering a moment in the vestibule to converse in whispers about the sad event. But there was no whispering in the house; only the funereal rustling of dresses as the women gathered to their seats disturbed the silence there. None could remember when the little church had been so full before. There was finally a waiting pause, an expectant dumbness, and then Aunt Polly entered, followed by the Harper family, all in deep black, and the whole congregation, the old minister as well, rose reverently and stood, until the mourners were seated in the front pew. There was another communing silence, broken at intervals by muffled sobs, and then the minister spread his hands abroad and prayed. A moving hymn was sung, and the text followed: "I am the Resurrection and the Life."

As the service proceeded, the clergyman drew such pictures of the graces, the winning ways, and the rare promise of the lost lads, that every soul there, thinking he recognized these pictures, felt a pang in remembering that he had persistently blinded himself to them always before, and had as persistently seen only faults and flaws in the poor boys. The minister related many a touching incident in the lives of the departed, too, which illustrated their sweet, generous natures, and the people could easily see, now, how noble and beautiful those episodes were, and remembered with grief that at the time they occurred they had seemed rank rascalities, well deserving of the cowhide. The congregation became more and more moved, as the pathetic tale went on, till at last the whole company broke down and joined the weeping mourners in a chorus of anguished sobs, the preacher himself giving way to his feelings, and crying in the pulpit.

There was a rustle in the gallery, which nobody noticed; a moment later the church door creaked; the minister raised his streaming eyes above his handkerchief, and stood transfixed! First one and then another pair of eyes followed the minister's, and then almost with one impulse the congregation rose and stared while the three dead boys came marching up the aisle, Tom in the lead, Joe next, and Huck in the rear! They had been hid in the unused gallery listening to their own funeral sermon!

Aunt Polly and the Harpers threw themselves upon their restored ones, smothered them with kisses and poured out thanksgivings, while poor Huck stood abashed and uncomfortable, not knowing exactly what to do or where to hide from so many unwelcoming eyes. He wavered, and started to slink away, but Tom seized him and said:

"Aunt Polly, it ain't fair. Somebody's got to be glad to see Huck."

"And so they shall. I'm glad to see him, poor motherless thing!" And the loving attentions Aunt Polly lavished upon him were the one thing capable of making him more uncomfortable than he was before.

Suddenly the minister shouted at the top of his voice: "Praise God from whom all blessings flow—SING!—and put your hearts in it!"

And they did. Old Hundred swelled up with a triumphant burst, and while it shook the rafters Tom Sawyer the Pirate looked around upon the envying juveniles about him and confessed in his heart that this was the proudest moment of his life.

## THE TRUCE ON TREASURE ISLAND[1]

*Robert Louis Stevenson*

Sure enough, there were two men just outside the stockade, one of them waving a white cloth; the other, no less a person than Long John Silver himself, standing placidly by.

It was still quite early, and the coldest morning that I think I ever was abroad in; a chill that pierced into the marrow. The sky was bright and cloudless overhead, and the tops of the trees shone rosily in the sun. But where Silver stood with his lieutenant all was still in shadow, and they waded knee deep in a low white vapor, that had crawled during the night out of the morass. The chill and the vapor taken together told a poor tale of the island. It was plainly a damp, feverish, unhealthy spot.

"Keep indoors, men," said the captain. "Ten to one this is a trick."

Then he hailed the buccaneer.

"Who goes? Stand, or we fire."

"Flag of truce," cried Silver.

The captain was in the porch, keeping

[1] From Robert Louis Stevenson, *Treasure Island.*

himself carefully out of the way of a treacherous shot should any be intended. He turned and spoke to us:

"Doctor's watch on the lookout. Dr. Livesey take the north side, if you please; Jim, the east; Gray, west. The watch below, all hands to load muskets. Lively, men, and careful."

And then he turned again to the mutineers.

"And what do you want with your flag of truce?" he cried.

This time it was the other man who replied.

"Cap'n Silver, sir, to come on board and make terms," he shouted.

"Cap'n Silver! Don't know him. Who's he?" cried the captain. And we could hear him adding to himself: "Cap'n, is it? My heart, and here's promotion!"

Long John answered for himself.

"Me, sir. These poor lads have chosen me cap'n, after your desertion, sir"—laying a particular emphasis upon the word "desertion." "We're willing to submit, if we can come to terms, and no bones about it. All I ask is your word, Cap'n Smollett, to let me safe and sound out of this here stockade, and one minute to get out o' shot before a gun is fired."

"My man," said Captain Smollett, "I have not the slightest desire to talk to you. If you wish to talk to me, you can come, that's all. If there's any treachery it'll be on your side, and the Lord help you."

"That's enough, cap'n," shouted Long John cheerily. "A word from you's enough. I know a gentleman and you may lay to that."

We could see the man who carried the flag of truce attempting to hold Silver back. Nor was that wonderful, seeing how cavalier had been the captain's answer. But Silver laughed at him aloud and slapped him on the back, as if the idea of alarm had been absurd. Then he advanced to the stockade, threw over his crutch, got a leg up, and with great vigor and skill succeeded in surmounting the fence and dropping safely to the other side.

I will confess that I was far too much taken up with what was going on to be of the slightest use as sentry; indeed, I had already deserted my eastern loophole and crept up behind the captain, who had now seated himself on the threshold, with his elbows on his knees, his head in his hands, and his eyes fixed on the water, as it bubbled out of the old iron kettle in the sand. He was whistling to himself, "Come, Lasses and Lads."

Silver had terrible hard work getting up the knoll. What with the steepness of the incline, the thick tree stumps, and the soft sand, he and his crutch were as helpless as a ship in stays. But he stuck to it like a man in silence, and at last arrived before the captain, whom he saluted in the handsomest style. He was tricked out in his best; an immense blue coat, thick with brass buttons, hung as low as to his knees, and a fine laced hat was set on the back of his head.

"Here you are, my man," said the captain, raising his head. "You had better sit down."

"You ain't a-going to let me inside, cap'n?" complained Long John. "It's a main cold morning to be sure, sir, to sit outside upon the sand."

"Why, Silver," said the captain, "if you had pleased to be an honest man, you might have been sitting in your galley. It's your own doing. You're either my ship's cook—and then you were treated handsome—or Cap'n Silver, a common mutineer and pirate, and then you can go hang!"

"Well, well, cap'n," returned the sea cook, sitting down as he was bidden on the sand, "you'll have to give me a hand up again, that's all. A sweet pretty place you have of it here. Ah, there's Jim! The top of the morning to you, Jim. Doctor, here's my service. Why, there you all are together like a happy family, in a manner of speaking."

"If you have anything to say, my man, better say it," said the captain.

"Right you were, Cap'n Smollett," replied Silver. "Dooty is dooty, to be sure. Well, now, you look here, that was a good lay of yours last night. I don't deny it was a good lay. Some of you pretty handy with a handspike end. And I'll not deny neither but what some of my people was shook—maybe all was shook; maybe I was shook myself; maybe that's why I'm here for terms. But you mark me, cap'n, it won't do twice, by thunder! We'll have to do sentry-go, and ease off a point or so on the rum. Maybe you think we were all a sheet in the wind's eye. But I'll tell you I was sober; I was on'y dog tired; and if I'd awoke a second sooner I'd a' caught you at the act, I would. He wasn't dead when I got round to him, not he."

"Well?" says Captain Smollett, as cool as can be.

All that Silver said was a riddle to him, but you would never have guessed it from his tone. As for me, I began to have an inkling. Ben Gunn's last words came back to my mind. I began to suppose that he had paid the buccaneers a visit while they all lay drunk together round their fire, and I reckoned up with glee that we had only fourteen enemies to deal with.

"Well, here it is," said Silver. "We want that treasure, and we'll have it—that's our point! You would just as soon save your lives, I reckon; and that's yours. You have a chart, haven't you?"

"That's as may be," replied the captain.

"Oh, well, you have, I know that," returned Long John. "You needn't be so husky with a man; there ain't a particle of service in that, and you may lay to it. What I mean is, we want your chart. Now, I never meant you no harm, myself."

"That won't do with me, my man," interrupted the captain. "We know exactly what you meant to do, and we don't care; for now, you see, you can't do it."

And the captain looked at him calmly, and proceeded to fill a pipe.

"If Abe Gray—" Silver broke out.

"Avast there!" cried Mr. Smollett. "Gray told me nothing, and I asked him nothing; and what's more I would see you and him and this whole island blown clean out of the water into blazes first. So there's my mind for you, my man, on that."

This little whiff of temper seemed to cool Silver down. He had been growing nettled before, but now he pulled himself together.

"Like enough," said he. "I would set no limits to what gentlemen might consider shipshape, or might not, as the case were. And, seein' as how you are about to take a pipe, cap'n, I'll make so free as to do likewise."

And he filled a pipe and lighted it; and the two men sat silently smoking for quite a while, now looking each other in the face, now stopping their tobacco, now leaning forward to spit. It was as good as the play to see them.

"Now," resumed Silver, "here it is. You give us the chart to get the treasure by, and drop shooting poor seamen, and stoving of their heads in while asleep. You do that, and we'll offer you a choice. Either you come aboard along of us, once the treasure shipped, and then I'll give you my affydavy, upon my word of honor, to clap you somewhere safe ashore. Or, if that ain't to your fancy, some of my hands being rough, and having old scores, on account of hazing, then you can stay here, you can. We'll divide stores with you, man for man; and I'll give my affydavy, as before, to speak the first ship I sight, and send 'em here to pick you up. Now you'll own that's talking. Handsomer you couldn't look to get, not you. And I hope"—raising his voice—"that all hands in this here blockhouse will overhaul my words, for what is spoke to one is spoke to all."

Captain Smollett rose from his seat, and knocked out the ashes of his pipe in the palm of his left hand.

"Is that all?" he asked.

"Every last word, by thunder!" answered John. "Refuse that, and you've seen the last of me but musket balls."

"Very good," said the captain. "Now you'll hear me. If you'll come up one by one, unarmed, I'll engage to clap you all in irons, and take you home to a fair trial in England. If you won't, my name is Alexander Smollett, I've flown my sovereign's colors, and I'll see you all to Davy Jones. You can't find the treasure. You can't sail the ship—there's not a man among you fit to sail the ship. You can't fight us—Gray, there, got away from five of you. Your ship's in irons, Master Silver; you're on a lee shore, and so you'll find. I stand here and tell you so; and they're the last good words you'll get from me; for, in the name of heaven, I'll put a bullet in your back when next I meet you. Tramp, my lad. Bundle out of this, please, hand over hand, and double quick."

Silver's face was a picture; his eyes started in his head with wrath. He angrily shook the fire out of his pipe.

"Give me a hand up!" he cried.

"Not I," returned the captain.

"Who'll give me a hand up?" he roared.

Not a man among us moved. Growling the foulest imprecations, he crawled along the sand till he got hold of the porch and could hoist himself again upon his crutch. Then he spat into the spring.

"There!" he cried, "that's what I think of ye. Before an hour's out, I'll stove in your old blockhouse like a rum puncheon. Laugh, by thunder, laugh! Before an hour's out, ye'll laugh upon the other side. Them that die'll be the lucky ones."

And with a dreadful oath he stumbled off, plowed down the sand, was helped across the stockade, after four or five failures, by the man with the flag of truce, and disappeared in an instant afterward among the trees.

## *Stories about Boys and Girls: Suggested Grades*

*Grade One*
- Lucky Little Lena
- Billy and Blaze

*Grade Two*
- Grandmother's Buttons
- Pita's Painted Pig

*Grade Three*
- Letters to Channy
- The Blue Teapot

*Grade Four*
- Mr. Murdle's Large Heart
- Jancsi and Kate

*Grade Five*
- Calypso
- Stories of Other Days in Old Bergen
- Swiss Family Robinson
- David and Goliath

*Grade Six*
- The Queen of the Pirate Isle
- Little Goody Two-Shoes

The Bears of Blue River
Hans Brinker and His Sister
The Far-Distant Oxus

*Grade Seven*
Little Women Plan Christmas
Christmas with the Cratchits
"Mark Twain"
Tom Sawyer and His Pirate Crew

*Grade Eight*
The Truce on Treasure Island

## *Books about Boys and Girls*

### *Grades One and Two*

Anderson, C. W., *Billy and Blaze,* illus. by the author. Macmillan.

Bacon, Peggy, *The Terrible Nuisance,* illus. by the author. Harcourt, Brace.

Baruch, Dorothy W., *I Know a Surprise,* illus. by George and Doris Hauman. Lothrop.

Bemelmans, Ludwig, *Hansi,* illus. by the author. Viking.

Bennett, Richard, *Skookum and Sandy,* illus. by the author. Doubleday, Doran.

Bianco, Margery, *The Hurdy-Gurdy Man,* illus. by Robert Lawson. Oxford.

Brock, Emma L., *Nobody's Mouse,* illus. by the author. Knopf.

Bryan, Dorothy, *Bobby Wanted a Pony,* illus. by Marguerite Bryan. Dodd Mead.

D'Aulaire, Ingri, and Edgar Parin d'Aulaire, *Ola,* illus. by the authors. Doubleday, Doran.

Flack, Marjorie, *Angus and the Ducks,* illus. by the author. Doubleday, Doran.

———, *Lucky Little Lena,* illus. by the author. Macmillan.

———, *William and His Kitten,* illus. by the author. Houghton Mifflin.

Hauman, George, and Doris Hauman, *Buttons,* illus. by the authors. Macmillan.

Haywood, Carolyn, *"B" Is for Betsy,* illus. by the author. Harcourt, Brace.

Heward, Constance, *Ameliar-Anne and the Green Umbrella,* illus. by Susan B. Pearse. Macrae.

———, *The Twins and Tabiffa,* illus. by Susan B. Pearse. Macrae.

Hill, Helen, and Violet Maxwell, *Charlie and His Puppy Bingo,* illus. by the authors. Macmillan.

Hogan, Inez, *Twin Kids,* illus. by the author. Dutton.

Hunt, Clara Whitehill, *About Harriet,* illus. by Maginel Wright Barney. Houghton Mifflin.

Lattimore, Eleanor Frances, *Little Pear,* illus. by the author. Harcourt, Brace.

Lenski, Lois, *Surprise for Mother,* illus. by the author. Stokes.

Lindman, Maj, *Snipp, Snapp, Snurr and the Red Shoes,* illus. by the author. Whitman.

Literature Committee of the Association for Childhood Education, *Told under the Blue Umbrella,* illus. by Marguerite Davis. Macmillan.

Newberry, Clare Turlay, *Barkis,* illus. by the author. Harper.

Petersham, Maud, and Miska Petersham (illustrators), *The Christ Child, as Told by Matthew and Luke.* Doubleday, Doran.

Sewell, Helen, *A Head for Happy,* illus. by the author. Macmillan.

Slocum, Rosalie, *Breakfast with the Clowns,* illus. by the author. Viking.

Smith, Susan, *The Christmas Tree in the Woods,* illus. by Helen Sewell. Nelson.

Stone, Amy Wentworth, *P-Penny and His Red Cart,* illus. by Hildegard Woodward. Lothrop.

Tousey, Sanford, *Cowboy Tommy's Roundup,* illus. by the author. Doubleday, Doran.

Wiese, Kurt, *Joe Buys Nails,* illus. by the author. Doubleday, Doran.

## *Grades Three and Four*

Beskow, Elsa, *Aunt Green, Aunt Brown, and Aunt Lavender* (trans. by Siri Andrews), illus. by the author. Harper.

Bianco, Margery. *A Street of Little Shops,* illus. by Grace Paull. Doubleday, Doran.

Brown, Esther, *Nanette of the Wooden Shoes,* illus. by the author. Macmillan.

Clark, Margery, *The Poppy Seed Cakes,* illus. by Maud and Miska Petersham. Doubleday, Doran.

Credle, Ellis, *Down, Down the Mountain,* illus. by the author. Nelson.

Dalgliesh, Alice, *The Blue Teapot,* illus. by Hildegard Woodward. Macmillan.

———, *Relief's Rocker,* illus. by Hildegard Woodward. Macmillan.

D'Aulaire, Ingri, and Edgar Parin d'Aulaire, *Children of the Northlights,* illus. by the authors. Viking.

De Angeli, Marguerite, *Petite Suzanne,* illus. by the author. Doubleday, Doran.

Hader, Berta, and Elmer Hader, *Billy Butter,* illus. by the authors. Macmillan.

Handforth, Thomas, *Mei Li,* illus. by the author. Doubleday, Doran.

Lathrop, Dorothy P., *Animals of the Bible,* illus. by the author. Stokes.

Moon, Grace, *The Book of Nah-wee,* illus. by Carl Moon. Doubleday, Doran.

Olcott, Virginia, *Anton and Trini, Children of the Alpland,* illus. by Constance Whittemore. Silver Burdett.

Petersham, Maud, and Miska Petersham, *Miki,* illus. by the authors. Doubleday, Doran.

Phillips, Ethel Calvert, *Calico,* illus. by Maginel Wright Barney. Houghton Mifflin.

Sawyer, Ruth, *Toño Antonio,* illus. by F. Luis Mora. Viking.

Sayers, Frances Clarke, *Bluebonnets for Lucinda,* illus. by Helen Sewell. Viking.

Seredy, Kate, *The Good Master,* illus. by the author. Viking.

Sperry, Armstrong, *One Day with Jambi in Sumatra,* illus. by the author. Winston.

Tousey, Sanford, *Steamboat Billy,* illus. by the author. Doubleday, Doran.

Van Stockum, Hilda, *A Day on Skates,* illus. by the author. Harper.

Washburne, Heluiz Chandler, *Letters to Channy,* illus. by Electra Papadopoulous. Rand McNally.

Wells, Rhea, *Coco, the Goat,* illus. by the author. Doubleday, Doran.

White, Stewart Edward, *The Magic Forest.* Macmillan.

Whitney, Elinor, *Timothy and the Blue Cart,* illus. by Berta and Elmer Hader. Stokes.

Wiese, Kurt, *Liang and Lo,* illus. by the author. Doubleday, Doran.

Wilder, Laura Ingalls, *The Little House on the Prairie,* illus. by Helen Sewell. Harper.

## *Grades Five and Six*

Burglon, Nora, *The Children of the Soil,* illus. by Edgar Parin d'Aulaire. Doubleday, Doran.

Chevalier, Ragnhild, *Wandering Monday,* illus. by James L. McCreery. Macmillan.

Coatsworth, Elizabeth, *Alice-All-by-Herself,* illus. by Marguerite de Angeli. Macmillan.

Dodge, Mary Mapes, *Hans Brinker; or, The Silver Skates,* illus. by George Wharton Edwards. Scribner.

Everson, Florence McClurg, and Howard Everson, *The Coming of the Dragon Ships,* illus. by Edgar Parin d'Aulaire. Dutton.

Forbes, Helen Cady, *Mario's Castle,* illus. by Marguerite de Angeli. Macmillan.

Goldsmith, Oliver (ascribed to), *The History of Little Goody Two-Shoes,* illus. by Alice Woodward. Macmillan.

Hamsun, Marie, *A Norwegian Farm* (trans. by Maida C. Darnton), illus. by Elsa Jemne. Lippincott.

Harte, Bret, *The Queen of the Pirate Isle,* illus. by Kate Greenaway. Warne.

Hull, Katherine, and Pamela Whitlock, *The Far-Distant Oxus.* Macmillan.

James, Will, *Look-See with Uncle Bill,* illus. by the author. Scribner.

Kent, Louise Andrews, *He Went with Marco Polo,* illus. by Cyrus LeRoy Baldridge and Paul Quinn. Houghton Mifflin.

Major, Charles, *The Bears of Blue River.* Macmillan.

Miller, Elizabeth Cleveland, *The Children of the Mountain Eagle,* illus. by Maud and Miska Petersham. Doubleday, Doran.

Nusbaum, Deric, *Deric in Mesa Verde,* illus. by photographs. Putnam.

Quiller-Couch, Arthur, and Others, *The Children's Bible.* Macmillan.

Rowe, Dorothy, *Traveling Shops,* illus. by Lynd Ward. Macmillan.

Sawyer, Ruth, *Roller Skates,* illus. by Valenti Angelo. Viking.

Shannon, Monica, *Dobry,* illus. by Atanas Katchomakoff. Viking.

Singer, Caroline, *Ali Lives in Iran,* illus. by Cyrus LeRoy Baldridge. Holiday House.

Snedeker, Caroline Dale, *Downright Dencey,* illus. by Maginel Wright Barney. Doubleday, Doran.

Spyri, Johanna, *Heidi* (trans. by Helen B. Dole), illus. by Marguerite Davis. Ginn.

Stein, Evaleen, *Gabriel and the Hour Book,* illus. by Adelaide Everhart. Page.

Stong, Phil, *Farm Boy,* illus. by Kurt Wiese. Dodd Mead

Tietjens, Eunice, *Boy of the Desert,* illus. by Will Hollingsworth. Coward-McCann.

Wiggin, Kate Douglas, *Rebecca of Sunnybrook Farm,* illus. by Helen M. Grose. Houghton Mifflin.

Wilder, Laura Ingalls, *On the Banks of Plum Creek,* illus. by Helen Sewell. Harper.

Wyss, Johann David, *Swiss Family Robinson* (ed. by C. E. Mitton), illus. by Harry Roundtree. Macmillan.

## *Grades Seven and Eight*

Alcott, Louisa M., *Eight Cousins,* illus. by Hattie Longstreet Price. Little, Brown.

———, *Little Men,* illus. by Reginald Birch. Little, Brown.

———, *Little Women,* illus. by Jessie Wilcox Smith. Little, Brown.

Bagnold, Enid, *National Velvet,* illus. by Laurian Jones. Morrow.

Bennett, John, *Master Skylark,* illus. by Reginald Birch. Appleton-Century.

Best, Herbert, *Garram, the Hunter,* illus. by Erick Berry. Doubleday, Doran.

Brink, Carol Ryrie, *Anything Can Happen on the River,* illus. by W. W. Berger. Macmillan.

Clemens, Samuel L. (Mark Twain), *The Adventures of Tom Sawyer,* illus. by Worth Brehm. Harper.

———, *The Adventures of Huckleberry Finn,* illus. by Worth Brehm. Harper.

———, *The Prince and the Pauper,* illus. by Robert Lawson. Winston.

Dickens, Charles, *A Christmas Carol,* illus. by Francis D. Bedford. Macmillan.

Field, Rachel, *Hepatica Hawks,* illus. by Allen Lewis. Macmillan.

Goodspeed, Edgar J., *The Junior Bible,* illus. by Frank Dobias. Macmillan.

Hawes, Charles Boardman, *The Dark Frigate.* Little, Brown.

Hewes, Agnes Danforth, *Spice and the Devil's Cave,* illus. by Lynd Ward. Knopf.

Kelly, Eric P., *The Trumpeter of Krakow,* illus. by Angela Pruszynska. Macmillan.

Lewis, C. Day, *Dick Willoughby,* illus. by H. R. Millar. Random House.

Lewis, Elizabeth Foreman, *Young Fu of the Upper Yangtze,* illus. by Kurt Wiese. Winston.

Meigs, Cornelia, *Rain on the Roof,* illus. by Edith Ballinger Price. Macmillan.

———, *Young Americans: How History Looked to Them While It Was in the Making,* illus. by Kurt Wiese. Ginn.

Mukerji, Dhan Gopal, *Ghond, the Hunter,* illus. by Boris Artzybasheff. Dutton.

Ransome, Arthur, *Swallows and Amazons,* illus. by Helene Carter. Lippincott.

Snedeker, Caroline Dale, *The Forgotten Daughter,* illus. by Dorothy P. Lathrop. Doubleday, Doran.

Stevenson, Robert Louis, *Treasure Island,* illus. by N. C. Wyeth. Scribner.

Tarkington, Booth, *Penrod: His Complete Story,* illus. by Gordon Grant. Doubleday, Doran.

# The Making of America

## BY COVERED WAGON [1]

*Emma L. Brock*

Something was happening in the house. That fact was clear even to my cornhusk mind, as I sat on the cherry chest of drawers in the dining room.

"Something is happening," I said to myself.

The early spring birds were piping in the sunshine. The ground was still soft with mud from the last snow. There was nothing strange in all that, but the family was behaving as it had never behaved before.

Sarah burst in at the kitchen door. Sarah never just walked in at a door. She ran in, or skipped in, or fell in. That day she burst in at the kitchen door and forgot to wipe her feet.

"Sarah," Mrs. Hodgetts said, "your feet."

"Oh," cried Sarah, wiping one toe on the braided rug. "Where is Drusilla? I must tell her about going to Minnesota."

So that was it. That was what all the stir was about. Going to Minnesota, going to Minnesota! I had heard about Minnesota before. Mr. Phineas Smith had talked a whole evening to Mr. Hodgetts about Minnesota, and Mr. Hodgetts had been a little queer ever since. It was way out west by the Indian country. It was wide flat prairie land with deep, rich, black soil—no rocks, no sand, no hills.

"You can grow corn as tall as a man," said Mr. Phineas Smith, spreading his red hands out above his head.

So it was Minnesota that was the cause of the excitement!

"I must wash all your clothes right away," said Sarah to me. "We are going as soon as the mud is dried up a bit," she added. "Oh, Drusilla, think of it! We are going out to Minnesota to live. Oh, Drusilla!"

Sarah smoothed down the two strands that were left of my yellow wool hair.

. . . . . . . . . .

I am a cornhusk doll. Aunt Polly made me out of cornhusks for Sarah. She tied a neck for me with heavy thread and she tied a waist, too. And she wound thread round and round my legs. She sewed on two jet beads for my eyes and stitched in some red silk for my mouth. Everybody says I am a very handsome doll when I have on my sprigged calico dress and red bonnet. I was proud to be going to Minnesota in a covered wagon!

[1] From Emma L. Brock, *Drusilla.*

Will Smith went with us. He was a very bony boy with more freckles than skin on his nose. He was the oldest child of Mr. Phineas Smith, who knew all about Minnesota.

Mr. Hodgetts fixed a covered wagon to travel in. He bent the trunks of young willow trees in large hoops over the wagon. And over the hoops he stretched a piece of heavy white canvas. That canvas would keep out the sun and the rain when we were on the road.

Mrs. Hodgetts *had* to take the four-poster bed, and the clock, and the kitchen stove, and the spinning wheel, and the cherry chest of drawers. Mr. Hodgetts decided he must take a trailer to hold all the things.

At last we were on our way.

. . . . . . . . . .

"Oop-hey, hey-ha-ha! Oh, oh, haw!" cried Mr. Hodgetts to the oxen.

The oxen tramped slowly, thud, thud, along the dusty road. They were about three times as wide as Mr. Hodgetts and they had twice as many feet, but they could not walk so fast. Even Will could walk faster than they could. It would take weeks to get to Minnesota. We had been traveling for two weeks already and we were not halfway there yet.

Some people who had more money than the Hodgetts did would take the train as far as the great Mississippi River, the Father of Waters, and there board the sidewheeler boats that paddled up the river to St. Paul. But the Hodgetts were far too poor for that.

"Oop-hey, hey-ha-ha! Oh, oh, gee!" cried Mr. Hodgetts to the oxen.

Sarah was sitting on the seat between Mrs. Hodgetts and Aunt Polly. It was rather crowded, because Aunt Polly was so lumpy. That is, Aunt Polly's pockets were so lumpy. Some of the things that would not go into the chest were in her pockets. The cooky cutter for one thing. Aunt Polly was making sure that the cooky cutter reached Minnesota.

"Don't sit too close to me, Sarah, or you will bend it," she said.

Sarah was sitting on one foot and holding me up so that I could look out over the brown backs of the oxen and watch the crooked dirty road creeping up on us. All through the day the wagon creaked along, trundling the squeaking trailer behind it. Daisy the cow stepped daintily after the trailer, stopping to snatch at some passing grass whenever she could.

In the afternoon when the sun was sinking low in the sky, Mr. Hodgetts found a clump of trees by a running stream and we made camp there.

"I will turn loose the oxen," said Mr. Hodgetts. "And then I will milk the cow."

"And I will set up the fireplace," said Will.

Will always set up the fireplace, because he liked to put things together.

"And I will lay the table," said Mrs. Hodgetts, as she spread the red and white checkered tablecloth on the ground and on it put the old dishes and the steel knives and forks.

"And I will let the chickens out of their crate," said Sarah.

The chickens ran clucking into the grass beside the road and began to peck and eat greedily.

"And I will gather firewood," said Will. He piled some branches beside the fireplace and brought a log or two from where they hung under the wagon beside the plow.

"And I will grind the coffee," said Sarah. Sarah put the coffee beans in the grinder and turned the handle. The coffee fell out in sharp brown bits.

While the others were busy with all this, Aunt Polly was picking a bunch of windflowers for the table.

"A bouquet of flowers makes it seem like home," Aunt Polly always said.

Over the fireplace they cooked their dinner. The fireplace was just two forked iron rods driven into the ground with a third rod resting on top of the others. From this iron rod they hung the coffee kettle, and on the coals they set the spider for the ham and the potatoes. Mrs. Hodgetts stirred up some biscuits and baked them in a kettle set down into the coals. There were dried apples for dessert.

The ham and the coffee cooking over the fire smelled so good that I wished I could be a real person who ate food and not just a cornhusk doll.

While they were eating dinner, the big black iron kettle filled with water was heating over the fire. After dinner Sarah washed the dishes. Mrs. Hodgetts washed the clothes, and Aunt Polly pinned them on the lines that were strung from the wagon to one of the trees. Aunt Polly always made a pattern of the clothes as she hung them up. First a towel, then a shirt, then a towel, then a shirt. First a white petticoat, then a pink dress, then a white petticoat, and then a blue dress. Mrs. Hodgetts said she did them that way because she was not a good housekeeper. But Aunt Polly said they were prettier hung like that.

After the dishes were done, Saran washed my clothes too, my petticoat and my nightgown and my sprigged calico dress, and hung them on a line by themselves.

Mr. Hodgetts was playing on his fiddle to make the washing shorter. He was playing "Pop goes the weasel." The words went like this:

All around the cobbler's bench
  The monkey chased the weasel.
The monkey thought 'twas all in fun.
  Pop goes the weasel!

When the washing was done Mrs. Hodgetts took out her knitting. She was making some wool socks for next winter. It could be very cold in Minnesota, everybody said —degrees and degrees below zero, perhaps thirty, perhaps even forty.

Will was riding a stick horse through the grass. It could travel much faster than the oxen could. Sarah was rolling her hoop. It bounced over the bumps.

Aunt Polly had pulled a low rocker from the trailer and was teetering back and forth on the bumpy ground. She was writing in her diary. This is what she wrote:

*Monday, May 16.* Yesterday we came to a little town and, as it was Sunday, we stopped and went to church there. The church was in the little white schoolhouse, and the people were very glad to see us and wished us good luck on our journey. We had dinner in a real house, and the lady gave me her recipe for boiled icing. I will try some as soon as the stove is set up in Minnesota. I gave her a pattern for a hooked rug, the one with the wreath of flowers in the center. She is going to make a dress like my pink calico. She has never seen one of those new-fangled sewing machines. I told her about the one I saw at second cousin Lydia's. She is sure that hand sewing is quicker. She thinks my ginger cookies are good keepers. I would like her for a neighbor, if only Minnesota were not so far away.

At twilight the chickens came hopping back to their crate and Sarah shut them in. And the oxen and Daisy strolled back to the wagon. Mr. and Mrs. Hodgetts spread the bedding under the wagon for the women and Sarah. Mr. Hodgetts and Will rolled themselves up in shawls and lay down beside the wagon wheels. While the pale moon was slipping up the sky, they all fell asleep. And they slept as hard as they could until the sun rose. Then they had pancakes and bacon, hitched up the oxen, and went on again.

The days passed by like that. Each one was just like the one before, the thud of the oxen's feet along the dusty road and the squeak of the wagon lurching over the ridges.

Only the evenings were different. On Tuesday nights they ironed the clothes they had washed on Monday. On Wednesday nights they mended the clothes they had ironed on Tuesday. On Thursday nights they churned the butter. On Friday nights they cleaned house and dusted out the covered wagon. On Saturday nights they baked the bread in the Dutch oven. On Sunday nights they sang hymns together to the music of Mr. Hodgetts' fiddle.

During the first two weeks we had passed through many towns and passed by many farmhouses. But as we trailed slowly toward the setting sun, the houses and towns were farther apart. And as we went north through Wisconsin, they grew fewer and fewer in number and the empty spaces became wider. It was a long, slow way to Minnesota.

It was nearly the first of June.

"We must be close to the Big River now," said Mr. Hodgetts one day. "See those low blue hills over there. They lie along the river. We should reach it by tomorrow."

"I wish I had a ginger cooky," said Will.

"Yes, I'm right sorry they are all gone," said Mr. Hodgetts.

"Oh, but they are not all gone," said Aunt Polly.

"But the keg is empty," said Will. "I took the last one yesterday."

"I have some right here in my bag," said Aunt Polly.

And there were some in the bag, a whole dozen of them wrapped in a napkin. And there were other things in that bag too. You could never guess how many. It was bulging every which way with the things that were in it.

That really was the last of the cookies.

"But just wait until we get the stove set up in Minnesota," said Aunt Polly.

The next day we came to a real town perched on the river bank. The tall blackened stacks of the mills puffed yellow smoke against the blue of the sky. Down on the river a white side-wheeler was on its way to St. Paul. On the deck people were laughing and trying to make themselves heard above the screaming noise that was coming from somewhere inside the boat.

"It's a calliope," cried Will, "a real calliope that goes by steam!"

The brown oxen lumbered down the slope to the ferry, where they had to wait while the ferryboat carried another wagon across the river. While they were waiting, Mr. Hodgetts bought a barrel of flour, and Aunt Polly traded an embroidery design for some peppermint drops. They all mailed letters back home to be carried down the river in a side-wheeler to the town where the railroad ended. There were no railroads west of the Big River then.

The oxen stamped onto the ferryboat, though they did not want to at all. They spread their nostrils and snorted and tossed their heads. But Mr. Hodgetts and two or three of the ferrymen pulled them and pushed them until they stumbled on, dragging the wagon after them.

Will was leading Daisy, and it took about six men and Mrs. Hodgetts and Sarah and me to get her on. She was so frightened that her eyes almost rolled out of her face. But after she was on, she did not mind at all and began chewing her cud as if she were in a field of daisies.

Will stood by the rail holding Daisy's rope and watching the big splashing wheel that made the ferryboat go. It was whirling round and churning up the water into white foam. Will was leaning over the rail to see how it worked. He always had to see how things worked. He hung farther and farther over the rail. He hung half over the rail, and then about three-quarters over the rail. And then he was all over the rail, his feet in the air.

Aunt Polly screamed, and so did everyone else. He would fall right down by the wheel and be drowned. Everyone rushed to the rail, and the ferrymen began to kick off their boots to jump in.

But Will did not fall into the river. He just held fast to Daisy's rope. He was on the water side of the rail, holding fast to Daisy's rope and looking surprised. And Daisy was on the boat side of the rail, with the rope pulling her head tightly against it, and looking more surprised than Will.

The ferrymen reached over the side and pulled Will up and set him on the deck.

"Lack-a-mercy-on-us!" cried Aunt Polly. "You might have been crushed by the wheel."

She began rubbing Will's hand that had held the rope. It was all red and scraped.

"We'll fix that up in a minute," said Aunt Polly. And she sat right down on the deck and pulled some ointment and some linen bandages from her bag and wrapped up Will's hand round and round.

Will's freckles were standing out against his white face.

"I won't do that again," he said.

After we had slid across the Father of Waters on the ferryboat, we climbed the steep bank on the other side. There were trees all round, oak and ash and walnut and cherry and hickory.

"Now we are in Minnesota," said Sarah.

"Oh, but wait," said Mr. Hodgetts. "This is only the beginning. Wait until we come to the prairie. That is really Minnesota."

And the next day we did. We turned out of the woodland along the river and came into the open. The prairie rolled on and on as far as we could see. The gay spring grass was dotted with wild flowers. Passenger pigeons were flying in great circles above us and making dark shadows on the prairie grass. There were clumps of trees here and there and one log cabin in the middle of plowed fields.

"This is Minnesota!" cried Mr. Hodgetts. His eyes were shining. "This is Minnesota!" He looked as if he had found the most precious thing in all the world.

Aunt Polly's earrings were bobbing against her plump neck until they danced with excitement.

Will and Sarah were jumping up and down and clapping their hands. Even Mrs. Hodgetts looked pink and happy.

"Was ever anything so beautiful!" She forgot to feel sorry about the home she had left so far behind her.

And I was so excited that I tipped off from the cherry chest of drawers and fell into the flour barrel. And I might have stayed there for days and days, until enough bread and biscuits had been made to reach me, if two gray mice had not pulled me out and dusted me off. The mice were going to Minnesota, too.

## CADDIE AND THE INDIAN CHIEF [1]

*Carol Ryrie Brink*

Clip-clop-clip sounded Betsy's hoofs across the field. There was a treacherous slime of mud on the surface, but underneath it the clods were still frozen as hard as iron. Then the bare branches of the woods were all around them, and Caddie had to duck and dodge to save her eyes and her hair. Here the February thaw had not succeeded in clearing the snow. It stretched gray and dreary underfoot, treacherously rotted about the roots of the big trees.

Caddie slowed her mare's pace and guided her carefully now. She did not want to lose precious time in floundering about in melting snow. Straight for the river she went. If the ice still held, she could get across here, and the going would be easier on the other side. Not a squirrel or a bird stirred in the woods. So silent! So silent! Only the clip-clop-clip of Betsy's hoofs.

Then the river stretched out before her, a long expanse of blue-gray ice under the gray sky.

"Carefully now, Betsy. Take it slowly, old girl." Caddie held a tight rein with one hand and stroked the horse's neck with the other. "That's a good girl. Take it slowly."

Down the bank they went, delicately onto the ice. Betsy flung up her head, her nostrils distended. Her hind legs slipped on the ice and for a quivering instant she struggled for her balance. Then she found her pace. Slowly, cautiously, she went daintily forward, picking her way, but with a snort of disapproval for the wisdom of her young mistress. The ice creaked, but it was still sound enough to bear their weight. They reached the other side and scrambled up the bank. Well, so much done! Now for more woods.

There was no proper sunset that day, only a sudden, lemon-colored rift in the clouds in the west. Then the clouds closed together again and darkness began to fall The ride was long, but at last it was over.

[1] From Carol Ryrie Brink, *Caddie Woodlawn*. This book was awarded the John Newbery Medal in 1935.

Blue with cold, Caddie rode into the clearing where the Indians had built their winter huts. Dogs ran at her, barking, and there was a warm smell of smoke in the air. A fire was blazing in the center of the clearing. Dark figures moved about it. Were they in war paint and feathers? Caddie's heart pounded as she drew Betsy to a stop. But, no, surely they were only old women bending over cooking pots. The running figures were children, coming now to swarm about her. There was no war paint! no feathers! Surely she and Father had been right! Tears began to trickle down Caddie's cold cheeks. Now the men were coming out of the bark huts. More and more Indians kept coming toward her. But they were not angry, only full of wonder.

"John," said Caddie, in a strange little voice, which she hardly recognized as hers. "Where is John? I must see John."

"John," repeated the Indians, recognizing the name the white men had given to one of their braves. They spoke with strange sounds among themselves, then one of them went running.

Caddie sat her horse, half-dazed, cold to the bone, but happy inside. The Indians were not on the warpath, they were not preparing an attack. Whatever the tribes farther west might be plotting, these Indians, whom Father and she trusted, were going about their business peacefully. If they could only get away now in time, before the white men came to kill them! Or, perhaps she could get home again in time to stop the white men from making the attack. Would those men whom she had heard talking by the cellar door believe a little girl when she told them that Indian John's tribe was at peace? She did not know. Savages were savages, but what could one expect of civilized men who plotted massacre?

Indian John's tall figure came toward her from one of the huts. His step was unhurried and his eyes were unsurprised.

"You lost, Missee Red Hair?" he inquired.

"No, no," said Caddie, "I am not lost, John. But I must tell you. Some white men are coming to kill you. You and your people must go away. You must not fight. You must go away. I have told you."

"You cold," said John. He lifted Caddie off her horse and led her to the fire.

"No understan'," said John, shaking his head in perplexity. "Speak too quick, Missee Red Hair."

Caddie tried again, speaking more slowly. "I came to tell you. Some bad men wish to kill you and your people. You must go away, John. My father is your friend. I came to warn you."

"Red Beard, he send?" asked John.

"No, my father did not send me," said Caddie. "No one knows that I have come. You must take your people and go away."

"You hungry?" John asked her and mutely Caddie nodded her head. Tears were running again and her teeth were chattering. John spoke to the squaws, standing motionless about the fire. Instantly they moved to do his bidding. One spread a buffalo skin for her to sit on. Another ladled something hot and tasty into a cup without a handle, a cup which had doubtless come from some settler's cabin. Caddie grasped the hot cup between her cold hands and drank. A little trickle of warmth seemed to go all over her body. She stretched her hands to the fire. Her tears stopped running and her teeth stopped chattering. She let the Indian children, who had come up behind her, touch her hair without flicking it away from them. John's dog came and lay down near her, wagging his tail.

"You tell John 'gain," said John, squatting beside her in the firelight.

Caddie began again, slowly. She told how the whites had heard that the Indians were coming to kill. She told how her father and she had not believed. She told how some of the people had become restless and planned to attack the Indians first. She begged John to go away from the Wisconsin country with his tribe while there was still time.

When Caddie had finished John grunted

and continued to sit on, looking into the fire. She did not know whether he had understood her. All about the fire were row on row of dark faces, looking at her steadily with wonder but no understanding. John knew more English than any of them, and yet, it seemed, he did not understand. Patiently she began again to explain.

But now John shook his head. He rose and stood tall in the firelight above the little white girl. "You come," he said.

Caddie rose uncertainly. She saw that it was quite dark now outside the ring of firelight, and a fine, sharp sleet was hissing down into the fire. John spoke in his own tongue to the Indians. What he was telling them she could not say, but their faces did not change. One ran to lead Betsy to the fire and another brought a spotted Indian pony that had been tethered at the edge of the clearing.

"Now we go," said the Indian.

"I will go back alone," said Caddie, speaking distinctly. "You and your people must make ready to travel westward."

"Red Hair has spoken," said John. "John's people go tomorrow." He lifted her onto her horse's back, and himself sprang onto the pony. Caddie was frightened again, frightened of the dark and cold, and uncertain of what John meant to do.

"I can go alone, John," she said.

"John go, too," said the Indian.

He turned his pony into the faint woods trail by which she had come. Betsy, her head drooping under a slack rein, followed the spotted pony among the dark trees. Farther and farther behind, they left the warm, bright glow of fire. Looking back, Caddie saw it twinkling like a bright star. It was something warm and friendly in a world of darkness and sleet and sudden, icy branches. From the bright star of the Indian fire, Caddie's mind leaped forward to the bright warmth of home. They would have missed her by now. Would Katie tell where she had gone? Would they be able to understand why she had done as she had?

She bent forward against Betsy's neck, hiding her face from the sharp needles of sleet. It seemed a very long way back. But at last the branches no longer caught her skirts.

Caddie raised her head and saw that they had come out on the open river bank. She urged Betsy forward beside the Indian pony.

"John, you must go back now. I can find my way home. They would kill you if they saw you."

John only grunted. He set his moccasined heels into the pony's flanks, and led the way onto the ice. Betsy shook herself with a kind of shiver all through her body, as if she were saying, "No! no! no!" But Caddie's stiff fingers pulled the rein tight and made her go. The wind came down the bare sweep of the river with tremendous force, cutting and lashing them with the sleet. Betsy slipped and went to her knees, but she was up again at once and on her way across the ice.

Caddie had lost the feeling of her own discomfort in fear for John. If a white man saw him riding toward the farm tonight, he would probably shoot without a moment's warning. Did John understand that? Was it courage or ignorance that kept John's figure so straight, riding erect in the blowing weather?

"John!" she cried. But the wind carried her voice away. "John!" But he did not turn his head.

Up the bank, through the woods, to the edge of the clearing they rode, Indian file. Then the Indian pony stopped.

Caddie drew Betsy in beside him. "Thank you!" she panted. "Thank you, John, for bringing me home. Go, now. Go quickly." Her frightened eyes swept the farmstead. It was not dark and silent as it had been the night before. Lanterns were flashing here and there, people were moving about, voices were calling.

"They're starting out after the Indians!" thought Caddie. "Father hasn't been able to stop them. They're going to massacre."

She laid her cold hand on the spotted

pony's neck. "John!" she cried. "John, you must go quickly now!"

"John go," said the Indian, turning his horse.

But, before the Indian could turn back into the woods, a man had sprung out of the darkness and caught his bridle rein.

"Stop! Who are you? Where are you going?" The words snapped out like the cracking of a whip, but Caddie knew the voice.

"Father!" she cried. "Father! It's me. It's Caddie!"

"You, Caddie? Thank God!" His voice was full of warm relief. "Hey, Robert, bring the lantern. We've found her. Caddie! My little girl!"

Suddenly, Father was holding her close in his arms, his beard prickling her cheek, and over his shoulder she could see Robert Ireton with a bobbing lantern that threw odd shafts of moving light among the trees. John, too, had dismounted from his pony, and stood straight and still, his arms folded across his chest.

"Oh, Father," cried Caddie, remembering again her mission and the last uncomfortable hours, "Father, don't let them kill John! Don't let them do anything bad to the Indians. The Indians are our friends, Father, truly they are. I've been to the camp and seen them. They mean us no harm."

"You went to the Indian camp, Caroline?"

"Yes, Father."

"That was a dangerous thing to do, my child."

"Yes, Father, but Kent and some of the men meant to go and kill them. I heard them say so. They said they wouldn't tell you they were going, and you weren't there. Oh, Father, what else could I do?"

He was silent for a moment, and Caddie stood beside him, shivering, and oppressed by the weight of his disapproval. In the swaying lantern light she searched the faces of the three men—Robert's honest mouth open in astonishment, Father's brows knit in thought, John's dark face impassive and remote with no one knew what thoughts passing behind it.

Caddie could bear the silence no longer. "Father, the Indians are our friends," she repeated.

"Is this true, John?" asked Father.

"Yes, true, Red Beard," answered John gravely.

"My people fear yours, John. Many times I have told them that you are our friends. They do not always believe."

"My people foolish sometime, too," said John. "Not now. They kill no white. Red Beard my friend."

"He brought me home, Father," said Caddie. "You must not let them kill him."

"No, no, Caddie. There shall be no killing tonight, nor any more, I hope, forever."

Over her head the white man and the red man clasped hands.

"I keep the peace, John," said Father. "The white men shall be your brothers."

"Red Beard has spoken. John's people keep the peace."

For a moment they stood silent, their hands clasped in the clasp of friendship, their heads held high like two proud chieftains. Then John turned to his pony. He gathered the slack reins, sprang on the pony's back and rode away into the darkness.

"Oh, my little girl," said Father. "You have given us a bad four hours. But it was worth it. Yes, it was worth it, for now we have John's word that there will be peace."

"But, Father, what about our own men? They meant to kill the Indians. I heard them."

"Those men are cowards at heart, Caddie. Their plans reached my ears when I got home, and I made short work of such notions. Well, well, you are shivering, my dear. We must get you home to a fire. I don't know what your mother will have to say to you, Caddie."

But, when they reached the farmhouse, the excitement of Caddie's return was overshadowed by another occurrence. Katie, who had sat pale and silent in a corner all during the search, rushed out of the house at the sound of Caddie's return.

"Caddie!" she cried, "Caddie!" Then suddenly she crumpled like a wilted flower, and had to be carried away to bed.

In the excitement of fetching smelling salts and water, Mrs. Woodlawn had only time to cry: "Caddie, my dear. You ought to be spanked. But I haven't time to do it now. There's a bowl of hot soup for you on the back of the stove."

In the kitchen all the children crowded around Caddie as she ate, gazing at her in silent admiration, as at a stranger from a far country.

"Golly, Caddie, didn't they try to scalp you?"

"Did they have on their war paint?"

"Did they wave their tomahawks at you?"

Caddie shook her head and smiled. She was so warm, so happy to be at home, so sleepy. . . .

The day after Caddie's ride to the Indian camp, life settled into the old routine. The neighbors went home again. No charred black ruins awaited them. The sturdy wilderness houses were just as they had left them, only dearer than ever before, and in the log barns hungry cows bawled lustily for food.

Everyone recognized now that the "massacree scare," which had started in the tavern, had been a false alarm. But the terror which it had inspired was not easily forgotten. Many people left the country for good, making their slow way eastward, their few possessions piled high in wagon or cart, their weary cows walking behind.

Tales of bravery or cowardice during the "scare" were told and retold around the winter fires and, at last, people were able to laugh at them instead of trembling. One of the tales the people of Dunnville loved best was of the fiery old man up river, who, although past sixty, left his old wife to defend the homestead with the only gun they owned, while he set out empty-handed to fight the Indians.

But, although it all came to nothing and folks could laugh at the "massacree scare" at last, still it left with many people a deeper fear and hatred of the Indians than they had ever felt before. The Indians themselves understood this. Now that the excitement was over, they were safe from even the most cowardly of the white men. But, nevertheless, they prepared to leave their bark huts and move westward for a time. They felt the stirring of the sap in the trees. A smell of spring in the winter air lured them. The old women made bundles of their furs and blankets and cooking pots and put them on pole and buckskin litters. The ponies pranced, the dogs barked. The Indian men refitted bowstrings, polished knives and guns, and prepared the canoes for a long portage over the ice.

One day, soon after the "scare," when Caddie came home from school, she saw an Indian pony tied to the rail fence near the kitchen door. Clara ran out of the front door to meet her.

"Oh, Caddie," she said, "do hurry. Indian John's in the kitchen and he wants to see you. He won't say a thing to the rest of us Father's away and Mother and Mrs. Conroy are nearly frightened out of their wits. He's got his horrible old dog with him and his scalp belt, too."

Caddie ran around the house and opened the kitchen door. Between the cook stove and the table sat John, bolt upright, with a large piece of dried apple pie in each hand. Solemnly he bit into first one piece and then the other, Mother and Mrs. Conroy peeping timidly at him from the dining-room door the while. His scalp belt lay on the kitchen table beside the empty pie tin and the clean fork and plate which city-bred Mother had laid for him so daintily. At his feet lay his dog, licking its front paw with a slow red tongue.

"Why, John, I'm glad to see you," said Caddie. She stooped and patted his dog. The dog stopped licking his paw for a moment and looked at Caddie with affectionate eyes.

"Him hurt," said John. "Him caught foot in trap."

Caddie bent closer over the foot. "Why, so he did. Poor thing!"

"You like him dog?" asked John. Absently he opened a square of calico which he had tied to his belt, disclosing an odd assortment of bones, bits of fat, and odds and ends of food. To this collection he added the last scrap of the dismembered pie, folded up the cloth, tied it again to his belt, and then knelt down to examine the dog.

"Of course, I like him. He's a good dog."

"Missee Red Hair got no dog?"

"No," said Caddie slowly, her eyes filling with tears. "Nero, our dog—he's lost."

"Look. John he go 'way. John's people go 'way. John's dog no can walk. John go far, far. Him dog no can go far. You keep?"

"Yes, John," said Caddie. "I'll keep him for you. May I, Mother?" Mrs. Woodlawn nodded at her from the dining-room door. "Oh, I'll be so glad to keep him, John. I love to have a dog."

"Good," said John. He straightened himself and folded his arms.

"Look, Missee Red Hair. You keep scalp belt, too?"

"The scalp belt?" echoed Caddie uncertainly. She felt the old prickling sensation up where her scalp lock grew as she looked at the belt with its gruesome decorations of human hair.

"Him very old," said John, picking up the belt with calm familiarity. "John's father, great chief, him take many scalps. Now John no do. John have many friend. John no want scalp. You keep?" John held it out.

Gingerly, with the tips of her thumb and first finger, Caddie took it. "What shall I do with it?" she asked dubiously.

"You keep," said the Indian. "John come back in moon of yellow leaves. John go now far, far. Him might lose. You keep?"

"Yes," said Caddie, "I keep. When you come back in the moon of yellow leaves, I will have it safe for you, and your dog, too."

"Missee Red Hair good girl," said John.

He drew his blanket around him and stalked out. From the doorway Caddie watched him go. His dog limped to the door, too, and Caddie had to put her arms around his neck to keep him from following.

"Good-by, John," she called. "Have a good journey!" John was already on his pony. He raised an arm in salute and rode quickly out of the farmyard.

"Well, of all things!" cried Mrs. Woodlawn, bustling into the kitchen with a great sigh of relief. "You do have a way with savages, Caroline Augusta Woodlawn! I declare, this kitchen smells to heaven of smoky buckskin. Let's open all the windows and doors for a minute and let it out. And, for mercy's sake, Caddie, put that awful scalp belt somewhere in the barn. I couldn't sleep of nights if I knew it was hanging in my house."

Caddie took the scalp belt and the dog out to the barn. She hid the scalp belt in a safe, dry place, where she could easily get it to show to the boys. They had gone part way to Eau Galle to meet Father. Wouldn't they be green with envy when they knew what they had missed?

There was an empty box stall in the barn. In it Caddie made a nice bed of hay for John's dog. She washed his hurt foot in warm water and brought him a bowl of warm milk. Then she covered him with an old horse blanket, and sat beside him, stroking the rough head. He was an ugly dog, without Nero's silky coat and beautiful eyes, but he licked her hand gratefully, and already Caddie loved him.

"I've got a dog," she whispered to herself. "I've got a dog of my very own to keep until John comes back." And she was unaccountably happy.

## TWO LITTLE CONFEDERATES [1]

*Thomas Nelson Page*

The raiders were up early next morning scouring the woods and country around.

[1] From Thomas Nelson Page, *Two Little Confederates.*

They knew that the fugitive Confederate soldiers could not have gone far, for the Federals had every road picketed, and their main body was not far away. As the morning wore on, it became a grave question at Oakland how the two soldiers were to subsist. They had no provisions with them, and the roads were so closely watched that there was no chance of their obtaining any. The matter was talked over, and the boys' mother and Cousin Belle were in despair.

"They can eat their shoes," said Willy, reflectively.

The ladies exclaimed in horror.

"That's what men always do when they get lost in a wilderness where there is no game."

This piece of information from Willy did not impress his hearers as much as he supposed it would.

"I'll tell you! Let me and Frank go and carry 'em something to eat!"

"How do you know where they are?"

"They are at our Robber's Cave, aren't they, Cousin Belle? We told the General yesterday how to get there, didn't we?"

"Yes, and he said last night that he would go there."

Willy's idea seemed a good one, and the offer was accepted. The boys were to go out as if to see the troops, and were to take as much food as they thought could pass for their luncheon. Their mother cooked and put up a luncheon large enough to have satisfied the appetities of two young Brobdingnagians, and they set out on their relief expedition.

The two sturdy little figures looked full of importance as they strode off up the road. They carried many loving messages. Their Cousin Belle gave to each separately a long whispered message which each by himself was to deliver to the General. It was thought best not to hazard a note.

They were watched by the ladies from the portico until they disappeared over the hill. They took a path which led into the woods, and walked cautiously for fear some of the raiders might be lurking about. However, the boys saw none of the enemy, and in a little while they came to a point where the pines began. Then they turned into the woods, for the pines were so thick the boys could not be seen, and the pine tags made it so soft under foot that they could walk without making any noise.

They were pushing their way through the bushes, when Frank suddenly stopped.

"Hush!" he said.

Willy halted and listened.

"There they are."

From a little distance to one side, in the direction of the path they had just left, they heard the trampling of horses' feet.

"That's not our men," said Willy. "Hugh and the General haven't any horses."

"No; that's the Yankees," said Frank. "Let's lie down. They may hear us."

The boys flung themselves upon the ground and almost held their breath until the horses had passed out of hearing.

"Do you reckon they are hunting for us?" asked Willy in an awed whisper.

"No, for Hugh and the General. Come on."

They rose, went tiptoeing a little deeper into the pines, and again made their way toward the cave.

"Maybe they've caught 'em," suggested Willy.

"They can't catch 'em in these pines," replied Frank. "You can't see any distance at all. A horse can't get through, and the General and Hugh could shoot 'em, and then get away before they could catch 'em."

They hurried on.

"Frank, suppose they take us for Yankees?"

Evidently Willy's mind had been busy since Frank's last speech.

"They aren't going to shoot *us*," said Frank; but it was an unpleasant suggestion, for they were not very far from the dense clump of pines between two gullies, which the boys called their cave.

"We can whistle," he said, presently.

"Won't Hugh and the General think we are enemies trying to surround them?" Willy objected. The dilemma was a serious one. "We'll have to crawl up," said Frank, after a pause.

And this was agreed upon. They were soon on the edge of the deep gully which, on one side, protected the spot from all approach. They scrambled down its steep side and began to creep along, peeping over its other edge from time to time, to see if they could discover the clearing which marked the little green spot on top of the hill, where once had stood an old cabin. The base of the ruined chimney, with its immense fireplace, constituted the boys' "cave." They were close to it, now, and felt themselves to be in imminent danger of a sweeping fusillade. They had just crept up to the top of the ravine and were consulting, when someone immediately behind them, not twenty feet away, called out:

"Hello! What are you boys doing here? Are you trying to capture us?"

They jumped at the unexpected voice. The General broke into a laugh. He had been sitting on the ground on the other side of the declivity, and had been watching their maneuvers for some time.

He brought them to the house-spot where Hugh was asleep on the ground; he had been on watch all the morning, and, during the General's turn, was making up for his lost sleep. He was soon wide awake enough, and he and the General, with appetites bearing witness to their long fast, were without delay engaged in disposing of the provisions which the boys had brought.

The boys were delighted with the mystery of their surroundings. Each in turn took the General aside and held a long interview with him, and gave him all their Cousin Belle's messages. No one had ever treated them with such consideration as the General showed them. The two men asked the boys all about dispositions of the enemy, but the boys had little to tell.

"They are after us pretty hotly," said the General. "I think they are going away shortly. It's nothing but a raid, and they are moving on. We must get back to camp tonight."

"How are you going?" asked the boys. "You haven't any horses."

"We are going to get some of their horses," said the officer. "They have taken ours—now they must furnish us with others."

It was about time for the boys to start for home. The General took each of them aside, and talked for a long time. Then the boys said good-by, and started in the direction of home.

After crossing the gully, and walking on through the woods for what they thought a safe distance, they turned into the path.

They were talking very merrily about the General and Hugh and discussing some romantic plan for the recapture of the horses from the enemy, when they came out of the path into the road, and found themselves within twenty yards of a group of Federal soldiers, quietly sitting on their horses, evidently guarding the road.

The sight of the blue-coats made the boys jump. They would have crept back, but it was too late—they caught the eye of the man nearest them. They ceased talking as suddenly as birds in the trees stop chirruping when the hawk sails over; and when one Yankee called to them, in a stern tone, "Halt there!" and started to come toward them, their hearts were in their mouths.

"Where are you boys going?" he asked, as he came up to them.

"Going home."

"Where do you belong?"

"Over there—at Oakland," pointing in the direction of their home, which seemed suddenly to have moved a thousand miles away.

"Where have you been?" The other soldiers had come up now.

"Been down this way." The boys' voices were never so meek before. Each reply was like an apology.

"Been to see your brother?" asked one who had not spoken before—a pleasant-looking fellow. The boys looked at him. They were paralyzed by dread of the approaching question.

"Now, boys, we know where you have been," said a small fellow, who wore a yellow chevron on his arm. He had a thin moustache and a sharp nose, and rode a wiry, dull sorrel horse. "You may just as well tell us all about it. We know you've been to see 'em, and we are going to make you carry us where they are."

"No, we ain't," said Frank, doggedly.

Willy expressed his determination also.

"If you don't, it's going to be pretty bad for you," said the little corporal. He gave an order to two of the men, who sprang from their horses, and, catching Frank, swung him up behind another cavalryman. The boy's face was very pale, but he bit his lip.

"Go ahead," continued the corporal to a number of his men, who started down the path. "You four men remain here till we come back," he said to the men on the ground, and to two others on horseback. "Keep him here," jerking his thumb toward Willy, whose face was already burning with emotion.

"I'm going with Frank," said Willy. "Let me go." This to the man who had hold of him by the arm. "Frank, make him let me go," he shouted, bursting into tears, and turning on his captor with all his might.

"Willy, he's not goin' to hurt you—don't you tell!" called Frank, squirming until he dug his heels so into the horse's flanks that the horse began to kick up.

"Keep quiet, Johnny; he's not goin' to hurt him," said one of the men, kindly. He had a brown beard and shining white teeth.

They rode slowly down the narrow path, the dragoon holding Frank by the leg. Deep down in the woods, beyond a small branch, the path forked.

"Which way?" asked the corporal, stopping and addressing Frank.

Frank set his mouth tight and looked him in the eyes.

"Which is it?" the corporal repeated.

"I ain't going to tell," said he, firmly.

"Look here, Johnny; we've got you, and we are going to make you tell us; so you might just as well do it, easy. If you don't, we're goin' to make you."

The boy said nothing.

"You men dismount. Stubbs, hold the horses." He himself dismounted, and three others did the same, giving their horses to a fourth.

"Get down!"—this to Frank and the soldier behind whom he was riding. The soldier dismounted, and the boy slipped off after him and faced his captor, who held a strap in one hand.

"Are you goin' to tell us?" he asked.

"No."

"Don't you know?" He came a step nearer, and held the strap forward. There was a long silence. The boy's face paled perceptibly, but took on a look as if the proceedings were indifferent to him.

"If you say you don't know—" said the man, hesitating in the face of the boy's resolution. "Don't you know where they are?"

"Yes, I know; but I ain't goin' to tell you," said Frank, bursting into tears.

"The little Johnny's game," said the soldier who had told him the others were not going to hurt Willy. The corporal said something to this man in an undertone, to which he replied:

"You can try, but it isn't going to do any good. I don't half like it, anyway."

Frank had stopped crying after his first outburst.

"If you don't tell, we are going to shoot you," said the little soldier, drawing his pistol.

The boy shut his mouth close, and looked straight at the corporal. The man laid down his pistol, and, seizing Frank, drew his hands behind him, and tied them.

"Get ready, men," he said, as he drew the boy aside to a small tree, putting him with his back to it.

Frank thought his hour had come. He thought of his mother and Willy, and wondered if the soldiers would shoot Willy, too. His face twitched and grew ghastly white. Then he thought of his father, and of how proud he would be of his son's bravery when he should hear of it. This gave him strength.

"The knot—hurts my hands," he said.

The man leaned over and eased it a little.

"I wasn't crying because I was scared," said Frank.

The kind looking fellow turned away.

"Now, boys, get ready," said the corporal, taking up his pistol.

How large it looked to Frank. He wondered where the bullets would hit him, and whether he would be left alone all night out there in the woods, and if his mother would come and kiss him.

"I want to say my prayers," he said, faintly.

The soldier made some reply which he could not hear, and the man with the beard started forward; but just then all grew dark before his eyes.

Next, he thought he must have been shot, for he felt wet about his face, and was lying down. He heard some one say, "He's coming to"; and another replied, "Thank God!"

He opened his eyes. He was lying beside the little branch with his head in the lap of the big soldier with the beard, and the little corporal was leaning over him throwing water in his face from a cap.The others were standing around.

"What's the matter?" asked Frank.

"That's all right," said the little corporal, kindly. "We were just a-foolin' a bit with you, Johnny."

"We never meant to hurt you," said the other. "You feel better now?"

"Yes, where's Willy?" He was too tired to move.

"He's all right. We'll take you to him."

"Am I shot?" asked Frank.

"No! Do you think we'd have touched a hair of your head—and you such a brave little fellow? We were just trying to scare you a bit and carried it too far, and you got a little faint—that's all."

The voice was so kind that Frank was encouraged to sit up.

"Can you walk now?" asked the corporal, helping him and steadying him as he rose to his feet.

"I'll take him," said the big fellow, and before the boy could move, he had stooped, taken Frank in his arms, and was carrying him back toward the place where they had left Willy, while the others followed after with the horses.

"I can walk," said Frank.

"No, I'll carry you, b-bless your heart!"

The boy did not know that the big dragoon was looking down at the light hair resting on his arm, and that while he trod the Virginia wood path, in fancy he was home in Delaware; or that the pressure the boy felt from his strong arms, was a caress given for the sake of another boy far away on the Brandywine. A little while before they came in sight Frank asked to be put down.

The soldier gently set him on his feet, and before he let him go kissed him.

"I've got a curly-headed fellow at home, just the size of you," he said softly.

Frank saw that his eyes were moist. "I hope you'll get safe back to him," he said.

"God grant it!" said the soldier.

When they reached the squad at the gate, they found Willy still in much distress on Frank's account; but he wiped his eyes when his brother reappeared, and listened with pride to the soldiers' praise of Frank's "grit," as they called it. When they let the boys go, the little corporal wanted Frank to accept a five-dollar gold piece; but he politely declined it.

## HITTY GOES TO SEA [1]

*Rachel Field*

As far as I can learn, I must have been made something over a hundred years ago in the State of Maine in the dead of winter. Naturally, I remember nothing of this,

[1] From Rachel Field, *Hitty: Her First Hundred Years.* This book was awarded the John Newbery Medal in 1929.

but I have heard the story told so often by one or another of the Preble family that at times it seems I, also, must have looked on as the Old Peddler carved me out of his piece of mountain-ash wood. It was a small piece, which accounts for my being slightly undersized even for a doll, and he treasured it greatly, for he had brought it across the sea from Ireland.

A piece of mountain-ash wood is a good thing to keep close at hand, for it brings good luck. That was the reason the Old Peddler had carried this about in the bottom of his pack ever since he had started peddling. Mostly he did his best business from May to November when roads were open and the weather not too cold for farmers' wives and daughters to stand on their doorsteps as he spread out his wares. But that year he tramped farther north than he had ever been before. Snow caught him on a road between the sea and a rough, woody country. The wind blew such a gale it heaped great drifts across the road in no time and he was forced to come knocking at the kitchen door of the Preble House, where he had seen a light.

Mrs. Preble always said she didn't know how she and Phoebe would have got along without the Old Peddler, for it took all three of them, besides Andy the chore-boy, to keep the fires going and to water and feed the horse, the cow, and the chickens in the barn. Even when the weather cleared, the roads were impassable for many days and all vessels stormbound in Portland Harbor. So the Peddler decided to stay on and help with odd jobs round the place till spring, since Captain Preble was off on his ship for months to come.

At that time, Phoebe Preble was a little girl with gay and friendly ways and fair hair that hung in smooth, round curls on either side of her face. It was for her that I was transformed from a piece of mountain-ash wood only six and a half inches high, not nearly so tall as a bayberry candle, into a doll of parts. My first memories, therefore, are of a square, pleasant room with brown beams and a great fireplace like a square cave, where flames licked enormous logs of wood and an old black kettle hung from an iron crane. The first words I ever heard were Phoebe's as she called to her mother and Andy: "See, now the doll has a face!"

They came over to peer at me as the Old Peddler held me between his thumb and forefinger, turning me this way and that in the firelight so my paint would dry. I can remember Phoebe's excitement over my features and her mother's amazement that the old man had been able to give such a small bit of wood a real nose and even a pleasant expression. Surely no one, they all agreed, had so much skill with a jackknife. That night I was left to dry on the mantelpiece with the light from the dwindling fire making strange shadows, with mice squeaking and scampering in and out of the walls, and the wind outside blowing through the branches of a great pine tree.

Phoebe's mother had decided that I was not to be played with until properly clothed. Phoebe was not a child who took readily to sewing, but her mother was firm, so presently out came needles and thread, thimbles and piece-bag, and I was being measured for my first outfit. It was to be of buff calico strewn with small red flowers, and I thought it very fine indeed. Phoebe's stitches were not always of the finest. She was apt to grow fidgety after ten or fifteen minutes of sewing; still, she was so anxious to play with me that she quite surprised us all by her diligence.

I do not remember exactly how I came by my name. At first, I was christened Mehitabel, but Phoebe was far too impatient to use so many syllables, and presently I had become Hitty to the whole household. Indeed, it was at Mrs. Preble's suggestion that these five letters were worked carefully in little cross-stitch characters upon my chemise.

"There," said Phoebe's mother when the last one was done, "now whatever happens to her she can always be sure of her name."

Summer passed. Captain Preble came home but in September made ready to sail on another long voyage. It was to be a whaling trip this time and he had bought more than half interest in the ship *Diana-Kate,* which was being repaired and fitted out in Boston. It was decided that Mrs. Preble and Phoebe and Andy, the chore-boy, and I would go with him on this voyage.

So it came about that one fine fall morning we all set off on the stage to Boston. There are no such stagecoaches nowadays, or such fine prancing horses to draw them. This one was painted red and yellow, and the four horses were matched in pairs, two grays and two chestnuts. The spokes of the wheels were painted black and when they turned very fast it made one quite dizzy, especially if one hung out of the window and looked down.

After a long trip on the stagecoach, we came to Boston and went on board the *Diana-Kate* to begin our voyage.

When Phoebe carried me up the steep steps of the companionway and on deck, we found the *Diana-Kate* running before the wind. Her square sails were billowing out in fine fashion and her bow dipped and rose to be lifted by great blue-green combers the like of which I had never seen before.

We made excellent runs our first months out. The weather was mild and fine and the winds brisk and steady. Different seamen as well as Andy took turns at helping Mrs. Preble in the little galley that served as kitchen, "tending the kettle halyards," they called it in their own particular sea talk.

Mrs. Preble soon grew used to the ship and when things had been going their best she was heard to declare that except for the lack of a few neighbors to drop in of an evening, and a decent sink for washing dishes, and a cow to give us milk, she could think of a lot worse places to spend one's days in. There were, of course, other times, such as Sundays, when she sighed remembering how many miles lay between us and Meeting-House Hill. Then she would call Andy and Phoebe to her to make sure that they had not forgotten the Commandments and the Twenty-Third Psalm.

Bill Buckle, a big sailor, was our constant companion and we were on such intimate terms with him that he even went as far as to loan Andy his jackknife and showed us all his best tattoo marks. Nearly all the men aboard were tattooed, but none could show such elaborate decorations as his, for there were mermaids and sea serpents in green on one arm, an anchor and a whale in blue on the other, while a clipper ship in full rig and three colors was sailing straight across his chest. Andy was very envious of these pictures, but it was rather discouraging to find how much Bill Buckle had paid to have them done. He did agree, however, to tattoo Andy's initials across his chest the first chance he got.

Phoebe felt a trifle left out when she heard this and was all for having mine done, too. This frightened me considerably and I was thankful enough when Bill came to my rescue by declaring that he didn't hold with tattooing for ladies. Kind Bill Buckle, I can see his great brown fingers now, his bristling black beard, and his eyes that squinted into pale blue slits when he looked far off to sea.

Another great favorite of ours was Jeremy Folger from Nantucket. He had had a fall from a yardarm in his youth, so he told us, and this had given him a hump on his back for life. It made him cut a queer figure but in no way unfitted him for ship's duties. In fact, Captain Preble counted himself lucky to have Jeremy aboard this trip, for he was known to be one of the best harpooners anywhere about. He had the keenest eyes as well as the steadiest aim. There was a rumor, which Andy and Phoebe firmly believed, that he could sight a whale spouting, or rather blowing, as they called it, fully nine miles away. He had no beard like the rest and his straw-colored hair was bleached almost white by the strong sea sunshine. This gave him the oddest appearance. To this day I do not know whether he was nearer twenty or seventy.

One night I heard Captain Preble tell his wife the only thing that bothered him was that "everything was *drawing* 'most too well." Just when that was it is difficult to remember, for there was little to separate one long, blue, salty day from the one that came before or after it. However, soon after we had come around that mysterious place they all called the Horn, the *Diana-Kate* struck a spell of bad weather. The storm came on quite suddenly late one afternoon and there was barely time to get canvas lashed and hatches battened down before we were in the teeth of it. No more sunny hours of leisure and yarn-spinning on deck, but two days and nights of pounding, tossing, and buffetings such as no pen can describe.

"Now don't you go and get wagdetty, Kate," Captain Preble told his wife, as he took a final look about the cabin to make sure all was tight before going on deck. "It won't be exactly smooth sailin' for a spell, but I've put through worse'n this is goin' to be. I mean to heave to and lay under bare poles till this is over with."

"Well, put on an extra pair of socks, Dan'l, an' take your muffler aloft," was all she said, but I could see that she was worried.

"What did he mean about layin' under bare poles?" Phoebe asked curiously.

"Means he don't dast have an inch of sail up," Andy told her. "Guess I'll go above an' have a look around."

"You won't do any such thing," Mrs. Preble spoke up briskly. "It's all the men can do to keep their footing on deck; you'd be washed overboard in no time. You come right in the galley with me and help get the fire goin' and some hot soup ready. Dear knows they'll need it tonight if they never did before."

Although it was long before the time, Phoebe and I were put to bed in her little bunk and tied in firmly with an old piece of flannel.

"Can't have you fallin' down and breakin' your bones," her mother said when she protested. "We've got trouble enough on our hands as 'tis."

So in bed we stayed, though it was impossible to sleep in all the racket going on about us. A single oil lamp hung in the main cabin just outside. This was the only light, dim and rather smoky at best, and now, with the ship reeling and plunging with such violence, it swung crazily about, making eerie shadows that frightened Phoebe into tears. But since no one heard her above the commotion, and if they had all were too busy to stop and reassure her, she finally ducked her head under the blankets and held me close.

"Oh, Hitty," she whispered, "I didn't think going to sea would be like this, did you?"

It seemed as if that night would never turn into morning, and when it did we were no better off, for it was almost as dark and noisy below as at midnight. To add to our discomfort, water poured down whenever the hatchway was opened, and even when it was not, it managed to seep in as often as a particularly huge wave broke over the *Diana-Kate's* bow and made her decks awash with tons of salt water. Already there were several inches on the cabin floor, and Mrs. Preble was in despair, trying to keep the fire alive.

"You'd best stay in your bunk same's Phoebe," the Captain told her on one of his few trips below. "I'd send one of the crew down to help you, but truth is I can't spare a one of 'em. She's sprung a leak for'ard and it takes four to keep her bailed out."

"Mercy, Dan'l!" I heard Mrs. Preble cry out. "Ain't that pretty bad?"

"Well, I can't say it's exactly good," he answered as he stood by the cabin door gulping down some hot tea she had brought him in a tin cup. "Trouble is we can't commence patchin' till this lets up. But it's bound to 'fore long, if we can just ride it out."

How that day passed I do not know. All I remember of it is the absolute certainty that the *Diana-Kate's* next downward plunge would surely send us to the bottom. Whenever she rose, shuddering and straining in every beam, I felt it must be for the last time, and then once more we would begin to sink down, down, till it seemed impossible we could ever again climb out of such a watery hollow.

The noise grew to be so great that even the men's shrillest shouts to one another could scarcely be heard above the sloshings and poundings, the thud and crash of waves breaking over and about us, and the wind that howled and tore at masts till it seemed they must crack in two. Indeed, during that second night of storm it increased with such violence that the accident occurred which was so nearly our finish.

By this time, what with the leak we had sprung and the force of the waves breaking over our bows, the foc's'le was partly under water. Those of the crew who ordinarily slept there must snatch the few winks of sleep allowed them in the cabin. Not that any part of the ship was dry now, but they were too wet from their struggles overhead to notice a few inches of water underfoot. Once or twice we caught sight of Jeremy or Bill Buckle or other special cronies, who were too spent and dripping to give us more than a nod or grin. It was no time for pleasantry, I can tell you.

Several of the men were gathered there trying to wring some of the wet from their soaked jackets when there came a particularly strong gust of wind. We could feel the *Diana-Kate* shiver under the force of it; and then came a sound of such horrid ripping and splintering that it makes me terrified to think of it even now. There followed a noise of hurrying feet on deck, more cracking, and Captain Preble bellowing out commands in a voice that sounded no bigger than a cricket chirping above the tumult.

"Cut her away, boys!" he was shouting. "Let her go—topsail an' all!"

I saw the three men who had been lounging in the cabin leap to their feet and go staggering up the companionway. Even in the wavering light of the oil lamp I could make out how pale Phoebe's mother had grown as she started up from her place in the bunk below us. She clung to the child with one hand, while with the other she kept herself from falling.

"What's happened, Mother? Are we going to sink?" Phoebe cried, seeing the fright in her face.

"Not if your father can help it," her mother answered, but her eyes were enormous and she never even noticed that she was standing in water to her ankles.

"I don't believe we will—not with Hitty aboard," Phoebe reminded her. "She's made of mountain-ash wood and you know that's sure to bring us good luck."

But Mrs. Preble was too anxious to hear her.

After what seemed a long time things quieted down somewhat above us. The men returned to the cabin and the Captain came down for a moment to reassure his wife. From him we learned that the main topmast had snapped in two and it had been necessary for several of the crew to climb up and cut it away, topsail, yardarm, and dear knows how much besides.

"Yes," he said, shaking the wet from his beard and eyebrows, "it's gone over the side and lucky we didn't follow it."

"Oh, Dan'l," his wife cried out, "can't you let me get you a dry shirt?"

But he was gone before she could make her way over to the chest.

Later on, Andy visited us. He had been with the men in the cabin and so had gathered much news about our situation. He crawled into our bunk and sat cross-legged at the foot while he regaled Phoebe with all he had learned.

"They thought we were gone for good that time," he told us. "Bill Buckle said it looked as if we were going to join the fishes in another five minutes, only for Jeremy and 'Lige cutting off the topmast and sail in such a hurry."

Well, at last it turned smooth and blue again, bluer than I have ever seen water before or since. We were in the South Seas now, heading for what the men all agreed was the best whaling ground, though what ground there was about these miles of sea I could not make out. The *Diana-Kate* seemed to be almost herself again after the accident she had suffered in the storm. Her leak had been patched, and a new topsail and mast concocted. The long boats were repainted and given thorough overhaulings, irons greased, harpoons sharpened, and ropes tarred in readiness for the first cry from the lookout that he saw a whale coming up to blow.

It was about this time that Phoebe Preble, as well as the ship, underwent some overhauling. As the weather had grown hotter and hotter she had discarded her woolens. But this was not enough. One by one, she shed first her merino dress, then her knitted stockings, then her flannel petticoats, and last of all her curls. These were removed with great ceremony in the presence of nearly all the crew, who gathered about the barrel on which she sat to make sure the job was properly done. 'Lige, who did all such services aboard ship, was as thorough with his scissors as with his other tools, and when he had finished, Phoebe's mother almost cried.

"This is what comes of taking her to sea," she lamented. "You wouldn't know her for the same child we fetched aboard."

Her father could not very well deny this, what with the freckles and tan she had acquired into the bargain. But he only laughed at his wife's head-shakings.

"Better have it off'n full of whale oil," he told her. "All she needs now is a pair of breeches. Guess I'll get Jim to cut down those old nankeens of Andy's. We won't be making a port for months, so who cares how she looks?"

So breeches it was, despite all her mother's protests.

I must confess to having some misgivings when I saw her in them, lest she might have changed her feelings for dolls. But she was as devoted to me as ever. I went with her everywhere and that is how I came to be upon such familiar terms with whales, an advantage such as few dolls can boast. First there would be the thrilling cry from the lookout aloft: "There she blows!" or, more often, just "Blo—o—ows!" Then the *Diana-Kate* would become all a-bustle. Our course must be changed to bring us as near as possible to where the pale jet of water, which the whale sent up like a fountain, had been last sighted. Meantime the longboats would be made ready to swing out at the order from Captain Preble to "lower an' fetch him." Sometimes five boats put out for the chase, more often three, the men bending briskly to their oars, as they sped toward that dark-gray mound that looked as big as Huckleberry Hill at home and yet disappeared as suddenly as it had come, to rise again at an entirely different spot.

Jeremy Folger was the first to "strike" a whale, but no one begrudged him the glory, for he had to drive more than one iron into the great creature and was himself all but swept into the sea when the whale nearly upset the longboat. It was a sperm whale of extraordinary size, such as any captain and crew might covet. All the men received shares of the oil, and so they were determined not to let such a prize escape. With Phoebe and Andy, I watched the boats lowered and saw them speed away, each leaving a white trail behind. There were five rowers in each of the three and their oar blades moved like one as they pulled away from us in the strong sea sunshine.

"Greasy luck, boys!" called Captain Preble as he watched them go.

How should I, a little wooden doll, be able to tell of such things—of those boats that looked no bigger than pea pods scurrying through the water toward that enormous gray shape that appeared and disappeared so mysteriously, sending its ghostly stream of water high in air? I cannot believe that I did actually see this for myself, and yet I know that it was so. Indeed, as luck would have it, the whale made such a wide circle in its fight that it brought up near enough for us to see much of the chase. Andy pressed close to the low rail, shading his eyes with his hands as he strained to make out the figures in the longboats.

"There 'tis!" he cried, so shrilly Phoebe almost dropped me over the side in her excitement to follow his pointing forefinger. "It's white-waterin' again. See it spout! Jeremy's boat's ahead. I can tell his red 'n' white shirt."

"Where?" Phoebe hopped up and down beside him, holding me close.

"Why, there, in the bow. Watch now, he's goin' to strike in a minute!"

The oars suddenly hung poised in midair and the little slip of a boat seemed about to vanish under the glistening dark mass above it.

But next thing I knew Andy was screaming out jubilantly that Jeremy had "struck his whale."

"Now they're off for a Nantucket sleighride," he told Phoebe. "That's what they call it," he explained, "when the harpoon's in fast and they can just pay out the rope an' follow him round."

"But I don't see the whale anywhere now," protested Phoebe.

"He'll be up again pretty quick," Andy assured her, "he can't get very far the way they've got him hooked."

It was certainly the truth. Presently the dark shape rose from the water again, struggling and plunging this time, trying to shake himself free. His great sides showed sleek and glittering in the sun, more water spouted into the air, and the sea was churned white and swirling by the gigantic lashings of his tail. How long he dragged the boat after him, or how many times he plunged under water to reappear again with more furious wallowings, I do not know.

The lashings grew less frequent, then they ceased altogether. The whale's great body rose a little more out of the water, then turned over slowly till a sharp black fin showed plainly. There came another shout from those on deck and still more from those in the boats.

"Well, we got him," said Captain Preble with satisfaction, as he turned to his wife. "Think maybe you could fix up somethin' extra in the grub line to celebrate?"

Next day the cutting-in began and I was to know the whale still more intimately. Even after all these years I can remember how it looked stretched out a full length alongside of the ship. By the time Phoebe brought me on deck the morning after our first chase, the men were lowering a little platform upon which they stood with long hooks, knives, and other implements. With ropes and various lines they managed to hoist the whale up, meantime having begun cutting it in such a manner that the blubber peeled off in long strips as neatly as if it had been an apple. But apple it was not as we very soon discovered once it was aboard and in the try-works.

I began to wonder how there would be any whale oil left to be stored in the casks, so much of it ran over the decks. But no one paid any attention to this except Mrs. Preble, who said she had never in all her days smelled such a smell or seen such a mess of grease. The men only laughed and said this was "greasy luck!" They went their different ways—some to toil at the hoisting and cutting, others to mince the hunks of blubber into pieces for the try-pots, and still others to skim off the scraps that kept the fires going night and day.

Thick black smoke rose and hung over us amidships like a queer umbrella, while at night the light of the fires made a dull red glow. This added to the heat and oiliness aboard. The men worked continuously with only a few hours off for rest.

"Got to push it through so's we can go after another," Captain Preble explained, as he came to eat his supper a few nights later, his hands so stiff from the work of cutting-in that he could scarcely hold his knife and fork.

Even Andy was pressed into service mincing and carrying. He went about very proudly, stripped to the waist like the rest, his trousers rolled to his knees. Sometimes his face was so black from oil and smoke that his blue eyes looked very strange in the midst of it and his red hair topping it even stranger. Phoebe and I were not allowed to venture very near the try-works. Her father had been firm about this.

"Can't have you gettin' underfoot an' maybe scalded," he told her.

So it came about that we took our place on an old barrel-head some yards away, but near enough to watch much of the work. I was relieved we were no nearer, for I had no desire to find myself swimming in the boiling try-pots and I might easily have slipped in along with a piece of blubber.

Scarcely was one whale turned into oil before they would be off for another, and, indeed, on one occasion, when a whole school of them was sighted, they took several and towed them back to the ship. It was strange to see these enormous gray bulks anchored nearby with small flags fastened to our irons to show they were our property. By this time a couple of other whaling vessels had arrived in the grounds. There was considerable rivalry among them, even though we were several miles from one another. There was talk among the men about going "gamming." One never hears that word nowadays, but then it was common enough among seafaring people. It meant paying social visits from one ship to another while at sea.

This was pleasant, and even I came to feel as much at home upon the world of wood and canvas as I had in the Preble farmhouse.

It seems strange that all this happened a hundred years ago and that of all the people on that voyage, only I am left. I have made other sea voyages on finer ships, but on none had I so many exciting adventures as befell me and my first little mistress, Phoebe Preble, on the whaling ship, *Diana-Kate.*

## A NIGHT RIDE IN A PRAIRIE SCHOONER[1]

*Hamlin Garland*

One afternoon in the autumn of 1868 Duncan Stewart, leading his little fleet of prairie schooners, entered upon the big prairie of northern Iowa, and pushed resolutely on into the west. His four-horse canvas-covered wagon was followed by two other lighter vehicles, one of which was driven by his wife, and the other by a hired freighter. At the rear of all the wagons, and urging forward a dozen or sixteen cattle, trotted a gaunt youth and a small boy.

The boy had tears upon his face, and was limping with a stone-bruise. He could hardly look over the wild oats, which tossed their gleaming bayonets in the wind, and when he dashed out into the blue joint and wild sunflowers to bring the cattle into the road he could be traced only by the ripple he made, like a trout in a pool.

He was a small edition of his father. He wore the same color and check in his hickory shirt, and his long pantaloons of blue denim had suspenders precisely like those of the men. Indeed, he considered himself a man, notwithstanding the tearstains on his brown cheeks.

It seemed a long time since leaving his native Wisconsin coolly behind, with only a momentary sadness, but now it seemed his father must be leading them all to the edge of the world, and Lincoln Stewart was very sad and weary.

"Company, halt!" called the Captain.

One by one the teams stopped, and the cattle began to feed (they were always ready to eat), and Mr. Stewart, coming back where his wife sat, said cheerily:

"Well, Kate, here's the big prairie I told you of, and beyond that blue line of timber you see is Sun Prairie, and home."

Mrs. Stewart did not smile. She was too weary, and the wailing of little Mary in her arms was dispiriting.

"Come here, Lincoln," said Mr. Stewart. "Here we are, out of sight of the works of man. Not a house in sight—climb up here and see."

Lincoln rustled along through the tall grass, and, clambering up the wagon wheel, stood silently beside his mother. Tired as

[1] From Hamlin Garland, *Boy Life on the Prairie.*

he was, the scene made an indelible impression on him. It was as though he had suddenly been transported into another world, a world where time did not exist; where snow never fell, and the grass waved forever under a cloudless sky. A great awe fell upon him as he looked, and he could not utter a word.

At last Mr. Stewart cheerily called: "Attention, battalion! We must reach Sun Prairie tonight. Forward, march!"

Again the little wagon train took up its slow way through the tall ranks of the wild oats and the drooping, flaming sunflowers. Slowly the sun sank. The crickets began to cry, the nighthawks whizzed and boomed, and long before the prairie was crossed the night had come.

Being too tired to foot it any longer behind the cracking heels of the cows, Lincoln climbed into the wagon beside his little brother, who was already asleep, and, resting his head against his mother's knee, lay for a long time, listening to the chuck-chuckle of the wheels, watching the light go out of the sky, and counting the stars as they appeared.

At last they entered the wood, which seemed a very threatening place indeed, and his alert ears caught every sound—the hoot of owls, the quavering cry of coons, the twitter of night birds. But at last his weariness overcame him, and he dozed off, hearing the clank of the whippletrees, the creak of the horses' harness, the vibrant voice of his father, and the occasional cry of the hired hand, urging the cattle forward through the dark.

He was roused once by the ripple of a stream, wherein the horses thrust their hot nozzles, he heard the grind of wheels on the pebbly bottom, and the wild shouts of the resolute men as they scrambled up the opposite bank, to thread once more the dark aisles of the forest. Here the road was smoother, and to the soft rumble of the wheels the boy slept.

At last, deep in the night, so it seemed to Lincoln, his father shouted: "Wake up, everybody. We're almost home." Then, facing the darkness, he cried, in western fashion, "Hello! the house!"

Dazed and stupid, Lincoln stepped down the wheel to the ground, his legs numb with sleep. Owen followed, querulous as a sick puppy, and together they stood in the darkness, waiting further command.

From a small frame house, near by, a man, with a lantern appeared.

"Hello!" he said, yawning with sleep. "Is that you, Stewart? I'd jest about give you up."

While the men unhitched the teams, Stewart helped his wife and children to the house, where Mrs. Hutchinson, a tall, thin woman, with a pleasant smile, made them welcome. She helped Mrs. Stewart remove her things, and then set out some bread and milk for the boys, which they ate in silence, their heavy eyelids drooping.

When Mr. Stewart came in, he said: "Now, Lincoln, you and Will are to sleep in the other shack. Run right along, before you go to sleep. Owen will stay here."

Without in the least knowing the why or wherefore, Lincoln set forth beside the hired man, out into the unknown. They walked rapidly for a long time, and, as his blood began to stir again, Lincoln awoke to the wonder and mystery of the hour. The strange grasses under his feet, the unknown stars over his head, the dim objects on the horizon, were all the fashioning of a mind in the world of dreams.

At last they came to a small cabin on the banks of a deep ravine. Opening the door, the men lit a candle, and spread their burden of blankets on the floor. Lincoln crept between them like a sleepy puppy, and in a few minutes this unknown actual world merged itself in the mystery of dreams.

When he woke, the sun was shining, hot and red, through the open windows, and the men were smoking their pipes by the rough fence before the door. Lincoln hurried out to see what kind of a world this was to which his night's journey had hurried him. It was, for the most part, a level land, covered with short grass intermixed with tall weeds, and with many purple and yellow flowers. A little way off, to the left, stood a small house, and about as far to the right was another, before which stood the wagons belonging to his father. Directly in front was a wide expanse of rolling prairie, cut by a deep ravine, while to the north, beyond the small farm which was fenced, a still wider region rolled away into unexplored and marvelous distance. Altogether it was a land to exalt a boy who had lived all his life in a thickly settled Wisconsin coolly, where the horizon line was high and small of circuit.

In less than two hours the wagons were unloaded, the stove was set up in the kitchen, the family clock was ticking on its shelf, and the bureau set against the wall. It was amazing to see how these familiar things and his mother's bustling presence changed the looks of the cabin. Little Mary was quite happy crawling about the floor, and Owen, who had explored the barn and found a lizard to play with, was entirely at home. Lincoln had climbed to the roof of the house, and was still trying to comprehend this mighty stretch of grasses. Sitting astride the roof board, he gazed away into the northwest, where no house broke the horizon line, wondering what lay beyond that high ridge.

While seated thus, he heard a distant roar and trample, and saw a cloud of dust rising along the fence which bounded the farm to the west. It was like the rush of a whirlwind, and before he could call to his father, out on the smooth sod to the south burst a platoon of wild horses, led by a beautiful roan mare. The boy's heart leaped with excitement as the shaggy colts swept round to the east, racing like wolves at play. Their long tails and abundant manes streamed in the wind like banners, and their imperious bugling voiced their contempt for man.

Lincoln clapped his hands with joy, and all of the family ran to the fence to enjoy the sight. A boy, splendidly mounted on a fleet roan, the mate of the leader, was riding at a slashing pace, with intent to turn the troop to the south. He was a superb rider, and the little Morgan strove gallantly without need of whip or spur. He laid out like a hare. He seemed to float like a hawk, skimming the weeds, and his rider sat him like one born to the saddle, erect and supple, and of little hindrance to the beast.

On swept the herd, circling to the left, heading for the wild lands to the east. Gallantly strove the roan with his resolute rider, disdaining to be beaten by his own mate, his breath roaring like a furnace, his nostrils blown like trumpets, his hoofs pounding the resounding sod.

All in vain; even with the inside track he was no match for his wild, free mate. The herd drew ahead, and, plunging through a short lane, vanished over a big swell to the east, and their drumming rush died rapidly away into silence.

This was a glorious introduction to the life of the prairies, and Lincoln's heart filled with boundless joy and longing to know it—all of it, east, west, north, and south. He had no further wish to return to his coolly home. The horseman had become his ideal, the prairie his domain.

## THE PINE-TREE SHILLINGS[1]

*Nathaniel Hawthorne*

Captain John Hull was the mint master of Massachusetts, and coined all the money that was made there. This was a new line of business; for in the earlier days of the colony the current coinage consisted of gold and silver money of England, Portugal, and Spain. These coins being scarce, the people were often forced to barter their commodities instead of selling them.

For instance, if a man wanted to buy a coat, he perhaps exchanged a bearskin for it. If he wished for a barrel of molasses, he might purchase it with a pile of pine boards. Musket bullets were used instead of farthings. The Indians had a sort of money, called wampum, which was made of clamshells; and this strange sort of specie

[1] From Nathaniel Hawthorne, *Grandfather's Chair*.

was likewise taken in payment of debts by the English settlers. Bank bills had never been heard of. There was not money enough of any kind, in many parts of the country, to pay the salaries of the ministers; so that they sometimes had to take quintals of fish, bushels of corn, or cords of wood, instead of silver or gold.

As the people grew more numerous, and their trade one with another increased, the want of current money was still more keenly felt. To supply the demand, the General Court passed a law for establishing a coinage of shillings, sixpences, and threepences. Captain John Hull was appointed to manufacture this money, and was to have about one shilling out of every twenty to pay him for the trouble of making them.

Hereupon, all the old silver in the colony was handed over to Captain John Hull. The battered silver cans and tankards, I suppose, and silver buckles, and broken spoons, and silver buttons of worn-out coats, and silver hilts of swords that had figured at court—all such curious old articles were doubtless thrown into the melting pot together. But by far the greater part of the silver consisted of bullion from the mines of South America, which the English buccaneers—who were little better than pirates—had taken from the Spaniards, and brought to Massachusetts.

All this old and new silver being melted down and coined, the result was an immense amount of splendid shillings, sixpences, and threepences. Each had the date, 1652, on the one side, and the figure of a pine tree on the other. Hence they were called pine-tree shillings. And for every twenty shillings that he coined, you will remember, Captain John Hull was entitled to put one shilling into his own pocket.

The magistrates soon began to suspect that the mint master would have the best of the bargain. They offered him a large sum of money if he would give up that twentieth shilling which he was continually dropping into his own pocket. But Captain Hull declared himself perfectly satisfied with the shilling. And well he might be; for so diligently did he labor that in a few years his pockets, his money bags, and his strong box were overflowing with pine-tree shillings.

When the mint master had grown very rich, a young man, Samuel Sewell by name, came a-courting his only daughter. His daughter—whose name I do not know, but we will call her Betsey—was a fine, hearty damsel, by no means so slender as some young ladies of our own days. On the contrary, having always fed heartily on pumpkin pies, doughnuts, Indian puddings, and other Puritan dainties, she was as round and plump as a pudding herself. With this round, rosy Miss Betsey did Samuel Sewell fall in love. As he was a young man of good character, industrious in his business, and a member of the church, the mint master very readily gave his consent.

"Yes, you may take her," said he, in his rough way, "and you'll find her a heavy burden enough!"

On the wedding day, honest John Hull dressed himself in a plum-colored coat, all the buttons of which were made of pine-tree shillings. The buttons of his waistcoat were sixpences; and the knees of his smallclothes were buttoned with silver threepences. Thus attired, he sat with great dignity in Grandfather's chair; and being a portly old gentleman, he completely filled it from elbow to elbow. On the opposite side of the room, between her bridesmaids, sat Miss Betsey. She was blushing with all her might, and looked like a full-blown peony, or a great red apple.

There, too, was the bridegroom, dressed in a fine purple coat and gold-lace waistcoat, with as much other finery as the Puritan laws and customs would allow him to put on. His hair was cropped close to his head, because Governor Endicott had forbidden any man to wear it below the ears. But he was a very personable young man; and so thought the bridesmaids and Miss Betsey herself.

The mint master also was pleased with his new son-in-law; especially as he had courted Miss Betsey out of pure love, and had said nothing at all about her portion. So, when the marriage ceremony was over, Captain Hull whispered a word to two of his men-servants, who immediately went out, and soon returned, lugging in a large pair of scales. They were such a pair as wholesale merchants use for weighing bulky commodities; and quite a bulky commodity was now to be weighed in them.

"Daughter Betsey," said the mint master, "get into one side of these scales."

Miss Betsey—or Mrs. Sewell, as we must now call her—did as she was bid, like a dutiful child, without any question of the why and wherefore. But what her father could mean, unless to make her husband pay for her by the pound (in which case she would have been a dear bargain), she had not the least idea.

"And now," said honest John Hull to the servants, "bring that box hither."

The box to which the mint master pointed was a huge, square, iron-bound, oaken chest; it was big enough for four children to play at hide-and-seek in. The servants tugged with might and main, but could not lift it, and were finally obliged to drag it across the floor. Captain Hull then took a key from his girdle, unlocked the chest, and lifted its ponderous lid. Behold! it was full to the brim of bright pine-tree shillings, fresh from the mint; and Samuel Sewell began to think that his father-in-law had got possession of all the money in the Massachusetts treasury. But it was only the mint master's honest share of the coinage.

Then the servants, at Captain Hull's command, heaped double handfuls of shillings into one side of the scales, while Betsey remained in the other. Jingle, jingle, went the shillings, as handful after handful was thrown in, till, plump and ponderous as she was, they fairly weighed the young lady from the floor.

"There, son Sewell!" cried the honest mint master, resuming his seat in Grandfather's chair, "take these shillings for my daughter's portion. Use her kindly, and thank Heaven for her. It is not every wife that's worth her weight in silver!"

## JACQUES AND THE LITTLE CHIEF [1]

*Frances Gaither*

In 1702 Monsieur de Bienville built a fort at Mobile, which for some time was the seat of government of the French province of Louisiana. In the colony was a French lad named Jacques Duval. Bienville sent Jacques inland to live for two years with the Indians to learn their language and customs. Later he became very valuable as an interpreter. During his stay with the Indians he became fast friends with Little Chief, an Indian boy of his own age.

The month when the corn ripened was called the Green-eared Moon—as in France one would have said July or August. It was greeted with elaborate and mystic ritual. First, all the Indian people cleaned their houses and burned every grain of the old corn and all of their old soiled deerskins and breechclouts. Then the square was sprinkled with sand and decked with green boughs and armfuls of blossoming trumpet vine and all the many-colored wild flowers that gemmed the prairies. Jacques didn't see what happened next, because no one but the warriors could stay in the square while the new holy fire was being kindled.

In the first days of the Green-eared Moon, everybody fasted. But at last came the day when the old women gathered the ripe corn and the young women ran about between the houses each shielding with her palm a smoking brand from the holy fire. And then the bright flames woke before every door and the good smells started and soon the feasting began.

Some of the new corn was roasted whole in the ear. Some was pounded with young green chestnuts and packed back into the green corn blades, where corn and chestnuts cooked together. Some of it was mixed with bears' oil and molded into thin cakes

[1] From Frances Gaither, *The Painted Arrow.*

and baked on flat stones in the ashes. There was sagamité, of course, cooked in every sort of way, with fresh fruit and dry, with beans, with squash, with venison. There were peaches and apples heaped high in bright new baskets. There were rabbits and squirrels roasted whole and sweet potatoes moistened with hickory milk. There was watermelon with an inside like rose-colored snow, which melted in the mouth as if it actually were snow and left after it a cool, delicious taste.

The warriors went about new-painted with vermilion and ocher, their heads nodding with their finest feathers and horns. Hot as it was, some of them got out their most treasured deerskin mantles, dressed as soft as chamois and drawn all over with bright-colored pictures of their exploits in war and hunt. They wore bracelets of feathers or beads or deer-ribs bent and polished, and necklaces of bears' teeth or shell beads with engraved shell pendants. The women dancers fastened tortoise shells to their garter-like leg bands, filled with clattering gravel stones, and hundreds of small wild hoofs and all the bright and tinkling metal things their chiefs had brought up from the French settlement. In some of the dances they wore masks made of big gourds grotesquely carved and painted.

Dancing went on all night long and all day, too, until the ground was trodden into furrows. People from the neighboring villages came and without a word of greeting fell to dancing. The chief's daughter got up from her couch and began to dance with all her might as if she had never been ill in her life. Sometimes the dancers let the rattling things down their legs make a deafening clatter. But sometimes they moved so that they made no noise at all. They danced about great bonfires, shielding their faces from the glare with fans of turkey feathers. And now and then a kick from a dancer sent flames and sparks leaping up into the high tree branches.

When the dancers stopped to rest, they gathered about the old mythkeeper in his woven white robe, firelight reddening his wise, wrinkled face. And he willingly laid aside his carving. And, fingering those chaplets on which a rattlesnake rattle stood for a war, perhaps, a point of buck horn for a great storm out of the Gulf, he recited the oldest and most beloved traditions of their people.

A singer came up from the country of their former enemies—those with whom the Iron Hand and Messieurs d'Iberville and de Bienville had contrived to have them smoke the calumet of peace—and sitting down close beside their holy fire like a blood brother sang all the songs of his people, their one-time enemies. Some of the songs were so old that they were half-forgotten now and some were so new that no alien ear had ever heard them before.

One afternoon there was a great ball-play out upon the prairie. People gathered from the sister villages of the nation. Many brought all their skins and ornaments to wager on the game. The players were naked and painted all over, one team with white clay, one with red. They carried in their hands long scoop-like rackets, called ball-sticks. And they ran and leaped in the sunshine after the stuffed deerskin ball.

One night the warriors sat in a circle about the red-painted pole while the chief went to strike it with his great, edged war-club, or "headbreaker," and chanted:

The lightning clove an oak tree
And so was I born,
Sinewy and hard as oak wood,
Swift-leaping as the sky-fire
That springs from cloud to cloud
On summer nights.
The lightning was my father,
An oak tree was my mother . . .
Who shall gainsay it?

He paused and looked about him. The warriors loosed a great *hou* of approval from their chests and shook their chichicois. The chief struck the pole again with his club.

The thunder of my bow
Scatters fear
Like a storm from the Gulf.
My uncle, the wind,
Himself has winged my arrows.
My father has touched their tips
With his own fire
That they may carry the death spark
Straight to the hearts of my enemies . . .
Does any man doubt it?

When he sat down, the warriors rose in the order of their distinction and chanted each his own prowess. Even the boys were allowed to strike the pole and tell, not what they had done of course, but what they were going to do when they were men. If a boy was timid and spoke poorly, the chiefs and warriors were silent and looked at the ground. But if one was fearless and eloquent, they applauded him.

When the Little Chief's turn came, he stood as straight as the red pole itself, flung his chin high and with an odd shining look in his black eyes told of all he dreamed of doing for the glory of his people. When he finished, the warriors and chiefs fetched great whoops of approval out of their deep chests blazoned all over with the insignia of their brave deeds.

Jacques dug his nails against his palms and stole away by himself. He had a feeling that was part pride and part pain. He hated to think of the Little Chief wearing a warrior's swan-feather crown on his head and scalps at his belt.

He walked slowly away through the trees. Behind him in the square, the drums and chichicois and voices took up the rhythm of the Red Ant Dance. It was quite dark under the trees, but beyond them it was nearly as bright as day. The moon was a week old now. The ground in front of the house like a temple was spattered with brightness. And the wooden bear with a man's head up over the door was black against the shining sky. A mockingbird lit on the bear-thing's head and began to sing.

Jacques walked across the island of light and, still thinking of the Little Chief's speech, curiously fingered the dried scalps hanging on the poles before the temple-like house. A black shadow lay on the silver ground when Jacques turned around, but it was instantly swallowed up in the tree shadows. Somebody had been watching him. Would the Indians call what Jacques had just done some sort of desecration? He froze into stillness. Fireflies threaded the close-woven shade. Far away beat the drums, the chichicois, the stamping feet, the chanting voices, endless and mysterious. A wind bent branches rustling downward over Jacques' head. The dried scalps rattled crisply against the poles.

Jacques' straining ears caught a vagrant hint of sound, a mere flash, swift as a firefly and glinting like a firefly, too—such a sound precisely as a saint's medal makes swinging like a little bell clapper. Jacques laughed aloud with relief when he heard the sound by which he always recognized the Little Chief's nearness. He flung himself into the dark toward the faint glint of sound. His arms closed on a naked body. The Little Chief taken unaware tumbled backward, but his arms closed around Jacques and Jacques, too, went down. The two boys rolled over and over like puppies. But only for a moment. The Little Chief hurried to drag Jacques out into the moonlight where he could piece out speech with gestures, as needful to make Jacques understand.

Listen. In Jacques' own tribe far away across the ocean had they a mythkeeper?

Jacques hesitated.

"Why, yes," he said after a moment. "A priest we call him."

"And has he taught you the old beloved legends of your people?"

"Yes," said Jacques, still puzzled.

"I will teach you all I know," said the Little Chief, panting with eagerness, "if you will tell me stories of the white men's country."

Jacques laughed aloud and flung his arm around the Little Chief's shoulder. Oh, he had enough tales to last for months: all the priest's stories from the lives of saints and heroes; all Aunt Gabrielle's chimney-corner tales of Hop o' My Thumb and his company; all Jacques' own adventures. He could tell of the château they visited the time they took the anchovies from the north coast of Brittany up the River Loire; of the walled town where Jacques' home was and the king's high-towered arsenal; of ships and sailors and Mardi Gras, which is the French people's Green-eared Moon, when they put on masks and sing and dance in the streets.

Jacques thought it must be toward the end of September when they began burning the country over. The crisp air came spiced with the charred fragments of leaves and grass. A mighty sound of popping came out of the canebrakes as though whole armies of musketeers lay in ambush here. All the woods grew dark with smoke. And through the tall grass and goldenrod over the prairies waved little red flags of flame. A small rain came to wet the singed prairies and new grass sprang up soft as down to tempt the deer. The ground was suddenly spangled over with mushrooms as thick as stars in the Milky Way—the White Dog's Road, the Indians called it. Grapes ripened, purple and amber. Sweet gum oozed fragrant resin and its leaves turned the color of rich port wine. Hickory nut trees turned clear yellow, and that gave, in the places where they stood, an odd effect of sunlight in the smoky forests. Light seemed to come, too, from the persimmons strung like gold lanterns along bare branches. The mockingbirds burst into a second season of song.

There was no more work to be done in the fields now. The corn and the dried fruit and the barbecued scimitar-like slices of pumpkin were all stored in the cribs set like French dovecotes on high stilts, well polished to discourage mice. The men hunted a little but mostly they busied themselves getting ready for the great winter hunt. All day long they polished arrows or labored at deer-head decoys stretched over hooped laths, the antlers patiently hollowed out so they should weigh upon the hunting pack scarcely more than a dry hollow gourd. The women again swung their corn carriers against their shoulders by the deerskin forehead straps and scattered over the country to reap a second harvest. The boys, Jacques and the Little Chief in their midst, went along to help fill the hampers. They swept up the starry mushrooms out of the meadows, gleaned wild rice in the marshes, disputed the right of the bears to the juicy muscadines festooning the high trees, and went into the groves where all the ground was fat with hickory nuts and the bright persimmons hung in air as big as hens' eggs and as mellow as good French butter.

The women squeezed the persimmons over cane sieves to get the skin and seeds out, rolled the paste into broad flat cakes and roasted them over fires in the woods. They hung up the big blue muscadines and dried them on the stem like sweet raisins from Greece.

Soon flocks of wild pigeons came flying so thick that they clouded over the copper sun. Swans and ducks and geese gathered about the marshes and lakes. Every low place was like a fair in the market square of a busy French town. Stray hunters unwise enough to camp near any water could not sleep for the noise the wild fowl made. The ducks and geese have chiefs, the Indians said, and "old wise men" who meet every fall in their council house in the far north to decide when the tribe shall move south, just as the Indians themselves had leaders who fixed the time for setting out northward on the winter hunt.

There never had been a time when fowl had been so plentiful—at least the notched sticks and shell bead chaplets of the myth-keeper carried the record of none. The boys with torches of blazing lightwood knots went through the woods at night and knocked down the roosting pigeons out of the trees by the bagful. In the daytime they took turkey skins dressed with the heads on and lay down behind fallen trees until the turkeys stepped mincingly out of the deeper woods in search of ripe nettle seed or red acorns. Then they lifted the decoys up on their fists and gobbled like turkeys to entice their game near enough to be caught.

The Little Chief stuffed a duck skin with straw and set it afloat on a pond, and when the ducks that were flying over settled around it he swam under water, as noiselessly as an eel, seized the ducks' feet, tucked the heads under his belt, and swam ashore with them alive and squawking.

The women wanted all the down feathers they could get for making blankets and shawls. They wove the feathers, as the wigmakers of France wove hair, on nets of coarse bark thread till the nets were covered all over on both sides with silky bright shag. The women couldn't have too many duck feathers and the boys themselves were very fond of roast duck. Jacques, lips twisting in a little rueful smile, wished he could have shared some of his with good Monsieur Bosset. Did Monsieur Bosset, he wondered wistfully, still boast as much as ever of the way they cook duckling at Rouen?

Jacques and the Little Chief were really friends now. They were never separated. When the sun came burning up beyond the blue bare treetops, they went running together over the frosty ground to swim in the ice-cold river. And at night when the warm, crowded town house was noisy with chichicois and dancing feet and dim with smoke of pipes and lightwood knots, they lay on one bearskin and whispered together. The Little Chief never got tired of hearing Jacques talk about the white men's country and, good as his word, he gave in exchange one after another of the mythkeeper's stories exactly as he had learned them.

Now it was a tale of the Ancient of Terrapins: ". . . not the little helpless terrapin we have in these days but the first of all terrapins, mighty and heavy as a bear." Now it was a story about a Sint-holo, the sacred horned snake which lived along big creeks or in caves: "Once, the old men say, a hunter came upon a Sint-holo fighting with the Thunder . . ." Or it was the story of the Nameless Young Man: "There was once a young man who had no name, they say. Unluckily for him the tribe had smoked the calumet of peace with all its enemies. So the young man could not go out to war and get a man's name for people to call him by or a swan feather crown for his temples. This was a matter of grief and shame to his parents and to the maiden who loved him and to the young man, too. For, though he grew to be as tall and strong as the great chief himself, still he had to go on lighting the warrors' pipes for them like a boy and heaping the lightwood knots in the square for the fires at evening . . ."

Story after story they told each other, and they had other things to talk about, besides. More than anything else now they talked about the winter hunt. They were both going, everybody was in fact—except a half-dozen ancients no longer fit to travel —even the mythkeeper, old as he was, and the babies who would have to ride like corn in baskets against the women's shoulders. Jacques was to carry his gun. No other boy had a gun of course—not even half of the warriors had any. Jacques was thankful now for the edict which had seemed so hard last summer. But for the old men he'd have wasted all of his powder and shot in the cornfields and he would have had none left now. As it was, his powder horn was barely half full and his shot pouch all too flabby. In the brief hour he had tarried at the French fort before setting off again with the Indians, nobody had thought to replenish his ammunition. So precious was ammunition hereabout that the braves made shot molds of clay and melted up everything metal they had got from the French: skillets and kettles, even nails and buttons.

Jacques had just twenty rounds left. He and the Little Chief counted the shot a hundred times, turning the bag up carefully over a gourd cup and fingering the balls of lead as greedily as if they had been minted doubloons. It was well understood that the Little Chief was to fire ten shots and Jacques ten. They couldn't spare one shot for practice, but the Little Chief over and over went through the motions of loading and firing. They were in sworn agreement to use arrows whenever possible. And they would disregard the meaner sort of game altogether—a bear or so, perhaps, but no rabbits or squirrels and no beaver.

"Anybody can kill a beaver," the Little Chief said scornfully. And from the talk in the town house at night it was clear that all the men were of his opinion.

One of the women took her needle of heron's bone and her deer-sinew thread and fashioned a pair of moccasins for Jacques. The mythkeeper put down his still unfinished pipe bowl to make for him a "deer-call" out of a bit of cane. And he taught Jacques as many of the seven ancient songs to call up deer as were now remembered:

Deer, deer, come sweeten your tongue
On the fat juicy acorns
Lying here around me. . . .

And:

Nearer and nearer I creep in my deer mask—
Where are you hiding, deer?
Are you drinking there by the stream
Out of sight among the tall ferns?
Or are you lying in yonder shady grove?
If that is where you are,
I shall find you, deer.
I shall steal upon you
In my well-made deer mask.
I shall cry:
Awake, arise, stand up—
The hunter is here with his arrows.

Even the horned man searched in his pouch among the seed pods of swamp flag and the bits of twisted roots for a charm to give Jacques. He drew out first a root of the plant called deer-tail, but he put it back and looked further. He found at last a wisp of velvet from the horns of a young deer, over which he mumbled a charm—the very best talisman, the Little Chief declared, not only for deer but for any sort of game.

Jacques grinned at the Little Chief's solemn faith. But he tucked the downy scrap into his shot pouch all the same.

At last the chiefs and old wise men met in the town house and decided it was time to go. The hunters fasted every day for three days, and each night when they dreamed of any animal they believed it was the game they were sure to kill. The women made ready the usual traveling equipment: the deerskins to sleep on, the warm buffalo coverings, the little bags of reddish parched meal and a gourd cup apiece to stir up the cold gruel in.

The sun was just coming up when they stepped out from the shelter of the trees and houses. The sky was red and purple across the round-humped prairie. The ground was covered all over with frost that crumpled like starched lace under Jacques' new moccasins. Carrying his gun on his shoulder and munching the barbecued persimmon loaf which he and the Little Chief had just broken in half between them, he felt tingling and ecstatic. He had felt like that once before—when was it? Oh, yes, to be sure, it was the day Monsieur d'Iberville had said he might come along as ship's boy to the New World and dowered him with a great bundle of fine clothes from the king. What a child he had been!

The place where they pitched their winter camp was eight sleeps as the Indians reckoned, or eight days' journey, away from home, in a grove of chestnuts on the southern slope of a very high hill, with a clear spring flowing in a ravine below it. As soon as they arrived the men set to building shelters of bark and evergreen boughs. The women opened the travel packs. Jacques and the Little Chief were sent with a skin bag to fetch water from the spring. They came upon bear tracks. Jacques, by some incredible chance, was the first to see them. He guessed they were the footprints of a man walking barefoot, but the Little Chief stooping found the print of claws at the ends of the toes. Jacques dropped the water bag to fly for his gun.

"Wait," said the Little Chief. How did they know it was not an ambush? These were rich hunting grounds. Their northern enemies sometimes came here.

"But you said yourself it was bears' claws," argued Jacques, almost dancing with impatience.

Bears' claws can be fastened on men's feet. Just last winter in these very hunting grounds an unwary hunter had been enticed to his death that way. The Little Chief cautiously followed the tracks to the foot of a tall elm which had a great hollow about forty feet up and the bark deeply scratched by claws climbing up and down. The Little Chief laid his ear close to the tree and Jacques did, too. They heard a low hum-hum-hum. At last the Little Chief nodded—yes, it was a bear. Jacques threw down the water sack and ran back up the slope.

At the camp he ran straight to the tree where his gun leaned, calling out the tidings as he ran. They all gathered about him to hear the particulars. And one of the old men promptly ordered Jacques not to touch his gun. With every man in camp and every quiver full of arrows that was perhaps mere common sense. But Jacques was terribly disappointed.

However, there was no time to mope. He had to guide them to the bear tree, and as soon as they got there he and the other boys had to gather some dried rotten wood which holds fire well and tie it into bundles with strips of bark. The men half felled a near-by sapling and made it lean like a ladder over against the bear tree. Then one of the young men fastened the bundles of dried wood about his girdle, took a long stick in his hand, and climbed up the leaning sapling. He set fire to the bundles of wood one by one and with his stick poked them down into the hollow. Almost at once they could hear the bear snuffing in the tree. The women and boys were made to stand back and the men got ready with stretched bows in case the man who had been chosen to shoot first should merely wound the bear and he should turn upon them—a wounded bear is very dangerous. At last the fire got too hot inside the tree and the bear came out. He climbed down backward like a man. A bow twanged and he toppled, a single arrow swaying like a rooted reed just behind his shoulder. He was as big as a French carriage horse, and as soft and black as if a velvet pall had been flung over him.

Some of the women ran up to the dead bear with their keen-edged cane knives, and the rest hurried back to the camp to stir up the fires and get the kettles on. The hunters went off to try their luck at getting a deerskin to hold the bear fat. Soon the camp in the chestnut grove was perfumed with the smell of roasting and boiling bear meat. It smelled good, too, after eight days of cold meal-and-water gruel. And it was astonishing how good it did taste at last, eaten without salt or bread or even sagamité.

So it happened that Jacques' powder and shot were kept until he and Little Chief went on a hunting expedition alone. The Little Chief was certain they could bring down the white deer that the Indians believed led a large herd in these woods.

They did see the white deer, or at least so the Little Chief said. Jacques could never be sure. Against the dark trees he saw the herd streaming by like meteors or phantoms.

"There!" cried the Little Chief. "There! The great buck in front—wasn't he white?"

Jacques gulped and shook his head. He didn't know. Who can tell the color of a shooting star?

But when the Little Chief fired, a fine russet-colored buck lay stretched on the ground.

## DICK FINDS THE "WHEEL OF FORTUNE"[1]

*Cornelia Meigs*

They passed through valleys, over green hills, skirting the yellow fields which had given up their abundance of grain to the harvest. The stretches of woods began to be greater and greater, for they were coming into more unsettled country. For a great many miles their way led along the shore of the Susquehanna River, a broad clear stream with a wide valley between forested hills.

They waited, a little impatiently on the boys' part, for their turn at Chamber's Ferry, the only means at hand for crossing the river. The big flat boat moved in the most leisurely manner across the smooth water, pushed by long poles worked by the men on board. A great crowd of horses, vehicles and men were waiting, a stage-coach which had bumped over the rough way from Lancaster, white-topped wagons in great numbers, some laden to the bows with boxes and barrels, some of them carrying families and their goods to find a new home beyond the Susquehanna. There were mail riders, too, with bags of letters swung from their saddles, exchanging news, as time passed, with the men who stood near. They had much to tell of President Washington and the new capital at Philadelphia.

Everyone must await his turn; the mail carriers went first, then the others in order of arriving, two wagons and their horses at a time. Marcus Horner's pack train and the two boys got aboard at last and slid across to the green banks and the deep, worn track on the other side. And presently, as they went forward on their journey, they could see the mountains rising up before them, high, deep-forested barriers, which their way must cross.

They stopped to trade at the wayside towns, at the blacksmith shops, and even at some of the farmhouses. They moved very slowly, so that days and finally weeks went by, and they were still journeying westward. Salt, gunpowder, quinine, needles, and coffee, all the things which were not to be had in this back country seemed to have been packed in Marcus Horner's saddlebags. The loads lightened and the train moved forward more quickly.

It was getting to be very cold; the mountains above them were white as they came nearer and nearer to the great ridge over which they must climb. Marcus Horner gave away the last package of drugs to a thin mother with an ailing child, the two sitting on a wagon seat waiting to be ferried over the Juniata River. There were more fur caps and rifles and rough-coated horses now in those crowds which still waited to pass over the river; there were very few wheeled vehicles, only the boldest and the sturdiest having come so far.

There were still inns beside the road, but the company that gathered in the great room and that lay down to sleep beside the fire were ruder and noisier; they growled complaints that the food was nothing but deer and partridge and wild duck, with no good farm-raised beef and mutton. The stony hillsides were not laid out in a checkerboard of fields of different shades of yellow; their wild grass was nibbled short by sheep, for herds and flocks of them were always coming into view, gray patches on the cleared slopes.

At every inn and at every blacksmith shop where they happened to stop, Dick would remember to ask the question, "Does anyone hereabouts know of South Down sheep? Where could I get some wool of that kind?"

They had all heard of it, the breed seemed to do well on this higher, cooler stretch of country. But no one could tell him just where he was to go or exactly whom to ask, so that a real fleece of the proper wool did not come into his hands.

"I can pick it up on the way back," he thought. He resolved to ask even oftener than before when they were on the homeward road. His mother so wanted the South

[1] From Cornelia Meigs, *Wind in the Chimney*.

Down wool, for the wool she had been able to get was not the best for weaving the fine cloth and figured bed coverlids which she could make so beautifully. Dick thought with pride how brave his mother had been to bring her three children from England and make a new home in America. He was proud too that now his earnings could be added to those from his mother's weaving. He was sure he could find the wool his mother wanted.

Marcus Horner began to press forward more quickly, for what was left in the packs, mostly gunpowder, was to be sold only in Pittsburgh. The trail grew steeper and steeper, one could no longer call it even the semblance of a road. On the second day of climbing, torrents of cold rain began to fall about them, the leaves were all gone from the trees, and the birds went whirling by them as though carried away, as the leaves were, by the roaring autumn gale.

"When you get to the top of the ridge, you can look off to the western country," Marcus Horner told them, as they scrambled upward. But long before they reached the height toward which they were striving, the cold rain had turned into sleet which blew in their faces and made the horses dance and flinch, most unwilling to go up the steep trail in the face of the ice-laden wind. There was no place of shelter where they could stop, the only thing was to go forward. The pack animals spread out along the way, Horner leading, Dick a good space behind him with several horses between, Caspar bringing up the rear. The rough ground over which they were going seemed to grow rougher. Marcus Horner hesitated and stopped and waited for Dick to come up.

"The horses won't look where they are going and I can scarcely see, myself," Horner said. "I don't know, I'm not sure but that we have got off the trail." They pushed a little farther and suddenly came up against an impassable mass of rocks and broken trees. "We *are* off the trail," he said.

In that blinding storm it would be hard indeed to find the way back. The horses drew together, standing in a forlorn huddle, with their tails to the wind. The last of them came staggering up, Caspar riding behind, tugging at the rein of his ungainly mount.

"Why are you stopping?" he called above the wind as he came close. "Is this the way to go? Speckle doesn't like it."

"I happen not to have been over just this trail before," Horner said. "The men in the last town gave me such directions that I was sure we could not make a mistake. But somehow, we have missed the way." He looked about him, at the ice cover which was beginning to spread over the ground, at the broken rocks, and the waste all around them. He did not need to say that there was danger in staying where they were, and much greater danger in moving blindly on.

"I've been over this way," Caspar said unexpectedly. "And so has old Speckle, we were with a pack train a year ago and made this same crossing of the mountains. I thought from the way Speckle was trying to turn that we were not going the right way. I'll give her her head and she'll lead us right, I'm certain she knows."

There seemed no other thing to try. Caspar swung round and patted the white mare on the neck. She set off confidently, going almost into the wind, which no horse would do unless she were sure of where she meant to go. The others came stumbling after her, over the icy rocks, round a big boulder, on smoother going which did indeed seem to mean that they were on the trail. Up they went, half a mile farther, then, wrapped in stinging clouds of icy rain and scarcely able to see even the things nearest them, they began to feel, by the action of the horses' great muscles between their knees, that they were going down, and not up. A little farther, and they dropped below the storm, saw open ground all about, and could spy, far off, the lower lands and meandering rivers of western Pennsylvania. The old mare, with her long ears poked forward, led the way and the others came gratefully after her.

They rode into Pittsburgh on the afternoon of a short, sunny day that was really winter. Snow lay on the roofs of the cabins and of the bigger houses, and was heavy on the eaves of the Hickory Tree Inn. At the ends of the lanes and roadways, they could look at hills above or river banks below, drifted in snow or white with ice. Big flatboats and long French bateaux were frozen in where they lay along the shore, their toiling progress over, now, until another spring. Men with fur caps pulled low and in buffalo-hide coats walked the streets. Caspar, riding beside Dick, leaned from his saddle to touch his friend on the arm. "Look, there at the corner, by the flagstaff, an Indian!"

Red men's ears are quick and the tall chief with a blanket girded about him and a single feather in his hair turned to look at the boys. Dick had not been long in America, but he was never to forget that first sight of an Indian face, so different in shape from anyone he had ever seen in England, narrow where most faces were wide, the eyes narrow too and so very bright, the straight black hair sweeping back from the high dark forehead. There was no way in the world that one could guess what the Indian was thinking of those two boys in homespun garments and with red mufflers wound round their necks up to the ears, mounted on the weary pack horses, who had come all the way from the seaboard country. He gave them a long careful stare, and then turned about indifferently to look once more at the river and the ice, and the snowy hills rising beyond it.

It was a day or two later while Dick was standing on the river front, with the broad Ohio before him, with bags of grain, barrels of molasses, kegs of turpentine, piled-up billets of pig iron, all about, that a man in wagoner's clothes, whom he had never seen before, put a paper into his hand. As Dick stared at it in surprise, the other explained, in a thick, friendly, German voice that "a friend of mine, who goes only so far as Harrisburg, haf give me this to bring to you in Pittsburgh. He said a little girl, a nice little girl, on the Lancaster Road asked him would he take it west to reach her brother, traveling with Marcus Horner. We all know Horner, it was not hard to find you and him."

Dick read the message, so carefully written in Debby's big square writing: ". . . we miss you. Don't forget the South Down wool. . . . See if anybody knows how to weave a Wheel of Fortune quilt. We think we can keep our house if you will bring home the pattern."

That was a challenge indeed, although for the life of him Dick could not see what a Wheel of Fortune quilt had to do with the little house on Cherry Hill. But his faith in Debby's judgment was, somehow, quite firm. She would not have said it if this did not mean the way out. His eyes, as he stood thinking, were on the busy scene before him, but what he really saw was a tall hedge, a gap in the branches and a little stone house with shuttered windows, waiting for them to come and live and be happy inside. He saw the bright room and the fire aflame on the hearth. Even above all the shouting about him, the guttural voices of Indians and the hoarse shouts of the keelboat men, he could hear within his memory another sound, like nothing else in the world, the sound of wind in the chimney. Yes, they would keep that house, if he had to walk over every mile of Pennsylvania seeking what they needed.

Marcus Horner's business of buying furs to carry home did not move very quickly, but at last it was finished and the bales were packed for the start home. Dick knew certainly of one farmer at least who had South Down wool, and had been told just where to find him. He had not had such good luck in the matter of the Wheel of Fortune quilt, because no one to whom he spoke had ever heard of such a thing. The furs were abundant, however, and the whole pack train was as well loaded as when they set out from Elizabethtown. They buckled the girths, looked to the shoes for the last time and set their faces homeward.

They were still on the western side of the mountain range, beginning to mount into the foothills, when they came to the farmhouse where Dick had been advised to stop for the prized wool. Yes, they had it, there was a good roll of it left from the last shearing, Marcus Horner was to pay for it out of Dick's earnings. The purchase was made in the big farm kitchen, from the friendly housewife, of whom Dick asked his often-repeated question, "Do you know how to weave a Wheel of Fortune quilt? Do you know of anyone who does?"

The farmer's wife thought a minute. "Wheel of Fortune, Wheel of Fortune," she repeated. "It does seem to me I have heard the name of that pattern and not so long since, though it is nothing that I know how to weave." She pondered for some minutes, then her face brightened. "Why, yes, it was Miranda Solent, who's married to my husband's cousin and lives away off the road, up in the hills. Her folks brought a Wheel of Fortune quilt from England with them and I did hear Miranda tell once that she had the pattern. But it's miles from here on the hill trail, and all out of your way."

Dick looked beseechingly at Marcus Horner. Surely he would not object to their spending a day more on this great quest. It was true that they must hurry, now they were once started, for the snows of winter would soon make the mountains quite impassable. But Horner knew, by now, all that the Wheel of Fortune really meant. He had the woman explain to them just how Dick could reach the Solent farm, and how, by riding a higher trail, he could cut across a ridge and meet them again at the foot of the real mountain range.

"I should like to let Caspar go with you," he said, "but one man can't manage so many horses as we have now. Jason will be all the company we can give you, and you had better take along that bundle that has your own things in it. You might by chance get snowbound for some days."

They parted company, therefore, with Dick and the gray lead horse, Jason, setting boldly out along the hill trail which the farmer so carefully described to him. By this time he had certainly had enough travel on mountain tracts to have learned much about finding his way. He felt ten years older in experience than the boy who had started so confidently with Marcus Horner from Cherry Hill.

The day was bright, fortunately, so that the darkness came as late as the gray November day would allow. He could look back at the whole valley like a map below him, could even see the smoke from the houses of Pittsburgh. He knew that broad view was very beautiful, but he could think of nothing, really, but his errand. He rode steadily onward.

He knew the Solent farmhouse at once from the description, long and low-roofed, seeming to be set into the hill, so closely did it stand against the wooded slope. Part of it was built of logs, but the newer portion was of boards and hand-hewn timbers, with a row of bright windows. There was a neat garden space before the house, where even the snow could not hide the orderly rows of lilac and rose bushes. He got down stiffly from Jason; it had been a long ride, and had only been accomplished just in time, for it was already almost dark. He knocked at the door and, after listening a moment, heard a husky voice call from inside, "Come in."

The door led him straight into the kitchen, with its fireplace so big that it simply was a stone-walled end of the room with a deep hearth and enormous chimney space. So close did the house stand to the hill that a spring above had been led down to trickle into a niche in the wall, filling a copper basin which stood below it and flowing away in a cool stream down through the wall again. The firelight shone on bright pans and scoured pots. The gay curtains at the windows were looped back to show the wide white landscape of woods and mountains. No house that Dick had seen, even close to the big towns, seemed so pleasant, so beautiful and so full of peace. Yet there was no busy housekeeper in sight, only a very tall and broad-shouldered boy, sitting by the fire with his knee propped up on a stool. He turned about, and smiled a welcome as Dick came in.

"My father and mother are down at the barn, seeing to the milking. I had an accident chopping a tree, a while ago, and I'm no use on the place just now." Some natural good manners kept him, evidently, from asking curiously what it could be which had brought a stranger so far into the hills where casual visitors never came.

Richard saw that the boy was reaching, with difficulty, to put another log on the fire, and he lifted it instead and stirred the dying blaze. "How long ago was your knee hurt?" he asked.

"Oh, a month or more. We were very lucky, we sent down word to Pittsburgh if a doctor went through to have him come up and see me, and someone came, hardly more than a week after. He was a splendid man, in a great hurry to get on with his journey, but he stayed here a day and a night and showed us exactly what to do. He said it would get all well, but I couldn't move it for a month."

They talked while Dick waited, so that the younger boy learned that his host's name was Joseph Solent, that he had been born on the hillside farm and knew no other life than that of the hills.

"My mother tells me about England, for she was born there," he said, "but it sounds like something so far away I never think of it as real." It seemed hard for him to picture how another boy would know all about the busy streets of an English town, with its crooked lanes and gabled houses, just as well as he knew the rustling pathways of the Pennsylvania hill country. The two were busy in talk, when the back door opened and Joe's mother came in.

She was as small as her great son was tall. She was quick and alert and bright-eyed, and as neat as a wax figure, even though she had just been helping to put the stock of the whole farm to bed. Her husband came in behind her, carrying the milk pails, a giant of a man with a silent, friendly smile. Mrs. Solent went about, lighting candles, laying the table with a place for the guest, stirring things in pots on the fire, cutting bread and opening jars of strawberry jam all at once, and at the same time she talked busily and asked a brisk succession of kindly questions. How had he heard of them; was Cousin Anna, who had sent him, quite well; did business seem to be brisk on the Pittsburgh water front; were there many farmhouses now along the Lancaster Road; how did Philadelphia look; had he seen President Washington in his great coach?

It seemed that, after coming to America when she was a girl, she had lived for a while in Philadelphia before she married and moved into the West country. She exclaimed with delight when she found that Dick was so newly come from England and could tell her news of a land which seemed so unbelievably far away from the Pennsylvania mountains. Much indeed did she have to ask, and there was much gay laughter over her questions and Dick's answers and the comments of the other two.

"I've seen Washington myself, often enough, for I was one of his soldiers," her husband said at last in his slow, deep voice, "but I never caught sight of him in a great coach, no, indeed. The last time I laid eyes on him he was mounted on his great gray charger, riding home from Yorktown, and the end of the war. I never thought that any face could look so weary or so happy."

Both Joe and his father were eager to hear anything Dick had to tell of his journeying with Marcus Horner. "We came in an ox cart, and it carried easily all we owned," the elder Solent observed while his son added, "Wagons sometimes go all the way to the new land beside the Ohio River now and out into Kentucky. I'm going there myself, when I can walk again and when Pop doesn't need me for a while."

His mother sighed a little; but he spoke with such depth of eagerness that she offered no protest. When the father has pressed a long way into the wilderness to establish his home, the son is very apt to take up his ax and his gun and press even farther. Whatever the women think, they do not say it.

The meal was almost ended before they asked at last concerning Dick's errand and listened in the silence of deep interest as he told them of the little stone house on Cherry Hill, of his mother's weaving and even of the noise the wind made in the chimney. He brought out Debby's letter, and Mrs. Solent read it and puzzled over it, for no one, so far, had been able to guess, from that request in big, firm writing, just how the house could be kept for them all by means of a Wheel of Fortune quilt.

She shrewdly guessed the answer when she said, "People sometimes set great store by one special kind of a coverlid. It must be, somewhere, there is a person wanting both the farm and the quilt, equally enough for the Wheel of Fortune to tip the balance."

"And do you have the pattern?" It was her son who asked it, speaking even more anxiously than Dick.

"My grandmother certainly had it," Mrs. Solent answered, knitting her brows in thought. "I remember the quilt itself, a beautiful thing, but all worn to bits before I grew up. I have my grandmother's weaving patterns, but I don't have time, myself, for making figured coverlids, so the directions for making them lie there in the cupboard where I haven't touched them for years."

She got up, took the candle and opened the door of the little storage place in the wall. A bundle of yellow scraps of paper, all sizes and shapes came out of the dark recess and she began turning them over. "Here's Bachelor's Fancy, and Double Snowballs, and Muscadine Hulls," she named them one after another. "Why, I haven't thought of that for years, and here's Rosepath that the Swedish woman in Cottage Lane showed my mother how to make." She went through them one by one; there was every name fancy could conjure up, it seemed, except the one they wanted. There were only three left, then only two strips of yellow curling paper, then one. Even her hands were trembling a little, and both the boys were breathless as they watched over her shoulder. Here was only a collection of lines and crosses, just like all the rest, but, in neat perfect little writing in the upper corner, were the words "Wheel of Fortune." Joe let out a great hurrah that echoed in all the corners of the shadowy room.

They worked until far into the night to make a copy of the faded pattern on its cracked and crumpled paper which was more than a hundred years old. It took long rummaging to find a suitable strip of paper, then lines had to be ruled upon it like those on which music notes are written, then tiny crosses had to be made, each in its exact space, and gone over again and again to verify every mark, otherwise the pattern could never be properly woven. The two boys held the ends of the paper steady, for the long strip had been rolled for years, and tended to curl itself up the moment it was released from their firm hold. Joe's father held the candle, very carefully lest it drip, but just in the right place to let the best light follow that row of crosses which meant so much. Mrs. Solent bent over the table, hardly breathing, so earnest was she in the matter of getting the task perfectly accomplished. It was a long, long piece of work, and it was after midnight when it came to an end, when she set the last mark and wrote in the corner, as neatly and as beautifully as her grandmother had done, "Wheel of Fortune."

Then Dick brought in his roll of blankets and she made up a bed in Joe's room and told her family and guest very firmly that it was time they all got to bed. Joe was helped, limping painfully, to his own couch, and the house fell into silence.

Dick lay awake for some time, excited, glad, and at the same time greatly puzzled. He ought to pay these generous people something for what they had given him, but what should it be? He knew they would refuse money; and yet he knew also that they were poor and in need of many things. What could he do, what should he do? He went to sleep still wondering, and still, as he slipped into dreams, conscious vaguely that something very pleasant had happened to make everyone happy.

When he awoke the first gray light was just showing behind the windows. Even then he heard his hostess stirring in the kitchen, building up the fire for breakfast. The clear yellow behind the mountain top gave promise of a fine day for his long ride to meet Marcus Horner.

He was still struggling with his unsolved problem of payment as he ate a hearty breakfast, took under his arm the package of lunch which Mrs. Solent thrust upon him, and listened to Joe's final directions as to how he was to find the appointed spot for meeting Marcus Horner and Caspar. He tried to say some word of what he wanted to offer, but he was so quickly silenced that he had not the courage to go on.

He walked out of the house, carrying his blanket roll, and found that Joe's father had already saddled Jason and brought him to the door. He said good-by to Joe, who had been assisted back to his seat near the fire. The tall boy's face looked drawn, not with pain, but with the cruel thought that here was one who could mount and ride away and here was the other who could not move from within those imprisoning four walls. They did not have much to say, but each knew all of what the other was thinking. Mrs. Solent and her husband came out in the cold to stand on the step and see Dick mount. Suddenly a magnificent thought, exactly the right thought, struck him.

"I forgot something," he muttered, and unstrapped his blanket roll as though to see that everything was inside. From the very heart of it he plucked his most cherished possession, his horse bells with silver in the metal that he had earned by helping Tom Garwick. In two strides he was in the kitchen again and had put them in Joe's hands. "For you, when you make your march to the West," he said, and was gone before the other could reply.

The ride across the hills was successfully accomplished, as was also the long journey back toward the land of turnpikes and stone farmhouses and great warm barns. How well they knew the way now, and how well they knew each other, he and Caspar and Marcus Horner. Both the boys, when they got home, must go to school for the winter term, but when spring came, Marcus Horner, so he promised, would take them over this road again.

It was a great moment for Dick at home when he unrolled his pack of possessions and produced the bale of South Down wool and the tiny roll of paper with that beautifully written "Wheel of Fortune" in the corner. To Debby and her mother, the rows of lines and crosses made the most exciting document they had ever seen.

In time the quilt was woven and it saved Cherry Hill Cottage for them, but that is another story.

## ABE LINCOLN GROWS UP[1]

*Carl Sandburg*

When he was eleven years old, Abe Lincoln's young body began to change. As the months and years went by, he noticed his lean wrists getting longer, his legs too, and he was now looking over the heads of other boys. Men said, "Land o' Goshen, that boy air a-growin'!"

As he took on more length, they said he was shooting up into the air like green corn in the summer of a good corn-year. So he grew. When he reached seventeen years of age, and they measured him, he was six feet, nearly four inches, high, from the bottoms of his moccasins to the top of his skull.

These were years he was handling the ax. Except in spring plowing-time and the fall fodder-pulling, he was handling the ax nearly all the time. The insides of his hands

[1] From Carl Sandburg, *Abe Lincoln Grows Up*.

took on callus thick as leather. He cleared openings in the timber, cut logs and puncheons, split fire wood, built pigpens.

He learned how to measure with his eye the half-circle swing of the ax so as to nick out the deepest possible chip from off a tree trunk. The trick of swaying his body easily on the hips so as to throw the heaviest possible weight into the blow of the ax —he learned that.

On winter mornings he wiped the frost from the ax handle, sniffed sparkles of air into his lungs, and beat a steady cleaving of blows into a big tree—till it fell—and he sat on the main log and ate his noon dinner of corn bread and fried salt pork—and joked with the gray squirrels that frisked and peeped at him from high forks of near-by walnut trees.

He learned how to make his ax flash and bite into a sugar maple or a sycamore. The outside and the inside look of black walnut and black oak, hickory and jack oak, elm and white oak, sassafras, dogwood, grapevines, sumac—he came on their secrets. He could guess close to the time of the year, to the week of the month, by the way the leaves and branches of trees looked. He sniffed the seasons.

Often he worked alone in the timbers, all day long with only the sound of his own ax, or his own voice speaking to himself, or the crackling and swaying of branches in the wind, and the cries and whirs of animals, of brown and silver-gray squirrels, of partridges, hawks, crows, turkeys, sparrows, and the occasional wildcats.

The tricks and whimsies of the sky, how to read clear skies and cloudy weather, the creeping vines of ivy and wild grape, the recurrence of dogwood blossoms in spring, the ways of snow, rain, drizzle, sleet, the visitors of sky and weather coming and going hour by hour—he tried to read their secrets, he tried to be friendly with their mystery.

So he grew, to become hard, tough, wiry. The muscle on his bones and the cords, tendons, cross-weaves of fiber, and nerve centers, these became instruments to obey his wishes. He found with other men he could lift his own end of a log—and more too. One of the neighbors said he was strong as three men. Another said, "He can sink an ax deeper into wood than any man I ever saw." And another, "If you heard him fellin' trees in a clearin', you would say there was three men at work by the way the trees fell."

He was more than a tough, long, rawboned boy. He amazed men with his man's lifting power. He put his shoulders under a new-built corncrib one day and walked away with it to where the farmer wanted it. Four men, ready with poles to put under it and carry it, didn't need their poles. He played the same trick with a chicken house; at the new, growing town of Gentryville near by, they said the chicken house weighed six hundred pounds, and only a big boy with a hard backbone could get under it and walk away with it.

He took shape in a tall, long-armed cornhusker. When rain came in at the chinks of the cabin loft where he slept, soaking through the book Josiah Crawford loaned him, he pulled fodder two days to pay for the book, made a clean sweep, till there wasn't a blade left on a cornstalk in the field of Josiah Crawford.

His father was saying the big boy looked as if he had been roughhewn with an ax and needed smoothing with a jackplane. "He was the ganglin'est, awkwardest feller that ever stepped over a ten-rail snake fence; he had t' duck to git through a door; he 'peared to be all j'ints."

His stepmother told him she didn't mind his bringing dirt into the house on his feet; she could scour the floor; but she asked him to keep his head washed or he'd be rubbing the dirt on her nice whitewashed rafters. He put barefoot boys to wading in a mud puddle near the horse trough, picked them up one by one, carried them to the house upside down, and walked their muddy feet across the ceiling. The mother came in, laughed an hour at the foot tracks, told Abe he ought to be spanked—and he cleaned the ceiling so it looked new.

Abe knew the sleep that comes after long hours of work outdoors, the feeling of simple food changing into blood and muscle as he worked in those young years clearing timberland for pasture and corn crops, cutting loose the brush, piling it and burning it, splitting rails, pulling the crosscut saw and the whipsaw, driving the shovel-plow, harrowing, planting, hoeing, pulling fodder, milking cows, churning butter, helping neighbors at house-raisings, logrollings, corn-huskings.

He found he was fast, strong, and keen when he went against other boys in sports. On farms where he worked, he held his own at scuffling, knocking off hats, wrestling. The time came when around Gentryville and Spencer County he was known as the best "rassler" of all, the champion. In jumping, foot-racing, throwing the maul, pitching the crowbar, he carried away the decisions against the lads of his own age always, and usually won against those older than himself.

He earned his board, clothes, and lodgings, sometimes working for a neighbor farmer. He watched his father, while helping make cabinets, coffins, cupboards, window frames, doors. Hammers, saws, pegs, cleats, he understood firsthand, also the scythe and the cradle for cutting hay and grain, the corn-cutter's knife, the leather piece to protect the hand while shucking corn, and the horse, the dog, the cow, the ox, the hog. He could skin and cure the hides of coon and deer. He lifted the slippery two-hundred-pound hog carcass, head down, holding the hind hocks up for others of the gang to hook, and swung the animal clear of the ground. He learned where to stick a hog in the under side of the neck so as to bleed it to death, how to split it in two, and carve out the chops, the parts for sausage grinding, for hams, for "cracklings."

Farmers called him to butcher for them at thirty-one cents a day, this was when he was sixteen and seventeen years old. He could "knock a beef in the head," swing a maul and hit a cow between the eyes, skin the hide, halve and quarter in, carve out the tallow, the steaks, kidneys, liver.

And the hiding-places of fresh spring water under the earth crust had to be in his thoughts; he helped at well-digging; the wells Tom Lincoln dug went dry one year after another; neighbors said Tom was always digging a well and had his land "honeycombed"; and the boy, Abe, ran the errands and held the tools for the well-digging.

When he was eighteen years old, he could take an ax at the end of the handle and hold it out in a straight horizontal line, easy and steady—he had strong shoulder muscles and steady wrists early in life. He walked thirty-four miles in one day, just on an errand, to please himself, to hear a lawyer make a speech. He could tell his body to do almost impossible things, and the body obeyed.

Growing from boy to man, he was alone a good deal of the time. Days came often when he was by himself all the time except at breakfast and supper hours in the cabin home. In some years, more of his time was spent in loneliness than in the company of other people. It happened, too, that this loneliness he knew was not like that of people in cities who can look from a window on streets where faces pass and repass. It was the wilderness loneliness he became acquainted with, solved, filtered through body, eye, and brain, held communion with in his ears, in the temples of his forehead, in the works of his beating heart.

He lived with trees, with the bush wet with shining raindrops, with the burning bush of autumn, with the lone wild duck riding a north wind and crying down on a line north to south, the faces of open sky and weather, the ax which is an individual one-man instrument, these he had for companions, books, friends, talkers, chums of his endless changing soliloquies.

His moccasin feet in the wintertime knew the white spaces of snowdrifts piled in whimsical shapes against timber slopes or blown in levels across the fields of last year's cut corn stalks; in the summertime his bare feet toughened in the gravel of green streams while he laughed back to the chatter of bluejays in the red-haw trees or while he kept his eyes ready in the slough quack-grass for the cow-snake, the rattler, the copperhead.

He rested between spells of work in the springtime when the upward push of the coming out of the new grass can be heard, and in autumn weeks when the rustle of a single falling leaf lets go a whisper that a listening ear can catch.

He found his life thrown in ways where there was a certain chance for a certain growth. And so he grew. Silence found him; he met silence. In the making of him as he was, the element of silence was immense.

## INVINCIBLE LOUISA AS A NURSE [1]

*Cornelia Meigs*

The city of Washington lay silent in the raw cold of a cloudy December day, silent and listening. It was almost as if the people walking to and fro in the broad streets were afraid to speak aloud; it was as though they were all straining their ears for a sound too far off to be actually heard. A great battle was going forward. That was official news, brought to the tall, gaunt man in the White House, who was even now walking up and down the long office room, waiting and listening just as was every one else. Rumors were flocking in—General Burnside, the Union commander, was splendidly victorious—General Burnside was in utter rout with all his forces. Rumors of a battle always contradict one another for a little while, until finally the truth comes drifting in. The truth came at last. It was news of a signal defeat of the Union troops at Fredericksburg. Close behind it came the rumble of heavy wheels, as the ambulances brought the thousands of wounded to the hospitals of Washington.

Louisa Alcott's new life as a nurse had just begun. She had not learned very much about her duties as yet, only which ward was to be hers, how the meals of fat pork and dishwater coffee were served, how many different people must be applied to before an order for bandages and medicine could be filled. The hospital to which she had been sent was in Georgetown, on high ground just outside Washington. The building had once been a large hotel, wherein slatternly housekeeping with lazy, casual servants had held sway for years. Upon the accumulation of dirt and dilapidation, there had been poured the hastily gathered equipment of a hospital—flimsy iron cots, dingy mattresses, hard pillows, bedding and crockery and surgeons' supplies in all the necessarily enormous quantities.

It had looked, nevertheless, like an imposing place to Louisa as she drove up in the dark, saw the rows of lighted windows and the guards at the door. The recollection of her travels was still like a great adventure upon her, so unused was she to even so modestly brief a journey as this. May and Julian to see her off in Concord, the night spent in Boston with Cousin Lizzie Wells, a few last pangs of wonder and foreboding, then Anna and John Pratt saying good-by before the puffing train bore her southward! To go from Boston to Washington was an elaborate process in 1862; one journeyed by train to New London, by boat to New York, took another inexpressibly early train from Jersey City and reached Washington long after dark. She had studied her traveling companions with edification; she had chuckled delightedly over the tribulations of hoop-skirted ladies trying to go to bed in the narrow cabin berths of the steamer.

As Philadelphia went past the car windows she pressed her nose to the pane and wished that she could stop a little to see more of her "native city." When she came at last to her journey's end, was carried in

[1] From Cornelia Meigs, *Invincible Louisa: The Story of the Author of Little Women.* This book was awarded the John Newbery Medal in 1934.

a bumping cab over the long drive to Georgetown, when she finally dismounted, stiff with lengthy, uncomfortable traveling, the first sensation which came over her was a wave of terrific shyness. All these strange people, a crowd of men about the doors—how was she to face them; what was she supposed to do first? She walked forward boldly, was admitted, welcomed and taken to her room.

A tiny apartment it was, for which the words bare and dreary would give too rich a description. Two inhospitable iron beds told her that she was to share it with another nurse. Half the window panes were broken, and, opposite the curtainless opening, the innumerable windows of a great hospital in a church across the way, stared in upon her. It was inadequately warmed by a narrow fireplace, in which a pair of bricks supported one end of a log, which, too big for the aperture, extended out into the room and had to be pushed into the fireplace by degrees as the wood burned away. The closet was tiny, full of cockroaches and loud with the scampering of rats. She was warned at once to leave nothing of value lying about, as both the colored and the white hospital attendants were rapacious thieves.

When she was introduced to her duties in the ward, she looked about in dismay at the rows of sagging beds, the dirty floors, the unwashed windows, and the long corridors, haunted with evil smells. The comfortable, plain neatness of the house in Concord seemed a thing of which she had dreamed, so remote it appeared to be from this vast dismal place. But she had come to work and, no matter what the circumstances were, work she would do. There was no lack of it. A nurse had just given out, ill, and her place was thrust upon Louisa, so that, with no training and with insufficient knowledge, she found herself immediately superintendent of a ward containing forty beds. Those who occupied them were suffering variously from measles, diphtheria, and typhoid.

The hospital nevertheless was not crowded just then; most of the patients were recovering to a certain degree, so that the pressure for the first three days was not unendurable. She began to get acquainted with her fellow workers, with the faces on the pillows, faces which very soon learned to brighten as she came near. Even without surgical skill or proper knowledge, Louisa was a rare nurse. She might be shy, weary or sick at heart, but even here she always remained good company.

Like the others, she had waited through the long dark day for news from Fredericksburg and had gone to bed, worn out with apprehension. At three o'clock in the morning she was awakened by the general summons—

"The wounded are coming."

They came streaming in, filling every vacant bed and cot, waiting in the halls, laid upon pallets on the floor. Those who could walk stood in dismal groups about the stoves, cold, wet, and dirty. They had been fighting in the rain and mud for three days, and, when they were hurt, were bundled into the ambulances with only the briefest of emergency treatment. Louisa, who thought that she was used to sickness and nursing, had no experience of anything like this.

"What do I do first?" she asked desperately of a superior, hurrying past.

"Wash them," was the brief reply.

So, armed with a tin basin, a towel so rough that it might be made of sandpaper, and a cake of brown soap which, at home, she would have used only for scrubbing the floor, she advanced upon her task. She began with the man in the bed nearest her, a person so covered with dirt that his own family might not have known him. She commenced to draw off his ragged uniform, working easily and gently as she knew how to do, holding her breath for fear a groan of pain would reproach her efforts.

"May your bed above be aisy, darlin', for the day's work you are doin'," said a rich, cheerful voice. Louisa, hearing it, laughed aloud with relief. Faces on the long row of pillows turned and smiled and the Irish soldier laughed with her. It was a good beginning.

During the first days and nights which followed she was nothing but a bundle of tired aches, driven somehow by a determined will and a cool head. How much there was to do and what aimless confusion and lack of management there were to hinder the doing of it! There were calls for her in every direction and need for help even amongst those who had no strength to call. At first all those gray, worn faces looked alike to her; but little by little she began to know her horde of new patients, the cheery Irishman, the querulous, complaining man with a little wound, the big, patient Virginia blacksmith with a mortal one. It was on her first turn of night duty that she became acquainted with the little drummer boy and his friend Kit.

As she walked between the beds through the great candle-lit cave which had once been the hotel ballroom, she caught the noise of a stifled crying, a strange sound in that heroic company where even groans were comparatively rare. In the last bed was the smallest patient in the hospital, Billy, the drummer boy, aged only twelve. As Louisa bent over him, he broke into open, little-boy weeping.

"I dreamed that Kit was here and when I waked up he wasn't." He shook with sobs, as well as with the terrific chill which had waked him.

She quieted him as only Louisa really could have known how to do, and presently got his story from him, spoken softly lest the rest of the ward be disturbed. The yellow candle shone down upon his white, drawn, pitifully small face as he looked up at her and told her everything that had happened. Men were so badly needed in the army that the Government was obliged to accept boys to beat the rolling drums and blow the bugles. Billy had been the object of envy of all his young friends when he marched away with the regiment, thumping gloriously as they went down the road. He had drummed for long, weary marches, in the hot sun, in the rain and the snow; he had never lagged, though his legs were short and his strength only half that of a real soldier's. He fell ill with fever during the Fredericksburg campaign and was burning and shivering in his tent when the command came to go into battle.

He lay under the wavering canvas, hearkening to the boom of the guns, hearing the cheer of his comrades as they went into action. He could not move, he could only wait and wonder. He thought of each one whom he knew, the one who liked to tease him, the one who gave him good advice, and Kit, splendid Kit, who was his chief friend and the object of his adoration. Would the battle bring harm to Kit? That was his chief thought, as he lay there and watched the tent canvas shiver and tremble in the cold wind.

What was this he heard now, the sound of feet, thousands of feet going by the tent, not with the measured tread of marching, but with haste, with running panic?

Was this a retreat? Could it be possible that Kit—that General Burnside's army, had been forced back by the Johnny Rebs?

There was a voice at the tent door. Someone was standing against the light. It was Kit with the kindly face and the strong arms who gathered him up from his bed of blankets on the ground. Too weak to ask questions, Billy lay against his friend's shoulder and was carried away in that vast, dreary river of defeat which flowed down all the roads that led from Fredericksburg.

More than one voice said near them, "You're hurt yourself, Kit; let me take him."

But his comrade would not give him up. The endless shuffle of weary feet changed finally to the rumble of ambulance wheels, but still the two traveled on, still Kit's arm was around him. Billy fell into a long sleep of complete exhaustion and wakened only at the hospital door. He was being lifted, but by whose hands? Where was Kit? A battered soldier near him told him as gently as he could that Kit had—had gone. Billy would have cried out in anguish, but soldiers did not do that. He was one of the regiment; he must take this blow without whimpering. He did.

In the hospital he lay, silent and wide-eyed, facing his grief with unwavering spirit. It was that dream which betrayed him. He dreamed that Kit was with him again, that they were sitting together by the bivouac fire, laughing and joking as they had so often done. Kit's warm hand was on his shoulder, his strong voice was speaking just beside him—and suddenly he awoke to the shadowy ward, to the flickering lights from the candles and the glowing stove, to the rows of silent beds. Grief took him unawares and he wept, stifling the great sobs in the pillow as best he could. It was so that Louisa found him. It was into her ear that he poured out the whole story. For a whole hour she listened and comforted. At last he was cheered and quieted; at last he was dropping to sleep.

Louisa leaned back in her chair, to rest a minute and draw her breath; for it had taken all her strength and spirit to help the desolate little boy. How tired she was and how long the night! But she could be still for a little now, she thought, and gather courage again.

A step behind her made her start and turn about. A long rifleman from Pennsylvania had risen from his bed and was tramping down the ward, walking in the sleep of pain-ridden fever. She rushed to him and seized him by the arm, protesting and commanding. It was dangerous for him to be walking about with a serious wound; he must get back to bed at once.

"I'm going home," he announced, and tramped on. He would neither wake nor listen. Tall Louisa hanging on his arm was as nothing to his gigantic strength as he strode onward, repeating steadily, "I'm going home."

A huge fellow at the end of the ward, less seriously hurt than some of the others, rose from his blankets and came to her rescue. His powerful arms accomplished what her remonstrances could not; so that finally he led the wanderer back to his own place. Quiet settled down again; Billy was asleep, the lank Pennsylvanian was drifting into more peaceful dreams, muttering still now and then that he was going home.

That was what they all dreamed about in that crowded, ill-smelling place—home. Louisa knew it, for her own thoughts, at the back of her mind, were always on the clean perfume of pine-covered hills, on the glint of the river between green meadows, on the lighted windows in the friendly houses all along the road.

In the brief free hour between the night watch and the day, she wrote letters to her family of whom she thought so incessantly. The place that she was in was squalid and dreary; there was no romance in the sights she was seeing now, so she thought. But she was bound that they at home should see it all, just as she was always seeing them in the inner vision of her mind. As the days went by, she wrote and wrote, whenever she could snatch a minute, so that they too would become acquainted with the blacksmith John Sulie and jolly little Sergeant Bain, with Billy and Kit. She herself had learned to know Kit as well as though he were actually there, even though the knowledge came entirely through the chatter of Billy, who had taken her for his confidante. She was often so tired that the writing wavered on the page; but the picture that she drew in words was always clear.

She did not feel as strong and undaunted as she had intended to be. Although she did not know it, she was actually perishing for want of the fresh, bracing air which she had always breathed, of the spare, wholesome food which she was used to eating. She could have courage to steel her heart against the onslaughts of homesickness and the sight of suffering all about, but she could not steel her body against the poisons of that unhealthy place. She grew daily more thin and pale, but every one around her was far too busy to notice such a thing.

In spite of all she felt, Louisa could be nothing other than herself. The ward which she had in charge resounded with laughter, just as the old house in Concord had done. Here was suffering everywhere; but there were jokes everywhere also, since there is no place where something comic cannot be discovered. Some people thought the mirth unseemly; but the men laughed and loved her. The windows were nailed down; but she wrenched them loose and threw them open for a time every day, quite deaf to the dire prophecies of what the consequences might be. She made beds, carried trays and dressed wounds, and left her patients chuckling whenever she turned away to a new task. How she managed it she could not have told anyone. She did it by being Louisa.

## BLUE ARROW AND THE OUTLAWS [1]

*Constance Lindsay Skinner*

That afternoon Lachlan lay in the doorway of the dining tent, looking out on the mild day and the shining snow. Most of the well-fed diners had departed to their various tasks and amusements. The little group of gossips inside was composed of Meriwether Lewis, just returned that morning from St. Louis, William Clark, Silent Scot, Tuleko, Blue Arrow, Barking Water, and Daniel Boone, and the two trappers from Missouri who had accompanied Boone on his visit. Though Daniel maintained that he had come to the Illinois camp for no other purpose than to taste the far-famed cooking of Barking Water, he had really come to buy powder and lead for bullets, and six new rifles, from the expedition's stores, for himself and other hunters in La Charette. The two trappers, Biddle and Smith, had accompanied him to help carry the load home.

Lewis was telling Boone anecdotes of his former chief, Jefferson. But Lachlan's attention wandered under the spell of an old dream. Behind the tent there was a tall tree. Now it threw its lone blue shadow on the snow. That single shadow roused a keen memory in the lad, who had once been the adopted son of Alexander McGillivray, the dread White Leader of the Creeks. It brought back to him the day when White Alex's shadow had fallen across the garden grass in New Orleans just after Alex had learned that Lachlan Chate was not in sympathy with him and his Spanish allies in their intent to massacre the Tennessee settlers. Lachlan had waited breathlessly, looking not at the White Leader but at his shadow, to hear whether he was to live or die. Strangely now, here in the Illinois camp, this one innocent tree shadow on the snow seemed prophetic of menace.

Perhaps, he thought, the odd feeling it gave him was really due to the fact that Blue Arrow was putting the finishing touches with his knife to a blowgun. It was Gypsy John, the Venezuelan, a conspicuous figure in their lives in those perilous days, who had taught Blue Arrow how to make and use the silent, deadly blowgun invented by the Indians of his native jungles. And, in that same New Orleans garden, Blue Arrow had used it to kill, silently, the Spanish agent who held his pistol at Lachlan's breast. Yes, he argued, it must be the blowgun in Blue Arrow's hands which, by waking old memories, made a tree shadow seem to advance before the sun with a threat, here where all was clear and peaceful. With a determined effort he cast off the spell, and listened to the other men's conversation. Boone was talking now, about Pasky's band.

"It would be a good thing fer us an' t'other scattered settlers an' hunters, Cap'n Lewis, if you an' William was ter send out a score o' yer men ter hunt down that wolf, Pasky, an' his pack of outlaws, thieves, an' murderers. Both Biddle an' Smith's suffered from Pasky. Had their traps robbed. An' Smith was shot at from behind a tree."

"Missed me, by good luck," Smith said, grinning. He was a short, thickset man, very dark and heavily bearded. When he laughed, which was often, he showed all his gleaming white teeth. While he had been

[1] From Constance Lindsay Skinner, *Andy Breaks Trail.*

in camp, Andy and Lachlan had done their best to amuse him because they thought his way of laughing the funniest thing they had ever seen. When Smith laughed his big mouth opened wide; he shook, doubled up, slapped his thighs, and made no other sound. It was a noiseless laugh. The cousins were delighted with it. Tuleko imitated it on the sly. Wewoca, who saw a resemblance between Smith's antics and the sacred performances of a medicine man, thought Smith sacrilegious and thoroughly disapproved of him. Blue Arrow disliked him. It was rather a habit of Blue Arrow's to dislike strangers. There was nothing out of the way about Biddle. Nobody paid much attention to him. Smith talked for both.

"Well, we'd like to help the settlers," Clark said. "But we can't undertake to hunt down outlaws, and maybe lose some of the good men we've picked for the long trail to Oregon. Who is Pasky? Did he ever live in La Charette, or anywhere in Missouri?"

"Not so far as I know. They think mebbe he's a Spanish feller from down the river some place. We've got too few men in La Charette ter risk any of 'em in searchin' the wilderness fer Pasky's hangout."

"Biddle an' me reckons it's quite a piece north," said Smith. "Yer know our cabin, Dan'l. It's hid pretty well. But if Pasky'd come as far down as that, he'd likely have found it."

"If he'd found it, an' us inside it, we wouldn't be settin' here," said Biddle. "He's got a habit of sneakin' up ter a cabin, or a huntin' shelter, an' shootin' the men through the chinks in the walls. It's their guns an' powder he's after, of course. He's got ter git powder an' lead fer his men; an' more guns is always useful, too."

"What are ye roarin' about now, so loud an' silent?" Andy demanded of Smith, with a laugh. Smith slapped his thighs.

"Pasky always sets me laughin' this way. He's got all the settlers an' the hunters scared blue in the face; takes what he happens ter want from everybody—includin' their lives." He doubled up at that. "An' nobody ever gits the joke on *him*. I'm gittin' ter believe I'm the only boy that'll ever do it. Maybe because his name don't scare *me!* Yeh. This feller Pasky's got me thinkin' about him."

"Hasn't anybody ever seen him?" Lewis asked.

"I guess so," said Boone. "But they don't ever come back to tell about him. He's a killer. I believe men like Pasky are crazy."

"He must have belonged to a settlement once, unless he is a renegade who has been living with Indians." Lewis tossed a bone to Wolf; the dog crouched beside Wewoca.

"Well, it would be hard to trace him," Clark put in, "unless a posse was formed and made Pasky their special business. All the settlers in this territory spend half the year hunting and trapping. They come into the settlements for their powder, or else they bring it from St. Louis when they go down to market their furs. Some of those hunters, who seem to be peaceable men for a month or two in a settlement, may be Pasky and his band when they get out into the wilds."

"That's what Smith says," said Biddle.

"Yeh," Boone nodded. "My son, Nathan, didn't want me ter come fer the powder. But when Biddle an' Smith said they'd come along, I told Nathan he'd have ter be jedge an' mayor in my place—what yer call actin' magistrate—as I considered it my official duty ter git the powder an' some o' Wewoca's cookin'."

"Are ye a magistrate, Mister Colonel Boone?" Silent Scot asked respectfully.

"Yeh." The old scout's eyes twinkled. He brought out his wallet and carefully abstracted two folded pieces of paper from it. "This hyar paper," he held up one, "is near fallin' ter dust." He handed it to Lewis. "It's my commission as a British officer from Lord Dunmore way back in the war with the Shawanos. The year yer was born, Cap'n Lewis! When I was taken prisoner, years after, by British Indians, led by that mad Canadian De Quindre, an' haled off ter Detroit, the British governor thar paid me a lot o' respect after he seen that paper." He chuckled. "Now this, hyar," passing Lewis the other, "is a copy of a letter the new French governor of Upper Louisiana writ ter the American Commissioner, tellin' him the United States better keep me in office fer the good o' the country. See what he says? An' when the Spanish owned La Charette, afore turnin' it over ter the French, the Spaniard, who was governor, said about the same thing. Ain't any old hunter in the wilderness that's stood higher with more furren powers than old Dan'l Boone!" He chuckled again. Smith shook with soundless laughter.

Lewis unfolded the paper and scanned it.

"Listen, boys," he said, and read aloud: "'Mr. Boone is a respectable old man, just and impartial. He has already, since I appointed him, offered his resignation, owing to his infirmities. Believing I know his probity, I have induced him to remain, in view of my confidence in him, for the public good.' That's fine, Colonel, but deserved."

"I don't like that about infirmities, Daniel," said Clark. "I didn't know you'd been sick."

"Ain't. Them's the infirmities seizes on me worse'n the cramps every huntin' season, an' makes me wild ter step out in the woods, a free man. 'Stead o' havin' ter set ter home an' cut an' trim hickory rods fer the backs o' foolish men that don't know enough ter keep the peace an' do their work honest till I've thrashed 'em. Yeh. I'm the lawgiver in La Charette over in Mizzoura. An' the law is hickory. But my infirmities didn't git me let loose. So I took a trip, anyhow. Only I call it the official expedition of a magistrate's goin' fer powder." The men shouted with laughter.

The next morning Daniel started homeward with the guns and ammunition for the settlers of La Charette. Lewis had decided to make the trip with him, chiefly because he wanted to escape as much of the boredom of the camp as possible. Clark agreed cheerfully to his going. Clark was never bored anywhere. Lewis chose Lachlan and Andy to accompany him. Tuleko, of course, went with Andy. But, much to Blue Arrow's disgust, Lachlan told him to stay in camp and keep his eye on Barking Water. Wewoca had exhibited some dangerous powers of imagination lately and Lachlan feared what he might do next. The party was to spend the night in the shelter belonging to Biddle and Smith. With the assistance of the cousins and Tuleko, the two hunters would be able to get their store of deer hides out of the cache and take them to La Charette. They said that the cache, as well as their brush cabin, was well hidden, but Pasky had a gift for discovering caches of furs. "Seems ter smell 'em like a fox," as Smith said, with one of his soundless laughs.

Blue Arrow told his troubles sulkily to Wewoca, who was the cause of them. Barking Water's indignation knew no bounds.

"The spirits are even angrier than I am," he said, his eyes rolling and flaming. "But we forgive Lachlan Chate because he is a white man and therefore not very intelligent. What will you do?"

"I will follow them but will not let them know it until we reach La Charette. They are seven who go. But only four will return; and four are not enough if bad men are in that territory. It will be better to have me also for the journey home. Especially as, on the way there, while I am following along, I shall look about carefully for signs of this bad man called Pasky, and his braves."

"I will give you some marvelous food to take on your journey, and I will also give you the protection of my spirits. If you taste any new flavors in that village, bring me the recipe."

Blue Arrow gave the men two hours' start and then slipped out of camp on their trail. He had his rifle, hunting knife, and tomahawk, as a matter of course. He also took the blowgun, strung on his back, and a score of darts. He might want to shoot something on the out trip; and he could not use his rifle lest Boone's party hear the shot and investigate. Lachlan would be angry and would send him home. Blue Arrow intended to go to La Charette.

As sunset neared, he quickened his pace. Blue Arrow was a swift traveler and he carried no load. Just before dusk he caught sight of the party crossing an open stretch. An hour or so later, he discovered Smith and Biddle's hunting shelter. It was well hidden in the thick brush of a small ravine. Men could easily pass close to it, in going down the bank, and not see it. In following snowshoe or moccasin tracks, they could lose them here and have no idea where to look for them. Blue Arrow, not yet ready to announce his arrival, observed the shelter thoughtfully and had a better opinion of the men who made it. The clever disposal of brush and logs gave it the appearance of being only a thicker tangle in the undergrowth. He questioned whether he would have found it if he had come that way in daylight, instead of at night when the men did not travel in the wilderness. It was the glimmer of the light inside which had revealed it to him now.

He sat down to rest and to think. He had come up with the party; but what had he better do now? Make his presence known? It would be pleasanter to spend the night in the shelter with the others. Even though there was no roof except interlaced pine boughs, it must be much warmer in there. Hides suspended inside the brush walls took the edge off the chill wind; and evidently a small fire helped to make the place cozy. Yes, it would be nicer to sleep there than outside in the forest. But, when morning came, would he be allowed to go on to La Charette? If he had only Lachlan to deal with, he could probably persuade him. But there was Lewis, a disciplinarian.

If Blue Arrow had been asked, "What is the principal difference between a white soldier and an Indian brave?" he would have answered, "An Indian brave changes his mind as often as intelligence dictates, when new situations arise; but the white soldier, if he has once made a plan or given an order, sticks to it, even when it has become foolish." It was almost a certainty that Lewis would order him back to Wood River. How inviting the dim glow of fire looked! Before he found himself a safe cold spot to sleep in, he would creep close enough to peep into the shelter, at least, and see what amusing things the men were doing in which he could not share.

He took off his snowshoes and propped them against a tree, with his rifle beside them. The brush was too thick about the shelter for him to get through it on snowshoes. He had put his rifle by because he needed his hands to part the twigs and boughs before him so that his body could slip through noiselessly. Slowly and carefully, he moved over the few yards down to the camp.

The deerskin blankets, which had been hung to add warmth and to help shut out the light wind, did not overlap all the way up; and presently he found a wide chink in the brush wall where they parted. Now he had a good view of the group inside. To his surprise he saw two strangers there. They looked very much like any of the hunters and trappers of that region. Lachlan, Boone, and Lewis were sitting close together against the brush wall on a bed platform made of logs covered with pine boughs. Andy and Tuleko squatted on the ground in front of them near the fire. Smith was perched on a stump at Andy's left, a little distance from him. The strangers sat on the ground on the opposite side of the fire from Andy and Tuleko. Biddle was stacking the rifles against the wall behind them.

"Never mind about my gun," said Boone, waving off Biddle's offer to relieve him of it. "I kinder like ter set an' nurse it this way. Contracted the habit in my infancy an' they never could cure me of it."

Blue Arrow did not follow the words precisely, though he understood the white man's tongue fairly well now, even if he rarely cared to speak it. He was a conservative man; and he preferred to say whatever he had to say in Creek to Lachlan and to let Lachlan translate it. But he knew, in a general way, what white men were talking about. He saw that Tuleko also kept his gun. Always cautious, even suspicious, trusting no white man completely except Lachlan, Blue Arrow was displeased to see Lachlan, Andy, and Lewis sitting so carelessly at their ease with their guns not only out of reach, but on the far side of strange men. To be sure, Biddle had stacked the strangers' guns, too, as well as his own and Smith's. But suppose that bad Pasky band slipped up noiselessly over the soft snow and began shooting through the crannies in the walls of brush and flapping blankets!

Blue Arrow turned and glanced about sharply through the darkness, which, even here in the woods, was not black darkness because of the snow. His ears were strained for a possible sound. He resolved that, presently, he would get his rifle, hide his snowshoes, and climb into the tall tree that rose against the other side of the shelter and leaned its branches over the top of it. He would not sleep at all that night. He would do sentinel duty for a camp of fools! From the tree he would be able to see all the approaches to the shelter. And at the first sight of a man, or men, slinking up, he could wake the men inside with a rifle shot. A very lucky thing for them that he had disobeyed that silly order to stay at home and watch Barking Water!

He noticed that the small fire burned in a large, deep iron pan. The fire and its revealing light could be extinguished in an instant by overturning the pan. Yes, it was a clever camp. He wondered where the packs of powder were. Cached out of doors near by, doubtless. It was wise not to bring them into the small shelter where the fire was. The flaming pine chips snapped off sparks. Except in the matter of stacking the guns, Smith was not such a fool. He knew how to make a first-class camp; how to hide; how to protect powder.

Smith was talking now, pausing every few minutes to slap his thighs and rock with his soundless laugh.

"That was a good story about how the Shawanos tried to git yer in Kaintucky, Cap'n Lewis. Yer don't agree with Silent Scot that the Spanish might have set the Injuns onter yer? But I'll tell yer somethin' comical." He shook, showing all his teeth. "Down ter St. Louis, with my pack of marten pelts, I heard thar's a man that's let it be known he'll pay five hundred dollars fer the sight of yer dead body." He doubled up. Lewis burst out laughing.

"He didn't offer it to me when I was down there recently," he said. Smith nearly exploded. Everyone else roared with laughter, in watching him.

"That wasn't the best time ter do it. Might have made talk," Smith said, when he could speak. "But yer can bet the word's been passed about yer ter all the Spanish settlements up this way. Pasky'll have got wind of it, too. Only he wouldn't try a raid on yer big camp at Wood River. But if he knowed yer was settin' here—"

The thought amused him so much that he could not go on.

"All that ammunition you men are packin' would please Pasky a heap," one of the strangers said. He lit his pipe with a flaming twig from the fire.

"Yer know," said the other, "I been studyin' jes' now about some tracks Bill an' me seen a bit west of here when we was comin' ter yer camp. At the time we figgered Smith an' Biddle must have made 'em. But they wasn't enough tracks fer yer party, seven men; an' they wasn't heavy, like men carryin' loads. Might be a couple of hunters."

"Might be Pasky's scouts," said Biddle. He turned sharply. "Smith, I'm going out ter the cache an' see if anybody's been there. Them hides is worth money ter us."

"Want company?" Andy asked.

"No. 'Tain't far. Feel pretty sure it's all right. But hearin' about tracks kinder sets me on ter take a look."

"Well, I guess that's sensible," said Smith. "Here! Come back after yer gun!" he shouted indignantly, as Biddle made for the opening. "Ain't we made a rule never ter go outside without our rifles?"

"Gosh, it's only a few steps off! An' there ain't any Pasky men surroundin' us, or we'd all been shot by now." Biddle grumbled, but came back for his gun.

"Never let go yer gun, is my motto," said Boone.

"That'd earn yer the compliment of Pasky's first shot!"

Smith shook again. "It'd be sensible ter shoot the armed men first. Say, it's gettin' hot." He unbuttoned the loose fur jacket which he wore over his hunting shirt. Andy moved further from the fire.

Blue Arrow was alarmed when he saw Biddle step outdoors. While he could doubtless hide himself in the thick brush, his rifle and snowshoes were leaning against a tree, to be easily discovered if a man passed that way. He could not get them, for fear of being seen or heard by Biddle. He kept still and listened, to learn which direction Biddle was taking.

For some moments he heard nothing. Then there was a slight sound at the base of the big tree which branched over the shelter. A tiny flurry of light snow fell from a bough. Blue Arrow had seen nothing that looked like a fur pack cached in the tree; it must be high up among the top branches. He stood erect in the dense shadow and watched the figure of Biddle going up. But Biddle did not ascend into the higher branches. He paused in the crook of the big bough just over the widely laced natural roof of the shelter. Then he began to work his way slowly forward, sitting astraddle of it, his rifle in his hands.

Blue Arrow's suspicious nature and his swiftness in acting on his suspicions had been serviceable to Lachlan and his friends before this night. While the somber young Creek watched Biddle creep out on the bough, he had almost automatically slipped the blowgun from his back and set the dart. The light was bad for such shooting but he had no other gun. Biddle was pulling the trigger, with Boone as his target, no doubt, when the dart from the blowgun entered his head. His exploding rifle dropped from his hands and he pitched down. Blue Arrow shouted a warning in Creek to Lachlan. He fitted another dart. He dared not take time to get his rifle. He thrust the blowgun through the chink, and looked for Smith.

The two strangers had leaped for their rifles and now stood training them on Lewis' party across the fire.

"The first move out of any one of yer an' we shoot!" the man called "Bill" threatened.

Smith stood, laughing. He flung his fur jacket wide and flashed out two Spanish pistols.

"All yer powder an' yer guns an' five hundred dollars extry for the Cap'n's body. I'm Pasky!" he shouted.

At that moment both Biddle's body and his rifle, which had been caught on the slender roofing, crashed through. The surprise put Pasky and his two men off guard for a moment. Pasky straightened up, craned his neck, and stared at the ceiling. Blue Arrow shot him through the throat. He gurgled, dropped his pistols, and went down on his face.

"It is the blowgun," Blue Arrow called to Lachlan.

The silent death-dealing weapon from the unknown struck terror into the other bandits. They were afraid to fire. Tuleko quickly knocked one down with his rifle butt. By the time Blue Arrow entered the shelter, Tuleko and Andy had tied them up securely. Lachlan was looking at the dead Biddle.

"Pasky's livin'," he said. Andy nodded. "Cap'n Lewis says to nurse him up an' take him along."

Blue Arrow grunted. Watching his chance, he slipped over to Pasky and drove his knife through his heart. When Lewis discovered it he was very angry. He ordered Lachlan to tell Blue Arrow that as soon as they returned to Wood River, he would be discharged from the expedition for insubordination. Boone laid a hand on Lewis' shoulder.

"Son," he said gently, "listen ter me a minute. If Blue Arrow hadn't disobeyed yer orders an' follered us with that heathen South American gun, Pasky'd have got us all. Biddle'd have shot me first an' then picked off anybody he fancied. An' Pasky'd have collected that five hundred dollars on yer corpse. This ain't Virginny, son, whar yer been wearin' a uniform an' whar orders is orders. An' Blue Arrow ain't a militiaman. He's a Creek an' a scout an' a loyal friend, an' he's accustomed ter usin' his own jedgment—lucky fer us; mighty lucky! This ain't Virginny an' it ain't barracks. This is the frontier. Think it over, son, an' don't do wrong ter a Injun that's saved all our lives."

"I think you're right," Lewis answered thoughtfully. He smiled, added the title "Colonel," and saluted.

The old scout's eyes twinkled.

"I ain't been salooted in proper milit'ry style in a long time," he said. "It sure sets me up. An' I need it, fer I'm low in my mind, ter be took in so easy! Thought I knew Smith an' Biddle. I reckon we've got 'em all. Didn't need more'n four men ter play their game. Lookin' back over their actions ter-night, yer can see, Cap'n, they'd played it that way afore, till they was perfec' at it. Makin' friends, bringin' hunters in here that had furs or powder Pasky wanted, gittin' 'em separated from their guns, then Biddle, or any one of 'em, would start outside, Pasky'd make his holler about him comin' back fer his gun, an' Biddle'd come back, grumblin', take his gun, an' commence the shootin' from the tree; an' t'other three'd finish it inside. Clever an' smart!"

"Yes, it was a smart game, but it came to an end, thanks to Blue Arrow," Lewis answered.

"As fer these two Pasky men," Boone went on, "they'll come in handy, bein' husky, ter tote the powder ter La Charette." He turned a grim smile on the men, who were making desperate pleas for themselves now that affairs had gone against them. "Stop whinin' about Pasky leadin' yer astray," he said contemptuously. "I ain't listenin' ter a word from yer. When yer git ter La Charette ye'll have a fair an' square chance ter tell yer story ter the jedge when I bring yer afore the court fer trial. *I can guarantee yer that, 'coz I'm the court an' the jedge!"*

Lachlan led Blue Arrow aside and talked to him in Creek.

"Again you have saved my life, and, this time, the lives of my friends also. But it is bad to disobey Captain Lewis. Be careful not to do it again."

"Huh!" Blue Arrow grunted. "Tell him not to trust strangers, and never to sit at the opposite side of the camp from his gun! You are my brother; but nevertheless I must tell you that I am ashamed of you for your lack of caution. Now I will get my rifle, and then eat and go to sleep. Put more wood in the pan. I am cold."

"Blue Arrow's lost his respect for me, because I laid by my gun," Lachlan told Andy. "Only he was considerin' enough o' my feelin's to say it in Creek."

"Aye. But if ye want ter learn the feelin' o' scorn on yer skin when 'tis scaldin' hot, ye should hear Tuleko say it in Delaware," Andy answered ruefully. "An' we deserve it!"

"At last you restless lads have had some excitement," Lewis said, smilingly, when they were on the final lap of their homeward trip after leaving the Pasky men safely locked up in La Charette. "And it will only be a few weeks now till our boats pull out, on our way to Oregon!"

## BEING A BOY[1]

*Charles Dudley Warner*

One of the best things in the world to be is a boy, but it does not last long enough; just as you get used to being a boy, you have to be something else, with a good deal more work to do and not half so much fun. And yet every boy is anxious to be a man,

[1] From Charles Dudley Warner, *Being a Boy*. The incidents described in this story occurred a hundred years ago.

and is very uneasy with the restrictions that are put upon him as a boy. Good fun as it is to yoke up the calves and play work, there is not a boy on a farm but would rather drive a yoke of oxen at real work. What a glorious feeling it is when a boy is for the first time given the long whip and permitted to drive the oxen, walking by their side, swinging the long lash, and shouting "Gee, Buck!" "Haw, Golden!" "Whoa, Bright!" and all the rest of that remarkable language, until he is red in the face, and all the neighbors for half a mile are aware that something unusual is going on. If I were a boy, I am not sure but I would rather drive the oxen than have a birthday.

The proudest day of my boyhood in New England was one day when I rode on the neap of the cart, and drove the oxen, all alone, with a load of apples to the cider mill. I was so little, that it was a wonder that I didn't fall off, and get under the broad wheels. Nothing could make a boy, who cared anything for his appearance, feel flatter than to be run over by the broad tire of a cart wheel. But I never heard of one who was. As I said, it was a great day for me, but I don't remember that the oxen cared much about it. They sagged along in their great clumsy way, switching their tails in my face occasionally, and now and then giving a lurch to this or that side of the road, attracted by a choice tuft of grass. And then I "came the Julius Caesar" over them. I don't know that Julius Caesar ever drove cattle, though he must often have seen the peasants from the Campagna "haw" and "gee" them round the Forum (of course in Latin, a language that those cattle understood as well as ours do English); but what I mean is, that I stood up and "hollered" with all my might, as everybody does with oxen, as if they were born deaf, and whacked them with the long lash, just as the big folks did when they drove. I think now that it was a cowardly thing to crack the patient old fellows, and make them wink in their meek manner. I never liked lickings myself, and I don't know why an ox should like them.

Speaking of Latin reminds me that I once taught my cows Latin. I don't mean that I taught them to read it, for it is very difficult to teach a cow to read Latin or any of the dead languages—a cow cares more for her cud than she does for all the classics put together. But if you begin early you can teach a cow, or a calf (if you can teach a calf anything, which I doubt), Latin as well as English. There were ten cows, which I had to escort to and from the pasture night and morning. To these cows I gave the names of the Roman numerals, beginning with Unus and Duo, and going up to Decem. Decem was of course the biggest cow of the party, or at least she was the ruler of the others, and had the place of honor in the stable and everywhere else. I admire cows, and especially the exactness with which they define their social position. In this case, Decem could "lick" Novem, and Novem could "lick" Octo, and so on down to Unus, who couldn't lick anybody, except her own calf.

Besides Latin, I used to try to teach the cows a little poetry, and it is a very good plan. It does not do the cows much good, but it is very good exercise for a boy farmer. I used to memorize poems (the cows liked to listen to *Thanatopsis* about as well as anything), and repeat them when I went to the pasture, and as I drove the cows home through the sweet ferns and down the rocky slopes. It improves a boy's voice a great deal more than driving oxen.

Boys in general would be very good farmers if the notions about farming were not so different from those the boys have. What passes for laziness is very often an unwillingness to farm in a particular way. For instance, some morning in early summer John is told to catch the sorrel mare, harness her into the spring wagon, and put in the buffalo robe and the best whip, for father is obliged to drive over to the "Corners, to see a man" about some cattle, to talk with the road commissioner, to go to the store for the "women folks," and to attend to other important business; and very likely he will not be back till sundown. It must be very pressing business, for he drives off in this way somewhere almost every pleasant day, and appears to have a great deal on his mind.

Meantime, he tells John that he can play ball after he has done up the chores. As if the chores could ever be "done up" on a farm. He is first to clean out the horse stable; then to take a bill-hook and cut down the thistles and weeds from the fence corners in the home mowing-lot and along the road towards the village; to dig up the docks round the garden patch; to weed out the beet bed; to hoe the early potatoes; to rake the sticks and leaves out of the front yard; in short, there is work enough laid out for John to keep him busy, it seems to him, till he comes of age; and at half an hour to sundown he is to go for the cows, and, mind he don't run 'em!

"Yes, sir," says John, "is that all?"

"Well, if you get through in good season, you might pick over those potatoes in the cellar; they are sprouting; they ain't fit to eat."

John is obliged to his father, for if there is any sort of chore more cheerful to a boy than another, on a pleasant day, it is rubbing the sprouts off potatoes in a dark cellar. Then father mounts the wagon and drives away down the enticing road, with the dog bounding along beside the wagon, and refusing to come back at John's call. John half wishes he were the dog.

John looks after his father driving off in state, with the odorous buffalo robe and the new whip, and he thinks that is the sort of farming he would like to do. And he cries after his departing parent—

"Say, father, can't I go over to the farther pasture and salt the cattle?" John knows that he could spend half a day very pleasantly in going over to that pasture, looking for bird's nests and shying at red squirrels on the way, and who knows but he might see a sucker in the meadow brook, and perhaps get a jab at him with a sharp stick. He knows a hole where there is a whopper; and one of his plans in life is to go some day and snare him, and bring him home in triumph. It therefore is strongly impressed upon his mind that the cattle want salting. But his father, without turning his head, replies—

"No, they don't need salting any more'n you do!" And the old equipage goes rattling down the road, and John whistles his disappointment.

John goes to his chores, and gets through the stable as soon as he can, for that must be done; but when it comes to the outdoor work, that rather drags. There are so many things to distract the attention—a chipmunk on the fence, a bird in a near tree, and a hen-hawk circling high in the air over the barnyard. John loses a little time in stoning the chipmunk, which rather likes the sport, and in watching the bird to find where its nest is; and he convinces himself that he ought to watch the hawk, lest it pounce upon the chickens, and therefore, with an easy conscience, he spends fifteen minutes in hallooing to that distant bird, and follows it away out of sight over the woods, and then wishes it would come back again. Then a carriage with two horses, and a trunk on behind, goes along the road; and there is a girl in the carriage who looks out at John, who is suddenly aware that his trousers are patched on each knee and in two places behind; and he wonders if she is rich, and whose name is on the trunk, and how much the horses cost, and whether that nice-looking man is the girl's father, and if that boy on the seat with the driver is her brother, and if he has to do chores; and as the gay sight disappears John falls to thinking about the great world beyond the farm, of cities, and people who are always dressed up, and a great many other things of which he has a very dim notion. Then a boy, whom John knows, rides by in a wagon with his father, and the boy makes a face at John, and John returns the greeting with a twist of his own visage and some symbolic gestures. All these things take time. The work of cutting down the big weeds gets on slowly, although it is not very disagreeable, or would not be if it were play. John imagines that yonder big thistle is some whiskered villain, of whom he has read in a fairy book, and he advances on him with "Die, ruffian!" and slashes off his head with the bill-hook; or he charges upon the rows of mullein stalks as if they were rebels in regimental ranks, and hews them down without mercy. What fun it might be if there were only another boy there to help. But even war, single handed, gets to be tiresome. It is dinner-time before John finishes the weeds, and it is cow-time before John has made much impression on the garden.

Going after the cows was a serious thing in my day. I had to climb a hill, which was covered with wild strawberries in the season. Could any boy pass by those ripe berries? And then in the fragrant hill pasture there were beds of wintergreen with red berries, tufts of columbine, roots of sassafras to be dug, and dozens of things good to eat or to smell, that I could not resist. It sometimes even lay in my way to climb a tree to look for a crow's nest, or to swing in the top, and to try if I could see the steeple of the village church. It became very important sometimes for me to see that steeple; and in the midst of my investigations the tin horn would blow a great blast from the farmhouse, which would send a cold chill down my back in the hottest days. I knew what it meant. It had a frightfully impatient quaver in it, not at all like the sweet note that called us to dinner from the hayfield. It said, "Why on earth doesn't that boy come home? It is almost dark, and the cows ain't milked!" And that was the time the cows had to start into a brisk pace and make up for lost time. I wonder if any boy ever drove the cows home late, who did not say that the cows were at the very farther end of the pasture, and that "Old Brindle" was hidden in the woods, and he couldn't find her for ever so long! The brindle cow is the boy's scapegoat, many a time.

No other boy knows how to appreciate a holiday as the farm-boy does; and his best ones are of a peculiar kind. Going fishing is of course one sort. The excitement of rigging up the tackle, digging the bait, and the anticipation of great luck; these are pure pleasures, enjoyed because they are rare. Tramping all day through bush and brier, fighting flies and mosquitoes, and branches that tangle the line, and snags that break the hook, and returning home late and hungry, with wet feet and a string of speckled trout on a willow twig, and having the family crowd out at the kitchen door to look at 'em, and say, "Pretty well done for you, bub; did you catch that big one yourself?"—this is pure happiness, the like of which the boy will never have again, not if he comes to be selectman and deacon and to "keep store."

But the holidays I recall with greatest delight were the day in spring and the one in the fall, when we went to the distant pasture land. In the spring we drove the young cattle and colts there to stay for the summer, and in the fall we brought them back again. It was a wild and rocky upland where our great pasture was, many miles from home, the road to it running by a brawling river, and up a dashing brookside among the hills. What a day's adventure it was! It was like a journey to Europe. The night before, I could scarcely sleep for thinking of it, and there was no trouble about getting me up at sunrise that morning. The breakfast was eaten, the luncheon was packed in a large basket, with bottles of root beer and a jug of switchel, which packing I superintended with the greatest interest; and then the cattle were to be collected for the march, and the horses hitched up. Did I shirk any duty? Was I slow? I think not. I was willing to run my legs off after the frisky steers, who seemed to have an idea they were going on a lark, and frolicked about, dashing into all gates and through all bars except the right ones. How cheerfully I yelled at them; it was a glorious chance to "holler," and I have never since heard any public speaker who could make more noise.

The whole day was full of excitement and freedom. We were away from the farm; we saw other farms and other people at work; I had the pleasure of marching along, and swinging my whip, past boys whom I knew. Every turn of the road, every bend and rapid of the river, the great boulders by the wayside, the watering-troughs, the giant pine that had been struck by lightning, the mysterious covered bridge over the swift, foamy river, the chance eagle in the blue sky, the sense of going somewhere—why, as I recall all these things I feel that even a general with a mounted regiment clattering at his heels, and crowds of people cheering, could not have been as happy as was I, a boy in short jacket and shorter pantaloons, trudging in the dust that day behind the steers and colts, cracking my blackstock whip.

I wished the journey would never end; but at last, by noon, we reached the pastures and turned in the herd; and after making the tour of the lots to make sure there were no breaks in the fences, we took our luncheon from the wagon and ate it under the trees by the spring. This was the supreme moment of the day. This was the way to live; this was like the Swiss Family Robinson, and all the rest of my delightful acquaintances in romance. Baked beans, rye-and-Indian bread (moist, remember), doughnuts and cheese, pie, and root beer. What richness!

The winter season, too, is a good time on a farm, but the winter is not all sliding down hill for the farmer-boy, by any means; yet he contrives to get as much fun out of it as from any part of the year.

The farmer-boy likes to have winter come for one thing, because it freezes up the ground so that he can't dig in it; and it is covered with snow so that there is no picking up stones, nor driving the cows to pasture. He would have a very easy time if it were not for the getting up before daylight to build the fires and do the chores. Nature intended the long winter nights for the farmer-boy to sleep; but in my day he was expected to open his sleepy eyes when the cock crew, get out of the warm bed and light a candle, struggle into his cold pantaloons, and pull on boots in which the thermometer would have gone down to zero, rake open the coals on the hearth and start the morning fire, and then go to the barn to "fodder."

The frost was thick on the kitchen windows, the snow was drifted against the door, and the journey to the barn, in the pale light of dawn, over the creaking snow, was like an exile's trip to Siberia. The boy was not half awake when he stumbled into the cold barn, and was greeted by the lowing and bleating and neighing of cattle waiting for their breakfast. How their breath steamed up from the mangers, and hung in frosty spears from their noses. Through the great lofts above the hay, where the swallows nested, the winter wind whistled, and the snow sifted. Those old barns were well ventilated.

I used to spend much valuable time in planning a barn that should be tight and warm, with a fire in it if necessary in order to keep the temperature somewhere near the freezing point. I couldn't see how the cattle could live in a place, where a lively boy, full of young blood, would freeze to death in a short time if he did not swing his arms and slap his hands, and jump about like a goat. I thought I would have a sort of perpetual manger that should shake down the hay when it was wanted, and a self-acting machine that should cut up the turnips and pass them into the mangers, and water always flowing for the cattle and horses to drink. With these simple arrangements I could lie in bed, and know that the chores were doing themselves. It would also be necessary, in order that I should not be disturbed, that the crow should be taken out of the roosters, but I could think of no process to do it. It seems to me that the hen breeders, if they know as much as they say they do, might raise a breed of crowless roosters, for the benefit of boys, quiet neighborhoods, and sleepy families.

There was another notion that I had about kindling the kitchen fire, that I never carried out. It was to have a spring at the head of my bed, connecting with a wire, which should run to a torpedo which I would plant over night in the ashes of the fireplace. By touching the spring I could explode the torpedo, which would scatter the ashes and uncover the live coals, and at the same time shake down the sticks of wood which were standing by the side of the ashes in the chimney, and the fire would kindle itself. This ingenious plan was frowned on by the whole family, who said they did not want to be waked up every morning by an explosion. And yet they expected me to wake up without an explosion. A boy's plans for making life agreeable are hardly ever heeded.

I never knew a boy farmer who was not eager to go to the district school in the winter. There is such a chance for learning, that he must be a dull boy who does not come out in the spring a fair skater, an accurate snowballer, and an accomplished slider-down-hill, with or without a board, on his seat, on his stomach, or on his feet. Take a moderate hill, with a foot-slide down it worn to icy smoothness, and a "go-round" of boys on it, and there is nothing like it for whittling away boot-leather. The boy is the shoemaker's friend. An active lad can wear down a pair of cowhide soles in a week so that the ice will scrape his toes. Sledding or coasting is also slow fun compared to the "bareback" sliding down a steep hill over a hard, glistening crust. It is not only dangerous, but it is destructive to jacket and pantaloons to a degree to make a tailor laugh. If any other animal wore out his skin as fast as a schoolboy wears out his clothes in winter, it would need a new one once a month. In a country district school patches were not by any means a sign of poverty, but of the boy's courage and adventurous disposition. Our elders used to threaten to dress us in leather and put sheet-iron seats in our trousers. The boy *said* that he wore out his trousers on the hard seats in the schoolhouse ciphering hard sums.

The winter evenings of the farmer-boy in New England could not be said to be gay. A remote farmhouse, standing a little off the road, banked up with sawdust and earth to keep the frost out of the cellar, blockaded with snow, and flying a blue flag of smoke from its chimney, looks like a besieged fort. On cold and stormy winter nights, to the traveler wearily dragging along in his creaking sleigh, the light from its windows suggests a house of refuge and the cheer of a blazing fire. But it is no less a fort, into which the family retire when the New England winter on the hills really sets in.

The boy is an important part of the garrison. He is not only one of the best means of communicating with the outer world, but he furnishes half the entertainment and takes two-thirds of the scolding of the family circle. "That boy" brings life into the house; his tracks are to be seen everywhere, he leaves all the doors open, he hasn't half filled the wood-box, he makes noise enough to wake the dead; or he is in a brown study by the fire and cannot be stirred, or he has fastened a grip into some Crusoe book which cannot easily be shaken off.

Of course he had the evenings to himself, after he had done the chores at the barn, brought in the wood and piled it high in the box, ready to be heaped upon the great open fire. It was nearly dark when he came from school (with its continuation of snowballing and sliding), and he always had an agreeable time stumbling and fumbling around in barn and wood-house, in the waning light.

John used to say that he supposed nobody would do his chores if he did not get home till midnight; and he was never contradicted. Whatever happened to him, and whatever length of days or sort of weather was produced by the almanac, the cardinal rule was that he should be at home before dark.

Of course, John had nothing to do all the evening, after his chores—except little things. While he drew his chair up to the table in order to get the full radiance of the tallow candle on his slate or his book, the women of the house also sat by the table knitting and sewing. The head of the house sat in his chair, tipped back against the chimney; the hired man was in danger of burning his boots in the fire. John might be deep in the excitement of a bear story, or be hard at writing a composition on his slate; but whatever he was doing, he was the only one who could always be interrupted. It was he who must snuff the candles, and put on a stick of wood, and toast the cheese, and turn the apples, and crack the nuts. He knew where the fox-and-geese board was, and he could find the twelve-men-Morris. Considering that he was expected to go to bed at eight o'clock, one would say that the opportunity for study was not great, and that his reading was rather interrupted.

No wonder that John was not sleepy at eight o'clock; he had been flying about all evening while the others had been yawning before the fire. He would like to sit up just to see how much more solemn it would become as the night went on; he wanted to tinker his skates, to mend his sled, to finish that chapter. Why should he go away from that bright blaze, and the company that sat in its radiance, to the cold and solitude of his chamber? Why didn't the people who were sleepy go to bed?

How lonesome the old house was; how cold it was, away from that great central fire in the heart of it; how its timbers creaked as if in the contracting pinch of the frost; what a rattling there was of windows, what a concerted attack upon the clapboards; how the floors squeaked, and what gusts from round corners came to snatch the feeble flame of the candle from the boy's hand. How he shivered, as he paused at the staircase window to look out upon the great fields of snow, upon the stripped forest, through which he could hear the wind raving in a kind of fury, and up at the black flying clouds, amid which the young moon was dashing and driven on like a frail shallop at sea. And his teeth chattered more than ever when he got into the icy sheets, and drew himself up into a ball in his flannel nightgown, like a fox in his hole.

For a little time he could hear the noises downstairs, and an occasional laugh; he could guess that now they were having cider, and now apples were going round; and he could feel the wind tugging at the house, even sometimes shaking the bed. But this did not last long. He soon went away into a country he always delighted to be in; a calm place where the wind never blew, and no one dictated the time of going to bed to any one else.

## THE HOOSIER SCHOOLMASTER[1]

*Edward Eggleston*

"Want to be schoolmaster, do you? You? Well, what would *you* do in Flat Crick deestrick *I'd* like to know? Why, the boys have driv off the last two, and licked the one afore them like blazes. You might teach a summer school, when nothin' but children come. But I 'low it takes a right smart *man* to be schoolmaster in Flat Crick in the winter. They'd pitch you out of doors, sonny, neck and heels, afore Christmas."

The young man, who had walked ten miles to get the school in this district and who had been mentally reviewing his learning at every step he took, trembling lest the committee should find that he did not know enough, was not a little taken aback at this greeting from "old Jack Means," who was the first trustee that he lighted on. The impression made by these ominous remarks was emphasized by the glances which he received from Jack Means's two sons. The older one eyed him from the top of his brawny shoulders with that amiable look which a big dog turns on a little one before shaking him. Ralph Hartsook had never thought of being measured by the standard of muscle. This notion of beating education into young savages in spite of themselves dashed his ardor.

He had walked right to where Jack

[1] From Edward Eggleston, *The Hoosier Schoolmaster.*

Means was at work shaving shingles in his own front yard. While Mr. Means was making the speech which we have set down above, and punctuating it with expectorations, a large brindle bulldog had been sniffing at Ralph's heels, and a girl in a new linsey-woolsey dress, standing by the door, had nearly giggled her head off at the delightful prospect of seeing a new schoolteacher eaten by the ferocious brute.

The disheartening words of the old man, the immense muscles of the young man who was to be his rebellious pupil, the jaws of the ugly bulldog, and the heartless giggle of the girl gave Ralph a delightful sense of having precipitated himself into a den of wild beasts. Faint with weariness and discouragement and shivering with fear, he sat down on a wheelbarrow.

"You, Bull!" said the old man to the dog, which was showing more and more a disposition to make a meal of the incipient pedagogue, "you, Bull! git aout, you pup!" The dog walked sullenly off, but not until he had given Ralph a look full of promise of what he meant to do when he got a good chance.

Ralph wished himself back in the village of Lewisburg, whence he had come.

"You see," continued Mr. Means, spitting in a meditative sort of way, "you see, we a'n't none of your saft sort in these diggin's. It takes a *man* to boss this deestrick. Howsumdever, ef you think you kin trust your hide in Flat Crick schoolhouse I ha'n't got no 'bjection. But ef you git licked, don't come on us. Flat Crick don't pay no 'nsurance, you bet! Any other trustees? Wal, yes. But as I pay the most taxes, t'others jist let me run the thing. You can begin right off a Monday. They a'n't been no other applications. You see, it takes grit to apply for this school. The last master had a black eye for a month. But, as I wuz sayin', you can jist roll up and wade in. I 'low you've got spunk, maybe, and that goes for a heap sight more'n sinnoo with boys. Walk in, and stay over Sunday with me. You'll hev' to board roun', and I guess you better begin here."

Ralph did not go in, but sat out on the wheelbarrow, watching the old man shave shingles, while the boys split the blocks and chopped wood.

Bull smelled of the newcomer again in an ugly way, and got a good kick from the older son for his pains. But out of one of his red eyes the dog warned the young schoolmaster that *he* should yet suffer for all kicks received on his account.

"Ef Bull once takes a holt, heaven and yarth can't make him let go," said the older son to Ralph by way of comfort.

It was well for Ralph that he began to "board roun' " by stopping at Mr. Means's. Ralph felt that Flat Creek was what he needed. He had lived a bookish life; but here was his lesson in the art of managing people, for he who can manage the untamed and strapping youths of a winter school in Hoopole County has gone far toward learning one of the hardest of lessons. And in Ralph's time things were worse than they are now.

The older son of Mr. Means was called Bud Means. What his real name was Ralph could not find out, for in many of these families the nickname of "Bud," given to the oldest boy, and that of "Sis," which is the birthright of the oldest girl, completely bury the proper Christian name. Ralph saw his first strategic point, which was to capture Bud Means.

After supper the boys began to get ready for something. Bull stuck up his ears in a dignified way, and the three or four yellow curs who were Bull's satellites yelped delightedly and discordantly.

"Bill," said Bud Means to his brother, "ax the master ef he'd like to hunt coons. I'd like to take the starch out uv the stuck-up feller."

"Nough said," was Bill's reply.

"You durn't do it," said Bud.

"I don't take no sech a dare," returned Bill, and walked down to the gate, by which Ralph stood watching the stars come out and half wishing he had never seen Flat Creek.

"I say, mister," began Bill, "mister, they's

a coon what's been a eatin' our chickens lately, and we're goin' to try to ketch the varmint. You wouldn't like to take a coon hunt nor nothin', would you?"

"Why, yes," said Ralph, "there's nothing I should like better, if I could only be sure Bull wouldn't mistake me for the coon."

And so, as a matter of policy, Ralph dragged his tired legs eight or ten miles, on hill and in hollow, after Bud and Bill and Bull and the coon. But the raccoon climbed a tree. The boys got into a quarrel about whose business it was to have brought the ax and who was to blame that the tree could not be felled. Now, if there was anything Ralph's muscles were good for, it was climbing. So, asking Bud to give him a start, he soon reached the limb above the one on which the raccoon was. Ralph did not know how ugly a customer a raccoon can be, and so got credit for more courage than he had. With much peril to his legs from the raccoon's teeth, he succeeded in shaking the poor creature off among the yelping brutes and yelling boys.

Ralph could not help sympathizing with the hunted animal, which sold its life as dearly as possible, giving the dogs many a scratch and bite. It seemed to him that he was like the raccoon, precipitated into the midst of a party of dogs who would rejoice in worrying *his* life out, as Bull and his crowd were destroying the poor raccoon. When Bull at last seized the raccoon and put an end to it, Ralph could not but admire the decided way in which he did it, calling to mind Bud's comment, "Ef Bull once takes a holt, heaven and yarth can't make him let go."

But as they walked home, Bud carrying the raccoon by the tail, Ralph felt that his hunt had not been in vain. He fancied that even red-eyed Bull, walking uncomfortably close to his heels, respected him more since he had climbed that tree.

"Purty peart kind of a master," remarked the old man to Bud, after Ralph had gone to bed. "Guess you better be a little easy on him. Hey?"

But Bud deigned no reply. Perhaps because he knew that Ralph heard the conversation through the thin partition.

Ralph woke delighted to find it raining. He did not want to hunt or fish on Sunday, and this steady rain would enable him to make friends with Bud. I do not know how he got started, but after breakfast he began to tell stories. Out of all the books he had ever read he told story after story. And "old man Means" and "old *Miss* Means" and Bud Means and Bill Means and Sis Means listened with great eyes while he told of Sinbad's adventures, of the Old Man of the Sea, of Robinson Crusoe, of Captain Gulliver's experiences in Lilliput, and of Baron Munchausen's exploits.

Ralph had caught his fish. The hungry minds of these backwoods people were refreshed with the new life that came to their imaginations in these stories. For there was but one book in the Means library, and that, a well-thumbed copy of "Captain Riley's Narrative," had long lost all freshness.

"I'll be dog-on'd," said Bill, emphatically, "ef I hadn't ruther hear the master tell them whoppin' yarns than go to a circus the best day I ever seed!" Bill could pay no higher compliment.

What Ralph wanted was to make a friend of Bud. It's a nice thing to have the seventy-four-gun ship on your own side, and the more Hartsook admired the knotted muscles of Bud Means the more he desired to attach him to himself. So, whenever he struck out a peculiarly brilliant passage, he anxiously watched Bud's eye. But the young Philistine kept his own counsel. He listened, but said nothing, and the eyes under his shaggy brows gave no sign. Ralph could not tell whether those eyes were deep and inscrutable or only stolid. Perhaps a little of both. When Monday morning came, Ralph was nervous. He walked to school with Bud.

"I guess you're a little skeered by what the old man said, a'n't you?"

Ralph was about to deny it, but on reflection concluded that it was best to speak the truth. He said that Mr. Means's description of the school had made him feel a little downhearted.

"What will you do with the tough boys? You a'n't no match for 'em." And Ralph felt Bud's eyes not only measuring his muscles but scrutinizing his countenance. He only answered: "I don't know."

"What would you do with me, for instance?" and Bud stretched himself up as if to shake out the reserve power coiled up in his great muscles.

"I sha'n't have any trouble with you."

"Why, I'm the wust chap of all. I thrashed the last master, myself."

And again the eyes of Bud Means looked out sharply from his shadowing brows to see the effect of this speech on the slender young man.

"You won't thrash me, though," said Ralph.

"Pshaw! I 'low I could whip you in an inch of your life with my left hand, and never half try," said young Means, with a threatening sneer.

"I know that as well as you do."

"Well, a'n't you afraid of me, then?" and again he looked sidewise at Ralph.

"Not a bit," said Ralph, wondering at his own courage.

They walked on in silence a minute. Bud was turning the matter over.

"Why a'n't you afraid of me?" he said presently.

"Because you and I are going to be friends."

"And what about t'others?"

"I am not afraid of all the other boys put together."

"You a'n't! The mischief! How's that?"

"Well, I'm not afraid of them because you and I are going to be friends, and you can whip all of them together. You'll do the fighting, and I'll do the teaching."

The diplomatic Bud only chuckled a little at this; whether he assented to the alliance or not Ralph could not tell.

When Ralph looked round on the faces of the scholars—the little faces full of mischief and curiosity, the big faces full of an expression which was not further removed than second-cousin from contempt—when young Hartsook looked into these faces, his heart palpitated with stage fright. There is no audience so hard to face as one of schoolchildren, as many a man has found to his cost. Perhaps it is because no restraint can keep down their laughter when you do or say anything ridiculous.

Hartsook's first day was hurried and unsatisfactory. He was not master of himself, and consequently not master of anybody else. When evening came, there were symptoms of insubordination through the whole school. Poor Ralph was sick at heart. He felt that if there had ever been the shadow of an alliance between himself and Bud, it was all "off" now. It seemed to Hartsook that even Bull had lost his respect for the teacher.

Half that night the young man lay awake. At last comfort came to him. A reminiscence of the death of the raccoon flashed on him like a vision. He remembered that quiet and annihilating bite which Bull gave. He remembered Bud's certificate, that "Ef Bull once takes a holt, heaven and yarth can't make him let go." He thought that what Flat Creek needed was a bulldog. He would be a bulldog, quiet, but invincible. He would take hold in such a way that nothing should make him let go. And then he went to sleep.

In the morning Ralph got out of bed slowly. He put his clothes on slowly. He pulled on his boots in a bulldog mood. He tried to move as he thought Bull would move if he were a man. He ate with deliberation, and looked everybody in the eyes with a manner that made Bud watch him curiously. He found himself continually comparing himself with Bull. He found Bull possessing a strange fascination for him. He walked to school alone, the rest having gone on before. He entered the schoolroom preserving a cool and dogged manner. He saw in the eyes of the boys that there was mischief brewing. He did not dare sit down in his chair for fear of a pin. Everybody looked solemn. Ralph lifted the lid of his desk. "Bow-wow! wow-wow!" It was the voice of an imprisoned puppy, and the school giggled and then roared. Then everything was quiet.

The scholars expected an outburst of wrath from the teacher. For they had come to regard the whole world as divided into two classes, the teacher on the one side representing lawful authority, and the pupils on the other in a state of chronic rebellion. To play a trick on the master was an evidence of spirit; to "lick" the master was to be the crowned hero of Flat Creek district. Such a hero was Bud Means; and Bill, who had less muscle, saw a chance to distinguish himself on a teacher of slender frame. Hence the puppy in the desk.

Ralph Hartsook grew red in the face when he saw the puppy. But the cool, repressed, bulldog mood in which he had kept himself saved him. He lifted the dog into his arms and stroked him until the laughter subsided. Then, in a solemn and set way, he began:

"I am sorry," and he looked round the room with a steady, hard eye—everybody felt that there was a conflict coming—"I am sorry that any scholar in this school could be so mean"—the word was uttered with a sharp emphasis, and all the big boys felt sure that there would be a fight with Bill Means, and perhaps with Bud—"could be so *mean*—as to—shut up his *brother* in such a place as that!"

There was a long, derisive laugh. The wit was indifferent, but by one stroke Ralph had carried the whole school to his side. By the significant glances of the boys, Hartsook detected the perpetrator of the joke, and with the hard and dogged look in his eyes, with just such a look as Bull would give a puppy, but with the utmost suavity in his voice, he said:

"William Means, will you be so good as to put this dog out of doors?"

There was a moment of utter stillness; but the magnetism of Ralph's eye was too much for Bill Means. The request was so polite, the master's look was so innocent and so determined. Bill often wondered afterward that he had not "fit" rather than obeyed the request. But somehow he put the dog out. He was partly surprised, partly inveigled, partly awed into doing just what he had not intended to do. In the week that followed, Bill had to fight half a dozen boys for calling him "Puppy Means." Bill said he wished he'd licked the master on the spot. 'Twould 'a' saved five fights out of the six.

And all that day and the next, the bulldog in the master's eye was a terror to evildoers. At the close of school on the second day Bud was heard to give it as his opinion that "the master wouldn't be much in a tussle, but he had a heap of thunder and lightning in him."

## THE PONY EXPRESS[1]

*Charles L. Skelton*

As the days passed, the sunlight slanted more and more sharply through the door way of the Mud Springs station. The buffalo grass, brown since midsummer, shrank closer to the cold dry hills. The dwarf plum trees in the coulees turned from dull green to red and brown, then all at once stood huddled, leafless. The buttes along the Platte, as Jeff passed them on his rides to and from Fort Laramie, stood outlined against a sky of softened blue. It was autumn, autumn of 1860.

Back in the States, a political campaign was closing, full of portent. North and South, uneasy, distrustful, watching each other, waited. Out on the high plains and in the sagebrush country powerful Indian tribes—the Sioux, the Arapahoes, the Cheyennes, wary, distrustful, watched the growing white invasion of their hunting lands, and waited.

The Pony Express was known now, East and West, as the surest, speediest carrier across the troubled continent. The silk-

[1] From Charles L. Skelton, *Riding West on the Pony Express.*

wrapped packets of tissue-paper letters and dispatches in the battered mochilas were getting thicker as the Express built up a reputation for fast, regular runs. Sun-blasted deserts, high mountain ranges, sagebrush wastes, wind-whipped short-grassed plains, the menace of Indians, the jealous rivalry of the Butterfield stage line on the far southern route—the Pony Express was running despite them all.

Now, just ahead, another hazard loomed. Winter was coming—the drifting snows, the cruel storms, the bitter cold of the high plains and the intermountain country.

Jeff's shadow in the late October noonday was long on the bare, hoof-marked ground in front of the Mud Springs station. He finished reading the letter Lacy had handed him and paced a few short turns, easing his muscles after a hundred miles in the saddle. Southward, down the Julesburg trail, Bill Johnson was going out of sight, carrying the mochila Jeff had brought in from Laramie. Lacy spoke from the open doorway:

"What's the word, Jeff? How's your brother making it, that is, if that was about him? Bill thought it probably was."

Anxiety was in Jeff's voice. "He isn't getting along very well. They took that bullet out, and the place healed up, but there's still something the matter with his right side. He can't ride yet; tried it and couldn't hardly get up into the saddle. Doctor told him not to try it any more for a while."

"That's tough, sure. He was figuring on coming back out here, wasn't he?"

"Yes. Slade told him he'd take him on again, when he got well." Jeff's face darkened as he thought of Chet, who loved to ride, unable to swing into the saddle. His hand unconsciously stole to the holster that still held the Colt he had carried on his long ride from Laramie. "Queer nobody ever sees or hears anything more about Pete Anderson. I'd like to run into him, just once," he said, meaningly.

"He may be in Texas by this time," Lacy suggested. "Nobody seems to be bothering the Express any more; my guess is that Anderson has cleared out for good."

Jeff had no words for the instinctive dissent he felt.

"What's the news from the Fort, Jeff?" Lacy asked. There had been little chance for conversation in the scrambled moment in which Jeff had arrived and Bill departed.

"I didn't get any news. The Indians are quiet, and so is everything else. What'd Bill have to say? Julesburg's the place to get news."

"Well," Lacy began, importantly, "Bill says they're going to make a special run with the election returns."

"Clear through, you mean?"

"Yeah, from one end of the wire to the other—Fort Kearny to Fort Churchill. They're out to break the record."

Jeff by this time was standing close to his partner, he had forgotten about being tired. "When's the election?"

"First Tuesday in November, whenever that is." Lacy dived into the station and came out quickly, holding a tiny calendar. "November sixth, that's a week from tomorrow."

"Well, I'll try to do my part, if they want a fast run. But don't skimp the ponies on feed, Jack. Give 'em a few extra dippers of oats."

"Think I don't know how to feed?" Lacy retorted, edgily. "Come out and look 'em over. See if they ain't in good shape right now."

Jeff, grinning because he had piqued Lacy so easily, followed him to the stable. There, in the squat log building, stood four Express horses. The one Jeff had ridden in from the west was stained with sweat; the sleek coats and well-carded manes and tails of the others showed that Lacy knew how to use brush and currycomb. The herby, pungent smell of prairie hay scented the stable as the horses and the seldom-used mules munched along the manger row.

"A stationman has a great life," Lacy grumbled, "with the riders hollering for him to sling in more feed and the superintendent telling him to make supplies go as far as he can." He raised the lid of a wooden bin and noted the contents. "D'you know, Jeff," he went on, "it's a fright the way this feed costs. This corn and oats was freighted all the way from St. Joe– I'll bet it cost Russell, Majors, and Waddell ten cents a pound just to haul it out here, besides whatever they had to pay for it back there. We've still got some of the wild hay that was cut down in the river bottom this summer. When that runs out, I reckon they'll have to freight in some from back East."

"Well, you don't have to pay for it," Jeff chaffed, "and I don't want you to starve these nags. Not Mack, anyway." He rubbed the rangy black's nose. "For a fast run, I reckon Mack's the one I better start with, that day. What d'you think?"

"He's about the best of the bunch. I'd take him, or Pieface." He glanced at the sweat-marked bay Jeff had ridden in.

"Did Bill have any more news?" Jeff asked, as they went back to the cabin.

"No, nothing much. Said the rush to the Pike's Peak diggings is slowing up. Heavy travel on the stage East, he said, people getting out of the mountains before winter comes. Good deal of dust coming out by stage—ten thousand dollars worth day before yesterday."

Jeff had thought little about the election, but the order for a special run brought it sharply to his mind. "Who you reckon will be elected, Jack?" he demanded.

"How do I know? I'm buried alive here, you might say. Don't see anybody but you and Bill, and twice a month the stage driver. I haven't seen a newspaper since that one Bill fetched up from Julesburg a couple of weeks ago, and it was a month old when he got hold of it. I reckon Douglas will get it; hope so, anyhow."

"I hope Abe Lincoln gets it," Jeff returned.

"That long-legged rail splitter! He'd make a fine President, wouldn't he? Ugly as a mud fence!"

"He's not, either!" Jeff's eyes flashed. He faced Lacy with hands unconsciously clenched. "Don't talk that way about him!"

"Keep your shirt on," Lacy said, coldly. "No use for us to get worked up. It'll all be settled without any of our say-so. What makes you think so much of Lincoln?" he added, curiously.

Fragments of talk heard back in Missouri, bits of scanty newspaper reading had formed a picture in Jeff's mind. It was real to him, but he found it hard to explain.

"Well," he began, "he was a poor boy. He lived in a log cabin, and he had to work mighty hard to get any kind of a start. He could outrassle any of his crowd. And he was so honest he walked three or four miles to give back a few cents to some woman, after he'd made a mistake in change when he was clerking in a store. I bet you he's all right!"

Lacy's lips twitched with amusement.

"What's so funny?" Jeff demanded.

Lacy's glance went round the room—the dirt floor, the rusty sheet-iron stove, the log walls hung with scanty, battered cooking utensils and ropes and saddles, the stray wisps of dry grass sticking down between the roof-poles. "I just happened to think," he drawled, "that if being poor and living in a log house helps a fellow so much, why maybe—"

"Somebody's coming yonder," Jeff interrupted.

Lacy instantly joined him in the doorway; their distance-trained eyes peered south.

The eastbound Pony Express trail ran almost due south from Mud Springs. The farthest point of the trail that could be seen from the station was a mile away. There, sharp against the skyline, an approaching horseman showed for a moment, then disappeared as the trail dipped into lower ground. The trail was little traveled. The boys stood watching. Soon, nearer, the rider showed again, coming on at a gallop.

"Looks like Slade," Jeff said.

"It *is* Slade," Lacy exclaimed.

"Don't forget to call him Captain," Jeff warned, low-voiced, as the rider neared.

"I know enough for that," his companion muttered.

"Hello, boys! How's everything?" Slade hailed.

"All right, Captain," they replied as one, their eyes on the muscular, hard-faced man who swung lightly to the ground. He tied his horse to a ring in the log wall of the station, and faced the boys.

"We're going to run a special mochila through from Fort Kearny with the election returns," he announced. He spoke almost gently. "It will probably leave on November seventh. I want you to put it through without a minute's unnecessary delay." His eyes, keen, and in that moment almost genial, flicked Jeff.

"All right, sir," Jeff replied.

"We'll be on the lookout," Lacy added, quickly.

"You boys have some pay coming," Slade continued. "Let's go inside." He led the way. Lacy slid a chair forward. Slade unbuckled his gun belt and laid it on the table. The chair he took, Jeff noted, faced the door; the guns in the holsters were never far from his hands. Next he unbuckled a money belt; it sagged in his grasp and lay heavy beside the guns.

"Here you are, Lacy," he said, as he opened the belt. He deftly stacked a little pile of coin and slid it across the rough planks. "Sign this receipt, will you?" There were seven gold eagles and a five-dollar piece in Lacy's stack.

"Next." Slade spoke briskly. His swift fingers formed another stack; he looked at Jeff. There were twelve eagles and a five-dollar piece—a month's wages for a Pony Express rider—in the stack he shoved across the table.

Jeff hastily signed the receipt and took the coins. Slade replaced his money belt and put on his guns. His glance once more rested on Jeff. "Have you heard from your brother lately?" he asked.

Jeff told him about the letter that had just come.

"That may turn out all right yet," Slade said, in a tone of kindly assurance. "Gunshot wounds are uncertain, but I've seen worse-looking cases than your brother get well. We'll hope for the best."

He got up and paced about the room. "How are you getting along?" he demanded. "Anything going wrong? Anybody been bothering you?"

"No, sir," they both assured him.

"How are your supplies holding out?"

"We've got grub enough for a couple of weeks, sir," Lacy answered. "The wood is getting low, and so is the grain."

"I'll send a load of each up in a few days."

He stepped lightly to the door and outside. The boys followed him.

"Don't forget, I want good time on that special run," he added, in almost silky tones, as he swung into the saddle.

"We'll do our best, Captain."

With no other word, without a backward glance, Slade took the trail toward Fort Laramie.

Noon of November 7, 1860, at Fort Kearny. Mose Sydenham's store was full of men. This little sod house was notion store, post office, and, just lately, something more. Something new, thrilling. The soldiers and civilians wedged into the place were all watching the railed-off corner where a rough table held telegraph instruments and batteries.

A wire from Omaha, strung along the Platte bottoms on green cottonwood poles, had reached Fort Kearny less than a week before. The commandant hemmed and hawed about assigning room for a telegraph office in any of the military buildings at the fort. So Sydenham had cleared a space in one corner of his own little establishment. Here now, while the tense crowd waited, Ellsworth, the operator, sat at his key.

Those who could not wedge their way into the store stood grouped outside in front. "He'll have a good day to start," suggested one man to another beside him, sniffing the mild air. "Yes, but this is a weather-breeder," returned the other, glancing at the tall flagstaff where the United States flag hung limp, outlined against an overcast sky.

Like others of the group, they watched with friendly eyes a youth who stood there holding a horse. Bronzed, lithe, alert the lad; slim, trim, eager the horse. The lad wore buckskin; the handle of a Colt's revolver showed in his holster, the tan mochila of the Pony Express was fitted over his horse's saddle. Narrow red and white and blue ribbons dangled from saddle and bridle; a bow of ribbons showed on the lad's arm.

Inside, the sounder on the table clicked and chattered. Ellsworth scribbled on sheets of tissue. The jammed room was hushed, no sound came but the sharp staccato of the key and the rustle of tissue paper. Suddenly Ellsworth got up. His voice trembled: "Lincoln is elected!"

A stir, a murmur, ran through the crowd. No cheers. Cool heads had advised against any demonstration, no matter what news the wire brought. Some faces darkened, some lit up with thankfulness. The air was tense.

Ellsworth pushed through the crowd to the door; the division agent of the Pony Express went with him. The agent hurried out to the waiting horse and rider. He stuffed a sheaf of tissue-paper messages into one of the mochila's compartments, locked it, and pocketed the key. "Let 'er go, Jim," he said. "Lively, now!"

The lad swung into the saddle and the horse bounded away. Now a cheer broke from the crowd. Feeling was high and divided about the election, but they all admired the Pony Express.

Ellsworth went back to his key. He called Omaha, got a response, and clicked off a message for the Eastern press:

"Fort Kearny, Wed., Nov. 7

"An extra Pony Express with the election returns for California left here for Fort Churchill at 1 o'clock today. It took also a considerable number of private telegrams. Both horse and rider were decorated with ribbons, etc., and they departed amid the cheers of a large gathering. This run is expected to be quicker than any ever yet made between here and the outer station of the California telegraph line. The ponies leaving St. Joseph Thursday 8th and Sunday 11th are also to make double-quick time, calling here for the latest telegraphic dates. Weather mild with tokens of rain."

Jeff, pacing back and forth in front of the squat Mud Springs station late that afternoon, turned nervously to Lacy: "Jack, if they started from Kearny sometime this evening, when d'you reckon they'd get here?"

Lacy considered. "Two hundred miles to Julesburg, about sixty-five on up here. Trail ought to be in good shape now. Around noon tomorrow, or a little after, I'd say."

The lad glanced back at Fort Kearny through the dust. The crowd at Sydenham's had shrunk to a blur in the distance. He grinned as he tore off the fluttering ribbons that annoyed his horse and himself. He crouched lower over the saddle horn to lessen the air's retarding pull, and to speak: "Flint, old boy, let's go!" The rangy stride lengthened in instant response; the bursts of dust exploded faster behind the thudding hoofs.

Midforenoon of the next day, Jeff was restlessly alert. "Let's stack the grub pile for dinner pronto and get it over with," he suggested. "Bill may show up sooner than we figured."

"All right," Lacy assented. He stirred the embers in the little stove, added pine slivers and a chunk. " 'Twon't take long to warm these beans. I'll fry some bacon. Want potatoes?"

"No, let 'em go this time. Make some coffee strong enough to hold up an iron wedge."

"Iron wedge? That's a new one to me, Jeff."

"That's what they say in Missouri, where I lived, when coffee is right strong—that it'll hold up an iron wedge."

"Well, I'll see what I can do."

Jeff, in the doorway, kept his eyes down the Julesburg trail. His gaze narrowed as a black dot bobbed up against the sky line on the ridge a mile away. "Somebody's coming. I bet it's Bill!" he shouted. He caught up a handful of hardtack and stuffed the pockets of his slicker. "Let that stuff go!" he exclaimed, as Lacy lingered at the stove. Together they hurried out to the stable, Jeff buckling his gun belt as he strode, Lacy carrying saddle and bridle.

"Want Mack?" Lacy asked.

"Yep."

Jeff caught up the saddle and eased it into place on the nervous black while Lacy slipped the bridle on. He drew up the latigos with quick jerks. Lacy led Mack out. Jeff followed close. A yell sounded down trail, above the quickening beat of hoofs. Another instant and Bill Johnson pulled up his panting, foam-splashed pony.

"Hi, fellows!" he greeted. "Here's your special! Lincoln's elected!"

"Good!" Jeff exclaimed. He tugged at the mochila; it stuck to Bill's saddle. Bill helped with a hard jerk; the thing came loose. They flung it over the other saddle while Lacy clung to the dancing pony's bit. Jeff strapped his slicker down behind the cantle, caught his stirrup, and swung up. Lacy let go. A clatter of hoofs on hard ground, and the election special darted out of Mud Springs.

The pair left behind waved a farewell to Jeff, then turned to the station's open door.

"Just in time for dinner, Bill," Lacy invited. "You can have the plate I put down for Jeff. He didn't have time to take a bite." He poked more wood into the stove, then straightened up with a jerk and smote his hip in vexed remembrance. "I clean forgot to put down the time," he exclaimed, pulling out his record book. " 'Twasn't much over a minute, was it, Bill?"

"Naw, hardly that much. What time is it now?" He glanced at the watch Lacy drew. "Ten eighteen? Make it in at ten fifteen and out at ten sixteen and you'll be close enough."

Jeff held the headstrong black in for a little way. Then he bent lower in the saddle and slackened the rein a trifle. "All right, Mack," he urged, "come on."

Mack shot forward in instant response. Jeff had to check him; it took more talk, a skilled hand on the rein, to settle the rangy, eager horse down into a long, ground-covering gallop that ate the trail up smoothly, swiftly.

The election was now a matter of history. North and South knew the result. Fearfully or hopefully, in winterbound New England villages, on cotton and cane plantations swept by the soft airs of the Gulf, men waited to see what would come next.

A great metropolitan journal of the North looked at the matter complacently: "It is not to be supposed that the election of Abraham Lincoln as President of these United States—conspicuous and glorious triumph as it is—will at once restore the country to political harmony and quiet, though we are convinced that the agitation raised in the South will gradually and surely subside into peace."

A dispatch from Washington sounded less peaceful: "A large quantity of arms was yesterday shipped from our arsenal to the South. But the place of destination remains a secret."

And from Charleston, South Carolina, came this word: "There is no longer any possible doubt that the state will secede. . . . The struggle is over, and we are merely perfecting the secession arrangements."

But in the far, imperial West, in new, busy ports of the Pacific, in remote mining camps, in rich wide valleys beneath a genial sun, men waited yet for word of the nation's verdict. The American empire, that had grown so fast, that seemed now about to crumble into fragments, had for its best communicating tie between East and West a scanty line of bronzed young horsemen, coursing from station to lonely station through the land of sagebrush and desert, stopping not for night or day or storm or fair. Couriers of empire, these boys of the Pony Express!

Gallant the riders; the ponies fleet of foot. Yet, so vast the land to be crossed, ten days went by while a mochila was being carried on regular schedule from the Missouri River to Sacramento. This election ride was special.

For all the rangy black's toughness and bottom he was panting and faltering when Jeff swung down at the relay station.

"Put him right through, didn't you?" remarked the stationman.

"Well, you know the orders."

"Sure. I got the one you like for you, Jeff."

"I see."

He was changing over mochila and slicker with quick jerks as he spoke. He caught his stirrup. The man held the raw-boned dun horse, letting go as Jeff's weight settled into the saddle. The horse snorted, bucked, then straightened out in a reaching gallop that speedily left the squat, cedar-pole station far behind. The November sun was low in the overcast sky. The ice-fringed Platte ran cold and swift between its endless sandbars on Jeff's right; the lonely trail slipped past.

He brought the "ornery" dun into the next station subdued, foam-wet, quivering. Another change, to a speedy, nervy bay. Then on, without a moment's rest.

The smell of coming storm, damp yet crisp, was borne on the night air. A chilling wind from mountain ranges pressed against horse and rider. Jeff slowly lost the high-keyed feeling that had held him up. He was cold, dizzy, dead-tired, when he slid off his gasping, faltering horse in the yellow circle of lantern light at Laramie station.

"Boy, you've been traveling!" called the stationman. "What's the news?"

Jeff tugged at the mochila. "Lincoln's elected!" he gasped.

The waiting rider, brown, slim, hard, smiled as he caught the stiff square of leather and clapped it down over the fresh and fretting pony's saddle. "Here goes!" he cried, above the wind and the quick clatter of his pony's feet. Then he was gone into the black and threatening night.

Ahead in bleak darkness lay lonely stations, tiny outposts in an empty land—Horseshoe, Labonte Creek, Platte Bridge, Willow Springs, Independence Rock, Devil's Gate, and the three treacherous crossings of the icy Sweetwater in its rocky canyon. Beyond that was Ice Slough, Burnt Ranch, wind-swept South Pass, and the desolate stretch to Fort Bridger.

The West Coast was far, very far, from the rest of the nation. Word of the special mochila's progress got back to the Pony Express stations only gradually. It was the night of Thursday, November 8, that Jeff brought the special into Laramie. It was the forenoon of Thursday, November 22, that he pulled into Mud Springs on one of his regular eastbound runs. Gaunt and hollow-eyed from the unending saddle grind, he slid stiffly to the ground and announced to Lacy and waiting Bill Johnson:

"That extra got to Salt Lake in good time, anyhow!"

"Did? What was the time? Who told you?"

"Joe Jackson brung the word to Laramie. They set her down in Salt Lake City in three days and four hours from Fort Kearny."

"Going some, I'll say!"

"Good thing they had their election when they did, I reckon, if they wanted the news to get through quick," Jeff went on, wearily. "Been snowing for two days and a night when this left Salt Lake."

*This* was the brown, battered mochila. Bill Johnson caught it from Jeff, eased it expertly over his saddle, stepped into the leather.

"So long, fellers."

The eastbound mail, once more, was out of Mud Springs.

## *The Making of America: Suggested Grades*

*Grade Four*
- By Covered Wagon

*Grade Five*
- Caddie and the Indian Chief
- Two Little Confederates
- Hitty Goes to Sea

*Grade Six*
- A Night Ride in a Prairie Schooner
- The Pine-Tree Shillings
- Jacques and the Little Chief
- Dick Finds the "Wheel of Fortune"

*Grade Seven*
- Abe Lincoln Grows Up
- Invincible Louisa as a Nurse
- Blue Arrow and the Outlaws

*Grade Eight*
- Being a Boy
- The Hoosier Schoolmaster
- The Pony Express

## *Books about the Making of America*

### *Grades Three and Four*

Albert, Edna, *The Little Pilgrims to Penn's Woods,* illus. by Esther Brown. Longmans.

Birney, Hoffman, *Mountain Chief,* illus. by Jean Macdonald Porter. Penn.

Brock, Emma L., *Drusilla,* illus. by the author. Macmillan.

Coatsworth, Elizabeth, *Dancing Tom,* illus. by Grace Paull. Macmillan.

Coatsworth, Elizabeth, *Away Goes Sally,* illus. by Helen Sewell. Macmillan.

D'Aulaire, Ingri, and Edgar Parin d'Aulaire, *George Washington,* illus. by the authors. Doubleday, Doran.

———, *Abraham Lincoln,* illus. by the authors. Doubleday, Doran.

Duvoisin, Roger, *And There Was America,* illus. by the author. Knopf.

Flack, Marjorie, *Humphrey: One Hundred Years along the Wayside with a Box Turtle,* illus. by the author. Doubleday, Doran.

Hayes, Marjorie, *The Little House on Runners,* illus. by George and Doris Hauman. Little, Brown.

Keelor, Katharine, *Little Fox,* illus. by Frederick Richardson. Macmillan.

Orton, Helen Fuller, *The Treasure in the Little Trunk,* illus. by Robert Ball. Stokes.

Perkins, Lucy Fitch, *The American Twins of the Revolution,* illus. by the author. Houghton Mifflin.

Phillips, Ethel Calvert, *Ride-the-Wind,* illus. by Herbert M. Stoops. Houghton Mifflin.

Seredy, Kate, *Listening,* illus. by the author. Viking.

White, Eliza Orne, *Where Is Adelaide?* illus. by Helen Sewell. Houghton Mifflin.

## Grades Five and Six

Bailey, Carolyn Sherwin, *Tops and Whistles,* illus. by Grace Paull. Viking.

Brink, Carol Ryrie, *Caddie Woodlawn,* illus. by Kate Seredy. Macmillan.

Bransom, Paul, and Helen Dean Fish, *Animals of American History,* illus. by Paul Bransom. Stokes.

Coatsworth, Elizabeth, *The Golden Horseshoe,* illus. by Robert Lawson. Macmillan.

———, *Five Bushel Farm,* illus. by Helen Sewell. Macmillan.

Crawford, Phyllis, *"Hello, the Boat!"* illus. by Edward Laning. Holt.

Field, Rachel, *Hitty: Her First Hundred Years,* illus. by Dorothy P. Lathrop. Macmillan.

Gaither, Frances, *The Painted Arrow,* illus. by Henry Pitz. Macmillan.

Garland, Hamlin, *Boy Life on the Prairie.* Harper.

Grey, Katharine, *Rolling Wheels,* illus. by Frank Schoonover. Little, Brown.

Hader, Berta, and Elmer Hader, *The Picture Book of the States,* illus. by the authors. Harper.

Hawthorne, Nathaniel, *Grandfather's Chair,* illus. by Frank T. Merrill. Houghton Mifflin.

Lenski, Lois, *Phebe Fairchild: Her Book,* illus. by the author. Stokes.

Meigs, Cornelia, *The Covered Bridge,* illus. by Marguerite de Angeli. Macmillan.

———, *Wind in the Chimney,* illus. by Louise Mansfield. Macmillan.

Orton, Helen Fuller, *Hoof-Beats of Freedom,* illus. by Charles De Feo. Stokes.

Page, Thomas Nelson, *Two Little Confederates,* illus. by John W. Thomason. Scribner.

Parton, Ethel, *Vinny Applegay,* illus. by Margaret Platt. Viking.

Phillips, Ethel Calvert, *A Story of Nancy Hanks,* illus. by Kleber Hall. Houghton Mifflin.

Rogers, Frances, *Big Miss Liberty,* illus. by the author. Stokes.

Russell, I. K., and Howard R. Driggs, *Hidden Heroes of the Rockies,* illus. by Herman Palmer. World Book.

Schultz, James Willard, *Sinopah, the Indian Boy,* illus. by E. Boyd Smith. Houghton Mifflin.

Skinner, Constance Lindsay, *Becky Landers, Frontier Warrior.* Macmillan.

## Grades Seven and Eight

Allee, Marjorie Hill, *Off to Philadelphia,* illus. by David Hendrickson. Houghton Mifflin.

Bell, Frederic J., *Room to Swing a Cat,* illus. by Pauline Glidden Bell. Longmans.

Benét, Laura, *The Hidden Valley,* illus. by Kurt Wiese. Dodd Mead.

Berry, Erick, *Homespun,* illus. by Harold Von Schmidt. Lothrop.

Coatsworth, Elizabeth, *Here I Stay,* illus. by Edwin Earle. Coward-McCann.

Cormack, Maribelle, and William P. Alexander, *Land for My Sons: A Story of the Pennsylvania Wilderness,* illus. by Lyle Justis. Appleton-Century.

Eggleston, Edward, *The Hoosier Schoolmaster.* Scribner.

Field, Rachel, *Calico Bush,* illus. by Allen Lewis. Macmillan.

Hartman, Gertrude, *These United States, and How They Came to Be.* Macmillan.

Hewes, Agnes Danforth, *Glory of the Seas,* illus. by N. C. Wyeth. Knopf.

Jackson, Helen Hunt, *Ramona,* illus. by Herbert M. Stoops. Little, Brown.

Longstreth, T. Morris, *In Scarlet and Plain Clothes.* Macmillan.

Malkus, Alida Sims, *Caravans to Santa Fe,* illus. by Marie A. Lawson. Harper.

———, *Eastward Sweeps the Current,* illus. by Dan Sweeney. Winston.

Meigs, Cornelia, *Invincible Louisa: The Story of the Author of Little Women.* Little, Brown.

———, *Master Simon's Garden,* illus. by Frances White. Macmillan.

Pease, Howard, *Long Wharf,* illus. by Manning de V. Lee. Dodd Mead.

Sandburg, Carl, *Abe Lincoln Grows Up,* illus. by James Daugherty. Harcourt, Brace.

Singmaster, Elsie, *Emmeline,* Houghton Mifflin.

Skelton, Charles L., *Riding West on the Pony Express,* illus. by Paul Quinn Macmillan.

Skinner, Constance Lindsay, *Andy Breaks Trail.* Macmillan.

———, *Debby Barnes, Trader,* illus. by John Rae. Macmillan.

Thompson, Wolfe, *Moccasins on the Trail,* illus. by Richard H. Rogers. Longmans.

Warner, Charles Dudley, *Being a Boy,* illus. by Clifton Johnson. Houghton Mifflin.

# Workers and Their Work

## TONY, THE STEAM SHOVEL MAN[1]

*Henry B. Lent*

Tony is the man who runs the steam shovel. He wears a bright red handkerchief about his neck. He twirls his shiny black mustache and smiles. In one hand he carries his lunch box, full of good things to eat when the twelve o'clock whistle blows. It is a hard job to run a steam shovel, but Tony is very strong.

Today Tony must dig out a great hole in the earth, so that other men can start to build a tall apartment house. This hole is called an "excavation." A big red truck, shining in the sunlight, is already starting to chug slowly down the steep wooden runway into the hole toward the steam shovel. This truck, and many others like it, will haul away the dirt as fast as the steam shovel can dig it up. They carry the dirt to the edge of the city, where they dump it and come back for more.

It is still early in the morning when Tony walks down the runway and clambers up into the cab of his steam shovel. His helper shovels coal into the great boiler, for he must have a red-hot fire to make plenty of steam. Finally the steam hisses. Psss! Psss! The big shovel is ready to start work.

The steam shovel looks very much like a small house on wheels. At one end is the cab, or driver's place. Here are the levers which operate the shovel. At the other end is the big boiler with its smokestack sticking up through the roof. The shovel itself is really a huge bucket which scoops up more dirt than many men could dig up with their ordinary shovels. It takes only a few big bucketfuls of dirt to fill a large dump truck.

Now the red truck is down close to the steam shovel. Tony pulls a lever with his strong arms. The heavy iron bucket drops down. He pulls another lever. The big scoop digs into the earth. In a jiffy the bucket is heaping full. Then Tony presses a large pedal with his foot. The bucket rises high into the air. Tony must watch very carefully now! He pulls another lever and the bucket swings slowly around, over the truck. When it is just right, the truck driver waves his hand. Quick as a wink, Tony jerks the cord, and plop! the bottom of the bucket opens and the dirt falls into the truck with a loud noise.

When the truck is loaded full with dirt and stones, the driver starts his engine, and

[1] From Henry B. Lent, *Diggers and Builders*.

the truck climbs up the steep planks out of the hole, to make room for the next truck. Chug . . . chug . . . chug . . . ever so slowly, for the truck has a heavy load.

Sometimes men walk behind the truck with big blocks of wood which they quickly slip under the wheels if the engine begins to sputter. This prevents the truck from rolling back into the hole.

All day long Tony pushes and pulls the big levers of his steam shovel. Bucketful after bucketful, the dirt comes up and is emptied into the trucks.

Finally the hole becomes so large that Tony must move the steam shovel forward, where there is more dirt to scoop up. Have you ever seen a steam shovel move? It rolls along slowly on little wheels that run along a big, flat sort of chain. Because it crawls very much like a caterpillar, this is called a "caterpillar tread." The little wheels move the giant steam shovel quite easily, even up over bumps and rough places.

Tony's helper must keep shoveling coal into the boiler all day long to keep the fire burning. In the boiler, directly over the hot fire, are pipes of water. As the fire burns fiercely, the water boils and turns into steam. Steam is very powerful. It drives the pistons on huge railroad locomotives . . . and in Tony's steam shovel, the steam drives the pistons which turn the wheels and gears—and this is the machinery which makes the giant digger work. Black smoke pours out of the stack each time he shovels. Sometimes red sparks shoot up into the air.

For many days Tony and his hissing steam shovel dig and dig, deeper and deeper. At last he cannot even see up over the top of the steep sides of the hole his shovel has dug.

Finally, when there is no more dirt to be taken out, Tony jumps down from his cab and looks about him. He has dug a deep hole. But he is very wise. He knows exactly how to get out. Do you know how he does it?

Tony walks up to the foreman. "We're ready to move, boss," he says. "If your men will give us a hand, we'll soon be out of here." The men carry heavy timbers over to the steam shovel. They lay them down close together so that they make a plank road leading right up to the steep runway that the trucks have been using. Everything is ready. Tony climbs back into his steam shovel. Now then, everybody must get out of the way!

What a puffing and snorting as the steam shovel starts to climb up, up, out of the hole! Sometimes it slips back a little, but Tony opens the throttle, turns on more steam, and it keeps on moving. When he reaches the top, Tony steers it right onto a big low trailer which is hitched to a truck. Then the truck driver tows Tony and his steam shovel away, to dig another hole somewhere else.

Every day, as Tony works, many people stop to watch him and his steam shovel. His hands are too busy to wave to the boys and girls who watch him from the fence up above the hole, but Tony always has a smile. For he likes children.

Perhaps, some day, *you* will see Tony and his steam shovel digging.

## WAY PING, MASTER OF BOATS[1]

*Dorothy Rowe*

"Stand away, stand away, Son," called Father to the little boy who stood on the narrow deck and looked off to the west. "It is time to drop the anchor so our boat may rest for the night. Stand away, my Son."

Way Ping had just been thinking that this boat was the nicest home in the world in the summertime. He was so glad he and Father and Mother and the new Sister lived on it. He had to work hard and help Father, but all the time he worked he could hear the brown waves slap the nose of the boat, and he could see the sunshine run over the deck like gold water. It was the moving of the boat with the

[1] From Dorothy Rowe, *The Rabbit Lantern, and Other Stories of Chinese Children.*

wind that made the sunlight run about like water. Father had told him that.

It was evening now, and Way Ping had been watching the sunset make the reeds along the bank look like tall, black soldiers marching and marching but never going anywhere. Oh, indeed, a Chinese boat was a most joyful home. Way Ping had quite forgotten how long he had stood there. It seemed as if his heart had gone away to talk to the clouds and to follow the birds that went flying across the sky to their homes in the south. So when Father called to him, Way Ping jumped quickly, and his heart came running back to him, and he said:

"Yes, Father, I hear, and tonight I shall not let a brown wave come up and splash me. Did you see that wave last night, Father? It acted as if it wanted to push me down and jump on me, but when I ran away and laughed, it only threw some spray in my face and went back again. Aren't waves funny, Father? There, the anchor is down in the mud now, isn't it? I know the sound when it hits the bottom of the river."

The boat pulled a little bit at the anchor chain, then it drifted around until its stern rested near the reeds on the bank. When the boat was still, Father put a board from the deck to the land, took a big market basket, and went off on shore to buy food for supper. Father always bought the food in the little villages that were near the river's edge. He turned as he went off and called to Way Ping, "I'm going, Son. Remember, remember well, while I am gone you are the Master of the Boat. Watch that no harm comes to it. Take care of the Mother and Sister and tighten the anchor chain if the boat rocks loose."

Of course Way Ping was very proud. Father always made him the Master of the Boat when he was gone, and Way Ping was very careful. He loved the boat so much. It was such a pretty boat. The bottom of it was quite flat, but the two ends reached high into the air like the curved points of a new gold moon. The wood of the boat was gold colored, too, and rubbed bright with Chinese oil. There were two masts, and two square sails made of yellow cloth.

Way Ping went up to see if the sails were tight for the night. He tried the ropes and tied good knots at the ends. There was one very big sail and one little one. Sometimes only the big sail was up. That was when the wind was blowing high and puffed the yellow sail out very full. Then the little sail lay down near the deck, floppy and tired. Way Ping was always sorry for the second sail when it could not stand up and push the wind and shine in the sun. So tonight he gave the little sail a soft pat as he tied it tightly. He said to it, "Never mind because you have to lie still now. It's night time and you must get rested for tomorrow. I think tomorrow you will stand up against the wind."

Then Way Ping had to go to the front of the boat to see if the little lamp that stayed there all night was lit. He did know for sure that Father had lit it, but since he was Master now maybe he ought to see if it was quite all right.

On the front of the boat were painted two big, round, red eyes. They were the eyes of the ship. They did not look like eyes, but Way Ping knew they were, for Father had explained, "Those, Son, are the eyes of our boat. They can see farther and surer than your eyes and mine. They never go to sleep. They watch all day and all night to keep us safe. The boat's eyes see through the fog. They see other ships that pass us in the dark at night. They frighten away bad spirits who come to hurt us. You must be careful, Son, never to make the boat angry at us so it would shut its eyes."

All the time Way Ping had lived on the boat he had been careful. Now he looked to see if the light was burning brightly. In the light he could see the eyes and he thought they were very friendly. He liked the ship's eyes. They had always been good to him and his Mother and Father. Even the new Sister had been held up to see the eyes. She liked the bright red color of them and she said, "Ah goo, ah goo," and spit bubbles on her blue bib.

The next thing Way Ping did was to see if the cargo in the back of the ship was all right. The big jars of oil that Father was taking in the boat were piled high in the back. Way Ping thought they looked quite safe. They were very important, for it was because of this oil that Way Ping's Father had to take his boat on the long journey. You see, in China there are not so many trains, and almost no motor trucks, and not very many good roads. To Chinese people the river is a wide road, the Road of Boats, and when a man wants to send things from one city to another he gets a boat to carry them for him. And some one has to live on that boat and take care of it. Way Ping's Father was a boatman. He had filled his boat with these earthen jars of bean oil, and was taking them two hundred miles up the river to a merchant in Nanking. All day long he sailed the boat up the brown river and if there was a moon for light and the wind had not gone away, sometimes the boat would sail all night, too. But usually at night the boat was anchored by the shore and Father would walk off to the land as he had tonight. Always while Father was gone Way Ping was Master of the Boat and very, very proud.

The most exciting place in the boat, except right by the big sail when the wind blew hard, was the room down under the deck where Way Ping slept, where Mother cooked the meals and took care of the Sister. It was a low, dark room. To go down to it Way Ping pulled a ring in a certain board, the board came up like a door, and there were little steep wooden steps to climb down.

Mother and Sister were down there now, and Way Ping thought he would call down to see if they were all right before he went to fix the anchor for the night. So he pulled the ring, opened the little door, and called down, "Oh, Mother, you there? You quite all right? Where is the little Sister? Father hasn't come back with the supper yet, but he'll be home soon, I think."

Mother's voice called back, "Yes, Son, I make the fire of reed grass back here, and the little Sister is safe asleep in her corner. Are the sails fast? Take care that the anchor does not slip. Be careful. Big Son."

Way Ping started off to see about the anchor, but just at that minute he heard a little cry down the stairs. "Oh," thought he, "May-May is awake and crying. Mother is busy, so I had better go down and pat her to sleep again."

Very, very quietly he climbed down the stairs and walked across the half-dark room to the corner where little Sister was lying. She didn't have any bed. She just had two big blue quilts wrapped round and round her and she usually lay quite happy on the floor. The rocking of the boat was her cradling, and the sound of the reeds swishing against the boat was her lullaby. But now she was hungry, for she had slept a long time, so she cried and kicked her fat brown legs and waved her fat brown arms. She cried and kicked till she had almost unrolled from the quilts. Way Ping rolled her up again gently. "Ai yaa," he said, "such kickings! You ought to be a boy, May-May. Then when you grow up you could be a big, strong boatman. Don't cry. I'll turn you west now. Did you dream all the east dreams about the sun coming up like a great gold fish and getting tangled in the clouds?" Of course May-May didn't understand Way Ping, but she knew his voice, and it was nice to be turned to the west. Way Ping patted her softly, softly, and sang the song his Mother sang to him when he was a baby:

Mother of Dreams  
This little child cries  
For the west dreams now.  
Long has she slept  
With her face to the east,  
Now she is turned to the west—  
Mother of Dreams, Mother of Dreams.  
Send her the west dreams now.

Hush, baby, hush.
Dreams of the sunset,
Dreams of the dusk,
Dreams of the birds going home.
West dreams, rest dreams
From the Mother of Dreams to you.

It seemed as if the boat helped to put May-May to sleep. It rocked back and forth, back and forth. Way Ping wondered if the anchor chain was holding. As soon as May-May slept he ran up to see about the anchor. It seemed as he went up the stairs that the boat moved in a strange way, and when he got on deck he could not see the lights of the village. He ran around the deck, and then he saw his boat was really moving, going away from the shore. First he was too frightened to move. What would Father say? How could he ever get back to the village to find Father? Oh, why had he not tightened the anchor chain first of all? He wanted to cry. Then, like a real voice he seemed to hear Father say, "You are the Master of the Boat, Son." So he had to be brave.

"I'll call Mother," he said. "We've got to get the boat steered around and the big sail put up." So he ran to the back and called Mother. She left her fire and came quickly. "Don't be afraid, Son," she said. "We are two and you are strong. We will get back to land again."

Way Ping never worked so hard. He pulled in the anchor that had been dragging along in the mud, and he and Mother got the big sail up, and he steered. He and Mother talked to the boat as they worked. They said to the eyes, "Help us, eyes of the boat. Watch in the dark for us. We can see so little and we are not very good at this work."

Way Ping felt as if the boat really heard and helped them, for suddenly out of the dark came Father's voice, and there they were nearly to the shore again. Father said, "Here I am, here I am, Son of mine. Steer west, more west. There, drop the sail." And then Father jumped on the boat from the land and fastened the anchor quite tightly.

Mother sat on the deck and rested. Way Ping looked at Father and said, "Was I a bad Master of the Boat, Dada?"

"No, Little Son, a good Master you were, for when trouble came you remembered what I had told you of winds and sails, and the boat knew your voice and obeyed. Come now, I have brought fish balls and bean sprouts for supper. Come, Master of Boats, come, Little Son."

## THE SMALL YELLOW TRAIN[1]

*Alice Dalgliesh*

"David," said Aunt Melissa, "there are times when I truly believe your questions will drive me crazy!"

"He's at it all day long," said Aunt Ann. "What makes the steam engine go, and how big is it, and what does it look like? I can't answer the questions. Why do folks want to bother their heads about those new-fangled affairs, anyway?"

"Why, indeed!" agreed Aunt Melissa.

David said nothing for a few minutes. He was sorry he had annoyed the aunts. They had been so kind to him since he had come to stay in their comfortable house. He would be with them until his father and mother came home from a long voyage in his father's ship. Perhaps he should not talk so much about the new locomotive, not even if all the town of Albany was talking about it.

"I didn't mean—" said David.

"Neither did I," said Aunt Melissa, hastily.

"Well," suggested Aunt Ann, "I've heard there is a man in town who is showing a picture of the queer contraption. Perhaps if we took David to see it he would find the answers to some of his questions."

David sat up straight, his eyes shining.

"A good plan," said Aunt Melissa. "We'll go this very afternoon."

So, like most of the other people in Albany, the aunts and David went to see the picture. It was cut out of black paper

[1] From Alice Dalgliesh, *America Travels.*

and it had been made by a man who actually rode on the train the first time it carried passengers. Now he was showing it in his studio and charging a small admission fee.

As David came into the room he gave a little gasp. There was the picture, a big one, longer than David himself, all across the wall on one side of the room. Now he knew just how the train looked!

People were talking about the picture.

"It's wonderful!" they said. "Just like magic. Cut out of a piece of black paper with a pair of common scissors. And see the engineer! It's David Matthews himself, not quite as large as life, but twice as natural. The way Mr. Brown makes these likenesses is astonishing."

It was hard to get David away from the picture of the train, he could have looked at it all day long.

"Now he will be satisfied," said Aunt Ann.

But David was not satisfied. He had a great many more questions to ask and he wanted to see the train with his own eyes. At last the day came when he found courage to tell the aunts that he wanted more than anything in the world to ride on the small yellow train. When he told them they were shocked. They were horrified. They were terrified.

"Have you heard the tales of what happened on the first trip?" they asked. "Why it jerked so that Sally Jones was thrown from her seat. Her father lost his hat and never did find it again!"

"And the sparks! Mrs. Burton had a big hole burned in her new dress. The ladies who were in the open cars had to put up parasols to keep the sparks and cinders off their clothes."

"Sally said her face was black from the smoke."

"It is a very remarkable invention, David, but a most dangerous and uncomfortable way to travel."

All this did not discourage David in the least. It simply made him wish more than ever that he could ride on the train. In fact he knew he would never be quite happy until he had done so.

The aunts knew this too. So, because they were really very fond of David, they began to talk in this way:

"He does so want to go," said Aunt Melissa.

"Perhaps it is not so bad after all. I hear they have made improvements."

"Sally Jones always makes things seem worse than they are."

"And Elizabeth has begged us to bring David to visit her in Schenectady."

"Do you think we might try it?"

David could scarcely believe his ears when the aunts told him they had decided to travel by the train. When the day came it was bright and sunny. It took quite a while to get ready. Both aunts wore their second-best silk dresses and David's hair was brushed to a remarkable neatness. The aunts had hired a carriage to drive to the place from which the train started. As this was David's special day, he was allowed to ride in front with the coachman.

Aunt Melissa and Aunt Ann were safely settled in the carriage. The coachman cracked his whip. They were off! David braced his feet against the dashboard and looked sideways at the coachman. He looked solemn and cross, so David did not speak. There was silence for a long time. Then the coachman looked at David.

"Going to ride on the train, I hear?"

"Yes," said David.

"H'm," said the coachman. "More time than sense. What do folks want with them steam engines anyway, puffing and snorting and scaring the horses half out of their wits? Thirty miles an hour it goes! I say no good will come of people shooting around the country like skyrockets. Give me horses!"

"But it's a very wonderful invention," ventured David.

"H'm!" said the coachman. "That may be. But did you hear about the steam locomotive that blew up down Charleston way? Folks scattered all over the tracks. Horses for me!"

David could think of nothing to say. He hoped Aunt Ann and Aunt Melissa had not heard the conversation, for there was still time to turn back. Now they were at the place from which the train started. There was a steep hill leading into the town, and people thought that engines could run only on level ground. So there was a little car on which passengers sat while a stationary engine pulled them up to the top of the hill. The aunts did not care for this at all.

The car reached the top of the slope. The passengers stepped off—and there was the *De Witt Clinton* engine with its train! Shivers chased up and down David's spine and his stomach seemed to be turning over. The little engine stood on the track puffing as if impatient to be off. It looked just like the picture—and, sure enough, there was David Matthews, the engineer! Next to the engine was the tender with wood for fuel, and behind that the coaches, bright yellow with orange trimmings. Some of the passengers chose to sit on top of the coaches, but the aunts were sure it would be safer inside. Besides, they remembered about the sparks. Now they were all settled. The conductor came to collect the tickets.

"All aboard!" The conductor climbed on a small seat behind the tender and blew a long blast on a tin horn. "All aboard!"

"Can't we get out even now?" asked Aunt Ann, nervously clasping and unclasping her mittened hands.

"Nonsense, Ann," said Aunt Melissa. "We must do it for David's sake." Her voice was firm, but her knees were trembling.

S-s-s-s-ssss! a great sound of steam.

S-s-s-s-ssss! Chuff! They were off!

It was jerky, but not nearly as bad as Sally Jones had said it was. Undoubtedly there had been changes and improvements. How quickly they traveled! The coaches rocked and swayed. The engine puffed out great clouds of black smoke. The aunts sat bolt upright, hands clasped tightly on their laps, looking perfectly miserable. David looked perfectly happy. He talked all the time.

"We're out in the country now! Oh, look at those cows, they're scared of us!"

"Look at those children on the fence. They're so surprised to see me riding on the train!"

"O-oh! We scared a horse! See him go down the road!"

"Ouch! There's a spark on me. It's all right, I put it out."

"Your cheek is all black, Aunt Melissa. No, not that one, the other one."

"There's another horse that's scared! I wonder what he thinks we are."

After a time David did not talk so much and the aunts did not sit so stiffly. They were getting quite accustomed to riding on the train. Aunt Ann began to look out of the windows with a good deal of pleasure.

"After all . . . Melissa . . ."

"After all you *like* it, don't you, Aunt Ann?" asked David.

Aunt Ann swallowed hard and looked the other way. Aunt Melissa answered.

"Why, yes, David, it seems almost pleasant. We shall undoubtedly use the train a number of other times."

David leaned back in his seat with a deep sigh of happiness.

"I shall go with you every time," he said. "And when I grow up I shall drive an engine just like David Matthews. Won't that be fine, Aunt Melissa?"

But Aunt Melissa had not time to answer for they were at the end of the line.

"Schenectady! Schenectady! All out!"

The journey on the small yellow train was over.

## RUSTY PETE, COW PONY[1]

*Doris Fogler* and *Nina Nicol*

Rusty Pete is a chunky, well-built white cow pony with a wavy white mane and tail. His ears and the sides of his head are rust-colored.

He lives on the "Lazy A B" ranch in

[1] From Doris Fogler and Nina Nicol, *Rusty Pete of the Lazy A B.*

southeastern Montana, on the border of the Crow Indian Reservation.

Alan Wallace and his twelve-year-old sister, Mary Lou, are the owners of the "Lazy A B." Singing Mink, a Crow woman, is boss of the kitchen. She has taken care of Mary Lou ever since the death of her mother and father, and loves her tomboyish little charge with all her heart.

The ranch takes its name from the brand which marks all the Wallace horses and cattle. This is the way the brand looks—➤ B—and because the "A" is lying on its side, it is called "Lazy."

It is a ranch of fifteen hundred acres, half of which is level or gently rolling land. On this, wheat, oats, and hay are grown, and there is also a vegetable garden. The rest of the ranch is cut up by deep coulees where many horses and cattle graze, and where they find shelter from the cold wind in the winter.

The house is a low, rambling building with a big screened porch. Around the house is a fence to keep out any too-familiar stock. At the back are a barn, corrals built of poles, wagon sheds, blacksmith shop, and various small outbuildings. Near the kitchen is a root-cellar where the vegetables are kept.

Almost any day Rusty Pete can be seen taking a sun bath in the round corral by the barn. He is trustworthy and gentle, and is kept close at hand for Mary Lou's exclusive use.

He was born on the open range and roamed freely for four years before he even wore a halter. He is a range horse at heart, and when he does get loose he is very hard to catch, for he knows cowboys and their ways.

Out of the corner of his eye, any fine summer morning, he may see Mary Lou at the ranch house door. She is wearing her big cowboy hat. A bright red handkerchief is knotted around the collar of her flannel shirt, and she has on her oldest khaki breeches and high boots.

"Oh, dear!" Rusty Pete will be saying to himself. "This looks like work!"

For him work often means "riding the fence." For it is his duty and Mary Lou's to follow the ranch fences up the hills, down the coulees, and into every corner, to see that the wires are all tightly stapled to the cedar posts, that the posts are all up, and that no gates are left open. If any repair requires too much strength, Mary Lou reports it to Alan, who fixes it himself.

Then she and Pete must see that all of the "Lazy A B" stock is inside the ranch fences, and that any other stray stock is outside.

Horses and cattle know no property rights. When the grain begins to ripen it is a great temptation to break through the fences and enjoy a feast. Pete and Mary Lou must drive out these intruders.

"Round-up" time is always a busy time for Pete. Alan borrows him and takes him away with a string of four or five of his own horses. Cattle that have been roaming on the range all summer are brought in to central locations, and riders from different ranches separate their cattle from the rest. All the cattle are branded with their owner's brand, just as Alan's cattle are marked "➤ B."

Pete and Alan often help hold the herd, guarding them and chasing back any adventurers who try to break away. When Alan is roping, Pete knows just when to stop, bracing himself and facing the roped animal. He is not afraid of the rope, and much experience has taught him to keep it tight and not get tangled up in it.

Rusty Pete is very wise in the ways of his world, extra-wise when it somes to bluffing. He pretends to be wild and fierce, but is really gentle and willing. He will never intentionally hurt anyone, especially his beloved mistress, Mary Lou.

One day when Mary Lou called good-by to Alan and Singing Mink, and came down the path, Rusty Pete didn't actually mind. But, being young and full of life, he got ready to express his opinion.

In the cool, shadowy barn, the harness hung from a row of pegs along the wall. There were intricate trappings for the work horses, an orderly litter of bridles, halters, ropes and hobbles, and several saddles each dangling by a stirrup.

Pete's outfit hung nearest the door. It was new, and Mary Lou took good care of it. The bridle had a flower-stamped headstall, and three gleaming gold conchos down each cheek strap and one in the center of the brow band. It was a gift from Alan on her last birthday. The saddle he had given her at Christmas. It was a regular stock saddle any cowboy might be proud of, and bore the same flower design as the bridle. Mary Lou vowed no calf should ever chew the tie-strings on this saddle as one had on her old saddle! She took down the bridle and went into the corral.

Pete, who had no intention of being caught without some fun, gave her quite a chase under the hot sun. He finally stopped long enough for her to grasp his mane. She put the bit in his mouth, slipped the bridle over his rusty ears, and buckled the throat latch.

She led him to the barn by the long reins. When these reins were let trail on the ground, Rusty Pete was supposed to consider himself tied. He did—sometimes! Now he objected to being caught and bridled on general principles. But he objected to being saddled for a more personal reason.

The man who first taught Pete about saddles, had little patience when Pete, frightened and not understanding why the heavy flapping affair should be strapped so securely to his back, fought desperately.

The sight of a saddle always brought back this unpleasant memory to Pete. Of course he knew Mary Lou wouldn't hurt him; but the man who broke him had given him such a beating that Pete simply had to include some strenuous objecting in the routine of saddling up.

Mary Lou understood this, and was very patient. Pete backed the length of the corral and reared. A few times he had even thrown himself over backward.

"Now, feller," coaxed Mary Lou, "quit performing for the grand stand. There's no movie camera handy, so all this 'Wild West' stuff is wasted."

"O Alfalfa!" snorted Pete. "I might as well stand still and get it over with! You always win!"

Mary Lou smoothed the gay saddle-blanket over his back, taking care there were no creases or wrinkles in it to make his back sore.

She swung the heavy saddle expertly over the blanket, looped the latigo through the cinch ring, and drew the cinch up tight. She fastened her rope at the right side of the saddle, and led Pete out of the corral gate.

"That's over," said Rusty Pete, with a relieved sigh. "It's rather nice to be going somewhere. Let's go!"

With the reins and a fistful of his mane in her left hand, and a good grip on the saddle horn with her right, Mary Lou put her left foot in the left stirrup, and swung up into the saddle as Pete started off.

They soon reached the highest land on the ranch. Mary Lou hoped they might see the missing horses she and Pete were to go after.

To the north and west stretched the grain fields and pastures of the benchland. Beyond, in the north, lay the green and gold checkerboard of the irrigated valley. Then rose line after line of bluffs, becoming bluer in the distance.

To the east, past the hills, rows of sandstone bluffs, dotted with pines, led to the river in the valley, tracing the courses of ancient streams.

The broken hilly country in the south, with its shades of gold, rose, and mauve, showed soft and beautiful as a Persian rug. Beyond this, flat-topped and blue, were the Pryor Mountains; and far to the west lay the jagged Bear-Tooth Range of the Rockies. On clear days Mary Lou could see four more distant mountain ranges.

No horses were in sight, so she turned Pete in the likeliest direction.

Scattered clumps of wild plum and chokecherry bushes grew on the steep sides of the coulees. Down by the shallow waters of the creeks that ran in some of the coulees, cottonwood and box elder trees cast their shade. But no trees at all offered shade on the hills.

It was hot!

"It wasn't hot in the corral," sighed Pete, "just comfortably warm. And that lovely cool shadow by the barn—"

He slowed up and pretended to be frightened at a rock. He shied at a fence post, tried to wheel and run back to the ranch.

"Pete, stop your nonsense," scolded Mary Lou severely. "You never notice such trifles when you are headed for home! Come on, big boy, we must find those horses that strayed away last week."

Rusty Pete knew when she meant business. He knew that her quirt hung on the saddle horn, and that unless he buckled down and stopped fooling, he would get a good-natured slap with it. So he loped along meekly enough, and at the first coulee he half slid down the steep bank, dislodging the stones and digging his iron-shod hoofs into the ground to keep his balance. Then he daintily picked his way across the stony bed of a dry creek and scrambled up the other side. From the top of the next hill they saw a herd of perhaps forty horses grazing about a mile away.

They went near enough to see that this was one of Chief Plenty Coos' fine pinto herds, and that none of the "Lazy A B" horses were among them.

On the sunny side of Wet Creek, not far off, a smaller herd grazed. All the "Lazy A B" strays were there except brown Nellie and two yearlings.

Rusty Pete slid down the next coulee, and around the next bend they found the stragglers. With them was a horse from a neighboring ranch—a ten-year-old unbroken buckskin.

And Nellie had a brand-new possession—a wobbly-legged colt.

They stopped beside Nellie, and the colt, frightened, staggered awkwardly to its little hoofs and huddled close to her side. Nellie watched anxiously, wondering what Mary Lou would do.

"What a beautiful baby, Mrs. Nellie!" nickered Pete softly. "Black all over, and a white star on his forehead. And—bless my oats—a white forefoot!" Then, turning to the buckskin: "As to you, what are you doing here, you old loafer?"

The big buckskin snorted, switched his black tail, and took a few steps toward Pete. Pete squealed, tugged at his reins, shook his head, and stamped a foot.

He so evidently wanted to mix in this affair that, although they were a good two miles from the ranch and it might mean that she would have to walk home, Mary Lou's curiosity won. She jumped down and let him go.

Pete flew straight for the buckskin. The buckskin was no coward, and met him halfway. They reared and struck viciously at each other with their forefeet; then down again, snorting, biting. Each tried to circle around to get in a good kick with his hind feet.

Nellie and her colt and the two yearlings had made off toward the other "Lazy A B" horses. Pete and the intruder made a few more wicked plunges at each other; and with a last wild kick from Pete, the buckskin trotted off toward his home, head up, mane and tail flying, not admitting defeat, simply leaving.

Mary Lou was glad to see that neither horse had been hurt. Her leniency to Pete was rewarded by the sight of him trotting over the opposite hill after Nellie. But the herd would have none of him while he wore his saddle and bridle—even his special friends snapped at him when he tried to work his way to Nellie's side.

So Pete wandered back toward Mary Lou, pretending he had meant all the time to let her catch him.

Delighted to get him so easily, she mounted and rode toward the herd.

The colt was still learning how to use his awkward legs. He tested their possibilities with little hops and skips, and even kicked once or twice.

"Guess we shall have to call you 'Skipper,'" laughed Mary Lou. "I reckon you are strong enough to drift on over to the ranch. Hey, Pete, let's get busy and bring them in!"

They headed the horses up the coulee toward home, and past the prairie-dog town on the next hill.

The prairie dogs were very busy with their daily affairs. The village fathers, sitting up tall and dignified on their mounds, looked just like so many stakes driven into the ground. However, they were very alert sentinels, and chattered warning and advice to the others scampering around.

As the horses approached, the prairie dogs barked defiance, jerking their tails at each bark. They were very brave until the horses got close. Then they barked very fast, keeping time with their tails, and disappeared into their holes.

The horses were indifferent to the scolding—or maybe, warning. Had they been racing, they would have taken notice, for many a running horse has broken his leg by stepping into a prairie-dog hole.

"What kind of noise do they make?" Mary Lou asked Pete. "It isn't a bark and it isn't a squeak.

"Alan says little brown owls live in the same holes with them," she continued, "and rattlesnakes, too! I hope the snakes are all asleep or off visiting distant relations."

They slowly followed the back trail, picking the easiest going for the benefit of Skipper. On the side of the last coulee, a boarded-up spring made a clear, cool water hole. The horses were drinking as Alan rode over the hill on his big black horse, Chester Bad Boy.

"Thought we'd ride over and help," he called.

"Pete and I sure don't need any help to bring in a bunch of horses," said Mary Lou, indignantly. "We're traveling slow 'cause of Nellie's new youngster."

Alan reined up and grinned at Skipper, who was investigating the water hole.

"Looks like the makin's of a good little cayuse." he said.

When the horses were in the corral, Mary Lou tried to make friends with Skipper. He was shy and frightened, and would have none of this queer two-legged creature. Nellie, worried, circled the corral, Skipper always on her far side, running in and out among the milling horses. For such a youngster, he was very elusive.

Alan was out by the blacksmith shop. Mary Lou finally called to him.

"Oh, Alan, please help me catch Skipper. I want to make friends with him, and even Nellie is suspicious!"

Alan climbed through the corral bars and soon they had Skipper cornered. By being very gentle, Mary Lou convinced him he was safe with her. It had been a big day for him, and he lay down wearily.

Mary Lou sat down beside him and took his head in her lap.

"Don't be scared, little feller," she crooned. "You're home, and nothing will hurt you." She rubbed his neck, and the spot-which-likes-to-be-rubbed behind the ears. Worn out from the journey and the excitement, he fell asleep.

Nellie stood at Mary Lou's shoulder, watching.

"She is always kind and gentle," said Nellie to herself. "I guess she won't hurt him. I don't know why I ran from her. Nevertheless, you never can tell what might happen. I'll stick around."

So she stood guard until Singing Mink called Mary Lou in to dinner.

## CHILDREN OF HAITI[1]

*Arna Bontemps* and *Langston Hughes*

Popo and Fifina were walking barefooted behind two long-eared burros down the highroad to the little seacoast town of Cape Haiti. Bags, woven of grass, were hung across the backs of the pack animals, and in these were all the belongings of their family. Popo and Fifina were moving. They were moving from their grand-

[1] From Arna Bontemps and Langston Hughes, *Popo and Fifina: Children of Haiti.*

mother's home in the country to a new home in town.

Their parents, Papa Jean and Mamma Anna, were peasant farmers. But they had grown tired of the life on their lonely hillside, and they were going to Cape Haiti, where Papa Jean planned to become a fisherman.

The sunshine was like gold. The little dusty white road curved ribbonlike among the many hills. It was overhung with the leaves of tropical trees. On the warm countryside there was no sound but the droning of insects and the sudden crying of bright birds. There was no hurry or excitement. And the burros' lazy steps set the speed for the little band of travelers.

From the rear of their tiny caravan, Popo could see the members of his family stretched along the road, one after another, like a line of ducks. First was Papa Jean himself, a big powerful black man with the back torn out of his shirt. He wore a broad turned-up straw hat and a pair of soiled white trousers; but, like all peasants of Haiti, he was barefooted. He walked proudly, and there was a happy bounce in his step as he led his little family toward the town of his dreams.

Next came Mamma Anna with the baby, Pensia, swinging from her side as Haitian babies do. Mamma Anna was also barefooted, and she wore a simple peasant dress and a bright peasant headcloth of red and green. She was a strong woman with high glossy cheek bones. She followed her husband step for step in the dusty road. The two loaded burros came next. They were shaggy animals, and their heads were lowered as they trudged along. Great bright-winged flies rode on their flanks and buzzed around their heads.

Fifina, Popo's ten-year-old sister, walked so close behind the second burro that she could reach out her hand and smack him on the flanks if he stopped to nibble grass on the roadside. She wore a little blue dress that reached her knees.

But Popo, who walked behind her, was only eight, and all he wore was a shirt that didn't even reach his waist. At home he wouldn't have been wearing this; but when a person is making a long journey to an important town like Cape Haiti, he has to dress up a little. So Popo had worn his Sunday clothes. And Sunday clothes for black peasant boys in Haiti usually consist of nothing more than the single shirt Popo was wearing to town.

Like all dressed-up people, Popo was proud of himself this afternoon. He was proud also to be going to town to live by the ocean and to see new wonders. So while the little procession swung slowly along, he frisked about like a young colt, stamping the dust and kicking up his heels. Late in the day, near their journey's end, the road led up a hill and they passed between thickets of dense foliage. Beautiful flowering trees were plentiful, their blossoms red like fire, or white as milk.

Looking back, Popo could see forests of palms, mangoes, banana trees, and coffee bushes bordering the road; but he spent very little time in looking back. His mind was set on reaching the top of the hill. He wanted to get a glimpse of the town that was to be their home, and the great ocean from which Papa Jean would fish food and make a living for his family.

Papa Jean was perspiring as he led the way up the mountain. His naked back flashed like metal in the sun.

"Do you think we're almost to the top?" Popo asked Fifina.

"It isn't far," she said. "But you won't help us to get there any sooner by frisking around as you do."

"I can hardly wait, Fifina! If Papa Jean would let me, I could run ahead and be at the top in a minute. Why do you suppose he makes me stay back here, Fifina?"

"Why, it's plain as anything. It's because he knows you'd run so far ahead we could never catch you."

Popo became silent. He couldn't understand the ways of old people. And his thoughts made him sad. "Oh, my!" he said to himself. Then he settled back into the slow gait of the others and made up his mind to be patient till they reached the hilltop.

Presently Papa Jean reached the high point and stood with his hands on his hips. A few moments later Mamma Anna reached his side. Popo could see their backs against the sky—Papa Jean and Mamma Anna standing on the top of the world at the place where the mountain touches the sky. They were in the middle of the road, and soon the faithful burros were there also. One stopped beside Popo's mother and the other beside his father. Then Fifina reached the top and stood beside one of the burros; but before she got there Popo forgot his place, ran ahead of her, and took his stand beside the other animal.

"Well, here we are," Papa Jean said.

"H'm," Mamma Anna hummed without parting her lips. "H'm." She was pleased.

"How fine!" Fifina exclaimed. "Oh, how fine the ocean is! And what a big town!"

Really the town was small, but, compared with the villages Fifina had seen, it was quite impressive.

Popo said nothing. He was too excited to speak, but his eyes swept the whole bright scene below.

This is what he saw: rows of small white houses and buildings that stretched along the curved water front almost as far as his eyes could reach, old ruins and battlements overlooking the water at several places, trees growing right down to the water's edge, sailboats in the harbor moving under a slow steady wind, others being sculled by half-naked men, and a number of tiny rocking boats anchored along the beach.

"We've got to keep moving," Papa Jean said, after a long pause. "We've got to get unpacked before night."

"H'm," Mamma Anna agreed.

Fifina clapped her hands in excitement, and Popo danced with glee as the party of travelers took their former positions in the road and started down the hillside to their new home.

. . . . . . . . . . .

The next day, in the heat of the morning, Popo lay in the doorway naked. There was no reason why he should wear his little dress-up shirt now, so he rolled in the dirt happily, and without fear of soiling a garment. He felt more comfortable than he had been since the beginning of their journey two days before.

At that early hour there was very little wind stirring, and there was almost no activity on the streets. The trees of the yard were still, their leaves powdered by white dust. The two burros were sleeping in their places at the back of the yard, and the usual tropical flies were buzzing their bright wings about the animals' heads.

Presently Fifina and Mamma Anna came to the door with their arms full of soiled clothes.

"We're going to wash today," Mamma Anna said to Popo. "You come with us, if you like."

Popo didn't really feel like moving at the moment. He was so comfortable on the warm ground he felt that he might have stayed there the rest of the day. But he managed to draw himself up and to roll his eyes at Mamma Anna's suggestion. After all, it might not be a bad idea to follow Mamma Anna and Fifina to the washing place. He might have a chance to play in the water. That *would* be a treat. Popo sprang to his feet.

"Yes, indeed, Mamma," he exclaimed. "I'd like to go very much. But where will you wash the things—at the fountain at the next corner?"

"Oh, no, son, not there. The fountain is all right for washing dishes or milk cans, or even for bathing babies like Pensia, but it is better to wash clothes in the stream that runs along the street." Then Mamma Anna put the clothes she was carrying in Popo's arms. "Here. You carry these. I'll go back and get Pensia."

Pensia, like Popo, wore no clothes at all, only a bead on a cord around her neck. She was a quiet and well behaved baby, and she seemed as delighted as any one to be going out for the morning work.

The stream along the street was no bigger than the stream in some gutters after a rain. But it was clean sparkling water from the mountain springs flowing in a little stone gully for the convenience of people who did not have private wells in their houses.

While Mamma Anna and Fifina washed the pieces of clothing, one by one, Popo and Baby Pensia played in the water. Popo took good care of his baby sister and seated her on the edge of the little stream where her feet could reach the water while he ran up and down the middle of the stream splashing in every direction and having the time of his life.

Soon Popo noticed other women coming with their clothes to the little streams. They took their places farther up the street and began beating their garments in the water in the same way Mamma Anna washed. They took each garment, dampened and soaped it, then put it on the rocky edge of the gully and gave it a good pounding with a wooden stick while the soapy water ran out of it. Before long there was a line of busy women that reached almost the whole length of the street. Other youngsters like Popo were playing in the water, and other babies like Pensia were sitting with their feet in the stream. Occasionally a dog or a goat came to the stream to drink. The day that had seemed so dull and quiet a little while earlier was now full of sounds and movements.

There were by now, too, many people passing along the streets with bundles on their heads. Among them was one youngster who attracted the attention of Popo and Fifina—a little smiling black girl who carried a large wooden tray on her head and a small folding stool on one arm. She carried her burden lightly and happily, as if she had been used to balancing things on her head a long time.

All Haitian youngsters learn to carry burdens on their heads. Popo already knew the trick. He could go to the store for a bar of soap or a basket of fruit and bring it home on his head just as expertly as the little girl was carrying her tray. That was a fine thing for a playful boy like Popo, since he could forget the burden on his head and at the same time have his hands free to play.

But the little girl with the wooden tray and the broad smile was not out to play. She was on a business errand, and Popo could see that her tray was loaded with things to sell. When she was near enough, she unfolded her stool, put it on the ground, and set the tray upon it.

Popo's eyes popped, and his mouth began to water, for he was looking at a great collection of stick candy, large sugary peppermint sticks of pink and white. It was a soft crumbly kind of stick candy; it had a fine peppermint smell, and when the little girl removed the tray from her head she had to shoo the tropical bees and flies away. A whole swarm of them had been sitting happily on the sweet sticks as they traveled along the road uncovered in the sunshine.

"Will you have a stick of candy?" the little girl asked. "It's a penny a stick and awfully good. My mother just made it. Will you buy a stick?"

Popo turned to his mother with a pleading glance, but she was shaking her finger in the air. Fifina looked up eagerly. But pennies are scarce in Haiti. And Mamma Anna was not at all sure that she could afford to spend two or three of them that day for candy.

"Please, mamma," Popo said softly.

"We haven't had a taste of candy for months," Fifina begged.

The mother paused, thinking.

"I don't know," she said. "Not now anyhow. But maybe when the morning's work is done, when the little girl passes here on her way home, you may each have a stick."

Popo clapped his hands and gave an excited leap in the water. Fifina showed her happiness by bringing the back of her hand across her open mouth in a little gesture. Then the girl gathered up her wares, folded her chair across her arm, and started down the street again. Fifina and Mamma

Anna returned to their clothes, and once again Popo splashed and galloped in the water. Baby Pensia, who kicked her feet, gurgling, seemed also to understand.

When the washing was done, Mamma Anna wrung the clothes as dry as she could and stacked them in a large tin pan. The loaded pan she lifted quickly to her head. Then, leaving Fifina and Popo to attend to Pensia, she started off toward home, a great pile of whiteness balanced on her head.

At home Mamma Anna unfolded her clothes and spread them carefully on the grass around the house. There was no such thing as a clothes line in anybody's yard.

"Will there be anything for me to do?" Popo asked.

"Oh, yes," Mamma Anna told him. "I will need you to go down by the roadside and get me some soap weed to wash dishes. I used the last bit of bar soap on the clothes, and if you are to have your stick candy, I shan't be able to spend pennies for another bar. You will have to get me a good supply of soap weed."

"I'll go too," Fifina offered. "I know a soap bush better than he does."

The two youngsters went running down the path. And sure enough Fifina led Popo to a large clump beside the roadside. They tore off a few leaves to try it out. Rubbing the leaves between the hands produced a lather not unlike that from moistened soap.

"These will do," Fifina said. "Let's gather as many leaves as we can carry in our hands."

"All right," Popo went to work eagerly.

Ten or fifteen minutes later, when Popo and Fifina and Mamma Anna were at the fountain and Baby Pensia, getting a real bath, was covered with white suds that looked like wool, the little candy girl returned. Her tray was not empty, but it was plain that she had made sales since passing the family at the washing place. True to her word, Mamma Anna took two pennies from a pocket of her skirt and bought one stick for Fifina and one for Popo. Fifina's was white and Popo's was pink.

"Pensia can have a taste of each," she explained. "She does not need a whole stick."

"Glook!" said Pensia, crowing at the sight of the candy. "O–oo! Glook!"

## LITTLE TONINO [1]

*Helen Hill* and *Violet Maxwell*

If you should go on board a big ship and sail east for days and days across the Atlantic Ocean you would pass through the Straits of Gibraltar into the Mediterranean Sea, with Africa on your right and Europe on your left. Then, if you sailed northeast for a few days you would come to a land where the mountains slope straight down to the sea, and this is the South of France which in the old days was called the Kingdom of Provence.

If you should leave the ship, and get into an automobile, and drive up and up along the winding white road straight into the mountains, you would come to a little gray old town perched high on the top of a precipice with a high wall all around it. Here you would have to leave the automobile and walk up a steep, cobbled street that would lead you to the gate of the old town. The name of the old town is Nouvilo.

Now Nouvilo means *new town,* and I haven't a doubt that seven or eight hundred years ago Nouvilo really *was* new, and the houses stood beautifully upright, and were white and shining. But now Nouvilo is very old indeed, so old that the houses are all crooked and seem to lean against each other for support. They are too old to stand upright! In the very crookedest house of all lives a little Provençal boy called Tonino.

The back of Tonino's house bulges over the town wall, which grows right out of the side of the cliff. The front door of Tonino's house opens onto a little narrow street, so narrow that if a donkey cart comes along

[1] From Helen Hill and Violet Maxwell, *Little Tonino.*

you have to climb somebody's doorstep to get out of the way!

Tonino's house has two front doors, one very narrow leading up the corkscrew stone steps to the kitchen. The kitchen is very big and is the living room as well. Next to the kitchen is a smaller room where sleep Tonino's grandmother and his sister Nanou. Then another flight of corkscrew stairs leads up to the big bedroom, which belongs to Tonino's father and mother, and a tiny little room that is Tonino's own.

The other front door, very wide and studded with nails, leads into a large room level with the street. And here live all the animals except Minou, the cat, who sleeps in the kitchen. There's Lavanda, the goat, and there's Mius, the big pompous cock with beautiful green tail-feathers, who lords it over seven hens and ever so many chickens. Here also live Mignonetto, the big mother donkey, and her little donkey, Tintourlet.

Tintourlet is Tonino's very own donkey and I will tell you exactly how he came to him. Two years ago on Christmas Eve, when Tonino and Nanou were putting their shoes in the fireplace in the kitchen for Papo Noël to fill with presents, Tonino suddenly thought of the donkey, Mignonetto. At that time Mignonetto lived all alone on the ground floor with Mius, the cock, and the hens, as Lavanda had not yet come to live with them.

Tonino felt very sorry for Mignonetto all alone among the chickens on Christmas Eve. So, without saying a word to anyone, Tonino took his other shoe down to the stable and put it near Mignonetto's stall so that Papo Noël should remember Mignonetto when he went his rounds and maybe bring her a gift of juicy red carrots.

On Christmas morning everybody sleeps late, especially those who have been to church at midnight on Christmas Eve. But Tonino woke as soon as it was light and ran downstairs in his nightshirt to see what Papo Noël had brought to Mignonetto, and what do you think he found? Lying beside Mignonetto was a little baby donkey!

You can imagine how pleased and excited Tonino was and how he rushed upstairs and pounded first on his grandmother's door and then on his mother's door as he shouted at the top of his lungs, "Mameto, Papo, Mamo! Papo Noël has put a baby donkey in Mignonetto's shoe!"

You can imagine also how amazed Tonino's father and mother and grandmother were when they heard this astounding news, until Tonino explained to them that he had put his own shoe beside Mignonetto so that Papo Noël should not forget her but would bring her a present also, and *he had.*

Then Tonino's father said, "Well, Tonino, you shall have this baby donkey for your very own until he is full-grown and has to be sold, so as he is your donkey you shall choose his name."

Tonino thought and thought of ever so many names, but at last he decided to just call him *Tintourlet,* which means "little and sweet and darling."

Tintourlet was nearly grown up now; he could carry light loads on his back and every day when they all went out to their little farm that was nearly a mile from the town, Tonino rode on Tintourlet's back a part of the way, giving Nanou her turn too.

One day Tonino was feeling very sad. He had heard his father and mother talking together the evening before. They were talking about Tintourlet, his little donkey. His mother was saying what a pity it would be to have to sell Tintourlet, as the children were so fond of him, and his father had answered: "I know it is very sad, but I don't see how we can keep Tintourlet *another* winter. We can keep him till next summer, when he will be full-grown, but we must sell him then. We do not really need two donkeys and, as the price of grain has gone up, it would be too expensive just to keep him for a plaything."

That is what Tonino heard, and are you surprised that he was feeling sad? That is why, when afternoon school was over, instead of running gayly down the hill as he usually did, he walked very slowly, with his head bent down, so that he did not see Monsieur Nirascou till he tapped him on the shoulder and said: "Hello, Tonino! Tomorrow I am going to take a load of decorated pottery down to Pouget. They will be lighting the Great Fire. How would you like to come along?"

You can believe that Tonino was delighted. He forgot his sorrow about Tintourlet and jumped right up into the air with joy. He said: "Thank you, Monsieur Nirascou. If Papo and Mamo will give their permission, I would just love to come with you!"

Papo and Mamo and Mameto were very glad that Tonino should have such a treat. So on Saturday morning Tonino got out of bed at five o'clock, while it was still quite dark, for Monsieur Nirascou was to start from the big square at six.

His Mamo got up also and made Tonino a big bowl of hot cocoa so that he should be nice and warm when he started. When Tonino had eaten some bread that was left from the day before, and had drunk his hot cocoa, he put on his warm cape, and his Mamo wound his long scarf round his neck and kissed him on both cheeks; and then he ran along the dark streets till he came to the big square.

Monsieur Nirascou had already finished harnessing his big white horse, Louiset, to the cart, which was laden with big baskets of pottery carefully packed. When he saw Tonino he called out: "Good morning, Tonino. You are just in time. Another five minutes and I should have been out of the gate and you would have had to run to catch up with us."

Tonino laughed as he climbed up on the seat. Louiset began to jog quickly down the long uneven road, through the gate, across the bridge, to the smooth main road.

It was still dark, for the sun gets up very late a few weeks before Christmas even in countries where there is no ice or snow, and where the flowers bloom all through the year. But soon the sky began to grow pink in the east and at last the sun popped up behind a mountain.

Very soon after, they saw Pouget perched up on its hill. All the old towns are on the tops of hills in the country of Provence, that part of France where Tonino lived. They were built there so that the watchmen on the city walls in the old days could see the enemy approaching and close the gates and give warning to all the men of the town.

Tonino was very much interested, because he had never seen any other town before. Nouvilo was built on such a high and steep hill that Tonino had never been to *any* other town yet. It might have been easy to go down into the valley, but think of the tremendous climb to get up again!

The hill on which Pouget was built was not very high, and Louiset did not have to stop to rest very often as she pulled the cart up the winding road. Just before they reached the city gate Monsieur Nirascou told Louiset to stop, for the pottery studio with the great oven was outside the city wall.

It was a long group of low buildings that had once been a farmhouse, with its barns and outhouses. Already people were at work. There were several carts from other villages and men were unloading pottery which they had brought to be baked in the Great Fire. At a long trestle a woman was painting pots a bright yellow.

It looked like most interesting work and Tonino could not bear to tear himself away; but of course he had to help Monsieur Nirascou and two men who came out of the pottery shed to unload the pottery. It is true that the baskets were too heavy for Tonino to carry, but he had to be there in case his help was needed, so he followed Monsieur Nirascou and the two men into the building.

First they passed through one big room where Tonino just caught a glimpse of a man doing most fascinating things with lumps of clay, then down a passage which became hotter and hotter until they came to a large room—and one whole side of the room was an enormous furnace and oven. All around on the ground were baskets filled with pottery and two men were placing the little bowls and cooking pots and jugs and cups and saucers on big tiles, which they then pushed into the huge oven that had shelves all the way up, wide enough to hold the tiles.

When all Monsieur Nirascou's pottery had been unloaded and carried into the room of the Great Fire, Monsieur Nirascou said to Tonino: "I am going out for an hour as I have business in the town; if you like, you can come with me and I will give you a syrup to drink at the café, or you can stay here and watch the men at work."

But Tonino chose to stay and find out exactly what everybody was doing, in spite of the delicious syrup that he would miss.

He soon went back into the first room, where he had seen the man working with clay, and he found that it was the most interesting thing that he had ever seen in his life. It was Monsieur Vernandou, the master potter, who was working here. He was sitting at what, at first glance, looked like a round table. When Tonino came nearer he saw that the table was really a solid wheel, and in the middle of the wheel there was what looked like a table leg that joined a lower wheel to the top wheel.

Monsieur Vernandou put his foot on the lower wheel and pushed it so that both wheels spun round and round, and—what do you think? The lump of clay which he had placed on the middle of the top wheel began to get smooth and round; and, though he hardly seemed to touch it, the clay began to grow till it became the shape of a cooking pot. Then, as the pot whirled round and round, he put his hand into it and with a broken piece of pottery he scooped it out so that the cooking pot became round and smooth inside. And all the time it was turning and becoming rounder and smoother. At last the potter stopped the wheel, and there stood a beautiful pot.

It was very soft, as it was made of soft clay; and of course, as the clay is very sticky, the pot was stuck fast. But the master potter took a piece of string and passed it under the pot to loosen it from the wheel. Then he lifted it ever so gently onto a long plank which stood on trestles beside the wheel, and which was already half covered with finished pots. But the pot that Tonino had been watching was still not quite finished: the spout and the handle were still lacking.

First the master potter pinched one side of the pot with his finger and thumb, and there was a beautiful spout. Then he took a smooth little stick of clay from a row of them lying at one end of the plank, and he curved the soft stick and stuck both ends to the pot on the opposite side from the spout—and the pot was finished.

Monsieur Vernandou was called a master potter because he could make not only cups and saucers and pots and plates, but also beautiful pitchers and graceful vases. In fact he could make anything that he wanted to out of clay. Tonino thought this was the most interesting work he had ever seen and his eyes grew bigger and bigger as he watched Monsieur Vernandou take another lump of clay and put it on the wheel, and turn the bottom wheel with his foot so that both wheels whirled round and round again, and another smooth round pot began to grow before his astonished eyes.

In about three minutes it also was finished and loosened with the string and placed on the plank. Then, as soon as the spout was pinched and the handle fitted, the master potter started right in again and made another pot, and another, until the whole plank was covered with pots all exactly alike.

Tonino was thrilled; he watched everything that the potter did, how he worked his feet to make the wheel turn round, and how he hollowed the pot out with his thumb and smoothed it with a broken piece of tile even as the pot was turning round and round. And as he watched all these things Tonino became sure that, if only he could try, he could make a pot himself on that fascinating wheel.

At last, when the master potter had made seven pots, one right after another, and the plank was full of smooth round pots, he stopped and said to Tonino: "You have been watching me a long time now, so you must know exactly how it is done. How would you like to have a try yourself?"

Tonino said: "Oh! I would like to make something on that wheel more than anything in the world!"

Monsieur Vernandou said, "A pot is rather a ticklish thing for a beginner, but just you watch while I make a cup for you, and see if you can make one for yourself."

He took a smaller lump of clay and put it on the wheel and worked his foot in just the same way as when he was making big pots, and soon the little lump of clay was turned into a little shallow round bowl. As it whirled round he sliced off the irregular top of the bowl with the broken piece of pottery.

"Some potters nowadays," said Monsieur Vernandou, "use all sorts of tools, a different one for everything they want to do. But I find I can do everything better with a broken piece of rounded pottery. That is what my grandfather used, and he taught me when I was about your age, and *he* was a better potter than any man living now."

Then Monsieur Vernandou loosened the cup from the wheel and placed it on the end of the plank. He took a tiny piece of clay which he rolled round between his fingers and curved into the shape of a handle, and he fastened it to the shallow little bowl—and there was the cup all complete!

Next the master potter invited Tonino to sit in his seat in front of the wheel, and, as it was too low for Tonino, he put a box on it to make it higher. He handed Tonino a ball of clay and told him to round it out inside with his thumb when the wheel turned. Of course Tonino could not turn the wheel himself; his legs were not nearly long enough to reach the lower wheel. So the master potter turned it for him; and, as it turned round faster and faster, the cup began to grow round and smooth.

But suddenly, Tonino must have pressed his thumb down too hard—for there was no bottom left to the cup and it caved in and left off looking like a cup at all! For a moment Tonino felt quite discouraged, but the master potter told him that no one could expect to make a perfect cup the first time. "My grandfather showed me again and again before I made a cup that was fit to be fired!" said he.

He rolled the clay up into a ball again and, as he stood at the wheel, he turned it and made another perfect cup while Tonino watched him so closely that he hardly breathed. The next time Tonino tried he was much more successful. It was not until he began to smooth out the cup with the broken piece of pottery that he spoiled his second cup. However, Tonino was not discouraged this time; he had felt the clay growing round and smooth inside as he hollowed it with his thumb.

Again the master potter made a cup and, as he finished it with the piece of broken pottery, he showed Tonino how to hold it, and the *next* time Tonino tried he really produced a cup that looked like a cup! Of course it was not all perfectly round and smooth inside and out, like the master potter's, but it was a *cup,* as anyone could see. Putting the handle on was very easy; Tonino was able to do that the first time he tried, and he took the string and passed it between the cup and the wheel and placed his cup very gently on the plank beside the cooking pots that had been made by the master potter.

Monsieur Vernandou was delighted with Tonino's cup. He said: "My boy, you have the potter's touch and the potter's eye, and that is a gift without which you can never be a master potter. When you are a big boy, come back to me and I will take you as my apprentice and teach you the secrets of my trade so that some day you shall be a master potter yourself!"

Then the kind master potter showed Tonino all around the studio, and he explained everything to him. He told him that the pots that he had made that morning must be left on the planks for days and days till they were quite dry, and then the woman that Tonino had seen in the yard would paint them a beautiful bright yellow on the outside and a reddish brown on the inside, and they would be stacked on shelves until the next time that the Great Fire should be lit. Then they would be baked till they were absolutely fireproof, and they would be packed in crates and taken to the railway and sent all over France—and some were shipped to England and even as far away as to the United States of America!

The master potter showed Tonino also the pottery that was ready to be baked, not only pots and pitchers, but pretty double salt cellars and butter dishes and cups and saucers and egg cups that had been painted by the children of Nouvilo and other small towns near by. Tonino admired them enormously and wished that he could paint well enough to do some himself.

Then the master potter gave him a large lump of clay and said: "When you get home you must try to make something interesting with this. Even without a wheel you can make little trays and salt cellars, and when they are dry you can paint them and decorate them. Perhaps Monsieur Nirascou will bring them down next time there is a Great Fire and I will have them fired for you. If they are good enough, perhaps when the agent who buys all my pottery comes around he will buy yours, too!"

Here was an idea! Tonino had already quite decided that he would be a master potter when he grew up, but now he knew that he could begin to be a potter right away. Perhaps he could not make cups and saucers and bowls without a potter's wheel, but he felt sure that he could make fascinating little trays and salt cellars like those the children of Nouvilo had decorated. He would get some paint and paint them, and later the agent would buy them. Tonino's head was full of plans. Perhaps he could learn to make such beautiful pottery that the agent would give him enough money to buy the grain to feed Tintourlet so that he need not be sold next summer after all!

Then Monsieur Nirascou came in. He had been busy loading the unpainted pottery into his cart to take back for the children of Nouvilo to decorate before the next Great Fire.

So Tonino said good-by to his kind friend, the master potter, and thanked him again and again for his kindness. Then he climbed up beside Monsieur Nirascou and off they drove, and all the way home Tonino chattered to Monsieur Nirascou about the things that he was going to make with his big lump of clay that the master potter had given him.

And he said, "Do you think I could possibly make a potter's wheel myself so that I could make bowls and cups and saucers too, like those you are taking back to Nouvilo now?"

But Monsieur Nirascou was not encouraging. He said: "I don't know. A potter's wheel would be a difficult thing to make, but there are things you can make without one. People have made pottery since the world began, and doubtless they made it before the potter's wheel was invented. I was a master potter myself and I used to work in Pouget before I hurt my arm in the war, so I can tell you a lot about it. But there is one truth, and that is that, if you really have it in you to become a master potter, you will know what to do with it as soon as you get the soft clay in your hands. If you can learn to make simple little things with your hands alone, undoubtedly one day the potter's wheel will arrive and you will own one yourself."

When Tonino got home he sat down on the hearthstone with his sister Nanou and took the lump of clay and smoothed it and molded it and pinched it. He had decided to first make a cup, but alas and alack, he could not make the cup look round and even like the cup made on the potter's wheel. It *would* bulge out on one side or the other. Nanou thought it was a beautiful cup, but Tonino was not satisfied and at last he gave it up and squeezed the clay all up in a ball again and tried to think what he should make instead of a cup.

While he was thinking he looked out of the window and saw Tintourlet and Mingonetto, each tethered to a tree, and at last he had an idea. He took a small lump of clay and he molded it and pushed it here and pulled it there. All the time he was working he looked out of the window and watched Tintourlet. At last he showed Nanou what he had done, and she was so surprised that she nearly fell over backward when she saw that Tonino had made a little figure of Tintourlet, with his big head and his long ears and his four little legs, the two front legs together and the two hind legs together, as they were not so likely to break that way.

As for Tonino, he was just as much astonished as was Nanou at the marvelous thing that he had made out of a lump of clay.

Then Nanou said, "Make Lavanda, Tonino, see if you can make Lavanda!" And Tonino looked at Lavanda, who was ambling around, nibbling the grass and enjoying herself very much indeed.

Tonino looked and looked, and all the time he was looking he was modeling the clay and smoothing it here and pinching it there until at last he had made Lavanda, with her head down nibbling the grass. And of course he did not forget her little pointed ears and her little horns; and then Tonino made a little platform of clay for Tintourlet and Lavanda to stand upon.

Then Nanou said: "Oh, Tonino, how beautiful they would look if they were painted! If Tintourlet were painted a beautiful gray and his nose white, and Lavanda were painted white with black spots, and if the grass were painted green! Why, they would look as if they were alive! Do you know that Suzetto, who is in my class, has started decorating pottery for the pottery studio at Pouget? And she has lovely paints, red and white and blue and yellow and purple and green. I wonder, if I beg her ever so hard if she would lend us a little of her paints? Perhaps she would if we were to take the figures of Tintourlet and Lavanda over to her house and show them to her!"

Tonino was delighted with this idea of Nanou's. He jumped around the room, he was so excited. "Oh, won't that be splendid! And look here, Nanou, we will put the figures in a safe place so that they can dry, because they must be absolutely dry before we can paint them. What do you think? Monsieur Nirascou has promised that the next time there is a Great Fire, he will take mine along with the other pottery and Monsieur Vernandou has promised to bake them, and then perhaps the agent who buys the master's pottery will buy mine also."

And Tonino did make pottery! But he was not satisfied to make plain cups, he modeled little animals to decorate the cups. He made other pottery, and Nanou painted them all. He found a market for all he could make and the money was more than enough to buy all the grain Tintourlet could eat. In fact, it was not long until Tintourlet was in danger of getting so fat that he would not be able to get in the stable door!

## PLOWING[1]

*Henry B. Lent*

A farmer's life is a busy one. There are so many things to do! When it gets dark at night we are always tired and ready for bed. We are having lots of fun, though, staying out here at Grindstone Farm.

One day we decide to go fishing in the brook, up near the pasture where it is good and deep. Hank makes some fishing poles for us and tells us where to find the pools where the fish bite best. We dig some worms and set out right after breakfast, with Prince trotting at our heels. In less than an hour we catch nine big speckled brook trout. We are very proud of our skill

[1] From Henry B. Lent, *Grindstone Farm.*

at fishing, especially when Mrs. Lee says that she will fix them for our supper.

Fishing is fun, but best of all we like to help with the jobs that have to be done around the farm.

Plowing is the first job every farmer has to do in the spring. The soil becomes soft enough to plow as soon as the frost is out of the ground. Each year the soil must be plowed, or turned under. This makes the crops grow better.

One morning, when Mr. Lee and Hank are loading the milk cans on the truck after the morning milking, Mr. Lee says, "Hank, I want you to go to the creamery alone this morning. I will stay here and get the tractor and plow ready for a good day's work. I want to start plowing the stubble field where we are going to plant the corn."

"All right, Mr. Lee," Hank replies. "I'll be on my way and get back to help you as soon as I can."

He starts his engine and heads out the driveway in the truck.

"Come on, boys," says Mr. Lee. "I am going over to the shop and get the tractor started."

The shop is a large building just beyond the house. Mr. Lee tells us that every modern farmer has a shop like this to keep his tools and farm machinery in.

Part of the shop is a garage for the truck, the car, and the tractor. Another part of the building is a machine shop, with all kinds of tools. This is where the men do all their repair work. There is a stove here to keep the shop warm, for in the winter and on rainy days when other farm work is slack, Mr. Lee and Hank spend a great deal of time here keeping the machinery in repair and doing odd jobs that need being done.

There are workbenches here, with vises for holding things tight. Over the workbenches are many tools: hammers, saws, chisels, planes, braces, and bits. Underneath one of the benches are kegs of nails—big nails, medium-sized nails, and small nails. There is everything you could possibly want for doing work with wood.

On another wall there are tools for fixing engines and for working with iron and steel. Wrenches of all sorts, screwdrivers, wire-snippers, and files. There is also a shelf with boxes filled with nuts, bolts, and screws.

In the corner is a big grindstone. It is not the old-fashioned kind like the one on the sign that hangs in front of Mr. Lee's farm. This one is run by a gasoline engine with a leather belt.

Next to the machine shop is the implement shed. Farm tools, such as hoes, pitchforks, spades, mowing machines, hay rakes, plows, and cultivators are all kept in this building when not in use. If farm machines are left outdoors, they soon become rusty and old, like bicycles that are left out in the rain. A good farmer keeps all his implements well oiled and protected from rain and snow.

Mr. Lee opens the big sliding door and we go into the garage part of the shop.

Here is the tractor. What a beautiful machine it is! It is shiny and clean, just the way it must have looked when it came, brand new, from the factory. You would never guess that this tractor was two years old! Mr. Lee certainly has taken good care of it.

The four wheels are painted a bright red. There are steel ridges on the outside of the two big rear wheels, so that they can dig into the ground for more power. The engine is at the front. There is a seat and a steering wheel, too. There is nothing very fancy about a tractor. It is built for doing hard work.

"Isn't she a beauty, boys?" exclaims Mr. Lee. "Yes, sir! She is a regular little whirlwind for pep and power! You'd be surprised to know how much work this tractor can do, and how many different kinds of jobs. I use it to plow my fields, cultivate them, plant them, and then to harvest the crops. It is very useful for getting in the hay, grinding feed, sawing wood, pulling stumps, loading corn stalks into the silo, digging potatoes, and hauling the wagon and manure-spreader. It is never too hot for this *iron* horse, and the flies don't bother it at all!"

He laughs at his little joke.

"Of course, I use my team of horses for a great many jobs," he adds. "But when there is a good day's work to be done, give me the tractor!"

He looks at the gasoline gauge.

"Full."

He checks the oil.

"O.K."

Last of all, he unscrews the radiator cap to see if there is plenty of water.

"Even a tractor has to have a drink before it will work," he says.

He pours in a little more water. Now the radiator is full.

"I guess we're all set," he says as he bends down to grab the crank.

"As soon as she starts," he says, "you pull the throttle down a little so she won't stall."

Mr. Lee lifts up the crank with a quick jerk.

*Pfft! Pfft!* Nothing happens.

Once again he turns the crank.

*Pfft! Pop! Pop! Brrr!* There she goes! We pull the throttle open a little wider. The powerful engine is roaring away in fine style now.

"I'll drive her around to the implement shed, and hitch the plow on," Mr. Lee says.

He climbs up into the driver's seat, shifts into reverse, and backs the tractor out of the garage. We run ahead and open the door of the implement shed so that he can get out the plow.

"This is the plow we will use today," he says, as he climbs down off the tractor and comes into the shed. "This is what we call a two-bottom stubble plow."

He shows us how a plow is built, so that it pushes into the soil and turns it over as the tractor pulls it along. The front part of the plow is pointed. It is called a plowshare. This is the "business-end" of the plow. Another important part of the plow is the moldboard. This smooth steel part is curved, so that the soil slides over it and turns over as the plow passes.

Because this plow has two bottoms, it plows two furrows at a time, instead of just one. This saves a lot of time.

Mr. Lee backs the tractor up and bolts the big plow onto the rear. When the plow is fastened to the tractor there is a long lever that sticks up by the driver's seat. We ask Mr. Lee what it is for.

"This lever lifts the plow-bottoms so that they cannot dig into the ground," he replies. He pulls it to show us what happens.

"Now, you see, I can drive out to the field without letting the plows dig into the soil until I get there."

That is a good idea, we think. Mrs. Lee would not like it very much if we were to plow two deep furrows across the yard and all the way from the farmhouse to the field that we are going to plow!

Mr. Lee climbs into the driver's seat again.

"Well, here we go," he says.

He puts the tractor into gear and steers it down the lane to the field. We walk along behind.

Here comes Hank in the truck.

"I'll be right out there with you, Mr. Lee," he calls.

"All right, Hank," replies Mr. Lee. "I will start the plowing and turn it over to you when you come out."

The lane to the stubble field runs back of the truck garden. We run ahead and take down the fence bars that keep the cows out of the field. Just as we get the last rail down, Mr. Lee drives up with the tractor and turns into the field.

"Now then," he says, "I am going to start at this end of the field and plow around it, toward the middle, two furrows at a time."

He points the tractor so that it will plow a straight line, right down to the other end of the field. He releases the lever and points of the plow-bottoms dig down into the soil. He shifts into gear and starts off, with a wave of his hand. He gives the powerful little tractor plenty of gas. Puffing and snorting, it pulls the big double plow behind it. The earth curls back over the moldboards and drops flat into two neat straight furrows.

Now he is almost down at the far end of the field. With a quick twist of the steering wheel he turns the tractor around the corner.

When he has gone around the whole field once, he shifts into neutral and climbs down to talk to us.

"Hank is coming now. I will let him finish the job."

Hank walks over to the tractor.

"You take it now, Hank," Mr. Lee says. "Keep plugging away. The tractor is running like a top!"

"O.K., Mr. Lee," Hank replies. He climbs up into the driver's seat and starts off.

"It will take us about three days to plow this field," Mr. Lee explains. "Even with two plow-bottoms, it is hard to plow more than seven or eight acres a day. Now, boys, you may stay here and watch Hank, or you may come with me, if you want to. I am going to hitch up the team to the small sulky plow and get busy on the truck garden."

We tell Mr. Lee that we would like to watch him plow with the horses.

"That's fine," he says. "I will let you ride on their backs, and, if you think you are strong enough, I may even let you ride the plow."

That will be great!

The two horses, Dick and Tom, whinny when we come into the stable. Dick rubs his nose against Mr. Lee's coat. He knows that sometimes there is a lump of sugar there for them both.

"These horses are both Percherons," he tells us, as he starts to put on their heavy collars and work harness. Percherons are very big horses. Dick and Tom are both colored a dappled gray. Their muscles bulge out on their shoulders and legs. They are just about the biggest work horses we have ever seen!

"Percherons are big and strong," Mr. Lee says. "They are fast workers, too, and hardly ever get tired."

He lets us hold the reins and drive the team around to the implement shed where the sulky plow is kept. The sulky plow is not as big as the two-bottom plow that we fastened to the tractor. It has only one plow-bottom. There is a seat for the driver to sit on. It has a lever, too, for raising the plow off the ground.

We help Mr. Lee put the long wooden shaft between the two horses and hitch the traces to the whippletree.

Mr. Lee climbs onto the seat of the sulky plow and clucks to the horses. "Giddap, Tom! Dick!" and off we go to the truck garden, just beyond the house.

The truck garden is where Mr. Lee raises all his vegetables for market. The garden must be plowed every spring, to get the soil in good condition for the seeds that will soon be planted.

Before he starts plowing, Mr. Lee takes a soft brick from the tool kit fastened on the shaft of the plow.

"I want to scour the moldboard of the plow so that the dirt will slide off more easily," he says.

After he has rubbed it smooth and shiny, he climbs back on the seat and pulls the lever that drops the plow down ready to work. Dick and Tom brace their hind legs and start pulling the plow in a straight line along the edge of the field, close to the fence. The going is much easier here than it was in the stubble field. The soil is soft and rich, and turns easily when the plow runs through it.

When Mr. Lee reaches the end of the garden he turns to the left without stopping, and plows along the end of the field. Then he comes back down the other side. When he gets back to where we are standing, he has made a furrow all around the outside edge of the big garden.

"This is a good way to plow a field," he says. "It really saves time, because I do not have to stop and turn the team around at the end of each furrow. We just keep going, around and around the field, working toward the center. Each trip around is a little shorter than the time before, because we are always getting closer to the middle of the field."

This time around he lets us ride on Tom's back. He is such a tall horse that we cannot climb up, and there is no big stone or stump to stand on.

"Here," says Mr. Lee. "Just step on the shaft of the plow and walk right up. Then you can easily climb onto his back. Don't be afraid. Tom is very gentle. These horses never kick."

Up we go, right between the two big horses. Now it is easy to climb on. Tom's back is so broad that two or three people could ride on his back at the same time, the way the bareback riders do in the circus.

After this second trip around the outer edge of the field there are two furrows instead of just one. Mr. Lee stops to tighten up one of the traces.

"Would you like to try plowing?" he asks.

You bet we would!

"All right," he says. "Sit in the seat. Now hold the reins loosely in your hand. Dick and Tom don't really need to be driven when they are plowing. They are old-timers at this work. They know enough to follow the furrow. Now pull the lever and drop the plow-bottom down."

There it goes.

"Giddap, Tom! Giddap, Dick!"

It is not an easy job to sit on a sulky plow. It jerks quite a bit. When we come to the corner of the field we pull the left rein a little. Tom and Dick turn the corner without stopping. They are very smart horses. Dick walks right in the furrow, so that each new furrow is perfectly straight.

It is great fun to plow a field. The brown earth smells so good!

## BRIDGET GOES PROSPECTING[1]

*Berta* and *Elmer Hader*

Boone McBride whistled merrily as he led his new burro back to camp. His luck must be changing. To have bought such a fine young animal was good fortune indeed.

The next day the little burro carried a prospector's kit on her back. The pack was not heavy and she liked to be always on the move. She watched her master curiously as he chipped bits of rock off the ledges, while they wandered over the rugged mountain sides. Boone McBride was kind and gentle, and she trusted him. Though she balked at leading the way across some of the streams they came to, her master never lost his temper.

Day after day they plodded northward. Sometimes the trail was overgrown and McBride led the way. Sometimes the burro pushed on ahead, stopping from time to time to look around and see that her master was following. Days and weeks passed happily.

One day the trail they were following cut across some deep wagon ruts. McBride stopped. He had not seen anyone for weeks, and knew that a rancher named O'Shea had taken up a homestead here some years before. He and his wife and two children were the only people in the valley, their nearest neighbor was forty miles away. It was two years since Boone had seen the O'Sheas and he knew he would be welcome.

Boone turned from the trail and followed the wagon tracks. The ranch house stood in a small clearing. Its unpainted wood was a weather-beaten gray.

A dog barked as they drew near the house. A little girl about six years old stood on the porch and stared in amazement at Boone McBride and his burro, then in a wink she disappeared into the house. Before Boone had come much nearer, Brian O'Shea and his wife stood in the doorway with wide, welcoming smiles. The little girl peeked shyly from behind her mother's dress. The dog looked at the visitors suspiciously, but he stopped barking and his tail almost wagged. The burro kept an eye on the dog.

"Sure and it's me that said only this morning, Mary, it's high time Boone Mc-

[1] From Berta and Elmer Hader, *Midget and Bridget.*

Bride came this way. And here you are. And have you found that rich mine and—But come in, man, and rest your weary bones. Here am I asking a lot of fool questions of you." O'Shea stopped talking and helped untie the knots in the pack rope.

Boone took his pack from the back of the patient burro and turned her loose in the corral back of the house. But as soon as he left her she went into the barn to see what she could find.

Boone returned to the house to answer the many questions he knew would be asked. The O'Sheas lived so far away that they seldom had a visitor. Mrs. O'Shea, fresh and pretty, seemed just a girl. It was hard for her to be living so far from people. Their home was humble, their comforts few, but what they had they gladly shared. Boone told them all the friendly gossip he had picked up along his path.

The little girl, too, had a question and piped up in her tiny voice, "What's his name?"

"That is Mr. McBride, honey," answered her mother.

"I . . . I meant the little horsey's name," said the child.

"That little horsey is a burro," chuckled McBride. "Well . . . well now, that reminds me. I have never given her a name yet. Let me think. What shall I call her? I have had many burros. There was Chiquita and Pancho and Carlos and Sacramento and Bolivar." Boone counted them one by one on his fingers. "What would you name her?"

The little girl hung her head. "I don't know many names. Do you think she would like Bridget? That's my name."

"Splendid. It's a grand name and I'm sure she will be proud to have it. Bridget the burro shall be. Bring a pail of water and we'll christen her this minute."

In great glee the child fetched a pail of water and went with Boone to the barn. She sprinkled a few drops of water on the surprised little burro's nose while Boone said, "It's Bridget from now on you are. I hope you never bring disgrace on the fair name of Bridget. Here's a nice cool drink for you." Boone put the pail on the ground.

The burro drank the water gratefully. She looked at Boone and she looked at the little girl. Bridget was a nice name. Boone tied her in the corner stall.

When they returned to the house, little Danny O'Shea had given up chasing butterflies and grasshoppers because he was hungry and it must be nearly time for lunch. His sun-tanned face and sun-bleached hair showed very plainly that he spent as much time as possible out of doors.

"Hello, Mr. McBride," he said cheerily. "When did you come? I didn't see you." Danny was nine years old and remembered Boone's last visit with pleasure. He had been made rich then by a fine top and a bag of marbles, and now he could not help glancing at the pack lying on the porch.

"Can I help you in with the pack?" he asked Boone.

"Well, it is a pretty heavy pack for one man to manage all alone," said Boone. "Give me a hand, Danny, and we'll get it inside."

Danny felt very helpful as he picked up one end of the roll. It did not seem so heavy to him.

Bridget soon slipped outside again to see her namesake. She liked animals but was a little afraid of Tom and Ben, the work horses, because they were so big. Bess, the cow, was gentle as could be, but she looked very dangerous when she shook her horns or stretched her neck and mooed loudly. Bridget liked the burro because she was so small and looked so gentle. But as she entered the barn she heard a loud "hee-haw" which so startled her that she dropped the handful of grass she had gathered for the burro and ran back to the house.

"Bridget's making awful noises, Mr. McBride," she gasped.

Boone smiled. "I thought I heard her calling me," he said.

Boone and the children went to the barn. The burro brayed again.

"Burros know what is good for them," said Boone. "She wants to be out of doors as long as there is any sun." He untied the halter and led the burro outside, turning her loose in the small inclosed field with Bess, the cow.

"Animals are like people," said Boone. "They get lonesome with no one to talk to. If I didn't have my little burro, I would get very lonesome, too. Sometimes I don't have anyone else to talk to for weeks at a time."

"Gee," said Danny. "I never knew burros could talk. Daddy always said they were stupid."

"Stupid!" exclaimed Boone. "Why, many of those little animals are smarter than their owners and better prospectors, too. Why, I know a burro that found a rich mine for his owner."

"Gosh, Mr. McBride! Do you think your burro will find you a mountain of gold?"

"Maybe," said Boone. "I wouldn't be at all surprised if she did."

Boone stayed a week with the O'Sheas. Before leaving he unwrapped some mysterious parcels he had been carrying. Tobacco for his host and a bottle of perfume for Mrs. O'Shea. He opened a box and drew out a lovely little doll for rosy-cheeked Bridget. He handed little Danny a box of water colors and a pad of drawing paper.

"I noticed that you liked to make pictures the last time I was here," he said.

Stammering their thanks the children ran outside to examine their gifts.

It was with real regret that the rancher and his wife watched Boone's broad shoulders disappear as he followed his little burro around the bend in the road.

Boone was much farther north than he liked to be when the cool days and chill nights of late October told him it was time he headed for the warm desert lands.

Slowly they made their way south. Boone stopped to see his friend, big John Carlson, a miner, who lived in the mountains the year round.

Big John was disappointed that Boone was not staying for the winter. He pointed to the calendar and warned Boone of the danger of getting caught by a blizzard in the mountains.

"Don't be crazy, man," he said. "The snow will come any day. My nearest neighbors to the south are the Moystons. We haven't heard from them in a long time, but I think they are still homesteading. They are a good sixty miles from here, and most of the way is high in the mountains."

Boone had made up his mind to winter on the desert, and much against the pleadings of his friend he started south. He knew the trail and if a snow flurry did come, what of it? It would only be a light fall, no doubt, and he would soon be out of it.

Bridget was sorry when Boone threw the pack saddle on her back, for Dynamite, Carlson's burro, was good company. But when she found she was headed for the desert she hurried along the trail.

Boone made camp the third night and thanked his lucky stars that one more day would find them at the Moystons'. Bridget stayed near the camp fire eating the green grass contentedly.

Her soft muzzle in his face awakened him at dawn. The little burro seemed uneasy. She sensed danger. A great stillness hung over everything. Dark clouds filled the sky to the north. In a few minutes the pack was on Bridget's back and they hit the trail. Once through the pass in the mountains they would be safe. The Moystons lived in a sheltered valley at the foot of the next ridge. They pushed onward. Upward they climbed. The sky grew blacker, sometimes it was so dark in the woods it was hard to see the trail. Then it started to snow. The air became thicker and thicker with the falling snowflakes.

They could no longer see the trail, but Boone had been over it many times before and there were plenty of markers. He had blazed trees and chipped guiding signs on rocky ledges. They trudged onward and upward through the snow. Their only chance lay straight ahead. They must reach the pass. The snowstorm had become a blizzard. There was no turning back now.

"Now we are in for it and no mistake, old girl," said Boone aloud.

Bridget didn't like the snow blowing in her eyes and ears, but she plodded steadily along after her master. The wind howled and shrieked about them while snow piled up in high drifts.

Boone patted his little burro's drooping head. "I'll make it easier for you," he said, as he untied his pack from her back and placed it at the foot of a large hemlock.

Leading Bridget, Boone pushed on. The biting wind cut through his heavy garments and chilled him to the bone. He felt numb, but to stop now meant certain death. He staggered along, and Bridget struggled after him. They rounded a great scarred rock on the mountain side. The wind calmed down.

They were through the pass at last. Boone was exhausted. He stumbled and fell. He lay quiet in the soft snow. Bridget nudged him gently with her nose. Boone didn't move. Bridget bumped him harder, and Boone struggled to his feet. He grasped the burro's short mane. He must depend on his little pal to find the way down the mountain.

Bridget, too, was tired from the long strain, but she pushed on. Boone somehow managed to get on the burro's back. His head fell forward, and he clasped his hands as tight as he could around the burro's short little neck.

Bridget moved slowly and carefully down the trail. Sure-footed though she was, there were times when she hesitated. A misstep would send her master and herself hurtling down the mountain side.

Slowly but steadily they descended the mountain. Down, down, always down. Through drift after drift she plunged with her precious burden. Bridget was tired, so very tired she felt she could not go much farther. Then she saw a glow of light through the gray mist of falling snow. She knew that where there was a light most likely there was a man, too. At last she came to the house. She heard voices. She threw back her head and uttered a feeble bray, and then she waited. Why didn't they come? She moved nearer the house and brayed again.

Jerry Moyston and his wife Jill stopped talking and looked at each other. Could it be possible that they heard the braying of a burro outside their door—faintly at first, then loud and hoarse?

"Sounds like a Rocky Mountain canary, Jill," said Jerry. "But what could he be doing outside in this sort of weather?" He opened the door and looked out.

Through the blinding storm he saw the little gray burro standing knee-deep in snow. And there was something that looked like a man on her back. Jerry could hardly believe his eyes. He dashed out into the snow and lifted the unconscious Boone McBride from the little burro's back. With his wife's help he got Boone into the ranch house. They put him on a couch in the corner.

"It's Boone McBride, Jill, and he's almost frozen to death. Make him a hot drink while I try and warm him up. I think he'll come out of it all right."

It was some time before Boone realized where he was. His first question was, "Where's Bridget, my burro?"

"I'll take care of her, now that you are all right," said Jerry. He put on his great coat and fur hat and went out. The burro was gone, but he followed the tracks in the snow. They led to the sheltered side of the house where the little burro stood close to the wall. Her head and her long ears drooped, she was exhausted.

"It's a medal you deserve for this deed, little burro," said Jerry. "I don't know how you ever found your way here." He patted her forehead encouragingly. "Come along, I'll put you in the barn out of the wind. You rest a while and I'll bring you a nice warm mash that will make you as good as new." Jerry led tired Bridget to the warm barn and put her in a stall next to Comanche, his pinto cow pony.

Bridget was too tired to lie down on the

soft straw, but she closed her eyes. She hoped her master was all right now that she had found his friends. A little later Jerry returned with a pan of warm mash.

"Stow that away, ol' girl, and in the morning you will never know what a bad time you have been through." Jerry rubbed her nose gently and left the barn. The pinto pony looked at Bridget but asked no questions.

Bridget ate the warm mash. Then she lay down and slept.

The next day was bright and clear. The sun shone hotly down on the snow-covered hills. The countryside was white as far as you could see. The snow melted fast and Jerry rode his pinto pony back over the trail and found Boone's pack.

Boone McBride was as good as ever after a few days' rest. As for Bridget, the one night's rest was all she needed and she was ready to start on the trail the next morning. A day or so later Boone thanked his friends and again took to the trail. He had enjoyed his stay with the Moystons, but he was anxious to get started for he still had a long way to go.

When the heavy snows of winter blocked the roads and trails, Boone and Bridget were safely out of the snow country and slowly making their way across the sunny desert.

## THE FRENCH JONGLEURS[1]

*Katharine Gibson*

Long before the days of theaters, plays were sometimes given in churches to honor the Virgin or the saints. Such plays were religious, and were called miracle or morality plays. Those which were not religious were acted, in very early times, along the streets or in the open fields near some town or village. Curious performances were also given on the roadside by wandering bands of men and women called, in France, *"les jongleurs."* The jongleurs were not quite actors, nor yet minstrels, because they did not devote all their time to singing or to learning one part after another. They were perhaps more nearly the ancestors of our modern circus clown. They played tricks, juggled, trained animals, whistled, and danced; but unlike the clown they told many tales, and did much more than just make jokes. Sometimes their stories were quite serious. The jongleurs were proud of what they had to do, and proud of the cleverest in their bands.

They wandered over rough roads, stopping in villages or in quaint, walled towns where the streets were so narrow that the roofs of the houses nearly touched in friendly greeting. Their life was a hard one, full of weariness and uncertainty. Like gypsies they often had no place where they could sleep. Often there was little food, and in winter it was hard to keep warm. Yet they were merry, with the wide freedom of the skies and the laughter of men and women and the eager questions of little children to keep them company everywhere.

The jongleur was often an acrobat. He could stand on his head, walk on his hands, turn cartwheels, and he really preferred back somersaults to front ones. He carried tin swords and tasseled caps in his pack and often a tame rabbit or a trick crow. He was always followed by a dog that could dance on its hind legs, play dead, and jump through a hoop as easily as it could gnaw a bone. The jongleur was a bright-colored fellow, yellow, red, green, blue; and he jingled when he walked, with little bells; and he whistled when he talked, with a silver whistle or a reed pipe. He knew rhymes for every word, could make verses as he ran, and tell stories while he kept five balls whirling through the air.

It was the jongleur that kept people from forgetting many of the fine old tales, for there were no books in those days. Later, when there was printing, the tales of the jongleurs were put into books and we may read the books today.

[1] From Katharine Gibson, *The Golden Bird.*

## BEHIND THE BATTLEMENTS[1]

*Gertrude Hartman*

Inside the outer protecting wall of a medieval castle were a number of buildings, for a castle had to house many people. There were the stables for the horses, rough quarters for the grooms and hostlers, and barracks for the men-at-arms. There, also, were the shops of the armorers, the smith, the carpenter, and other workmen, and the little chapel where the lord and his family attended daily mass. Beyond the first courtyard was another stone wall protecting the inner courtyard and buildings.

The most important room in the castle was the hall, for it was the common meeting room of the household. It was a large rectangular room, loftly and spacious. The walls were of paneled wood or of gray stone, unplastered and rough. The floor, too, was flagged with great stones. Instead of a ceiling there were usually rafters of solid oak, often richly carved and ornamented in color. The windows of the finest halls were filled with beautiful stained glass, but in the dwellings of the less wealthy the glass was coarse and greenish and made in small round pieces, for glass in those days was too rare and expensive for ordinary use. At the end of the room was a big stone hearth where huge logs could be piled, to burn with cheerful blaze and warm the people during the long cold winter months.

In the early centuries carpets and rugs were rare. The floors were usually covered with rushes, which were fragrant and pleasant while they were fresh, but which in time often became dry and dirty. Shields and clusters of lances were hung on the walls. Other spaces were adorned with antlers and the heads of wild boar, while from the beams of the roof hung gay banners emblazoned with the coat of arms of the lord of the castle. In the fourteenth century the bare stone walls were often covered with tapestry, rich in color and design, on which were woven various scenes from history or a favorite romance of the times. These hangings brought warmth and beauty into the halls.

During the earlier centuries of the Middle Ages the hall served as living, dining, and sleeping place for everyone, with recesses used as retiring places by the family. But as people became more civilized the halls came to be used only for public functions, while the family of the lord lived in a more private apartment adjoining it.

A medieval bedroom lacked many of our modern conveniences, but it was beautiful. The floor was inlaid with checkered tiles, and the leaded windows were gay with heraldic glass. There was usually not much furniture in it—one or two chairs, with high carved back and arms; a small table; a footstool covered with silk; an oaken cupboard. The most striking piece of furniture was the bed. It was a stately four-poster, set in an alcove and canopied with beautiful curtains of damask or brocade, which could be drawn around to inclose it entirely, to keep out drafts. At the foot of the bed was a huge chest richly ornamented and carved with the emblem of the owner, in which clothes were kept. On the wall near one of the windows was a large crucifix of carved wood. Before it the lord and lady knelt on red silk cushions each night and morning to say their prayers.

In the lady's bower the lord's wife, with her handmaidens and numerous servingwomen, spent most of her time directing the spinning, weaving, embroidering and sewing, caring for her children, and managing the daily work of her big household. In addition she had her social duties, the most important of which were acting as a gracious hostess to guests, nursing wounded knights, and training pages in the ways of chivalry. A girl of the Middle Ages was taught the things a medieval lady was supposed to know. She learned to sing and to play accompaniments on some musical instrument. She must ride well. She must be skilled in needlework. She must know how to be beautiful at tournaments and other ceremonial occasions.

[1] From Gertrude Hartman, *Medieval Days and Ways.*

It was in the hall that the whole household gathered at mealtimes. Across one end of it was a platform—or dais—raised a step or two above the main floor, on which a high table was placed. In the center of the side near the wall was the seat for the lord, sometimes raised on a throne or an especially built high chair. His family and most honored guests were placed on each side of him, facing the rest of the company. No one was placed on the opposite side of the table. It was left entirely open so that the lord and his guests might see and be seen by the rest of the company. The other tables, long and narrow, were arranged down the whole length of the hall at right angles to the lord's table, with long benches along each side.

At one end of the hall was a passageway leading to the kitchen. Sometimes this was a near-by building separate from the hall. It was a large vaulted room, perhaps a hundred feet long, the headquarters for the servants, where a great deal of work had to be carried on. It had big ovens for baking and huge open fireplaces, where whole deer or sheep could be hung on spits and turned before the fire. Immense copper cauldrons hung over the fireplaces. There were large tables with solid oak tops, and on the walls hung many utensils—ladles, strainers, graters, saucepans, and so on.

Preparing the meals for a big house, with its many inmates and guests, was no easy matter, and the chief cook was a very important member of the household. His responsibilities were many. He had to provide all kinds of elaborate dishes and fancy table decorations. He must know how to make many complicated soups, stews, sauces, and desserts. He ruled over dozens of lesser cooks and scullions, for the richer households had from fifty to a hundred servants to cook and clean. As a mark of his office, he carried a large wooden spoon, which he used for testing the soups and other dishes and also for chastising those who failed to obey his orders.

Dinner at a rich nobleman's house might include as many as ten or twelve courses, mostly meat, game, and fish, finished off with a quantity of rich pastries and sweetmeats. When it was in preparation the kitchen presented a busy scene and was fragrant with appetizing odors, as the cooks and bakers employed all their art in preparing a variety of fancy dishes, and scullions ran about turning the meats on the spits or blowing up the fires with bellows.

Today we can scarcely appreciate the fondness of the medieval people for spices. Not only meat, but cake, bread, and wine were spiced. Every large household kept a store of spices, which were very expensive, and the "spicery" was superintended by a person whose duty it was to give out the proper quantities of these choice ingredients to the cooks.

Pastries made of chickens, grouse, pigeons, and other meats were often elaborate masterpieces of the cook's art.

Sometimes a cook would surprise his lord by making a huge pie full of little live birds, which fluttered out and flew high up in the air when the crust was cut open.

The usual time for dinner was ten or eleven o'clock in the morning. At that time trestles were brought in and tables arranged along the walls. The rich nobles prided themselves on their gold and silver plate, and silver dishes, cups, and tankards wrought with curious devices glistened on their tables; but in the houses of the less wealthy dishes were often made of wood or pewter. The huge saltcellar was the chief ornament of the table. It was usually of silver and was made in some ornamental shape, sometimes in the form of a stag or some other favorite animal. It had a very important significance, marking the division between the seats of people of rank and those of the common people.

Only knives and spoons were used in eating. Forks did not come into use until quite late in the Middle Ages. Because of the lack of forks there was no easy way of cutting the meat on the plate, so the cutting was done by the carver, who served the meat in small pieces to be taken up with the fingers or on a piece of bread.

Soft food was eaten with a spoon. Only one plate and drinking cup was placed for every two people, and it was always a courtesy for a knight and a lady to share the plate and cup.

As soon as the lord entered the hall a horn was sounded, and servitors brought in pitchers, basins, and napkins. Squires and small pages carried them around to the company, who washed their hands before they sat down to dinner. Then the guests were conducted to their seats at the tables, the places being very strictly assigned according to rank. Those to whom special honor was due were seated nearest the lord's table, the common folk were placed "below the salt," and the servants at the farthest end of the tables.

A burst of trumpets announced that all were seated; then the master cook entered, closely followed by other servants, bearing huge dishes of smoking viands which were duly presented to everyone in the order of his importance. Soon the tables were groaning under great quantities of food, as the stalwart serving men carried in course after course from the kitchen.

As there were no napkins, the much-needed basins, pitchers, and towels were passed around again after the meal. Then the guests left the tables, some to stroll in the garden. Young knights and ladies loved the open air and the bright sunshine. They would often spend whole afternoons in the pretty walled gardens of the castles, weaving garlands of flowers or conversing in the shade of the trees.

Supper was served at five in the afternoon. At supper the table was adorned with candlesticks of artistic design, but as these were often insufficient to light up the hall, servants sometimes held torches in their hands throughout the meal.

The nobility delighted in giving feasts. Almost any event afforded an excuse for a banquet, and special holidays like Easter, Christmas, Twelfth Night, all were celebrated with elaborate feasts. On such occasions a gay company would gather. The ladies were richly appareled in long robes of beautifully hued silk from the looms of old Cathay, some wrought with gold and silver thread, with long floating sleeves and richly embroidered girdles. The gentlemen were scarcely less brilliant in their long cloaks with rich fur at the neck and wrists, their varicolored hose and long pointed crimson shoes, with heavy gold chains around their necks and jeweled rings on their fingers. Then the old hall, with its timbered rafters from which gay banners hung, its tapestry-hung walls, its stained-glass windows, its tables glittering with gold and silver plate, and many tall tapering candles throwing a mellow light over everything, made indeed a splendid picture.

## BUCK, THE LEAD-DOG[1]

*Jack London*

"Eh? Wot I say? I spik true w'en I say dat Buck two devils."

This was Francois's speech next morning when he discovered Spitz missing and Buck covered with wounds. He drew him to the fire and by its light pointed them out.

"Dat Spitz fight lak devil, too," said Perrault, as he surveyed the gaping rips and cuts.

"But dat Buck fight lak two devils," was Francois's answer. "An' now we make good time. No more Spitz, no more trouble, sure."

While Perrault packed the camp outfit and loaded the sled, the dog-driver proceeded to harness the dogs. Buck trotted up to the place Spitz would have occupied as leader; but Francois, not noticing him, brought Sol-leks to the coveted position. In his judgment, Sol-leks was the best lead-dog left. Buck sprang upon Sol-leks in a fury, driving him back and standing in his place.

"Eh? eh?" Francois cried, slapping his thighs gleefully. "Look at dat Buck. Heem keel dat Spitz, heem t'ink to take de job."

[1] From Jack London, *The Call of the Wild.*

"Go 'way, Chook!" he cried, but Buck refused to budge.

He took Buck by the scruff of the neck, and though the dog growled threateningly, dragged him to one side and replaced Sol-leks. The old dog did not like it, and showed plainly that he was afraid of Buck. Francois was obdurate, but when he turned his back, Buck again displaced Sol-leks, who was not at all unwilling to go.

Francois was angry. "Now, I feex you!" he cried, coming back with a heavy club in his hand.

Buck remembered the man in the red sweater who had beaten him, and retreated slowly; nor did he attempt to charge in when Sol-leks was once more brought forward. But he circled just beyond the range of the club, snarling with bitterness and rage; and while he circled he watched the club so as to dodge it if thrown by Francois, for he was become wise in the way of clubs.

The driver went about his work, and he called to Buck when he was ready to put him in his old place in front of Dave. Buck retreated two or three steps. Francois followed him up, whereupon he again retreated. After some time of this, Francois threw down the club, thinking that Buck feared a thrashing. But Buck was in open revolt. He wanted, not to escape a clubbing, but to have the leadership. It was his by right. He had earned it, and he would not be content with less.

Perrault took a hand. Between them they ran him about for the better part of an hour. They threw clubs at him. He dodged. They cursed him, and his fathers and mothers before him, and all his seed to come after him down to the remotest generation, and every hair of his body and drop of blood in his veins; and he answered curse with snarl and kept out of their reach. He did not try to run away, but retreated around and around the camp, advertising plainly that when his desire was met, he would come in and be good.

Francois sat down and scratched his head. Perrault looked at his watch and swore. Time was flying, and they should have been on the trail an hour gone. Francois scratched his head again. He shook it and grinned sheepishly at the courier, who shrugged his shoulders in sign that they were beaten. Then Francois went up to where Sol-leks stood and called to Buck. Buck laughed, as dogs laugh, yet kept his distance. Francois unfastened Sol-lek's traces and put him back in his old place. The team stood harnessed to the sled in an unbroken line, ready for the trail. There was no place for Buck save at the front. Once more Francois called, and once more Buck laughed and kept away.

"T'row down de club," Perrault commanded.

Francois complied, whereupon Buck trotted in, laughing triumphantly, and swung around into position at the head of the team. His traces were fastened, the sled broken out, and with both men running they dashed out on to the river trail.

Highly as the dog-driver had forevalued Buck, with his two devils, he found, while the day was yet young, that he had undervalued. At a bound Buck took up the duties of leadership; and where judgment was required, and quick thinking and quick acting, he showed himself the superior even of Spitz, of whom Francois had never seen an equal.

But it was in giving the law and making his mates live up to it, that Buck excelled. Dave and Sol-leks did not mind the change in leadership. It was none of their business. Their business was to toil, and toil mightily, in the traces. So long as that was not interfered with, they did not care what happened. Billee, the good-natured, could lead for all they cared, so long as he kept order. The rest of the team, however, had grown unruly during the last days of Spitz, and their surprise was great now that Buck proceeded to lick them into shape.

Pike, who pulled at Buck's heels, and who never put an ounce more of his weight against the breast-band than he was compelled to do, was swiftly and repeatedly shaken for loafing; and ere the first day was done he was pulling more than ever before in his life. The first night in camp, Joe, the sour one, was punished roundly—a thing that Spitz had never succeeded in doing. Buck simply smothered him by virtue of superior weight, and cut him up till he ceased snapping and began to whine for mercy.

The general tone of the team picked up immediately. It recovered its old-time solidarity, and once more the dogs leaped as one dog in the traces. At the Rink Rapids two native huskies, Teek and Koona, were added; and the celerity with which Buck broke them in took away Francois's breath.

"Nevaire such a dog as dat Buck!" he cried. "No, nevaire! Heem worth one t'ousan' dollair! Eh? Wot you say, Perrault?"

Perrault nodded. He was ahead of the record now, and gaining day by day. The trail was in excellent condition, well packed and hard, and there was no new-fallen snow with which to contend. It was not too cold. The temperature dropped to fifty below zero and remained there the whole trip. The men rode and ran by turn, and the dogs were kept on the jump, with but infrequent stoppages.

The Thirty Mile River was coated with ice, and they covered in one day going out what had taken them ten days coming in. In one run they made a sixty-mile dash from the foot of Lake Le Barge to the White Horse Rapids. Across Marsh, Tagish, and Bennett (seventy miles of lakes), they flew so fast that the man whose turn it was to run, towed behind the sled at the end of a rope. On the last night of the second week they topped White Pass and dropped down the sea slope with the lights of Skaguay and of the shipping at their feet.

It was a record run. Each day for fourteen days they had averaged forty miles. For three days Perrault and Francois threw out their chests up and down the main street of Skaguay, while the team was the constant center of a worshipful crowd of dog-busters and mushers. Then three or four western bad men aspired to clean out the town, were riddled like pepperboxes for their pains, and public interest turned to other idols. Next came official orders. Francois called Buck to him, threw his arms around him, wept over him. And that was the last of Francois and Perrault. Like other men, they passed out of Buck's life for good.

A Scotch half-breed took charge of him and his mates, and in company with a dozen other dog-teams he started back over the weary trail to Dawson. It was no light running now, nor record time, but heavy toil each day, with a heavy load behind; for this was the mail train, carrying word from the world to the men who sought gold under the shadow of the Pole.

Buck did not like it, but he bore up well to the work, taking pride in it after the manner of Dave and Sol-leks, and seeing that his mates, whether they prided in it or not, did their fair share. It was a monotonous life, operating with machine-like regularity. One day was very like another. At a certain time each morning the cooks turned out, fires were built, and breakfast was eaten. Then, while some broke camp, others harnessed the dogs, and they were under way an hour or so before the darkness fell which gave warning of dawn. At night, camp was made. Some pitched the flies, others cut firewood and pine boughs for the beds, and still others carried water or ice for the cooks. Also, the dogs were fed. To them, this was the one feature of the day, though it was good to loaf around, after the fish was eaten, for an hour or so with the other dogs, of which there were fivescore and odd. There were fierce fighters among them, but three battles with the fiercest brought Buck to mastery, so that when he bristled and showed his teeth, they got out of his way.

Best of all, perhaps, he loved to lie near the fire, hind legs crouched under him, fore legs stretched out in front, head raised, and eyes blinking dreamily at the flames. Sometimes he thought of Judge Miller's big house in the sun-kissed Santa Clara Valley, and of the cement swimming-tank, and Ysabel, the Mexican hairless, and Toots, the Japanese pug; but oftener he remembered the man who had stolen him and brought him to the Yukon, the death of Curly, the great fight with Spitz, and the good things he had eaten or would like to eat. He was not homesick. The Sunland was very dim and distant, and such memories had no power over him now.

Sometimes he dreamed and whimpered low and suppressedly, or growled softly, till the half-breed cook shouted at him, "Hey, you Buck, wake up!" Whereupon the other world would vanish and the real world come into his eyes, and he would get up and yawn and stretch.

It was a hard trip, with the mail behind them, and the heavy work wore them down. They were short of weight and in poor condition when they made Dawson, and should have had a ten days' or a week's rest at least. But in two days' time they dropped down the Yukon bank from the Barracks, loaded with letters for the outside. The dogs were tired, the drivers grumbling, and to make matters worse, it snowed every day. This meant a soft trail, greater friction on the runners, and heavier pulling for the dogs; yet the drivers were fair through it all, and did their best for the animals.

Each night the dogs were attended to first. They ate before the drivers ate, and no man sought his sleeping-robe till he had seen to the feet of the dogs he drove. Still, their strength went down. Since the beginning of the winter they had travelled eighteen hundred miles, dragging sleds the whole weary distance; and eighteen hundred miles will tell upon the life of the toughest. But they kept on. Buck stood it, keeping his mates up to their work and maintaining discipline, though he too was very tired.

Thirty days from the time it left Dawson, the Salt Water Mail, with Buck and his mates at the fore, arrived at Skaguay. They were in a wretched state, worn out and worn down. Buck's one hundred and forty pounds had dwindled to one hundred and fifteen. The rest of his mates, though lighter dogs, had relatively lost more weight than he. Pike, the malingerer, who, in his lifetime of deceit, had often successfully feigned a hurt leg, was now limping in earnest. Sol-leks was limping, and Dub was suffering from a wrenched shoulder blade.

They were all terribly footsore. No spring or rebound was left in them. Their feet fell heavily on the trail, jarring their bodies and doubling the fatigue of a day's travel. There was nothing the matter with them except that they were dead tired. It was not the dead-tiredness that comes through brief and excessive effort, from which recovery is a matter of hours; but it was the dead-tiredness that comes through the slow and prolonged strength drainage of months of toil. There was no power of recuperation left, no reserve strength to call upon. It had been all used, the last least bit of it. Every muscle, every fibre, was tired, dead tired. And there was reason for it. In less than five months they had travelled twenty-five hundred miles, during the last eighteen hundred of which they had had but five days' rest. When they arrived at Skaguay, they were apparently on their last legs. They could barely keep the traces taut, and on the down grades just managed to keep out of the way of the sled.

"Mush on, poor sore feets," the driver encouraged them as they tottered down the main street of Skaguay. "Dis is de las'. Den we get one long res'. Eh? For sure. One bully long res'."

## TALKING WIRES[1]

*Clara Lambert*

The saga of the Telephone—that sounds queer! The Telephone—it is such an everyday thing, like walls and floors and windows. But there is a tale behind each ring that is full of heroic deeds as well as service—making this instrument the story of a great adventure.

[1] From Clara Lambert, *Talking Wires.*

First of all there are many, many hands that touch, feel, and make all the parts of the telephone instrument and the wires and cables that connect it. There are lumbermen in the forests who cut trees for poles; miners who get the copper, tin, lead, gold, platinum, coal, and other minerals from the ground; girls and men in huge factories who put together parts of the instrument, or who work machines that prepare the copper wire and lead cable. There are thousands of operators who connect people; linemen who put up poles and wires and keep the avenues of communication clear; men who fight blizzards, floods, and earthquakes. Behind them all are the engineers whose inventions, planning, and careful, continuous research, bind the system into a whole. Then there are the millions of people who use the telephone every minute of the day.

Out in the lonesome places of our country some farmers fight pests with the aid of the telephone; lonely people are less lonely because of it; and operators in their small offices are often heroines. Air pilots feel safer in the air, and *are* safer with it and the radio as co-workers; newspapermen keep the telephone wires going, not only with words, but with typewritten messages and photographs. Fishing vessels at sea and travelers on the huge liners have found themselves closer to land because of the radio telephone. Last but not least, are the thousands upon thousands of calls to the "butcher, the baker, the candlestick maker," and the "hello" that is sent to someone just for the sake of hearing a voice and the news of the everyday events of uneventful lives.

From coast to coast, over hills and valleys, plains and mountains, words travel faster than any one dreamed they could in 1876. When Alexander Graham Bell sent the first telephone message over his "improvement in telegraphy"—"Mr. Watson, come here, I want you"—in that year, he speeded up the world of communication and annihilated space. It is telephone wires that extend the concerts and programs of radio into great national networks, making this huge country of tremendous spaces and scattered settlements a more closely knit community. It has brought people together. It has helped change their thinking. It has given them a greater feeling of physical security.

The saga of the Telephone is the story of people all along the line—the users and the workers.

## THE PEARL DIVER[1]

*Charles Nordhoff*

The lagoon was calm that morning, calm as an inland lake, its surface ruffled at intervals by faint catspaws from the north. Looking back toward the pass, there was no land in sight—the blue water met the sky in an unbroken line. Ahead of us, at the northern end of the atoll, the seabeach was little more than a mile away, and the thunder of the breakers was borne to our ears, now loud, now soft, on flaws of air.

My uncle stood in the stern and I sat beside him; Fatu was in the bow, Ivi and Ofai at the oars. Once or twice Fatu motioned my uncle to change his course, to avoid the coral mushrooms rising to within a few inches of the surface, but in general the depth of the lagoon varied from six to twenty fathoms. Gazing down through the blue translucent water, I could see the strange forms of growing coral far beneath us; and sometimes, as the bottom turned sandy and the water shoaled, the lagoon shaded to purest emerald green. Clad only in a scarlet *pareu,* with his bronzed back and shoulders bare, Uncle Harry was leaning over the side, gazing intently at the bottom through a water glass. He had given the word to go slowly, and the men were resting on their oars.

"This is the place," he said; "we'll anchor here and let Ofai go down for a look."

[1] From Charles Nordhoff, *The Pearl Lagoon.*

While Fatu was paying out the anchor line, I took the glass and leaned over to see what I could make out. The water was about twelve fathoms deep, and far down beneath the whaleboat's keel I could distinguish the purple coral on the floor of the lagoon. Ofai, the Rangiroa boy, was preparing himself to dive. He coiled a long cotton line in the bottom of the boat, and made fast to one end of it a thirty-pound bulb of lead, like an enormous sinker. Then he adjusted his goggles and went over the side. While he lay in the water, drawing a series of deep breaths, Fatu passed him the weight. He allowed it to sink a yard beneath him, seized the rope between the toes of one foot, and took a grip, high up on the line, with his left hand.

"Go ahead!" ordered Fatu.

The diver filled his lungs with air, grinned at us like some goggle-eyed creature of the sea, and let go the gunwale. Coil after coil of line flew over the side, and a train of bubbles rose to the surface, hissing faintly. When the line ceased to run out, Fatu pulled in the slack till it stood taut from the bottom, and made it fast to a cleat. Gazing downward through the water glass, I found that I could see Ofai dimly, in the twilight of the depths. He was swimming close to the bottom, with strange slow motions of his arms and legs; at times he stopped as if examining something, and finally—after what seemed a longer time than any man could hold his breath—I saw him approach the rope, pull himself upright, and heave strongly with one hand. He seemed to shoot upward faster than he had gone down; an instant later his head broke water and he was expelling his breath with the eerie whistling sound I was to know so well. Then he shouted—the long-drawn yodeling cry which announces a lucky dive.

"Never have I seen shell of such a size!" he exclaimed, as he handed up a great coral-encrusted oyster and came clambering over the side. "It grows everywhere—the bottom was covered as far as my eyes could see!"

My uncle was opening the oyster with the blade of his clasp knife. It was a rough, roundish thing, uncouth to the eye, and a full eight inches across. He cut the muscle, felt skillfully but vainly for pearls under the fringe, tossed the soft body overboard, and handed the shells—still attached to the hinge—to me. Craning their necks to see, the natives exclaimed with wonder. When closed, the oyster might have been mistaken for an ugly lump of coral, picked up at random on the floor of the lagoon; when open, it displayed the changing opalescent shades of mother-of-pearl, fringed with a band of gold.

"Get up the anchor," ordered Uncle Harry; "we'll try again, a hundred yards farther on."

"There would be a sensation on Tahiti," he went on, turning to me, "if you showed the traders that shell! It's worth twenty dollars a ton more than the black-lipped variety, and the books say that it produces a great many more pearls. We'll do a bit of prospecting today, mark the best places, and let the men begin diving in the morning."

We wandered on for several hours, examining the bottom at each halt and marking the more likely spots with a small buoy, moored to the coral with a few fathoms of line. By mid-afternoon, our work seemed finished—we had found more shell than our men could bring up in all the months ahead of us. Our final halt was close to the reef, and there, in about ten fathoms of water, Ofai went overboard for the last time that day.

The coral was light-colored at this place and I could see every motion of the diver beneath us. Suddenly, when he had been about a minute under water, I saw him crouch and disappear in a crevice of the rock, and an instant later a long moving shadow passed beneath the boat.

"A shark!" exclaimed Fatu. My uncle sprang to the side.

I leaned over with the rest, watching

with acute suspense to see if the shark would move away. No—he had seen Ofai and was turning back toward the deep crevice in which the diver had taken refuge. Then the shark rose toward us and we saw him clearly—longer than our boat, livid-brown and hideous. An exclamation of horror went up from the men. There seemed nothing we could do. Thirty seconds passed; Ofai had been under water a minute and a half. My uncle had reached the limits of his endurance. He spoke to Fatu sharply:

"Your goggles! That knife! The other weight!"

The shark had approached the surface again, and as he turned to go down, before any of us could utter a cry of protest Uncle Harry went over the side, plunging downward with all the impetus of the heavy leaden bulb. It was an act of the most reckless courage; for in spite of the stories one reads, men do not attack the great sharks of the South Pacific in their own element.

Half sickened with suspense, I watched what followed: a drama played out in the limpid water beneath our boat. Grasping in his right hand a keen broad-bladed knife, my uncle shot down so fast that halfway to the bottom he overtook his monstrous antagonist. The shark was still intent upon Ofai; I saw him start and turn with a sweep of his tail as the man's body struck him and the thrust of a powerful arm sent the knife deep into his side. A pink cloud of blood gushed from the wound, and at that moment I saw Ofai emerge from his hiding place, seize the rope, and bound toward the surface of the lagoon. The diver's lungs must have been nearly bursting, and he mounted the rope with desperate speed. Now he was close to my uncle. The shark had circled, turning on his side with a livid gleam of his under parts, and was coming straight at the native. The monster reared—again I saw Uncle Harry raise his arm, saw the long knife sink home and the water reddened by a cloud of blood. The respite had been enough for Ofai; his head broke water with a gasp, and before a hand could be raised to help him he had seized the gunwale and was over the side of the boat.

My uncle was in desperate straits. He had been under water nearly a minute and was still eighteen or twenty feet beneath the surface. Fatu and Ivi were brave men and devoted to him, but it would have been insanity to think of going to his rescue now. I heard Fatu's voice, unreal and far-off, shouting to the men to move to the other side of the boat; I felt the boat list, and saw, out of the corner of my eye, the gigantic figure of the mate standing on the seat beside me, bent almost double as he watched the scene below.

Uncle Harry had dropped the weight at the first attack, and now, still grasping his knife, he made for the rope and seized it with his left hand. The shark had darted away as he felt the steel for the second time, but now he was returning straight for the antagonist he seemed to recognize at last. Moving with horrid deliberation, he reared almost vertically beneath the swimmer, and opened his great jaws. My uncle stopped himself with his left hand on the rope, gathered his body together, and drove the knife into the broad rounded snout beneath him—the shark's most vulnerable point. For a moment the monster lay stunned and motionless, and in that moment Uncle Harry nearly reached the surface of the lagoon. Fatu was bent double, his hands already in the water.

Then the shark seemed to regain his senses and came rushing upward grimly. I saw the muscles of the mate's arms standing out as though cast in bronze, I saw the swimmer's goggled face within a yard of the surface, and the great fish charging with open jaws, fearfully close behind. Then the whaleboat lurched as Fatu plunged his arms deep into the water, seized my uncle and swung him up and inboard with a single mighty heave.

The shark came crashing against the side of the boat—a blow that nearly stove in the planking and started a dozen seams.

A minute passed before my uncle sat up and lifted the goggles from his eyes. "Get the oars out," he gasped, "and pull for the shallow water yonder. Bale, you two, and look lively—that fellow means mischief!"

The shark was at the surface now, swimming in swift zigzags like a hound at fault. While Ofai and I baled and the others began to row, I glanced over my shoulder and saw the tall dorsal fin heading straight for us, so swiftly that the water rippled away on either side.

"Pull hard—he's after us!" shouted my uncle, standing in the stern with a twelve foot oar in his hand.

We were making for the shallows over a large coral mushroom, a hundred yards away, and the men were rowing at top speed, for they realized that our light boat gave little protection against such an enemy.

The shark drew rapidly abreast of us and as his head ranged alongside, Uncle Harry raised the oar and thrust down with all his strength. The blow was a glancing one, and before he recovered his weapon, the three-inch shaft of tough wood was between a pair of formidable jaws. My uncle's eyebrows went up as he raised what was left of the oar, sheared off as a child bites through a stick of candy. Next moment Ivi cried out, as the monster seized his sweep and wrenched it from his hands. I saw it float to the surface with a splintered blade—felt our boat shaken violently as the shark took the keel in his teeth. Then the bow grated on coral, and we leaped out in the shallows to pull the boat into the safety of a foot of water.

## CHRIS FARRINGTON: ABLE SEAMAN [1]

*Jack London*

"If you vas in der old country ships, a liddle shaver like you vood pe only der boy, und you vood wait on der able seamen. Und ven der able seaman sing out, 'Boy, der water jug!' you vood jump quick, like a shot, und bring der water jug. Und ven der able seaman sing out, 'Boy, my boots!' you vood get der boots. Und you vood pe politeful, und say 'Yessir' und 'No sir.' But you pe in der American ship, und you t'ink you are so good as der able seamen. Chris, mine boy, I haf ben a sailorman for twenty-two years, und do you t'ink you are so good as me? I vas a sailorman pefore you vas borned, und I knot und reef und splice ven you play mit topstrings und fly kites."

"But you are unfair, Emil!" cried Chris Farrington, his sensitive face flushed and hurt. He was a slender though strongly built young fellow of seventeen, with Yankee ancestry writ large all over him.

"Dere you go vonce again!" the Swedish sailor exploded. "My name is Mister Johansen, und a kid of a boy like you call me 'Emil!' It vas insulting, und comes pecause of der American ship!"

"But you call me 'Chris!' " the boy expostulated, reproachfully.

"But you vas a boy."

"Who does a man's work," Chris retorted. "And because I do a man's work I have as much right to call you by your first name as you me. We are all equals in this fo'castle, and you know it. When we signed for the voyage in San Francisco, we signed as sailors on the *Sophie Sutherland* and there was no difference made with any of us. Haven't I always done my work? Did I ever shirk? Did you or any other man ever have to take a wheel for me? Or a lookout? Or go aloft?"

"Chris is right," interrupted a young English sailor. "No man has had to do a tap of his work yet. He signed as good as any of us, and he's shown himself as good—"

"Better!" broke in a Nova Scotia man. "Better than some of us! When we struck the sealing-grounds he turned out to be next to the best boat-steerer aboard. Only French Louis, who'd been at it for years, could beat him. I'm only a boat-puller,

[1] From Jack London, *Dutch Courage.*

and you're only a boat-puller, too, Emil Johansen, for all your twenty-two years at sea. Why don't you become a boat-steerer?"

"Too clumsy," laughed the Englishman, "and too slow."

"Little that counts, one way or the other," joined in Dane Jurgensen, coming to the aid of his Scandinavian brother. "Emil is a man grown and an able seaman; the boy is neither."

And so the argument raged back and forth, the Swedes, the Norwegians and Danes, because of race kinship, taking the part of Johansen, and the English, Canadians and Americans taking the part of Chris. From an unprejudiced point of view, the right was on the side of Chris. As he had truly said, he did a man's work, and the same work that any of them did. But they were prejudiced, and badly so, and out of the words which passed rose a standing quarrel which divided the forecastle into two parties.

The *Sophie Sutherland* was a seal-hunter, registered out of San Francisco, and engaged in hunting the furry sea animals along the Japanese coast north to Bering Sea. The other vessels were two-masted schooners, but she was a three-master and the largest in the fleet. In fact, she was a full-rigged, three topmast schooner, newly built.

Although Chris Farrington knew that justice was with him, and that he performed all his work faithfully and well, many a time, in secret thought, he longed for some pressing emergency to arise whereby he could demonstrate to the Scandinavian seamen that he also was an able seaman.

But one stormy night, by an accident for which he was in nowise accountable, in overhauling a spare anchor chain he had all the fingers of his left hand badly crushed. And his hopes were likewise crushed, for it was impossible for him to continue hunting with the boats, and he was forced to stay idly aboard until his fingers should heal. Yet, although he little dreamed it, this very accident was to give him the long-looked-for opportunity.

One afternoon in the latter part of May the *Sophie Sutherland* rolled sluggishly in a breathless calm. The seals were abundant, the hunting good, and the boats were all away and out of sight. And with them was almost every man of the crew. Besides Chris, there remained only the captain, the sailing-master and the Chinese cook.

The captain was captain only by courtesy. He was an old man, past eighty, and blissfully ignorant of the sea and its ways; but he was the owner of the vessel, and hence the honorable title. Of course the sailing-master, who was really captain, was a thorough-going seaman. The mate, whose post was aboard, was out with the boats, having temporarily taken Chris's place as boat-steerer.

When good weather and good sport came together, the boats were accustomed to range far and wide, and often did not return to the schooner until long after dark. But for all that it was a perfect hunting day, Chris noted a growing anxiety on the part of the sailing-master. He paced the deck nervously, and was constantly sweeping the horizon with his marine glasses. Not a boat was in sight. As sunset arrived, he even sent Chris aloft to the mizzen-topmast-head, but with no better luck. The boats could not possibly be back before midnight.

Since noon the barometer had been falling with startling rapidity, and all the signs were ripe for a great storm—how great, not even the sailing-master anticipated. He and Chris set to work to prepare for it. They put storm gaskets on the furled topsails, lowered and stowed the foresail and spanker and took in the two inner jibs. In the one remaining jib they put a single reef, and a single reef in the mainsail.

Night had fallen before they finished, and with the darkness came the storm. A low moan swept over the sea, and the wind struck the *Sophie Sutherland* flat. But she righted quickly, and with the sailing-master at the wheel, sheered her bow into within five points of the wind. Working as well as he could with his bandaged hand, and with the feeble aid of the Chinese cook, Chris went forward and backed the jib over to the weather side. This with the flat mainsail, left the schooner hove to.

"God help the boats! It's no gale! It's a typhoon!" the sailing-master shouted to Chris at eleven o'clock. "Too much canvas! Got to get two more reefs into that mainsail, and got to do it right away!" He glanced at the old captain, shivering in oilskins at the binnacle and holding on for dear life. "There's only you and I, Chris—and the cook; but he's next to worthless!"

In order to make the reef, it was necessary to lower the mainsail, and the removal of this after pressure was bound to make the schooner fall off before the wind and sea because of the forward pressure of the jib.

"Take the wheel!" the sailing-master directed. "And when I give the word, hard up with it! And when she's square before it, steady her! And keep her there! We'll heave to again as soon as I get the reefs in!"

Gripping the kicking spokes, Chris watched him and the reluctant cook go forward into the howling darkness. The *Sophie Sutherland* was plunging into the huge head seas and wallowing tremendously, the tense steel stays and taut rigging humming like harp strings to the wind. A buffeted cry came to his ears, and he felt the schooner's bow paying off of its own accord. The mainsail was down!

He ran the wheel hard-over and kept anxious track of the changing direction of the wind on his face and of the heave of the vessel. This was the crucial moment. In performing the evolution she would have to pass broadside to the surge before she could get before it. The wind was blowing directly on his right cheek, when he felt the *Sophie Sutherland* lean over and begin to rise toward the sky—up—up—an infinite distance! Would she clear the crest of the gigantic wave?

Again by the feel of it, for he could see nothing, he knew that a wall of water was rearing and curving far above him along the whole weather side. There was an instant's calm as the liquid wall intervened and shut off the wind. The schooner righted, and for that instant seemed at perfect rest. Then she rolled to meet the descending rush.

Chris shouted to the captain to hold tight, and prepared himself for the shock. But the man did not live who could face it. An ocean of water smote Chris's back and his clutch on the spokes was loosened as if it were a baby's. Stunned, powerless, like a straw on the face of a torrent, he was swept onward he knew not whither. Missing the corner of the cabin, he was dashed forward along the poop runway a hundred feet or more, striking violently against the foot of the foremast. A second wave, crushing inboard, hurled him back the way he had come, and left him half-drowned where the poop steps should have been.

Bruised and bleeding, dimly conscious, he felt for the rail and dragged himself to his feet. Unless something could be done, he knew the last moment had come. As he faced the poop, the wind drove into his mouth with suffocating force. This brought him back to his senses with a start. The wind was blowing from dead aft! The schooner was out of the trough and before it! But the send of the sea was bound to breach her to again. Crawling up the runway, he managed to get to the wheel just in time to prevent this. The binnacle light was still burning. They were safe!

That is, he and the schooner were safe. As to the welfare of his three companions he could not say. Nor did he dare leave the wheel in order to find out, for it took every second of his undivided attention to keep the vessel to her course. The least fraction of carelessness and the heave of the sea under the quarter was liable to thrust her into the trough. So, a boy of one hundred and forty pounds, he clung to his herculean task of guiding the two hundred straining tons of fabric amid the chaos of the great storm forces.

Half an hour later, groaning and sobbing, the captain crawled to Chris's feet. All was lost, he whimpered. He was smitten unto death. The galley had gone by the board, the mainsail and running-gear, the cook, everything!

"Where's the sailing-master?" Chris demanded when he had caught his breath after steadying a wild lurch of the schooner. It was no child's play to steer a vessel under single-reefed jib before a typhoon.

"Clean up for'ard," the old man replied. "Jammed under the fo'c'sle-head, but still breathing. Both his arms are broken, he says, and he doesn't know how many ribs. He's hurt bad."

"Well, he'll drown there the way she's shipping water through the hawse-pipes. Go for'ard!" Chris commanded, taking charge of things as a matter of course. "Tell him not to worry; that I'm at the wheel. Help him as much as you can, and make him help"—he stopped and ran the spokes to starboard as a tremendous billow rose under the stern and yawed the schooner to port—"and make him help himself for the rest. Unship the fo'castle hatch and get him down into a bunk. Then ship the hatch again."

The captain turned his aged face forward and wavered pitifully. The waist of the ship was full of water to the bulwarks. He had just come through it, and knew death lurked every inch of the way.

"Go!" Chris shouted, fiercely. And as the fear-stricken man started, "And take another look for the cook!"

Two hours later, almost dead from suffering, the captain returned. He had obeyed orders. The sailing-master was helpless, although safe in a bunk; the cook was gone. Chris sent the captain below to the cabin to change his clothes.

After interminable hours of toil, day broke cold and gray. Chris looked about him. The *Sophie Sutherland* was racing before the typhoon like a thing possessed. There was no rain, but the wind whipped the spray of the sea mast-high, obscuring everything except in the immediate neighborhood.

Two waves only could Chris see at a time—the one before and the one behind. So small and insignificant the schooner seemed on the long Pacific roll! Rushing up like a maddening mountain, she would poise like a cockleshell on the giddy summit, breathless and rolling, leap outward and down into the yawning chasm beneath, and bury herself in the smother of foam at the bottom. Then the recovery, another mountain, another sickening upward rush, another poise, and the downward crash.

For three hours more, Chris held the *Sophie Sutherland* before the wind and sea. He had long since forgotten his mangled fingers. The bandages had been torn away, and the cold, salt spray had eaten into the half-healed wounds until they were numb and no longer pained. But he was not cold. The terrific labor of steering forced the perspiration from every pore. Yet he was faint and weak with hunger and exhaustion, and hailed with delight the advent on deck of the captain, who fed him all of a pound of cake-chocolate. It strengthened him at once.

He ordered the captain to go forward and cut loose the jib-halyard and sheet. When he had done so, the jib fluttered a couple of moments like a handkerchief, then tore out of the bolt-ropes and vanished. The *Sophie Sutherland* was running under bare poles.

By noon the storm had spent itself, and by six in the evening the waves had died down sufficiently to let Chris leave the helm. It was almost hopeless to dream of the small boats weathering the typhoon, but there is always the chance of saving human life, and Chris at once applied himself to going back over the course which he had fled. He managed to get a reef in one of the inner jibs and two reefs in the spanker, and then, with the aid of the watch-tackle, to hoist them to the stiff breeze that yet blew. And all through the night, tacking back and forth on the back track, he shook out canvas as fast as the wind would permit.

The injured sailing-master had turned delirious and between tending him and lending a hand with the ship, Chris kept the captain busy. "Taught me more seamanship," as he afterward said, "than I'd learned on the whole voyage." But by daybreak the old man's feeble frame succumbed, and he fell off into exhausted sleep on the weather poop.

Chris, who could now lash the wheel, covered the tired man with blankets from below, and went fishing in the lazaretto for something to eat. But by the day following he found himself forced to give in, drowsing fitfully by the wheel and waking ever and anon to take a look at things.

On the afternoon of the third day he picked up a schooner, dismasted and battered. As he approached, close-hauled on the wind, he saw her decks crowded by an unusually large crew, and on sailing in closer, made out among others the faces of his missing comrades. And he was just in the nick of time, for they were fighting a losing fight at the pumps. An hour later they, with the crew of the sinking craft, were aboard the *Sophie Sutherland*.

Having wandered so far from their own vessel, they had taken refuge on the strange schooner just before the storm broke. She was a Canadian sealer on her first voyage, and as was now apparent, her last.

The captain of the *Sophie Sutherland* had a story to tell, also, and he told it well —so well, in fact, that when all hands were gathered together on deck during the dogwatch, Emil Johansen strode over to Chris and gripped him by the hand.

"Chris," he said, so loudly that all could hear, "Chris, I gif in. You vas yoost so good a sailorman as I. You vas a bully boy und able seaman, und I pe proud for you!"

"Und Chris!" He turned as if he had forgotten something, and called back, "From dis time always you call me 'Emil' mitout der 'Mister!' "

## NEW YORK TO PARIS[1]

*Charles A. Lindbergh*

At New York we checked over the plane, engine, and instruments, which required several short flights over the field.

When the plane was completely inspected and ready for the trans-Atlantic flight, there were dense fogs reported along the coast and over Nova Scotia and Newfoundland, in addition to a storm area over the North Atlantic.

On the morning of May 19th (1927), a light rain was falling and the sky overcast. Weather reports from land stations and ships along the great circle course were unfavorable and there was apparently no prospect of taking off for Paris for several days at least. In the morning I visited the Wright plant at Paterson, New Jersey, and had planned to attend a theatre performance in New York that evening. But at about six o'clock I received a special report from the New York Weather Bureau. A high pressure area was over the entire North Atlantic and the low pressure over Nova Scotia and Newfoundland was receding. It was apparent that the prospects of the fog clearing up were as good as I might expect for some time to come. The North Atlantic should be clear with only local storms on the coast of Europe. The moon had just passed full and the percentage of days with fog over Newfoundland and the Grand Banks was increasing so that there seemed to be no advantage in waiting longer.

We went to Curtiss Field as quickly as possible and made arrangements for the barograph to be sealed and installed, and for the plane to be serviced and checked.

We decided partially to fill the fuel tanks in the hangar before towing the ship on a truck to Roosevelt Field, which adjoins Curtiss on the east, where the servicing would be completed.

I left the responsibility for conditioning the plane in the hands of the men on the field while I went into the hotel for about

[1] From Charles A. Lindbergh, *We*.

two and one-half hours of rest; but at the hotel there were several more details which had to be completed and I was unable to get any sleep that night.

I returned to the field before daybreak on the morning of the twentieth. A light rain was falling which continued until almost dawn; consequently we did not move the ship to Roosevelt Field until much later than we had planned, and the take-off was delayed from daybreak until nearly eight o'clock.

At dawn the shower had passed, although the sky was overcast, and occasionally there would be some slight precipitation. The tail of the plane was lashed to a truck and escorted by a number of motorcycle police. The slow trip from Curtiss to Roosevelt was begun.

The ship was placed at the extreme west end of the field heading along the east and west runway, and the final fueling commenced.

About 7:40 A.M. the motor was started and at 7:52 I took off on the flight for Paris.

The field was a little soft due to the rain during the night and the heavily loaded plane gathered speed very slowly. After passing the halfway mark, however, it was apparent that I would be able to clear the obstructions at the end. I passed over a tractor by about fifteen feet and a telephone line by about twenty, with a fair reserve of flying speed. I believe that the ship would have taken off from a hard field with at least five hundred pounds more weight.

I turned slightly to the right to avoid some high trees on a hill directly ahead, but by the time I had gone a few hundred yards I had sufficient altitude to clear all obstructions and throttled the engine down to 1750 R.P.M. I took up a compass course at once and soon reached Long Island Sound where the Curtiss Oriole with its photographer, which had been escorting me, turned back.

The haze soon cleared, and from Cape Cod through the southern half of Nova Scotia the weather and visibility were excellent. I was flying very low, sometimes as close as ten feet from the trees and water.

On the three hundred mile stretch of water between Cape Cod and Nova Scotia I passed within view of numerous fishing vessels.

The northern part of Nova Scotia contained a number of storm areas and several times I flew through cloudbursts.

As I neared the northern coast, snow appeared in patches on the ground and far to the eastward the coastline was covered with fog.

For many miles between Nova Scotia and Newfoundland the ocean was covered with caked ice, but as I approached the coast the ice disappeared entirely and I saw several ships in this area.

I had taken up a course for St. Johns, which is south of the great Circle from New York to Paris, so that there would be no question of the fact that I had passed Newfoundland in case I was forced down in the north Atlantic.

I passed over numerous icebergs after leaving St. Johns, but saw no ships except near the coast.

Darkness set in about 8:15 New York time, and a thin, low fog formed through which the white bergs showed up with surprising clearness. This fog became thicker and increased in height until within two hours I was just skimming the top of storm clouds at about ten thousand feet. Even at this altitude there was a thick haze through which only the stars directly overhead could be seen.

There was no moon and it was very dark. The tops of some of the storm clouds were several thousand feet above me and at one time, when I attempted to fly through one of the larger clouds, sleet started to collect on the plane, and I was forced to turn around and get back into clear air immediately and then fly around any clouds which I could not get over.

The moon appeared on the horizon after about two hours of darkness; then the flying was much less complicated.

Dawn came at about 1 A.M. New York time, and the temperature had risen until there was practically no remaining danger of sleet.

Shortly after sunrise the clouds became more broken, although some of them were far above me and it was often necessary to fly through them, navigating by instruments only.

As the sun became higher, holes appeared in the fog. Through one the open water was visible, and I dropped down until less than a hundred feet above the waves. There was a strong wind blowing from the northwest and the ocean was covered with white caps.

After a few miles of fairly clear weather, the ceiling lowered to zero and for nearly two hours I flew entirely blind through the fog at an altitude of about 1500 feet. Then the fog raised and the water was visible again.

On several more occasions it was necessary to fly by instrument for short periods; then the fog broke up into patches. These patches took on forms of every description. Numerous shorelines appeared, with trees perfectly outlined against the horizon. In fact, the mirages were so natural that, had I not been in mid-Atlantic and known that no land existed along my route, I would have taken them to be actual islands.

As the fog cleared I dropped down closer to the water, sometimes flying within ten feet of the waves and seldom higher than two hundred.

There is a cushion of air close to the ground or water through which a plane flies with less effort than when at a higher altitude, and for hours at a time I took advantage of this factor.

Also, it was less difficult to determine the wind drift near the water. During the entire flight the wind was strong enough to produce white caps on the waves. When one of these formed, the foam would be blown off, showing the wind's direction and approximate velocity. This foam remained on the water long enough for me to obtain a general idea of my drift.

During the day I saw a number of porpoises and a few birds but no ships, although I understand that two different boats reported me passing over.

The first indication of my approach to the European Coast was a small fishing boat which I first noticed a few miles ahead and slightly to the south of my course. There were several of these fishing boats grouped within a few miles of each other.

I flew over the first boat without seeing any signs of life. As I circled over the second, however, a man's face appeared, looking out of the cabin window.

I have carried on short conversations with people on the ground by flying low with throttled engine, shouting a question, and receiving the answer by some signal. When I saw this fisherman I decided to try to get him to point towards land. I had no sooner made the decision than the futility of the effort became apparent. In all likelihood he could not speak English, and even if he could, he would undoubtedly be far too astounded to answer. However, I circled again and closing the throttle as the plane passed within a few feet of the boat, I shouted, "Which way is Ireland?" Of course the attempt was useless, and I continued on my course.

Less than an hour later a rugged and semi-mountainous coastline appeared to the northeast. I was flying less than two hundred feet from the water when I sighted it. The shore was fairly distinct and not over ten or fifteen miles away. A light haze coupled with numerous local storm areas had prevented my seeing it from a long distance.

The coastline came down from the north, curved over toward the east. I had very little doubt that it was the southwestern end of Ireland, but in order to make sure I changed my course towards the nearest point of land.

I located Cape Valentia and Dingle Bay, then resumed my compass course towards Paris.

After leaving Ireland I passed a number of steamers and was seldom out of sight of a ship.

In a little over two hours the coast of

England appeared. My course passed over Southern England and a little south of Plymouth; then across the English Channel, striking France over Cherbourg.

The English farms were very impressive from the air in contrast to ours in America. They appeared extremely small and unusually neat and tidy with their stone and hedge fences.

I was flying at about a fifteen-hundred-foot altitude over England and as I crossed the Channel and passed over Cherbourg, France, I had probably seen more of that part of Europe than many native Europeans. The visibility was good and the country could be seen for miles around.

People who have taken their first flight often remark that no one knows what the locality he lives in is like until he has seen it from above. Countries take on different characteristics from the air.

The sun went down shortly after passing Cherbourg and soon the beacons along the Paris-London airway became visible.

I first saw the lights of Paris a little before ten P.M., or five P.M. New York time, and a few minutes later I was circling the Eiffel Tower at an altitude of about four thousand feet.

The lights of Le Bourget were plainly visible, but appeared to be very close to Paris. I had understood that the field was farther from the city, so continued out to the northeast into the country for four or five miles to make sure that there was not another field farther out which might be Le Bourget. Then I returned and spiralled down closer to the lights. Presently I could make out long lines of hangars, and the roads appeared to be jammed with cars.

I flew low over the field once, then circled around into the wind and landed.

After the plane stopped rolling I turned it around and started to taxi back to the lights. The entire field ahead, however, was covered with thousands of people all running towards my ship. When the first few arrived, I attempted to get them to hold the rest of the crowd back, away from the plane, but apparently no one could understand, or would have been able to conform to my request if he had.

I cut the switch to keep the propeller from killing some one, and attempted to organize an impromptu guard for the plane. The impossibility of any immediate organization became apparent, and when parts of the ship began to crack from the pressure of the multitude I decided to climb out of the cockpit in order to draw the crowd away.

Speaking was impossible; no words could be heard in the uproar and nobody apparently cared to hear any. I started to climb out of the cockpit, but as soon as one foot appeared through the door I was dragged the rest of the way without assistance on my part.

For nearly half an hour I was unable to touch the ground, during which time I was ardently carried around in what seemed to be a very small area, and in every position it is possible to be in. Everyone had the best of intentions, but no one seemed to know just what they were.

The French military flyers very resourcefully took the situation in hand. A number of them mingled with the crowd; then, at a given signal, they placed my helmet on an American correspondent and cried: "Here is Lindbergh." That helmet on an American was sufficient evidence. The correspondent immediately became the center of attraction, and while he was being taken protestingly to the Reception Committee via a rather devious route, I managed to get inside one of the hangars.

Meanwhile a second group of soldiers and police had surrounded the plane and soon placed it out of danger in another hangar.

The French ability to handle an unusual situation with speed and capability was remarkably demonstrated that night at Le Bourget.

Ambassador Herrick extended me an invitation to remain at his Embassy while I was in Paris, which I gladly accepted. But grateful as I was at the time, it did not take me long to realize that a kind Providence had placed me in Ambassador Herrick's hands. The ensuing days found me in situations that I had certainly never expected to be in and in which I relied on Ambassador Herrick's sympathetic aid.

These situations were brought about by the whole-hearted welcome to me—an American—that touched me beyond any point that any words can express. I left France with a debt of gratitude which, though I cannot repay it, I shall always remember. If the French people had been acclaiming their own gallant airmen, Nungesser and Coli, who were lost only after fearlessly departing in the face of conditions insurmountably greater than those that confronted me, their enthusiastic welcome and graciousness could not have been greater.

In Belgium as well, I was received with a warmth which reflected more than simply a passing curiosity in a trans-Atlantic flight, but which was rather a demonstration by the people of their interest in a new means of transportation which eventually would bring still closer together the new world and the old. Their welcome, too, will be a cherished memory for all time.

In England, I experienced one final unforgettable demonstration of friendship for an American. That spontaneous wonderful reception during my brief visit seemed typical of what I had always heard of the good sportsmanship of the English.

My words to all those friends in Europe are inadequate, but my feelings of appreciation are boundless.

## SAND HOGS [1]

*Margaret Norris*

The sand hog is a useful animal better known to the engineer than to the zoologist. As he grunts along at the roots of our cities we cannot hear his voice; every sound he makes is muffled by the compressed air in which he works.

He is the unsung hero of every tunnel thrown open to traffic. He sets the caissons in our bridge piers, or in the deep foundations from which many of our proudest buildings rise. Every day he risks his life against the mud and strength of some river. But he wears rubber boots and clothes caked with mud, and so he does not step into the limelight. As he burrows along quietly and inconspicuously, we are scarcely aware he is there.

Who is this sand hog, and how does he work under the river bed?

He is a hybrid growth of industry, a cross between the miner and the deep-sea diver. He must know what the miner knows of blasting, excavating, and timbering. He must have the diver's knowledge of compressed air, plus leather lungs and iron heart in order to work in it. But he lacks the miner's protection of rock. The river bed is soft mud and silt. At any moment it may cave in on him, flooding the tunnel with water. If this happens, he lacks the protection of the diver's helmet and waterproof suit. He must have the cool courage and resourcefulness of both to rescue himself in a catastrophe. Like the cat he must have nine lives and be ready to lose eight of them, if necessary, to push the hole through.

## RIDING THE GIRDERS [2]

*Margaret Norris*

Up from the city streets goes the skyscraper, higher and ever higher until its tower pierces the clouds, a misty outline of shining steel and pale moon-colored masonry. A few years ago a twenty-story building was high. People looked from its top windows and grew dizzy. Then other buildings shot up which made twenty-story structures look like mushrooms. Today buildings rival one another in height, until the distinction of being the highest in the world is as transitory as if written in the

[1] From Margaret Norris, *Heroes and Hazards.*
[2] *Ibid.*

sand. The Woolworth Tower with its fifty-four stories was dwarfed by the Chrysler Building, with a pointed, shimmering spire which is fifty feet higher than the Eiffel Tower. This, in turn, was outdone by the Empire State Building, twelve hundred and fifty feet from base to summit, the highest man-made structure—one hundred and two stories including the tower. Yet, it is quite possible that within the next decade some new steel giant may rise to eclipse this, as well.

How high can a skyscraper go? Architects say, as high as the air is breathable. Steel can stand any strain. Elevator men maintain that one hundred and fifty stories is the feasible limit. After that the car must travel so fast as to make passage uncomfortable, and the expense would make it logical to charge passengers a fare for the ride.

Before the elevator was invented, six stories was the limit. Even our grandfathers with their sturdy calves refused to climb any higher.

Nowadays, in gauging the height of a building, the first factor to be considered is the condition of the substrata. Chicago saw the first skyscraper, but New York now builds higher and probably always will do so, for Manhattan Island is solid rock, while the site of Chicago is sandy soil. The fear has been expressed that some day the sheer weight of her buildings will make Manhattan Island sink into the sea. But this fear is groundless. It has been proved that the rock excavated for the foundations of a great building invariably outweighs the building itself. The innumerable towers of fantastic height which adorn the New York skyline have actually lightened Manhattan's load.

A skyscraper, whether of six stories or of sixty, is a very special thing—namely, a steel skeleton, the walls of which bear no weight but are merely curtains of masonry. The load is taken off the walls by crossbeams of structural steel which, riveted together, support the floor of each story. Thus, from the architect's standpoint the building might rise indefinitely.

Structural steel is the factor which binds together the whole skyscraper. Until iron was replaced by steel it was not possible to build to such heights. For iron beams and columns have to be bolted together, while steel can be riveted. No bolt is as strong as a rivet, which, forced redhot into the punch-hole, fills it up, fuses with its walls, and becomes an integral part of both floor beam and column.

With the use of steel has come into existence a fearless, daring type of workman, who walks the naked girders and rivets the skyscraper together. These men are called structural ironworkers. The description is misleading, for they actually work on steel, not on iron.

Of the thirty-two trades that enter into the building of a skyscraper, the ironworker runs the greatest risk. No one who works on a building is safe. The construction company planks and decks, puts out riggers and barricades to protect the public, but the men who do the actual construction take tremendous hazards.

Most of the trades, however, are protected by union requirements for safety which are recognized and respected. For instance, the bricklayer works on a scaffold which must be at least four planks wide with a guard rail around it and a planked roof over it to ward off falling objects. But the steelworker strides across needle beams (a needle beam is four inches wide) at heights to make a professional rope-walker cringe. Two hundred, five hundred feet up in the air, he spans the fathomless gulf between one steel column and another on a narrow ten-inch plank, carrying heavy tools or an armful of planks, with nothing between him and eternity except his own uncanny skill, his nerve, and his fine sense of balance. Instead of sweet music such as accompanies the circus or stage acrobat, he has the terrific noise of the rivet hammers.

Yet, "The sound of the rivets is sweet music to me," said one assistant foreman, a big husky fellow with a twinkle in his eye. "It means the work is going O.K."

For these men poised precariously on the top do heavy, highly skilled work. They shift and swing clumsy steel burdens capable of destroying everything if they fall; raise and lower vast girders and beams, each painstakingly numbered to correspond with the architect's drawing, until every rivet hole fits to a sixteenth of an inch with some other rivet hole; bolt up the columns, plumb them up, toss and drive red-hot rivets. It is labor that is actual—and dangerous—and hard.

But the strange sense of security these men feel while defying the laws of gravity is really the outgrowth of caution, so constant, so deeply ingrained that it has become unconscious, part and parcel of their beings. The swift graceful ease with which they move through the tall spider web of steel gives an outward impression of recklessness. But this is erroneous. The ironworker who takes a risk seldom lives to boast of it. Rather, an ironworker does dangerous work so cautiously that finally it is not dangerous.

This is why he can walk the topmost beam of a building whose height is one of the miracles of our century.

So, while many lament that the machine age is making robots and automatons of men, here is one type of workman, the steel man, the very spirit of the skyscraper, a direct product of the power age, whose personality the machine age exalts.

## ROBINSON CRUSOE [1]

*Daniel Defoe*

I was now landed, and safe on shore, and began to look up and thank God that my life was saved. I cast my eyes to the stranded vessel, where, the breach and froth of the sea being so big, I could hardly see it, it lay so far off; and considered, how had it been possible to get on shore.

After I had solaced my mind with the comfortable part of my condition, I began to look round me, to see what kind of place I was in, and what was next to be done. And I soon found my comforts abate, and that, in a word, I had a dreadful deliverance; for I was wet, had no clothes to shift me, nor anything either to eat or drink, to comfort me; neither did I see any prospect before me but that of perishing with hunger, or being devoured by wild beasts; and that which was particularly afflicting to me was that I had no weapon, either to hunt and kill any creature for my sustenance, or to defend myself against any other creature that might desire to kill me for theirs. In a word, I had nothing about me but a knife, a tobacco pipe, and a little tobacco in a box. This was all my provision; and this threw me into terrible agonies of mind, that for a while I ran about like a madman. Night coming upon me, I began, with a heavy heart, to consider what would be my lot if there were any ravenous beasts in that country, seeing at night they always come abroad for their prey.

All the remedy that offered to my thoughts, at that time, was to get up into a thick, bushy tree, like a fir, but thorny, which grew near me, and where I resolved to sit all night, and consider the next day what death I should die, for as yet I saw no prospect of life. I walked about a furlong from the shore, to see if I could find any fresh water to drink, which I did, to my great joy; and having drunk, and put a little tobacco in my mouth to prevent hunger, I went to the tree, and getting up into it, endeavored to place myself so that if I should sleep I might not fall. And having cut me a short stick, like a truncheon, for my defense, I took up my lodging; and being excessively fatigued, I fell fast asleep, and slept as comfortably as, I believe, few could have done in my condition, and found myself more refreshed with it than I think I ever was on such an occasion.

When I waked it was broad day, the weather clear, and the storm abated, so that the sea did not rage and swell as be-

[1] From Daniel Defoe, *The Life and Surprising Adventures of Robinson Crusoe.*

fore; but that which surprised me most was that the ship was lifted off in the night from the sand where she lay, by the swelling of the tide, and was driven up almost as far as the rock, where I had been so bruised by the wave dashing me against it. This being within about a mile from the shore where I was, and the ship seeming to stand upright still, I wished myself on board, that at least I might save some necessary things for my use.

When I came down from my apartment in the tree I looked about me again, and the first thing I found was the boat, which lay, as the wind and sea had tossed her up, upon the land, about two miles on my right hand. I walked as far as I could upon the shore to have got to her; but found a neck or inlet of water between me and the boat which was about half a mile broad; so I came back for the present, being more intent upon getting at the ship, where I hoped to find something for my present subsistence.

A little after noon I found the sea very calm, and the tide ebbed so far out that I could come within a quarter of a mile of the ship. And here I found a fresh renewing of my grief; for I saw evidently that, if we had kept on board, we had been all safe; that is to say, we had all got safe on shore, and I had not been so miserable as to be left entirely destitute of all comfort and company, as I now was. This forced tears to my eyes; but as there was little relief in that, I resolved, if possible, to get to the ship. So I pulled off my clothes, for the weather was hot to extremity, and took to the water.

When I came to the ship my difficulty was still greater to know how to get on board; for, as she lay aground, and high out of the water, there was nothing within my reach to lay hold of. I swam round her twice, and the second time I espied a small piece of rope, which I wondered I did not see at first, hanging down by the forechains so low that with great difficulty I got hold of it, and by the help of that rope got up into the forecastle of the ship. Here I found that the ship was bulged, and had a great deal of water in her hold; but that she lay so on the side of a bank of hard sand, or rather earth, that her stern lay lifted up upon the bank, and her head low, almost to the water. By this means all her quarter was free and all that was in that part was dry; for you may be sure my first work was to search, and to see what was spoiled and what was free. And, first, I found that all the ship's provisions were dry and untouched by the water, and being very well disposed to eat, I went to the bread room, and filled my pockets with biscuit, and ate it as I went about other things, for I had no time to lose. Now I wanted nothing but a boat, to furnish myself with many things which I foresaw would be very necessary to me.

It was in vain to sit still and wish for what was not to be had; and this extremity roused my application. We had several spare yards, and two or three large spars of wood, and a spare topmast or two in the ship; I resolved to fall to work with them, and I flung as many of them overboard as I could manage for their weight, tying every one with a rope, that they might not drive away. When this was done, I went down the ship's side, and pulling them to me, I tied four of them together at both ends, as well as I could, in the form of a raft, and laying two or three short pieces of plank upon them, crossways, I found I could walk upon it very well, but that it was not able to bear any great weight, the pieces being too light. So I went to work, and with the carpenter's saw I cut a spare topmast into three lengths, and added them to my raft, with a great deal of labor and pains. But the hope of furnishing myself with necessaries encouraged me to go beyond what I should have been able to have done upon another occasion.

My raft was now strong enough to bear any reasonable weight. My next care was what to load it with, and how to preserve what I laid upon it from the surf of the sea, but I was not long in considering this.

I first laid all the planks or boards upon it that I could get, and having considered well what I most wanted, I first got three of the seamen's chests, which I had broken open and emptied, and lowered them down upon my raft; the first of these I filled with provisions—viz., bread, rice, three Dutch cheeses, five pieces of dried goat's flesh (which we lived much upon), and a little remainder of European corn, which had been laid by for some fowls which we brought to sea with us, but the fowls were killed. There had been some barley and wheat together; but, to my great disappointment, I found afterwards that the rats had eaten or spoiled it all.

By now I found the tide began to flow, though very calm; and I had the mortification to see my coat, shirt, and waistcoat, which I had left on shore upon the sand, swim away. As for my breeches, which were only linen, and open-kneed, I swam on board in them and my stockings. However, this put me upon rummaging for clothes, of which I found enough, but took no more than I wanted for present use, for I had other things which my eye was more upon; as, first, tools to work with on shore; and it was after long searching that I found out the carpenter's chest, which was indeed a very useful prize to me, and much more valuable than a ship-lading of gold would have been at that time. I got it down to my raft, whole as it was, without losing time to look into it, for I knew in general what it contained.

My next care was for some ammunition and arms. There were two very good fowling pieces in the great cabin, and two pistols. These I secured first, with some powder horns, a small bag of shot, and two old rusty swords. I knew there were three barrels of powder in the ship, but knew not where our gunner had stowed them; but with much search I found them, two of them dry and good, the third had taken water. Those two I got to my raft, with the arms. And now I thought myself pretty well freighted, and began to think how I should get to shore with them, having neither sail, oar, nor rudder; and the least capful of wind would have overset all my navigation.

I had three encouragements: first, a smooth, calm sea; secondly, the tide rising, and setting in to the shore; thirdly, what little wind there was blew me towards the land. And thus, having found two or three broken oars belonging to the boat, and besides the tools which were in the chest, two saws, an ax, and a hammer. With this cargo I put to sea. For a mile, or thereabouts, my raft went very well, only that I found it drive a little distant from the place where I had landed before; by which I perceived that there was some indraft of the water, and consequently, I hoped to find some creek or river there, which I might make use of as a port to get to land with my cargo.

As I imagined, so it was. There appeared before me a little opening of the land. I found a strong current of the tide set into it; so I guided my raft as well as I could, to keep in the middle of the stream.

But here I had like to have suffered a second shipwreck, which, if I had, I think verily would have broken my heart; for knowing nothing of the coast, my raft ran aground at one end of it upon a shoal, and not being aground at the other end, it wanted but a little that all my cargo had slipped off towards the end that was afloat, and so fallen into the water. I did my utmost, by setting my back against the chests, to keep them in their places, but could not thrust off the raft with all my strength; neither durst I stir from the posture I was in; but holding up the chests with all my might, I stood in that manner near half an hour, in which time the rising of the water brought me a little more upon a level; and, a little after, the water still rising, my raft floated again, and I thrust her off with the oar I had into the channel, and then driving up higher, I at length found myself in the mouth of a little river, with land on both sides, and a strong current or tide running up. I looked on both sides for a proper place to get to shore, for I was not willing to be driven too high up the river; hoping in time to see some ship at sea, and therefore resolved to place myself as near the coast as I could.

At length I spied a little cove on the right shore of the creek, to which, with great pain and difficulty, I guided my raft, and at last got so near that, reaching ground with my oar, I could thrust her directly in. But here I had like to have dipped all my cargo into the sea again; for that shore lying pretty steep—that is to say, sloping—there was no place to land, but where one end of my float, if it ran on shore, would lie so high, and the other sink lower, as before, that it would endanger my cargo again.

All that I could do was to wait till the tide was at the highest, keeping the raft with my oar like an anchor, to hold the side of it fast to the shore, near a flat piece of ground, which I expected the water would flow over; and so it did. As soon as I found water enough, for my raft drew about a foot of water, I thrust her upon that flat piece of ground, and there fastened or moored her, by sticking my two broken oars into the ground—one on one side, near one end, and one on the other side, near the other end; and thus I lay till the water ebbed away, and left my raft and all my cargo safe on shore. . . . I found also that the island I was in was barren, and, as I saw good reason to believe, uninhabited, except by wild beasts, of which, however, I saw none. . . .

I now began to consider that I might yet get a great many things out of the ship which would be useful to me, and particularly some of the rigging and sails, and such other things as might come to land; and I resolved to make another voyage on board the vessel, if possible. And as I knew that the first storm that blew must necessarily break her all in pieces, I resolved to set all other things apart till I got everything out of the ship that I could get. Then I called a council—that is, to say, in my thought—whether I should take back the raft; but this appeared impracticable. So I resolved to go as before, when the tide was down; and I did so, only that I stripped before I went from my hut, having nothing on but a checkered shirt, a pair of linen drawers, and a pair of pumps on my feet.

I got on board the ship as before, and prepared a second raft; and having had experience of the first, I neither made this so unwieldy nor loaded it so hard, but yet I brought away several things very useful to me; as, first, in the carpenter's stores I found two or three bags full of nails and spikes, a great screw-jack, a dozen or two of hatchets, and, above all, that most useful thing called a grindstone. All these I secured, together with several things belonging to the gunner, particularly two or three iron crows, and two barrels of musket bullets, seven muskets, and another fowling piece, with some small quantity of powder more, a large bagful of small shot, and a great roll of sheet lead; but this last was so heavy I could not hoist it up to get it over the ship's side.

Besides these things, I took all the men's clothes that I could find, and a spare fore-topsail, a hammock, and some bedding; and with this I loaded my second raft, and brought them all safe on shore, to my very great comfort. I was under some apprehension during my absence from the land that my provisions might be devoured on shore; but when I came back I found no sign of any visitor . . .

Having got my second cargo on shore—though I was obliged to open the barrels of powder, and bring them by parcels, for they were too heavy, being large casks—I went to work to make me a little tent, with the sail and some poles which I cut for that purpose; and into this tent I brought everything that I knew would spoil either with rain or sun; and I piled all the empty chests and casks up in a circle round the tent, to fortify it from any sudden attack, either from man or beast.

When I had done this, I blocked up the door of the tent with some boards within, and an empty chest set up on end without; and spreading one of the beds upon the ground, laying my two pistols just at my head, and my gun at length by me, I went to bed the first time, and slept very quietly all night. I was very weary and heavy; for the night before I had slept little, and had labored very hard all day, as well to fetch those things from the ship as to get them on shore.

I had the biggest magazine of all kinds now that ever was laid up, I believe, for one man; but still I was not satisfied, for while the ship sat upright in that posture I thought I ought to get everything out of her that I could; so every day, at low water, I went on board, and brought away something or other; but particularly, the third time I went, I brought away as much of the rigging as I could, as also all the small ropes and rope twine I could get, with a piece of spare canvas, which was to mend the sails upon occasion, and the barrel of wet gunpowder. In a word, I brought away all the sails, first and last; only that I was fain to cut them in pieces, and bring as much at a time as I could, for they were no more useful to me for sails, but as mere canvas only.

But that which comforted me more still was, that at last of all, after I had made five or six such voyages as these, and thought I had nothing more to expect from the ship that was worth my meddling with —I say, after all this, I found a great hogshead of bread, three large runlets of rum, a box of fine sugar, and a barrel of fine flour: this was surprising to me, because I had given over expecting any more provisions except what was spoiled by the water. I soon emptied the hogshead of the bread, and wrapped it up, parcel by parcel, in pieces of the sails, which I cut out; and, in a word, I got all this safe on shore also, though at several times.

The next day I made another voyage, and now, having plundered the ship of what was portable and fit to hand out, I began with the cable; cutting the great cable into pieces such as I could move, I got two cables and a hawser on shore, with all the ironwork I could get; and having cut down the spritsail-yard and the mizzen-yard, and everything I could to make a large raft, I loaded it with all those heavy goods and came away; but my good luck began to leave me, for this raft was so unwieldy, and so overladen, that after I was entered the little cove, where I had landed the rest of my goods, not being able to guide it so handily as I did the other, it overset, and threw me and all my cargo into the water; as for myself, it was no great harm, for I was near the shore; but as to my cargo, it was great part lost, especially the iron, which I expected would have been of great use to me; however, when the tide was out I got most of the pieces of cable ashore, and some of the iron, though with infinite labor; for I was fain to dip for it into the water, a work which fatigued me very much. After this, I went every day on board, and brought away what I could get.

I had now been thirteen days on shore, and had been eleven times on board the ship, in which time I had brought away all that one pair of hands could well be supposed capable of bringing; though I verily believe, had the calm weather held, I should have brought away the whole ship, piece by piece; but preparing the twelfth time to go on board, I found the wind began to rise; however, at low water I went on board, and though I thought I had rummaged the cabin so effectually that nothing more could be found, yet I discovered a locker with drawers in it, in one of which I found two or three razors, and one pair of large scissors, with some ten or a dozen of good knives and forks; in another I found about thirty-six pounds' value in money—some European coin, some Brazil, some pieces of eight, some gold, and some silver.

I smiled to myself at the sight of this money. "Oh!" said I aloud, "what art thou good for? Thou art not worth to me—no, not the taking off the ground; one of those knives is worth all this heap. I have no manner of use for thee; e'en remain where thou art, and go to the bottom, as a creature whose life is not worth saving." However, upon second thoughts, I took it away; and wrapping all in a piece of canvas, I began to think of making another raft; but while I was preparing this, I found the sky overcast, and the wind began to rise, and in a quarter of an hour it blew a fresh gale from the shore. It presently occurred to me that it was in vain to pretend to make a raft with the wind offshore; and that it was my business to be gone before the tide of flood began, otherwise I might not be able to reach the shore at all. Accordingly, I let myself down into the water, and swam across the channel which lay between the ship and the sands, and even that with difficulty enough, partly with the weight of the things I had about me, and partly from the roughness of the water; for the wind rose very hastily, and before it was quite high water it blew a storm. But I was gotten home to my little tent, where I lay, with all my wealth about me very secure. It blew very hard all that night, and in the morning, when I looked out, behold, no more ship was to be seen.

## SCHUMANN-HEINK'S FIRST CONTRACT [1]

*Mary Lawton*

I had studied singing three years, when Marie Wilt—the famous soprano, one of the greatest that ever lived—came to Graz. She was a wonder! One day she sang coloratura parts like the Queen in *The Magic Flute,* and the next, Valentine, in *Les Huguenots*. She was bad-tempered—a big woman, fat and disagreeable as could be, but what a voice! Nearest to her voice was Nordica. Dear Nordica!

About this time I got a chance to sing the alto part in the Ninth Symphony of Beethoven with Marie Wilt. But even then I didn't know the notes, for I remember Wilt said to my teacher,

"Why, she doesn't know it!"

And my teacher replied: "Oh, never mind that—I can teach it to her by ear. She is intelligent and very musical. I know she will be very good for this part. You can depend upon it."

So this was my first public singing, with Marie Wilt. She sang the soprano and I the alto part. It was a great day for me when I sang with this wonderful opera singer. Marie Wilt looked splendid and had on a beautiful dress, too. I was a homely little thing, famous even then for my homeliness, and I had no nice clothes, and only old shoes made in the barracks by the soldiers! So I must have been a funny sight beside the great Wilt. When I sang that time, I had on a black dress made from one of Mother's, but I did have beautiful hair anyway, and took great pains fixing it, and I stuck a red rose in it, too—extra—for the occasion. Also, most important, I got about six dollars for that singing.

The first thing, I gave two dollars to my mother, kept some for myself, and the rest I gave to my bird. He had such a little house—cage, you call it—to live in, and that always made me feel badly, so I went to a secondhand store and bought a nice, big cage for him. Much later, when I went home from Dresden, he was still alive, but not singing. And it was a grateful thing that he opened his mouth wide as soon as I came into the room and almost sang his head off! He remembered me, you see. So it was a good thing for the canary bird, too, that I sang in Beethoven's Ninth Symphony.

I suppose I should have used some of the money for decent shoes, but I bought instead the first white curtains we ever had—secondhand, of course, but still white curtains—and so one of my dreams was fulfilled. You see, we had very little furniture —not even real beds. I remember the mattresses. They were only big sacks—the kind soldiers use—stuffed with straw. But I had such a way to make them that they were smooth like the finest beds. We had only rough military blankets for sheets. Then

[1] From Helen Ferris, *When I Was a Girl,* and Mary Lawton, *Schumann-Heink, Last of the Titans.*

for furniture we had boxes made like long sofas. Mother could use them for packing when we moved from place to place. And these had on top the sacks with straw, like the beds, only sewed through, so the stuffing didn't move. Then it was covered with cretonne and tacked on to the boxes and made to look like a real couch. The boxes were specially made; we always packed the stuff in them when we made a move. This was our furniture—and a cradle. Always the cradle! So, you see, the secondhand white curtains were a great event in our household.

I cannot remember the time, in early years, when the pennies didn't have to be counted, and we had sometimes as little food as we had furniture.

Father was in the barracks, and every officer had a piece of land allotted him. The pay of the soldiers and officers was so small that land was a godsend, and we worked every inch of it. We planted potatoes, turnips, cabbage, onions, etc., and a certain salad called *raddicci,* an Italian vegetable. In the summer the leaves are eaten for salad. We had this always for supper—a big bowl of salad was our evening meal at this time. That was all, unless there were cucumbers by a bit of good luck, then they were served only to Father and Mother, as they were a great luxury. Olive oil was out of the question, but we had plenty of vinegar—we got a barrel for a penny. But for oil we had only linseed oil, you call it here. That was cheap, but it didn't taste any too well, I recollect. A piece of bread and this salad was our supper always, except at the first of the month, when Mother had a little money on hand. Then we had a feast! She'd rub a little lard and flour together and make a kind of gravy into which she would put some spinach. Then she'd take a big piece of bread, rub it on both sides with garlic, and spread on the spinach gravy, and would say, "Now, children, see, I give you a fine supper tonight."

And, oh, how we always counted the days to the first of the month!

Poor Mother, how she managed I don't know. Of course, we always owed the grocery some money. At the first of every month we would pay as much as we could, but there was always something owing. Just before my sister was born, Mother was feeling so sick and had such an appetite for—what do you think?—just a piece of cheese! She said to me:

"Oh, Tini, I would so like a piece of Swiss cheese. How I wish I could have it now!"

"Well, I will go and get it," I said.

"But, my child, we have no money," she answered. "Swiss cheese is very expensive."

"Oh, never mind that," I said. "I'll get it for you."

So I went to the big fat grocery woman. She was sitting in front of her shop with all the neighbors around her, chattering. But I ran up to her and said,

"Oh, please, will you give me a piece of Swiss cheese?" putting on the sweetest face I could.

"*Swiss* cheese! *Swiss* cheese! How can that be done? Have you the money?"

"No, I haven't," I said.

"Well, then," she screamed, "you can't have it, that's all! Be off!"

"But," I said, "I *must* have some Swiss cheese. My mother is sick and wants it right away."

And then that old fatty just opened her mouth wide and roared. "Oh, who ever heard of a *sick* person wanting cheese! That's nonsense!"

I began to cry and said: "Oh, but my mother *is* sick, and she wants that Swiss cheese now."

That wicked old woman didn't relent, just kept shaking her head. "No, no, you cannot have it."

And then I had a bright thought. I knew she loved to see me dance, so I said:

"Oh, if you will give me the cheese for my mother, I will dance for you the czardas. I will sing it and dance it all for you, but first, *please,* my cheese. Mother is waiting."

"Oh, oh!" she grumbled. "You'll get the

cheese, and you won't come back! You'll have some excuse—your father, or something!"

"No, no," I said, "I'll come back, I promise you."

Well, my promises weren't much good at this time, but anyway she took a chance, because she loved the czardas so, and gave me a piece of Swiss cheese, wrapped it in a little paper, and I ran home with it tight in my hand, and said,

"Here it is, Mother, and that old fatty won't put it on the grocery bill, for I'm going back to sing and dance for her the czardas!"

Of course, poor Mother was delighted, and said: "Tini, you are a rascal—but you surely have a brain. Thank God for that!" So she kissed me and said, "Run quick now, before your father comes home."

And I said, "What! Will he scold me?"

"Never mind," she said. "Go quick—quick."

So I ran back to that old fatty, and there she sat waiting, with all the neighbors crowding about. So I sang and danced in fine style, and at the end she gave me an apple as a reward.

It was Graz, where I began to study singing, that I want to tell you about now—a word in memory of the people who were so kind and fed me in the days when I was always hungry.

There lived in Graz then a Fräulein Erich, the daughter of Colonel von Erich. I passed their house every day to go to my singing lessons. They had a big house and lived in the finest part of town. I ran always at the last minute for my lessons, because there was so much work at home. One day, as I was hurrying along, my songs in my arms—very important looking, of course—the Colonel's wife was sitting in the window working. She happened to look up, and I noticed that she followed me with her eyes, so the next day I greeted her—kissed my hand to her in grand style—which turned out afterward a good thing for me. Every day, when I ran by, I made some kind of greeting. So after a while she beckoned me to come in.

Of course, I was tickled to death at that, for as you know I was always hungry, and I scented food in the air. I was like a dog—I could smell it a mile away!

You know, in Austria, every one in the afternoon drinks coffee and has rolls and cakes to eat. Well, it smelled so good, that coffee, and the first day I went in I just couldn't help it, for right away I said,

"Oh, you must make wonderful coffee here—it smells so good!"

That, of course, was pretty fresh of me, but they all laughed and said,

"And would you like to have some of our good coffee?"

"I should say so," I answered.

"And who are you?" Frau Erich inquired.

Well, I told her, I was Tini Roessler; that I went twice a week to my singing lessons with Marietta von Leclair. Oh, I told her the whole story of my life—all for a cup of coffee!—and they were all very interested at once. That was the beginning of our friendship.

It was a wonderful room they took me into, with pictures of all their ancestors hanging on the walls and everything so beautiful. One of the daughters, Louisa, took a great fancy to me and an interest in my singing. So twice a week, after my lessons, it was arranged that I stop on my way home. The coffee was put in the stove to keep hot, and the rolls, too. The old Colonel, the father, was happy to have me come in, for it brought youth to that lonely house. He would talk and talk to me and ask all kinds of questions.

"And what have you studied today?" he would ask, and I answered him—with my mouth full of bread and butter, of course. First, I began with one roll and one cup of coffee, then I had two rolls, then four, and then, came sandwiches and cake too! Yes, I must say I ate "to beat the band!" During the four years I studied with Marietta, I always stopped for afternoon coffee on my way home. The father and mother died years after, but Louisa kept the friendship with me until she died. I always called her "Tante Louisa." I was her idol, and she followed my career always with love and sympathy. It was a wonderful friendship for me. A little garden spot in my life—even to this day it lives.

And now I must tell you of a wonderful thing that happened later, when the great opera singer, Materna, heard my voice. This, too, was in Graz. Wilhelm Kienzl was a famous composer of that time, and it was his beloved mother, Frau Nini Kienzl—whom I always called "Tante Nina Kienzl"—who took such an interest in me. She was a remarkable woman. She held a sort of salon at that time, and had celebrities from everywhere around her—playwrights, singers, sculptors, poets, philosophers. She always had the deepest interest in me, and I was often invited to her house. Of course, I had no nice clothes, so I kept in the background and just listened. But sometimes I sang, and it was there that the great Materna heard me, and LeBatt, the tenor, too. You see, Tante Nina Kienzl was the most elegant and highly educated person you can imagine, and my experience in her house was my first entrance to anything like society. It was most brilliant—wonderful! She took care of me with such affection! She had no daughter of her own, but she had a great kindness for all children. My poverty, I know, touched her heart, and she always tried to help me. It was another big step in my career, when Materna heard me sing. Materna was then one of the most famous German prima donnas. She sang first in light opera and then went into grand opera. She was very, very dark, but with a grand, imposing figure—and a great voice and personality—one of the most wonderful singers of her time.

LeBatt, the tenor, came with Materna from the Imperial Opera in Vienna. And it was there in Graz that Tante Nina Kienzl had Materna hear my voice.

"You will be surprised," she said to Materna, "you will be surprised, I tell you, when you hear this voice. I know how this child is struggling, and I want you to hear and like her, too."

So I sang for Materna. She listened quietly and said: "Why, yes, it is beautiful—a really beautiful voice, but she is much too young for opera. (I was only fifteen.) What can you do with a child like this? It's no use. She's impossible. Short, homely, undernourished, poverty-stricken, no appearance—nothing— Oh, no, no! Never!"

And so it was. I was homely. I made a poor appearance and had nothing then to say for myself. I was bashful—I always was —although I suppose I'd have hard work to make any one believe it now!

So, in spite of Tante Nina Kienzl, Materna was not interested in me at all.

But LeBatt, the tenor, was much kinder. He said, "I will speak for her—I will speak for this child to our Director." And then he asked me, "Do you think you can come to Vienna to sing for our Director?"

Of course, I said, "Yes," although I didn't have a penny for the journey. I thought and thought—and then came a bright idea. At that time one of Tante Nina Kienzl's friends, Field Marshal Benedikt, was in pension at Graz, Graz being the city of pensioners, you know. So I went to Tante Nina Kienzl and said:

"I beg of you to do me a favor. You can introduce me to Field Marshal Benedikt (he was very rich, through his wife), and as the child of an Austrian officer I could perhaps get money for the journey to Vienna."

So we were invited for dinner, and I will never forget that occasion as long as I live. Mother was there, of course, and Tante Nina Kienzl, and my teacher, Marietta von Leclair, very excited.

Well, I sang, and the outcome of it all was, he gave me fifty *gulden*—God love him!—and that is how I first went to Vienna.

Yes, I went to Vienna—to the Director—and sang. I sang "Ah, Mon Fils," and "The Drinking Song" from *Lucrezia Borgia*—the "Brindisi," they generally called it—which made me famous in the United

States long years after—though at that time I didn't know anything about the United States.

Well, I had a good success, but that wasn't enough. The Director (Zauner was his name) listened to me patiently, and then turned to LeBatt, and said, shrugging his shoulders:

"Well, what you want? What's all the fuss? Look at her! With such a face—and such poverty—nothing! What do you want? What do you expect?"

And then to me: "No, no, my dear child," waving his hands. "Go home, quick, and ask your kind friends who helped you to come to Vienna to buy you instead a sewing machine, and learn to be a good dressmaker maybe, or something like that—but a singer—an *opera* singer! No! Never—never in this world!"

So home I went, heartbroken!

And Father, when he heard the news, flew into a temper. "Well," he said, "I thought so—I told you so! That settles it. Now you go to school and learn to be a teacher. That at least is a *decent* profession, and I don't want to hear anything more, ever again, about theaters or actresses or opera singers—nothing like that! You be a teacher!"

Poor Mother, of course, was heartsick, too; she felt with me. But my teacher, Marietta von Leclair, was simply furious! She said to my father:

"You do not understand—you understand nothing! You don't understand even your child! You don't know her yet at all."

Mother told me about it after. I wasn't present, of course.

"You are the most cruel father—you are simply the meanest man I ever met in all my life. To kill the ambition of your own child! It is a crime! And I tell you that Tini is what I feel she is, and will prove to you and the world what I know she will prove."

She still had such a confidence in me, you see.

Then later on I told her, "Father said I must now give up my singing." No more lessons!

"Nonsense," she replied. "Never listen to him any more. You come for your lessons just the same. He's away all day and has not to know anything about it. Forget him!"

Then there came a little bit of a man. He was an agent, Levi was his name, and he came to Graz to make engagements for singers, and went to my teacher, of course. He said how the whole Vienna opera house was buzzing—talking about this new singer with the contralto voice—this young girl that sang there.

"Now," he said, "I am interested in young talent, and I telegraphed to the Dresden Royal Opera, and they are willing to pay the expenses and hear her there. And if they find she is what they think, and has talent and voice, they will make a contract with her, I'm sure."

So when my teacher Marietta von Leclair heard all this, she came right away to my mother.

"Now," she said, "*this* is the real opportunity! I know positively that this child will have a success. It is a sign of God!"

But poor Mother said: "Yes—perhaps. But we can not go a *second* time to the Field Marshal."

"We don't have to," cried Marietta. "We can borrow the money somewhere, because the opera will pay it back. She will have a success this time, I know."

"But suppose she doesn't," replied Mother, "and then we cannot pay the debts?"

"Never mind, Mother, never mind," I cried. "I'll get it somehow."

I was so excited at this good news that I thought right away of another plan. A schoolmate of mine had married a rich man in Graz, and he was interested in me, too. So I went to him, and when I told him of my opportunity, he said right away:

"Now, here are 400 *gulden*. Take them—do anything you want with them, but first get some real clothes! You cannot go to Dresden looking like that. Buy yourself a decent dress! And buy also some real shoes!"

You see, I still had those old soldier shoes, made in the barracks.

I took his advice. But first I gave 200 *gulden* to my mother, that she, too, could get a dress. Poverty is so terrible. My heart aches still again when I think of those black days.

But this time I didn't say anything to my father about my trip. I lied because I thought it was necessary. I said to him:

"Father, I'm invited with a school friend to go on a visit to the mountains, but I'll be back soon—in a week."

Well, it doesn't sound a very good lie now, after all these years, but it was sufficient then. He believed me. Poor Father!

So, all alone, I went to Dresden. My feelings you can imagine. I went to the Hotel Weber, where Sembrich lived when she was young. I had already bought the new dress and hat and shoes, so I presented a decent appearance for the first time in my life. There were three other singers to be heard on trial—all contraltos. Well, they sang first, I was the last. To me who sat listening, they sounded so beautiful! I thought: "Oh, I am nothing to compare to them. I have no chance here!" And my heart dropped down into my new boots!

Well, when my turn came, I sang my same songs, "Ah, Mon Fils!", and "The Drinking Song." I did my very best—I had to succeed this time! When I was through, Plateu, an old Hanover aristocrat—a big, wonderful man (he was the *intendant-impresario*—like Gatti-Casazza at the Metropolitan, in the United States) said:

"It is a very beautiful voice, I will engage you. I'll pay you 3,600 marks the first year, 4,600 marks the second year, and the third year I pay you 5,000 marks—so you will go up all the time. After the first year, if you disappoint us, I have, of course, the right to cancel the contract. In addition, you can sing in the cathedral, too."

Well, I was so overcome, I could only stare at him and nod my head. I couldn't speak.

"Now, we will make the contract," he went on. "You will sign first, and then we have to send it to the King, and if he is satisfied, everything is well and good."

So I had my contract for 3,600 marks. I hardly knew what a mark was—I had seen so little money.

"Now," he said, "after you sign, and it comes back from the King, then your father must sign it, too. We will send it to you."

But that was not all, for when he told me I must come back in September to begin my engagement, I burst out crying and said:

"Herr Director, you tell me I must be back in September—but that is impossible! In October we expect another baby, and my mother—what will she do without me? I must help my mother! I must be there!"

And this man—well he just stared at me, then the tears ran in his old eyes, he was so touched.

"You poor child," he said. Oh, I remember how he looked at me standing there.

"You poor, blessed child! Don't worry. Everything will be all right."

But I still asked, "What will Mother do without me?"

"Oh," he said, "she can keep a servant *now*—she will not need you."

That comforted me, and so I signed the contract.

My first engagement!

Happy? I should say so! I came home, and they had given me 200 marks to make the expenses. I had to go to Vienna to get the train for home—a whole day and a night. I had my new dress—but I was carefull not to wear it on the train. I tied it up in a package and put my old one on, in spite of the new contract.

When Father saw me, he said: "Well, and did you have a good visit? You don't look as if you'd been in the mountains. You look pale, Ernestine. *How is that?*"

"It is all right, Father," I said. "Now I can tell you the truth. I was not in the mountains at all!"

"But *where* have you been, then?"

"In Dresden, Father."

"In *Dresden?* And with whom, Ernestine?"

"Alone!"

Oh, you should have seen him! "What does this mean?" he said, turning to my mother. "Did you know about this?"

"Yes, I knew about it, Hans," she replied, smiling.

And then it started—the row! But when I said I had a contract with the Dresden opera, he just laughed and laughed.

"Oh, ho! Oh, ho! And you say they paid for your trip?" he roared. "Well, that is very decent of them, I must say."

But when I told him the King had to sign the contract,

"Oh, the King wouldn't bother with a contract with you. Is this another fine story that you tell me?"

Poor Father! He didn't understand—he simply couldn't believe it. And I was a little bit frightened, too, and began to wonder if it was true myself. Then at last, two weeks after, the postman came with a big envelope with the seal from the Dresden Royal Opera—the contract!

And Mother! When she saw that envelope, she just put her head down on the table and cried and cried! She was all broken to pieces. Then she held me in her arms with such a look on her face—for she knew that good fortune had come to me at last.

"Tini! Tini!" she cried, "God in heaven bless you! But what shall I do without you?"

"Oh," I told her, "the Director says you can now keep a servant, and I will send you all I can, always."

Then Mother talked very seriously, and told me I must dress well and keep strong and eat good food. "You can have proper food now, thank God."

And then came her great triumph when she showed the contract to Father, and said, "Now, I hope, Hans, you are satisfied at last and will believe your child, for here is the contract, with the King's signature!"

But Father—how he looked at it! "Why," he grumbled, "she gets more money than I get—and she'll make more money than I do!" He couldn't believe it—even then.

And I was proud like a peacock! And Father was proud, in his heart. He was a mighty good Father, but he was always frightened for me.

"God only knows what will happen to you, Tini, you are so young," he said.

Well, his fears were useless, because from the very first, I had one big protection: *I was homely*. I had nice hair and black eyes, but a yellow complexion, always. Yes, I was homely—and I knew it. That is why vanity never bothered me. I knew from the beginning how homely I was. But, homely or not—nothing mattered then. For at last I had my contract for the Dresden Royal Opera—signed by the King!

## JOHN HALIFAX FACES THE RIOTERS[1]

*Dinah Maria Mulock Craik*

It was the year 1800, long known in English households as "the dear year." The present generation can have no conception of what a terrible time that was—War, Famine, and Tumult stalking hand-in-hand, and no one to stay them. For between the upper and lower classes there was a great gulf fixed; the rich ground the faces of the poor, the poor hated, yet meanly succumbed to, the rich.

These troubles, which were everywhere abroad, reached us even in our quiet town of Norton Bury. For myself, personally, they touched me not, or, at least, only kept fluttering like evil birds outside the home-tabernacle,—for these two years with me had been very hard.

Though I had to bear so much bodily suffering, that I was seldom told of any worldly cares, still I often fancied things were going ill both within and without our doors. Jael, our housekeeper, complained in an under-key of being stinted, or boasted aloud of her own ingenuity in making ends meet; and my father's brow grew continually heavier, graver, sterner; sometimes so stern that I dared not wage, what was,

[1] From Dinah Maria Mulock Craik, *John Halifax, Gentleman.*

openly or secretly, the quiet but incessant crusade of my existence—the bringing back of John Halifax.

He still remained my father's clerk—nay, I sometimes thought he was even advancing in duties and trusts, for I heard of his being sent on long journeys up and down England to buy grain—my father, Abel Fletcher, having added to his tanning business the flour-mill hard by. But of these journeys my father never spoke; indeed he rarely mentioned John at all. He had not forgiven us for our adventure of two years before, when John and I had gone to Coltham to see Mrs. Siddons play *Lady Macbeth*. For three brief hours we hung upon her every breath, as if it could stay even the wheels of time. But it could not, and could not stay my father's anger, as we learned when we reached home. He had kept John as his clerk, but no longer as his son's companion. After that day, for two long years I never once saw the face of John Halifax. He was as inexorable as my father; no underhand or clandestine friendship would he admit—no, not even for my sake. I knew quite well, that until he could walk in openly, honorably, proudly, he never would re-enter my father's door.

One other fact I noticed: that a little lad, afterward discovered to be Jem Watkins, had somehow crept into our household as errand boy. I noticed, too, that the said Jem, whenever he came in my way, in house or garden, was the most capital "little foot-page" that ever invalid had; knowing intuitively all my needs, and serving me with an unfailing devotion.

Summer was passing. People began to watch with anxious looks the thin harvest fields—as Jael often told me, when she came home from her afternoon walks. "It was piteous to see them," she said; "only July, and the quartern loaf nearly three shillings, and meal four shillings a peck."

And then she would glance at our flour-mill, where for several days a week the water wheel was as quiet as on Sundays; for my father kept his grain locked up, waiting for what, he wisely judged, might be a worse harvest than the last. But Jael, though she said nothing, often looked at the flour-mill, and shook her head. And after one market day—when she came in rather "flustered," saying, there had been a mob outside the mill, until "that young man, Halifax" had gone out and spoken to them—she never once allowed me to take my rare walk under the trees; nor, if she could help it, would she even let me sit watching the lazy Avon from the garden wall.

One Sunday—it was the first of August, for my father had come back from meeting, very much later than usual; and Jael said he had gone, as was his annual custom on that his wedding day, to the Friends' burial ground on St. Mary's Lane, where, far away from her own kindred and people, my poor young mother had been laid—on this one Sunday, I began to see that things were going wrong. Abel Fletcher sat at dinner, wearing the heavy, hard look which had grown upon his face, not unmingled with the wrinkles planted by physical pain. For, with all his temperance, he could not quite keep down his hereditary enemy, gout; and this week it had clutched him pretty hard.

After dinner, my father sent for me and all his household.

He first addressed Jael. "Woman, was it thee who cooked the dinner today?"

She gave a dignified affirmative.

"Thee must give us no more such dinners. No cakes, no pastry kickshaws, and only wheaten bread enough for absolute necessity. Our neighbors shall not say that Abel Fletcher has flour in his mill, and plenty in his house, while there is famine abroad in the land. So take heed."

"I do take heed," answered Jael, staunchly. "Thee canst not say I waste a penny of thine. And for myself, do I not pity the poor? On First Day a woman cried after me about wasting good flour in starch—today, behold."

And with a spasmodic bridling up, she pointed to the *bouffante* which used to stand up stiffly round her withered old throat, and stick out in front like a pouter pigeon. Alas! it's glory and starch were alike departed; it now appeared nothing but a heap of crumpled and yellowish muslin. Poor Jael! I knew this was the most heroic personal sacrifice she could have made, yet I could not help smiling; even my father did the same.

"Dost thee mock me, Abel Fletcher?" cried she, angrily. "Preach not to others, while the sin lies on thy own head."

And I am sure poor Jael was innocent of any jocular intention, as advancing sternly, she pointed to her master's pate, where his long-worn powder was scarcely distinguishable from the snows of age. He bore the assault gravely and unshrinkingly, merely saying, "Woman, peace!"

"Nor while," pursued Jael, driven apparently to the last and most poisoned arrow in her quiver of wrath—"while the poor folk be starving in scores about Norton Bury, and the rich folk there will not sell their wheat under famine price. Take heed to thyself, Abel Fletcher."

My father winced, either from a twinge of gout or conscience; and then Jael suddenly ceased the attack, sent the other servants out of the room, and tended her master as carefully as if she had not insulted him. When, being at last relieved, he and I were sitting in the room alone, he said to me—

"Phineas, the tan-yard has thriven ill of late, and I thought the mill would make up for it. But if it will not, it will not. Wouldst thee mind, my son, being left a little poorer when I am gone?"

"Father!"

"Well, then, in a few days I will begin selling my wheat, as that lad has advised and begged me to do these weeks past. He is a sharp lad, and I am getting old. Perhaps he is right."

"Who, father?" I asked, rather hypocritically.

"Thee knowest well enough—John Halifax."

I thought it best to say no more.

On the Monday morning my father went to the tan-yard as usual. I spent the day in my bedroom. What was passing in the world, in the town, or even in the next street, was to me faint as dreams.

At dinner time I rose, went down stairs, and waited for my father; waited one, two, three hours. It was very strange. He never by any chance overstayed his time, without sending a message home, so I despatched Jem Watkins to the tan-yard to see after his master.

He came back with ill news. The lane leading to the tan-yard was blocked up with a wild mob. Even the stolid, starved patience of our Norton Bury poor had come to an end at last—they had followed the example of many others. There was a bread riot in the town.

God only knows how terrible those riots were; when the people rose in desperation to get food for themselves, their wives, and children. God only knows what madness was in each individual heart of that concourse of poor wretches, styled the mob, when every man took up arms, certain that there were before him but two alternatives, starving or—hanging.

"And where is my father?" I demanded of Jem, but he didn't know.

"Jael, somebody must go at once, and find my father."

"I am going," said Jael, who had already put on her cloak and hood. Of course, despite all her opposition, I went too.

The tan-yard was deserted; the mob had divided, and gone, one half to our mill, the rest to another that was lower down the river. I asked of a poor frightened bark-cutter if she knew where my father was. She thought he was gone for the "milling-tary," but Mr. Halifax was at the mill now—she hoped no harm would come to Mr. Halifax.

Even in that moment of alarm I felt a sense of pleasure. I did not know John had come already to be called "Mr. Halifax."

There was nothing for me but to wait here till my father returned. He could not surely be so insane as to go to the mill—and John was there. Terribly was my heart divided, but my duty lay with my father.

This minute I heard a footstep crossing the yard. No, it was not my father's—it was firmer, quicker, younger. I sprang from the bark-heap.

"Phineas!"

"John!"

What a grasp that was—both hands! And how fondly and proudly I looked up in his face—the still boyish face. But the figure was quite that of a man, now.

"Where is your father?" he asked.

"I wish I knew! Gone for the soldiers, they say."

"No, not that—he would never do that. I must go and look for him. Good-by." And he was gone.

In a few minutes I saw him and my father enter the tan-yard together. He was talking earnestly, and my father was listening—aye, listening—and to John Halifax! But whatever the argument was, it failed to move him. Greatly troubled, but staunch as a rock, my old father stood, resting his lame foot on a heap of hides. I went to meet him.

"Phineas," said John, anxiously, "come and help me. No, Abel Fletcher," he added, rather proudly, in reply to a sharp suspicious glance at us both; "your son and I only met ten minutes ago, and have scarcely exchanged a word. But we cannot waste time over that matter now. Phineas, help me to persuade your father to save his property. He will not call for the aid of the law, because he is a Friend, but he might get his own men to defend his property, and need not do what he is bent on doing—go to the mill himself."

I caught his arm—"Father, don't go."

"My son," said he, turning on me one of his "iron looks," as I used to call them, "my son, no opposition. Any who try that with me, fail. If those fellows had waited two days more, I would have sold all my wheat at a hundred shillings the quarter; now, they shall have nothing. It will teach them wisdom another time. Get thee safe home, Phineas, my son; Jael, go thou likewise."

But neither went. John held me back as I was following my father.

"He will do it, Phineas, and I suppose he must. Please God, I'll take care no harm touches him—but you go home."

That was not to be thought of. Fortunately, the time was too brief for argument, so the discussion soon ended. He followed my father, and I followed him. For Jael, she disappeared.

There was a private path from the tan-yard to the mill, along the river side; by this we went in silence. When we reached the spot, it was deserted; but farther down the river we heard a scuffling, and saw a number of men breaking down our garden wall.

"They think he is gone home," whispered John; "we'll get in here the safer. Quick, Phineas."

We crossed the little bridge; John took a key out of his pocket, and let us into the mill by a small door—the only entrance, and that was barred and trebly barred within.

The mill was a queer, musty, silent place, especially the machinery room, the sole flooring of which was the dark, dangerous stream. We stood there a good while—it was the safest place, having no windows. Then we followed my father to the top story, where he kept his bags of grain. There were a great many; enough, in these times, to make a large fortune—a cursed fortune, wrung out of human lives.

"Oh! how could my father—"

"Hush!" whispered John, "it was for his son's sake, you know."

But while we stood, and with a meaning but rather grim smile, Abel Fletcher counted his bags, worth almost as much as bags of gold—we heard a hammering at the door below. The rioters were come.

Miserable rioters—a handful of weak, starved men—pelting us with stones and words. One pistol shot might have routed them all, but my father's doctrine of non-resistance forbade. Small as their force seemed, there was something at once formidable and pitiful in the low howl that reached us at times.

"Bring out the bags! Us mun have bread!"

"Throw down thy corn, Abel Fletcher!"

"Abel Fletcher *will* throw it down to ye, ye knaves," said my father, leaning out of the upper window; while a sound, half curses, half cheers of triumph, answered him from below.

"That is well," exclaimed John, eagerly. "Thank you—thank you, Mr. Fletcher—I knew you would yield at last."

"Didst thee, lad?" said my father, stopping short.

"Not because they forced you—not to save your life, but because it was right."

"Help me with this bag," was all the reply.

It was a great weight, but not too great for John's young arm. He hauled it up.

"Now, open the window. Dash the panes through, it matters not. On to the window, I tell thee."

"But if I do, the bag will fall into the river. You cannot—oh, no!—you cannot mean that!"

"Haul it up to the window, John Halifax."

But John remained immovable.

"I must do it myself, then;" and in the desperate effort he made, somehow the bag of grain fell, and fell on his lame foot. Tortured into frenzy with the pain—or else, I will still believe, my old father would not have done such a deed—his failing strength seemed doubled and trebled. In an instant more he had got the bag half through the window, and the next sound we heard was its heavy splash in the river below.

Flung into the river, the precious wheat, and in the very sight of the famished rioters! A howl of fury and despair arose. Some plunged into the water, ere the eddies left by the falling mass had ceased, but it was too late. A sharp substance in the river's bed had cut the bag, and we saw thrown up to the surface, and whirled down the Avon, thousands of dancing grains. A few of the men swam, or waded after them, clutching a handful here or there; but by the mill pool the river ran swift, and the wheat had all soon disappeared, except what remained in the bag when it was drawn on shore. Over even that they fought like demons.

Abel Fletcher sat on his remaining bags, in an exhaustion that I think was not all physical pain. The paroxysm of anger past, he, ever a just man, could not fail to be struck with what he had done. He seemed subdued, even to something like remorse.

John looked at him, and looked away. For a minute he listened in silence to the shouting outside, and then turned to my father.

"Sir, you must come now. Not a second to lose. They will fire the mill next."

"Let them."

"Let them?—and Phineas is here!"

My poor father! He rose at once.

We got him downstairs—he was very lame—his ruddy face all drawn and white with pain; but he did not speak one word of opposition, or utter a groan of complaint.

The flour-mill was built on piles, in the centre of the narrow river. It was only a few steps of bridge to either bank. The little door was on the Norton Bury side, and was hid from the opposite shore, where the rioters had now collected. In a minute, we had crept forth, and dashed out of sight, in the narrow path which had been made from the mill to the tan-yard.

"Will you take my arm? We must get on fast."

"Home?" said my father, as John led him passively along.

"No, sir, not home; they are there before you. Your life's not safe an hour—unless, indeed, you get soldiers to guard it."

Abel Fletcher gave a decided negative. The stern old Quaker held to his principles still.

"Then you must hide for a time. Come to my room. You will be secure there. Urge him, Phineas—for your sake and his own."

But my poor broken father needed no

urging. Grasping more tightly both John's arm and mine, which for the first time in his life he leaned upon, he submitted to be led whither we chose. So, after this long interval of time, I once more stood in Sally Watkins' small attic; where ever since I first brought him there, John Halifax had lived.

"Now," said John, hastily smoothing his bed, so that my father might lie down, and wrapping his cloak round me—"you must both be very still. You will likely have to spend the night here. Jem shall bring you a light and supper. You will make yourself easy, Abel Fletcher?"

"Aye." It was strange to see how decidedly, yet respectfully, John spoke, and how quietly my father answered.

"And Phineas, you will take care of yourself. Good-by, I must be off."

"Whither?" said my father, rousing himself.

"To try and save the house and the tanyard. I fear we must give up the mill. No, don't hold me, Phineas. I run no risk; everybody knows me."

The evening passed very slowly. My father, exhausted with pain, lay on the bed and dozed.

After midnight—I know not how long, for I lost count of the hours by the Abbey chimes, and our light had gone out—after midnight I heard by my father's breathing that he was asleep. I was thankful to see it for his sake, and also for another reason.

I left him, and crept downstairs into Sally Watkins' kitchen. It was silent, only the faithful warder, Jem, dozed over the dull fire.

"Where is Mr. Halifax?" I asked.

"Doan't know, sir—wish I did! Wouldn't be long a-finding out though—on'y he says: 'Jem, you stop 'ere, wi' they' " (pointing his thumb up the staircase). "So, Master Phineas, I stop."

"Jem, lend me your coat and hat—I'm going out into the town."

Jem was so astonished that he stood with open mouth while I took the garments from him, and unbolted the door. At last it seemed to occur to him that he ought to intercept me.

"But, sir, Mr. Halifax said—"

"I am going to look for Mr. Halifax."

I stole along the dark alley into the street. It was very silent—I need not have borrowed Jem's exterior in order to creep through a throng of maddened rioters. There was no sign of any such, except that under one of the three oil-lamps that lit the night darkness of Norton Bury, lay a few smoldering hanks of hemp, well resined. They, then, had thought of that dreadful engine of destruction—fire.

On I ran, speeded by a dull murmur which I fancied I heard; and still there was no one in the street—no one except the Abbey watchman lounging in his box. I roused him, and asked if all was safe. Where were the rioters?

"What rioters?"

"At Abel Fletcher's mill; they may be at his house now—"

"Aye, I think they be."

"And will not one man in the town help him; no constables—no law?"

"Oh! he's a Quaker; the law don't help Quakers."

That was the truth—the hard, grinding truth—in those days. Liberty, justice, were idle names to Nonconformists of every kind.

I had forgotten this; bitterly I remembered it now. So, wasting no more words, I flew along the churchyard, until I saw, shining against the boles of the chestnut trees, a red light. It was one of the hempen torches. Now, at last, I had got into the midst of the rioters.

They were a mere handful—not above two score—apparently the relics of the band which had attacked the mill, joined with a few plow-lads from the country around. Wherever they had been ransacking, as yet they had not attacked my father's house; it stood up on the other side of the road, barred, black, silent.

I heard a muttering: "Th' old man bean't there." "Nobody knows where he be."

"Be us all y'ere?" said the man with the torch, holding it up so as to see round him. It was well then that I appeared as Jem Watkins. But no one noticed me, except one man, who skulked behind a tree, and of whom I was rather afraid, as he was apparently intent on watching.

"Ready, lads? Now for the rosin! Blaze 'un out."

But, in the eager scuffle, the torch, the only one alight, was knocked down and trodden out. A volley of oaths arose, though whose fault it was no one seemed to know; but I missed my man from behind the tree, nor found him till after the angry throng had rushed on to the nearest lamp. He looked round to see if none were by, and then sprang over the gate. Dark as it was, I thought I recognized him.

"John?"

"Phineas?" He was beside me in a bound. "We have a minute's time. I must have you safe. We must go into the house."

"Who is there?"

"Jael; she is as good as a host of constables; she has braved the fellows once tonight, but they're back again, or will be directly."

"And the mill?"

"Safe, as yet; I have had three of the tanyard men there since yesterday morning, though your father did not know. I have been going to and fro all night between there and here."

He tapped at the window. In a few seconds Jael had unbarred the door, let us in, and closed it again securely, mounting guard behind it with something that looked very like my father's pistols.

"Bravo!" said John, when we stood together in the barricaded house, and heard the threatening murmur of voices and feet outside.

"I have done all as thee bade me. Thee art a sensible lad, John Halifax. We are secure, I think."

Secure? Bolts and bars secure against fire? For that was threatening us now.

"They can't mean it! Surely they can't mean it!" repeated John, as the cry of "Burn 'un out!" rose louder and louder.

But they did mean it. From the attic window we watched them light torch after torch; sometimes throwing one at the house, but it fell harmless against the staunch oaken door, and blazed itself out on our stone steps. All it did was to show more plainly than even daylight had shown, the gaunt, ragged forms and pinched faces, furious with famine.

John, as well as I, recoiled at that miserable sight.

To my horror, he threw up the window wide, and leaned out.

"My men, I want to speak to you."

He might as well have spoken to the roaring sea. The only answer was a shower of missiles, which missed their aim. The rioters were too far off; our spiked iron railings, eight feet high or more, being a barrier which none had yet ventured to climb. But at length one random stone hit John on the chest.

I pulled him in, but he declared he was not hurt. Terrified, I implored him not to risk his life.

"Life is not always the first thing to be thought of," said he, gently. "Don't be afraid—I shall come to no harm. But I *must* do what I think right, if it is to be done."

While he spoke, I could hardly hear him for the bellowings outside. More savage still grew the cry—

"Burn 'em out! Burn 'em out! They be only Quakers!"

"There's not a minute to lose. Stop, let me think—Jael, is that a pistol?"

"Loaded," she said, handing it over to him with a kind of stern delight. Certainly, Jael was not meant to be a Friend.

John ran downstairs, and before I guessed his purpose, had unbolted the hall door, and stood on the flight of steps in full view of the mob.

There was no bringing him back, so of course I followed. A pillar sheltered me; I do not think he saw me, though I stood close behind him.

So sudden had been his act, that even the rioters did not seem to have noticed, or clearly understood it, till the next lighted torch showed them the young man standing there, with his back to the door—*outside* the door.

The sight fairly confounded them. Even I felt that for the moment he was safe. They were awed—nay, paralyzed, by his daring.

But the storm raged too fiercely to be lulled, except for one brief minute. A confusion of voices burst out afresh—

"Who be thee?" "Burn 'un, anyhow!" "Touch 'un, if ye dare."

There was evidently a division arising. One big man, who had made himself very prominent all along, seemed trying to calm the tumult.

John stood his ground. Once a torch was flung at him; he stooped and picked it up. I thought he was going to hurl it back again, but he did not; he only threw it down, and stamped it out safely with his foot. This simple action had a wonderful effect on the crowd.

The big fellow advanced to the gate, and called John by his name.

"Is that you, Jacob Baines? I am sorry to see you here."

"Be ye, sir?"

"What do you want?"

"Nought wi' thee. We wants Abel Fletcher. Where's um?"

"I shall certainly not tell you."

As John said this, again the noise arose, and again Jacob Baines seemed to have power to quiet the rest.

John Halifax never stirred. Evidently he was pretty well known. I caught many a stray sentence, such as "Don't hurt the lad."—"He were kind to my lad, he were."—"No, he be a real gentleman."—"No, he comed here as poor as us," and the like. At length, one voice, sharp and shrill, was heard above the rest.

"I say, young man, didst ever know what it was to be pretty nigh famished?"

"Aye, many a time. I know what it is to be hungry. I'm sorry for you—sorry from the bottom of my heart."

There was no mistaking that compassionate accent, nor the murmur which followed it.

"But what must us do, Mr. Halifax?" cried Jacob Baines. "Us be starved, a'most. What's the good o' talking to we?"

John's countenance relaxed. He went down to the locked gate.

"Suppose I gave you something to eat, would you listen to me afterwards?"

There rose up a frenzied shout of assent.

"You must promise to be peaceable," said John, again, very resolutely, as soon as he could obtain a hearing. "You are Norton Bury folk, I know you. I could get every one of you hanged, even though Abel Fletcher is a Quaker. Mind, you'll be peaceable?"

"Aye, aye! Some'at to eat; give us some'at to eat."

John Halifax called out to Jael; bade her bring all the food of every kind that there was in the house, and give it to him out of the parlor window. She obeyed—I marvel now to think of it—but she implicitly obeyed. Only I heard her fix the bar to the closed front door, and go back, with a strange, sharp sob, to her station at the hall window.

"Now, my lads, come in!" and he unlocked the gate.

They came thronging up the steps, not more than two score, I imagined, in spite of the noise they had made. But two score of such famished, desperate men, God grant I may never again see!

John divided the food as well as he could among them; they fell to it like wild beasts. Meat, cooked or raw, loaves, vegetables, meal; all came alike, and were clutched, gnawed, and scrambled for, in the fierce selfishness of hunger. Only a few sat and ate like rational human beings; and there was one, a little shrill-voiced man, who asked if he might "tak' a bit o' bread to the old wife at home?"

John called me aside, explained to me, and asked my advice and consent, as Abel

Fletcher's son, to a plan that had come into his mind. It was to write orders, which each man could present at our mill and receive a certain amount of flour.

"Do you think your father would agree?"

"I think he would."

"Yes," John added, pondering, "I am sure he would. And besides, if he does not give some, he may lose all. But he would not do it for fear of that. No, he is a just man; I am not afraid. Give me some paper, Jael."

He sat down as composedly as if he had been alone in the counting house, and wrote. Then to me he said, "Take the pen. It is your part to sign them, Phineas."

I obeyed.

"Isn't this better than hanging?" said John, to the men, when he had distributed the little bits of paper—precious as pound-notes—and made them all fully understand the same. "Why, there isn't another gentleman in Norton Bury, who if you had come to burn *his* house down, would not have had the constables or the soldiers shoot down one-half of you like mad dogs, and send the other half to the county gaol. Now, for all your misdoings, we let you go quietly home, well fed, and with food for your children, too. *Why,* think you?"

"I don't know," said Jacob Baines, humbly.

"I'll tell you. Because Abel Fletcher is a Quaker, and a Christian."

"Hurrah for Abel Fletcher! Hurrah for the Quakers!" they shouted, waking up the echoes down Norton Bury streets; which, of a surety, had never echoed to *that* shout before. And so the riot was over.

"Now, let us go and fetch your father home," said John.

We found him on John's bed, still asleep. But as we entered he woke. The daylight shone on his face—it looked ten years older since yesterday—he stared, bewildered and angry, at John Halifax.

"Eh, young man—oh! I remember. Where is my son—where's my Phineas?"

I fell on his neck as if I had been a child.

"Thee art not hurt? Nor any one?"

"No," John answered; "nor is either the house or the tan-yard injured."

He looked amazed. "How has that been?"

"Phineas will tell you. Or, stay, better wait till you are at home."

But my father insisted on hearing. I told the whole, without any comments on John's behavior; he would not have liked it; and, besides, the facts spoke for themselves. I told the simple, plain story—nothing more.

Abel Fletcher listened at first in silence. As I proceeded, he felt about for his hat, put it on, and drew its broad brim close down over his eyes. Not even when I told him of the flour we had promised in his name, the giving of which would, as we had calculated, cost him considerable loss, did he utter a word or move a muscle.

John, at length, asked him if he were satisfied.

"Quite satisfied."

But, having said this, he sat so long, his hands locked together on his knees, and his hat drawn down, hiding all the face except the rigid mouth and chin—sat so long, so motionless, that we became uneasy.

John spoke to him, gently, almost as a son would have spoken.

"Are you very lame still? Could I help you to walk home?"

My father looked up, and slowly held out his hand.

"Thee hast been a good lad, and a kind lad to us; I thank thee."

There was no answer, none. But all the words in the world could not match that happy silence.

By degrees, we got my father home. It was just such another summer morning as the one, two years back, when we two had stood, exhausted and trembling, before that sternly bolted door. We both thought of that day; I knew not if my father did also.

He entered, leaning heavily on John. He sat down in the very seat, in the very room, where he had so harshly judged us—judged him.

Something, perhaps, of that bitterness rankled in the young man's spirit now, for he stopped on the threshold.

"Come in," said my father, looking up.

"If I am welcome; not otherwise."

"Thee art welcome."

## *Workers and Their Work: Suggested Grades*

*Grade One*
- Tony, the Steam Shovel Man

*Grade Two*
- Way Ping, Master of Boats

*Grade Three*
- The Small Yellow Train
- Rusty Pete, Cow Pony
- Children of Haiti

*Grade Four*
- Little Tonino
- Plowing

*Grade Five*
- Bridget Goes Prospecting
- The French Jongleurs

*Grade Six*
- Behind the Battlements
- Buck, the Lead-Dog
- Talking Wires

*Grade Seven*
- The Pearl Diver
- Chris Farrington: Able Seaman
- New York to Paris
- Sand Hogs
- Robinson Crusoe

*Grade Eight*
- Riding the Girders
- Schumann-Heink's First Contract
- John Halifax Faces the Rioters

## Books about Workers and Their Work

### Grades One and Two

Baruch, Dorothy W., *Big Fellow,* illus. by Jay Van Everen. Harper.

Beskow, Elsa, *Pelle's New Clothes,* illus. by the author. Harper.

Gramatky, Hardie, *Little Toot,* illus. by the author. Putnam.

Hader, Berta, and Elmer Hader, *The Farmer in the Dell,* illus. by the authors. Macmillan.

Hanna, Paul R., Genevieve Anderson, and William S. Gray, *Peter's Family,* illus. by Clarence Biers. Scott, Foresman.

Huber, Miriam Blanton, *Cinder, the Cat,* illus. by A. Gladys Peck. American Book.

———, *Skags, the Milk Horse,* illus. by Curtiss Sprague. American Book.

Kuh, Charlotte, *The Deliverymen,* illus. by Kurt Wiese. Macmillan.

———, *The Postman,* illus. by Kurt Wiese. Macmillan.

Lenski, Lois, *The Little Airplane,* illus. by the author. Oxford.

Lent, Henry B., *Diggers and Builders,* illus. by the author. Macmillan.

Read, Helen S., *Mr. Brown's Grocery Store,* illus. by Eleanor Lee. Scribner.

Rowe, Dorothy, *The Rabbit Lantern, and Other Stories of Chinese Children,* illus. by Ling Lui Tang. Macmillan.

Waddell, John F., Lois Gadd Nemec, and Maybell G. Bush, *Helpers,* illus. by Eleanor Osborn Eadie and A. Gladys Peck. Macmillan.

### Grades Three and Four

Bontemps, Arna, and Langston Hughes, *Popo and Fifina: Children of Haiti,* illus. by E. Simms Campbell. Macmillan.

Dalgliesh, Alice, *America Travels,* illus. by Hildegarde Woodward. Macmillan.

E-Yeh-Shure (Blue Corn), *I Am a Pueblo Indian Girl,* illus. by Indian artists. Morrow.

Field, Rachel, *Little Dog Toby,* illus. by the author. Macmillan.

Fogler, Doris, and Nina Nicol, *Rusty Pete of the Lazy A B,* illus. by Doris Fogler. Macmillan.

Hill, Helen, and Violet Maxwell, *Little Tonino,* illus. by the authors. Macmillan.

Lent, Henry B., *Grindstone Farm,* illus. by Wilfrid S. Bronson. Macmillan.

Machetanz, Frederick, *Panuck: Eskimo Sled Dog,* illus. by the author. Scribner.

Peary, Marie Ahnighito, *The Red Caboose: With Peary in the Arctic,* illus. by Ferdinand H. Horvath. Morrow.

Petersham, Maud, and Miska Petersham, *The Story Book of Wheels, Ships, Trains, Aircraft,* illus. by the authors. Winston.

———, *The Story Book of Foods from the Fields,* illus. by the authors. Winston.

Purnell, Idella, *Pedro, the Potter,* illus. by Nils Hogner. Nelson.

Swift, Hildegarde Hoyt, *Little Blacknose,* illus. by Lynd Ward. Harcourt Brace.

Wells, Rhea, *An American Farm,* illus. by the author. Doubleday Doran.

## Grades Five and Six

Bailey, Carolyn Sherwin, *The Children of the Handicrafts,* illus. by Grace Paull. Viking.

Dobias, Frank, *The Picture Book of Flying,* illus. by the author. Macmillan.

Floherty, John J., *Fire Fighters: How They Work,* illus. by photographs. Doubleday, Doran.

Hader, Berta, and Elmer Hader, *Midget and Bridget,* illus. by the authors. Macmillan.

———, *The Picture Book of Travel,* illus. by the authors. Macmillan.

Hall, Charles Gilbert, *Through by Rail,* illus. by photographs. Macmillan.

Hartman, Gertrude, *Medieval Days and Ways,* illus. by Henry C. Pitz. Macmillan.

Hillyer, V. M., and Edward G. Huey, *A Child's History of Art.* Appleton-Century.

James, Will, *Young Cowboy,* illus. by the author. Scribner.

Johnson, Enid, *Runaway Balboa,* illus. by Anne Merriman. Harper.

Jones, Wilfred, *How the Derrick Works,* illus. by the author. Macmillan.

Lambert, Clara, *Talking Wires,* illus. by photographs. Macmillan.

London, Jack, *The Call of the Wild,* illus. by Paul Bransom. Macmillan.

McSpadden, J. Walker, *How They Sent the News,* illus. by photographs. Dodd Mead.

Mitchell, Lucy Sprague, *North America: The Land They Live In, for the Children Who Live There,* illus. by Kurt Wiese. Macmillan.

Naumburg, Elsa H., Clara Lambert, and Lucy Sprague Mitchell, *Skyscraper,* illus. by photographs. John Day.

Rogers, Frances, and Alice Beard, *Heels, Wheels and Wire,* illus. by Frances Rogers. Stokes.

## Grades Seven and Eight

Bormann, Henry H., *Bridges,* illus. by photographs. Macmillan.

Carroll, Gladys Hasty, *Land Spell,* illus. by William Siegel. Macmillan.

Cottler, Joseph, and Haym Jaffe, *Heroes of Civilization,* illus. by Forrest W. Orr. Little, Brown.

Craik, Dinah Maria Mulock, *John Halifax, Gentleman.* Macmillan.

Defoe, Daniel, *The Life and Surprising Adventures of Robinson Crusoe,* illus. by Warwick Goble. Macmillan.

Eaton, Jeanette, *Behind the Show Window,* illus. by photographs. Harcourt, Brace.

Ferris, Helen (editor), *When I Was a Girl,* illus. by Curtiss Sprague. Macmillan.

Floherty, John J., *Sons of the Hurricane,* illus. by photographs. Lippincott.

Gibson, Katharine, *The Goldsmith of Florence,* illus. by Kalman Kubinyi. Macmillan.

Hartman, Gertrude, *Machines, and the Men Who Made the World of Industry,* illus. by photographs. Macmillan.

Hibben, Thomas, *The Carpenter's Tool Chest,* illus. by the author. Lippincott.

Kelly, Eric P., *At the Sign of the Golden Compass,* illus. by Raymond Lufkins. Macmillan.

Kipling, Rudyard, *The Day's Work,* Doubleday, Doran.

Lindbergh, Anne Morrow, *Listen! The Wind.* Harcourt, Brace.

Lindbergh, Charles A., *We,* illus. by photographs. Putnam.

London, Jack, *Dutch Courage.* Macmillan.

Meigs, Cornelia, *Swift Rivers,* illus. by Peter Hurd. Little, Brown.

Nordhoff, Charles, *The Pearl Lagoon.* Little, Brown.

Norris, Margaret, *Heroes and Hazards,* illus. by photographs. Macmillan.

Raymond, Margaret Thompson, *Linnet on the Threshold,* illus. by Alida Conover. Longmans.

Pryor, William Clayton, and Helen Sloman Pryor, *Water—Wealth or Waste,* illus. by photographs. Harcourt, Brace.

Tinyanova, Helen, *Stradivari, the Violin-Maker* (trans. by Valentine Snow), illus. by Harrie Wood. Knopf.

Van Loon, Hendrik Willem, *The Story of Mankind,* illus. by the author. Liveright.

# *Books of Biography*[1]

## *Upper Grades*

Antin, Mary, *The Promised Land,* illus. by photographs. Houghton Mifflin.

Benz, Francis E., *Pasteur, Knight of the Laboratory,* illus. by James MacDonald. Dodd Mead.

Britt, Albert, *The Boys' Own Book of Frontiersmen.* Macmillan.

Brooks, Eldridge S., *The True Story of Christopher Columbus.* Lothrop.

Cody, William F., *Adventures of Buffalo Bill.* Harper.

Daugherty, James, *Their Weight in Wild-Cats,* illus. by the author. Houghton Mifflin.

Eaton, Jeanette, *Leader by Destiny: Washington, Man, and Patriot,* illus. by Jack Manley Rose. Harcourt, Brace.

———, *Young Lafayette,* illus. by David Hendrickson. Houghton Mifflin.

Ferris, Helen, *Here Comes Barnum,* illus. by Frank Dobias. Harcourt, Brace.

Green, Fitzhugh, *Bob Bartlett: Master Mariner,* illus. by photographs. Putnam.

Grenfell, Wilfred, *Adrift on an Ice-Pan.* Houghton Mifflin.

Hamilton, J. G. de Roulhac, and Mary Thompson Hamilton, *Life of Robert E. Lee for Boys and Girls,* illus. by photographs. Houghton Mifflin.

Hawthorne, Hildegarde, *Romantic Rebel: The Story of Nathaniel Hawthorne,* illus. by W. M. Berger. Appleton-Century.

Hawthorne, Hildegarde, and Esther Burnell Mills, *Enos Mills of the Rockies.* Houghton Mifflin.

James, Will, *Lone Cowboy,* illus. by the author. Scribner.

Keller, Helen, *The Story of My Life.* Doubleday, Doran.

Lagerlöf, Selma, *The Diary of Selma Lagerlöf* (trans. by Velma S. Howard), illus. by Johan Bull. Doubleday, Doran.

Meadowcroft, William Henry, *Boy's Life of Edison.* Harper.

Nicolay, Helen, *The Boys' Life of Abraham Lincoln,* illus. by Jay Hambridge. Appleton-Century.

Paine, Albert Bigelow, *The Boys' Life of Mark Twain.* Harper.

———, *The Girl in White Armor: The True Story of Joan of Arc.* Macmillan.

Proudfit, Isabel, *The Ugly Duckling, Hans Christian Andersen,* illus. by Malthé Hasselriis. McBride.

Richards, Laura E., *Florence Nightingale: The Angel of the Crimea.* Appleton-Century.

Rourke, Constance, *Davy Crockett,* illus. by James MacDonald. Harcourt, Brace.

Siple, Paul, *Scout to Explorer,* illus. by photographs. Putnam.

Steffens, Lincoln, *Boy on Horseback,* illus. by Sanford Tousey. Harcourt, Brace.

[1] Other books of biography have been included in previous lists of children's books.

Thomas, Lowell, *The Boys' Life of Colonel Lawrence,* illus. with photographs. Appleton-Century.

Washington, Booker T., *Up from Slavery: An Autobiography.* Houghton Mifflin.

Wheeler, Opal, and Sybil Deucher, *Mozart, the Wonder Boy,* illus. by Mary Greenwalt. Dutton.

———, *Joseph Haydn, the Merry Little Peasant,* illus. by Mary Greenwalt. Dutton.

White, Stewart Edward, *Daniel Boone, Wilderness Scout,* illus. by James Daugherty. Doubleday, Doran.

Wise, Winifred E., *Jane Addams of Hull House,* illus. by photographs. Harcourt Brace.

# *Newbery Medal Books*

The John Newbery Medal was established and endowed by Frederic G. Melcher, editor of *Publishers' Weekly*. It is awarded annually by the Children's Librarians' Section of the American Library Association for the most distinguished contribution to American literature for children published during the preceding year. The medal is named in honor of the famous London bookseller of the eighteenth century who was the first publisher to issue books especially for children.

1922 Van Loon, Hendrik Willem, *The Story of Mankind,* illus. by the author. Liveright.

1923 Lofting, Hugh, *The Voyages of Dr. Dolittle,* illus. by the author. Stokes.

1924 Hawes, Charles Boardman, *The Dark Frigate*. Little, Brown.

1925 Finger, Charles, *Tales from Silver Lands,* illus. by Paul Honoré. Doubleday, Doran.

1926 Chrisman, Arthur Bowie, *Shen of the Sea,* illus. by Else Hasselriis. Dutton.

1927 James, Will, *Smoky, the Cowhorse,* illus. by the author. Scribner.

1928 Mukerji, Dhan Gopal, *Gay-Neck,* illus. by Boris Artzybasheff. Dutton.

1929 Kelly, Eric P., *The Trumpeter of Krakow,* illus. by Angela Pruszynska. Macmillan.

1930 Field, Rachel, *Hitty: Her First Hundred Years,* illus. by Dorothy P. Lathrop. Macmillan.

1931 Coatsworth, Elizabeth, *The Cat Who Went to Heaven,* illus. by Lynd Ward. Macmillan.

1932 Armer, Laura Adams, *Waterless Mountain,* illus. by the author and Sidney Armer. Longmans.

1933 Lewis, Elizabeth Foreman, *Young Fu of the Upper Yangtze,* illus. by Kurt Wiese. Winston.

1934 Meigs, Cornelia, *Invincible Louisa: The Story of the Author of Little Women*. Little, Brown.

1935 Shannon, Monica, *Dobry,* illus. by Atanas Katchamakoff. Viking.

1936 Brink, Carol Ryrie, *Caddie Woodlawn,* illus. by Kate Seredy. Macmillan.

1937 Sawyer, Ruth, *Roller Skates,* illus. by Valenti Angelo. Viking.

1938 Seredy, Kate, *The White Stag,* illus. by the author. Viking.

1939 Enright, Elizabeth, *Thimble Summer,* illus. by the author. Farrar and Rinehart.

1940 Daugherty, James, *Daniel Boone,* illus. by the author. Viking.

1941 Sperry, Armstrong, *Call It Courage,* illus. by the author. Macmillan.

1942 Edmonds, Walter D., *The Matchlock Gun,* illus. by Paul Lentz. Dodd, Mead.

1943 Gray, Elizabeth Janet, *Adam of the Road,* illus. by Robert Lawson. Viking.

1944 Forbes, Esther, *Johnny Tremain,* illus. by Lynd Ward. Houghton Mifflin.

## *Caldecott Medal Books*

The Randolph Caldecott Medal, established and endowed by Frederic G. Melcher, is awarded annually by the Children's Librarians' Section of the American Library Association for the most distinguished American picture book for children published during the preceding year. The medal is named in honor of the famous English artist of the nineteenth century whose vigorous and delightful picture books have been loved by generations of children.

1938 Lathrop, Dorothy P., *Animals of the Bible,* illus. by the author. Stokes.

1939 Handforth, Thomas, *Mei Li,* illus. by the author. Doubleday, Doran.

1940. D'Aulaire, Ingri, and Edgar Parin d'Aulaire, *Abraham Lincoln,* illus. by the authors. Doubleday, Doran.

1941 Lawson, Robert, *They Were Strong and Good,* illus. by the author. Viking.

1942 McCloskey, Robert, *Make Way for Ducklings,* illus. by the author. Viking.

1943 Burton, Virginia Lee, *The Little House,* illus. by the author. Houghton Mifflin.

1944 Thurber, James, *Many Moons,* illus. by Louis Slobodkin. Harcourt, Brace.

## *Books That Are Easy to Read*

Children who do not read well present special problems in the teaching of literature. That such children are interested in books and capable of appreciating good ones is amply supported by experimental evidence.[1] Limited ability in reading, however, limits a child's pleasure in books and may lead to such discouragement that he will avoid reading altogether if he can or he may find satisfaction in unworthy books that are simple enough for him to read.

Modern school programs provide the means of identifying boys and girls deficient in reading skill and offer training to help them overcome such difficulties. Under the best of conditions, however, the problem of providing suitable material is not easy to solve. Such children need not only books simple enough for them to gain experience in reading but books that will attract and hold their interest. There is every reason also that they should be supplied with books of fine quality and unquestioned taste. We should be as careful in the quality of books we select for these readers as for other children, in fact we should use even greater discrimination, for these children will read fewer books. It should be kept in mind also that these children are not pleasantly disposed toward reading because it is difficult for them and in many cases negative attitudes become strong. We need, therefore, to make the experience as attractive in every way as we possibly can.

Of necessity, we must consider first the reading difficulty of the books we offer. If a child cannot read or understand a book, he cannot become interested in it. Over-age children are not attracted, however, to books with content planned for younger children, though the reading difficulty be suitable for them. They are interested in the same things that appeal to children with normal reading skill. To provide material dealing with subjects and situations that will satisfy them but written in language and style simple enough for them to read and understand is the problem.

In selecting books to meet the needs of these boys and girls, we look especially for strong narratives, with straightforward plot and action. Subtlety may prove confusing and the thread of the story be lost in a maze of characters or too long sustained suspense. The motives and purposes of the characters need to be simple and easily identified. The story should move forward, but climaxes and events should not come with too great suddenness for fear the reader may miss the point.

These children need varied and balanced experiences in reading as all children do. It is sometimes supposed that factual or informational books are best suited for these groups. Undoubtedly such books should have a place in their reading but not to the exclusion of narratives, for interest in

[1] For a more detailed discussion, see pages 16-17.

and digestion of classified knowledge requires high intelligence and well-defined purposes.

The following books have been found to be popular with children who do not read well, not only because they are easy to read but because their content, high in interest, appeals to a wide range of ages. Included are books of fantasy, real life, nature, humor, information, and adventure.

## *Primary Grades*

The books suggested in this group are suitable for boys and girls in *Grades Three* and *Four* who have first- and second-grade reading ability.

Aldredge, Edna M., and Jessie Fulton McKee, *Wags and Woofie,* illus. by Robert L. Dickey. Ginn.

Anderson, C. W., *Billy and Blaze,* illus. by the author. Macmillan.

Brann, Esther, *Patrick Was His Name,* illus. by the author. Macmillan.

Donaldson, Lois, *Karl's Wooden Horse,* illus. by Annie Bergmann. Whitman.

Flack, Marjorie, *The Story about Ping,* illus. by Kurt Wiese. Viking.

Gemmill, Jane Brown, *Joan Wanted a Kitty,* illus. by Marguerite de Angeli. Winston.

Huber, Miriam Blanton, *Cinder, the Cat,* illus. by A. Gladys Peck. American Book.

———, *Skags, the Milk Horse,* illus. by Curtiss Sprague. American Book.

Huber, Miriam Blanton, Frank Seely Salisbury, and Mabel O'Donnell, *I Know a Story,* illus. by Florence and Margaret Hoopes. Row, Peterson.

———, *It Happened One Day,* illus. by Mary Royt. Row, Peterson.

King, Marian, *Skeeta, a Wire-Haired Terrier,* illus. by Dorothy Bowden. Whitman.

Lindman, Maj, *Snipp, Snapp, Snurr and the Red Shoes,* illus. by the author. Whitman.

Lofting, Hugh, *The Story of Mrs. Tubbs,* illus. by the author. Stokes.

Miller, Jane, *Jimmy, the Groceryman,* illus. by Berta and Elmer Hader. Houghton Mifflin.

Orton, Helen Fuller, *The Little Lost Pigs,* illus. by Luxor Price. Stokes.

Williamson, Hamilton, *Baby Bear,* illus. by Berta and Elmer Hader. Doubleday, Doran.

———, *Little Elephant,* illus. by Berta and Elmer Hader. Doubleday, Doran.

———, *A Monkey Tale,* illus. by Berta and Elmer Hader. Doubleday, Doran.

## *Intermediate Grades*

The books suggested in this group are suitable for boys and girls in *Grades Five* and *Six* who have third- and fourth-grade reading ability.

Brown, Paul, *Crazy Quilt: The Story of a Piebald Pony,* illus. by the author. Scribner.

Brown, Paul, *War Paint, an Indian Pony,* illus. by the author. Scribner.

Carpenter, Frances, *Our Little Friends of the Arabian Desert,* illus. by Curtiss Sprague. American Book.

Clark, Margery, *The Poppy Seed Cakes,* illus. by Maud and Miska Petersham. Doubleday, Doran.

Credle, Ellis, *Down, Down the Mountain,* illus. by the author. Nelson.

Dalgliesh, Alice, *The Smiths and Rusty,* illus. by Berta and Elmer Hader. Scribner.

De Angeli, Marguerite, *Copper-Toed Boots,* illus. by the author. Doubleday, Doran.

Deming, Therese O., *Little Eagle,* illus. by E. W. Deming. Laidlaw.

Denison, Muriel, *Susannah, a Little Girl with the Mounties,* illus. by Marguerite Bryan. Dodd Mead.

Duplaix, Georges, *Gaston and Josephine in America,* illus. by the author. Oxford.

Gág, Wanda, *Tales from Grimm,* illus. by the author. Coward-McCann.

Gates, Arthur I., Miriam Blanton Huber, and Celeste Comegys Peardon, *We Grow Up,* illus. by Cyrus LeRoy Baldridge and C. B. Falls. Macmillan.

Hader, Berta, and Elmer Hader, *Billy Butter,* illus. by the authors. Macmillan.

Hill, Helen, and Violet Maxwell, *Charlie and His Friends,* illus. by the authors. Macmillan.

Huber, Miriam Blanton, Frank Seely Salisbury, and Mabel O'Donnell, *After the Sun Sets,* illus. by Nellie H. Farnam and Mary Royt. Row, Peterson.

King, Marian, *Kees,* illus. by Elizabeth Enright. Whitman.

Lattimore, Eleanor Frances, *Little Pear,* illus. by the author. Harcourt, Brace.

O'Donnell, Mabel, and Alice Carey, *If I Were Going,* illus. by Florence and Margaret Hoopes. Row, Peterson.

Orton, Helen Fuller, *The Treasure in the Little Trunk,* illus. by Robert Ball. Stokes.

Patch, Edith M., *Holiday Pond,* illus. by photographs. Macmillan.

Perkins, Lucy Fitch, *Farm Twins,* illus. by the author. Houghton Mifflin.

———, *Indian Twins,* illus. by the author. Houghton Mifflin.

Phillips, Ethel Calvert, *Marty Comes to Town,* illus. by George Schrieber. Houghton Mifflin.

Robinson, Tom, *Buttons,* illus. by Peggy Bacon. Viking.

Schawe, Louise R., *Pierre and the Fish Cart,* illus. by Mabel J. Woodbury. World Book.

Seredy, Kate, *Listening,* illus. by the author. Viking.

Tousey, Sanford, *Cowboy Tommy,* illus. by the author. Doubleday, Doran.

Wells, Rhea, *Judy and Grits and Honey,* illus. by the author. Doubleday, Doran.

———, *Zeke, the Raccoon,* illus. by the author. Viking.

Wiese, Kurt, *Karoo, the Kangaroo,* illus. by the author. Coward-McCann.

White, Eliza Orne, *Where is Adelaide?* illus. by Helen Sewell. Houghton Mifflin.

## *Upper Grades*

The books suggested in this group are suitable for boys and girls in *Grades Seven* and *Eight* who have fifth- and sixth-grade reading ability.

Akeley, Delia, *"J. T. Jr."—The Biography of an African Monkey,* illus. by photographs. Macmillan.

Altsheler, Joseph A., *Young Trailers.* Appleton-Century.

Baldwin, James, *Fifty Famous Stories Retold.* American Book.

Barbour, Ralph Henry, *The Spirit of the School.* Appleton-Century.

Blackmore, Richard D., *Lorna Doone* (adapted by Rachel Jordan, A. O. Berglund, and Carleton Washburne), illus. by Alexander Key. Scott, Foresman.

Bowman, James C., *Pecos Bill: The Greatest Cowboy of All Time,* illus. by Laura Bannon. Whitman.

Brink, Carol Ryrie, *Caddie Woodlawn,* illus. by Kate Seredy. Macmillan.

Carroll, Ruth, and Latrobe Carroll, *Luck of the Roll and Go,* illus. by Ruth Carroll. Macmillan.

Colum, Padraic, *The Boy Who Knew What the Birds Said,* illus. by Dugald Walker. Macmillan.

Crump, Irving, *The Boys' Book of Policemen.* Dodd Mead.

Darling, Esther Birdsall, *Baldy of Nome,* illus. by Hattie Longstreet Price. Penn.

Heyliger, William, *Don Strong of the Wolf Patrol.* Appleton-Century.

Lent, Henry B., *Wide Road Ahead!* illus. by Earle Winslow. Macmillan.

Moderow, Gertrude, Mary Yost Sandrus, Josephine Mitchell, and Ernest C. Noyes, *Six Great Stories,* illus. by Alexander Key. Scott, Foresman.

Moon, Grace, *Chi-Wee,* illus. by Carl Moon. Doubleday, Doran.

Morley, Margaret, *Donkey John of the Toy Valley.* McClurg.

Morrow, Honoré, and William J. Swartman, *Ship's Monkey,* illus. by Gordon Grant. Morrow.

O'Brien, Jack, *Silver Chief, Dog of the North,* illus. by Kurt Wiese. Winston.

———, *Valiant, Dog of the Timberline,* illus. by Kurt Wiese. Winston.

Otis, James, *Toby Tyler, or Ten Weeks with a Circus,* illus. by Richard Rodgers Harper.

Rolt-Wheeler, Francis, *The Boy with the U. S. Life Savers.* Lothrop.

Schultz, James Willard, *The Quest of the Fish-Dog Skin,* illus. by George Varian. Houghton Mifflin.

Stong, Phil, *Honk, the Moose,* illus. by Kurt Wiese. Dodd Mead.

White, Stewart Edward, *The Magic Forest.* Macmillan.

Wiggin, Kate Douglas, *The Birds' Christmas Carol,* illus. by Helen M. Grose. Houghton Mifflin.

Wilder, Laura I., *The Little House in the Big Woods,* illus. by Helen Sewell. Harper.

## *Student Activities*

1. Is there a collection of children's books of early date in your community? Many museums and libraries have such collections, some of them are very valuable and all of them are interesting. In recent years a number of private collectors also have added juvenilia to their collections. Original manuscripts of famous children's books are worth many thousands of dollars and certain first editions have sold for astonishing amounts. If there is a collection of such treasures near you, could you arrange to see it? Perhaps old residents of your community may own some old children's books that, even if they are not collectors' rare items, are certain to be interesting. The members of your class might be able to explore such possibilities and arrange an exhibit. Such an enterprise would undoubtedly interest the whole community.

2. Are there any children's book stores or departments in stores near you? If possible, visit such a shop and discover what books are in greatest demand. Do the books being offered reflect the reading tastes of the children in your community? What are the forces at work in the community that are favorable to ownership of books by children?

3. Explore if possible the newsstands in railway and bus stations located near you to discover what magazines are sold to children. What is the quality of the periodical literature being bought by children?

4. What children's magazines are to be found in the school and public libraries? Which ones are most read? What is the nature of their content?

5. Do you have access to a library that contains bound volumes of *St. Nicholas?* What enduring stories may be found there?

6. Do the ten-cent stores in your community carry a stock of children's books? You will find that the titles change frequently to build up repeat sales, but with care in selection some worthwhile books may be secured at low cost. Select a group of such books.

7. Assume that you are a teacher and have the authority to spend fifty dollars for books, exclusive of textbooks, for your schoolroom. How will you invest the money? Make lists of the books you would buy if you were located in one of the types of situations described below. You will of course want to get the most value to children from your expenditure and have as representative a library as possible. In it you will want to have a number of beautifully illustrated books, but you will find also that a number of cheap but good reprints of the classics may be bought, and from the textbook publishers you may secure a number of attractive but moderately priced story books. By careful planning you can extend the size of your library without sacrificing its quality.

Perhaps you are acquainted with the details of a particular school situation for which you would like to work out a selection of books. If so, substitute it for the problems that follow. Those given here represent four typical situations that may be duplicated at least partially in many different localities.

(a) One-room rural school, small enrollment but all ages of the elementary school. The children belong to a 4 H Club and are very alert and intelligent. From the county library you may borrow a small group of books each month—good editions of classics but no recent books. What selection of books will meet the needs of these wide-awake, practical youngsters?

(b) School in an average American community, two grades in each room. Choose the first and second grades, the third and fourth, the fifth and sixth, or the seventh and eighth, according to your interest. The children have some books in their homes but not many. The public library issues twenty books to each schoolroom at a time, but the funds of the library are limited and a teacher cannot be sure of getting particular titles.

(c) School in a residential community of considerable wealth. The children have books of their own and read well, but their interests are narrow. Select a particular grade in which you are interested and plan a library that will broaden the experience of the children and give them a better understanding of the world in which they live.

(d) School in a thickly populated industrial district where foreign languages are spoken in the homes. The public library is well equipped and generous in its loans, but the books are in the main too difficult because the children have language difficulties and many of them are retarded in reading. There is particular need and desire for books that give an understanding of American aims and purposes. Select a library for the primary, intermediate, or upper grades, keeping in mind that there is a wide range of ages and reading ability in each group.

## *References for Students*

Adams, Florence, and Elizabeth McCarrick, *Highdays and Holidays*. Dutton.

Andrews, Siri (editor), *Children's Catalog*. Wilson.

Barnes, Clara M., "Can Children Use a Library?" *Journal of National Education Association*, XXVI: 248.

Barry, Florence V., *A Century of Children's Books*. Doubleday, Doran.

Darton, F. J. Harvey, *Children's Books in England*, Chapters 8-10, 13-14. Macmillan.

Dillon, Josephine, "A Library Center in Action," *Elementary English Review*, XII: 127.

Field, E. M. (Mrs.), *The Child and His Book*, Wells, Garden, and Darton (London).

Frank, Josette, *What Books for Children?* Chapter 6. Doubleday, Doran.

Gardner, Emelyn E., and Eloise Ramsey, *A Handbook of Children's Literature*, Chapter 10. Scott, Foresman.

Halsey, Rosalie V., *Forgotten Books of the American Nursery*. Goodspeed.

Hazeltine, Mary E., *Anniversaries and Holidays*, American Library Assn.

Hewins, Caroline M., *A Mid-Century Child and Her Books*. Macmillan.

Hill, Ruth A., and Elsa de Bondeli, *Children's Books from Foreign Languages*. Wilson.

McCabe, Martha R., "Early American Juvenilia," *Elementary English Review*, XII: 251.

Moore, Annie E., *Literature Old and New for Children*, Chapters 7-8, 11-12. Houghton Mifflin.

———, "Magazines for Children," *Elementary English Review*, XIV: 58.

Moses, Montrose J., *Children's Books and Reading*. Kennerley.

Mott, Carolyn, and Leo Baisden, *The Children's Book on How To Use Books and Libraries*. Scribner.

Nolen, Eleanor Weakley, "The National Library Builds a Children's Book Collection," *The Horn Book*, XIV: 246.

Olcott, Frances J., *Good Stories for Anniversaries*, Houghton Mifflin.

Smith, Elva S., *The History of Children's Literature*. American Library Assn.

Smith, Nila Banton, *American Reading Instruction*. Silver, Burdett.

# *Appendix*

# AUTHORS OF CHILDREN'S BOOKS

THE following biographical sketches are necessarily brief, but they offer a means of acquaintance with the writers[1] whose material appears in *Story and Verse for Children.*

These accounts of the authors of children's books give us some insight into literature in the making. The lives of some of these writers reveal that the interests of childhood persisted into maturity. With these interests they kept also the delightful attitude of seeing things as children see them. In many cases it is clear that they were endowed in childhood with the ability for telling tales and making rhymes, and a sympathetic and stimulating environment furthered the development of native capacity. In a few cases we find that writing for children appeared relatively late in the lives of authors, native disposition finally winning out in the face of counter human purposes and circumstances of life. Poems and stories take on added charm and character as we see the forces in operation behind the literary productions.

Until comparatively recently many of the authors most widely read by children in America were British, but during the present century the number of juvenile writers in the United States has greatly increased. It is interesting to observe the geographical range in places of birth and residence of the men and women who have contributed to literature for children. Quiet rural surroundings and crowded industrial conditions furnish backgrounds with equal frequency. The comparatively simple social situations of a hundred and more years ago and the more complex ones of today have both produced writers with clear understanding of the needs of children, needs that are modified but not fundamentally changed by times and conditions.

Writers in foreign countries have contributed books which American children read in translation. Some of the well-known writers for children in the United States today have European beginnings and the mingling of influences of the old world and the new in their lives finds expression in their books. It is clear that books for children are not the result of any particular set of circumstances or conditions of living but are universal in

[1] All have been included except Elsie Finnimore Buckley and Susan Hartley Swett, about whom it has been impossible to secure information.

their origins and as varied in the sources from which they spring as the individual children who read them.

Information concerning the lives of the authors whose stories and poems appear in *Story and Verse for Children* is an addition to the student's acquaintance with children's literature. The facts are interesting in themselves, but they are especially valuable as they give insight and understanding by which the reader is better able to appreciate the work of the men and women who produce children's books.

ALCOTT, LOUISA M. (1832–1888), was a member of a cultured but improvident New England family. She lived in Concord, Massachusetts, and the families of Emerson and Hawthorne were her neighbors and friends. Her father, Bronson Alcott, was an educator and while never able to earn enough money to support the family, provided a happy childhood for Louisa and her three sisters. At fifteen, Louisa assumed financial responsibility for the family and kept them in comfortable circumstances the rest of her life by hard work in teaching and writing. She never married. Her most famous book, *Little Women,* is based upon her experiences as a child. It continues to be one of the books most loved by children, by boys as well as by girls. *Little Women* was followed by *Little Men* and a number of other stories which drew upon real and imaginary events of her childhood. During the Civil War she served for a time as a nurse in a Union hospital. Her experiences there, as well as a complete account of her busy and active life, are given by Cornelia Meigs in *Invincible Louisa: The Story of the Author of Little Women,* a biography of great interest to children.

ALDIS, DOROTHY (1897– ). Both of Dorothy Aldis' parents were writers for Chicago newspapers and she herself spent several years writing feature articles for a Chicago paper. She is the mother of four children. She has written several volumes of verse and several novels for adults, but she is best known for her three books of attractive verse for children: *Everything and Anything; Here, There and Everywhere;* and *Hop, Skip and Jump.*

ALEXANDER, CECIL FRANCES (1818–1895), was the wife of a Protestant archbishop in Ireland. She wrote some four hundred hymns, the best known of which is "There is a Green Hill Far Away." "All Things Bright and Beautiful," and "The Burial of Moses" have long had a place in collections of poems for children.

ALLINGHAM, WILLIAM (1824–1889), was the son of a banker in Donegal, in Ireland. He held positions in the customs service in Ireland and England and later became an editor for *Fraser's Magazine.* He knew Tennyson and Carlyle and was a close friend of Dante Gabriel Rossetti, who illustrated one of his books of verse. Allingham was an authority on ballads and his own verse reflects their spirit, color, and charm.

ANDERSEN, HANS CHRISTIAN (1805–1875), was one of the greatest storytellers of all literature. He did not regard his stories for children as important in his life work, but it is through them that he has become immortal. He was born in Odense, Denmark. His father was a poor cobbler, and his mother an ignorant and superstitious washerwoman. He was a queer, visionary child, caring little for school but listening eagerly to the folk stories of his country and reading all the plays he could borrow. He built a puppet theater and spent most of his time costuming his puppets and making plays for them. At fourteen he went to Copenhagen to become an opera singer. He tried to join a boys' chorus, but he had little talent for singing. He studied dancing, but his homely, awkward appearance made him a laughingstock. The theaters snubbed him. When he was nearly starving, a rich patron came to his aid, sent him to school, and kept him in school until he was a man. At twenty-four he began to write plays, novels, and poems, but it was not until he was thirty that he achieved any real success. In 1835, the year his first successful novel appeared, he published a small volume of the *Fairy Tales,* to be followed over a period of years by others in the series. These tales made him famous. He was acclaimed in all the countries of Europe and received by great people everywhere. He fell in love with Jenny Lind, the Swedish singer, but his courtship was unsuccessful and he never married. Many of his stories, particularly "The Ugly Duckling," seem to his readers to be autobiographical and to reflect his sensitiveness, his pride, and his persistence in finding an outlet for his genius in the face of handicaps and discouraging failures.

ANDERSON, C. W. (1891– ), was born in Nebraska, is now a resident of New York, with a summer home in New Hampshire. He is well known for his portraits of horses. He is the author of *Black, Bay, and Chestnut,* a book of drawings and life sketches of famous horses, and of three books about the little boy Billy and his horse Blaze: *Billy and Blaze, Blaze and the Gypsies,* and *Blaze and the Forest Fire.*

ASBJÖRNSEN, PETER C. (1812–1885), and MOE, JÖRGEN E. (1813–1882), worked so closely together in collecting the folklore of Norway that they are seldom named separately. Their friendship began when they were schoolboys and continued all their lives. Asbjörnsen was by profession a zoologist and an expert in forestry, Moe a professor of theology and a bishop. For many years they spent holidays and all other time they could find wandering on foot through the length and breadth of Norway, into the mountains and remote districts, collecting stories. In 1842 they published the first installment of their work, which was accepted all over Europe as a great contribution to comparative mythology as well as to literature. In 1859 the stories were translated into English by Dasent who preserved the fine literary style of the originals.

ASQUITH, HERBERT (1881– ), English poet and novelist, is the Earl of Oxford and Asquith. He was admitted to the bar in London in 1907, and from 1915 to 1918 served as captain in France and Flanders. Occasional items in his books of verse are suited and interesting to children. He is the author of *The Volunteers, A Village Sermon,* and *Pillicock Hill,* as well as several novels.

BACON, JOSEPHINE DASKAM (1876– ), was born in Connecticut, is a graduate of Smith College, and now lives in New York. Her husband is a lawyer and she is the mother of three children. Almost every year since 1900 has seen some publication of her work, prose or poetry. She has written a number of Girl Scout and other stories for girls and is a frequent contributor to magazines. In 1935 she was awarded the League of Nations prize for "Hymn for the Nations."

BACON, PEGGY (1895– ), Connecticut born, had an artist father. She is married to Alexander Brook, an artist, and has two children. Her dry points and etchings are well-known and a number are owned by the Metropolitan and other museums of art. Her work has been exhibited in galleries all over the country. She has received various prizes and a Guggenheim Fellowship. Some of her drawings are caricatures and most of them are humorous or satirical. She has written and illustrated several books for children: *The Lion-Hearted Kitten, Mercy and the Mouse, The Ballad of Tangle Street,* and *The Terrible Nuisance.*

BAIN, R. NISBET (1854–1909), was assistant librarian of the British Museum. He was an expert linguist and proficient in some twenty of the foreign tongues of northern and eastern Europe. He wrote extensively on Scandinavian, Polish, Hungarian, and Russian history and published a number of volumes on these subjects. He also contributed to the *Cambridge Modern History* and the eleventh edition of the *Encyclopaedia Britannica.* Bain's writings in history were based on source materials in the languages of the various countries, and he used the same method in his work in literature. In 1893 he translated Andersen's *The Little Mermaid and Other Stories,* and in 1895 wrote a sympathetic *Life of Hans Christian Andersen* based on Andersen's letters and private papers. In 1893 he translated from the Russian the *Shažki* of Nicholas Polevoi as *Russian Fairy Tales;* from the Finnish, Juhani Aho's *Squire Hellmann and Other Stories;* from the Danish, J. L. I. Lie's *Weird Tales from Northern Seas;* and from the Hungarian, Ignacz Kunos's *Turkish Fairy Tales and Folk Tales. Cossack Fairy Tales* (1894) was translated from the Ruthenian.

BAKER, EMILIE KIP, is a member of an old New York family and the wife of Franklin T. Baker, emeritus professor of English, Teachers College, Columbia University. She is the mother of four children. Her books for children are: *Out of the Northland, Stories of Old Greece and Rome, Stories from Northern Myths,* and *Children's Book of Poetry.*

BANGS, JOHN KENDRICK (1862–1922), was editor of *Harper's Weekly, Harper's Magazine, Life,* and *Puck.* He published more than thirty volumes of verse and humor, the best known of which are *The Houseboat on the Styx* and *The Foothills of Parnassus.* His lectures were very popular with American audiences.

BANNERMAN, HELEN, lives in Edinburgh, Scotland. As the daughter of an army chaplain, she spent her childhood in various corners of the British Empire. She married an army doctor and lived for thirty years in India, where she was a great help to her husband in his important work of stamping out plague. In 1889 when returning to India after leaving her two little girls in school in Scotland, she wrote and illustrated *The Story of Little Black Sambo* to send home to amuse them and to comfort herself on the long railway journey that took her away from her children. Thirty-seven years later a sequel, *The Story of Sambo and the Twins,* was written by Mrs. Bannerman, now a little, elderly lady in Scotland.

BARUCH, DOROTHY W. (1899– ), was born in San Francisco, of an old California family. She was educated at Bryn Mawr, Whittier, and Claremont colleges. She is now director of the preschool department and professor of education, Whittier College. She is the mother of two children and her work in education began with the establishment in Los Angeles of a coöperative nursery school for her own and other small children of the neighborhood in which she lived. She is the author of many children's books, both verse and prose, that have an educational purpose as well as outstanding literary value. Among them are: *A Day with Betty Anne, Big Fellow, Big Fellow at Work, I Like Animals,* and *I Like Machinery.*

BAYNES, ERNEST HAROLD (1868–1925), was born in Calcutta and lived during part of his childhood in England. He came with his parents to America at the age of eleven and spent the rest of his life here. After his marriage he made his home near a forest reservation in Sullivan County, New Hampshire. He filled notebooks with his observations of the habits of animals and took thousands of photographs of them. His lectures on nature subjects were popular and he was influential in saving the North American bison from extinction. Hundreds of animals were members of the Baynes household at various times and many of these animals were the subjects of his books for children. Some of the best known of his animal biographies are: *The Sprite: The Story of a Red Fox; Jimmy: The Story of a Black Bear Cub; Polaris: The Story of an Eskimo Dog;* and *My Wild Animal Guests.*

BEEBE, WILLIAM (1877– ), was born in Brooklyn and educated in New York. Since 1899 he has been curator of ornithology of the New York Zoölogical Society. He has directed many hazardous expeditions to study life in the jungle, in the desert, and at the bottom of the sea. He is a member of many scientific societies and renowned for his scientific researches. He is the author of many treatises and books dealing with birds and fishes. He is master of an extraordinarily vivid style of writing that makes his adventures with wild life as exciting as fiction. Many of his books are much liked by young people and the simpler portions, by children. Some of his most famous books are: *Jungle Peace; Jungle Days; Galápagos: World's End; The Arcturus Adventure; Beneath Tropic Seas;* and *Exploring with Beebe.*

BIANCO, MARGERY (1881– ), was born in London. She came to America when she was nine years old and with the exception of long visits to England, lived here until she was married. Then she made her home in Paris and Italy for some years, but in 1921 returned to the United States to live permanently. Her father was a distinguished classical scholar who believed that children were better educated with little formal teaching, consequently she had only a few actual years in school. As a child she had access to many books and always had many toys and pets. She began to write at seventeen and at twenty-one published a novel. It was not until after her two children were born that she began to write stories for children. Into them she put the toys of her childhood, *The Velveteen Rabbit, Poor Cecco, The Skin Horse,* and *The Little Wooden Doll.* The last was illustrated by her daughter, Pamela Bianco. She has written other fanciful stories and several realistic books about animals, in which figure the dogs and cats and other pets and wild creatures she has loved. She is one of the best known of present-day writers for children.

BLAKE, WILLIAM (1757–1827). The lyric perfection of William Blake's *Songs of Innocence* has long been the despair of poets who sought to imitate them, but it was not until comparatively recently that the public came to appreciate them. Though a strain of mysticism runs through them, their beauty and simplicity entitle them to representation in children's reading. Blake's genius, however, found its fullest expression in painting and design. He illustrated his own books and those of others, making his pictures and decorations in watercolor and translating them into copper engraving by a process he devised himself. His plates are considered among the finest ever produced.

BONTEMPS, ARNA (1902– ), was born in Alexandria, Louisiana. When he was four years old the family moved to California where he was educated. After graduating from college, he went to New York to teach. There he formed a close friendship with Langston Hughes and came to know other Negro artists of his own generation. Under a grant from the Julius Rosenwald Fund he visited Haiti and gathered material for several books, among them *Popo and Fifina: Children of Haiti,* which he and Langston Hughes wrote for children. Arna Bontemps is the author of several novels for adults; for children, in addition to *Popo and Fifina,* he has written *You Can't Pet a Possum* and *Sad-Faced Boy.* In the two latter he has reproduced colloquial Negro speech in a form easy for children to read.

BRALEY, BERTON (1882– ), has contributed more than 10,000 verses and 450 short stories to American magazines and newspapers. Many of his poems and stories have also been issued in book form. As reporter, special correspondent, and free-lance writer he has reported happenings from mines of Montana, war fields Europe, and scenes of disaster in the Far East.

BRINK, CAROL RYRIE (1895– ), was born in Idaho and educated in western colleges. Her husband is professor of mathematics at the University of Minnesota and they have two children. She began writing for children in 1925. *Caddie Woodlawn,* which was awarded the Newbery Medal in 1935, was based upon stories told by her grandmother, who was the "Caddie" of the story. For several years, Mrs. Brink has edited and published a volume of short stories selected from those that appear in children's magazines during the preceding year. She is also the author of *Anything Can Happen on the River, Mademoiselle Misfortune, Baby Island,* and *All Over Town.*

BROCK, EMMA L., was born at Fort Shaw, Montana. Her childhood was spent in army posts. She was educated at the University of Minnesota and in art schools in Minneapolis and New York. She has traveled a great deal and found material for children's stories in many picturesque places: *The Runaway Sardine,* in Brittany; *To Market! To Market!* in Holland; *The Greedy Goat,* in the Tyrolean Alps; *The Hen That Kept House,* in the French Basque country; *Little Fat Gretchen,* in the Black Forest of Germany; *Little Indian Boy,* in Taos, New Mexico; *The Pig with the Front Porch,* in the peninsula of Gaspé. From stories of pioneer days heard in Minnesota came *Drusilla.* All of these books have been illustrated by Miss Brock. She is one of the leading artist-authors in America.

BRONSON, WILFRID S. (1894– ), was born in Chicago and educated there. He has said that he was born wanting to draw and paint. When he was a child in public school he was very happy to be "borrowed" by various teachers to put decorations and pictures in colored chalk on their blackboards. During the war he was stationed near New York. Afterward he worked in several studios in New York painting murals, largely of animals. He spent five years as staff artist with an expedition collecting specimens and pictures for the oceanic exhibit in the Peabody Museum at Yale. *Fingerfins,* the story of a fish and his first book for children, was the result of that expedition. A later expedition to the Galápagos Islands gave him the story of the penguin, *Paddlewings. Pollwiggle's Progress* grew from observations of a frog in a pond on his own place in the Catskills. He has also illustrated books by other writers.

BROWNE, FRANCES (1816–1879), was born of a poor family in Donegal, Ireland. From the beginning she endured privations and hardships. When only eighteen months old she became blind as the result of an attack of smallpox. She received no education to speak of, but every evening she listened to her eleven brothers and sisters saying their lessons aloud and remembered every word she heard. Books were scarce in the village, but she borrowed every one she could and memorized everything that was read to her. She wrote her first poetry when she was seven years old. When she was twenty-one she went to live with a sister in Edinburgh and a few years later went to London. In spite of ill health and blindness, she wrote and published many novels, books of verse, and stories for children. She was very popular with the readers of her day, but only one book has lived, *Granny's Wonderful Chair.* It was first published in 1857 by the successors in business of John Newbery.

BROWNING, ROBERT (1812–1889), was one of the most famous of English poets and one of the most interesting personalities in English letters. His poetry has great depth, originality, and power, but his contribution to literature for children is not extensive. "The Pied Piper of Hamelin," "How They Brought the Good News from Ghent to Aix," and occasional songs from longer works are simple enough for children.

BRYANT, WILLIAM CULLEN (1794–1878), was the first of the major poets of America and the earliest of the famous "New England Poets." A generation ago American school children learned many of his poems, but a better understanding of children's interests in poetry has resulted in his verses being left for maturer ages. A few of his nature poems are suitable for children.

BURNS, ROBERT (1759–1796), is the well-loved Scottish poet, renowned for his portrayals of the everyday life of his people. His songs have the swing of folk ballads and his poems about common men and animals reveal his understanding heart. Children who are introduced to some of Burns' simpler verse may come as adults to know in his poetry the "pathos of little things and the humanity of big things."

CARMAN, BLISS (1861–1929), was a Canadian. He studied at Harvard and in 1889 came to live in the United States. In conjunction with the American poet, Richard Hovey, he produced four volumes of *Songs from Vagabondia* that were extremely popular in the eighteen-nineties. He wrote other volumes of verse, among them *April Airs.*

CARROLL, LEWIS (1832–1898), was the pen name of Charles Lutwidge Dodgson, a professor of mathematics at Oxford University. He was the oldest of eleven children and as a boy found many ways of amusing his brothers and sisters. He trained snails and toads, performed sleight-of-hand tricks, invented games, and made stories and pictures for their amusement. After receiving his degree at Oxford, he remained there as a teacher the rest of his life. He was a bachelor. He had many friends among children, particularly Alice Liddell and her two sisters, daughters of the dean of Christ Church College, Oxford. He enjoyed taking them boating on the Thames. One hot afternoon on the river he made up a story for them, a story of adventures that might have happened to Alice if she had gone underground. Alice liked the story so much that Dodgson wrote it down for her in a little hand-lettered book with pen-and-ink sketches that he made himself. Later George MacDonald, the author of *At the Back of the North Wind,* saw it and persuaded Dodgson to publish it for other children to read. This with Tenniel's illustrations became *Alice's Adventures in Wonderland.* Its success was so great that Dodgson continued the story in *Through the Looking Glass.* He also wrote for children, *The Hunting of the Snark, Sylvie and Bruno,* and several other volumes under the name of Lewis Carroll. In the meantime he published a number of scholarly mathematical treatises under his own name. To the end of his life, he never acknowledged publicly that he was Lewis Carroll. Alice Liddell, who became Alice Hargreaves, treasured the hand-lettered book for many years after the author's death. It is now one of the most valuable original manuscripts in the world. In 1932 Mrs. Hargreaves, then eighty years old, visited the United States to attend the celebration of the hundredth anniversary of Lewis Carroll's birth.

CARRYL, CHARLES EDWARD (1841–1920), was a broker on the New York Stock Exchange. Like Lewis Carroll, he wrote for children to please children, in this case his own son and daughter, and like Carroll, he wrote imaginatively and whimsically. *Davy and the Goblin* was published when he was forty-three, and *The Admiral's Caravan* a few years later. In both are many make-believe ventures with characters familiar to his children in their story books and with fanciful characters of his own devising. His son, Guy Wetmore Carryl, was also an author.

CARY, PHOEBE (1824–1871), and ALICE (1820–71), her sister, were born near Cincinnati and largely self-educated. In 1850 they moved to New York where, befriended by Horace Greeley, they gained an important place in literary circles. Alice was the first president of the first woman's club organized in New York. The two sisters were constant companions and their collected verse was published together. While Alice was recognized as the more gifted, Phoebe's poems have been longer remembered. Phoebe was the author of "The Leak in the Dike," and the hymn, "One Sweetly Solemn Thought."

CHEVALIER, RAGNHILD, was born in Bergen, Norway, of a French father and Norse mother. She lived in a home that was the meeting place of such people as Ibsen, Björnsen, and Grieg. She later lived in France, Spain, and the United States. *Wandering Monday* is based upon the memory of her happy childhood in Bergen.

CHILD, LYDIA MARIA (1802–1880), was born in Massachusetts and largely educated by her brother, a Unitarian minister and professor in Harvard Divinity

School. She was a tireless worker and a woman of wide influence. She edited *The Juvenile Miscellany,* the first monthly magazine for children in the United States, and wrote popular verse and fiction. She and her husband were ardent abolitionists and for four years edited an anti-slavery paper. Her books and articles won many recruits to the anti-slavery cause. She was also the author of one of the earliest American books on household economy, of a pioneer cookbook that was widely used, and of a history of women in several volumes.

CHUTE, MARCHETTE GAYLORD, lives in Nebraska. She is a graduate of the Art Institute of Chicago. She illustrated as well as wrote *Rhymes about Ourselves,* a book of verses about animals, pets, birthdays, Christmas, and other real things of interest to young children.

CLEMENS, SAMUEL L. (1835–1910), better known by his pen name, "Mark Twain," is one of the great figures of American literature. He is not only the foremost American humorist, but his writing covers an extraordinary range of style and subjects in which serious themes are expertly handled. His work is unqualifiedly American and full of a spirit of boyish zest in living. The materials of many of his books were drawn from his experiences as a child and as a young man. His boyhood was spent in Hannibal, Missouri, and is vividly pictured in *The Adventures of Tom Sawyer* and *The Adventures of Huckleberry Finn.* His father died when he was twelve years old and he left school and learned the printer's trade. He became an excellent compositor and wrote occasional paragraphs for papers on which he worked in various cities. The years from 1857 to 1861 he spent upon boats on the Mississippi River and became a pilot; this part of his life is pictured in *Life on the Mississippi.* The next three years, spent as a miner in Nevada, are chronicled in *Roughing It.* In 1864 he became a reporter on a San Francisco paper. In a few years his articles and lectures became very popular and led him to New York, where he entered upon forty years of literary activity that made him internationally famous. When *Tom Sawyer* was published, American boys immediately took it to their hearts. *Tom Sawyer* and *Huckleberry Finn* have had millions of readers and are as popular as ever today. *The Prince and the Pauper* is also much liked by boys and girls.

COATSWORTH, ELIZABETH (1893– ), was born in Buffalo and spent her childhood there except for long trips with her parents to various parts of the United States and Europe. She is a graduate of Vassar. After taking a Master's degree at Columbia, she spent a year in the Orient. She is the wife of Henry Beston, who also writes for children, and is the mother of two daughters. She now lives on "Chimney Farm" in Maine. She has contributed many distinguished books, both prose and verse, to the shelves of children's libraries. She has the faculty of writing successfully for a wide range of ages: *Dancing Tom* appeals to primary children, and *Here I Stay,* written for adults, is an outstanding book for boys and girls of the upper grades and high school. Both of these deal with pioneer America, as do *Away Goes Sally* and *Five Bushel Farm* for the intermediate grades. *Alice-All-by-Herself* is a story of a present-day girl in Maine and the adventures that happen to her day by day. Elizabeth Coatsworth writes realistic and fanciful stories with equal ease. *The Cat Who Went to Heaven,* a beautiful Japanese legend, won the Newbery Medal in 1931. She is also an able critic and writes many interesting reviews of children's books for leading magazines.

COLERIDGE, SAMUEL TAYLOR (1772–1834), the English poet, is best known for *The Rime of the Ancient Mariner.* He was a close friend of Wordsworth and Southey. His work was fragmentary but at times of singular beauty.

COLERIDGE, SARA (1802–1852), was the daughter of Samuel Taylor Coleridge, the English poet. Her poems were written for the pleasure of her own children and later published. She edited and arranged her father's works.

COLLODI, C. (1826–1890), was the pen name of Carlo Lorenzini, who was a native of Tuscany, a province of Italy, and later lived in the city of Florence. He took the name of "Collodi" from the village where his mother was born. Lorenzini was a soldier and newspaper editor and held high government positions. He said shortly before his death that *The Adventures of Pinocchio* was based upon many scrapes of his own boyhood. The story has been translated into many languages.

COLUM, PADRAIC (1881– ), is a native of Ireland. He came to the United States in 1914 and lives in New York and Connecticut. His many fine books for children have all been written in the United States. As a child in Ireland, he listened eagerly to the folk tales and songs of his native country. As a young man, he participated in the Celtic Revival in which the young people of Ireland studied the ancient language and traditions of their country. He was one of the founders of the Irish National Theatre and was associated with Lady Gregory, J. M. Synge, William Butler Yeats, and James Stephens. The Irish folklore he learned as a child he has woven into *The King of Ireland's Son, The Big Tree of Bunlahy,* and *The Island of the Mighty.* His interest in other traditional literature led him to make excellent re-tellings of Greek legends in *The Children's Homer* and *The Golden Fleece;* of the Norse, in *The Children of Odin;* of tales from various European lands, in *The Forge in the Forest;* and of *The Arabian Nights.* In *The White Sparrow* he has written a realistic story about birds with a background of Paris. He has also written many fine poems and is president of the Poetry Society of America.

CONKLING, HILDA (1910– ), is the daughter of the poet Grace Hazard Conkling, professor of English at Smith College. When a very little girl, Hilda began "talking" her poems to her mother, who wrote them down. Her first volume of poems, *Poems by a Little Girl,* was published when she was ten years old, though many of the poems had been written several years earlier. *Shoes of the Wind* appeared two years later. A collection from these two books has since been published under the title, *Silverhorn.* Today many children in progressive schools write attractive verse, but the poems of Hilda Conkling are more than the natural expression of a child, they reveal the genius of an extraordinary artist.

COOK, ELIZA (1818–1889), was an Englishwoman. Her poems were household favorites in her day but have now been largely forgotten. "The Old Armchair" and "King Bruce and the Spider" were the most popular of her many poems. The latter continues to interest children because of its story and homely sentiment.

COOPER, GEORGE (1840–1927), was born and lived in New York. He studied law under President Arthur. He wrote the lyrics for a number of songs and contributed many poems, principally about nature, to children's magazines.

CRAIK, DINAH MARIA MULOCK (1826–1887), was an Englishwoman. When she was ten years old she began to write verses, and at fourteen her first published poem appeared in an English newspaper. Lack of money and the responsibility of caring for a younger brother led her to the determination to earn a living by writing. Her first novel was published when she was twenty-three. It and succeeding books brought her money and literary fame. She was generous to those in need and particularly to less fortunate authors. *John Halifax, Gentleman,* the most famous of her books, was written for adults, but it has long had a strong appeal to young people. *The Little Lame Prince, The Adventures of a Brownie,* and *The Fairy Book* have been favorites with successive generations of children. Her writing is characterized by sincere feeling and is largely free of the artificiality that marked most of the fiction of her day.

CRANE, LUCY (1842–1882), was the sister of Walter Crane, the famous artist and illustrator of children's books. Her father was a well-known portrait painter and miniaturist. The childhood of Walter and Lucy Crane was spent among pictures and artists. In 1864 when Walter Crane began to publish his series of "toy-books" with colored illustrations, it was his sister, Lucy, who made the rhymed versions of the old nursery tales. She selected and arranged the music for *The Baby's Opera* and *The Baby's Bouquet,* and it was she who arranged the text for *The Baby's Own Aesop,* all of which carried Walter Crane's illustrations and decorations. Lucy translated and published *Household Stories from the Bros. Grimm,* which carried some of her brother's most famous drawings, notably the one of the "Goose Girl."

DALGLIESH, ALICE (1893– ), spent a happy childhood on the island of Trinidad in the West Indies. Her parents were English and when she was thirteen she went to live in England. At nineteen she came to the United States and studied at Pratt Institute and Teachers College, Columbia University. She became a kindergarten teacher at the Horace Mann School in New York and gave courses in children's literature at Teachers College, Columbia University. She is now children's book editor for Charles Scribner's Sons. She is an American citizen. She has a summer home at Sandy Cove, Nova Scotia, and that location forms the setting of many of her stories. She is the author of a large number of books of great interest to children in the primary grades. Among them are: *Relief's Rocker, The Blue Teapot, Roundabout, The Smiths and Rusty, The Young Aunts, America Travels,* and a collection of Mother Goose rhymes entitled *The Gay Mother Goose.* She has contributed widely to magazines, both for children and for parents and teachers.

DALY, T. A. (1871– ). Thomas Augustine Daly was born in Philadelphia and has spent most of his life there. Since 1891 he has been reporter, editor, and columnist on leading Philadelphia newspapers. He is also widely known as a lecturer. Some of the finest dialect verse written in America appears in his *Carmina* and *McAroni Ballads.* Beneath the comic situations in his poems, human sympathy is revealed, a sympathy that is genuine without being sentimental.

DASENT, GEORGE WEBBE (1817–1896), was in the English diplomatic service in Stockholm in 1840 when he met Jacob Grimm. At Grimm's suggestion he interested himself in Scandinavian folklore and a few years later issued an English version of stories from classic Norse mythology. This was the first of Dasent's many volumes that made available in English the traditional literature of the Norse countries. When Asbjörnsen and Moe published their collections of tales gathered from the humble folk of Norway, Dasent translated them into English and gave to children the matchless tales of "Boots" and "East of the Sun and West of the Moon." Dasent was appointed professor of literature at King's College, London, and in 1876 was knighted for his services to literature.

D'AULNOY, MADAME LA COMTESSE (1650–1705), was a figure in French court circles. She was witty and brilliant and became involved in the political intrigues of her time. The success of Perrault's *Contes de Ma Mère l'Oye (Tales of My Mother Goose),* published in France in 1697, led Madame D'Aulnoy to write and publish in 1698 twenty-four fairy tales drawn from traditional and literary sources. Her stories are much more complicated than Perrault's, and the backgrounds are sumptuous and ornate. Gold and silver are the meanest adornments in her tales; diamonds and rare jewels glitter everywhere. They are, however, very interesting tales, especially "The White Cat," "The Hind in the Wood," and "The Yellow Dwarf." Madame D'Aulnoy's stories were translated into English before Perrault's and were common in England as chapbooks in the eighteenth century. A very able translation was made by J. R. Planché (1796–1880), and the Planché text is used in the attractive collection compiled by Elizabeth MacKinstry and Rachel Field under the title, *The White Cat, and Other Old French Fairy Tales.*

DEFOE, DANIEL (1659–1731), was born and died in London. He had a very busy life, full of hardships and difficulties. He engaged in various lines of business, most of which resulted in failure. He suffered bankruptcy and illness. He held strong religious and political opinions and wrote nearly two hundred pamphlets defending them, some of which landed him in prison. It was not until he was fifty-five that he turned to the writing of fiction. *Robinson Crusoe* was published when he was sixty. It was an immediate success and the public believed it to be an account of true experiences. It was entirely fictitious as Defoe had never even been to sea. He intended the story as a device to carry the moralizing of which the complete edition was full, but the skill and patience with which he described the smallest incidents and trivial details of Crusoe's surprising adventures made it great realistic fiction.

DE LA MARE, WALTER (1873– ), was born in a little village in Kent but has lived for many years in London. He was a shy, dreamy boy and his schooldays were not very happy. When he was sixteen he edited and wrote most of a magazine issued at the school he attended. The following year he went to work in the statistical department of an oil company and spent eighteen years at work he disliked. During this period he wrote some verse, but when he was thirty-five he received a pension which enabled him to leave business and give his entire time to writing. He became famous with the publication of *Peacock Pie* in 1913. He is regarded by many critics as the greatest of living poets for children. In *Peacock Pie, A Child's Day, Down-Adown-Derry,* and other volumes of his verse are many poems suitable for children that are unsurpassed for beauty, grace, and true lyric quality. His work is varied and mixed, however, and some of it shows introspective and subtle influences beyond the grasp of average children. He is also the author of much prose, the best known of which is the beautifully written story, *The Three Mulla Mulgars.*

DICKENS, CHARLES (1812–1870), the great English novelist, wrote little intended directly for children, but *A Christmas Carol* will always keep his name among children's authors. He influenced the historical development of children's literature, for the power and strength of his novels helped to break the pattern of stilted moralistic writing common in children's books of his time. Throughout his life he wrote as the champion of the poor and oppressed.

DICKINSON, EMILY (1830–1886). The poetry of Emily Dickinson is considered by some critics the finest by a woman in the English language. She was born and died in Amherst, Massachusetts. She was a recluse and rarely set foot beyond her own doorstep, but she made a world within herself which she expressed in hundreds of startling poems. Her poems, not published until after her death, consist of compressed stanzas into which immensities of thought are packed. The peculiar flavor of Emily Dickinson, often childlike in its directness, deserves a place in children's experience with verse, though her poems do not appeal universally to children.

DITMARS, RAYMOND L. (1876– ), is curator of reptiles, in charge of the department of mammals, at the New York Zoölogical Park. His interest in natural history began as a boy when he collected snakes. At first his parents allowed him to keep his specimens only overnight, but later they let him have the entire upper floor of their New York house for them. When he was fifteen he went to work for the American Museum of Natural History, labeling and mounting insect specimens. Five years later he became a reporter for the *New York Times.* One of his assignments was an interview with Dr. Hornaday, director of the New York Zoölogical Park, and that acquaintance led to his becoming curator of reptiles there, a position he has held for forty years. He has conducted many valuable experiments in extracting venom from poisonous reptiles for medicinal use. He has explored and studied animals in tropical countries and made motion pictures of the animals in their native habitats. He has written many books on natural history; those of special interest to children are: *Strange Animals I Have Known, Thrills of a Naturalists's Quest, The Book of Insect Oddities,* and *The Forest of Adventure.*

DODGE, MARY MAPES (1831–1905), was the founder and for thirty years editor of *St. Nicholas Magazine.* Under her guidance it became the most popular magazine for boys and girls in America. She attracted the foremost writers in England and America. Bryant, Longfellow, Whittier, Louisa M. Alcott, Mark Twain, Frank R. Stockton, and Rudyard Kipling were among the contributors. Frances Hodgson Burnett's *Little Lord Fauntleroy* ran serially in *St. Nicholas* and was the most widely read story of its day. Mrs. Dodge herself wrote stories and poems which appeared in the magazine. Her best-known book, *Hans Brinker; or, The Silver Skates,* was first told to her two small boys at bedtime. She made it up as she went along, adding installments each evening. When it was published, it became instantly popular and continues today to hold its place in children's regard. Shortly after its publication, Mrs. Dodge visited Holland for the first time and found the book in Dutch translation in great demand there. The Dutch people considered it the most faithful story of Dutch life that had then been written. Though she had never been in Holland, she had been a careful reader of Dutch history. The success of *Hans Brinker* led to the founding of *St. Nicholas,* through which Mary Mapes Dodge rendered incalculable service to children and to children's literature.

DRINKWATER, JOHN (1882– ), the British poet and playwright, is best known for his play, *Abraham Lincoln.* He is the author of many outstanding volumes of verse and of much able criticism of poetry and poets. He has written two delightful books of verse for young children, *All about Me,* and *More about Me.*

DUNBAR, PAUL LAURENCE (1872–1908), is the most famous of the Negro poets of America. He was born at Dayton, Ohio, of parents who had been slaves. While writing the verses that became so famous, he was an elevator boy; later he had a position in the Library of Congress. He died of tuberculosis. He wrote several short stories and novels, but was at his best in *Lyrics of the Lowly Life* and *Lyrics of the Hearthside,* poems interpreting the life of his own people, many of them in dialect.

DUPLAIX, GEORGES, is a Frenchman now making his home in America. He is the author of several books for young children, among them *Gaston and Josephine,* and *Gaston and Josephine in America,* stories of two little French pigs who romp through many escapades. He also produced the hilarious and colorful drawings that accompany these stories. Mr. Duplaix has made a number of translations from French to English and English to French. His translations of Lida's stories have made available to American children her delightful books—*Plouf, the Little Wild Duck; Fluff, the Little Wild Rabbit;* and others. His translation of the work of Ernest Hemingway introduced Hemingway to the French public. He is now editor for the Whitman Publishing Company.

EATON, WALTER PRITCHARD (1878– ), is professor of playwriting at Yale University and an outstanding dramatic critic. He is popular as a lecturer on dramatic subjects and on gardens. He has written several plays, several books on the history of drama, a book of verse—*Echoes and Realities,* and a number of Boy Scout stories and stories of the outdoors for boys.

EGGLESTON, EDWARD (1837–1902), was born in a cultured home in southern Indiana. Because of frail health, he was self-educated, but well educated. In contrast to his home of culture and good books, he came in contact with illiterate people of the backwoods near him, from whom he later drew the literary material that made him famous. He became a Methodist circuit rider and traveled on horseback through Indiana. Later he was pastor of a church in Brooklyn, New York. In the meantime he began to write and publish stories in juvenile and other magazines. Eventually he gave up the ministry for editorial positions in Chicago and New York. His first notable story was *The Hoosier Schoolmaster,* which won immediate success. It was followed by *The Hoosier Schoolboy, The Circuit Rider,* and other stories of frontier and Indian life. He also wrote a comprehensive history of the United States.

EMERSON, RALPH WALDO (1803–1882), essayist and poet, was one of the most influential thinkers America has produced. His stimulating essays are beyond the grasp of children, as is most of his verse. "The Concord Hymn," however, presents in compact, musical form, a feeling of patriotism that children understand. It was written to be sung at the completion of the battle monument, July 4, 1837.

EWING, JULIANA HORATIA (1841–1885), was an outstanding writer for children and young people in the middle nineteenth century. One of a large family in Yorkshire, England, she played the role of storyteller to her brothers and sisters. They called her "Aunt Judy," and when her mother founded a magazine for children in 1866, the magazine was named *Aunt Judy's Magazine*. Nearly all of Juliana's writings appeared in this magazine before being published in book form. She married an army officer and many of her stories show the army influence, particularly *Jackanapes,* the most famous of her books. She was also the author of *Lob-Lie-by-the-Fire, Jan of the Windmill, A Flatiron for a Farthing, The Story of a Short Life,* and other stories and verse, all characterized by wholesome approach and literary style superior to most of the writing for children of the period.

FARJEON, ELEANOR (1881– ), is the author of a number of fine poems and fanciful stories for children. She was born in London and today divides her time between London and the Downs of Sussex. Her father was a novelist and her mother the eldest daughter of Joseph Jefferson, the great American actor famed for his impersonation of "Rip Van Winkle." She and her three brothers had an unusual childhood, with little time in school but surrounded by books and the companionship of their talented parents and other literary and artistic people. At seven she was writing poems and stories and typing them herself. In 1904 she spent a year in America with her grandfather. She has written several volumes of verse for children; among them are: *Gypsy and Ginger, Joan's Door, Come Christmas,* and *Over the Garden Wall.* She is at her best in poems of fairies and the supernatural. She has written two books of delightful fanciful stories: *Martin Pippin in the Apple Orchard* for children in the upper grades, and *Martin Pippin in the Daisy Field* for younger children.

FARRAR, JOHN (1896– ), was formerly editor of *The Bookman* and is now vice-president of the publishing firm of Farrar and Rinehart. He is the author of some pleasant verses that picture child experience.

FENTON, CARROLL LANE (1900– ), is a paleontologist, but throughout his study of fossils he has kept an interest in living animals. He was born in Iowa and spent his childhood there and in Canada. At the age of eight, he decided he would become a naturalist. When he was sixteen he published a paper on birds and at eighteen published his first paper on fossils. He was educated at the University of Chicago, and has taught at the Universities of Michigan, Cincinnati, and Buffalo. His wife is also a paleontologist and together they have made and reported various technical studies. Dr. Fenton is an artist and often makes the drawings for his books before he writes the text. His association with Dr. Edith Patch has produced several books on nature study for children that are valuable in subject-matter and high in interest. Among them are: *Desert*

*Neighbors, Forest Neighbors,* and *Mountain Neighbors,* for which Dr. Fenton also made the illustrations.

FERRIS, HELEN (1890– ), was born in Nebraska. Her father was a minister and her childhood was spent in various towns in Nebraska and Wisconsin. She was educated at Vassar College, where she served as college correspondent for several newspapers. Her first editorial position was in charge of *The Guardian,* the magazine of the Camp Fire Girls of America. She became in turn editor of *The American Girl,* and associate editor of *The Youth's Companion.* Since 1929 she has been editor-in-chief of the Junior Literary Guild. She has compiled several anthologies of interest to older girls: *When I Was a Girl, Five Girls Who Dared, Adventure Waits,* and *Love Comes Riding.* She is the author of *Girls Who Did, Here Comes Barnum,* and *Dody and Cap-tin Jenks,* the last a story for young children. Through her work with the Junior Literary Guild, Miss Ferris has rendered valuable service in making fine books available to children.

FIELD, EUGENE (1850–1895), one of the best-known of children's poets, was born in St. Louis. His mother died when he was six years old and he was brought up by relatives in New England. He cared little for school or for the several colleges he attended. When his father died and left him a small legacy, he spent it on a six-months' trip to Europe. He returned to St. Louis and, though only sixteen, married—a marriage that proved to be an extremely happy one. He went to work at the thing nearest at hand, journalism, which he followed sucessfully until his death. He worked on newspapers in St. Louis, Kansas City, Denver, and Chicago. For many years he wrote a widely read column called "Sharps and Flats" for the *Chicago Daily News.* In it appeared most of his verse and stories which were afterward published in book form. Field was a man of singularly happy disposition and was much loved by his friends and by the public. He was the father of eight children, three girls and five boys, and his companionship with his own children undoubtedly had much to do with the writing of his famous lullabies. No other poet has written so many beautiful lullabies. Many of his poems for children are humorous and a few employ child dialect. A third theme in his verse is undesirable for children though it was very popular with the adult readers of his column; it is that of death, particularly the death of children. Field's handling of this theme is distinctly sentimental and not at all an approach natural to children. He also wrote a number of fanciful, mystical tales, beautiful in style but not suited to children. In the ten volumes of his prose and verse, however, many childlike and delightful poems may be found.

FIELD, RACHEL (1894– ), is one of the most famous writers for children of the present day. Her background is that of New England; her childhood was spent in Massachusetts and for a number of years she has lived during the summer on a small island off the coast of Maine. She says she was an unpromising child and did not learn to read until after she was ten, though she had learned earlier to write. In high school she had great difficulty with mathematics and Latin, but wrote stories and verse with ease. She spent four years as a special student at Radcliffe, taking courses in English. It was there she wrote the play, "Three Pills in a Bottle." Her first book for children was one of verse, *The Pointed People,* which like several later books is illustrated with her own drawings. *Taxis and Toadstools,* and *Branches Green* added more verse for children; if she had written no prose, her verse alone would give her a distinguished place in children's literature. Some of her poems are about fairies and elves, but they are largely about real experiences in the city and out of doors. They are genuinely childlike and genuine poetry, and she never "talks down" to children either in her verse or stories. Her most famous story for children is *Hitty: Her First Hundred Years,* which was awarded the Newbery Medal in 1929. Other stories are: *Little Dog Toby, Hepatica Hawks, Calico Bush,* and *The Bird Began to Sing.* She has also written plays for children, and her novel for adults, *All This, and Heaven Too,* was a best-seller.

FLACK, MARJORIE (1898– ), is both author and illustrator of many picture story books that give great pleasure to young children. Her childhood was spent on the shore of Long Island Sound, where she played on the beach and cliffs and in the woods near by. When she was very young she began to draw pictures and to make up stories for her pictures. When she was eighteen, she went to New York to study art and soon after married Karl Larson, an artist. Many of her stories now in books were made up to please her daughter Hilma, when Hilma was very young. "Angus," "Wag-tail Bess," and other pets that figure in her stories were real animals. Her stories of real and imaginary happenings are simple and her illustrations are large and clear and full of action. Her well-loved picture story books include: *Ask Mr. Bear, Lucky Little Lena, Angus and the Ducks* and several other Angus books, *Humphrey the Box Turtle,* and *Tim Tadpole and the Great Bullfrog.* One of the most delightful of her books, *The Story about Ping,* the experiences of a little duck on the Yangtze River, was illustrated by Kurt Wiese, who lived for some years in China.

FLEMING, ELIZABETH, is a Scot but has lived most of her life in England. She is the author of six books for children; three of verse: *Gammon and Spinach, The Creepie Stool,* and *The Lucky Pedlar;* three of plays: *Fourteen Verse Plays, Brer Rabbit Plays,* and *Robin Hood Plays.* She is a contributor to *Punch, Country Life, Chambers' Journal,* and other periodicals, both grown-up and juvenile.

FOLLEN, ELIZA LEE (1787–1860), an American, was a voluminous writer. Her verse now seems old-fashioned, but it was loved by generations of children. Her most ambitious work was one for adults, a five-volume biography of her husband, Karl Follen, a political refugee from Germany who became professor of German literature at Harvard. He perished in the burning of a steamboat en route from New York to Boston. Mrs. Follen survived him by twenty years.

FROST, ROBERT (1875– ), the famous American poet, pictures the everyday things of his beloved New England so simply that many of his poems are well suited to children. He was born in San Francisco. When he was ten years old his father died and his mother took him to New England where his ancestors had lived for eight generations. He attended Dartmouth College and Harvard University. He settled down on a farm in New Hampshire and for a number of years struggled hard to make a living from the soil. For twenty years he wrote poetry without an audience. A few poems were published in magazines but were not popular. In 1912 he went to England and it was there his first book, *A Boy's Will,* was published and received recognition. With the American publication of *North of Boston* in 1914 he became famous. *New Hampshire* was published in 1923 and was awarded the Pulitzer prize for poetry. Frost received this award again in 1930 and 1937. He spent several years at the University of Michigan as "poet in residence," reading and sharing poetry with students. He is now professor of English at Amherst College and lecturer at Yale and Harvard. Frost's poetry is marked by quiet power. In his hands homely incidents and simple people take on significance and reality.

FYLEMAN, ROSE (1877– ), one of the best known of present-day writers for children, lives in London. She studied to be a teacher and taught for a short time. She also studied music and sang in concert. Her first poem, "There are fairies at the bottom of our garden," was published in *Punch.* Her fairy poems became so popular that she gave up other work to devote her time to writing. She has visited the United States several times and lectured here. She founded the delightful English magazine for children, *Merry Go Round.* She has written many poems for children, most of them about fairies. Her books of verse are: *Fairies and Chimneys, The Fairy Flute, Fairies and Friends, The Fairy Green, Fifty-one New Nursery Rhymes,* and *Gay Go Up.* She has also written several books of imaginative stories: *The Rainbow Cat, A Princess Comes to Our Town, A Little Christmas Book, Forty Good-Morning Tales,* and *Tea-Time Tales.*

GAITHER, FRANCES (1889– ), was born in Tennessee and has been closely identified with the South though she now lives in New York. She is the author of a number of historical pageants that have been produced in southern colleges and universities. For children of the upper grades she has written three adventure stories with careful and accurate backgrounds of early American history: *The Painted Arrow, The Scarlet Coat,* and *Little Miss Cappo.*

GARLAND, HAMLIN (1860–1940), is best known as the chronicler of "the Middle Border," the great western prairie across which covered wagons made a long trail bearing pioneer men and women to new homes. The development of New England had long figured in the literature of America, but Hamlin Garland focused attention upon the Middle West as a source of rich literary material. His contribution to literature was a significant one; for fifty years he wrote novels, biographies, and verse that pictured vividly the farm life of the great middle section of our country. Some of his books were planned for children, but others written for adults are suitable for children because of the clearness of his style and the sincerity of his purpose. His family migrated from New England to Wisconsin, where he was born. He spent his early life in the prairie sections of Wisconsin, Iowa, and South Dakota.[1] When he was twenty-one he went to Boston and during the years spent there began to write. He said he wrote his first stories of the prairie in a mood of homesickness, but homesickness soon crystallized into the determination to become the historian of the section he called "the Middle Border." In 1890 *Main-Traveled Roads* was published. In 1893 he returned to the West and was living in California at the time of his death. One of his best-known books, *A Son of the Middle Border,* was published in 1917. *A Daughter of the Middle Border,* 1921, received the Pulitzer prize for biography. *Boy Life on the Prairie* was written especially for children and pictures covered-wagon days vividly and without sentimentality. His verse, some

[1] For reminiscences of Hamlin Garland's early life, see "Books of My Childhood," pages 6 to 8 of this book.

of which appeared in *Boy Life on the Prairie* and more in *Prairie Songs,* is appealing to children. The wholesomeness of his realistic writing, both in verse and fiction, makes his books valuable for children.

GARRISON, THEODOSIA (1874– ), was born and still lives in New Jersey. She has contributed verse and stories to magazines. She has published three volumes of verse: *The Joy o' Life, Earth Cry,* and *The Dreamers.*

GIBSON, KATHARINE, is a member of the department of education of the Cleveland Museum of Art. She was born and spent her childhood in Indianapolis. Because of a difficulty of the eyes, she was educated by tutors at home. She is the wife of Dr. Frank S. C. Wicks, well-known Unitarian minister of Indianapolis. In connection with her work at the Cleveland Museum of Art, she has spent some time in Europe. Her book, *The Goldsmith of Florence,* contains stories of great craftsmen and artists. *The Golden Bird* gives traditional stories from various parts of the world and interesting accounts of the lands and periods from which the stories come. She has also written two fanciful books for young children: *The Oak Tree House,* and *Cinders.*

GILBERT, WILLIAM S. (1836–1911), English playwright and humorist, is best known as the librettist of *The Mikado, Pinafore, Iolanthe, The Pirates of Penzance,* and other classic comic operas for which Arthur Sullivan composed the music. His first book, *Bab Ballads,* was published in 1869. It is marked by perfect meter and ludicrous dilemmas, as are the operas. "The Yarn of the Nancy Bell," from *Bab Ballads,* is an unrivaled burlesque of "travelers' tales" and abounds in exaggerated humor that is very funny to children.

GOLDSMITH, OLIVER (1728–1774), author of *The Vicar of Wakefield, Deserted Village,* and *She Stoops to Conquer,* was born in Ireland of an English family. When he was seven years old, he was sent for two years to a village school kept by an old quartermaster who had an inexhaustible fund of stories about banshees, fairies, and legendary Irish heroes. The rest of Goldsmith's school life was unhappy. He was flogged by the masters as a dunce and ridiculed by the boys for his awkwardness and the ugly scars which smallpox had left on his face. At Trinity College, Dublin, he studied with little diligence and graduated with little distinction. For a time he wandered over Europe, begging his way and playing his flute for any who would listen. When he came to London in 1756, he was in dire straits to make a living. He finally got employment as a "hack writer," selling what he wrote to booksellers for whatever he could get and letting them publish his work anonymously. In this way he came to be connected with John Newbery, whom he admired and considered fair in his dealings, as shown by his tribute to Newbery in *The Vicar of Wakefield.* From 1759 until Newbery's death in 1767, Goldsmith worked for Newbery and it is reasonable to believe that he had much to do with Newbery's publications for children. *Mother Goose's Melody,* which appeared about 1760, is believed to have been edited by Goldsmith, and *The Renowned History of Little Goody Two-Shoes* is believed to have been written by Goldsmith. There is no positive evidence that he wrote *Goody Two-Shoes,* but the internal evidence is strong. The only book published by Newbery that can with certainty be ascribed to Goldsmith is *A History of England,* for young people, published in 1764, but Goldsmith was the only person in Newbery's employ with sufficient literary skill to have written *Goody Two-Shoes. The Vicar of Wakefield* became very popular, and *She Stoops to Conquer* was a dramatic success, but Goldsmith was extravagant and improvident and died in poverty. He was, however, generous and full of humor and much liked by his friends, among whom were Johnson, Burke, Reynolds, and Garrick.

GRIERSON, ELIZABETH W., was born on a sheep farm in Scotland, in the Sir Walter Scott country. She still spends half of the year on the farm where she was born. She was taught by a governess until she was twelve years old and then sent to Edinburgh to school. When her schooldays were over, she found time heavy on her hands and her first story for children was written as a diversion. Her stories were well received and she has since become the author of some twenty books for children. She knows thoroughly the folk tales and ballads of her native Scotland and her best-known books are: *Tales from Scottish Ballads, The Scottish Fairy Book,* and *The Book of Celtic Stories.* She is well known in Edinburgh for philanthropic work among the poor of that city.

GRIMM, JACOB (1785–1863), and WILHELM (1786–1859), German philologists known as the Brothers Grimm, were the founders of the science of folklore. The whole of the lives of the two brothers was passed together; they always lived under one roof, all their work was done together, and their property was held in common. The marriage of Wilhelm and the birth of his children did not in any way disturb their harmony. They both studied law but early became interested in historical and antiquarian investigation. They held posts in libraries together and in later life were appointed to professorships in Berlin and elected members of the Academy of Sciences. They made extensive researches and valuable contributions to the study of German language and grammar. From the beginning they were interested in national poetry and popular tales. From old manuscripts and books they gathered and published exhaustive accounts of Teutonic mythology. They were the first to collect folk tales directly from the folk, among whom the tales had been current for many generations.[1] In 1812–15 they published the first edition of the *Kinder- und Hausmärchen,* which have carried the name of the Brothers Grimm into every home of the civilized world.

HADER, BERTA, and ELMER, are wife and husband who together write and illustrate books for children. Berta was born in Mexico of American parents and came to California when very small. She spent two years at the University of Washington, studying journalism. She studied art in San Francisco and became a painter of miniatures. Elmer was born in California, studied art in San Francisco and Paris, and served as a camoufleur in the World War. After the war he returned to New York and to the painting of landscapes. Berta and Elmer had been fellow students in California and were married in New York in 1919. They have since given their entire time to writing and illustrating books for children. They live in a stone house overlooking the Hudson River not far from New York—a house they built with their own hands. They like to travel and have given book talks and drawn pictures for child audiences all over the country. They have an extraordinary understanding of children and of what children like in books. Their stories are wholesome and natural and while most of them are laid in familiar surroundings and deal with familiar sit-

[1] See pages 209, 389.

uations, they are alive and full of action. Their illustrations have this same naturalness and vitality—many of them are beautiful and all of them have force and a simplicity that is childlike. They work out their books together, both of them writing and drawing; then they revise each other's ideas until in the finished product it is hard to say what is the work of one and what of the other. Some of their best-liked books are: *Midget and Bridget; Billy Butter; Spunky; Cricket;* and *The Picture Book of Travel.*

HALLIWELL, JAMES ORCHARD (1820–1889), was born in London and educated at Cambridge. In 1872 he took the name of Halliwell-Phillips to satisfy the terms of a grandfather's will. He was one of the greatest of Shakespearean scholars and was responsible for establishing the Shakespeare Museum at Stratford-on-Avon. He made extensive researches in other early English literature and was the first to collect in a scientific manner the nursery rhymes and folk tales of England.[1] He gathered the rhymes and tales from the mouths of people, from chapbooks and early manuscripts, and preserved them in the form in which they had been known among the folk. He regarded the rhymes and tales as a significant part of English literature.

HARRIS, JOEL CHANDLER (1845–1908), creator of *Uncle Remus,* was born and spent his life in Georgia. He came of a poor family and was apprenticed as a boy to the printer's trade in the office of a country newspaper published on a plantation. He did his first writing for this paper and lived on the plantation for several years. Here he had access to a fine library, and in the evenings he went down to the slave quarters and heard the Negroes sing and tell the stories they knew so well. This was the beginning of his interest in the folk tales of the plantations, which he later told with such artistry as the stories of *Uncle Remus.* He created the character of the old slave storyteller, but he claimed no originality for the tales themselves, they are genuine folklore. After the Civil War he went to work for the *Atlanta Constitution,* and as editor of that paper did much to further the cause of the New South. He had many friends all over the United States, among them Theodore Roosevelt and James Whitcomb Riley. His home in Atlanta, called the "Wren's Nest," is now a museum. He published eight volumes of the *Uncle Remus* stories—stories famous all over the world. *Uncle Remus: His Songs and His Sayings* (which alone contains the story of the "Tar Baby") and *Nights with Uncle Remus* are the best known.

HARTE, BRET (1839–1902), is famous for his short stories of the gold rush in California. Though he is known as the chronicler of the "Golden West," only fifteen years of his life were spent in California. In San Francisco he worked as printer, newspaper reporter, and editor, and spent one year as professor at the University of California. The rest of his life was lived in New York and abroad. He died in England. His best-known stories are: "The Outcasts of Poker Flat," "The Luck of Roaring Camp," and "Tennessee's Partner." "The Queen of the Pirate Isle" is the only story that he wrote for children.

HARTMAN, GERTRUDE, was born in Philadelphia and now lives in New York. She was educated at Bryn Mawr and Teachers College, Columbia University. She taught English at several private schools and was director of the

[1] See pages 51, 209.

Merion Country Day School at Merion, Pennsylvania, and from 1924–30 edited the magazine, *Progressive Education.* She has been especially interested in writing informational material for children and young people. She is the author of *These United States, and How They Came to Be; The Making of the Constitution; The World We Live In, and How It Came to Be; Medieval Days and Ways; Machines, and the Men Who Made the World of Industry.*

HAUMAN, GEORGE, and DORIS, are a team of husband and wife who write and illustrate books for children. They both studied art in Boston and now live and work in Lexington, Massachusetts. They have a son, eleven years old. In producing *Buttons* and *Bread and Cheese,* both for young children, Mrs. Hauman wrote the story and her husband gave suggestions as the story progressed. In the same manner Mr. Hauman wrote *Happy Harbor,* for children somewhat older. When the text is written, they plan the design of the book together; Mr. Hauman makes up the book in dummy form and begins the drawings; Mrs. Hauman draws the children, and together they finished the drawings in the style decided upon for the book.

HAWTHORNE, NATHANIEL (1804–1864), the great American novelist, lived in New England. Three volumes of his stories written for children are: *Grandfather's Chair, A Wonder Book for Boys and Girls,* and *Tanglewood Tales.* The first comprises stories of early days in New England, and the latter two, versions of the old Greek myths. In the myths Hawthorne not only tells the tales in a style of absorbing interest, but imbues them with the idealism and high purpose characteristic of all his writing. Nathaniel Hawthorne's granddaughter, Hildegarde Hawthorne, is a present-day writer for children, well known for her biographies of famous people. In *The Romantic Rebel* she has told the story of her grandfather's life.

HILL, HELEN, and MAXWELL, VIOLET, are authors and illustrators who have collaborated on many books for children. Miss Hill is an American and Miss Maxwell is an Englishwoman. They have lived in France for many years. For children of the primary grades they have written and illustrated five books about a little American boy, Charlie, his pets and everyday adventures. *Charlie and His Puppy Bingo,* and *Charlie and His Kitten Topsy* are the best known of this group of stories. For children of the intermediate grades they have produced a number of stories of child life, peasant customs, and legends of southern France, based upon first-hand observation. Among them are: *Little Tonino, When Marius Was Ten, The Little Lost Shepherd,* and *The Golden Goat.*

HOGG, JAMES (1770–1835), Scottish poet, was a shepherd and his ancestors had been shepherds for centuries. He was self-taught as he tended his flocks. Sir Walter Scott helped him secure a publisher for some of his first poetry and later he was much lionized in his native parish and in Edinburgh and London. His poetry is marked by the spirit of fairy mythology and the rhythm of the old Scotch ballads.

HOLLAND, RUPERT SARGENT (1878– ), was born in Louisville, Kentucky. When he was six years old his family moved to Philadelphia. He was educated at Harvard and received a degree in law from the University of Pennsylvania. He practiced law for some years in Philadelphia, serving as attorney for the Legal Aid Society. He now lives in Wayne, Pennsylvania, and has a summer home on the Maine coast. He is the author of a series of books for children dealing with historic backgrounds: *Historic Boyhoods, Historic Girlhoods, Historic Railroads,* etc. He has also written a number of Boy Scout stories, of which *The Boy Scouts of Birch-Bark Island* was the first. A long list of mystery and adventure stories for boys and girls and some verse in children's magazines are of his authorship.

HOLLING, HOLLING CLANCY (1900– ), grew up on a farm in southern Michigan. His father, a superintendent of schools, loved the outdoors and taught him to observe and love nature. He studied art at the Art Institute of Chicago. After graduation he spent three years on the staff of the Field Museum, modeling and mounting specimens; during this time he studied anthropology under Dr. Ralph Linton. He made several field trips with expeditions for the museum, one to study Rocky Mountain goats in British Columbia. With material gathered on this trip, he wrote and illustrated *Rocky Billy: The Story of a Rocky Mountain Goat.* He and his wife, Lucille, also an artist, have made many pack and canoe trips into remote sections of the United States, Canada, and Mexico, studying and painting native Indian and wild life. They spent several years in pictorial advertising work in Chicago and have painted murals and designed Indian and early western interiors for buildings in various parts of the United States. For two years, in 1938 and 1939, they traveled in a studio trailer, gathering material and painting in western Canada and the United States. They now live in California. They work together on children's books; Mr. Holling writes the text and together they make the illustrations. In addition to *Rocky Billy,* they have written and illustrated: *The Book of Indians, The Book of Cowboys, Claws of the Thunderbird, Little Big-Bye-and-Bye, Little Buffalo Boy,* and other books for children.

HOLMES, OLIVER WENDELL (1809–1894), the delightful "Autocrat of the Breakfast Table," was one of the most versatile of American men of letters. He was a distinguished professor of medicine, a novelist, poet, and humorist. Many of his poems have the charming intimacy of conversation and the humorous ones are especially well suited to children.

HOOD, THOMAS (1799–1845), British humorist and poet, was one of the most popular writers of his day. He was famous for his humorous contributions to London magazines, but a few years before he died he championed the poor and oppressed in such poems as "The Song of the Shirt" and "The Bridge of Sighs." His earlier poems were graceful and delicate and many of them were about fairies.

HOSFORD, DOROTHY, was born and has lived most of her life in Pittsburgh. She was educated at the Carnegie Institute of Technology, and while in college was active in the publication of the undergraduate literary magazine. She became secretary of the Carnegie Library School and through her work as a librarian became interested in children's reading. A combination of this interest and a love of poetry led her to adapt William Morris's *Sigurd the Volsung* for older children, under the title, *Sons of the Volsungs.* She is the mother of twin sons, and now lives in Bradford, Pennsylvania.

HOUSMAN, A. E. (1859–1936), was born in England of a talented family. He was educated at Oxford, and all of his mature life was spent as professor of Latin at the University of London, and at Cambridge University. When *A Shropshire Lad* was published in 1896, Housman became internationally famous. After a silence of twenty-six years, his second volume, *Last Poems,* appeared in 1922. His poems, though beautiful, are ironic and pessimistic, and only a few quotations are suitable for children.

HOWITT, WILLIAM (1792–1879), was an English author of Quaker ancestry and education. He and his wife, Mary Howitt, worked together to produce wholesome and instructive literature for children. Mary translated many of Andersen's stories, and William wrote of nature and travel. Their writing seems old-fashioned today, but some of William Howitt's nature poems continue to have interest for children.

HUGHES, LANGSTON (1902– ), is a distinguished Negro poet. He was born in Missouri and was graduated from high school in Cleveland and from Lincoln University. His volume of verse, *The Dream Keeper, and Other Poems,* contains lyrics of great beauty, some serious poems, a number of rollicking songs, and some very fine "blues."

HULL, KATHARINE (1921– ), and WHITLOCK, PAMELA (1920– ), were respectively fifteen and sixteen years old in 1936 when a rainstorm brought them together and resulted in their collaborating to write *The Far-Distant Oxus.* In secret these English schoolgirls planned each chapter and then wrote the book in longhand on both sides of the paper, using several kinds of paper. They admired Arthur Ransome's *Swallows and Amazons* and other books he had written for children, so they sent the manuscript to him because, they wrote him, "we are not quite sure what to do with it." Ransome knew what to do with it, as did the publisher to whom he took it. Ransome wrote an interesting introduction for their book in which he tells how astonished he was to discover that these schoolgirl authors understood so well the craftmanship of writing and particularly the handling of plot.

HUNT, LEIGH (1784–1859), English critic, essayist, and poet, was a close friend of Keats, Shelley, and Byron. He was connected with various liberal newspapers and magazines and his opinions often landed him in difficulties. His whole life was one of political, financial, and domestic trouble, in spite of which he attained literary fame. His poem, "Abou Ben Adhem," has probably been quoted more often than any poem in the English language.

IRVING, WASHINGTON (1783–1859), was the first great American man of letters. Much of his work is marked by qualities that we think of as distinctively American—a mingling of the serious and comic, of fact and impossibility to produce a fabulous yarn told with the straightest of faces. In *The Sketch-Book* may be found the incomparable tales of "Rip Van Winkle" and "The Legend of Sleepy Hollow," in *The Tales of a Traveler* are weird adventures, and in *The Alhambra,* Moorish legends and fairy tales. Many critics think Irving is at his best in *The Knickerbocker History of New York.* An excellent edition of the last, arranged by Anne Carroll Moore, is available for older children.

IRWIN, WALLACE (1876– ), is well known for humorous verse and stories contributed to leading magazines. He was born in Oneida, New York, and now lives on Long Island. He spent some years in California, as a student at Stanford University and as special writer for San Francisco newspapers. His *Letters of a Japanese Schoolboy* is the best known of his prose, and *Nautical Lays of a Landsman,* of his verse.

JACKSON, LEROY F. (1881– ), was born in Canada but came to the United States when a small child. He was educated at the University of North Dakota, University of Chicago, and Harvard University. He has taught and directed schools in North Dakota, Minnesota, Washington, and North Carolina. He is the author of several books of songs and rhymes for young children. The jingles of *The Peter Patter Book* have some of the qualities of Mother Goose.

JACOBS, JOSEPH (1854–1916), was one of the great modern scholars of folklore. He was born in Australia and spent most of his life in England. In 1900 he came to the United States and lived here until his death in 1916. Many of the wonder stories that appear in his books were first told to his three children when they were small. His collections of folk tales, with their notes and introductions, are not only scientifically accurate, but his versions of the stories are delightful and interesting to children. *English Fairy Tales, More English Fairy Tales, Celtic Fairy Tales, More Celtic Fairy Tales,* and *Indian Fairy Tales* make an excellent library of folklore. He also produced editions of *The Fables of Aesop, Arabian Nights' Entertainments,* and *Reynard the Fox.* Jacobs was an authority on Jewish history and culture; he edited the *Jewish Encyclopaedia* and wrote *Jewish Contributions to Civilization,* the latter published after his death. He was a wonderfully gifted man and his pleasant, kindly disposition and inexhaustible humor endeared him to his many friends.

JORDAN, DAVID STARR (1851–1931), famous as the first president of Stanford University, had a wide influence upon American education. His liberal point of view extended to the education of children as well as to students of college age. *Science Sketches* was one of the first books for young people that presented scientific facts in an interesting and entertaining manner. The stories of *Knight and Barbara* are fanciful tales for very young children. Dr. Jordan was known internationally for his writings on science and on the prevention of war.

KEARY, ANNIE (1825–1879), was an English novelist, daughter of an Irish clergyman. Her best-known book was *Castle Daly,* an Irish story. In 1857 with Eliza Keary, she translated Norse tales under the title, *The Heroes of Asgard.* It continues to be one of the best sources for Norse myths.

KEATS, JOHN (1795–1821), the great English poet, was a tragic figure. He struggled with poverty and ill health and died from tuberculosis shortly after his third volume of poetry was published. Only a few of his beautiful poems are simple enough for children.

KILMER, JOYCE (1886–1918), was a graduate of Rutgers College and became a teacher, a book salesman, and an editor. In 1917 he enlisted as a private in the National Guard and was killed in action in 1918. Death came before his gift for poetry was fully developed, but "Trees" is one of the most popular poems of this century. "The House with Nobody in It" and "Delicatessen" show a deep love for humanity and are much liked by children.

KING, EDITH, was born in South Africa and has spent a large part of her life there. She was educated in England. For five years she lived on a remote farm in the Transvaal with a married sister, for whose children she wrote the *Veld Rhymes.* For eleven years she was principal of a government boarding and day school for girls at Bloemfontein in the Orange Free State. She loves the country and spends all the time she can there. Her poems for young children picture country sights and sounds in a simple, natural manner.

KIPLING, RUDYARD (1865–1936), was born in Bombay. His father was an artist, and for many years curator of the Lahore Museum in India. During the early years of his life, Rudyard Kipling spent most of his time with Indian nurses, *ayahs,* from whom he learned the native tales of the jungle animals that he later used so effectively as literary material. When he was six he was sent to England to school and remained there until he was seventeen. His school experiences are pictured in *Stalky & Co.*—he is "Beetle" in the story. At seventeen he returned to India and became assistant editor of a daily newspaper in Lahore. He spent seven happy years in this work and then went to England with a trunkful of stories of Indian life. He did not win immediate recognition and spent some time in dreary lodgings writing furiously, but soon the public discovered him and at twenty-six he was famous. In 1892 he married an American, Caroline Balestier, and lived for four years in her native city, Brattleboro, Vermont. Here two of his children were born and here he wrote *Captains Courageous, The Seven Seas, Many Inventions, The Jungle Book,* and *The Second Jungle Book.* The extraordinary beast stories of *The Jungle Books* brought him new fame and a new audience, that of children. In 1902 when he published the *Just So Stories,* illustrated by his own drawings, he was claimed by children everywhere as their own. In 1897 he wrote the poem "Recessional" on the occasion of Queen Victoria's second Jubilee. This and other poems, such as "Mandalay," "Gunga Din," "If—," and "The Ballad of East and West," became as popular as his stories. In 1907 he was awarded the Nobel Prize for Literature. His only son was killed in the World War, and from that time until his own death Kipling lived in seclusion in his home in Sussex.

LAMBERT, CLARA, was born in Minneapolis and educated there. After graduating from the University of Minnesota, she became assistant to Lucy Sprague Mitchell at the City and Country School in New York. She also worked under Elizabeth Irwin at the Little Red School House in New York. Out of these educational experiences, her books, *Manhattan Now and Long Ago, Skyscrapers, Talking Wires,* and other stories, grew. She is now Associate in Teacher Education for the Child Study Association of America. She is the mother of three children.

LANG, ANDREW (1844–1912), was born in Scotland, with a strain of gypsy blood in his veins. He was educated at St. Andrews University and Oxford University. He settled in London and became the greatest journalist of his day. He was a versatile scholar and writer in languages and in history, but he is best known today for his work in folklore. He searched for fairy stories and romances through the literature of England and all the European countries. *The Blue Fairy Book* was followed by fairy books designated by colors—red, brown, green, lilac, pink, violet, crimson, yellow, etc. He prepared a large number of these collections and for many years a new one was published each Christmas. They are still read with pleasure by British and American boys and girls. Lang's *Arabian Nights' Entertainments* is one of the best editions of that classic, and *The Nursery Rhyme Book,* one of the best collections of Mother Goose rhymes. His scholarly treatises on folklore include *Custom and Myth; Myth, Literature and Religion;* and *Social Origins.* His edition of *Perrault's Popular Tales* contains a very fine introduction and detailed notes. Lang was popular with his friends and loved by them for his good nature, but at times he attacked his fellow folklorists humorously but severely.

LANIER, SIDNEY (1842–1881), is a distinguished figure in American poetry though the number of poems he wrote is relatively small. He was a native of Georgia, served in the Confederate army throughout the Civil War, and contracted tuberculosis from which he never recovered. His life was a tragic one sustained by his genius as a poet and musician. He was a fine performer on the flute and played with leading orchestras in several cities. In spite of failing health he lectured brilliantly on literature at Johns Hopkins University. He prepared several volumes for boy readers in which the stories of Froissart, King Arthur, and the Mabinogion are retold in beautiful prose. His most famous poems are: "The Song of the Chattahoochee," "The Marshes of Glynn," "A Ballad of Trees and the Master," and "Dear Land of All My Love."

LATHROP, DOROTHY P. (1891– ), one of the most gifted of present-day illustrators of children's books, was born in Albany, New York. Her mother was a painter and her first interest in art came from playing in her mother's studio and being encouraged to use her mother's brushes and paints. Her sister, Gertrude, is a sculptor and the two share a studio at their home in Albany. Dorothy Lathrop studied at Teachers College, Columbia University, and taught for two years. She studied art at the Pennsylvania Academy of Fine Arts and the Art Students' League in New York. She began illustrating in 1918; her first book was *The Three Mulla Mulgars* by De la Mare. She has illustrated some thirty books for children, for eight of which she has also written the text. She works in oil, water color, pen and ink, and with the lithographic pencil. Her pictures of fairies are among the finest portrayals of fairies in the history of book illustration. She is equally successful in drawing animals—*Who Goes There?* and *Hide and Go Seek,* which she also wrote, are extraordinarily beautiful. In 1938 she received the Caldecott Medal, the first award ever given to a picture book for children, for her *Animals of the Bible.* Miss Lathrop's contribution to children's books is a large one, and each year she adds new volumes of grace and beauty.

LEAMY, EDMUND (1889– ), was born in Dublin, Ireland. His father and mother were writers of note. During the World War he served as a commissioned officer in East Africa. He has lived in the United States since 1918. When he was poetry editor of the *New York Sun* he "discovered" Nathalia Crane. He published poems she contributed, praised them highly, and invited the author to his office. He was astounded to find that she was a child less than ten years old. Mr. Leamy is the author of a large number of poems, short stories, articles, and editorials that have appeared in leading American magazines and newspapers.

LEAR, EDWARD (1812–1888), British artist and humorist, was the youngest of twenty-one children. His parents died when he was young and at fifteen he began to support himself by drawing sketches for books on natural history and medicine. When he was twenty he was employed by the Zoölogical Society of London and at twenty-one published a large collection of colored drawings of birds. The next four years were spent on the estate of the Earl of Derby, drawing the birds of his menagerie. These four years were happy and productive, for here Lear made many friends and in this happy atmosphere his flair for wit and nonsense developed. For the children of the family he made many absurd verses and pictures. Not only the children but all who saw them were delighted; years later they were gathered together and published as *The Book of Nonsense,* and people have laughed at them ever since. Other humorous books of Lear's authorship are: *The Book of More Nonsense, Nonsense Songs, Nonsense Stories and Alphabets, The Pelican Chorus,* and *The Jumblies,* which were originally illustrated by Lear himself and later editions by L. Leslie Brooke. Lear wrote nonsense verses for the amusement of himself and others, but his life work was painting. He was an indefatigable traveler, drawing and painting the scenes of his travels, and later exhibiting his paintings in London. He gave lessons in drawing and Queen Victoria was one of his pupils. The last twenty years of his life were spent in Italy. He was considered a first-rate artist, but his nonsense verse made his name famous all over the world.

LEIGH, HENRY S. (1837–1883), was an Englishman, contributor of humorous verse to *Punch* during one of its brilliant periods. His clever parodies were very popular.

LENT, HENRY B. (1901– ), was born in New Bedford, Massachusetts, and educated at Hamilton College and Yale University. He is now in the advertising business in New York and lives on a farm near Westport, Connecticut. During summer vacations when he was in college he worked with road construction crews, with gangs of building wreckers, with fishermen on schooners in the Bay of Fundy, and one summer drove a team of oxen on a Nova Scotia construction job. When he married and had two sons of his own, they asked so many questions that he got the idea of writing books for children picturing the everyday work of the world in story form. As a result he has written a number of informational books that young children like very much. Among them are: *Diggers and Builders, Grindstone Farm, Clear Track Ahead!, Full Steam Ahead!, Wide Road Ahead!* and *Tugboat.*

LIDA is French, the wife of Paul Fancher, the famous "Père Castor." They are both widely appreciated among French educators for their work in the "Père Castor" series. Several books for young children by Lida have been translated into English and published in the United States. In addition to *Plouf, the Little Wild Duck,* there are *Pompom, the Little Red Squirrel; Fluff, the Little Wild Rabbit; Scuff, the Seal;* and *Bruin, the Brown Bear.*

LINDBERGH, CHARLES A. (1902– ), is the American hero of aviation. In the book, *We,* he gives an account of his early life, of his experiences in the pioneer days of flying, and of his daring solo flight from the United States to France, which ended so successfully on May 21, 1927. His wife, Anne Morrow Lindbergh, describes more recent aviation ventures that she and her husband have shared in two beautifully written books, *Northward to the Orient* and *Listen, the Wind!*

LINDSAY, VACHEL (1879–1931), was born in Springfield, Illinois, in a house that had once belonged to Lincoln's sister and in which Lincoln had often been entertained. Lindsay's mother was a talented woman and the boy was brought up in an atmosphere of culture and wide reading. He was trained to be an artist and studied at the Art Institute of Chicago and the New York School of Art. Following art school, however, he spent his time tramping about the country, chanting and reciting his poems for all who would listen. His first volume of verse, *General Booth Enters into Heaven,* was published in 1913, and followed by *The Congo, and Other Poems* in 1914, both of which brought him well-deserved popularity. At the outbreak of the World War in 1914, he wrote the memorable poem, "Abraham Lincoln Walks at Midnight." For many years, almost up to the time of his death, he continued chanting his poems for audiences all over the country and became a national figure. His finest poems were written in the form of communal chants and have a primitive, pounding rhythm that is irresistible, especially to children. Children have appropriated many of his adult poems, but he wrote a number directly intended for children. His "poem games," such as "The Potatoes Dance" and "The Mysterious Cat" are alive with pulsating rhythm; "In Praise of Johnny Appleseed" has strong rhythm in a content of historical and ethical significance; other shorter poems have whimsical nonsense that children love.

LOFTING, HUGH (1886– ), was born in England of English-Irish parents. When he was eighteen he came to the United States and studied at the Massachusetts Institute of Technology. He completed his education in England, became a civil engineer, and built railroads in West Africa and Canada. In 1912 he married and settled in the United States. While serving with the British army in the trenches in France, he wrote and illustrated stories to send home to his children. They were so delighted with the stories and drawings that after the war his wife persuaded him to publish them in book form, and they became *The Story of Doctor Dolittle.* The second Doctor Dolittle book, *The Voyages of Doctor Dolittle,* received the Newbery Medal in 1923. Since that time Hugh Lofting has given his entire time to writing and illustrating books for children. There are ten books in the Doctor Dolittle series and two about Mrs. Tubbs—all abounding in delightful make-believe and humor. *Porridge Poetry* is a book of rhymes for very young children, and *The Twilight of Magic* is a medieval story for somewhat older children. Mr. Lofting now lives in Connecticut.

LOMAX, JOHN A. (1872– ), was born in Mississippi. He graduated from the University of Texas and was for some years a member of that faculty. He has rendered great service to American literature by his careful collection of cowboy songs and ballads. These half-forgotten ballads, typical of a picturesque phase of American civilization, are genuine folklore and deserve a place in our literature.

LONDON, JACK (1876–1916), was born in California of humble parents. His boyhood was dominated by gang life on the waterfronts of Oakland and San Francisco. When he was fifteen he bought a sloop in which he robbed the oyster beds of San Fransisco Bay at night. At seventeen he made a voyage on a seal-hunting schooner to Japan and the Bering Sea. On his return he wrote a story about a typhoon and sold it to a San Fransisco newspaper. This was his first published story. For some time he worked as a factory hand, coal-shoveler, and longshoreman, all the while eagerly reading books borrowed from the public library. He attended an Oakland high school for a year, working his way as a janitor. He crowded two years of high school work into three months of private study and passed the entrance examination into the University of California. After only one semester in the university, however, he joined the gold rush to the Klondike and spent a year in the Yukon. His stories began to attract attention and with the publication of *The Call of the Wild* when he was twenty-seven, he became famous. He continued to be a rover, exploring the slums of London and cruising the South Seas in his own yacht. He finally bought a ranch in California, where he settled down and wrote feverishly. Before his death at forty, he had produced over fifty books, chiefly fiction. His work was very uneven, but at his best he was master of the story of swift, red-blooded action. Many critics consider his stories of animals, *The Call of the Wild* and *White Fang,* as his best work.

LONGFELLOW, HENRY WADSWORTH (1807–1882), was one of the most loved of American writers, both for his poems and for his personal life. For a quarter of a century he taught foreign languages and literature at Bowdoin College and Harvard University. His poems were known all over the United States and Europe. The swing to realism in literature that took place after his death detracted from his popularity, but many critics believe that American literature viewed from a longer range of time than the present will accord a high place to the uniform excellence of Longfellow's representative poems.

LOWELL, AMY (1874–1925), born in Massachusetts of the famous Lowell family, had every advantage of education and travel. She chose poetry as a profession, and for ten years studied and practiced it before permitting any of her poems to be published. She was an able critic and became the leader and ardent defender of the school of so-called "new poetry" that came into literary prominence about 1914—new poetry in the sense that freer verse forms were employed and the subject-matter of poetry broadened to include all phases of life. Miss Lowell had an eccentric personality, but her volumes of verse and poetic criticism and her fine biography of Keats won for her a position of respect in literature.

LOWELL, JAMES RUSSELL (1819–1891), one of the New England poets, wrote racy Yankee dialect verses in *The Biglow Papers,* religious poetry in *The Vision of Sir Launfal,* dignified memorial verse in "The Harvard Commemoration Ode," as well as sonnets and ballads. He was a brilliant teacher and editor and his essays rank as high as his verse. He was minister to Spain and to England and was honored abroad as he was at home.

LUCAS, E. V. (1868–1938), was a versatile English writer. In addition to his books for children, he wrote charming humorous essays, biographies of distinction, and interesting accounts of travel—a total of more than a hundred titles. He was born at Brighton, and educated at University College, London. He early joined the staff of the *Sussex Daily News,* then the *London Globe,* and later became an editor of *Punch.* His writings for children comprise delightful verses and quietly humorous stories. He also compiled anthologies for children.

LUTHER, MARTIN (1483–1546), was born a peasant and became the leader of the German Reformation. His childhood was a happy one and as he early showed signs of high intelligence he received a good education. His sixty-three years of life were crowded with momentous happenings, but the "Cradle Hymn" seems to be an echo of his simple childhood.

McCORD, DAVID (1897– ), was born in New York but spent his boyhood in Oregon. He was educated at Harvard University and was for several years on the drama and music staff of the *Boston Evening Transcript.* He lives in Cambridge and is active in Harvard alumni affairs. He is a frequent contributor of verse to magazines. His books, *The Crows,* and *Bay Window Ballads,* reveal his skill in handling light verse and humorous themes. He has written many verses for children, some of which have been set to music.

McCRAE, JOHN (1872–1918), was a Canadian doctor. He served in the South African War, and in the World War was in charge of a field hospital in France, where he died of pneumonia. He wrote the poem, "In Flanders Fields," during the battle of Ypres. His poems were published in a volume that appeared shortly after his death.

McLEOD, IRENE RUTHERFORD (1891– ), is an Englishwoman. She has written several volumes of verse, of which *Songs to Save a Soul,* and *Before Dawn* are the best known.

MACDONALD, GEORGE (1824–1905), was born in a farmhouse in northern Scotland and spent his boyhood on the mountains and moors. He was educated at King's College, Aberdeen, and went to London as a tutor. He studied for the ministry and for a few years filled a pastorate in Sussex. His liberal views made him unpopular and he gave up the ministry for writing and lecturing. In forty-two years' time he produced fifty-two books novels, poems, essays, and stories. He was the father of eleven children and in his later life adopted three more children. His health was always poor and the last twenty-five years of his life were spent in Italy except for visits to England in the summers. He was gentle and lovable and many famous people were his friends. It was through his influence that Lewis Carroll was prevailed upon to publish *Alice's Adventures in Wonderland.* MacDonald's novels of Scottish peasant life brought him conspicuous success, but his fame today rests upon his books for children. *At the Back of the North Wind, The Princess and the Goblin, The Princess and Curdie,* and *The Light Princess* have a welcome place in children's libraries. These delightful make-believe stories embody high ideals without preachment.

MACKAYE, PERCY (1875– ), dramatist and poet, was born in New York, educated at Harvard University, and now lives at Cornish, New Hampshire. He has made extensive folk researches in the Appalachian Mountains and written and directed many community masques, pageants, and folk plays in various parts of the United States. He has translated plays and written a number of original ones. He has written and delivered many distinguished commemorative poems in honor of public events and heroes. In March, 1914, when the *Civic Forum* of New York presented a medal to Col. George W. Goethals for his work in building the Panama Canal, Percy MacKaye read his poem written for the occasion, "Goethals, the Prophet Engineer."

MAJOR, CHARLES (1856–1913), was an Indiana lawyer and novelist. He was the author of *When Knighthood Was in Flower,* published in 1898, and *Dorothy*

*Vernon of Haddon Hall,* published in 1902—two romantic novels of great popularity. *The Bears of Blue River,* published in 1901, is a dramatic account of boy life in Indiana in pioneer days.

MALLOCH, DOUGLAS (1877–1938), was born in Muskegon, Michigan, and made his home there and in Chicago. He was a newspaper reporter in Muskegon for a number of years, and from 1903 till his death was editor of *The American Lumberman.* He wrote many poems about the outdoors that were published in magazines and newspapers and later appeared in book form.

MARKHAM, EDWIN (1852–1940), was born in Oregon and spent his boyhood in California, where he worked at farming, blacksmithing, and herding sheep and cattle. He secured a college education and became a principal and superintendent of schools in California. From early boyhood he wrote poems but received little recognition until he was nearly fifty, when the publication of the poem, "The Man with the Hoe," made him famous. He is also the author of "Lincoln, the Man of the People," and other poems. The last forty years of his life were spent in or near New York.

MARQUIS, DON (1878–1937), humorist, poet, and playwright, was born in Illinois. For many years he was an editor on the staff of the *New York Sun* and later columnist on the *New York Herald Tribune. Dreams and Dust,* a volume of serious poems, was published in 1915. *The Old Soak,* a play published in 1921, was an outstanding dramatic success. The adventures in verse of his humorous characters, "Archy," the cockroach, and "Mehitabel," the alley-cat, delighted his many newspaper readers and were also published in book form. Don Marquis was much loved by the public and by his many friends.

MARSHALL, JIM, is the Far East correspondent of *Collier's Magazine.* The poem, "The Oregon Trail: 1851," first appeared in *Frontier and Midland,* a literary magazine edited by Professor H. G. Merriam at the University of Montana.

MARTIN, JOHN, is the pen name of Morgan Shepard. For twenty years he and Helen Waldo edited and published *John Martin's Book,* a magazine for children that had much to do with improving the quality of illustrations in books and periodicals for children. John Martin is a native of San Francisco but has lived for many years in New York. He was for some time director of children's radio programs for the National Broadcasting Company. He has written numerous rhymes and verses for children, published in his own and other magazines. He has edited several classics for children, the best known of which are *The Children's Munchausen* retold from Raspe's *Adventures of Baron Munchausen,* and *The Wolf's-Head and the Queen,* retold from William Morris's *Child Christopher.*

MASEFIELD, JOHN (1878– ), is the present poet laureate of England. He went to sea at an early age and worked for several years as a common sailor. At one time he landed in New York with five dollars and stayed nearly three years working at any rough jobs he could find. When he was twenty-four he read Chaucer for the first time and determined to become a poet. His first volume, *Salt-Water*

*Ballads,* was published in 1902 and has been followed by many others. Many critics believe Masefield to be the greatest poet of this century. In his poems real life, often hard and ugly, is pictured with solemn beauty. Mr. Masefield also writes excellent prose. *Jim Davis, A Bird of Dawning,* and *Victorious Troy* are adventure stories much liked by high-school students; *The Midnight Folk,* and *The Box of Delights* are make-believe stories of interest to children in the intermediate grades.

MEIGS, CORNELIA (1885– ), was born in Rock Island, Illinois, and spent her childhood in Keokuk, Iowa. She is now professor of English at Bryn Mawr College and her summers are spent in Vermont. She grew up in a storytelling family and many of the stories concerned her ancestors. From early childhood she was absorbed in accounts of historic adventure and this interest was deepened by her study of history at Bryn Mawr College. Her first writing was done while she was teaching in a private school in Davenport, Iowa, where she told her stories to children and listened to their criticisms. In the summers she has had her sisters' children with her and they have made a critical audience for her stories. Few writers for children have received such consistent praise for all their books. In 1927, *Trade Wind* received the Beacon Hill Bookshelf Prize, and in 1934 *Invincible Louisa* was awarded the Newbery Medal. Her stories are historically accurate and delightful in plot and characterization. Other well-liked books of her authorship are: *Wind in the Chimney, Rain on the Roof, The Pool of Stars, As the Crow Flies, The Covered Bridge, The Scarlet Oak, Master Simon's Garden, The Willow Whistle, Young Americans,* and *The Wonderful Locomotive.*

MILLAY, EDNA ST. VINCENT (1892– ), is the foremost woman poet in America today. She was born in Maine, educated at Vassar College, and now lives with her husband, Eugen Boissevain, on a farm in upstate New York. She has not written intentionally for children, but many of her beautiful poems are simple enough for children. *The Ballad of the Harp Weaver,* thought of as an adult poem, has a strong appeal for boys and girls of the upper grades if read to them. In *Second April,* also, are poems suitable for children. A compilation of her poems, entitled *Poems Selected for Young People,* has been issued.

MILLER, "JOAQUIN" (1841–1913), was born, it is said, in Indiana, in "a covered wagon, pointed west." He spent his adventurous youth in the West, and his best poetry was written about the West. When he was a young man he wrote an article in defense of a Mexican bandit named Joaquin Murietta; the name "Joaquin" became associated with Miller and he retained it instead of his less romantic given name, Cincinnatus Heine. He received little recognition as a poet until his first book, *Songs of the Sierras,* was published at his own expense in London in 1870 and at once made him famous. He came back to the United States and became a journalist in Washington, but a few years later returned to California and lived in Oakland until his death. None of his later verse achieved the popularity of *Songs of the Sierras* except "Columbus," which was written in 1896 and expressed in the figure of Columbus the same steadfastness of purpose that drove the American pioneers westward.

MILLER, MARY BRITTON (1883– ), came of New England heritage. Orphaned by the sudden death of her parents when she was four years old, she and her four brothers and sisters were brought up in her grandmother's home in Springfield, Massachusetts. She and her twin sister, whom she called her "identical self," romped and played in the rose gardens, terraced orchards, and wide lawns of the beautiful old New England place. She now lives in New York and is unmarried. Her book of verse for children, *Menagerie,* has a number of vivid sketches of animals, drawn with touches of humor, and several poems of deeper meaning—all robust and free of any tone of patronizing. She has also written three volumes of unusual verse for adults: *Without Sanctuary, Intrepid Bird,* and *Songs of Infancy.* The last, while a book for adults, pictures the thoughts and feelings of childhood.

MODEROW, GERTRUDE, is assistant director of research for the public schools of Louisville, Kentucky. She was educated at the University of Chicago and taught mathematics in high school. She has conducted investigations and experiments in the teaching of slow pupils of junior high-school age. SANDRUS, MARY YOST, lives in Charleston, West Virginia. She was educated at Hood College and the University of Chicago. She taught English in Pennsylvania high schools and became especially interested in the problems of dull children. For several years she was connected with the state department of education of West Virginia. MITCHELL, JOSEPHINE, teaches extension classes for the Southwestern Louisiana Institute. She formerly taught in junior high school and the Louisville Normal School. NOYES, ERNEST C., was educated at Yale and Harvard universities. He taught English in high school and has been for some years assistant superintendent of schools of Allegheny County, Pennsylvania. Miss Moderow, Mrs. Sandrus, Miss Mitchell, and Mr. Noyes have collaborated in producing *Six Great Stories,* retold versions of classic stories, prepared especially to meet the needs of boys and girls in the upper elementary grades who do not read well. The vocabulary and sentence structure of their versions have been subjected to experimentation and arranged to suit the capacity of children 13 years old with mental development and reading ability of average children 10 years old.

MOORE, CLEMENT C. (1779–1863), was born and lived all his life on an estate in Chelsea, then outside New York but now West Twenty-third Street in downtown New York. His father was Bishop of New York and President of Columbia College and officiated at the inauguration of Washington. Clement was educated at Columbia and became a scholar of oriental literature and professor of Biblical learning at the Theological Seminary of New York. On Christmas Eve, 1822, Dr. Moore read to his children a poem he had written for them, "A Visit from St. Nicholas." A friend of the family later heard the poem and the following year sent it to a newspaper, the *Troy Sentinel,* where it was published anonymously. In 1837, a slender collection of verse entitled *The New York Book of Poetry,* contained the immortal poem. The Moore home has been torn down to make way for skyscrapers, but each year on Christmas Eve, the children in the vicinity of the New York churchyard where Clement C. Moore lies buried form a candlelight procession to his grave.

MORLEY, CHRISTOPHER (1890– ), was born at Haverford, Pennsylvania. His boyhood was spent in Baltimore where his father was professor of mathematics at Johns Hopkins University. He was educated at Haverford College and was a Rhodes scholar at Oxford. He became in turn an editor of the *Ladies*

*Home Journal,* the *Philadelphia Evening Public Ledger,* and the *New York Sun.* He now contributes a column, entitled "The Bowling Green," to the *Saturday Review of Literature.* He has not written directly for children, but some of his poems in *Chimney Smoke* and *The Rocking Horse* are suitable for children and and many of his essays and stories are liked by young people. *Parnassus on Wheels* and *The Haunted Bookshop* are dear to book lovers, and *Where the Blue Begins* is a fantasy somewhat after the manner of James M. Barrie. His novel, *Kitty Foyle,* is very popular.

MORRIS, WILLIAM (1834–1896), English poet and artist, was in spirit a medieval knight or an adventurous Viking. The medievalism that inspired his poetry found expression also in arts and crafts. He founded industries that brought back the spirit of the Middle Ages in house decoration—furniture, wall hangings, carpet-weaving, painted glass and tiles, and tapestries—and set styles that still inspire the makers of beautiful things. He established a printing press and issued beautifully printed and decorated books that set a standard which typographers still attempt to reach. He was a man of prodigious imagination and while he worked at painting and designing, poems and tales took shape in his mind. Between 1868 and 1870 he wrote *The Earthly Paradise,* a storehouse of poetic romance. In 1876 appeared *Sigurd the Volsung,* an epic poem of heroic vigor and movement. He also wrote a large number of prose tales and romances. These poems and stories as William Morris wrote them are too long and complicated for children to read, but adaptations of them bring to children a literature full of color and action and supply ideals of courtesy and faith.

MORROW, ELIZABETH (1873– ), was born in Cleveland, Ohio, and lives in Englewood, New Jersey. She was educated at Smith College and the Sorbonne in Paris. She is a trustee and has served as acting president of Smith College. She is active in philanthropic work and is the mother of four children, one of whom is Anne Morrow Lindbergh. Her husband was Dwight W. Morrow, late ambassador to Mexico. While in Mexico, Mrs. Morrow wrote the story for children, *The Painted Pig.* She has written a volume of verse and contributed articles and verse to magazines.

MORTON, DAVID (1886– ), was born in Kentucky, educated at Vanderbilt University, and is now professor of English at Amherst College. He has not written for children, but some of the poems in *Ships in Harbour* are liked by children. He has written other volumes of verse: *Harvest, A Man of Earth, Earth's Processional,* and *Spell against Time.* He has also compiled anthologies of verse and written several books on the criticism and history of poetry.

NICOL, NINA (1895– ), was born in New Hampshire and spent her childhood in New England. She studied painting in Boston and New York and sculpture in Paris. While a student in Paris she began to write stories for children, the first of which were published in England. When she returned to the United States she and Doris Fogler wrote *Rusty Pete of the Lazy A B.* The cow pony of the story is a real pony that Miss Fogler had owned and ridden on her ranch in Montana. Mrs. Nicol now makes her home in Hollywood, California, where she lives with her young son. She has written the script for several radio programs and motion pictures on the subject of health education for children.

NORDHOFF, CHARLES (1887– ), was born in London of American parents. He was brought to the United States at the age of three, lived on a ranch in California, and was educated at Stanford and Harvard universities. In 1916 he went to France and joined the Lafayette Flying Corps, a squadron of American volunteers in the French army. There he met James Norman Hall. After demobilization they collaborated in editing a history of the Lafayette Flying Corps. Then they went to live in the island of Tahiti, in the South Pacific Ocean. There they have remained ever since and together have written a number of books, the best known of which are *Mutiny on the Bounty, Men against the Sea,* and *Pitcairn's Island.* During the early years of their residence in Tahiti, they worked separately. During this time Nordhoff wrote two books for boys, *The Pearl Lagoon* and *The Derelict,* stories of adventure in the South Seas. He and Hall collaborated in writing another book for boys, *Falcons of France,* a story of the World War.

NORRIS, MARGARET, was educated at Smith College and became a reporter on a Chicago newspaper. As a reporter she interviewed all kinds of people, from murderers to visiting royalty. She became interested in the daredevils of industry —the unknown men in hazardous occupations who risk their lives to help turn the wheels of civilization. To get the stories of these heroes she tracked them to their jobs and talked with them at work. Her book, *Heroes and Hazards,* is the result. She is now a free-lance writer and lives in New York. She has contributed a number of articles and stories to magazines.

PAGE, THOMAS NELSON (1853–1922), was born and grew up on a plantation in Virginia. When he was eight years old he saw his father ride away to join the Confederate army. During the next four years, soldiers passing and guns booming near by were frequent experiences. At one time he went to see his father on the battlefield and spent the night in his father's tent. After the Civil War was over and most of the slaves were gone, he did farm work on the plantation. He was educated at Washington and Lee University, studied law at the University of Virginia, and practiced law in Richmond. When he was twenty-seven he wrote his first story, "Marse Chan," based upon true incidents of the Civil War. The success of "Marse Chan" led him to write other stories which were included in his first book, *In Ole Virginia. Two Little Confederates,* his most popular book for children, was based upon his own boyhood experiences during the Civil War. His style is the most graceful of all writers of his time who undertook to depict the Negro character and ante-bellum plantation life. He also wrote several books on Christmas, the best known of which is *Santa Claus's Partner.* When he was forty he went to live in Washington, D. C., and much of his writing was done there. He was appointed ambassador to Italy by Woodrow Wilson and filled that post during the World War.

PAGET-FREDERICKS, JOSEPH (1903– ), was born in San Francisco of English and Russian parents. He was educated at the University of California and studied under Sargent and other artists. He has taken part in a number of pageants and is a talented classical dancer. His pictures have been exhibited in galleries in different cities. He has illustrated several books for boys and girls; among them, *Poems of Edna St. Vincent Millay Selected for Young People.* His own verse for children, *Green Pipes,* was written when he was a boy, but it was not published until 1929 when it was issued with his own illustrations.

PARKER, ARTHUR C. (1881– ), is an anthropologist, and director of the Rochester Museum of Arts and Sciences, Rochester, New York. His great-grandfather, a Seneca Indian, was a private in the war of 1812. His grandfather was secretary of the Seneca Nation and a graduate engineer. His mother and father were teachers at the Cattaraugus Seneca Reservation in Erie County, New York, where he was born. When he was nine years old his father became statistician for the New York Central Railroad and the family went to live in the vicinity of New York City. The first nine years of the boy's life and many succeeding summers were spent on the reservation. Many Indians of the tribe came to his parents' house and told the children stories of earlier days. When he reached maturity, the Bear Clan of the tribe gave him the name of Gawaso Wanneh, a hereditary title borne by the war captain, which means "the great snowslide." Before going to the Rochester Museum, Mr. Parker served as archaeologist at the American Museum of Natural History, the Peabody Museum, and the New York State Museum. He is the author of *Archaeological History of New York,* and other scientific books and reports. He is an expert on the history of the Iroquois-Seneca Indians and on Indian affairs, and has made valuable collections of Indian myths and tales. In 1937 he was awarded the Indian Achievement Medal. His excellent books for children portray the Indian with accuracy and understanding. *The Indian How Book* explains many of the things about Indian life and customs that children wish to know. *Rumbling Wings,* and *Skunny Wundy* give interesting literary versions of Indian folk tales.

PATCH, EDITH M. (1876– ), is an entomologist, and since 1903 has been in charge of the department of entomology of the Maine Agricultural Experiment Station. She was born and spent her early childhood in Massachusetts. When she was eight years old her parents moved to Minnesota; there she went to school, and in 1901 graduated from the University of Minnesota. Later she studied at the University of Maine and Cornell University. Her childhood on a farm was a happy one; exploring the outdoors, she early developed a love of nature and a special interest in insects. During her senior year in high school she wrote an essay about the monarch butterfly that was read to younger childern in the school and much liked by them. Her teacher extracted from her a promise that some day she would write nature stories for children. The next twenty years were filled with scientific research to aid farmers in the control of insects and she wrote many scientific bulletins, but it was not until 1920 that she kept her promise and published *Hexapod Stories* for children. Since that time she has written many books and stories for children. She has the faculty of presenting accurate scientific information in a form that appeals to children. Her books abound in intimate sketches of strange little animals, fishes, and insects. Some of her books are: *Holiday Pond, Holiday Meadow, Holiday Hill, Holiday Shore, Forest Neighbors, Mountain Neighbors,* and *Desert Neighbors.*

PERRAULT, CHARLES (1628–1703), came of a distinguished French family. He was educated for the law but practiced only a short time. He held several important public posts, and through his efforts the Tuileries gardens were saved for the children of Paris when it was proposed to reserve them for royal use. He was elected to the French Academy, and after 1683 gave all his time to literature, writing poetry and scholarly criticism. He was a vigorous and popular character with much influence in literary and court circles. It was the fashion at the court of Louis XIV to pretend admiration for a life of simplicity, and nobles and ladies masqueraded in the costumes of shepherds and shepherdesses. Telling romantic fairy stories became a popular court diversion in which Perrault participated. In 1697 he published a little volume of eight prose tales,[1] called on the frontispiece, *Contes de Ma Mère l'Oye (Tales of My Mother Goose).* Evidently Perrault thought it unbecoming for a scholar of his standing to publish fairy tales, so he said they were written by his young son who had learned the stories from his nurse. Perhaps his son did hear them in this way; undoubtedly Perrault had himself heard them in this way in his own childhood. Perrault's other elaborate volumes have long since been forgotten, but these tales live on. Though children do not know the name of their benefactor, their love of "Cinderella," "Little Red Riding Hood," and the other tales, has made Perrault immortal.

PIPER, EDWIN FORD (1871– ), is professor of English at the University of Iowa. He was born and educated in Nebraska. He is the author of *Barbed Wire and Wayfarers,* and other volumes of poetry. He is a contributor of verse to magazines.

POE, EDGAR ALLAN (1809–1849), was one of the great geniuses of American letters. Some of the details of his life are obscure, but it was filled with misfortune and tragedy. In 1836 he married his cousin, Virginia Clemm, then only thirteen years old. She was an invalid for several years before her death in 1847. "Annabel Lee" was written in her memory. No poet excels Poe in picturing the dignity of sorrow in beautiful language and rhythm. His short stories of mystery, horror, and the supernatural are the most perfect of their type in literature.

POTTER, BEATRIX, is an Englishwoman. Her ancestors were hardy yeomen and weavers of Lancashire. Much of her childhood was spent in the Scottish Highlands. Her first writing was that of hymns after the style of Isaac Watts, but she was discouraged at the result. About 1893 she wrote a series of letters to amuse the little invalid son of a friend; one of the letters was *The Tale of Peter Rabbit,* but it was not published until 1900. She has since written *Benjamin Bunny, Jemima Puddle-Duck, Squirrel Nutkin, The Tailor of Gloucester, Two Bad Mice, The Roly Poly Pudding,* and other make-believe stories of great charm and interest to young children. Her own delightful illustrations accompany the stories. Many of the settings for her stories are her own farm in the south Lake District of England, where she now lives.

RANDS, WILLIAM BRIGHTY (1823–1882), was an efficient reporter in the House of Lords who supplemented his income by writing on a variety of subjects. He contributed to most of the periodicals of his time, both for children and adults. He used at least three pen names. Under the name of "Matthew Browne," he wrote *Chaucer's England,* an authoritative work. The children's books by which he is best remembered are *Lilliput Lyrics, Lilliput Lectures,* and *Lilliput*

[1] For titles of the tales and further discussion, see pages 208, 209.

*Legends.* His fairy stories were liked by children at the time they appeared, and his verse is still of interest. He understood a child's point of view and his writing rose above the mediocrity common in children's books of his period.

RASPE, RUDOLPH ERICH (1737–1794), is believed to have been the author of the original version of the *Adventures of Baron Munchausen,* though the tales were subsequently elaborated by others. An English edition published three years after the death of Raspe seems to establish his authorship, but German editions ascribed the stories to other authors. Raspe was born in Hanover, Germany, and was a librarian and professor. He was a brilliant scholar, wrote on numerous subjects, and was an authority on antique jewelry. As the years went by he became a greater scamp than scholar. In 1775 he was commissioned by a rich patron to buy gems in Italy, but he sold the gems for his own profit. Threatened with arrest, he decamped to London. For some years he lived in England and gained considerable prominence as a writer. From 1782 to 1788 he was assay master at a mine in Cornwall, and it is believed that he wrote *Munchausen* during that time. Shortly after, he went to Scotland and pretended to discover a valuable mine. When it was discovered that he had "salted" the ground, he absconded to Ireland where he died a few years later. He is said to have given the manuscript of *Munchausen* to a friend to be translated, which probably accounts for the confusion as to authorship.

RILEY, JAMES WHITCOMB (1849–1916), known as the "Hoosier poet," was born and spent his life in Indiana. He came of a good family. His father was a lawyer and expected his son to study law, but at eighteen Riley joined a troupe of entertainers and toured the country in a wagon. He beat the drum, painted the scenery, and wrote new versions for the company's songs. When he came back home, he joined the staff of the *Indianapolis Journal;* his first poems were published in that paper. As a boy he delighted in writing rhymes and his mother encouraged him. When he was twenty-seven, he decided seriously to become a poet. He sent some of his verses to Henry Wadsworth Longfellow, who wrote to him encouragingly. In the years that followed, he wrote about one thousand poems, many of them in dialect and most of them picturing the simple virtues of everyday life. He had something of Burns' power to touch the heart. Many of his poems were written for children and record his own happy childhood. He traveled extensively throughout the United States, reading his poems to enthusiastic audiences. He was showered with honors and became a national figure. He never married. In his lifetime the school children of Indianapolis flocked to his home to bring him good wishes on his birthday, October the seventh.

ROBERTS, CHARLES G. D. (1860–    ), has been called the "dean of Canadian literature." He came of a distinguished literary family and Bliss Carman is his cousin. He grew up in a home of plain living and high thinking. His father, an Episcopal rector, spent many hours reading aloud to his children and gave them the run of his fine library. The boy Charles loved nature and spent much time in the woods of New Brunswick near his home. He made a brilliant record in college, both in scholarship and in athletics. He taught for some years in the University of King's College in Nova Scotia, but resigned at the age of thirty-five to give his time to writing. He lived in New York for a while, and was living in England at the outbreak of the World War. He joined the army, became an officer, and rose to the rank of major. Since 1925 he has made his home in Toronto. He began to write poetry at sixteen; for some years his writing was entirely verse. He is best known, however, for his animal stories for children, which he began to write in the 'eighties. He was the forerunner of Ernest Thompson Seton as a writer of modern nature stories. Like Seton, he has been criticized for attributing too much intelligence to animals, but his stories are much liked by young readers. He is the author of some fifty books, among which are: *The Kindred of the Wild, Hoof and Claw, The Feet of the Furtive, Kings in Exile, Children of the Wilds, The Wisdom of the Wilderness,* and *Neighbors Unknown.*

ROBERTS, ELIZABETH MADOX (1885– ), was born near Springfield, Kentucky, and still makes her home there. She was educated at the University of Chicago and lived for some time in New York. She is the author of the remarkable novel, *The Time of Man;* other novels and short stories of her authorship reveal the true literary artist. Her writing for children is confined to a slender volume of verse, entitled *Under the Tree,* which first appeared in 1922 and has become one of the classics of children's literature. It is hard to analyze the strength and charm of Miss Roberts' poetry. She writes about simple, everyday experiences of children, but she sees with the eyes of a child, feels as a child feels, and expresses these things with simple but consummate artistry. "The Butterbean Tent" is an experience that all children create in one form or another; in "Christmas Morning" the events of the Nativity merge naturally with the child's own family life; in such poems as "The Rabbit," "The Hens," and "The Woodpecker," the identification of the child with the animal world is complete and satisfying.

ROBINSON, W. W. (1891– ), lives in Los Angeles. He has spent his entire life in southern California, except for a year and a half's service in the army in France. He is a specialist in land titles, and has written several pamphlets and books for adults about the Spanish grandees and great ranchos of southern California. *The Beasts of the Tar Pits* and *Ancient Animals* were written to satisfy his young nephew, Bobby. Bobby became greatly interested in prehistoric animals and spent many hours in the museum looking at the mounted skeletons and animals, but he was unhappy because there were no books about them simple enough for him to read. Mr. Robinson's books are illustrated by his wife, Irene B. Robinson.

ROSSETTI, CHRISTINA G. (1830–1894), was born and lived her whole life in London. Her father was a scholarly exile from Italy, and though poor he gathered about him a group of Italian and English intellectuals. Her brother was Dante Gabriel Rossetti, who became a famous poet and painter. Christina was a shy, retiring child and grew into a grave, serious woman. She never married; she was twice sought in marriage, but refused each suitor because of differences in religion. Her health was always frail, and in the latter part of her life she became an invalid and lived in seclusion. She was educated entirely by her mother, and her first poem was written in honor of her mother's birthday when Christina was eleven years old. When she was seventeen her first book of poems was published, but it was not until the publication of *Goblin Market* in her thirty-first year that she gained recognition as a poet. She was past forty when *Sing-Song* appeared. Her verse is tender and musical; and though delicate, it is sincere and childlike.

ROWE, DOROTHY (1898– ), was born in Rome, New York, and went to China when she was nine weeks old. Her childhood was spent in Nanking and other cities in China. She was taught by her parents until ready for high school in Shanghai. She came to America for her college education at Goucher College. She is the wife of Benjamin March, lecturer on the art of the Far East, and the mother of one daughter. Her childhood in China was a happy one, and she was very fond of her Chinese nurse who told her the fairy stories of China. When she came to America she missed the things in China that she loved, so she wrote about them for boys and girls. Her books are *The Rabbit Lantern, The Moon's Birthday, Traveling Shops,* and *The Begging Deer,* the last a collection of Japanese stories.

SANDBURG, CARL (1878– ), was born in Galesburg, Illinois, the son of a Swedish immigrant. At thirteen he went to work, and for seven years earned his living by driving a milk wagon, washing dishes in hotels, making bricks, harvesting wheat, and other jobs through which he gained firsthand the knowledge of industrial America that he portrays so vigorously in his poetry. After serving in the Spanish-American War, he worked his way through Lombard College, and there he edited the college paper. Since 1910 he has been in newspaper work and is now on the editorial staff of the *Chicago Daily News.* The publication of *Chicago Poems* in 1915 has been followed by other volumes of verse–*Cornhuskers; Smoke and Steel; Slabs of the Sunburnt West; Good Morning, America;* and *The People, Yes.* In his poems are factories belching smoke, wheels turning, and men at work; but there is quiet, too, the quiet of the prairies and of silent city streets. His language is the everyday speech of Americans and the rhythms he employs are fitted to his subjects, ranging from the heavy, noisy tones of his poems that picture stark realism to the soft overtones of "Fog." Some of Mr. Sandburg's poems are too mature in emotional experience for children, but others are simple and clear and bring to children something more robust than much poetry that follows a more conventional pattern. A selection of his verse for children has been published under the title, *Early Moon.* Sandburg is also a master of strong vital prose, as is evident from *Abraham Lincoln: The Prairie Years.* The story of Lincoln's boyhood, taken from that book, has been issued for boys and girls under the title, *Abe Lincoln Grows Up.* In 1939 he completed his biography of Lincoln with the publication of *Abraham Lincoln: The War Years,* in four volumes. For young children he has written *Rootabaga Stories* and *Rootabaga Pigeons*–make-believe tales of original content, full of poetry, nonsense, and philosophy.

SAXE, JOHN GODFREY (1816–1887), lived in Vermont. He graduated from Middlebury College and was a lawyer and newspaper editor. His satirical and humorous verse was very popular with a large reading public at the time he lived, but today he is remembered largely for his fable in verse, "The Blind Men and the Elephant."

SCOTT, SIR WALTER (1771–1832), is the great Scottish poet and novelist. His novels, *Ivanhoe, The Talisman, Quentin Durward,* and *Kenilworth,* are read with interest by young people of high-school age; a few ballads and short quotations from his long poems, *Marmion, The Lay of the Last Minstrel,* and *The Lady of the Lake,* are enjoyed by children.

SEREDY, KATE (1896– ), was born in Budapest, Hungary. Her father was a schoolteacher in Budapest and she grew up in a home filled with good books and good music. As a child she listened to the conversation of her mother and father and their friends, conversation supposed to be "too old for a child to understand," but from which she learned respect for words and ideas. Her father held her to a high standard of doing well everything she undertook, and the same high quality of work was demanded by her instructors in the Academy of Art in Budapest. During the World War she served for two years as a nurse in a war hospital. After the war she illustrated two books that were published in Hungary, then she came to the United States where she has lived ever since. The first book she illustrated in the United States was a textbook in primary reading; she has illustrated a number of books written by other authors, among them *Caddie Woodlawn* by Carol Ryrie Brink. In 1935 appeared the first book both written and illustrated by Kate Seredy—*The Good Master,* much of the story of which is taken from her own life. *The Singing Tree,* published in 1939, is a continuation of the story begun in *The Good Master.* The most distinguished book of which she is the author-illustrator is *The White Stag,* an epic tale of Hungary, written in the stirring English that seems as natural a medium for her as her native tongue. *The White Stag,* illustrated by heroic drawings of great beauty, was awarded the Newbery Medal in 1938. *Listening,* written for younger children, is the story of an early American house in which the author lived and the book reconstructs the historic events of which the house was a part. Miss Seredy has an astonishing ability for restoring neglected houses and land, and driving a tractor and directing her farm are among her interests.

SEWELL, HELEN (1896– ), was born at Mare Island Navy Yard in California, where her father, a naval officer, was stationed. Her mother died when she was small, and in 1902 her father was appointed governor of Guam and she accompanied him to the island. She says the rest of her life pales beside the memory of the two years spent in the gorgeous coloring of Guam. Her father died there and she was sent back to relatives in the eastern part of the United States. Her ability in drawing had already developed and from that time on, all her education and interests were centered upon art. She has been very successful in illustrating books for children. Her pictures may be found in books by Elizabeth Coatsworth, Eliza Orne White, Laura Ingalls Wilder, and others. When she began to write the text as well as make the illustrations for children's books, she revealed a clear understanding of the things children like. Among the attractive books of which she is author-illustrator are: *A Head for Happy, Ming and Mehitable,* and *Blue Barns.* Her pictures for *Cinderella* are especially charming.

SKELTON, CHARLES L., was born and grew up on a farm in northern Illinois. After graduating from the University of Illinois, he spent several years in business. A long illness sent him to the West to live. He spent a winter in a cabin on the Saskatchewan prairie, and drove four hundred miles in a buckboard from the cabin down into Montana, looking for a homestead. For five years he was in business in Pierre, South Dakota. He has written a number of short stories and serials for boys and conducts stamp-collecting departments in several papers and magazines. *Riding West on the Pony Express* is his first book.

SKINNER, CONSTANCE LINDSAY (1879–1939), daughter of pioneers, was born at her father's fur trading post in British Columbia. Her childhood associates were fur traders, French Canadian *voyageurs,* and Indians. Books lined the walls of the living room of her father's log house; from them she was taught by her parents until she was old enough to be sent to school in Vancouver. As a schoolgirl she wrote for Canadian newspapers; later she worked on the *Los Angeles Times, Los Angeles Examiner,* and *Chicago American.* She gave up journalism, went to New York, and began a long career of free-lance writing. She wrote poetry and novels for adults, but some of her best writing was done in her stories of America for boys and girls. Her frontier childhood gave her a rich store of memories, careful research furnished authentic backgrounds, and her gift for storytelling and characterization—all combined to make these books outstanding. Some of their titles are: *Andy Breaks Trail; Silent Scot; The White Leader; Roselle of the North; Becky Landers: Frontier Warrior;* and *Debby Barnes: Trader.*

SOUTHEY, ROBERT (1774–1843), was poet laureate of England and the author of many books, both poetry and prose. Little of his work is remembered today except two poems. "The Inchcape Rock," a ballad of the sea, and "The Battle of Blenheim," a telling satire against war. Of special interest to students of children's literature is Southey's connection with the nursery tale, "The Three Bears." In the years just before his death, Southey published five volumes of miscellaneous articles and papers in a series entitled *The Doctor.* In this collection is "The Story of the Three Bears," in a form much as we know it today except that a bad-mannered old woman played the role now given to Goldilocks. This is probably the first appearance in print (1837) of the story, but Joseph Jacobs discovered in oral tradition what he believed to be an older version of the same tale known as "Scrapefoot," in which a fox has the part taken by the old woman in Southey's version. In introducing the story in *The Doctor,* Southey did not claim to be doing more than repeating a popular tale, but in doing so he preserved a story that continues to be loved by succeeding generations of children.

STEEL, FLORA ANNIE (1847–1929), was an Englishwoman who spent many years in India, where her husband held an office in the government. As inspectress of schools, she gained an insight into the native life and character. She carefully collected folk tales of India, which she published in 1894 under the title, *Tales of the Punjab.* She also wrote several novels of Indian life, a popular history of India, and her own autobiography. Her interest in folk tales extended to those of her own country, and she prepared an interesting collection entitled *English Fairy Tales,* which was illustrated by Arthur Rackham.

STEPHENS, JAMES (1882– ), Irish novelist and poet, is an ardent nationalist who has done much to preserve Irish tradition in story and verse. In prose he is best known by *The Crock of Gold;* among his volumes of verse are: *The Rocky Road to Dublin, Songs from the Clay,* and *Reincarnations.* His poetry, marked by sincerity and enlivened by touches of humor and fantasy, is mainly for adults, but occasional poems are suitable for children. *Irish Fairy Tales,* for older children, is written in poetic prose which reveals the beauty of the ancient literature of Ireland.

STEVENSON, LIONEL (1902– ), was born in Edinburgh, Scotland, and spent the first five years of his life in Ireland. The remainder of his boyhood was lived in isolated sections of Canada, and he and his mother ran a rural general store and post office in British Columbia while the men of the family were in France during the World War. He was educated at the University of British Columbia, the University of California, and Oxford University. He is now professor of English literature at the University of Southern California. He is a talented actor and has appeared with Little Theater groups. He has written much delightful verse. "In a Desert Town" was written on his return to his home in Arizona after a stay in England. He is the author of *The Wild Irish Girl,* and *Dr. Quicksilver,* literary biographies for adults.

STEVENSON, MABEL ROSE (1875– ), was born in Ireland, in County Donegal. In her own words, "I lived in that remote and beautiful corner of northwest Ireland until 1907. There is much fairy lore still lingering in that region. Many natural objects, such as thorn bushes and strangely shaped rocks, have their legends. I absorbed much of the belief in fairies and still retain it." Her poem, "Springtime in Donegal," and others, reflect her childhood. Mrs. Stevenson and her son, Lionel, have been close companions, living abroad, in Canada, and in the United States.

STEVENSON, ROBERT LOUIS (1850–1894), is an outstanding figure in literature for children; two of its great classics bear his name, *Treasure Island* and *A Child's Garden of Verses.* His whole life was a struggle against ill health, but he wrote many books and had a wide circle of friends whom he charmed by his gaiety and wit. He was born in Edinburgh, Scotland. Much of his childhood was spent in bed, cared for by his faithful nurse, Alison Cunningham, to whom he later dedicated *A Child's Garden of Verses.* His father was a builder of lighthouses and wished his son to continue the profession. Robert Louis's health improved so that he was able to attend the university and study engineering, but the outdoor life was too hard for him and he gave up engineering for the study of law. Later he discovered that writing was his work and he studied it with great concentration and worked with great perseverance in spite of frequent illness. Traveling in France for his health, he met an American, Mrs. Fanny Osbourne, with whom he fell in love. He followed her to America and they were married in 1880. They tried living in various climates in the United States and Europe, and finally settled down in Samoa, where Stevenson lived for four happy years before his death. He was very fond of his stepson, Lloyd Osbourne, for whom he wrote the story, *Treasure Island,* putting into it the things Lloyd liked. Then came *Kidnapped, The Black Arrow, The Strange Case of Dr. Jekyll and Mr. Hyde,* and other matchless stories and many equally fine essays. *A Child's Garden of Verses,* published in 1885, marked a turning point in verse for children. Instead of the moralizing common in children's poetry at the time, Stevenson wrote of the happenings of his own childhood in a simple, childlike, and beautiful manner. Here, play, story books, weather, the seasons, and imaginative experiences natural to children are pictured in the way they seem to children.

TAYLOR, ANN (1782–1866), and JANE (1783–1824), were the daughters of gifted parents, and their childhood in the English countryside of Suffolk was a happy one. There were plays and picnics and lessons at home. While they were still small, they wrote poems as a part of every day's occupations. Some of their verse was later accepted by a children's magazine and the editor asked for more. The result was a book, *Original Poems for Infant Minds,* published in 1804. This was quite a remarkable book for the time. Previously children's poems had been in the main accounts of early death or rhymed warnings of the dire results of wrong-doing, but the Taylors wrote about animals, the outdoors, and home life. Their poems were not great ones, but they were loved by children and some of them still have interest. The sisters collaborated on two other volumes of verse for children. Ann married a clergyman and lived to be very old; Jane was unmarried and died at forty-one.

TAYLOR, EDGAR (1793–1839), was born at Banham, in Norfolk, England, and went to London in 1814. He became a prosperous solicitor. He made a digest of English constitutional law, a revised version of the New Testament, and translated a number of medieval manuscripts. He is remembered, however, for his translation of the folk tales collected by the Brothers Grimm. The first series of Taylor's translations appeared in 1823 under the title, *Grimms' Popular Stories,* and in 1826 other stories were added to make a total of fifty-five. Taylor published them anonymously, evidently thinking them less important than his other literary work. He was helped in translating and editing the tales by his sister, Emily Taylor, a writer of historical stories and books of instruction for children. Taylor's was the first English translation of Grimm, and with Cruikshank's famous drawings became one of the most significant books for children ever published.

TEASDALE, SARA (1884–1933), was born in St. Louis of an old American family. Ill health permitted only limited formal education, but she had access to fine books which she read eagerly. She traveled extensively and after her marriage to Ernst Filsinger, made her home in New York. Her verse received early recognition and honors came to her. *Rivers to the Sea, Flame and Shadow, Dark of the Moon,* and other volumes reveal the delicate, cameo-like beauty and dignified simplicity of her lyrics. A selection of her poems for boys and girls has been issued under the title, *Stars Tonight.*

TENNYSON, ALFRED (1809–1892), is the great English poet, author of *In Memoriam, The Idylls of the King, The Princess,* and many other poems known all over the civilized world. In the great range of Tennyson's work may be found a number of poems simple enough for children—delicate lyrics and stories in verse. "Gareth and Lynette," the simplest of *The Idylls of the King,* may be read aloud to upper-grade boys and girls who are interested in the King Arthur stories; selected portions of other *Idylls* will have meaning for older children who know the epic in prose form.

THACKERAY, WILLIAM MAKEPEACE (1811–1863), was one of the foremost English novelists, the author of *Vanity Fair, Pendennis, The Newcomes,* and *Henry Esmond.* He was a vivid caricaturist and often illustrated his own works. At one time he made some drawings to amuse some child friends and from them developed *The Rose and the Ring,* his famous nonsense story for children. Thackeray's verse was a small part of his literary work, but his sense of humor found an outlet in several wholly extravagant poems at which both children and grown-ups have laughed.

TIPPETT, JAMES S. (1885– ), was born and grew up on a farm in Missouri. There he learned to see things and to enjoy animals, workers, and all kinds of farm experiences. He was educated in Missouri and at Teachers College, Columbia University. He has been a teacher for nearly thirty years—teaching children in Missouri and New York, college students at Peabody College and the University of Pittsburgh, and serving as principal of public schools in Missouri and private day schools in Connecticut. He is now curriculum adviser for schools in North Carolina. He lives at Chapel Hill, North Carolina, in the winter, and at Scotland, Connecticut, in the summer. Much of his time is given to writing for children. From 1922 to 1928, Mr. Tippett taught primary children at Lincoln School, Teachers College, Columbia University; the creative atmosphere of the school and the interesting activities and experiences of the children started him to writing. A play farm in the schoolroom was the inspiration for *The Singing Farmer.* Other books of verse for young children followed: *I Live in a City, I Go A-Traveling, I Spend the Summer,* and *A World To Know.* All his verse for children is simple and childlike and enriches familiar experiences and familiar things. He has also written stories of the outdoors for very young children.

TROWBRIDGE, JOHN TOWNSEND (1827–1916), lived in Cambridge, Massachusetts. At one time he was associate editor of *Our Young Folks' Magazine,* in which in 1867 appeared his humorous poem, "Darius Green and His Flying Machine." Many years passed and Trowbridge was an old man, more than eighty years old, when he first saw an airplane. He wrote other poems, also a number of adventure stories for boys, among them *Cudjo's Cave,* which present-day readers still find interesting.

UNTERMEYER, JEAN STARR (1886– ), was born in Zanesville, Ohio. She was educated in private schools in Ohio and New York. She studied music abroad and sang in concerts in Vienna and London. In 1907 she married the poet, Louis Untermeyer, from whom she was later divorced. She now lives in New York and is a frequent contributor of verse to magazines. Her volumes of verse are: *Growing Pains, Dreams Out of Darkness,* and *Winged Child.* Though she has not written purposely for children, some of her poems are suitable for them.

VAN DYKE, HENRY (1852–1933), was born in Germantown, Pennsylvania, and educated at Princeton University and Princeton Theological Seminary. He entered the ministry and was for some years pastor of the Brick Presbyterian Church in New York. He was professor of English literature at Princeton for more than twenty years, and was appointed ambassador to the Netherlands by Woodrow Wilson. He was the author of a long list of books of verse, short stories, and essays on religious and philosophical subjects. His skill in writing both prose and verse and the sense of optimism pervading all he wrote brought him a very large reading audience.

WADSWORTH, WALLACE (1894–1933), was a native of Indiana and lived most of his life in Indianapolis. He was educated at Butler University, and later became publishers' representative for several book publishers. His business required extensive travel and gave him an opportunity to collect folk stories in different parts of the United States. This was literary material which he used effectively in books for children. *Paul Bunyan and His Great Blue Ox* is an excellent version of the American yarn told in a form simple enough for children. *The Real Story Book* is a collection of familiar stories for young children. Mr. Wadsworth's early death prevented the completion of other books he had planned for boys and girls.

WARNER, CHARLES DUDLEY (1829–1900), was a native of Massachusetts and his boyhood was spent there. He was educated at Hamilton College and the University of Pennsylvania. He was for years on the editorial staff of *Harper's Magazine.* He was the author of many essays and sketches; his restrained humor, wholesome love of the outdoors, and suggestive comment on life and affairs made him very popular. He worked for prison reform and other movements for the public good, about which he lectured extensively. The *Library of the World's Best Literature* was issued under his editorship. *Being a Boy* is a delightful account of his own experiences when he was a boy a hundred years ago in New England.

WASHBURNE, HELUIZ CHANDLER (1892– ), was born in Cincinnati and studied art in Philadelphia. She has been a commercial artist, also fashion adviser for a large department store in Chicago. She has traveled extensively in Europe, Asia, and North Africa. She is the wife of Carleton Washburne, the educator, and the mother of three children. She lives in Winnetka, Illinois. In collaboration with her husband she has written a number of informational books for children. *Letters to Channy* are real letters written to her little son when she and her husband were traveling in the Orient.

WATTS, ISAAC (1674–1748), was an English theologian and writer of hymns. He was pastor of an Independent congregation in London, and his religious opinions were very liberal for the period in which he lived. He was the author of many hymns, some of which are sung today. He was a firm believer in the value of rhymes in teaching children; his *Divine and Moral Songs For Children* (1715) were written to teach children religious principles and rules of conduct. While his purpose was serious, and even stern, he undoubtedly wrote to please children, for some of the verses show tenderness and a real love of children. They are unique in children's literature; written two hundred years ago, they represent the first poetry consciously written for children.

WELLES, WINIFRED (1893– ), was born in Connecticut, educated there, and still makes her home there. She says she has known no children well except herself and her son, and it was when his experiences began to revive memories of her own childhood that she combined the two and wrote the poems in *Skipping Along Alone.* This is a remarkable little volume and places Winifred Welles in the front rank of present-day poets for children. Some of her verse may be compared with that of Elizabeth Madox Roberts; she has the same quality of seizing upon the essence of a child's real experience and expressing it in simple, beautiful words. Other poems of hers that picture experience beyond the border of reality have the haunting, eerie quality of Walter de la Mare. There are no conventional fairies in *Skipping Along Alone,* but "Green Moth," "Behind the Waterfall," and "The Angel in the Apple Tree" are adventures in imagination that children know to be genuine.

WHEELER, WILLIAM A. (1833–1874), was a lexicographer. He was born in Leicester, Massachusetts, and educated at Bowdoin College. From 1856 to 1860 he worked upon Worcester's dictionary and from 1860 to 1864, upon a revision of Webster's dictionary. In 1867 he became assistant superintendent of the Boston Public Library. His connection with literature for children is his collection, *Mother Goose's Melodies,* published in 1869. The text for the rhymes is drawn from Halliwell's *Nursery Rhymes of England* with a few additional rhymes from other sources. Considerable space is given by Wheeler to the contention that Mother Goose was a real personage, a Mrs. Elizabeth Vergoose, of colonial Boston, who sang the rhymes to her grandchildren. This legend, which at one time gained considerable credence in New England, was based upon a supposed publication of the rhymes by one Thomas Fleet in Boston in 1719. Such a volume would have antedated John Newbery's *Mother Goose's Melody* by some forty years, but no copies of the Fleet edition or any proof that it ever existed have been found; in fact, the theory has been generally discredited. Wheeler added nothing to the literary history of the famous rhymes, but the collection is a good one and the old-fashioned illustrations are interesting.

WHITMAN, WALT (1819–1892), was the maker of a new type of poetry in the United States. In form his verse was a radical change from the measured cadences of Tennyson and the New England poets; its lack of regularly recurring rhyme or meter was profoundly disturbing to many of his readers and caused much controversy. Many poets since have developed verse in free forms but none have achieved greater strength and power. In content, too, Whitman's verse broke with tradition; he wrote of the work done by men and women and how they felt about it, the awakening of new ideas, and the many influences at work in a democracy. During the Civil War he served in hospitals in Washington, nursing wounded soldiers and helping in any way he could. He greatly admired Lincoln, and two of his best-known poems were written in sorrow at Lincoln's death—"When Lilacs Last in the Door-Yard Bloomed," and "O Captain! My Captain!"

WHITTIER, JOHN GREENLEAF (1807–1892), is second only to Longfellow in popularity among American poets. His life was a simple one, spent in the rural surroundings of New England which he pictured so effectively in "Snow-Bound." He was a Quaker, deeply devout, and a strong abolitionist. He is best known for his short narrative poems; among them, "Skipper Ireson's Ride," and "Barbara Frietchie."

WILWERDING, WALTER J. (1891– ), was born in Winona, Minnesota, and educated in Minneapolis. He studied under well-known artists and became an animal painter. He has made several expeditions to East Africa, sketching and painting wild animal life. He has illustrated a number of children's books by various authors, and written animal stories and nature articles for magazines. He is both author and illustrator of the following books for children—*Jangwa: The Story of a Jungle Prince; Keema of the Monkey People; Punda: The Tiger Horse; Tembo: The Forest Giant.* He now lives in Connecticut.

WOLFE, HUMBERT (1885– ), was born in Italy but went to England as a child. He was educated at Oxford, entered the British Civil Service, and became a valued member of the Ministry of Labour. His satires and lampoons against the government have been popular with the British public, and his verse has much of the same humor, spicy accent, and unexpectedness. *Kensington Gardens,* published in 1924, attracted favorable attention both in England and America.

WORDSWORTH, WILLIAM (1770–1860), the great English poet, portrayed nature and man's relation to nature with moving dignity and beauty. His poetry is too profound for children. A thoughtful child, however, will appreciate one of Wordsworth's simpler poems, such as "Daffodils."

WYLIE, ELINOR (1885–1928), was one of the most brilliant of recent American women poets. Her first volume of verse, *Nets To Catch the Wind* (1921), and the second, *Black Armour* (1923), revealed an intensity of feeling and mastery of form that brought her many admirers. The emotional content of most of her poems is too mature for children, but an occasional one, such as "Velvet Shoes," presents familiar experience with a delightful delicacy that children can share. Elinor Wylie also wrote several outstanding novels. She was the wife of the poet, William Rose Benét.

WYNNE, ANNETTE (1885– ), was born in Brooklyn, New York, and was educated at the University of California and New York University. Her first job was on a newspaper in Portland, Oregon. Then she went to Alaska where she taught for some time. She learned to speak the Indian language and her pupils called her by an Indian name which meant "Good Luck." She returned to the United States and taught in an elementary school in Brooklyn and later in a New York high school. From childhood she made up rhymes about everything around her. She has published two volumes of verse for young children—*For Days and Days,* and *All through the Year.* Most of these poems were written for her young pupils and for the children of a club which she directed in a settlement house in New York.

WYSS, JOHANN DAVID (1743–1818), was a Swiss pastor in Berne. He told the stories of *Swiss Family Robinson* to his son while they took long walks in the country. The son, JOHANN RUDOLF WYSS (1781–1830), later became professor of philosophy at Berne and a poet of importance; he was the author of the Swiss national anthem. The younger Wyss arranged his father's stories for publication, and they were issued in Zurich in two parts, in 1812 and 1813. The earliest English translation was published by William Godwin in 1814—a translation from the original German, believed to have been made in part by the poet Shelley. This earliest English version was much shorter than the original, but between 1824 and 1826 there appeared in France a version by Madame De Montholieu that ran to five volumes, in which a new ending and many new adventures had been added to the story apparently with the consent of Wyss's son. Most of the English versions now generally known were probably taken from the French. The rather involved way in which the story has reached English and American readers has had nothing to do with its popularity—it has always been in demand. A number of different American editions, some illustrated by famous artists, have been published. It has been pointed out that the background of natural history in the book is frequently not in line with scientific facts, for in the story fruits and animals native to half the globe are found growing naturally upon one tropical island. Neither this nor the extravagantly labored piety has had the slightest effect in dulling the interest of the book for young readers, who for generations have accepted it merely as an absorbing tale of a courageous family.

## *References for Students*

*Authors Today and Yesterday.* S. J. Kunitz and Howard Haycraft. Wilson.

*British Authors of the Nineteenth Century.* S. J. Kunitz and Howard Haycraft. Wilson.

*Children's Books in England.* F. J. Harvey Darton. Macmillan.

*Contemporary Illustrators of Children's Books.* Bertha E. Mahony and Elinor Whitney. Women's Educational and Industrial Union (Boston).

*Dictionary of National Biography.* Macmillan.

*Encyclopedia Americana.*

*Encyclopaedia Britannica.* Eleventh and Fourteenth Editions.

*The Junior Book of Authors.* S. J. Kunitz and Howard Haycraft. Wilson.

*Living Authors.* "Dilly Tante." Wilson.

*National Cyclopaedia of American Biography.* White.

*New International Encyclopaedia.* Dodd Mead.

*Who's Who.*

*Who's Who in America.*

# LIST OF SELECTIONS

## Suggested Grades[1]

### Grade One

*Verse*

"A farmer went riding," 54
A Visit from St. Nicholas (*Clement C. Moore*), 88
At the Seaside (*Robert Louis Stevenson*), 78
"Baa, baa, black sheep," 58
Bed in Summer (*Robert Louis Stevenson*), 74
Birthdays (*Marchette Gaylord Chute*), 77
"Blow, wind, blow," 58
"Bow, wow, wow," 53
"Bye, baby bunting," 53
Choosing a Kitten, 95
Clouds, 106
"Cobbler, cobbler, mend my shoe," 58
"Come, butter, come," 54
"Cushy cow bonny," 54
"Diddle, diddle, dumpling," 53
"Ding, dong, bell," 57
Frogs at School (*George Cooper*), 95
"Girls and boys, come out to play," 57
"Hey! diddle, diddle," 54
"Hickory, dickory, dock," 54
"Higgledy, piggledy, my black hen," 55
"Humpty-Dumpty," 59
"Hush-a-bye, baby," 53
"I have a little sister," 59
"Jack and Jill," 54
"Jack be nimble," 55

[1] For discussion of grade placement of stories and verse for children, see pages 41, 42. The grades given are suggestive only. The needs and interests, as well as the ages, of particular children or groups of children should determine the grades in which materials are used.

Jack-in-the-Pulpit (*Rupert Sargent Holland*), 107
"Little Betty Blue," 55
"Little Bo-peep," 58
"Little Boy Blue," 55
"Little Jack Horner," 55
"Little Miss Muffet," 55
"Little Robin Redbreast," 56
Merry-Go-Round (*Dorothy W. Baruch*), 78
Mice (*Rose Fyleman*), 95
"Mistress Mary," 54
Mouse (*Hilda Conkling*), 94
"Old King Cole," 58
"Once I saw a little bird," 56
"One, two, buckle my shoe," 57
"Pat-a-cake," 53
"Polly, put the kettle on," 54
Presents (*Marchette Gaylord Chute*), 77
"Pussy-cat, where have you been," 54
Rain (*Robert Louis Stevenson*), 106
"Ride a cock-horse to Banbury Cross," 53
"Sing a song of sixpence," 57
Skyscrapers (*Rachel Field*), 89
The Bird's Nest (*John Drinkwater*), 93
The Caterpillar (*Christina G. Rossetti*), 93
The Hairy Dog (*Herbert Asquith*), 95
The House Cat (*Annette Wynne*), 95
The Huntsmen (*Walter de la Mare*), 83
The Little Turtle (*Vachel Lindsay*), 94
The Moon's the North Wind's Cooky (*Vachel Lindsay*), 105
"The north wind doth blow," 56
The Rabbit (*Edith King*), 93
"The rose is red," 54
The Sleepy Song (*Josephine Daskam Bacon*), 75
The Squirrel, 94
The Swing (*Robert Louis Stevenson*), 78
The Three Little Kittens (*Eliza Lee Follen*), 169
The White Window (*James Stephens*), 106
The Wind (*Robert Louis Stevenson*), 106
The Woodpecker (*Elizabeth Madox Roberts*), 93
"There was an old woman lived under a hill," 55
"There was an old woman who lived in a shoe," 57
"There were three jovial huntsmen," 56
"This little pig went to market," 53
Time To Rise (*Robert Louis Stevenson*), 73
To China (*Leroy F. Jackson*), 77
"To market, to buy a fat pig," 53

Troubles (*Dorothy Aldis*), 77
"Twenty white horses," 59
Washing (*John Drinkwater*), 76
Watching Clouds (*John Farrar*), 106
"Wee Willie Winkie," 55
Who Has Seen the Wind? (*Christina G. Rossetti*), 105
"Willy boy, where are you going," 58
Woolly Lambkins (*Christina G. Rossetti*), 94

*Stories*

Aiken-Drum, the Brownie, 221
Ask Mr. Bear (*Marjorie Flack*), 393
Billy and Blaze (*C. W. Anderson*), 551
Blue Barns (*Helen Sewell*), 490
Little Red Riding Hood, 219
Lucky Little Lena (*Marjorie Flack*), 550
Mr. Vinegar, 224
The Gingerbread Boy, 214
The Old Woman and Her Pig, 216
The Straw Ox, 218
The Tale of Peter Rabbit (*Beatrix Potter*), 455
The Three Bears, 215
The Three Billy Goats Gruff, 213
Tony, the Steam Shovel Man (*Henry B. Lent*), 705

## Grade Two

*Verse*

A Bird (*Emily Dickinson*), 97
"A cat came fiddling," 58
A Child's Day Begins (*Walter de la Mare*), 73
A Friend in the Garden (*Juliana Horatia Ewing*), 96
A Good Play (*Robert Louis Stevenson*), 79
A Visit from Mr. Fox, 169
All Things Bright and Beautiful (*Cecil Frances Alexander*), 163
Alone (*Joseph Paget-Fredericks*), 79
An Explanation of the Grasshopper (*Vachel Lindsay*), 95
"As round as an apple," 59
Boats Sail on the Rivers (*Christina G. Rossetti*), 106
Bob White (*George Cooper*), 97
Busy Carpenters (*James S. Tippett*), 143
Christmas Morning (*Elizabeth Madox Roberts*), 82
Cradle Hymn (*Martin Luther*), 163
"God bless the master of this house," 56
Hiawatha's Childhood (*Henry Wadsworth Longfellow*), 170

"I had a little pony," 57
"If all the seas were one sea," 59
Indian Children (*Annette Wynne*), 152
"Intery, mintery, cutery-corn," 58
Is the Moon Tired? (*Christina G. Rossetti*), 105
"Little King Boggen," 58
"Little Nancy Etticoat," 59
Little Star (*Jane Taylor*), 108
Lullaby (*Paul Laurence Dunbar*), 74
My Bed Is a Boat (*Robert Louis Stevenson*), 74
My Shadow (*Robert Louis Stevenson*), 76
Night Was Creeping (*James Stephens*), 106
"Old Mother Hubbard," 61
Over the Garden Wall (*Eleanor Farjeon*), 79
"Pease-porridge hot," 58
Pretty Cow (*Ann Taylor*), 96
Skipping Ropes (*Dorothy Aldis*), 76
Sweet and Low (*Alfred Tennyson*), 107
Taxis (*Rachel Field*), 139
The Birches (*Walter Pritchard Eaton*), 107
The Child and the Fairies, 87
The Cow (*Robert Louis Stevenson*), 96
The Duck (*Edith King*), 96
The Frost Pane (*David McCord*), 109
The Land of Counterpane (*Robert Louis Stevenson*), 78
The Owl and the Pussy-Cat (*Edward Lear*), 121
The Pasture (*Robert Frost*), 96
The Raggedy Man (*James Whitcomb Riley*), 80
The Secret, 97
"This is the house that Jack built," 60
"Three blind mice," 55
Three Lovely Holes (*Winifred Welles*), 78
Where Go the Boats? (*Robert Louis Stevenson*), 138
Wynken, Blynken, and Nod (*Eugene Field*), 75

*Stories*

Drakesbill, 238
Grandmother's Buttons (*George* and *Doris Hauman*), 552
Jack and the Beanstalk, 234
Lazy Jack, 225
Little Black Sambo (*Helen Bannerman*), 456
Pita's Painted Pig (*Elizabeth Morrow*), 553
Plouf, the Little Wild Duck (*Lida*), 491
The Elves and the Shoemaker, 237
The First Christmas Tree (*Rose Fyleman*), 394
The Lad Who Went to the North Wind, 232

The Lion and the Mouse (*Aesop*), 299
The Three Little Pigs, 226
The Traveling Musicians, 229
The Wolf and the Seven Young Goslings, 231
Way Ping, Master of Boats (*Dorothy Rowe*), 706
Why the Bear Is Stumpy-Tailed, 230

## Grade Three

*Verse*

A Child's Grace (*Robert Burns*), 162
"As I was going to St. Ives," 59
As Joseph Was A-Walking, 163
Behind the Waterfall (*Winifred Welles*), 90
Brown Bee (*William Brighty Rands*), 101
Carpenter (*E. V. Lucas*), 143
Cat (*Mary Britton Miller*), 98
"Cock-a-doodle-doo," 55
Do You Know? (*Christina G. Rossetti*), 99
Dogs and Weather (*Winifred Welles*), 99
Fairies (*Rose Fyleman*), 86
Green Moth (*Winifred Welles*), 90
"I had a little nut-tree," 56
"I saw a ship a-sailing," 56
If Only . . . (*Rose Fyleman*), 80
"In marble halls as white as milk," 59
King Bruce and the Spider (*Eliza Cook*), 173
"Monday's child," 59
Oak Leaves (*Elizabeth Coatsworth*), 111
Roads (*Rachel Field*), 138
Seeds (*Walter de la Mare*), 107
Silver (*Walter de la Mare*), 108
"Simple Simon," 60
Skating (*Herbert Asquith*), 80
Some One (*Walter de la Mare*), 86
Thanksgiving Day (*Lydia Maria Child*), 81
The Angel in the Apple Tree (*Winifred Welles*), 90
The Blackbird (*Humbert Wolfe*), 98
The Butterbean Tent (*Elizabeth Madox Roberts*), 81
The City Mouse and the Garden Mouse (*Christina G. Rossetti*), 98
The Duel (*Eugene Field*), 122
The Elf Singing (*William Allingham*), 87
The Hens (*Elizabeth Madox Roberts*), 100
The Horseshoe (*Edna St. Vincent Millay*), 138
The Lamb (*William Blake*), 163
The Lord Is My Shepherd (*The Bible: Psalm 23*), 166

The Lucky Snail (*Winifred Welles*), 97
The Night Will Never Stay (*Eleanor Farjeon*), 108
The Peddler's Caravan (*William Brighty Rands*), 139
The Raggle, Taggle Gypsies, 173
The Sun's Travels (*Robert Louis Stevenson*), 108
The Swallow (*Christina G. Rossetti*), 98
The Wonderful Weaver (*George Cooper*), 109
The Wonderful World (*William Brighty Rands*), 108
"There was a crooked man," 60
"There was an old man who lived in a wood," 62
"There was an old woman tossed up in a basket," 60
Wild Animals (*Elizabeth Fleming*), 98
Wintertime (*Robert Louis Stevenson*), 109

*Stories*

Boots and His Brothers, 241
Brier Rose, 258
Children of Haiti (*Arna Bontemps* and *Langston Hughes*), 715
Cinderella, or the Little Glass Slipper, 254
East of the Sun and West of the Moon, 264
Hansel and Gretel, 247
Hide and Go Seek (*Dorothy P. Lathrop*), 496
Letters to Channy (*Heluiz Chandler Washburne*), 554
Rusty Pete, Cow Pony (*Doris Fogler* and *Nina Nicol*), 711
Skunks (*Edith M. Patch*), 496
Snow-White and Rose-Red, 251
Snow-White and the Seven Dwarfs, 243
The Blue Teapot (*Alice Dalgliesh*), 560
The Crow and the Pitcher (*Aesop*), 300
The Gentleman in Brown (*Margery Bianco*), 493
The Lion-Hearted Kitten (*Peggy Bacon*), 458
The Princess on the Glass Hill, 259
The Small Yellow Train (*Alice Dalgliesh*), 709
The Tinder Box (*Hans Christian Andersen*), 395
The Town Mouse and the Country Mouse (*Aesop*), 302
The Wind and the Sun (*Aesop*), 302

## Grade Four

*Verse*

A Circus Garland (*Rachel Field*), 82
A Lobster Quadrille (*Lewis Carroll*), 122
A Strange Wild Song (*Lewis Carroll*), 124
A Tragic Story (*William Makepeace Thackeray*), 126
April (*Sara Teasdale*), 107
Evening at the Farm (*John Townsend Trowbridge*), 144

Glimpse in Autumn (*Jean Starr Untermeyer*), 110
He Prayeth Best (*Samuel Taylor Coleridge*), 162
Hills (*Hilda Conkling*), 111
In a Desert Town (*Lionel Stevenson*), 111
Mr. Nobody, 82
My Dog (*John Kendrick Bangs*), 100
Nonsense Verses (*Edward Lear*), 124
"Peter Piper," 60
Psalm of Those Who Go Forth before Daylight (*Carl Sandburg*), 143
Queen Mab (*Thomas Hood*), 87
Robin Hood and the Ranger, 179
"Robert Rowley," 60
Springtime in Donegal (*Mabel Rose Stevenson*), 90
Stopping by Woods on a Snowy Evening (*Robert Frost*), 110
Thanksgiving (*The Bible: Psalm 100*), 166
The Blind Men and the Elephant (*John Godfrey Saxe*), 176
The Garden Year (*Sara Coleridge*), 110
The Leak in the Dike (*Phoebe Cary*), 171
The Mysterious Cat (*Vachel Lindsay*), 100
The Old Woman of the Roads (*Padraic Colum*), 164
The Plaint of the Camel (*Charles Edward Carryl*), 121
The Runaway (*Robert Frost*), 99
The Sea Shell (*Amy Lowell*), 140
The Strange Man, 125
The Table and the Chair (*Edward Lear*), 123
The Wilderness Is Tamed (*Elizabeth Coatsworth*), 152
The Wind and the Moon (*George MacDonald*), 112
The Year's at the Spring (*Robert Browning*), 111
"There was a man in our town," 60
"Thirty days hath September," 59
"Three children sliding on the ice," 60
Up the Airy Mountain (*William Allingham*), 88
Yet Gentle Will the Griffin Be (*Vachel Lindsay*), 88

*Stories*

By Covered Wagon (*Emma L. Brock*), 635
Jancsi and Kate (*Kate Seredy*), 565
Jimmie, the White Sparrow (*Padraic Colum*), 513
Keeping Still in the Woods (*Charles G. D. Roberts*), 505
Little Tonino (*Helen Hill* and *Violet Maxwell*), 719
Mr. Murdle's Large Heart (*Margery Bianco*), 557
Plowing (*Henry B. Lent*), 725
Puss in Boots, 275
Rocky Billy Goes Visiting (*Holling Clancy Holling*), 502
The Ant and the Grasshopper (*Aesop*), 301
The Dog and the Shadow (*Aesop*), 301

The Frog and the Ox (*Aesop*), 300
The Ghost of the Great White Stag (*Arthur C. Parker*), 309
The Hare and the Tortoise (*Aesop*), 300
The Horny Ones (*Edith M. Patch* and *Carroll Lane Fenton*), 511
The King of the Crocodiles, 270
The Magic Fish-Bone (*Charles Dickens*), 459
The Mice in Council (*Aesop*), 301
The Midnight Voyage (*John Masefield*), 399
The Princess and the Pea (*Hans Christian Andersen*), 406
The Tar Baby (*Joel Chandler Harris*), 465
The Well Story (*Joel Chandler Harris*), 466
The White Cat (*Madame la Comtesse D'Aulnoy*), 407

## *Grade Five*

*Verse*

A Boy's Song (*James Hogg*), 83
A Merry Heart (*The Bible: Proverbs 15*), 167
A Salute to Trees (*Henry van Dyke*), 115
Aladdin (*James Russell Lowell*), 91
Autumn Fancies, 114
Barbara Frietchie (*John Greenleaf Whittier*), 158
Children of the Wind (*Carl Sandburg*), 102
Fog (*Carl Sandburg*), 114
Hiawatha's Canoe (*Henry Wadsworth Longfellow*), 178
Horses Chawin' Hay (*Hamlin Garland*), 101
Little Busy Bee (*Isaac Watts*), 101
Little Orphant Annie (*James Whitcomb Riley*), 83
Lone Dog (*Irene Rutherford McLeod*), 101
Meg Merrilies (*John Keats*), 184
Milk-White Moon, Put the Cows to Sleep (*Carl Sandburg*), 113
Mother to Son (*Langston Hughes*), 162
Paul Revere's Ride (*Henry Wadsworth Longfellow*), 153
Plowing: A Memory (*Hamlin Garland*), 144
Robin Hood and Little John, 181
Song for a Little House (*Christopher Morley*), 164
Song of the Parrot (*Elizabeth Coatsworth*), 140
Swift Things Are Beautiful (*Elizabeth Coatsworth*), 114
The Battle of Blenheim (*Robert Southey*), 176
The Height of the Ridiculous (*Oliver Wendell Holmes*), 123
The Plowman of Today (*Hamlin Garland*), 145
The Tevins (*Henry S. Leigh*), 126
The Walrus and the Carpenter (*Lewis Carroll*), 126
The Wind in a Frolic (*William Howitt*), 111
Three Kings Came Riding (*Henry Wadsworth Longfellow*), 177

Travel (*Robert Louis Stevenson*), 140

*Stories*

Aladdin and the Wonderful Lamp, 278
Beasts of the Tar Pits (W. W. Robinson), 519
Bridget Goes Prospecting (*Berta* and *Elmer Hader*), 729
Caddie and the Indian Chief (*Carol Ryrie Brink*), 639
Calypso (*Elizabeth Coatsworth*), 568
David and Goliath (*The Bible: I Samuel 17*), 602
Doctor Dolittle and the Pushmi-Pullyu (*Hugh Lofting*), 471
Fairyfoot (*Frances Browne*), 415
Fin McCoul and the Giant (*Joseph Jacobs*), 313
Hercules and the Wagoner (*Aesop*), 302
Hitty Goes to Sea (*Rachel Field*), 648
Paddlewings Grows Up (*Wilfrid S. Bronson*), 521
Pinocchio (*C. Collodi*), 420
Stories of Other Days in Old Bergen (*Ragnhild Chevalier*), 570
Swiss Family Robinson (*Johann David Wyss*), 574
The Elephant's Child (*Rudyard Kipling*), 467
The First Harp (*Padraic Colum*), 317
The Fox and the Grapes (*Aesop*), 301
The French Jongleurs (*Katharine Gibson*), 733
The Milkmaid and Her Pail (*Aesop*), 302
The Tiger, the Brahman, and the Jackal, 298
The Ugly Duckling (*Hans Christian Andersen*), 430
Tom Thumb, 272
Two Little Confederates (*Thomas Nelson Page*), 644

## Grade Six

*Verse*

A Hot-Weather Song (*Don Marquis*), 131
A Nautical Ballad (*Charles Edward Carryl*), 128
An Indian Summer Day on the Prairie (*Vachel Lindsay*), 116
Columbus (*Joaquin Miller*), 153
Concord Hymn (*Ralph Waldo Emerson*), 153
Dear Land of All My Love (*Sidney Lanier*), 152
How They Brought the Good News from Ghent to Aix (*Robert Browning*), 174
I Hear America Singing (*Walt Whitman*), 145
In Flanders Fields (*John McCrae*), 160
July (*Susan Hartley Swett*), 115
Lady Clare (*Alfred Tennyson*), 189
Lochinvar (*Sir Walter Scott*), 188
O Captain! My Captain! (*Walt Whitman*), 159
Primer Lesson (*Carl Sandburg*), 162

Robin Hood and Allen-a-Dale, 182
The Angler's Reveille (*Henry van Dyke*), 102
The Clinker, 148
The Falling Star (*Sara Teasdale*), 113
The House with Nobody in It (*Joyce Kilmer*), 164
The Planting of the Apple-Tree (*William Cullen Bryant*), 115
The Poplars (*Theodosia Garrison*), 114
The Village Blacksmith (*Henry Wadsworth Longfellow*), 145
The Yarn of the Nancy Bell (*William S. Gilbert*), 128
The Zebra Dun, 146
This Is My Rock (*David McCord*), 116
Travel (*Edna St. Vincent Millay*), 139
When the Drive Goes Down (*Douglas Malloch*), 146

*Stories*

A Night Ride in a Prairie Schooner (*Hamlin Garland*), 655
Alice Goes Down the Rabbit-Hole (*Lewis Carroll*), 473
Behind the Battlements (*Gertrude Hartman*), 734
Buck, the Lead-Dog (*Jack London*), 736
Dick Finds the "Wheel of Fortune" (*Cornelia Meigs*), 666
Hans Brinker and His Sister (*Mary Mapes Dodge*), 659
Jacques and the Little Chief (*Frances Gaither*), 659
Jangwa Begins To Hunt (*Walter J. Wilwerding*), 530
Little Daylight (*George MacDonald*), 423
Little Goody Two-Shoes, 591
Pandora (*Emilie Kip Baker*), 334
Paul Bunyan (*Wallace Wadsworth*), 478
Riquet with the Tuft, 296
Talking Wires (*Clara Lambert*), 739
The Bears of Blue River (*Charles Major*), 596
The Emperor's New Clothes (*Hans Christian Andersen*), 434
The Far-Distant Oxus (*Katherine Hull* and *Pamela Whitlock*), 605
The Heroes of Asgard (*A.* and *E. Keary*), 318
The Making of the Hammer (*Emilie Kip Baker*), 320
The Pine-Tree Shillings (*Nathaniel Hawthorne*), 657
The Prince and the Giant's Daughter, 285
The Queen of the Pirate Isle (*Bret Harte*), 583
The Winged Horse (*Nathaniel Hawthorne*), 337
What We Found in a Fox Den (*Ernest Harold Baynes*), 525

## Grade Seven

*Verse*

A Prayer (*Edwin Markham*), 165
A Thing of Beauty (*John Keats*), 165
A Vagabond Song (*Bliss Carman*), 118

Daffodils (*William Wordsworth*), 118
Darius Green and His Flying Machine (*John Townsend Trowbridge*), 131
Hymn to the Night (*Henry Wadsworth Longfellow*), 117
In Praise of Johnny Appleseed (*Vachel Lindsay*), 155
Loveliest of Trees (*A. E. Housman*), 114.
Navaho Prayer (*Edward S. Yeomans*), 165
Old Ships (*David Morton*), 141
The Bugle Song (*Alfred Tennyson*), 91
The Discoverer of the North Cape (*Henry Wadsworth Longfellow*), 184
The Merry Miner, 130
The Prairie Schooner (*Edwin Ford Piper*), 157
The Sun (*Emily Dickinson*), 116
Whoopee Ti Yi Yo, Git Along Little Dogies, 147

*Stories*

Abe Lincoln Grows Up (*Carl Sandburg*), 672
Blue Arrow and the Outlaws (*Constance Lindsay Skinner*), 679
Chris Farrington: Able Seaman (*Jack London*), 743
Christmas with the Cratchits (*Charles Dickens*), 611
Invincible Louisa as a Nurse (*Cornelia Meigs*), 675
Little Women Plan Christmas (*Louisa M. Alcott*), 609
"Mark Twain" (*Cornelia Meigs*), 613
New York to Paris (*Charles A. Lindbergh*), 749
Rip Van Winkle (*Washington Irving*), 482
Robinson Crusoe (*Daniel Defoe*), 753
Sand Hogs (*Margaret Norris*), 751
The Bold Dragoon (*Washington Irving*), 482
The Fair Jehane (*Katharine Gibson*), 369
The Pearl Diver (*Charles Nordhoff*), 740
The Story of a Stone (*David Starr Jordan*), 535
The Story of Odysseus (*Padraic Colum*), 345
The Winning of Atalanta (*Elsie Finnimore Buckley*), 350
Tom Sawyer and His Pirate Crew (*Samuel L. Clemens*), 619
With Helmet and Hose (*William Beebe*), 527

## *Grade Eight*

*Verse*

A Nautical Extravagance (*Wallace Irwin*), 130
Abou Ben Adhem (*Leigh Hunt*), 166
Annabel Lee (*Edgar Allan Poe*), 191
Between Two Loves (*T. A. Daly*), 134
Charity (*The Bible: I Corinthians 13*), 167
Goethals, the Prophet Engineer (*Percy MacKaye*), 148
In School Days (*John Greenleaf Whittier*), 186
It Is Not Far (*Sara Teasdale*), 116

John Anderson, My Jo (*Robert Burns*), 198
Miracles (*Walt Whitman*), 119
My Own, My Native Land (*Sir Walter Scott*), 160
Sea Fever (*John Masefield*), 141
Skipper Ireson's Ride (*John Greenleaf Whittier*), 196
The Courtin' (*James Russell Lowell*), 186
The Deacon's Masterpiece (*Oliver Wendell Holmes*), 135
The Oregon Trail: 1851 (*Jim Marshall*), 157
The Passing of the Buffalo (*Hamlin Garland*), 156
The Pied Piper of Hamelin (*Robert Browning*), 193
The Secret of the Machines (*Rudyard Kipling*), 149
The Snow (*John Greenleaf Whittier*), 117
The Thinker (*Berton Braley*), 150
The Ticket Agent (*Edmund Leamy*), 141
Velvet Shoes (*Elinor Wylie*), 118

*Stories*

Baron Munchausen Goes to the Moon (*Rudolph Erich Raspe*), 485
Being a Boy (*Charles Dudley Warner*), 685
Gareth and Lynette (retold from *Alfred Tennyson*), 362
John Halifax Faces the Rioters (*Dinah Maria Mulock Craik*), 764
Riding the Girders (*Margaret Norris*), 751
Schumann-Heink's First Contract (*Mary Lawton*), 758
Sigurd the Volsung (*Dorothy Hosford*), 324
The Capture of the Giant Armadillo (*Raymond L. Ditmars*), 538
The Hoosier Schoolmaster (*Edward Eggleston*), 691
The Nightingale (*Hans Christian Andersen*), 691
The Pony Express (*Charles L. Skelton*), 695
The Truce on Treasure Island (*Robert Louis Stevenson*), 626

# PRONOUNCING GLOSSARY

Achilles à kĭl′ ēz
Aershot är′ skŏt
Aesir ē′ sĭr
Agamemnon ăg à mĕm′ nŏn
Aladdin à lăd′ ĭn
Alcinous ăl sĭn′ ō ŭs
Alcott ôl′ kŭt
Aldis ôl′ dĭs
Allah ăl′ à
Amaro ä mä′ rō
Amphidamas ăm fĭ′ dà màs
Andvari än dwä′ rē
Aphrodite ăf rō dī′ tē
Apuleius ăp ū lē′ yŭs
Araby ăr′ à bĭ
Arcturus ärk tū′ rŭs
Artemis är′ tē mĭs
Artzybasheff är″ tzē băsh′ ĕf
Asbjörnsen äs byĕrn′ sĕn
Asgard äs′ gärd
Atalanta ăt à lăn′ tà
Athene à thē′ nē
Audhumla ou͜ thōōm′ lä
Aulis ôl′ ĭs

Baldur bôl′ dĕr
Baruch bâr′ ŭk
Beebe bē′ bē
Bellerophon bĕ lĕr′ ō fōn
Beskow bĕs′ kō
Bewick bū′ ĭk
Bianco bē ăn′ kō
Bienville byăn vĕl′
Blenheim blĕn′ ĭm
Bontemps bŏn tăm′
Bragi brä′ gē
Brer brŭh

Brindisi brēn′ dē zē
Brobdingnagian brŏb″ dĭng năg′ ĭ ăn
Bruges brōō′ jĭz
Brynhild brōōn′ hĭlt
Buri Bōō′ rē

Caldecott kŏl′ dĕ kŏt
Calydon kăl′ ĭ dŏn
Calypso kà lĭp′ sō
Camerino kä mā rē′ nō
Campagna käm pän′ yä
Carabas kâr′ à băs
Cendfind kĕnd′ fīnd
Chaleur shä lōōr′
Cham kăm
Chevalier, Ragnhild shē và lyā′, rā yĭn hĭlt
Chimaera kī mē′ rà
Chimalpopoca chē″ mäl pō pō′ kä
Chiquita chē kē′ tà
*cholla* chōl′ yä
Clymene klī mē′ nē
Coli kō′ lē
Collodi kŏl lō′ dē
Colum, Padraic kŏl′ ŭm, pŏd′ rĭg
Columbkill kŏl′ ŭm kĭl
Cuhullin kōō hōō′ lĭn
Cyclops (sing.) sī′ klŏps
Cyclopes (plu.) sī klō′ pēz
Cythera kĭth′ ĕ rà

Daedalus dĕd′ à lŭs
Dalgliesh dăl′ glēsh
Damariscotta dăm″ à rĭs kŏt′ à
Dasent dā′ sĕnt
D'Aulaire, Parin dō lâr′, pà răn′
D'Aulnoy dōl nwä′
De la Mare dĕ là mâr′

D'Iberville dē bĕr vēl′
De Quindre dĕ kăn′ dr
Donegal dŏn ĕ gäl′
Duval, Jacques do͞o väl,′ zhäk

Eau Galle ō găl′
Epimetheus ĕp ĭ mē′ thūs
Eris ĕr′ ĭs
Erzeroum ĕrz′ ro͞om

Fafnir fäv′ nĭr
Farjeon fär′ jŏn
Farrar fă rär′
Fatima fä′ tē mä
Faustina fous tē′ nä
Favosites făv″ ō sī′ tēz
Fifina fē fē′ nä
Findaragh fĭn dâr′ ȧ
Francois frŏn swä′
Freyr frār
Frigga frĭg′ gä

Gág gäg
Galápagos gä lä′ pä gōs
Gareth găr′ ĕth
Gargantua gär găn′ tu ȧ
Gatti-Casazza gä′ tī - kä zä′ tsä
Gawain gä′ wān
Geppetto jĕ pĕt′ tō
Ghent gĕnt
Ginnungagap yĭn′ o͞on gä gäp″
Gladsheim gläts′ hām
Graeme grām
Graz gräts
Gretel grā′ t'l
Guadalupe gwä thä lo͞o′ pē

Hader hā′ dẽr
Hainault ĕ nō′
Hans hänz
Hardangerfjord här′ däng ẽr fyôrd
Hasselt häs′ ĕlt
Helicon hĕl′ ĭ kŏn
Hera hē′ rȧ
Hermod hẽr′ mŏd
Hodur Hō′ dẽr
Holger Danske hōl′ gẽr däns′ kĕ
Housman hous′ măn

Icarus ĭk′ ȧ rŭs
Ivi ē′ vē

Jael jā′ ĕl
Jancsi Jăn′ sĭ
Jataka jä′ tä kȧ
Jehane zhän
*jongleur* zhôn glûr′
Jotunheim yô′ tŏn hām
Jovita hō vē′ tä
*jufvrow* jo͞o frou′
Juniata jo͞o″ nĭ ăt′ ȧ

Kauai kä o͝o ä′ ē
Khama kä′ mä
Kienzl kēn′ tz'l
Kristiania krĭs tyä′ nē ȧ
Kuu ko͞o

La Brea lä brā′ ä
La Charette lä shä rĕt′
Laertes lā ẽr′ tēz
Lanier lȧ nēr′
Lavanda lȧ vän′ dȧ
Le Bourget lĕ bo͞or zhĕ′
Lokeren lō′ kẽr ĕn
Loki lō′ kē
Loire lwȧr
Lorenzini lō rĕn zē′ nē
Louiset lo͞o ĭ zĕt′
Lycia lĭsh′ ĭ ȧ
Lyonors lī″ ō nôrs′

MacKaye m'kī′
McGillivray m'gĭl′ ĭ vrā
Maenads mē′ năds
Maeve māv
Máli mä′ lē
Mardi Gras mär″ dē grä′
M'Coul m'ko͞ol′
Mameto mä mā′ tō
Medusa mĕ dū′ sȧ
Meigs mĕgz
Meilanion mī lăn′ ĭ ŏn
Menelaus mĕn ĕ lā′ ŭs
Menomonee mĕ nŏm′ ŏ nē
Mignonetto mĭn yŭn ĕt′ tō
Milne mĭln
Minou mĭn o͞o′
*mochila* mō chē′ lä
Modred mō′ drĕd
Moe, Jörgen mō, yẽr′ gĕn
Mukerji, Dhan Gopal mo͞o kẽr′ jē, dhän gō′ päl

Mustapha mo͞os′ tä fä
Mycenae mī sē′ nē

Nanou năn o͞o′
Nirascou nēr äs ko͞o′
Nizam nĭ zäm′
Nouvilo no͞o vē′ lō
Nungesser nŭn zhĕ sā′

Odin ō′ dĭn
Odysseus ō dĭs′ ūs
Olaf ō′ läf
Oonagh o͞o′ nȧ
Orleans ôr lā än′
Outagamie o͞o tȧ găm′ ĭ
Oxus ŏk′ sŭs

Paget pădg′ ĕt
Parthenius pär thē′ nĭ ŭs
Pedro pā′ drō
Pegasus pĕg′ ȧ sŭs
Penelope pē nĕl′ ō pē
Perrault pĕ rō′
Peti pā′ tē
Phthia thī′ ä
Pinocchio pĭn ōk′ ĭ ō
Pirene pī rē′ nē
Pita pē′ tä
Plouf plo͞of
Pogány pō gä′ nē
Polyphemus pŏl ĭ fē′ mŭs
Popo pō′ pō
Poseidon pō sī′ dŏn
Pouget po͞o zhĕ′
Priordon prī′ ĕr dŏn
Provence prö väns′

Rangiroa răn″ gē rō′ ȧ
Raoul rä o͞ol′
Regin rā′ yĭn
Riquet rĭ′ kĕ
Rossetti rō sĕt′ ē
Rousseau ro͞o sō′
Rowe rou
Ruadh, Mari rū′ ä, môr′ ē

*sagamite* sä gä″ mĭ tā′
Sangamon săn′ gȧ mŏn
Schiedam skē däm′
Schoenus skē′ nŭs
Schumann-Heink sho͞o″ män - hīngk′
Seredy shēr′ ĭ dĭ
Shawano shä wä′ nō
Sigurd zē′ go͞ort
Sindri sĭn′ drē
Slieveleague slēv′ lēg
Stanislaus stăn′ ĭs lô
Stutly stŭt′ lĭ

Telemachus tē lĕm′ ȧ kŭs
Tenniel tĕn′ yĕl
Thetis thē′ tĭs
Tintourlet tăn″ to͞or lā′
Tlaxochimaco tläs″ ō chē mä′ kō
Tongres tŏn′ gr
Tonino tō nē′ nō
Tournaise to͞or nā′
Trebizond trĕb′ ĭ zŏnd″
Tyr tĭr

Valhalla văl hăl′ ȧ
Vanir vä′ nĭr
Van Loon văn lōn′
Vernandou vĕr nän do͞o′
Vidar vē′ där
*vizier* vĭ zēr′
Volsung vŏl′ so͞ong

Weser vā′ zĕr
Wiese, Kurt vē′ zĕ, ko͞ort
Wyss vĭs

Zeus zūs

## *References for Students*

*Century Cyclopedia of Names.*
*International Book of Names.* C. O. Sylvester Mawson. Crowell.
*The Junior Book of Authors.* S. J. Kunitz and Howard Haycraft. Wilson.
*New International Dictionary.* Webster. Merriam.
*Pronunciation of 10,000 Proper Names.* M. G. and M. S. Mackey. Dodd Mead.
*What's the Name, Please.* Charles Earle Funk. Funk and Wagnalls.

# INDEX

"A cat came fiddling," 58
"A farmer went riding," 54
Abbott, J., 388-389
*Abe Lincoln Grows Up,* C. Sandburg, 672
*Abou Ben Adhem,* L. Hunt, 166
Adolescents, book for, 11, 308
Aesop, 209, 210, 386; *The Lion and the Mouse,* 299; *The Wind and the Sun,* 300; *The Frog and the Ox,* 300; *The Hare and the Tortoise,* 300; *The Crow and the Pitcher,* 300; *The Ant and the Grasshopper,* 301; *The Mice in Council,* 301; *The Dog and the Shadow,* 301; *The Fox and the Grapes,* 301; *The Town Mouse and the Country Mouse,* 302; *Hercules and the Wagoner,* 302; *The Milkmaid and the Pail,* 302
*Aiken-Drum, the Brownie,* 221
*Aladdin,* J. R. Lowell, 91
*Aladdin and the Wonderful Lamp,* 6, 278
Alcott, L. M., 13, 14, 792; *Little Women Plan Christmas,* 609
Aldis, D., 792; *Troubles,* 77; *Skipping Ropes,* 77
Alexander, C. F., 792; *All Things Bright and Beautiful,* 163
*Alice Goes Down the Rabbit-Hole,* L. Carroll, 473
*Alice in Wonderland,* L. Carroll, 390; illustration from, 28; selections from, 122, 473
*All Things Bright and Beautiful,* C. F. Alexander, 163
Allingham, W., 792; *The Elf Singing,* 87; *Up the Airy Mountain,* 88
*Alone,* J. Paget-Fredericks, 79
America, poems about, 152-160; stories about, 635-702
American folklore, 209-210, 378-379, 390; selections from, 146, 147, 214, 309, 436, 465, 466, 478
American Library Assn., 13, 391, 779, 780
Andersen, H. C., 389-390, 792; *The Tinder Box,* 395; *The Princess and the Pea,* 406; *The Ugly Duckling,* 430; *The Emperor's New Clothes,* 434; *The Nightingale,* 445
Anderson, C. W., 793; *Billy and Blaze,* 551
*Angel in the Apple Tree, The,* W. Welles, 90
*Angler's Reveille, The,* H. van Dyke, 102
*Annabel Lee,* E. A. Poe, 191
*Ant and the Grasshopper, The,* Aesop, 301
*April,* S. Teasdale, 107
*Arabian Nights' Entertainment, The,* 6, 209; selection from, 278
Artzybasheff, B., 20, 37; illustration by, 37
"As I was going to St. Ives," 59
*As Joseph Was A-Walking,* 163
"As round as an apple," 59
Asbjornsen, P., and J. Moe, 209, 793
*Ask Mr. Bear,* M. Flack, 393
Asquith, H., 792; *Skating,* 80; *The Hairy Dog,* 95
*At the Seaside,* R. L. Stevenson, 78
Authors, biographical notes on, 791-840
*Autumn Fancies,* 114

"Baa, baa, black sheep," 58
Bacon, J. D., 793; *The Sleepy Song,* 75
Bacon, P., 793; *The Lion-Hearted Kitten,* 458

Bain, R. N., 218, 794
Baker, E. K., 794; *The Making of the Hammer,* 320; *Pandora,* 334
Ballads, 52, 70-71, 386; selections from, 125, 146, 147, 169, 173, 179, 181, 182; *see also* Stories in verse
Bamberger, F. E., 20
Bangs, J. K., 794; *My Dog,* 100
Bannerman, H., 794; *Little Black Sambo,* 456
*Barbara Frietchie,* J. G. Whittier, 158
*Baron Munchausen Goes to the Moon,* R. E. Raspe, 485
Baruch, D. W., 794; *Merry-Go-Round,* 78
*Battle of Blenheim, The,* R. Southey, 176
Baynes, E. H., 794; *What We Found in a Fox Den,* 525
*Bears of Blue River, The,* C. Major, 596
*Beasts of the Tar Pits,* W. W. Robinson, 519
*Bed in Summer,* R. L. Stevenson, 74
Bedford, F. D., 32
Beebe, W., 795; *With Helmet and Hose,* 527
*Behind the Battlements,* G. Hartman, 734
*Behind the Waterfall,* W. Welles, 90
*Being a Boy,* C. D. Warner, 685
Beskow, E., 34
*Between Two Loves,* T. A. Daly, 134
Bewick, T., 25; illustrations by, 26
Bianco, M., 795; *The Gentleman in Brown,* 493; *Mr. Murdle's Large Heart,* 557
Bible, *The Lord Is My Shepherd* (Psalm 23), 166; *Thanksgiving* (Psalm 100), 166; *A Merry Heart* (Proverbs 15), 167; *Charity* (I Corinthians 13), 167; *David and Goliath* (I Samuel 17), 602
*Billy and Blaze,* C. W. Anderson, 551
Biographical notes, 791-840
Biography, books of, 777
Birch, R., 32
*Birches, The,* W. P. Eaton, 107
*Bird, A,* E. Dickinson, 97
*Bird's Nest, The,* J. Drinkwater, 93
*Birthdays,* M. G. Chute, 77
*Blackbird, The,* H. Wolfe, 98
Blake, W., 71, 795; *The Lamb,* 163
*Blind Men and the Elephant, The,* J. G. Saxe, 176
"Blow, wind, blow," 58
*Blue Arrow and the Outlaws,* C. L. Skinner, 679
*Blue Barns,* H. Sewell, 490
*Blue Teapot, The,* A. Dalgliesh, 560
*Boats Sail on the Rivers,* C. G. Rossetti, 106
*Bob White,* G. Cooper, 97
*Bold Dragoon, The,* W. Irving, 482
Bontemps, A., 796; *Children of Haiti,* 715
Book Week, Children's, 391
Books, children's, lists of, Mother Goose, 65; Verse, 200-202; Old tales, 304-306; Legends and hero tales, 377-378; Modern, 451-454, 488-489, 547-549, 630-634, 702-704, 774-776, 777-778, 779-780, 782-784; *see also* References for students
*Books of My Childhood,* H. Garland, 6
*Boots and His Brothers,* 241
"Bow, wow, wow," 53
Boys and girls, poems about, 73-84; stories about, 550-629
*Boy's Song, A,* J. Hogg, 83
Braley, B., 796; *The Thinker,* 150
*Bridget Goes Prospecting,* B. and E. Hader, 729
*Brier Rose,* 258
Brink, C. R., 796; *Caddie and the Indian Chief,* 639
Broadsides, 386
Brock, E. L., 38, 796; *By Covered Wagon,* 635
Bronson, W. S., 796; *Paddlewings Grows Up,* 521
Brooks, L. L., 31; illustration by, 32
*Brown Bee,* W. B. Rands, 101
Browne, Frances, 797; *Fairyfoot,* 415
Browning, E. B., 4
Browning, R., 797; *The Year's at the Spring,* 111; *How They Brought the Good News from Ghent to Aix,* 174; *The Pied Piper of Hamelin,* 193
Bruner, H. B., 14-15
Bryant, W. C., 797; *The Planting of the Apple-Tree,* 115
*Buck, the Lead-Dog,* J. London, 736
Buckley, E. F., *The Winning of Atalanta,* 350
*Bugle Song, The,* A. Tennyson, 91
Burns, R., 797; *A Child's Grace,* 162; *John Anderson, My Jo,* 198
*Busy Carpenters,* J. S. Tippett, 143
*Butterbean Tent, The,* E. M. Roberts, 81

*By Covered Wagon,* E. L. Brock, 635
"Bye, baby bunting," 53

*Caddie and the Indian Chief,* C. R. Brink, 639
*Caddie Woodlawn,* C. R. Brink, illustration from, 36; selection from, 639
Caldecott, R., 31, 391, 780; illustration by, 31
Caldecott Medal books, 780
*Calypso,* E. Coatsworth, 568
*Capture of the Giant Armadillo, The,* R. L. Ditmars, 538
Carman, B., 797; *A Vagabond Song,* 118
*Carpenter,* E. V. Lucas, 143
Carroll, L., 390, 797; *A Lobster Quadrille,* 122; *A Strange Wild Song,* 124; *The Walrus and the Carpenter,* 126; *Alice Goes Down the Rabbit-Hole,* 473
Carryl, C. E., 798; *The Plaint of the Camel,* 121; *A Nautical Ballad,* 128
Cary, P., 795; *A Leak in the Dyke,* 171
*Cat,* M. B. Miller, 98
*Caterpillar, The,* C. G. Rossetti, 94
Chapbooks, 25, 387; illustration from, 25
*Charity,* Bible (I Corinthians 13), 167
Chevalier, R., 798; *Stories of Other Days in Old Bergen,* 570
*Child and the Fairies, The,* 87
Child, L. M., 798; *Thanksgiving Day,* 81
*Children of Haiti,* A. Bontemps and L. Hughes, 715
*Children of the Wind,* C. Sandburg, 102
Children's interests in pictures, 20-21
Children's interests in reading, 12-18, 45, 51, 69-70, 207, 210, 212, 390, 785
*Child's Day Begins, A,* W. de la Mare, 73
*Child's Grace, A,* R. Burns, 162
*Choosing a Kitten,* 95
*Chris Farrington: Able Seaman,* J. London, 743
Christmas, poems about, 77, 82, 88, 163, 177; stories about, 394, 555, 573, 609, 611
*Christmas with the Cratchits,* C. Dickens, 611
Chute, M. G., 799; *Birthdays,* 77; *Presents,* 77
*Cinderella,* 207, 254
*Circus Garland, A,* R. Field, 82
*City Mouse and the Garden Mouse, The,* C. G. Rossetti, 98
Clemens, S. L., 14, 613, 799; *Tom Sawyer and His Pirate Crew,* 619
*Clinker, The,* 148
*Clouds,* 106
Coatsworth, E., 799; *Oak Leaves,* 111; *Swift Things Are Beautiful,* 114; *Song of the Parrot,* 140; *The Wilderness Is Tamed,* 152; *Calypso,* 568
"Cobbler, cobbler, mend my shoe," 58
"Cock-a-doodle-doo," 55
Coleridge, S., 800; *The Garden Year,* 110
Coleridge, S. T., 800; *He Prayeth Best,* 162
Collodi, C., 800; *Pinocchio,* 420
Colum, P., 800; *The Old Woman of the Roads,* 164; *The First Harp,* 317; *The Story of Odysseus,* 345; *Jimmie, the White Sparrow,* 513
*Columbus,* J. Miller, 153
"Come, butter, come," 54
Comenius, J. A., *Orbis Pictus,* 23, 24, 387
*Concord Hymn,* R. W. Emerson, 153
Conkling, H., 800; *Mouse,* 94; *Hills,* 111
Cook, E., 800; *King Bruce and the Spider,* 173
Cooper, G., 800; *Frogs at School,* 95; *Bob White,* 97; *The Wonderful Weaver,* 109
*Courtin', The,* J. R. Lowell, 186
*Cow, The,* R. L. Stevenson, 96
*Cradle Hymn,* M. Luther, 163
Craik, D. M. M., 231, 251, 254, 272, 275, 296, 801; *John Halifax Faces the Rioters,* 764
Crane, L., 28, 247, 801
Crane, W., 28; illustration by, 29
Crothers, S. M., 51
*Crow and the Pitcher, The,* Aesop, 300
Cruikshank, G., 26, 27; illustrations by, 26, 27
Curry, C. M., 14-15
"Cushy cow bonny," 54

*Daffodils,* W. Wordsworth, 118
Dalgliesh, A., 801; *The Blue Teapot,* 560; *The Small Yellow Train,* 709
Daly, T. A., 801; *Between Two Loves,* 134
*Darius Green and His Flying Machine,* J. T. Trowbridge, 131
Dasent, G. W., 209, 213, 230, 232, 241, 259, 264, 801
Daugherty, J., 32

D'Aulaire, E. P. and I., 35, 36
D'Aulnoy, Madame, 802; *The White Cat,* 407
*David and Goliath,* Bible (I Samuel 17), 602
Day, T., 388
*Deacon's Masterpiece, The,* O. W. Holmes, 135
*Dear Land of All My Love,* S. Lanier, 152
Defoe, D., 802; *Robinson Crusoe,* 753
De la Mare, W., 72, 802; *The Huntsmen,* 73; *A Child's Day Begins,* 73; *Some One,* 86; *Seeds,* 107; *Silver,* 108
*Dick Finds the "Wheel of Fortune,"* C. Meigs, 666
Dickens, C., 803; *The Magic Fish-Bone,* 459; *Christmas with the Cratchits,* 611
Dickinson, E., 803; *A Bird,* 97; *The Sun,* 116
"Diddle, diddle, dumpling," 53
"Ding, dong, bell," 57
*Discoverer of the North Cape, The,* H. W. Longfellow, 184
Ditmars, R. L., 803; *The Capture of the Giant Armadillo,* 538
*Do You Know?* C. G. Rossetti, 99
*Doctor Dolittle and the Pushmi-Pullyu,* H. Lofting, 471
Dodge, M. M., 803; *Hans Brinker and His Sister,* 599
*Dog and the Shadow, The,* Aesop, 301
*Dogs and Weather,* W. Welles, 99
*Drakesbill,* 238
Dramatization, 211, 379, 381
Drinkwater, J., 804; *Washing,* 76; *The Bird's Nest,* 93
*Duck, The,* E. King, 96
*Duel, The,* E. Field, 122
Dull children, reading of, 16-17, 781-784
Dunbar, P. L., 804; *Lullaby,* 741
Dunn, F. W., 15-16
Duplaix, G., 491, 804

*East of the Sun and West of the Moon,* 264
Eaton, W. P., 804; *The Birches,* 107
Eggleston, E., 7-8, 804; *The Hoosier Schoolmaster,* 691
*Elephant's Child, The,* R. Kipling, 467; illustration from, 35
*Elf Singing, The,* W. Allingham, 87
*Elves and the Shoemaker, The,* 237
Emerson, R. W., 805; *Concord Hymn,* 153
*Emperor's New Clothes, The,* H. C. Andersen, 434
Enjoyment of literature, 3-5, 44, 51, 69-72, 207, 211, 212, 392, 781-782
*Evening at the Farm,* J. T. Trowbridge, 144
Ewing, J. H., 805; *A Friend in the Garden,* 96
Experimental studies, 12-18, 20, 21
*Explanation of the Grasshopper, An,* V. Lindsay, 95

*Fables of Aesop, The, see* Aesop
*Fair Jehane, The,* K. Gibson, 369
*Fairies,* R. Fyleman, 86
Fairies and make-believe, poems about, 86-91; stories about, 393-450, 459, 471, 473; *see also* Fairy tales, Folk tales, Legends
Fairy tales, 207, 210, 389, 390; *see also* Folk tales, Humor, Legends, Make-believe stories
*Fairyfoot,* Frances Browne, 415
*Falling Star, The,* S. Teasdale, 113
Falls, C. B., 38
*Far-Distant Oxus, The,* K. Hull and P. Whitlock, 605
Farjeon, E., 72, 805; *Over the Garden Wall,* 79; *The Night Will Never Stay,* 108
Farrar, J., 805; *Watching Clouds,* 106
Fenton, C. L., 805; *The Horny Ones,* 511
Ferris, H., 758, 806
Field, E., 70, 806; *Wynken, Blynken, and Nod,* 75; *The Duel,* 122
Field, R., 72, 806; *A Circus Garland,* 82; *Skyscrapers,* 89; *Roads,* 138; *Taxis,* 139; *Hitty Goes to Sea,* 648
*Fin McCoul and the Giant,* J. Jacobs, 313
*First Christmas Tree, The,* R. Fyleman, 394
*First Harp, The,* P. Colum, 317
Flack, M., 34, 807; *Ask Mr. Bear,* 393; *Lucky Little Lena,* 550
Fleming, E., 807; *Wild Animals,* 98
*Fog,* C. Sandburg, 114
Fogler, D., *Rusty Pete, Cow Pony,* 711
Folk tales, 10, 207-212, 304-306, 307-308, 379-380, 389-390; selections from, 213-302; *see also* Legends
Follen, E. L., 807; *The Three Little Kittens,* 169
Foreign lands, poems about, 90, 108, 140, 141, 171; stories about, 553, 554, 565, 570, 599, 605, 706, 715, 719, 740

*Fox and the Grapes, The,* Aesop, 301
*French Jongleurs, The,* K. Gibson, 733
*Friend in the Garden, A,* J. H. Ewing, 96
*Frog and the Ox, The,* Aesop, 300
*Frogs at School,* G. Cooper, 95
Frost, A. B., 32; illustration by, 33
Frost, R., 72, 807; *The Pasture,* 96; *The Runaway,* 99; *Stopping by Woods on a Snowy Evening,* 110
Fyleman, R., 72, 808; *If Only . . .,* 80; *Fairies,* 86; *Mice,* 94; *The First Christmas Tree,* 394

Gàg, W., 34
Gaither, F., 808; *Jacques and the Little Chief,* 659
*Garden Year, The,* S. Coleridge, 110
*Gareth and Lynette,* retold from A. Tennyson, 362
Garland, H., 808; *Books of My Childhood,* 6; *Horses Chawin' Hay,* 101; *Plowing: A Memory,* 144; *The Plowman of Today,* 145; *The Passing of the Buffalo,* 156; *A Night Ride in a Prairie Schooner,* 655
Garrison, T., 809; *The Poplars,* 114
*Gentleman in Brown, The,* M. Bianco, 493
*Ghost of the Great White Stag, The,* A. C. Parker, 309
Gibson, K., 809; *The Fair Jehane,* 369; *The French Jongleurs,* 733
Gilbert, W. S., 809; *The Yarn of the Nancy Bell,* 128
*Gingerbread Boy, The,* 214
"Girls and boys, come out to play," 57
*Glimpse in Autumn,* J. S. Untermeyer, 110
"God bless the master of this house," 56
*Goethals, the Prophet Engineer,* P. MacKaye, 148
Goldsmith, O., 50, 387, 388, 809; *Little Goody Two-Shoes,* 591
*Good Play, A,* R. L. Stevenson, 79
Goodrich, S. G., *see* Parley, Peter
Graded lists of selections, discussion of, 41-42; Mother Goose, 63-64; Verse, 84, 91, 103, 119, 136, 142, 150, 160, 168, 198; Old tales and legends, 303, 376; Modern stories, 450, 487, 546, 629, 702, 773, 841-852.
*Grandmother's Buttons,* G. and D. Hauman, 552
Greek myths and legends, 307, 308, 334-361
*Green Moth,* W. Welles, 90
Greenaway, K., 30, 31; illustration by, 30
Grierson, E. W., 285, 810
Grimm, J. and W., 26-27, 209, 229, 237, 243, 247, 258, 389, 810
Guideposts to living, poems about, 162-168

Hader, B. and E., 35, 36, 810; *Bridget Goes Prospecting,* 729
*Hairy Dog, The,* H. Asquith, 95
Halliwell (Phillips), J. O., 51, 53-62, 209, 216, 224, 225, 811
Handforth, T., 38
*Hans Brinker and His Sister,* M. M. Dodge, 599
*Hansel and Gretel,* 247
*Hare and the Tortoise, The,* Aesop, 300
Harris, J. C., 390, 811; *The Tar Baby,* 465; *The Well Story,* 466; *see also Uncle Remus*
Harte, B., 811; *The Queen of the Pirate Isle,* 583
Hartman, G., 811; *Behind the Battlements,* 734
Hauman, G. and D., 812; *Grandmother's Buttons,* 552
Hawthorne, N., 812; *The Winged Horse,* 337; *The Pine-Tree Shillings,* 657
*He Prayeth Best,* S. T. Coleridge, 162
*Height of the Ridiculous, The,* O. W. Holmes, 123
*Hens, The,* E. M. Roberts, 100
*Hercules and the Wagoner,* Aesop, 302
*Heroes of Asgard, The,* A. and E. Keary, 318
"Hey! diddle, diddle," 54
*Hiawatha's Canoe,* H. W. Longfellow, 178
*Hiawatha's Childhood,* H. W. Longfellow, 170
"Hickory, dickory, dock," 54
*Hide and Go Seek,* D. P. Lathrop, 496
"Higgledy, piggledy, my black hen," 55
Hill, H., and V. Maxwell, 812; *Little Tonino,* 719
*Hills,* H. Conkling, 111
History, American, *see* America
History of children's literature, 3, 21-40, 49-52, 70-72, 207-210, 385-392, 791-840
*Hitty Goes to Sea,* R. Field, 648
Hogg, J., 812; *A Boy's Song,* 83
Holland, R. S., 812; *Jack-in-the-Pulpit,* 107

Holling, H. C., 813; *Rocky Billy Goes Visiting,* 502
Holmes, O. W., 813; *The Height of the Ridiculous,* 123; *The Deacon's Masterpiece,* 135
Hood, T., 813; *Queen Mab,* 87
*Hoosier Schoolmaster, The,* E. Eggleston, 691
*Horn Book Magazine, The,* 391
Hornbooks, 22, 285; illustration of, 22
*Horny Ones, The,* E. M. Patch and C. L. Fenton, 511
*Horses Chawin' Hay,* H. Garland, 101
*Horseshoe, The,* E. St. V. Millay, 138
Hosford, D., 813; *Sigurd the Volsung,* 324
*Hot-Weather Song, A,* D. Marquis, 131
*House Cat, The,* A. Wynne, 95
*House with Nobody in It, The,* J. Kilmer, 164
Housman, A. E., 813; *Loveliest of Trees,* 114
*How They Brought the Good News from Ghent to Aix,* R. Browning, 174
Howitt, W., 814; *The Wind in a Frolic,* 111
Huber, M. B., 14-15, 16-17, 221, 464, 466
Hughes, L., 814; *Mother to Son,* 162; *Children of Haiti,* 715
Hull, K., and P. Whitlock, 814; *The Far-Distant Oxus,* 605
Humor, 10, 17, 27, 51, 71, 72; poems of, 121-136; stories of, 455-487
"Humpty-Dumpty," 59
Hunt, L., 814; *Abou Ben Adhem,* 166
*Huntsmen, The,* W. de la Mare, 83
"Hush-a-bye, baby," 53
*Hymn to the Night,* H. W. Longfellow, 117

"I had a little nut-tree," 56
"I had a little pony," 57
"I have a little sister," 59
*I Hear America Singing,* W. Whitman, 145
"I saw a ship a-sailing," 56
"If all the seas were one sea," 59
*If Only . . . ,* R. Fyleman, 80
Illustrated books, 19-40, 43, 45, 780
*In a Desert Town,* L. Stevenson, 111
*In Flanders Fields,* J. McCrae, 160
"In marble walls as white as milk," 59
*In Praise of Johnny Appleseed,* V. Lindsay, 155
*In School Days,* J. G. Whittier, 186
Indian, American, poems about, 152, 165, 170, 178; stories about, 309, 639, 659, 679
*Indian Children,* A. Wynne, 152
*Indian Summer Day on the Prairie, An,* V. Lindsay, 116
Informational books, 9-10, 547, 702, 774, 777
"Intery, mintery, cutery-corn," 58
*Invincible Louisa as a Nurse,* C. Meigs, 675
Irving, W., 390, 814; *Rip Van Winkle,* 436; *The Bold Dragoon,* 482
Irwin, W., *A Nautical Extravagance,* 130
*Is the Moon Tired?* C. G. Rossetti, 105
*It Is Not Far,* S. Teasdale, 116

"Jack and Jill," 54
*Jack and the Beanstalk,* 234
"Jack be nimble," 55
*Jack-in-the-Pulpit,* R. S. Holland, 107
Jackson, L. F., 815; *To China,* 77
Jacobs, J., 209, 234, 299-302, 815; *Fin McCoul and the Giant,* 313
*Jacques and the Little Chief,* F. Gaither, 659
*Jancsi and Kate,* K. Seredy, 565
*Jangwa Begins To Hunt,* W. J. Wilwerding, 530
Jataka tales, 305
*Jimmie, the White Sparrow,* P. Colum, 513
*John Anderson, My Jo,* R. Burns, 198
*John Halifax Faces the Rioters,* D. M. M. Craik, 764
*John Martin's Book,* 392
Jordan, A. M., 13
Jordan, D. S., 815; *The Story of a Stone,* 535
*July,* S. H. Swett, 115
Junior Literary Guild, 391, 806
*Just So Stories,* R. Kipling, 390; illustration from, 35; selection from, 467

Keary, A. and E., 815; *The Heroes of Asgard,* 318
Keats, J., 815; *A Thing of Beauty,* 165; *Meg Merrilies,* 184
*Keeping Still in the Woods,* C. G. D. Roberts, 505
Kilmer, J., 815; *The House with Nobody in It,* 164
King, E., 816; *The Rabbit,* 93; *The Duck,* 96
*King Bruce and the Spider,* E. Cook, 173

*King of the Crocodiles, The,* 270
Kipling, R., 390, 816; illustration by, 35; *The Secret of the Machines,* 149; *The Elephant's Child,* 467

*Lad Who Went to the North Wind, The,* 232
*Lady Clare,* A. Tennyson, 189
*Lamb, The,* W. Blake, 163
Lambert, C., 816; *Talking Wires,* 739
*Land of Counterpane, The,* R. L. Stevenson, 78
Lang, Andrew, 31, 51, 54, 55, 58, 59, 209, 238, 278, 811
Lanier, S., 817; *Dear Land of All My Love,* 152
Lathrop, D. P., 20, 39, 817; illustration by, 40; *Hide and Go Seek,* 496
Lawson, R., 38
Lawton, M., *Schumann-Heink's First Contract,* 758
*Lazy Jack,* 225
*Leak in the Dyke, The,* P. Cary, 171
Leamy, E., 817; *The Ticket Agent,* 141
*Leap of Roushan Beg, The,* H. W. Longfellow, 192
Lear, E., 71, 390, 818; *The Owl and the Pussy Cat,* 121; *The Table and the Chair,* 123; *Nonsense Verses,* 124
Legends and hero tales, 307-376
Leigh, H. C., 818; *The Twins,* 126
Lenski, L., 38
Lent, H. B., 818; *Tony, the Steam Shovel Man,* 705; *Plowing,* 725
*Letters to Channy,* H. C. Washburne, 554
Library, children's, 12, 43, 390, 785-786
Lida, 818; *Plouf, the Little Wild Duck,* 491
Lima, M., 13
Lindbergh, C. A., 818; *New York to Paris,* 747
Lindsay, V., 72, 819; *Yet Gentle Will the Griffin Be,* 89; *The Little Turtle,* 94; *An Explanation of the Grasshopper,* 95; *The Mysterious Cat,* 100; *The Moon's the North Wind's Cooky,* 105; *An Indian Summer Day on the Prairie,* 116; *In Praise of Johnny Appleseed,* 155
*Lion and the Mouse, The,* Aesop, 299
*Lion-Hearted Kitten, The,* P. Bacon, 458
"Little Betty Blue," 55
*Little Black Sambo,* H. Bannerman, 456
"Little Bo-peep," 58
"Little Boy Blue," 55
*Little Busy Bee,* I. Watts, 101
*Little Daylight,* G. MacDonald, 423
*Little Goody Two-Shoes,* 591
"Little Jack Horner," 55
"Little King Boggen," 58
"Little Miss Muffet," 55
"Little Nancy Etticoat," 59
*Little Orphant Annie,* J. W. Riley, 83
*Little Red Riding Hood,* 208, 219
"Little Robin Redbreast," 56
*Little Star,* J. Taylor, 108
*Little Tonino,* H. Hill and V. Maxwell, 719
*Little Turtle, The,* V. Lindsay, 94
*Little Women Plan Christmas,* L. M. Alcott, 609
*Lobster Quadrille, A,* L. Carroll, 122
*Lochinvar,* W. Scott, 188
Lofting, H., 819; *Doctor Dolittle and the Pushmi-Pullyu,* 471
Lomax, J. A., 146, 147, 819
London, J., 819; *Buck, the Lead-Dog,* 736; *Chris Farrington: Able Seaman,* 743
*Lone Dog,* J. R. McLeod, 101
Longfellow, H. W., 820; *Hymn to the Night,* 117; *The Village Blacksmith,* 145; *Paul Revere's Ride,* 153; *Hiawatha's Childhood,* 170; *Three Kings Came Riding,* 177; *Hiawatha's Canoe,* 178; *The Discoverer of the North Cape,* 184; *The Leap of Roushan Beg,* 192
*Lord Is My Shepherd, The,* Bible (Psalm 23), 166
*Loveliest of Trees,* A. E. Housman, 114
Lowell, A., 820; *The Sea Shell,* 140
Lowell, J. R., 820; *Aladdin,* 91; *The Courtin',* 186; *The Singing Leaves,* 190
Lucas, E. V., 820; *Carpenter,* 143
*Lucky Little Lena,* M. Flack, 550
*Lucky Snail, The,* W. Welles, 97
*Lullaby,* P. L. Dunbar, 74
Luther, M., 820; *Cradle Hymn,* 163

McCord, D., 821; *The Frost Pane,* 109; *This Is My Rock,* 116
McCrae, J., 821; *In Flanders Fields,* 160
McGuffey's Readers, 7
McLeod, J. R., 821; *Lone Dog,* 101

MacDonald, G., 821; *The Wind and the Moon,* 112; *Little Daylight,* 423
MacKaye, P., 821; *Goethals, the Prophet Engineer,* 148
MacKinstry, E., 38; illustration by, 38
Magazines, children's, 7, 391-392, 785
*Magic Fish-Bone, The,* C. Dickens, 459
Major, C., 821; *The Bears of Blue River,* 596
Make-believe stories, 210, 393-450; *see also,* Fairies and make-believe, Fairy tales, Folk tales, Humor, Legends
*Making of the Hammer, The,* E. K. Baker, 320
Malloch, D., 822; *When the Drive Goes Down,* 146
Mark Twain, *see* Clemens, S. L.
*"Mark Twain,"* C. Meigs, 613
Markham, E., 822; *A Prayer,* 165
Marquis, D., 822; *A Hot-Weather Song,* 131
Marshall, J., 822; *The Oregon Trail,* 157
Martin, John, 822; *Baron Munchausen Goes to the Moon,* 485
Masefield, J., 72, 822; *Sea Fever,* 141; *The Midnight Voyage,* 399
*Meg Merrilies,* J. Keats, 184
Meigs, C., 823; *"Mark Twain,"* 613; *Dick Finds the "Wheel of Fortune,"* 666; *Invincible Louisa as a Nurse,* 675
Melcher, F. G., 391, 779, 780
Mellinger, B. E., 21
*Merry Heart, A,* Bible (Proverbs 15), 167
*Merry Miner, The,* 130
*Merry-Go-Round,* D. W. Baruch, 78
*Mice,* R. Fyleman, 95
*Mice in Council, The,* Aesop, 301
*Midnight Voyage, The,* J. Masefield, 399
*Milkmaid and Her Pail, The,* Aesop, 302
*Milk-White Moon, Put the Cows To Sleep,* C. Sandburg, 113
Millay, E. St. V., 823; *The Horseshoe,* 138; *Travel,* 139
Miller, J., 823; *Columbus,* 153
Miller, M. B., 823; *Cat,* 98
Milne, A. A., 72
*Miracles,* W. Whitman, 119
"Mistress Mary," 54
Modern literature for children, discussion of, 385-392
Moderow, G., M. Y. Sandrus, J. Mitchell, and E. C. Noyes, 362, 824
"Monday's child," 59
*Moon's the North Wind's Cooky, The,* V. Lindsay, 105
Moore, C. C., 824; *A Visit from St. Nicholas,* 88
Morley, C., 824; *Song for a Little House,* 164
Morris, W., 324, 369, 825
Morrow, E., 825; *Pita's Painted Pig,* 553
Morton, D., 825; *Old Ships,* 141
Mother Goose, 49, 50, 208, 827, 838
Mother Goose rhymes, 47-66
*Mother to Son,* L. Hughes, 162
*Mouse,* H. Conkling, 94
*Mr. Murdle's Large Heart,* M. Bianco, 557
*Mr. Nobody,* 82
*Mr. Vinegar,* 224
*My Bed Is a Boat,* R. L. Stevenson, 74
*My Dog,* J. K. Bangs, 100
*My Own, My Native Land,* W. Scott, 160
*My Shadow,* R. L. Stevenson, 76
*Mysterious Cat, The,* V. Lindsay, 100
Myths, *see* Legends and hero tales

Nature, poems about, 93-119; stories about, 490-547
*Nautical Ballad, A,* C. E. Carryl, 128
*Nautical Extravagance, A,* W. Irwin, 130
*Navaho Prayer,* E. S. Yeomans, 165
*New England Primer, The,* 22-23, 385-386; illustration from, 23
*New York to Paris,* C. A. Lindbergh, 747
Newbery, J., 50, 337-338, 391, 779
Newbery Medal books, 779
Nicholson, W., 38
Nicol, N., 825; *Rusty Pete, Cow Pony,* 711
*Night Ride in a Prairie Schooner, A,* H. Garland, 655
*Night Was Creeping,* J. Stephens, 106
*Night Will Never Stay, The,* E. Farjeon, 108
*Nightingale, The,* H. C. Andersen, 445
*Nonsense Verses,* E. Lear, 124
Nordhoff, C., 826; *The Pearl Diver,* 740
Norris, M., 826; *Sand Hogs,* 751; *Riding the Girders,* 751
Norse myths and legends, 307, 308, 318-334

*O Captain! My Captain!* W. Whitman, 159
*Oak Leaves,* E. Coatsworth, 111

O'Donnell, M., 221
"Old King Cole," 58
"Old Mother Hubbard," 61
*Old Ships,* D. Morton, 141
*Old Woman and Her Pig, The,* 216
*Old Woman of the Roads, The,* P. Colum, 164
"Once I saw a little bird," 56
"One, two, buckle my shoe," 57
*Orbis Pictus,* J. A. Comenius, 23, 387; illustration from, 24
*Oregon Trail, The,* J. Marshall, 157
*Over the Garden Wall,* E. Farjeon, 79
*Owl and the Pussy-Cat, The,* E. Lear, 121

*Paddlewings Grows Up,* W. S. Bronson, 521
Page, T. N., 826; *Two Little Confederates,* 644
Paget-Fredericks, J., 826; *Alone,* 79
*Pandora,* E. K. Baker, 334
Parker, A. C., 827; *The Ghost of the Great White Stag,* 309
Parley, Peter, 388
*Passing of the Buffalo, The,* H. Garland, 156
*Pasture, The,* R. Frost, 96
"Pat-a-cake," 53
Patch, E. M., 827; *Skunks,* 496; *The Horny Ones,* 511
*Paul Bunyan,* W. Wadsworth, 478
*Paul Revere's Ride,* H. W. Longfellow, 153
*Pearl Diver, The,* C. Nordhoff, 740
"Pease-porridge hot," 58
*Peddler's Caravan, The,* W. B. Rands, 139
Perrault, C., 49, 208-209, 219, 254, 258, 275, 296, 387, 827
"Peter Piper," 60
Petersham, M. and M., 35, 36
*Pied Piper of Hamelin, The,* R. Browning, 193
*Pine-Tree Shillings, The,* N. Hawthorne, 657
*Pinocchio,* C. Collodi, 420
Pioneers, poems about, 155, 157-158; stories about, 596, 635, 639, 655, 666, 679, 695, 729
Piper, E. F., 828; *The Prairie Schooner,* 157
*Pita's Painted Pig,* E. Morrow, 553
*Plaint of the Camel, The,* C. E. Carryl, 121
*Planting of the Apple-Tree, The,* W. C. Bryant, 115
*Plouf, the Little Wild Duck,* Lida, 491
*Plowing,* H. B. Lent, 725
*Plowing: A Memory,* H. Garland, 144
*Plowman of Today, The,* H. Garland, 145
Poe, E. A., 828; *Annabel Lee,* 191
Poetry, *see* Verse
"Polly, put the kettle on," 54
*Pony Express, The,* C. L. Skelton, 695
*Poplars, The,* T. Garrison, 114
Potter, B., 828; *The Tale of Peter Rabbit,* 455
*Prairie Schooner, The,* E. F. Piper, 157
*Prayer, A,* E. Markham, 165
*Presents,* M. G. Chute, 77
*Pretty Cow,* A. Taylor, 96
*Primer Lesson,* C. Sandburg, 162
*Prince and the Giant's Daughter, The,* 285
*Princess and the Pea, The,* H. C. Andersen, 406
*Princess on the Glass Hill, The,* 259
*Psalm of Those Who Go Forth before Daylight,* C. Sandburg, 143
Puppetry, 211, 379, 381
*Puss in Boots,* 275
"Pussy cat, where have you been," 54
Pyle, H., 32

*Queen Mab,* T. Hood, 87
*Queen of the Pirate Isle, The,* B. Harte, 583

*Rabbit, The,* E. King, 93
Rackham, A., 33; illustration by, 34
*Raggedy Man, The,* J. W. Riley, 14-15, 80
*Raggle, Taggle Gypsies, The,* 173
*Rain,* R. L. Stevenson, 106
Rands, W. B., 828; *Brown Bee,* 101; *The Wonderful World,* 108; *The Peddler's Caravan,* 139
Rare books, children's, 21, 22, 23, 24, 25, 26, 50, 51, 385, 386, 387, 785
Raspe, R. E., 829; *Baron Munchausen Goes to the Moon,* 485
Reading ability, 4, 42, 781
References for students, 44-46, 66, 203-204, 380-381, 786-787, 840, 843
"Ride a cock-horse to Banbury Cross," 53
*Riding the Girders,* M. Norris, 751
Riley, J. W., 829; *The Raggedy Man,* 14-15, 80; *Little Orphant Annie,* 83
*Rip Van Winkle,* W. Irving, 436

*Riquet with the Tuft,* 296
*Roads,* R. Field, 138
"Robert Rowley," 60
Roberts, C. G. D., 829; *Keeping Still in the Woods,* 505
Roberts, E. M., 72, 830; *The Butterbean Tent,* 81; *Christmas Morning,* 82; *The Woodpecker,* 93; *The Hens,* 100
Robin Hood, 308, 387; ballads about, 179, 181, 182
*Robin Hood and Allen-a-Dale,* 182
*Robin Hood and Little John,* 181
*Robin Hood and the Ranger,* 179
Robinson, W. W., 830; *Beasts of the Tar Pits,* 519
*Robinson Crusoe,* D. Defoe, 753
*Rocky Billy Goes Visiting,* H. C. Holling, 502
Rossetti, C. G., 71, 830; *Woolly Lambkins,* 94; *The Caterpillar,* 94; *The Swallow,* 98; *The City Mouse and the Country Mouse,* 98; *Do You Know?* 99; *Is the Moon Tired?* 105; *Who Has Seen the Wind?* 105; *Boats Sail on the Rivers,* 106
Rousseau, J. J., 388
Rowe, D., 831; *Way Ping, Master of Boats,* 706
*Runaway, The,* R. Frost, 99
*Rusty Pete, Cow Pony,* D. Fogler and N. Nicol, 711

*St. Nicholas Magazine,* 214, 392
Salisbury, F. S., 221
*Salute to Trees, A,* H. van Dyke, 115
*Sand Hogs,* M. Norris, 751
Sandburg, C., 72, 831; *Children of the Wind,* 102; *Milk-White Moon, Put the Cows To Sleep,* 113; *Fog,* 114; *Psalm of Those Who Go Forth before Daylight,* 143; *Primer Lesson,* 162; *Abe Lincoln Grows Up,* 672
*Sandford and Merton, The History of,* T. Day, 388
Saxe, J. G., 831; *The Blind Men and the Elephant,* 176
*Schumann-Heink's First Contract,* M. Lawton, 758
Scott, W., 831; *My Own, My Native Land,* 160; *Lochinvar,* 188
Sea, the, poems about, 130, 140, 141, 148; stories about, 399, 527, 648, 706, 740, 743
*Sea Fever,* J. Masefield, 141
*Sea Shell, The,* A. Lowell, 140
*Secret, The,* 97
*Secret of the Machines, The,* R. Kipling, 149
*Seeds,* W. de la Mare, 107
Seegers, J. C., 14
Selecting books for children, 3-5, 6, 9-11, 12-18, 20-21, 33, 35, 41, 42, 43, 44, 51, 69-70, 207, 210-212, 390, 392, 785-786
Seredy, Kate, 36-37, 832; illustration by, 36; *Jansci and Kate,* 565
Sewell, H., 38, 832; *Blue Barns,* 490
*Sigurd the Volsung,* D. Hosford, 324
*Silver,* W. de la Mare, 108
"Simple Simon," 60
"Sing a song of sixpence," 57
*Singing Leaves, The,* J. R. Lowell, 190
*Skating,* H. Asquith, 80
Skelton, C. L., 832; *The Pony Express,* 695
Skinner, C. L., 833; *Blue Arrow and the Outlaws,* 679
*Skipper Ireson's Ride,* J. G. Whittier, 196
*Skipping Ropes,* D. Aldis, 77
*Skunks,* E. M. Patch, 496
*Skyscrapers,* R. Field, 89
*Sleepy Song, The,* J. D. Bacon, 75
*Small Yellow Train, The,* A. Dalgliesh, 709
*Snow, The,* J. G. Whittier, 117
*Snow-White and Rose-Red,* 251
*Snow-White and the Seven Dwarfs,* 243
*Some One,* W. de la Mare, 86
*Song for a Little House,* C. Morley, 164
*Song of the Parrot,* E. Coatsworth, 140
Southey, R., 215, 833; *The Battle of Blenheim,* 176
*Springtime in Donegal,* M. R. Stevenson, 90
*Squirrel, The,* 94
Steel, F. A., 215, 219, 226, 270, 298, 833
Stephens, J., 833; *The White Window,* 105; *Night Was Creeping,* 106
Stevenson, L., 834; *In a Desert Town,* 111
Stevenson, M. R., 834; *Springtime in Donegal,* 90
Stevenson, R. L., 13, 71, 834; *Time To Rise,* 73; *Bed in Summer,* 74; *My Bed Is a Boat,* 74; *My Shadow,* 76; *At the Seaside,* 78; *The Swing,* 78; *The Land of Counterpane,* 78; *A Good Play,* 79; *The Cow,* 96; *The Wind,* 106; *Rain,* 196; *The Sun's*

*Travels,* 108; *Wintertime,* 109; *Where Go the Boats?* 138; *Travel,* 140; *The Truce on Treasure Island,* 626
*Stopping by Woods on a Snowy Evening,* R. Frost, 110
Stories in verse, 169-198; *see also* Ballads
*Stories of Other Days in Old Bergen,* R. Chevalier, 570
*Story of Odysseus, The,* P. Colum, 345
*Story of a Stone, The,* D. S. Jordan, 535
Storytelling, 42, 211, 379, 381
*Strange Man, A,* 125
*Strange Wild Song, A,* L. Carroll, 124
*Straw Ox, The,* 218
Student activities, 42-43, 65, 202-203, 379-380, 785-786; *see also* Suggestions for students, References for students
Suggestions for students, 41-42, 69-70, 72; *see also* Student activities, References for students, Graded lists of selections
*Sun, The,* E. Dickinson, 116
*Sun's Travels, The,* R. L. Stevenson, 108
*Swallow, The,* C. G. Rossetti, 98
*Sweet and Low,* A. Tennyson, 76
Swett, S. H., *July,* 115
*Swift Things Are Beautiful,* E. Coatsworth, 114
*Swing, The,* R. L. Stevenson, 78
*Swiss Family Robinson,* J. D. Wyss, 574

*Table and the Chair, The,* E. Lear, 123
*Tale of Peter Rabbit, The,* B. Potter, 455
*Talking Wires,* C. Lambert, 739
*Tar Baby, The,* J. C. Harris, 465
*Taxis,* R. Field, 139
Taylor, A. and J., 71, 834; *Pretty Cow,* 96; *Little Star,* 108
Taylor, E., 26, 209, 229, 237, 243, 258, 835
Teasdale, S., 835; *April,* 107; *The Falling Star,* 113; *It Is Not Far,* 116
Tenniel, J., 21, 27; illustration by, 28
Tennyson, A., 835; *Sweet and Low,* 76; *The Bugle Song,* 91; *Lady Claire,* 189; *Gareth and Lynette* (retold from), 362
Terman, L. M., 13
Thackeray, W. M., 835; *A Tragic Story,* 126
*Thanksgiving,* Bible (Psalm 100), 166
*Thanksgiving Day,* L. M. Child, 81
"The north wind doth blow," 56
"The rose is red," 54
"There was a crooked man," 60
"There was a man in our town," 60
"There was an old man who lived in a wood," 62
"There was an old woman lived under a hill," 55
"There was an old woman tossed up in a basket," 60
"There was an old woman who lived in a shoe," 57
"There were three jovial huntsmen," 56
*Thing of Beauty, A,* J. Keats, 165
*Thinker, The,* B. Braley, 150
"Thirty days hath September," 59
*This Is My Rock,* D. McCord, 116
"This is the house that Jack built," 60
"This little pig went to market," 53
*Three Bears, The,* 215
*Three Billy Goats Gruff, The,* 213
"Three blind mice," 55
"Three children sliding on the ice," 60
*Three Kings Came Riding,* H. W. Longfellow, 177
*Three Little Kittens, The,* E. L. Follen, 169
*Three Little Pigs, The,* 226
*Three Lovely Holes,* W. Welles, 78
*Ticket Agent, The,* E. Leamy, 141
*Tiger, the Brahman, and the Jackal, The,* 298
*Time To Rise,* R. L. Stevenson, 73
*Tinder Box, The,* H. C. Andersen, 395
Tippett, J. S., 836; *Busy Carpenters,* 143
*To China,* L. F. Jackson, 77
"To market, to buy a fat pig," 53
*Tom Sawyer and His Pirate Crew,* S. L. Clemens, 619
*Tom Thumb,* 272
*Tony, the Steam Shovel Man,* H. B. Lent, 705
*Town Mouse and the Country Mouse, The,* Aesop, 302
*Tragic Story, A,* W. M. Thackeray, 126
Transportation, poems about, 138, 139, 141, 148, 149, 157; stories about, 635, 648, 655, 695, 709, 729, 736, 743, 747, 751
*Travel,* E. St. V. Millay, 139
*Travel,* R. L. Stevenson, 140
Travel, poems about, 102, 108, 138-142; stories about, 485, 554, 635, 648, 709, 747
*Traveling Musicians, The,* 229

*Troubles,* D. Aldis, 77
Trowbridge, J. T., 836; *Darius Green and His Flying Machine,* 131; *Evening at the Farm,* 144
*Truce on Treasure Island, The,* R. L. Stevenson, 626
Twain, Mark, *see* Clemens, S. L.
"Twenty white horses," 59
*Two Little Confederates,* T. N. Page, 644
Typography in children's books, 19, 20, 21

*Ugly Duckling, The,* H. C. Andersen, 430
*Uncle Remus,* 208, 210, 390; illustration from, 33; selections from, 465, 466
Untermeyer, J. S., 836; *Glimpse in Autumn,* 110
*Up the Airy Mountain,* W. Allingham, 88

*Vagabond Song, A,* B. Carman, 118
Van Dyke, H., 836; *The Angler's Reveille,* 102; *A Salute to Trees,* 115
Variety in children's reading, 9-11, 41, 42, 51, 72, 207, 211, 390, 786
*Velvet Shoes,* E. Wylie, 118
Verse for children, 10, 51, 53-62, 69-204
*Village Blacksmith, The,* H. W. Longfellow, 145
*Visit from Mr. Fox, A,* 169
*Visit from St. Nicholas, A,* C. C. Moore, 88
Vogel, M., 13

Wadsworth, W., 836; *Paul Bunyan,* 478
*Walrus and the Carpenter, The,* L. Carroll, 126
Ward, L., 39; illustration by, 39
Warner, C. D., 837; *Being a Boy,* 685
Washburne, C., 13
Washburne, H. C., 837; *Letters to Channy,* 554
*Washing,* J. Drinkwater, 76
*Watching Clouds,* J. Farrar, 106
Watts, I., 71, 837; *Little Busy Bee,* 101
*Way Ping, Master of Boats,* D. Rowe, 706
"Wee Willie Winkle," 55
*Well Story, The,* J. C. Harris, 466
Welles, Winifred, 72, 837; *Three Lovely Holes,* 78; *The Angel in the Apple Tree,* 90; *Behind the Waterfall,* 90; *Green Moth,* 90; *The Lucky Snail,* 97; *Dogs and Weather,* 99
Welsh, C., 50
*What We Found in a Fox Den,* E. H. Baynes, 525
Wheeler, W. A., 51, 54, 57, 838
*When the Drive Goes Down,* D. Malloch, 146
*Where Go the Boats?* R. L. Stevenson, 138
*White Cat, The,* Madame D'Aulnoy, 407
*White Window, The,* J. Stephens, 105
Whitman, W., 838; *Miracles,* 119; *I Hear America Singing,* 145; *O Captain! My Captain!* 159
Whittier, J. G., 838; *The Snow,* 117; *Barbara Frietchie,* 158; *In School Days,* 186; *Skipper Ireson's Ride,* 196
*Who Has Seen the Wind?* C. G. Rossetti, 105
*Whoopee Ti Yi Yo, Git Along Little Dogies,* 147
*Why the Bear Is Stumpy-Tailed,* 230
Wiese, K., 38
*Wild Animals,* E. Fleming, 98
*Wilderness Is Tamed, The,* E. Coatsworth, 152
"Willy boy, where are you going," 58
Wilwerding, W. J., 838; *Jangwa Begins To Hunt,* 530
*Wind, The,* R. L. Stevenson, 106
*Wind and the Moon, The,* G. MacDonald, 112
*Wind and the Sun, The,* Aesop, 300
*Wind in a Frolic, The,* W. Howitt, 111
*Winged Horse, The,* N. Hawthorne, 337
*Winning of Atalanta, The,* E. F. Buckley, 350
*Wintertime,* R. L. Stevenson, 109
*With Helmet and Hose,* W. Beebe, 527
*Wolf and the Seven Young Goslings, The,* 231
Wolfe, H., 838; *The Blackbird,* 98
*Wonderful "One-Hoss Shay," The,* O. W. Holmes, 135
*Wonderful Weaver, The,* G. Cooper, 109
*Wonderful World, The,* W. B. Rands, 108
*Woodpecker, The,* E. M. Roberts, 93
*Woolly Lambkins,* C. G. Rossetti, 94
Wordsworth, W., 839; *Daffodils,* 118
Work and workers, poems about, 143-150; stories about, 705-773
Wylie, E., 839; *Velvet Shoes,* 118

*Wynken, Blynken, and Nod,* E. Field, 75
Wynne, A., 839; *The House Cat,* 95; *Indian Children,* 152
Wyss, J. D., 839; *Swiss Family Robinson,* 574

*Yarn of the Nancy Bell, The,* W. S. Gilbert, 128
*Year's at the Spring, The,* R. Browning, 111
Yeomans, E. S., *Navaho Prayer,* 165
*Yet Gentle Will the Griffin Be,* V. Lindsay, 89
*Youth's Companion, The,* 392

*Zebra Dun, The,* 146